Electronic Configurations of the Elements

Element	K	L	M	4s	4p	4d	4f	5s	5p	5d	5f	5g	6s	6p	6d	6f	6g	6h	7
55. Cs	2	8	18	2	6	10		2	6				1						
56. Ba	2	8	18	2	6	10		2	6				2						
57. La	2	8	18	2	6	10		2	6	1			2						
58. Ce	2	8	18	2	6	10	2	2	6				2						
59. Pr	2	8	18	2	6	10	3	2	6				2						
60. Nd	2	8	18	2	6	10	4	2	6				2						
61. Pm	2	8	18	2	6	10	5	2	6				2						
62. Sm	2	8	18	2	6	10	6	2	6				2						
63. Eu	2	8	18	2	6	10	7	2	6				2						
64. Gd	2	8	18	2	6	10	7	2	6	1			2						
65. Tb	2	8	18	2	6	10	9	2	6				2						
66. Dy	2	8	18	2	6	10	10	2	6				2						
67. Ho	2	8	18	2	6	10	11	2	6				2						
68. Er	2	8	18	2	6	10	12	2	6				2						
69. Tm	2	8	18	2	6	10	13	2	6				2						
70. Yb	2	8	18	2	6	10	14	2	6				2						
71. Lu	2	8	18	2	6	10	14	2	6	1			2						
72. Hf	2	8	18	2	6	10	14	2	6	2			2						
73. Ta	2	8	18	2	6	10	14	2	6	3			2						
74. W	2	8	18	2	6	10	14	2	6	4			2						
75. Re	2	8	18	2	6	10	14	2	6	5			2						
76. Os	2	8	18	2	6	10	14	2	6	6			2						
77. Ir	2	8	18	2	6	10	14	2	6	7			2						
78. Pt	2	8	18	2	6	10	14	2	6	9			1						
79. Au	2	8	18	2	6	10	14	2	6	10			1						
80. Hg	2	8	18	2	6	10	14	2	6	10			2						
81. Tl	2	8	18	2	6	10	14	2	6	10			2	1					
82. Pb	2	8	18	2	6	10	14	2	6	10			2	2					
83. Bi	2	8	18	2	6	10	14	2	6	10			2	3					
84. Po	2	8	18	2	6	10	14	2	6	10			2	4					
85. At	2	8	18	2	6	10	14	2	6	10			2	5					
86. Rn	2	8	18	2	6	10	14	2	6	10			2	6					
87. Fr	2	8	18	2	6	10	14	2	6	10			2	6					1
88. Ra	2	8	18	2	6	10	14	2	6	10			2	6					2
89. Ac	2	8	18	2	6	10	14	2	6	10			2	6	1				2
90. Th	2	8	18	2	6	10	14	2	6	10			2	6	2				2
91. Pa	2	8	18	2	6	10	14	2	6	10	2		2	6	1				2
92. U	2	8	18	2	6	10	14	2	6	10	3		2	6	1				2
93. Np	2	8	18	2	6	10	14	2	6	10	5		2	6					2
94. Pu	2	8	18	2	6	10	14	2	6	10	6		2	6					2
95. Am	2	8	18	2	6	10	14	2	6	10	7		2	6					2
96. Cm	2	8	18	2	6	10	14	2	6	10	7		2	6	1				2
97. Bk	2	8	18	2	6	10	14	2	6	10	8		2	6	1				2
98. Cf	2	8	18	2	6	10	14	2	6	10	10		2	6					2
99. Es	2	8	18	2	6	10	14	2	6	10	11		2	6					2
100. Fm	2	8	18	2	6	10	14	2	6	10	12		2	6					2
101. Md	2	8	18	2	6	10	14	2	6	10	13		2	6					2
102. —	2	8	18	2	6	10	14	2	6	10	14		2	6					2
103. Lw	2	8	18	2	6	10	14	2	6	10	14		2	6	1				2

ADVANCED INORGANIC CHEMISTRY

A Comprehensive Text

SECOND EDITION

ADVANCED INORGANIC CHEMISTRY

A Comprehensive Text

F. ALBERT COTTON

PROFESSOR OF CHEMISTRY
MASSACHUSETTS INSTITUTE OF TECHNOLOGY
CAMBRIDGE, MASSACHUSETTS

and

GEOFFREY WILKINSON, F.R.S.

PROFESSOR OF INORGANIC CHEMISTRY
IMPERIAL COLLEGE OF SCIENCE AND TECHNOLOGY
UNIVERSITY OF LONDON, ENGLAND

Second Revised and Augmented Edition

INTERSCIENCE PUBLISHERS
A DIVISION OF JOHN WILEY & SONS
NEW YORK · LONDON · SYDNEY

Preface to the Second Edition

Although the basic structure of the text is unaltered, we have rearranged several sections and have brought up to date essentially all of the factual material. The vast amount of recent literature has meant an increase in the size of the book, but it is intended to be a *teaching* text and not a reference book and it is our view that it is better to have too much material on hand rather than too little, since sections can always be omitted.

In response to numerous requests, we have improved on the handling of documentation of which there are three levels. First, for the great majority of long known and well established facts and theories, no explicit reference is given since such material can be readily located through standard reference texts and treatises, listed at the end of the text.

Secondly, some material not so available appears in review articles and monographs; a pertinent list is provided at the end of each chapter.

Finally, we have introduced as footnotes in each chapter, some original research references. These cover broadly the period from January 1962 to August 1965 and are intended primarily for teachers and research workers as guide references to recent work.

We take this opportunity to thank all those who gave us their comments on the first edition.

F. A. Cotton
Cambridge, Massachusetts

G. Wilkinson
London, England

Preface to the First Edition

It is now a truism that, in recent years, inorganic chemistry has experienced an impressive renaissance. Academic and industrial research in inorganic chemistry is flourishing, and the output of research papers and reviews is growing exponentially.

In spite of this interest, however, there has been no comprehensive textbook on inorganic chemistry at an advanced level incorporating the many new chemical developments, particularly the more recent theoretical advances in the interpretation of bonding and reactivity in inorganic compounds. It is the aim of this book, which is based on courses given by the authors over the past five to ten years, to fill this need. It is our hope that it will provide a sound basis in contemporary inorganic chemistry for the new generation of students and will stimulate their interest in a field in which trained personnel are still exceedingly scarce in both academic and industrial laboratories.

The content of this book, which encompasses the chemistry of all of the chemical elements and their compounds, including interpretative discussion in the light of the latest advances in structural chemistry, general valence theory, and, particularly, ligand field theory, provides a reasonable achievement for students at the B.Sc. honors level in British universities and at the senior year or first year graduate level in American universities. Our experience is that a course of about eighty lectures is desirable as a guide to the study of this material.

We are indebted to several of our colleagues, who have read sections of the manuscript, for their suggestions and criticism. It is, of course, the authors alone who are responsible for any errors or omissions in the final draft. We also thank the various authors and editors who have so kindly given us permission to reproduce diagrams from their papers: specific acknowledgments are made in the text. We sincerely appreciate the secretarial assistance of Miss C. M. Ross and Mrs. A. B. Blake in the preparation of the manuscript.

F. A. COTTON
Cambridge, Massachusetts

G. WILKINSON
London, England

Contents

PART THREE

Chemistry of the Transition Elements

Abbreviations

The following list of abbreviations, most of which are commonly adopted in the inorganic research literature, will be employed in this text.

All temperatures are in °C unless specifically denoted °K.

A	Angstrom unit, 10^{-8} cm
acacH	acetylacetone
acac	acetylacetonate anion
am.	ammonia
aq	aquated, water
asym.	asymmetric or antisymmetric
b	boiling point
bu	butyl, C_4H_9
bz	benzene
cp	cyclopentadienyl, C_5H_5
d.	decomposes
d-	dextrorotation
diars	*o*-phenylenebisdimethylarsine, $C_6H_4(AsMe_2)_2$
diglyme	diethyleneglycoldimethylether
dipy	2,2'-dipyridyl
DMF	dimethylformamide, $HCONMe_2$
$DMGH_2$	dimethylglyoxime
$DMGH^-$	anion of same
DMSO	dimethylsulfoxide, Me_2SO
$EDTAH_4$	ethylenediaminetetraacetic acid
$EDTAH_{4-n}^{n-}$	anions of same
en	ethylenediamine, $NH_2CH_2CH_2NH_2$
esr	electron spin resonance
Et	ethyl, C_2H_5
ev	electron volt
f	freezing point
g	gaseous state
h	Planck's constant
ICCC	International Coordination Chemistry Conference
IR	infrared
IUPAC	International Union of Pure and Applied Chemistry
l	liquid state
l-	levorotation
L	ligand

LCAO	linear combination of atomic orbitals
m	melting point
M	central atom in compound
Me	methyl, CH_3
MO	molecular orbital
nmr	nuclear magnetic resonance
ox	oxalate ion, $C_2O_4{}^{2-}$
Ph	phenyl, C_6H_5
phen	1,10-phenanthroline
pn	propylenediamine (1,2-diaminopropane)
Pr	propyl, C_3H_7
py	pyridine
QAS	tris(o-phenylarsinophenyl)arsine
R	alkyl or aryl group
R	gas constant
s.	solid state
s	spin quantum number
str.	infrared stretching frequency
sub.	sublimes
sym.	symmetrical
THF	tetrahydrofuran
tn	1,3-diaminopropane(trimethylenediamine)
tren	β,β',β''-triaminotriethylamine, $N(CH_2CH_2NH_2)_3$
TTA	thenoyltrifluoroacetone, $C_4H_3SCOCF_3$
U	lattice energy
UV	ultraviolet
VB	valence bond
X	halogen or pseudo halogen
Z	atomic number
ε	molar extinction coefficient
ν	frequency, cm^{-1}
μ	magnetic moment, in Bohr magnetons
χ	magnetic susceptibility
θ	Curie–Weiss constant

Some useful constants and conversion factors are given inside the back cover.

PART ONE

General Theory

1

The Electronic Structures of Atoms

Ultimate explanations for all chemical phenomena must lie in the structures of the atoms. While there is little chance that such explanations can be formulated in a rigorous or complete way in the near future, even the partial and tentative explanations which are part of contemporary chemical theory are founded on knowledge of atomic structure.

Rutherford's work (1911) on the scattering of α particles (helium nuclei) by matter showed that the nucleus contains nearly all of the mass and all of the positive charge within a very small volume. Present-day estimates of nuclear radii are $\sim 10^{-12}$ cm. However, from various lines of evidence we know that the radii of entire atoms are of the order of 10^{-8} cm, or, of the order of an Angstrom unit. Thus an atom has a group of electrons distributed through a sphere several Angstroms in diameter with a dense positively charged nucleus at the center of the sphere.[1]

With the exception of isotope effects in light atoms, the nucleus has little influence on chemical behavior other than in determining the number of electrons surrounding it. However, certain spectroscopic techniques, notably nuclear magnetic resonance, depend on specific properties of nuclei such as magnetic moment and spin, and on the effects of external electron density upon them.

Since the chemical properties of atoms and molecules depend almost exclusively upon the extra-nuclear arrangements, it is desirable to begin an account of inorganic chemistry with a précis of some basic facts and principles concerning the electronic structure of atoms.

Beginning around the turn of this century, physicists made certain discoveries during studies of emission of radiation from hot bodies, the ejection of electrons from surfaces by radiation (photoelectric effect), and

[1] For a discussion of the nucleus, its structure and properties, see G. Friedlander, J. W. Kennedy and J. M. Miller, *Nuclear and Radiochemistry*, 2nd ed., Wiley, New York, 1964.

later, atomic spectra, which forced them to conclude that for phenomena on the atomic and subatomic scales energy is *not* continuously variable. Instead, energy can take only certain values which are integral multiples of basic units called *quanta*. The energies of these systems are thus said to be *quantized*. The quantization of energy was first proposed by Planck and later, in connection with the photo-electric effect, by Einstein. As a result of their work we have the fundamental relation between the frequency of light, ν, and the energy, E (of the quanta)

$$E = \mathbf{h}\nu \tag{1-1}$$

in which the energy is expressed in ergs, the frequency in cycles per second and the proportionality constant, $\mathbf{h}$, called Planck's constant, has the value 6.6252×10^{-27} erg-sec.

There is a very important physical concept underlying equation 1-1 Although it is well known that light has the properties of wave motion and can for many purposes be regarded purely as waves, in dealing with the atomic processes in which it is generated or absorbed it must be regarded as a stream of energy packets or quanta, each having the energy prescribed by equation 1-1 according to the frequency, ν. Thus, when an atom undergoes a transition releasing some energy, E, one quantum of light with frequency $E/\mathbf{h}$ always appears, not, for example, two quanta of different frequencies with energies adding up to the correct total. Conversely, when an atom absorbs radiant energy in order to make a transition involving an increase in energy by the amount E, it will only absorb one quantum of light of frequency $E/\mathbf{h}$ and not two or more quanta with differing frequencies even if the energies of the several quanta total E. These simple facts make it possible for us to infer in a direct way the separations of various energy states of an atom or molecule from the frequencies of light emitted or absorbed.

1-1. Bohr's Theory of Atoms

The culmination of the development of the concept of quantization, prior to the advent of wave mechanics, was Bohr's theory of the hydrogen atom. By postulating that the angular momentum of the electron about the nucleus could take only values which are integral multiples, n, of $\mathbf{h}/2\pi$, where $\mathbf{h}$ is again Planck's constant, but otherwise using only simple relationships from classical mechanics, Bohr derived equations 1-2 and 1-3 for the radius and energy, respectively, of the electron in its various orbits about the nucleus.

$$r = \frac{n^2\mathbf{h}^2}{Z4\pi^2\mu e^2} = n^2 \frac{a_0}{Z} \tag{1-2}$$

$$E = -Z^2 \frac{2\pi^2\mu e^4}{n^2\mathbf{h}^2} = -\frac{R}{n^2} \tag{1-3}$$

In these equations Z is the charge on the nucleus in atomic units ($Z = 1$ for H), $\mathbf{h}$ is Planck's constant, e is the charge of the electron and μ is the reduced mass† of the electron (very nearly equal to m, the actual mass of the electron). The number n, introduced to quantize the angular momentum, is called a *quantum number*. The symbol a_0, which is the radius of the most stable orbit ($n = 1$) of the hydrogen atom, is called the *Bohr radius*. It is equal to 0.529 Angstroms and is often used as a unit of length in atomic physics. The quantity R, called the *Rydberg* or *Rydberg constant*, is seen to be the product of fundamental constants.

Bohr's theory was in remarkable agreement with many experimental facts and provided the first satisfactory explanation of the line spectra of atoms (cf. Fig. 1-5, page 15). For example, one can compute easily from equation 1-3 the energy required to ionize the atom in its ground state, that is, to separate the electron and proton to an infinite separation with each at rest. This energy is simply R and is indicated in Figure 1-5 by the arrow marked I, which is the customary generic symbol for ionization energies. The value so computed is in good agreement with the experimentally measured value. Moreover, by assuming that a hydrogen atom in any given state characterized by an n value n' may make a transition to another state which is characterized by n'', either absorbing energy if $n'' > n'$ or radiating energy if $n'' < n'$, Bohr was able to calculate the frequencies of all of the lines observed in the absorption and emission spectra of the hydrogen atom using equation 1-3 with a value of R calculated from the values of the fundamental constants which compose it. All of these had been measured independently. In Figure 1-5 the arrows indicate a few of the transitions responsible for well-known lines in the hydrogen emission spectrum.

Remarkable as was the success of the Bohr theory (as amended by Sommerfeld to consider elliptical as well as circular orbitals), it soon became evident that the basic idea of the electron as a small charged particle obeying exactly the same laws (aside from the quantum restriction on its angular momentum) as are obeyed by macroscopic bodies is incorrect. Theoretical physicists therefore sought a new form of mechanics applicable to atomic and subatomic phenomena.

1-2. The Beginning of Wave Mechanics

The basic idea in wave mechanics is that for so small a body as the electron we cannot say, as Bohr did, precisely where it is and where it is going at a definite moment. We can only state the relative *probability* of

† Letting M = mass of nucleus, $\mu = mM/(m + M)$.

its being at a given place and having a certain momentum at a certain time. This may appear at first sight to be a somewhat vague state of affairs, but actually we are able to know quite enough to deal with problems of atomic and molecular structure.

We shall consider only a limited form of wave mechanics, namely, that part of the theory which deals with *stationary states*. A stationary state is one which persists for a long period of time unless subject to outside stimuli. The energy states of the hydrogen atom are stationary states of that system.

According to wave mechanics any system—an atom, a molecule, an electron in free space, etc.—is described by a *state function* or *wave function*, symbolized by ψ, which is a function of the coordinates of all the particles constituting the system. That is, the magnitude of ψ depends only on the positions in space of all the particles. We shall return later to further discussion of the physical meaning of the quantity ψ.

In order to understand why ψ is called a wave function, and why wave mechanics presupposes that we cannot precisely define the position of an electron, we may consider some developments in physics which occurred just prior to the formulation of wave mechanics by the physicist Erwin Schrödinger. De Broglie had suggested in 1924 that just as light, usually considered to be undulatory in nature, did behave under certain circumstances as if it consisted of particles (the quanta discussed above), so, very small particles such as electrons might also have wave properties. From certain theoretical considerations he was led to propose that we could associate with a beam of electrons a wavelength, λ, given by

$$\lambda = \frac{\mathbf{h}}{p} \tag{1-4}$$

where $\mathbf{h}$ is again Planck's constant, and p is the momentum of an electron in the beam, that is, its mass times its velocity.

The physical reality of this wave nature of the electron was demonstrated in 1927–28 by Davisson and Germer and by Thomson who showed that a beam of electrons could be diffracted by a suitable grating (the atoms in a crystal of gold) in a manner analogous to the diffraction of a beam of light.

The fact that systems of small particles manifest wave properties, at least under certain conditions, suggests the possibility of describing such systems with equations similar to those which are known to describe other kinds of wave motion, for example, the waves which run along a vibrating string or the wave motion attributed to electromagnetic radiation. Indeed it is possible to begin with the wave equation appropriate to electromagnetic waves and, by certain substitutions, convert it into an equation appropriate to matter. Although these substitutions are dictated by physical reasoning, they are *basically arbitrary* and acceptable *only* because they lead to an equation which experience has shown will enable us to get correct answers to physical problems. We therefore prefer simply to state the *wave equation* as a postulate since, for chemists, the prime concern is with the application of the wave equation to atomic and molecular systems rather than with the physical and mathematical background which led Schrödinger to propose it.

The Wave Equation. The form of the wave equation which applies to stationary states of a system can be written in an exceedingly simple symbolic form:

$$\mathscr{H}\psi = E\psi \qquad (1\text{-}5)$$

where $\mathscr{H}$ represents a certain way of expressing the total energy of the system, and E is the numerical value of that energy. For all systems which will normally concern us as chemists, the total energy is just the sum of the kinetic energy, T, and the potential energy, V, that is,

$$H = T + V \qquad (1\text{-}6)$$

This relation was first demonstrated by the theoretical physicist, Hamilton, and H is frequently called the Hamiltonian of a system.

As an illustration, let us consider the Bohr model of the hydrogen atom. For simplicity, we shall assume that the heavy nucleus (which is nearly but not quite immobile as the electron goes around it) is fixed. Then, all of the kinetic energy, T, of the system is just the kinetic energy of the electron and is given by

$$T = \tfrac{1}{2}mv^2 \qquad (1\text{-}7)$$

where m is the mass of the electron, and v is its velocity. The potential energy of the system is just that resulting from the electrostatic interaction (the gravitational forces are $\sim 10^{18}$ times smaller) and can thus be expressed as

$$V = -\frac{e^2}{r} \qquad (1\text{-}8)$$

where e is the electronic charge, and r is the radius of the orbit; the minus sign arises because one charge is $+e$ and the other is $-e$. Therefore, for the hydrogen atom the Hamiltonian, in classical (i.e., pre-quantum mechanical) physics, is

$$H = \tfrac{1}{2}mv^2 - \frac{e^2}{r} \qquad (1\text{-}9a)$$

For a reason which will become apparent presently, we prefer to write equation 1-9a in the form

$$H = \frac{p^2}{2m} - \frac{e^2}{r} \qquad (1\text{-}9b)$$

where we have simply used the definition of the momentum of the electron, $p = mv$.

Now, the way in which we go from the classical description of this or any other system to the description in wave mechanics is to take its classical Hamiltonian (eq. 1-9) and make certain substitutions. An exact prescription of these rules would involve mathematics beyond the scope of this book, but we can give a simplified and illustrative account.

The basic rule is that wherever a momentum occurs in the classical Hamiltonian, we replace it with a derivative of the form:

$$\frac{\mathbf{h}}{2\pi i}\left(\frac{\partial}{\partial x} + \frac{\partial}{\partial y} + \frac{\partial}{\partial z}\right) \tag{1-10}$$

Thus, the Hamiltonian for the hydrogen atom in its wave mechanical form, $\mathscr{H}$, is

$$\mathscr{H} = -\frac{\mathbf{h}^2}{8\pi^2 m}\left(\frac{\partial^2}{\partial x^2} + \frac{\partial^2}{\partial y^2} + \frac{\partial^2}{\partial z^2}\right) - \frac{e^2}{r} \tag{1-11}$$

If we now substitute this form of the Hamiltonian into the general form of the wave equation (eq. 1-5), we obtain

$$\mathscr{H}\psi = \left[-\frac{\mathbf{h}^2}{8\pi^2 m}\left(\frac{\partial^2}{\partial x^2} + \frac{\partial^2}{\partial y^2} + \frac{\partial^2}{\partial z^2}\right) - \frac{e^2}{r}\right]\psi = E\psi \tag{1-12}$$

This is the wave equation for the hydrogen atom. We have seen, to a certain extent, how it is obtained, but much remains to be said about what it means and how to solve it.

The Meaning of the Wave Equation. Equation 1-12 tells us that we should take the indicated second derivatives of a function, ψ, add them together, and multiply by $-\mathbf{h}^2/8\pi^2 m$. If to this we then add $(-e^2/r)\psi$, we shall have something identical with $E\psi$. When we have found a function, ψ, which permits us to do this, that function is said to be a solution of the wave equation and is called a *wave function*. In general, there will be many different functions, $\psi_1, \psi_2, \ldots, \psi_i$, which will be solutions, each giving a value of the energy, $E_1, E_2, \ldots E_i$.

But still, to know what the wave equation "means" we must know what ψ "means." From the fact that we take the second derivatives of ψ with respect to the coordinates x, y and z of the electron, it follows that ψ must be a function of these coordinates. In fact, $\psi(x, y, z)$ has a particular value for any particular combination of values of x, y and z; or, to put it another way, at any point in space (where we use the position of the proton as the origin of the coordinate system) specified by the coordinates x, y and z, ψ has a certain value.

The physical meaning of this value is that *it is related to the probability that the electron will be found at that point.* The exact form of the relation is very simple. The probability, P, of finding the electron at the point (x, y, z) is given by

$$P = \psi(x, y, z)\psi^*(x, y, z) \tag{1-13}$$

ψ^* is the complex conjugate of ψ; since ψ can have imaginary values, we must in general multiply it by its complex conjugate in order that P be real. The probability of finding the electron at any point may be large or small, even zero, but, obviously, it cannot be imaginary. Of course, if ψ is real, $\psi^* = \psi$, and equation 1-13 simply says that the probability equals the square of ψ.

From this definition of the physical significance of ψ, it follows that any such function must satisfy the following requirements:

1. It must have only one value at each and every point because—whatever the values of x, y and z—there must be only one definite answer to the question "What is the probability that the electron is at the point (x, y, z)?"

2. It must not have the value ∞ at any point.

3. Its absolute values at all points must be such that

$$\int_{-\infty}^{+\infty} \int_{-\infty}^{+\infty} \int_{-\infty}^{+\infty} \psi(x, y, z)\psi^*(x, y, z) \, dx \, dy \, dz = \int \psi\psi^* \, d\tau = 1 \tag{1-14}$$

The left term in equation 1-14 gives us the sum of the probabilities of finding the electron at each point throughout all space. Since there is one electron and it must be somewhere, this total probability must then equal one. The middle term in equation 1-14 is simply a shorthand for the left term where τ is a general symbol for all the coordinates, the integration is understood to be over all coordinates, and ψ is understood to be a function of all coordinates. When a wave function satisfies this condition it is said to be *normalized*.

When equation 1-12 is rewritten in spherical polar coordinates (see page 11) it can be solved and a set of wave functions is obtained. Let us now examine one of these in some detail in order to gain insight into the physical meaning of ψ. We shall use the one of lowest energy, ψ_1, which has the following rather simple form:

$$\psi_1 = \frac{\exp(-r/a_0)}{\sqrt{\pi} \, a_0^{3/2}}$$

Here, a_0 again stands for the Bohr radius and r is the distance from the nucleus. In Figure 1-1 is a plot of ψ_1 and also of ψ_1^2. It should be recognized that these functions are spherically symmetrical, since their values do not depend on the angles θ and ϕ. It can be seen that ψ_1 satisfies the

1*

requirements for an acceptable wave function in that it is (*a*) single-valued, (*b*) never infinite and (*c*) normalized.

Another way of depicting the function ψ_1 is shown in Figure 1-2. This picture may be interpreted in several ways.

1. We may imagine having a very large number of hydrogen atoms. At a certain time the electrons in each atom will in general each be at a different distance from the nucleus. If we were to superpose pictures of all of these atoms, we would obtain Figure 1-2.

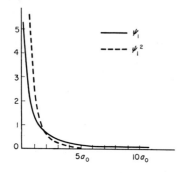

Fig. 1-1.   Plot of ground state wave function ψ_1 and ψ_1^2 for hydrogen atom.

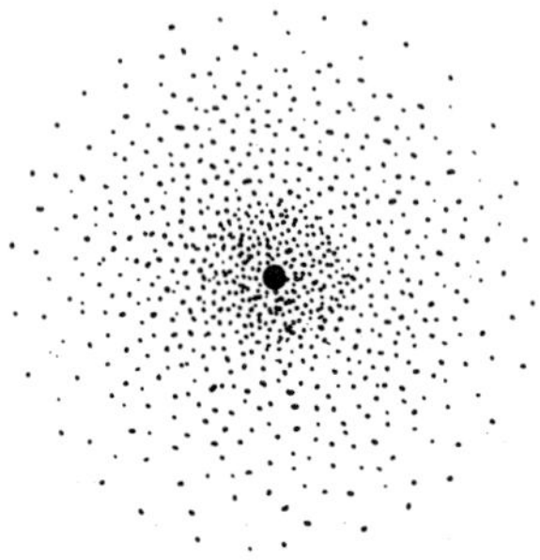

Fig. 1-2.   A representation of the ground state wave function of the hydrogen atom.

2. We may take only one atom and observe it many times as the electron changes its position with respect to the nucleus. If we shade each small region of space in proportion to how often we find the electron in it, we obtain Figure 1-2.

3. We may abandon altogether our picture of the electron as a tiny hard body moving around the proton and regard it instead as a certain amount of negative charge and mass which is distributed, or smeared out, around the nucleus as required by equation 1-13. In this case Figure 1-2 represents roughly what we would "see" if we could look at the atom. This last view may be a little difficult to get used to, but is undoubtedly the most useful one to take.

Let us now see how the wave mechanical picture of the ground state of the hydrogen atom—with its smeared-out electron—compares with Bohr's picture. Suppose we consider the space around the nucleus to be divided into an infinite number of infinitesimally thin concentric spherical shells and ask what is the probability that the electron will be found in each of these. The total volume of such a shell, of thickness Δr, is $4\pi r^2 \Delta r$, and the total probability of finding the electron within it is $(4\pi r^2 \Delta r)\psi_1^2$. In Figure 1-3 we have plotted $4\pi r^2 \psi_1^2$ against r. The maximum lies at a value of r equal to a_0. Now a_0, as we have said, is called the Bohr radius because it is the radius of the lowest orbital of the Bohr hydrogen atom. Thus, although Bohr's model of the hydrogen atom led to the conclusion that in the ground state the electron would *always* be found going around the proton on a circular path exactly a_0 in radius, wave mechanics says only that this is the *most probable* radius.

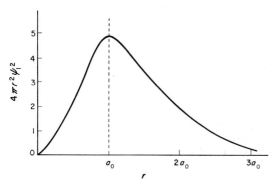
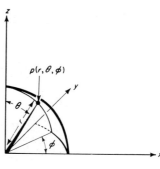

Fig. 1-3. Probability density function, $4\pi r^2\psi_1{}^2$, for the ground state orbital of the hydrogen atom.

Fig. 1-4. The polar coordinate system.

1-3. The Hydrogen Atom

All treatments of the electronic structures of atoms, however sophisticated they may become in their final stages, begin by considering the solutions to the wave equation for the simplest of all atoms, the hydrogen atom.

When the wave equation for the hydrogen atom (1-12) is written in terms of spherical polar coordinates r, θ and ϕ, which are coordinates related to the Cartesian coordinates x, y and z as illustrated in Figure 1-4, it takes the form

$$\frac{1}{r^2}\cdot\frac{\partial}{\partial r}\left(r^2\frac{\partial\psi}{\partial r}\right) + \frac{1}{r^2\sin\theta}\frac{\partial}{\partial\theta}\left(\sin\theta\frac{\partial\psi}{\partial\theta}\right)$$
$$+ \frac{1}{r^2\sin^2\theta}\frac{\partial^2\psi}{\partial\phi^2} + \frac{8\pi^2m}{\mathbf{h}^2}\left(E + \frac{e^2}{r}\right)\psi = 0 \quad (1\text{-}15)$$

Solution of the Wave Equation for the Hydrogen Atom. To solve equation 1-15, we may look for solutions of the general form

$$\psi = R(r)\,\Theta(\theta)\,\Phi(\varphi)$$

in which we write ψ, which is in general a function of all three coordinates r, θ and φ, as a product of $R(r)$, a function only of r, $\Theta(\theta)$, a function only of θ and $\Phi(\varphi)$, a function only of φ. If we substitute this expression into equation 1-15 and rearrange we get

$$\frac{1}{R}\frac{\partial}{\partial r}\left(r^2\frac{\partial R}{\partial r}\right) + \frac{8\pi^2\mu}{\mathbf{h}^2}\left(E + \frac{e^2}{r}\right)r^2$$
$$= -\frac{1}{\Theta\sin\theta}\frac{d}{d\theta}\left(\sin\theta\frac{d\Theta}{d\theta}\right) - \frac{1}{\Phi\sin^2\theta}\frac{d^2\Phi}{d\varphi^2} \quad (1\text{-}16)$$

Now the LHS of equation 1-16 depends only on r whereas the RHS depends only on θ and φ. Consequently, in order for equation 1-16 to hold for all values of r, θ and φ, each side must separately equal a constant, λ. Thus we write, with a little rearrangement:

$$\frac{\sin\theta}{\Theta}\frac{d}{d\theta}\left(\sin\theta\frac{d\Theta}{d\theta}\right) + \lambda\sin^2\theta = -\frac{1}{\Phi}\frac{d^2\Phi}{d\varphi^2} \quad (1\text{-}17)$$

and

$$\frac{1}{r^2}\frac{d}{dr}\left(r^2\frac{dR}{dr}\right) + \left[\frac{8\pi^2\mu}{\mathbf{h}^2}\left(E + \frac{e^2}{r}\right) - \frac{\lambda}{r^2}\right]R = 0 \quad (1\text{-}18)$$

Now inspection of equation 1-17 shows that for the same reason we separated equation 1-16 into equation 1-17 and 1-18, we can separate equation 1-17 into equations 1-19 and 1-20:

$$\frac{\sin\theta}{\Theta}\frac{d}{d\theta}\left(\sin\theta\frac{d\Theta}{d\theta}\right) + \lambda\sin^2\theta = m^2 \quad (1\text{-}19)$$

$$\frac{d^2\Phi}{d\varphi^2} = -m^2\Phi \quad (1\text{-}20)$$

where m is some constant. We now have three separate equations, 1-18, 1-19 and 1-20, whose solutions will tell us how the form of the wave functions of the hydrogen atom depends on the coordinates r, θ and φ, respectively.

We can begin by solving equation 1-20. It is easily found that the only solutions which satisfy the requirements for good wave functions are

$$\Phi = (2\pi)^{-1/2}\exp{(im\varphi)} \quad (1\text{-}21)$$

in which m must be a positive or negative integer; m is therefore a quantum number. Now it is found that the solutions to equation 1-19 are rather complicated when written out in their general form and we shall not give the general solution here. The most important point is that all of these solutions, that is, the various Θ's are functions of the quantum numbers

l and m. l may take only positive integral values and m may take all integral values from $-l$ to $+l$ for any given value of l:

$$l = 0, 1, 2, 3, \ldots$$
$$m = l,\ (l-1),\ (l-2),\ \ldots,\ 0,\ -1,\ \ldots,\ -l$$

Finally, when equation 1-18 is solved in terms of l which is related to λ by the expression $\lambda = l(l+1)$, a set of radial wave functions is obtained. In so doing, we also solve equation 1-18 for the energy of the system

$$E_n = -\frac{1}{n^2}\frac{2\pi^2\mu^2 e^4}{\mathbf{h}^2} \tag{1-22}$$

where n is still another quantum number and may take all positive integral values from 1 to ∞. Furthermore, the possible values which l may have are related to the value of n so that

$$l = (n-1),\ (n-2),\ \ldots,\ 0$$

It will be noted that the energy of the hydrogen atom is found to depend only on the quantum number n, which is called the *principal quantum number*.

The Hydrogen Atom Orbitals. We shall now examine some of the wave functions which are solutions to equation 1-15, specifically, the first fourteen in increasing order of energy. These functions, which are usually called *orbitals*, describe the spacial distribution of electron density about the nucleus. Each one is uniquely identified by its quantum numbers n, l and m. Table 1-1 lists these orbitals for a *hydrogen-like* atom, that is, for a one electron atom with a nuclear charge of Z electronic units. The hydrogen atom itself is the particular case of $Z = 1$; other hydrogen-like atoms are Li^{2+}, C^{5+}, F^{8+}, etc.

Table 1-1 also lists the general symbols for these orbitals, each of which consists of a number and a letter. The number is simply the principal quantum number. The letters correspond to the values of l in the following way:

$$l = 0 \quad 1 \quad 2 \quad 3 \quad 4 \quad 5$$
$$s \quad p \quad d \quad f \quad g \quad h$$

The first four letters are arbitrary for historical reasons, but following f they go in alphabetical order. Note that the general symbol does not distinguish between orbitals with the same values of n and l but differing values of m. We shall discuss symbols for indicating the difference between each of the three p orbitals or five d orbitals shortly.

The three quantum numbers n, l and m which arise in the solution of the wave equation may each be considered to have a physical meaning.

TABLE 1-1

Orbitals of a Hydrogen-like Atom

Quantum numbers n	l	m	General symbol	Radial wave function[a]	Angular wave function	Explicit symbol
1	0	0	$1s$	$2(Z/a_0)^{3/2}e^{-\rho}$	$(2\sqrt{\pi})^{-1}$	$1s$
2	0	0	$2s$	$2^{-3/2}(Z/a_0)^{3/2}(2-\rho)e^{-\rho/2}$	$(2\sqrt{\pi})^{-1}$	$2s$
2	1	0	$2p$	$2^{-1}\cdot6^{-1/2}(Z/a_0)^{3/2}\rho e^{-\rho/2}$	$2^{-1}\cdot3^{1/2}\pi^{-1/2}\cos\theta$	$2p_z$
2	1	1		''	$2^{-1}\cdot3^{1/2}\pi^{-1/2}\sin\theta\cos\phi$	$2p_x$
2	1	-1		''	$2^{-1}\cdot3^{1/2}\pi^{-1/2}\sin\theta\sin\phi$	$2p_y$
3	0	0	$3s$	$2\cdot81^{-1}\cdot3^{-1/2}(Z/a_0)^{3/2}(27-18\rho+2\rho^2)e^{-\rho/3}$	$(2\sqrt{\pi})^{-1}$	$3s$
3	1	0	$3p$	$4\cdot81^{-1}\cdot6^{-1/2}(Z/a_0)^{3/2}(6\rho-\rho^2)e^{-\rho/3}$	$2^{-1}\cdot3^{1/2}\pi^{-1/2}\cos\theta$	$3p_z$
3	1	1		''	$2^{-1}\cdot3^{1/2}\pi^{-1/2}\sin\theta\cos\phi$	$3p_x$
3	1	-1		''	$2^{-1}\cdot3^{1/2}\pi^{-1/2}\sin\theta\sin\phi$	$3p_y$
3	2	0	$3d$	$4\cdot81^{-1}\cdot30^{-1/2}(Z/a_0)^{3/2}\rho^2 e^{-\rho/3}$	$4^{-1}\cdot5^{1/2}\pi^{-1/2}(3\cos^2\theta-1)$	$3d_{z^2}$
3	2	1		''	$2^{-3/2}\cdot30^{1/2}\pi^{-1/2}\sin\theta\cos\theta\cos\phi$	$3d_{xz}$
3	2	-1		''	$2^{-3/2}\cdot30^{1/2}\pi^{-1/2}\sin\theta\cos\theta\sin\phi$	$3d_{yz}$
3	2	2		''	$4^{-1}\cdot15^{1/2}\pi^{-1/2}\sin^2\theta\cos2\phi$	$3d_{x^2-y^2}$
3	2	-2		''	$4^{-1}\cdot15^{1/2}\pi^{-1/2}\sin^2\theta\sin2\phi$	$3d_{xy}$

[a] $\rho = Zr/a_0$; Z = nuclear charge.

As indicated in equation 1-22, the quantum number n gives a measure of the energy of an electron in an orbital.   Somewhat loosely, but quite commonly, one speaks of the energy of the orbital.   The orbital with the smallest value of n (i.e., 1) has the *lowest*, that is, most negative energy. As n increases, the energies of the orbitals increase, becoming less negative. In the limit of $n = \infty$, the energy becomes zero; the electron is then no longer bound to the nucleus.   Beyond this there is a continuous range of energies—called the continuum—in which the electron has zero binding energy and any arbitrary amount of kinetic energy.   The difference in

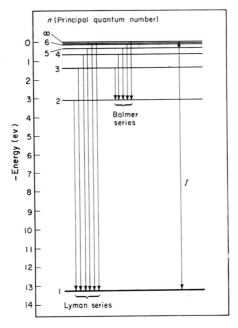

Fig. 1-5.   Simplified energy level diagram of the hydrogen atom, showing some of the spectral series.

energy between the states with $n = 1$ and $n = \infty$ is the ionization energy of the atom.   The transitions of the atom from a series of excited states to a common lower state are responsible for the various series of spectral emission lines.   Figure 1-5 indicates these energy relationships.

The quantum number n is also a measure of the mean radial distance of the electron density from the nucleus, as shown in Figure 1-6.

The quantum number l can be taken as the measure of the *classical angular momentum* of the electron, although in wave mechanics this concept is not physically defined because we no longer visualize the electron as a discrete body with a definite position and velocity. The actual magnitude of the orbital angular momentum is given by $\sqrt{l(l+1)}\mathbf{h}/2\pi$, where $\mathbf{h}$ is Planck's constant. For convenience, $\mathbf{h}/2\pi$ is often taken as the unit of angular momentum. Thus, we would then say that s electrons have zero angular momentum, p electrons ($l = 1$) have $\sqrt{1(1+1)} = \sqrt{2}$ units, d electrons ($l = 2$) have $\sqrt{6}$ units, and so forth.

The quantum number m, tells how the orbital angular momentum is oriented relative to some fixed direction. For reasons which will become clear in later sections, we shall henceforth use the symbol m_l. The rule that m_l can take only the values $l, l-1, \ldots, -(l-1), -l$ means that the

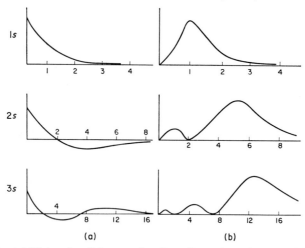

(a)   (b)

Fig. 1-6. (a) Plots of radial wave function, R, against r/a_0. (b) Plot of density distribution functions, $4\pi r^2 \psi^2$, against r/a_0. Ordinates only relative; note different abscissa scales.

vector representing orbital angular momentum can be directed only in such ways that it has components of these magnitudes in the reference direction. Actually, the angular momentum vector should be regarded as precessing about the reference direction, tracing out a cone of height m_l, as shown in Figure 1-7 for a p orbital.

We shall now examine the spacial form of s, p and d orbitals in detail. For each orbital the form is determined by both the radial and the angular parts of the wave function. Figure 1-6a shows the radial parts of the first three s orbitals. Note that the $1s$ function never crosses the zero line, while the $2s$ function crosses it once and the $3s$ function crosses it twice. For p orbitals and d orbitals the pattern is similar in that the first such orbital ($2p$, $3d$) has a radial function which never crosses zero, the second orbital of each type ($3p$, $4d$) has a radial function which crosses zero once,

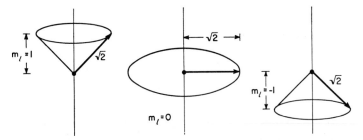

Fig. 1-7. The three projections of the angular momentum vector of length $\sqrt{l(l+1)} = \sqrt{1(1+1)} = \sqrt{2}$, for a p orbital to give m_l values of 1, 0 and -1.

and so on. Figure 1-6b shows how the electron density varies with radial distance. The functions plotted are proportional to $r^2\psi^2$. Obviously, whenever the wave functions themselves cross zero, the radial electron density function must touch zero. However, it is the angular parts of the wave functions which are of more interest and importance, and we shall now examine these for each of the three types of orbital.

s Orbitals. Let us consider first the s orbitals. Note that there is an s orbital in every *principal shell*, that is, in every group of orbitals with the same principal quantum number. It may be inferred from Table 1-1 that all s orbitals are spherically symmetrical since they all have an angular wave function which is independent of the angles θ and ϕ. The radial dependence of the first three s orbitals is plotted in Figure 1-6. The most important features of these plots to be noted are:

1. The number of *nodes*. Nodes are surfaces at which ψ and consequently ψ^2 go to 0. For s orbitals the number of these *radial nodes* is always $(n-1)$. These nodes are spherical surfaces.

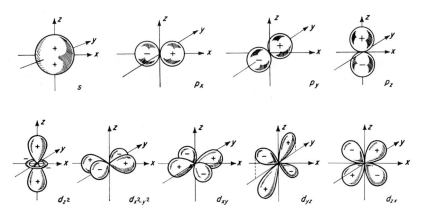

Fig. 1-8. Balloon pictures of s, p and d atomic orbitals.

2. The electron density is concentrated farther out as the value of n increases, and, in general, the radial density function has its largest value beyond the last node.

Another simple and commonly used representation of the spatial properties of orbitals is that shown in Figure 1-8. These balloon pictures are constructed so that the skin of the balloon includes within it most (say, $\sim 90\%$) of the electron density. The sign of the wave function is also given. The picture of the s orbital is actually only correct in sign for the $1s$ orbital since for all others there will be concentric spherical regions in which the sign alternates, always being positive in the innermost region. However, the main purpose of placing the signs on these diagrams is to show how the sign varies as a function of angle, and for all s orbitals the sign is independent of angle in any given spherical shell.

p Orbitals. Beginning with $n = 2$, each principal shell has three p orbitals. From Table 1-1 we see that these depend upon the angles θ and ϕ and thus are not spherically symmetrical. The three p orbitals in each set are classified as p_x, p_y and p_z. Let us look first at the $2p_z$ orbital. It is completely symmetric about the z axis, has no radial nodes and appears roughly as shown in Figure 1-8. Note that the signs of the two *lobes* are different. The p_x and p_y orbitals have exactly the same radial functions as the p_z orbital. They may easily be shown, using the angular wave functions in Table 1-1, to have the shapes indicated in Figure 1-8. The purpose of the brackets in Table 1-1 is to indicate that the p_x and p_y orbitals are *not* identical with $\psi_{2,1,1}$ and $\psi_{2,1,-1}$, respectively. These two ψ's are actually complex, but appropriately normalized sums and differences of them give the real functions called p_x and p_y. Note that the signs of the orbitals are strictly correct only for $2p$ orbitals where there are no radial nodes and an entire lobe has the same sign. For any p orbital, however, it is true that at a given radius the signs of the two lobes are opposite.

d Orbitals Beginning with $n = 3$, each principal shell will have a set of five d orbitals. All d orbitals of a given set have the same radial dependence, but differ considerably in their angular distribution. The balloon pictures in Figure 1-8 are obtained by plotting the wave functions in Table 1-1. Note the following features of the d orbitals:

1. The d_{z^2} orbital is symmetrical around the z axis.

2. The d_{xy}, d_{yz} and d_{zx} orbitals are exactly alike except that they lie in the xy, yz and zx planes, respectively.

3. The $d_{x^2-y^2}$ orbital is exactly like the d_{xy} orbital except that it is rotated by $45°$ around the z axis so that its lobes are directed along the axes.

Now that we have discussed the complete set of orbitals of the hydrogen atom and examined the lower ones in some detail, we may point out an important property of these orbitals which will be of use later. This is the property of *orthogonality*, which means that the net overlap between any two of these orbitals is exactly zero. This may easily be seen by examining Figure 1-8. For example, if we draw the $1s$ and the $2p_z$ orbitals on the same set of axes (Fig. 1-9), it is clear that the regions of space in which the two lobes of the p orbital overlap the s orbital are exactly equal, but the signs of these overlaps are opposite, so that the net overlap is zero. This orthogonality may be expressed mathematically by writing

$$\int \psi_s \psi_p \, d\tau = 0 \qquad (1\text{-}23)$$

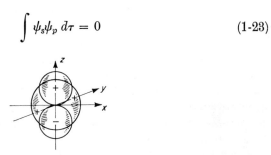

Fig. 1-9.   Diagram indicating the net zero overlap between an s and a p orbital.

1-4. Electron Spin

The electron possesses an inherent angular momentum, called spin. Experiment shows that magnitude of the angular momentum, again in units of $\mathbf{h}/2\pi$, is given by the expression $\sqrt{s(s+1)}$, in which s, the spin quantum number, takes the value $\frac{1}{2}$. With respect to a reference direction, the spin may be aligned to give components of $\frac{1}{2}$ or $-\frac{1}{2}$. By analogy to m_l, we define the quantum number m_s, and say that its values are limited to $\pm\frac{1}{2}$. Therefore, in addition to the quantum numbers n, l, m_l, it is also necessary to specify a value of m_s in order to indicate completely the state of an electron in an atom.

The spin of the electron, which corresponds to the classical concept of rotation of the spherical electron about an axis through its center, causes it to have an inherent magnetic moment. The direction of this moment coincides with the direction of the m_s vector. Thus, whenever there are two electrons with different m_s values, their magnetic moments are opposed and cancel one another. However, every electron which cannot be matched with another having the opposite m_s value to its own contributes to the magnetism of the atom or molecule in which it occurs. The subject will be discussed in more detail later (Chapter 25), but until then (with only an occasional exception such as the NO molecule), it will be sufficient just to recognize that magnetic moments of atoms and molecules having unpaired electrons will be proportional to the number of unpaired electrons.

If a single electron occupies a p, d or higher orbital, there are both orbital and spin angular momenta, and according to the rules of wave mechanics these may combine to give total angular momentum, $\sqrt{j(j+1)}$, in two ways. The quantum number j may be either $l + s$ or $l - s$, that is j may be $l \pm \frac{1}{2}$. The energy of the atom is different for the two values of j.

1-5. The Exclusion Principle

Having discussed all of the quantum numbers required to specify the state of an electron in a hydrogen atom, we shall now consider the electronic structure of atoms with two or more electrons. First, however, we must introduce one more restriction on the behavior of electrons, known as *Pauli's exclusion principle*, after the physicist Wolfgang Pauli who first recognized and formulated this restriction. It can be stated in several ways, but a statement which is useful for our purposes is: *No two electrons in one atom can have an identical set of quantum numbers.*

1-6. The Aufbau Principle; Configurations of Many-electron Atoms

By the term *configuration* of an atom, we mean the distribution of electrons among the various orbitals. The aufbau principle (German *Aufbau*, "building up") is used to deduce the electronic configurations of multielectron atoms by building them up, that is, by adding protons and electrons to the hydrogen atom. In its simplest form the aufbau principle states that we should place the electrons of a multielectron atom in a set of orbitals formally the same as those for hydrogen, filling them in the order of decreasing stability and taking account of the exclusion principle. The order of energies of the orbitals in multielectron atoms is somewhat the same as the order for the hydrogen orbitals, but differences, to be discussed below, do occur. In assuming that the multielectron atom has a set of orbitals corresponding to the hydrogen orbitals, we are really assuming that one electron does not interact with the other electrons, but acts as though it were the only electron there. This is a satisfactory assumption except that each electron will tend to modify the effect which the electrostatic field of the nucleus has on each of the other electrons. Further discussion of this point is given in Section 1-10.

The ground state of the hydrogen atom can be specified as $1s$, meaning that the single electron occupies a $1s$ orbital. In this case we need not specify the spin of this electron since it has no effect on the energy, and we need not consider the exclusion principle since there is only one electron. Actually in a large number of hydrogen atoms in free space, half of the m_s values would be $+\frac{1}{2}$ and half of them $-\frac{1}{2}$. The next element in order of increasing atomic number is helium with two electrons. Its electronic structure is worked out as follows. If we start with the nucleus, He^{2+}, and add one electron we have a hydrogen-like atom, He^+, and the electron will occupy the $1s$ orbital. It can be assigned the quantum numbers $n = 1$, $l = 0$, $m_l = 0$, $m_s = \frac{1}{2}$, where the choice of $+\frac{1}{2}$ for m_s is arbitrary. Now, where will the second electron go in the process $He^+ + e = He$? The $1s$ orbital is still the most stable one so that the electron will go into it since this can be done without violating the exclusion principle. This second electron has the quantum numbers $n = 1$, $l = 0$, $m_l = 0$, $m_s = -\frac{1}{2}$. This set differs from the first only in the spin, so that both electrons in the helium atom in its ground state are $1s$ electrons. This electron configuration is symbolized $1s^2$, the superscript indicating the number of electrons of the type specified. The spins of the two electrons are said to be *paired*. The atom is not paramagnetic.

With the configuration $1s^2$ the first principal shell is filled. Thus, when we come to lithium with three electrons, the first two go in to give Li^+ the configuration $1s^2$, but the remaining electron will have to enter the next most stable orbital, namely, $2s$. Thus the electronic configuration of Li is $1s^2 2s$. It has already been noted that in the hydrogen atom the energies of the orbitals increase with increasing n. While in the hydrogen atom there is no energy difference between an ns and an np level, there is a difference decidedly in favor of the ns level in all multielectron atoms (see below). That is why the third electron of Li has been assigned as $2s$ rather than $2p$. The beryllium atom, which has four electrons, has the configuration $1s^2 2s^2$, and all electron spins are paired. When we reach boron, which has five electrons, the configuration must be $1s^2 2s^2 2p$, and there is one unpaired spin due to the $2p$ electron.

When we come next to carbon, which has six electrons, we can easily enough decide that the electron configuration of its ground state must be $1s^2 2s^2 2p^2$, but we have as yet no basis for deciding whether the spins of the two $2p$ electrons will be paired or unpaired. Pairing is not required by the exclusion principle since the two electrons which have $n = 2$, $l = 1$ can have the same spin and differ in their m_l values. The answer to this question is provided by a rule-of-thumb called Hund's first rule, which we shall discuss more fully later (page 30). For the present, we can state the import of this rule in a form particularly suitable for present purposes, viz., so long as the exclusion principle permits, electrons with the same n

and l values will also have the same m_s values, thus, necessarily, occupying orbitals with different m_l values. Thus, for carbon the particular $1s^2 2s^2 2p^2$ configuration which occurs is that in which the two p orbitals are different, and the atom has paramagnetism corresponding to two unpaired electron spins. Similarly, for nitrogen the configuration is $1s^2 2s^2 2p^3$, and the p electrons are spread out among the three $2p$ orbitals with identical m_s values.

At oxygen we add a fourth $2p$ electron and this must enter a $2p$ orbital already occupied. Its n, l and m_l quantum numbers will then be identical with those of the electron already occupying this orbital, so these two electrons must have their spins opposed. Thus in the oxygen atom there is a paramagnetism corresponding to two unpaired spins. In fluorine the configuration is $1s^2 2s^2 2p^5$, and there is only one unpaired electron spin. Neon has the configuration $1s^2 2s^2 2p^6$ and is not paramagnetic. At this point all orbitals in the first and second principal shells are filled.

As in hydrogen, the next most stable orbitals after the $2s$ and $2p$ levels are the $3s$ and $3p$ orbitals. Consequently, beginning with sodium, $Z = 11$, and going through to argon, $Z = 18$, eight electrons are added in a manner quite analogous to the filling of the second shell. Beyond this, however, the pattern of levels deviates further from that for hydrogen. We might have expected that potassium, with $Z = 19$, would have the configuration [Ar]$3d$, where [Ar] represents a core with the configuration of argon, that is, $1s^2 2s^2 2p^6 3s^2 3p^6$. Actually the configuration of potassium is [Ar]$4s$. In order to understand this deviation from the hydrogen pattern as well as the general rule that $E_{ns} < E_{np}$, let us pause to consider in more detail the assumption implicit in the aufbau principle, namely, that a multi-electron atom ought to have a set of orbitals formally similar to those for a one-electron atom like hydrogen.

In a hydrogen or hydrogen-like atom the energy of an electron in a particular orbital depends only on the quantity Z/n^2, or, for a particular atom, on the quantum number n (see eq. 1-22). Thus, for example, the $3s$, $3p$ and $3d$ orbitals should all have the same energy. (Actually there are slight differences due to higher order effects.) An electron in one of these orbitals in hydrogen feels the presence of exactly one positive charge at the nucleus. Now, in the sodium atom an electron in, say, the $3s$ orbital feels a greater nuclear charge. If the $3s$ electron spent all of its time in regions completely outside of that occupied by the electrons of the neon core, then the charge of $+11$ on the nucleus would be shielded by the charge of -10 of the neon core, and the $3s$ electron would feel a net nuclear charge of exactly $+1$. However, this is not the case because the $3s$ wave function has a finite value even at the nucleus (Fig. 1-6) where it is subject to the full nuclear charge. Figure 1-10 illustrates how the $3s$ electron in sodium *penetrates* the neon core. Rather than being perfectly shielded so that the *effective nuclear charge*, Z^*, would be 1.0, it is, in fact, imperfectly shielded so that the effective nuclear charge is ~ 2. Now, the $3p$ orbital is also partly penetrating but not as much as the $3s$ orbital; consequently, it feels an effective nuclear charge between 1 and 2. The $3d$ orbital is practically nonpenetrating, and Z^* for it is very nearly 1.0. Thus, when the neon core is complete, there are appreciable differences in the energies of these orbitals such that the order of stability is $3s$, $3p$, $3d$.

In the region of argon and potassium in the sequence of elements, the shielding effects of inner, filled orbitals are such that the $4s$ orbital is less shielded than the $3d$ orbitals and hence more stable, whereas the $4p$ orbitals are not only more shielded than the $4s$, as usual, but also more shielded than the $3d$ orbitals. Thus the order of energies is $3s$, $3p$, $4s$, $3d$, $4p$. Similarly, following $4p$, the $5s$ orbital is more stable than $4d$. Now, in the

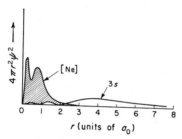

Fig. 1-10.   Penetration of the $3s$ orbital into the neon core, [Ne], in the sodium atom.

fourth principal shell we have the first set of f orbitals. These do not, however, follow the $4d$ orbitals. Instead, again mainly because of differences in the degrees of penetration of the core, they are less stable than the $5p$ and $6s$ orbitals. The complete list of the orbitals for neutral atoms, in the order in which they are filled is: $1s$, $2s$, $2p$, $3s$, $3p$, $4s$, $3d$, $4p$, $5s$, $4d$, $5p$, $6s$, $4f$, $5d$, $6p$, $7s$, $6d \sim 5f$....

The electronic structures of most of the remaining atoms which are known can be worked out using this order and the principles discussed above. There are certain minor anomalies which will be discussed at appropriate places in the text. A complete list of the elements and their ground state electron configurations is given inside the front cover.

1-7. The Periodic Table

The title "*the* periodic table" is perhaps inappropriate since literally hundreds of different forms of a periodic table of the elements have been devised. The first ones date from long before the advent of the modern theory of atomic structure and were based upon comparison of the chemical properties of the elements. It was Mendeléev who first devised tables essentially similar to those used today. A common contemporary "long form" type will be found inside the back cover of this book.

The vertical sequences in the table are called *groups*, and the horizontal sequences are called *periods*. Certain of the groups have acquired trivial names which are very commonly used. The group Ia elements (excluding hydrogen) are the *alkali metals*. Group IIa consists of the *alkaline earth metals*, group Ib of the *coinage metals*. The VIIb elements are the *halogens*. The group 0 elements are the *noble gases*, although the terms "rare gases" and "inert gases" are also encountered. The group VIb elements are sometimes called the *chalcogens*, but this term is not as common as the others mentioned.

The basic reason given by Mendeléev for the groupings was the similarity of the valences of the elements in a given group.

These similarities can now be explained in terms of the electronic structures of the atoms. We can now also understand why the metals Ag, Cu and Au, although formally similar to the metals Li, Na, K, Rb and Cs in having stable +1 oxidation states, are otherwise not very similar to these elements. In the Li group there is one valence electron outside of a very stable, rigid noble gas core, whereas in the Cu group, the outer electron has beneath it a complete *d* shell which is not particularly resistant to loss of electrons and is rather soft and deformable. We can also see why the formal similarities of the oxidation states of elements with partially filled *d* shells to those of elements which have only *s* and *p* electrons in their outer shells are really only formal. Certainly N and V have no genuine chemical similarities. In contemporary forms of the periodic table, these sequences of elements in which *d* and *f* shells are being filled, called *transition series*, are set apart from the *nontransition elements*. The sequences Li–Ne and Na–Ar are called the first short period and the second short period, respectively. The sequences Sc–Ni, Y–Pd and La–Pt (excluding the fourteen elements following immediately after La) are called the first, second and third transition series, respectively. The fourteen elements Ce–Lu, in which the 4*f* orbitals are being filled, are called the *rare earths* or the *lanthanides* (because the 4*f* electrons have little effect on their chemical properties, they all resemble lanthanum chemically). The elements in the sequence Th to element 104 are called the *actinides*, although on the whole their resemblance to actinium is not nearly so close as that of the lanthanides to lanthanum. The elements in the three transition series, where *d* shells are being filled, are sometimes called the "*d*-block elements". The lanthanides and actinides together are correspondingly called the "*f*-block elements".

1-8. The States Derived from Electronic Configurations

In general, a given electronic configuration does not correspond to a single *state* of the atom or ion. For our purposes, we shall regard a state as being characterized by particular values of (1) energy, (2) orbital angular momentum and (3) spin angular momentum. A state so characterized corresponds to the spectroscopist's *multiplet*. The term multiplet is used because, in fact, there are a number of components of the state which, in general, differ in energy by much less than one such state differs from another. These components of the state or multiplet have different values of the total angular momentum, which is a result of the combination of the orbital and spin angular momenta. Now the three characteristic quantities of a state of the system have magnitudes which are determined by the manner in which the three corresponding quantities for each of the individual electrons combine to produce the resultant quantities for the entire group of electrons. Even for the simplest cases, this is a complicated matter which cannot be dealt with entirely rigorously. However, we are fortunate in finding, from experiment, that for the lighter atoms (up to, approximately, the lanthanides) nature follows a scheme which can be understood to a fairly accurate level of approximation using a set of relatively simple rules. This set of rules may be designated the *Russell–Saunders* or *LS* coupling scheme, and it forms the subject of this section.

Each electron in an atom has a set of quantum numbers, n, l, m_l, m_s; it is the last three which are of concern here. Just as l is used, as $\sqrt{l(l + 1)}$, to indicate the orbital angular momentum of a single electron, there is a quantum number L such that $\sqrt{L(L + 1)}$ gives the total orbital angular momentum of the atom. The symbol M_L is used to represent a component of L in a reference direction and is analogous to m_l for a single electron. Similarly, we use a quantum number S to represent the total electron spin angular momentum, given by $\sqrt{S(S + 1)}$, in analogy to the quantum number s for a single electron. There is the difference here that s is limited to the value $\frac{1}{2}$, whereas S may take any integral or half-integral value beginning with 0. Components of S in a reference direction are designated by M_S, analogous to m_s.

Symbols for the states of atoms are analogous to the symbols for the orbitals of single electrons. Thus the capital letters S, P, D, F, G, H, ... are used to designate states with $L = 0, 1, 2, 3, 4, 5, \ldots$. The use of S for both a state and a quantum number is unfortunate, but in practice seldom causes any difficulty. The complete symbol for a state also indicates the total spin, but not directly in terms of the value of S. Rather, the number of different M_S values, which is called the *spin multiplicity*, is used. Thus, for a state with $S = 1$, the spin multiplicity is 3 because there are three M_S values, 1, 0, -1. In general the spin multiplicity is equal to $2S + 1$, and is indicated as a left superscript to the symbol for L. The following examples should make the usage clear.

$$\text{For } M_L = 4,\ S = \tfrac{1}{2}, \text{ the symbol is } {}^2G$$

$$\text{For } M_L = 2,\ S = \tfrac{3}{2}, \text{ the symbol is } {}^4D$$

$$\text{For } M_L = 0,\ S = 1, \text{ the symbol is } {}^3S$$

In speaking or writing of states with spin multiplicities of 1, 2, 3, 4, 5, 6, . . . we call them respectively, *singlets, doublets, triplets, quartets, quintets, sextets,* . . . . Thus, the three states shown above would be called doublet G, quartet D and triplet S, respectively.

As in the case of a single electron, we may sometimes be interested in the total angular momentum, that is the vector sum of L and S. For the entire atom this is designated J. When required, J values are appended to the symbol as right subscripts. For example, a ${}^4D$ state may have any of the following J values, the appropriate symbols being indicated:

L	M_S	J	Symbol
2	$\tfrac{3}{2}$	$\tfrac{7}{2}$	${}^4D_{7/2}$
2	$\tfrac{1}{2}$	$\tfrac{5}{2}$	${}^4D_{5/2}$
2	$-\tfrac{1}{2}$	$\tfrac{3}{2}$	${}^4D_{3/2}$
2	$-\tfrac{3}{2}$	$\tfrac{1}{2}$	${}^4D_{1/2}$

In order to determine what states may actually occur for a given atom or ion, we begin with the following definitions, which represent the essence of the approximation we are using:

$$M_L = m_l^{(1)} + m_l^{(2)} + m_l^{(3)} + \ldots + m_l^{(n)}$$

$$M_S = m_s^{(1)} + m_s^{(2)} + m_s^{(3)} + \ldots + m_s^{(n)}$$

in which $m_l^{(i)}$ and $m_s^{(i)}$ stand for the m_l and m_s values of the ith electron in an atom having a total of n electrons.

In general it is not necessary to pay specific attention to all the electrons in an atom when calculating M_L and M_S since those groups of electrons which completely fill any one set of orbitals (s, p, d, etc.) collectively contribute zero to M_L and to M_S. For instance, a complete set of p electrons includes two with $m_l = 0$, two with $m_l = 1$ and two with $m_l = -1$, the sum, $0 + 0 + 1 + 1 - 1 - 1$, being zero. At the same time, half of the electrons have $m_s = \tfrac{1}{2}$ and the other half have $m_s = -\tfrac{1}{2}$, making M_S equal to zero. The generalization to any filled shell should be obvious. Therefore, we need only concern ourselves with partly filled shells.

For a partly filled shell, there is always more than one way of assigning m_l and m_s values to the various electrons. All ways must be considered except those which are either prohibited by the exclusion principle or are physically redundant, as will be explained presently. For convenience we shall use symbols in which $+$ and $-$ superscripts represent $m_s = +\frac{1}{2}$ and $m_s = -\frac{1}{2}$ respectively. Thus, when the first electron has $m_l = 1$, $m_s = +\frac{1}{2}$, the second electron has $m_l = 2$, $m_s = -\frac{1}{2}$, the third electron has $m_l = 0$, $m_s = +\frac{1}{2}$, etc., we shall write $(1^+, 2^-, 0^+, \ldots)$. Such a specification of m_l and m_s values of all electrons will be called a *microstate*.

Let us now consider the two configurations $2p3p$ and $2p^2$. In the first case, our freedom to assign quantum numbers m_l and m_s to the two electrons is unrestricted by the exclusion principle since the electrons already differ in their principal quantum numbers. Thus microstates such as $(1^+, 1^+)$ and $(0^-, 0^-)$ are permitted. They are not permitted for the $2p^2$ configuration, however. Secondly, since the two electrons of the $2p3p$ configuration can be distinguished by their n quantum numbers, two microstates such as $(1^+, 0^-)$ and $(0^-, 1^+)$ are physically different. However, for the $2p^2$ configuration, such a pair are actually identical since there is no *physical* distinction between "the first electron" and "the second electron." For the $2p3p$ configuration there are thus $6 \times 6 = 36$ different microstates, while for the $2p^2$ configuration six of these are nullified by the exclusion principle and the remaining 30 consist of pairs which are physically redundant. Hence, there are but 15 microstates for the $2p^2$ configuration.

TABLE 1-2
Tabulation of Microstates for a p^2 Configuration

(a)

M_L	M_S		
	1	0	-1
2		$(1^+,1^-)$	
1	$(1^+,0^+)$	$(1^+,0^-)(1^-,0^+)$	$(1^-,0^-)$
0	$(1^+,-1^+)$	$(1^+,-1^-)(0^+,0^-)(1^-,-1^+)$	$(1^-,-1^-)$
-1	$(-1^+,0^+)$	$(-1^+,0^-)(-1^-,0^+)$	$(-1^-,0^-)$
-2		$(-1^+,-1^-)$	

(b)

M_L	M_S		
	1	0	-1
2			
1	$(1^+,0^+)$	$(1^-,0^+)$	$(1^-,0^-)$
0	$(1^+,-1^+)$	$(1^-,-1^+)(0^+,0^-)$	$(1^-,-1^-)$
-1	$(-1^+,0^+)$	$(-1^-,0^+)$	$(-1^-,0^-)$
-2			

Table 1-2a shows a tabulation of the microstates for the $2p^2$ configuration, in which they are arranged according to their M_L and M_S values. It is now our problem to deduce from this array the possible values for L and S. We first note that the maximum and minimum values of M_L are 2 and -2, each of which is associated with $M_S = 0$. These must be the two extreme M_L values derived from a state with $L = 2$ and $S = 0$, namely a ^1D state. Also belonging to this ^1D state must be microstates with $M_S = 0$ and $M_L = 1$, 0 and -1. If we now delete a set of five microstates appropriate to the ^1D state, we are left with those shown in Table 1-2b. Note that it is not important which of the two or three microstates we have removed from a box which originally contained several, since the microstates occupying the same box actually mix among themselves to give new ones. However, the *number* of microstates per box is fixed, whatever their exact descriptions may be. Looking now at Table 1-2b, we see that there are microstates with $M_L = 1$, 0, -1 for each of the M_S values, 1, 0, -1. Nine such microstates constitute the components of a ^3P state. When they are removed, there remains only a single microstate with $M_L = 0$ and $M_S = 0$. This must be associated with a ^1S state of the configuration. Thus, the permitted states of the $2p^2$ configuration—or any np^2 configuration—are ^1D, ^3P and ^1S. It is to be noted that the sum of the degeneracies of these states must be equal to the number of microstates. The ^1S state has neither spin nor orbital degeneracy; its degeneracy number is therefore 1. The ^1D state has no spin degeneracy but is orbitally $2L + 1 = 5$-fold degenerate. The ^3P state has 3-fold spin degeneracy and 3-fold orbital degeneracy giving it a total degeneracy number of $3 \times 3 = 9$. The sum of these degeneracy numbers is indeed 15.

For the $2p3p$ configuration the allowed states are again of the types of S, P and D, but now there is a singlet and a triplet of each kind. This can be demonstrated by making a table of the microstates and proceeding as before. It can be seen perhaps more easily by noting that for *every* combination of $m_l^{(1)}$ and $m_l^{(2)}$ there are four microstates, with spin assignments $++$, $+-$, $-+$ and $--$. One of these, either $+-$ or $-+$, can be taken as belonging to a singlet state and the other three belong then to a triplet state. It will be noted that the sum of the degeneracy numbers for the six states ^3D, ^1D, ^3P, ^1P, ^3S, ^1S is 36, the number of microstates.

For practice in using the LS coupling scheme, the reader may verify, by the method used for np^2 that an nd^2 configuration gives rise to the states ^3F, ^3P, ^1G, ^1D and ^1S, and that an np^3 configuration gives the states ^4S, ^1P, ^1D.

While the method shown for determining the states of an electron configuration will obviously become very cumbersome as the number of electrons increases beyond perhaps 5, there is, fortunately, a relationship which makes many of the problems with still larger configurations tractable. This relationship is called the *hole formalism*, and with it a partially filled shell of n electrons can be treated either as n electrons or as $N - n$ positrons, where N represents the total capacity of the shell. As far as electrostatic interactions of electrons among themselves are concerned, it makes no difference whether they are all positively charged or all negatively charged since the energies of interaction are all proportional to the product of two charges. It is actually rather easy to see that the hole formalism must be true, for, whenever we select a microstate for n electrons in a shell of capacity N, there remains a set of m_l and m_s values which could be used by $N - n$ electrons.

The several states derived from a particular configuration have different energies. However, purely theoretical evaluation of these energy differences is neither easy nor accurate, since they are expressed as certain integrals representing electron–electron repulsions, which cannot be precisely evaluated by computation. However, when there are many terms arising from a configuration, it is usually possible to express all of the energy differences in terms of only a few integrals. Thus, when the energies of just a few of the states have been measured, the others may be estimated with fair accuracy, though not exactly, because the coupling scheme itself is only an approximation. The magnitudes of the energy differences are generally comparable to energies of chemical bonds and chemical reactions. For example, the energies of the ^1D and ^1S excited states of the carbon atom in the configuration $1s^2 2s^2 2p^2$ are ~ 25 and ~ 56 kcal/mole, respectively, above the ^3P ground state.

In this book, the major use for the energy differences between states will be in the treatment of transition metal ions by the crystal and ligand field theories. Thus, further discussion of the energies will be deferred until then (Chapter 26).

As mentioned before, each state of the type ^{2S+1}L actually consists of a group of substates with different values of the quantum number J. The energy differences between these substates are generally an order of magnitude less than the energy differences between the various states themselves, and usually they can be ignored in ordinary problems of chemical interest. However, in certain cases, for example, in understanding the magnetic properties of the lanthanides (see Chapter 31) and in nearly all problems with the very heavy elements (those of the 3rd transition series and the actinides), these energy differences are of great significance and cannot be ignored. Indeed, for the very heavy elements they become comparable in magnitude to the energy differences between the ^{2S+1}L states. When this happens, the LS coupling method becomes inherently unreliable, and different, more complex treatments must be used.

The cause of the separation between substates with different J values is direct coupling between the spin and orbital angular momenta of the electrons. In the LS coupling scheme, this is assumed to be negligible. Thus, as stated, we assume that the $m_l^{(i)}$ add only to one another and the $m_s^{(i)}$ add only to one another. When coupling between $m_l^{(i)}$ and $m_s^{(i)}$ for each electron becomes *very* strong, it is possible to utilize another relatively simple method to determine states of the electron configuration. In this method, known as the jj coupling scheme, one assumes that the states arise from the various combinations of j values for each electron. In the jj coupling scheme, the quantum numbers M_L and M_S no longer are meaningful and the states are characterized by other quantum numbers. Since jj coupling will not find any direct application in the later parts of this book, we shall not discuss it further here.

1-9. Hund's Rules

Although the general problem of assessing the relative energies of all the ^{2S+1}L states of a configuration is a complex one beyond the scope of this book, there does exist a set of essentially empirical rules which can tell us which state will be the *ground state*, that is, the most stable one. There is actually sufficient theoretical backing for these rules (which, however, we shall omit) to justify the statement that they are as reliable as the LS coupling scheme itself. In other words, in a case where Hund's rules fail, we have no business speaking of the $^{2S+1}L_J$ states anyway. These rules are:

1. The ground state will always have the highest value of spin multiplicity.
2. If several states have the highest spin multiplicity, the most stable one will be that which has the highest value of L.
3. The energies of the substates will increase as the J values increase for a state derived from a configuration of a shell less than half full; the order of the substates is reversed when the shell is more than half full.

We have already used Hund's first rule, in a slightly different form, in discussing the configurations of many-electron atoms (sec. 1-6). In its present form, we see that it alone tells us that for the np^2 configuration the ^3P state is the ground state. For the nd^2 configuration, Hund's first rule tells us that the ground state must be either ^3F or ^3P; the second rule pinpoints ^3F as the ground state.

It should be emphasized that Hund's rules are generally applicable only to the ground state. They are *not* useful for determining the order of the other states in general.

1-10. Orbitals in Many-electron Atoms

We have seen how electron configurations of many-electron atoms can be built up by filling the proper number of hydrogen-like orbitals in order of increasing energy and in accord with the exclusion principle. It has been noted briefly (page 20) that each of these orbitals is influenced by the electrons occupying the others, and certain shifts in the relative energies of orbitals, due to penetration effects, have been noted. In this section these effects will be discussed further.

As indicated in the discussion relating to equations 1-15 to 1-22, the wave functions for hydrogen-like orbitals are products of a radial function, R, and two angular functions, Θ and Φ. It is the latter functions, which depend on the quantum numbers l and m_l, that determine the type of orbital, e.g., p_x, p_y, p_z, d_{xy}, d_{z^2}, etc., we are dealing with. These characteristic angular functions can be assumed to be invariant to the presence of electrons in other orbitals. However, the presence of an electron in one orbital has an influence upon the radial function of all other orbitals in an atom, since each radial wave function depends on the effective nuclear charge (see Table 1-1), and the interpenetration of orbitals causes the occupation of one to influence the effective nuclear charge for the others.

This line of reasoning led Hartree to devise a method for calculating radial wave functions for the orbitals in many-electron atoms. Hartree's procedure is an iterative one which begins with an assumed set of radial wave functions for each of the occupied orbitals of an atom. Then, for each orbital a new radial function is calculated for an electron in this orbital moving in the field provided by the nucleus and all of the other electrons in the assumed orbitals. As a result, all of the initial radial functions are somewhat altered, giving a new set, which are better approximations than those of the first set. Again, the radial function for each orbital is recalculated, using the field provided by the nucleus and the second set of radial functions for the orbitals of all other electrons. Thus a third, still better, set of radial wave functions is obtained. This procedure is repeated many times until the functions in the nth set differ negligibly from those in the $(n-1)$th set. The self-consistent functions so obtained, multiplied by the appropriate hydrogenic angular functions, Θ and Φ, are called *Hartree orbitals*.

A further refinement, which we shall not explain in detail, is to include the effects of exchange energies, which vary with the radial wave functions. The orbitals obtained in this way are called *Hartree–Fock* orbitals. They provide the best description of the electron distributions in many-electron atoms which can be obtained within the electron configuration approximation. They also provide the best starting point for calculating the magnitude of overlap of orbitals in chemical bonds (see page 72).

1-11. Ionization Potentials or Ionization Energies

It is always possible to detach one or more electrons from an atom, ion or molecule if sufficient energy is provided to do the necessary work. The minimum energy required to remove an electron from an atom, ion or molecule, leaving each without any kinetic energy, is called the *ionization potential*. For a given species, the energy required to remove the first electron is called the first ionization potential, and so on. Note that the first ionization potential of, say, Cl_2^+ is the same as the second ionization potential of Cl_2. By convention, the *algebraic signs of all ionization potentials are positive*. The symbol I is usually used to signify an ionization potential.

The first ionization potentials of the elements vary in relation to their positions in the periodic table, as shown in Figure 1-11. With the exception

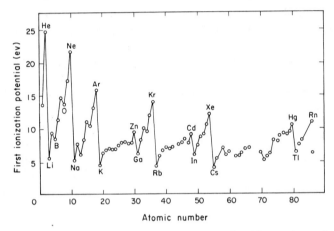

Fig. 1-11. Variation in first ionization potentials with atomic number.

of mercury, the maxima in the curve all occur at noble gases, and the deeper minima all occur with the alkali metals. These facts show that the closed configurations of the noble gases are most difficult to disturb by removal of an electron, whereas the lone electron outside of a noble gas configuration, which is the common feature of each alkali metal atom, is very easy to remove. Furthermore, although there are irregularities, the potentials rise steeply in going from an alkali metal to the following noble gas. These facts can be accounted for on the basis of the shielding of one electron by others.

As we go from, say, sodium, with a nuclear charge of 11 to argon with a nuclear charge of 18, the eight electrons which are also added are all in the same principal shell. Because the radial wave functions of all electrons in the same shell are either identical or very similar, no one electron spends much time between the nucleus and any other electron. Thus the extent to which these electrons shield one another from the steadily increasing nuclear charge is slight. For example, the effective nuclear charge for the $3s$

electron in sodium is ~ 2, whereas that for the s or p electron in argon is ~ 6.7. It is this substantially greater restraining force which is responsible for the much tighter binding of the electrons.

For a given atom the ionization potentials always increase in the order $I_1 < I_2 < I_3 < \ldots < I_n$. This is obviously due to the fact that removal of a negative charge from a species of charge $+k$ ($k = 0, 1, 2 \ldots$) must be easier than removal of a negative charge from a similar species of charge $+(k + 1)$ or greater.

1-12. Electron Affinities

In general, it is also possible to attach an additional electron to any atom, ion or molecule. The energy which is *released* when this takes place is called the *electron affinity* of the species, usually symbolized A. It will be noted that this sign convention is *opposite* to the one stated above, but this definition of electron affinity is so well established that we must accept it as it is. Negative electron affinities do exist—that is, when the species concerned does not "want" another electron and must be forced to accept it—but the cases of greatest interest are those in which the electron affinity is positive.

Table 1-3 lists some representative electron affinities. Note that in

TABLE 1-3

Some Electron Affinities of Atoms in Electron Volts

H	0.747[a]	N	~ -0.1[d]
F	3.45[b]	S	2.07[e]
Cl	3.61[b]	Li	0.54[a]
Br	3.36[b]	Na	0.74[a]
I	3.06[b]	Be	~ -0.6[a]
O	1.47[c]	Mg	~ -0.3[a]

[a] H. A. Skinner and H. O. Pritchard, *Trans. Faraday Soc.*, **49**, 1254 (1953).
[b] R. S. Berry and C. W. Riemann, *J. Chem. Phys.*, **38**, 1540 (1963).
[c] L. M. Branscomb, *Nature*, **182**, 248 (1958).
[d] A. P. Ginsburg and J. M. Miller, *J. Inorg. Nucl. Chem.*, **7**, 351 (1958).
[e] L. M. Branscomb and S. J. Smith, *J. Chem. Phys.*, **25**, 598 (1956).

many cases the accuracy is low. This is because, unlike ionization potentials, which can usually be directly measured spectroscopically, electron affinities are usually measured by less accurate, often indirect, methods.

The halogens have the highest electron affinities, a fact which may be attributed to their completing noble gas configurations upon acquisition of one electron. On the other hand, for the alkali metals, which do not bind their outermost electron very strongly to begin with, the electron

2 + A.I.C.

affinities are very low: ~ 17 kcal/g-atom for sodium and hydrogen and probably close to zero for the others. Beryllium and magnesium also have small negative electron affinities.

As might be expected, second electron affinities of atoms (e.g., $O^- + e = O^{2-}$) are all negative so far as is known. This is because of the electrostatic repulsion of the second electron by the negative charge on the ion. Finally, it may be noted that the electron affinity of an atom is numerically equal to the ionization potential of the corresponding anion.

The electron affinities of certain transition metals have also been estimated[2]; gold, which is known to form the compound Cs^+Au^- has a value about 2.2 ev while Ag, Cu, Pd and Pt have values not less than about 1 ev.

References

Harris, L. and A. L. Loeb, *Introduction to Wave Mechanics*, McGraw-Hill, New York, 1963.

Herzberg, G., *Atomic Spectra and Atomic Structure*, Dover, New York, 1944. A classic which presents lucidly and succinctly "what every chemist should know" about atomic spectra and the electronic structure of atoms.

Hochstrasser, R. M., *Electrons in Atoms*, Benjamin, New York, 1964. A good introductory text.

Kauzmann, W., *Quantum Chemistry*, Academic Press, New York, 1957. Contains a good introduction to mathematical treatment of atomic structure.

Linnett, J. W., *Wave Mechanics and Valency*, Wiley, New York, 1960. A short and lucidly written introduction which can be recommended.

Slater, J. C., *Quantum Theory of Atomic Structure*, Vol. I, McGraw-Hill, New York, 1960. A very fine introduction to the necessary wave mechanics which carries the theory of atomic structure with elegance and clarity through most topics of importance to inorganic chemistry.

Vedeneyev, V. I., *et al.*, *Bond Energies, Ionization Potentials and Electron Affinities*, Arnold, London, 1965.

[2] R. S. Nyholm, *Congress on Catalysis* Vol. I, page 83, North Holland Publishing Co., Amsterdam, 1965.

2

The Nature of Ionic Substances

2-1. Introduction

The reason atoms combine to form chemical compounds is that, when the several atoms approach one another closely, their electron clouds interact in such a way that the energy of the system is lowered. We can also say that the interactions are such as to produce forces of attraction. In this chapter we consider one of the simplest kinds of attractive force, namely, the electrostatic attraction between ions of opposite charge. There are a vast number of solid compounds which can be considered as very closely approximating aggregates of positive and negative ions interacting in a purely electrostatic manner. We shall first consider the energetics of perfectly ionic materials, assuming the existence of a certain arrangement of the ions in the lattice, and we shall then consider the various kinds of lattices which commonly occur, the factors favoring one or another type of lattice, and the effects of deviations from the idealized concept of an ionic substance.

Most ionic compounds are formed by combination of elements near "opposite ends" of the periodic table. They are usually oxides, sulfides or halides of the electropositive metals such as those of groups I, II and III and the transition series. Lead in the $+2$ oxidation state also forms more or less ionic salts, and large oxo anions—ClO_4^-, CO_3^{2-}, NO_3^- and others—form ionic salts with many metal ions. The main requirements for the formation of ionic compounds, that is, those solids which consist of an array of positive and negative ions held together almost entirely by the coulomb forces between the oppositely charged ions, are that the metal ions have a relatively low ionization potential and that the nonmetal atoms or radicals have a relatively high electron affinity. In general the electron affinities are considerably less than the ionization potentials, but even where the difference is not large, e.g., ca. 2.5 kcal/g-atom between Cs and Cl, other factors must be involved in the formation of ionic solids. Similarly, in view of the fact that the electron affinity of oxygen (for the acquisition of two electrons to form the oxide ion) is actually negative, it may seem surprising that so many oxides are ionic. An explanation for this and similar facts will be given in this chapter.

2-2. Lattice Energies of Ionic Crystals

As an example of an *idealized* ionic substance let us consider a 1:1 compound of the type $(M^+)(X^-)$. M^+ is a cation, spherical in shape, incompressible, and having a sharply defined surface. Similarly, X^- is a spherical anion, also incompressible and having a definite size. This kind of model is commonly called a hard-sphere electrostatic model. When these cations and anions are brought together in large and equal numbers, they will arrange themselves in a regular array in which they tend to occupy the minimum volume and have the least electrostatic energy. (The dependence of the geometry of the array on the relative sizes of the two ions is discussed later.) Let us assume that the arrangement adopted is that shown in Figure 2-1, the type of lattice arrangement occurring in sodium chloride.

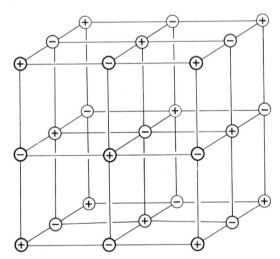

Fig. 2-1. The sodium chloride structure.

Let us call the M—X distances r. Using Figure 2-1 and simple trigonometry it can be shown that an M^+ ion is surrounded by six X^- ions (nearest neighbors) at a distance r, twelve M^+ ions (second nearest neighbors) at a distance $\sqrt{2}r$, eight more distant X^- ions at $\sqrt{3}r$, six M^+ ions at $2r$, twenty-four more X^- ions at $\sqrt{5}r$, etc. The electrostatic interaction energy of the M^+ ion with each of these surrounding ions is equal to the product of the charge on each ion, Z^+ and Z^-, divided by the distance. Hence the total electrostatic energy of this positive ion can be written

$$E = \frac{6e^2}{r} (Z^+)(Z^-) + \frac{12e^2}{\sqrt{2}r} (Z^+)^2 + \frac{8e^2}{\sqrt{3}r} (Z^+)(Z^-) + \frac{6e^2}{2r} (Z^+)^2 \cdots$$

$$= -\frac{e^2|Z|^2}{r} \left(6 - \frac{12}{\sqrt{2}} + \frac{8}{\sqrt{3}} - \frac{6}{2} + \frac{24}{\sqrt{5}} \cdots \right) \tag{2-1}$$

Actually, it is possible to set up the general formula for the terms in equation 2-1 from geometrical considerations. The sum of all these terms, that is, the sum of an infinite series, is called the *Madelung constant*. It should be clear that the value of the Madelung constant is characteristic of the geometrical arrangement and independent of the particular ions or their charges (i.e., they might both be doubly or triply charged). The above series converges to a value of 1.747558 ... and can be evaluated to any required degree of accuracy. In many cases the series diverge, and the evaluation of the Madelung constants for such structures requires considerable mathematical manipulation. The Madelung constants for many commonly occurring lattices have been calculated.[1]

If we made a mole (N ion pairs) of the compound MX, then NE would be the energy of the process

$$M^+(g) + X^-(g) = MX(s) \tag{2-2}$$

This is so because if we wrote out an expression for the electrostatic energy of an X^- ion it would be identical with equation 2-1. If we added the electrostatic energies for a mole of each ion, the result would be twice the true electrostatic energy per mole because we would be counting each pairwise interaction twice. Thus NE is the electrostatic potential energy per mole for a hard-sphere ionic solid with the NaCl structure.

In the hard-sphere model the M^+—X^- distance is fixed by the sum of the radii of M^+ and X^-. We know that real atoms are not rigid spheres, and their equilibrium separation in an ionic solid must therefore be a consequence of some short-range repulsive force due to overlapping of their electron clouds which comes into play as they approach. Born proposed the simple assumption that the repulsive force between two ions could be represented by the expression B'/r^n in which B' and n are constants, as yet undetermined, characteristic of the ion pair concerned. We can therefore write, for the repulsive energy of a particular ion in a crystal,

$$E_{rep} = \frac{B}{r^n} \tag{2-3}$$

---

[1] See T. C. Waddington, *Adv. Inorg. Chem. Radiochem.*, **1**, 157 (1956) for a tabulation.

where B is related to B' by the crystal geometry. The total electrostatic energy of the crystal, that is, the *inherently negative* lattice energy, U, is then given by

$$U = \frac{N(Z^+)(Z^-)Ae^2}{r} + \frac{NB}{r^n} \qquad (2\text{-}4)$$

where A is the Madelung constant. This energy, U, is exactly the energy of reaction 2-2, if these are the only forces involved. There is a relation between B and n which may be determined if we recognize that in the equilibrium state of the crystal ($r = r_0$) the energy is a minimum as a function of r. Thus

$$\left(\frac{dU}{dr}\right)_{r=r_0} = 0 = -\frac{A(Z^+)(Z^-)Ne^2}{r_0{}^2} - \frac{nNB}{r_0{}^{n+1}} \qquad (2\text{-}5)$$

which yields

$$B = -\frac{A(Z^+)(Z^-)e^2}{n}r_0{}^{n-1} \qquad (2\text{-}6)$$

Substituting equation 2-6 into equation 2-4, we obtain

$$U = N(Z^+)(Z^-)A\frac{e^2}{r_0}\left(1 - \frac{1}{n}\right) \qquad (2\text{-}7)$$

The numerical value of n can be derived from measurements of the compressibility of the solid and may also be estimated theoretically. The experimentally derived values and the values calculated by Pauling for noble gas-like ions are given in Table 2-1. It can be seen that the ex-

TABLE 2-1

Sample n Values

Determined by experiment		Estimated from theory	
Compound	n	Noble gas configuration of ion	n
LiF	5.9	He	5
LiCl	8.0	Ne	7
LiBr	8.7	Ar	9
NaCl	9.1	Kr	10
NaBr	9.5	Xe	12

perimental values are reasonably close to the averages of the appropriate theoretical estimates. It can also be seen that even if the n used is off by 1.0, the lattice energy will be in error only by 1–2%.

In very accurate calculations some correction factors are required because equation 2-4 does not take account of other minor forces. There are three main refinements.

1. *Inclusion of van der Waals forces.* Van der Waals forces operate between all atoms, ions or molecules, but are relatively very weak. They are due to attractions between oscillating dipoles in adjacent atoms and vary approximately as $1/r^6$. They can be calculated from the polarizabilities and ionization potentials of the atoms or ions.

2. *Use of a more rigorous expression for the repulsive energy.* The simple Born expression (eq. 2-3) for the repulsive energy is not strictly correct from quantum mechanical considerations. More refined expressions do not greatly change the results, however.

3. *Consideration of "zero point energy" of the crystal.* The "zero point energy" of the crystal is that energy of vibration of the ions which the crystal possesses even at the absolute zero. This can be calculated from the lattice vibration frequencies.

The data given in Table 2-2 indicate the relative importance of the various contributions to the lattice energy.

TABLE 2-2

Components of Lattice Energy

(In electron volts)

Energy	LiF	NaCl	CsI
Coulomb	−12.4	−8.92	−6.4
Repulsion	+1.9	+1.03	+0.63
Van der Waals	−0.17	−0.13	−0.48
Zero point	+0.17	+0.08	+0.3

The calculation of lattice energies of ionic compounds is very important since, in general, there is no *direct* way to measure them experimentally, although they can be obtained from certain experimental data using the Born-Haber cycle which is discussed immediately below. For example, the heat of vaporization of NaCl does not give the lattice energy because up to the highest temperatures at which accurate measurements can be made the gas phase consists of NaCl molecules (or ion pairs), and it has so far proved impossible to get an accurate estimate of the heat of dissociation of $NaCl(g)$ into $Na^+(g)$ and $Cl^-(g)$ since $NaCl(g)$ normally dissociates into atoms.

2-3. The Born-Haber Cycle

The heats of formation of various ionic compounds show tremendous variations. In a general way, we know that many factors contribute to the over-all heat of formation, namely, the ionization potentials, electron affinities, heats of vaporization and dissociation of the elements, and the lattice energy of the compound. The Born-Haber cycle is a thermodynamic cycle which shows the interrelation of these quantities and enables us to see how variations in heats of formation can be attributed to the variations in these individual quantities. In order to construct the Born-Haber cycle we consider the following thermochemical equations, using NaCl as an example.

$$
\begin{array}{ll}
\text{Na(s)} = \text{Na(g)} & \Delta H_{\text{subl}}(\text{Na}) \\
\text{Na(g)} = \text{Na}^+(\text{g}) + e^- & I_{\text{Na}} \\
\tfrac{1}{2}\text{Cl}_2(\text{g}) = \text{Cl(g)} & \tfrac{1}{2}\Delta H_{\text{diss}}(\text{Cl}_2) \\
\text{Cl(g)} + e^- = \text{Cl}^-(\text{g}) & -A_{\text{Cl}} \\
\text{Na}^+(\text{g}) + \text{Cl}^-(\text{g}) = \text{NaCl(s)} & U \\
\hline
\text{Na(s)} + \tfrac{1}{2}\text{Cl}_2(\text{g}) = \text{NaCl(s)} & \Delta H_f(\text{NaCl})
\end{array}
$$

The net change expressed by the last equation can be achieved by carrying out the preceding five steps successively, as indicated in Figure 2-2, which is an example of the Born-Haber cycle.

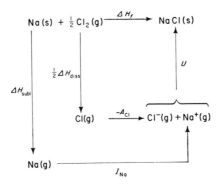

Fig. 2-2.   Born-Haber cycle for NaCl.

The energies are interrelated by the equation

$$\Delta H_f = \Delta H_{\text{subl}} + I + \tfrac{1}{2}\Delta H_{\text{diss}} - A_{\text{Cl}} + U \qquad (2\text{-}8)$$

The Born-Haber cycle is used to calculate any one of the quantities in equation 2-8 when all of the others are known or to provide a check on the internal consistency of a complete set of these quantities. Normally, ΔH_f, ΔH_{subl}, I and ΔH_{diss} are known. Direct measurement of electron affinities is usually rather difficult, and only for the halogens have really accurate values been obtained. In these cases the cycle can then be used as a check on the calculated lattice energies, which, when all refinements are included, are found to be quite accurate. For example, the calculated lattice energy of NaCl is 7.94 ev, and the value obtained from the Born-Haber cycle is 7.86 ev, a difference of $\sim 1\%$. Since we have such checks to give us confidence in the accuracy of computed lattice energies, the cycle is more commonly used to determine electron affinities. For example, the electron affinity of oxygen is a very important quantity which cannot be measured directly, if for no other reason than that it is highly negative, namely, -7.3 ev. This value has been obtained by applying the Born-Haber cycle to various ionic oxides.

The Born-Haber cycle is also valuable as a means of analyzing and correlating the variations in stability of various ionic compounds. As an example, it enables us to explain why MgO is a stable ionic compound despite the fact that the Mg^{2+} and O^{2-} ions are both formed endothermically, not to mention the considerable energies required to vaporize Mg(s) and to dissociate $O_2(g)$. ΔH_f is highly negative despite these opposing tendencies because the lattice energy of MgO more than balances them out.

The Born-Haber cycle also enables us to understand why most metals fail to form stable ionic compounds in low valence states (e.g., MnCl, CaCl, AlO, etc.). Let us consider a metal M with 1st and 2nd ionization energies of 160 and 300 kcal/mole respectively (fairly typical values). Suppose this metal forms a chloride, MCl_2, with the fluorite structure (see page 48), and let us assume that the monochloride would have the NaCl structure. For simplicity we shall also assume $r_{M^{2+}} = r_{M^+} = 1.00$ A, although of course the M^+ ion would be larger than M^{2+} and this would further decrease the lattice energy of MCl. For the two compounds, MCl and MCl_2, the Born-Haber cycles are as follows:

MCl		MCl_2	
Reaction	Energy (kcal/mole)	Reaction	Energy (kcal/mole)
(1) $M(s) = M(g)$	ΔH_{subl}	$M(s) = M(g)$	ΔH_{subl}
(2) $M(g) = M^+(g) + e^-$	160	$M(g) = M^{2+}(g) + 2e^-$	460
(3) $\frac{1}{2}Cl_2(g) = Cl(g)$	29	$Cl_2(g) = 2Cl(g)$	58
(4) $Cl(g) + e^- = Cl^-(g)$	-87	$2Cl(g) + 2e^- = 2Cl^-(g)$	-174
(5)[a] $M^+(g) + Cl^-(g) = MCl(s)$	-184	$M^{2+}(g) + 2Cl^-(g) = MCl_2(s)$	-1061
(6) $M(s) + \frac{1}{2}Cl_2(g) = MCl(s)$	$-82 + \Delta H_{subl}$	$M(s) + Cl_2(g) = MCl_2(s)$	$-717 + \Delta H_{subl}$

[a] Calculated using Madelung constants of 1.748 and 5.039 for the NaCl and CaF_2 structures respectively, with $r_{Cl^-} = 1.81$ A and taking n, the Born exponent, as 9.

It can be seen that while the energies of reactions (1)–(4) favor MCl over MCl_2 by 242 kcal/mole, this is completely overwhelmed by the fact that

2*

the lattice energies favor MCl_2 by 877 kcal/mole. From the above figures it can be shown that for the reaction

$$2MCl(s) = MCl_2(s) + M(s) \tag{2-9}$$

$\Delta H = -553 - \Delta H_{subl}$ kcal/mole.

2-4. Other Thermochemical Cycles: Hydration and Ligation Energies

Although this subject is not an inherent part of the general theory of ionic solids, it is somewhat related and it is convenient to treat it at this point, since other thermodynamic cycles are similar in principle to the Born-Haber cycle. Their purpose is to enable us to estimate energies of processes not subject to direct experimental measurement or theoretical computation by properly combining the results of other measurements and computations.

The hydration energy of an ion is defined as the energy released in the process:

$$Z^{\pm x}(g) + \infty H_2O(l) = Z^{\pm x}(aq)$$

It should be clear that energy will be *released* in such a process, since there are forces of attraction between the dipolar water molecules and the ions (see Fig. 2-10); it is to be noted that *both* positive and negative ions will be hydrated—or, quite generally, solvated if non-aqueous solvents such as CH_3OH are used—but of course the positive ends of the dipole of the solvent molecules will approach the anion closest. From another point of view, the process is one in which a charge is moved from a medium of low dielectric constant and zero polarizability (the vacuum; $\epsilon = 1$) to one of higher dielectric constant and appreciable electric polarizability.

For an ionic salt, say NaCl, we consider the cycle shown in Figure 2-3.

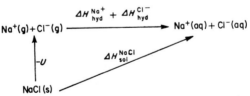

Fig. 2-3. A thermochemical cycle including ionic hydration energies for Na^+ and Cl^-.

The corresponding thermochemical equation is:

$$\Delta H_{hyd}^{Na^+} + \Delta H_{hyd}^{Cl^-} = U + \Delta H_{sol}^{NaCl} \tag{2-10}$$

U, the lattice energy, is obtainable by computation using the ionic model of the compound or by using a Born-Haber cycle, as discussed earlier. ΔH_{sol}^{NaCl} is easily determined by experiment. Thus, the sum of the hydration energies of the cation and the anion may be calculated. Unfortunately, there is no purely thermochemical way to separate this sum of hydration energies into its two parts. However, methods have been devised for doing so; these methods are not rigorous, and the errors involved are not known with certainty, but they are probably not more than a few kcal/mole. Table 2-3 gives some representative hydration energies.[2]

TABLE 2-3
Some Representative Hydration Energies, kcal/mole[a]

Li^+	124.4	NH_4^+	72.5 ± 5.5
Na^+	97.0	$(CH_3)_4N^+$	32 ± 8
K^+	77.0	F^-	120.8 ± 3.5
Rb^+	71.9	Cl^-	86.8 ± 3.1
Cs^+	66.1	Br^-	80.3 ± 3.5
Mg^{2+}	459.1	I^-	70.5 ± 3.5
Ba^{2+}	325.2	ClO_4^-	57 ± 4
Sc^{3+}	631.3	OH^-	110 ± 8

[a] According to ref. 2, the uncertainties should be at least $\pm 2.5\,n$ kcal/mole, where n is the charge on the ion, unless larger uncertainties are quoted.

We define the *ligation* (or *complexation*) *energy*, E_{lig}, as the energy released when a gaseous ion combines with a group of gaseous ligands (anions or neutral molecules) to form a gaseous complex (see Chapter 5). A general equation is:

$$M^{n+}(g) + xL^{x-}(g) = [ML_x]^{n-x}(g) \qquad (2\text{-}11)$$

Obviously, direct measurement is not possible. One way to estimate such energies[3] is to use a cycle such as that shown in Figure 2-4 for Cs_2CoCl_4,

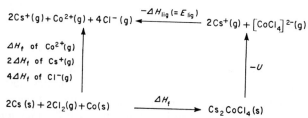

Fig. 2-4. A thermochemical cycle which includes the energy of formation of gaseous $[CoCl_4]^{2-}$ from gaseous Co^{2+} and Cl^- ions.

a substance consisting in the crystalline state of Cs^+ ions and $[CoCl_4]^{2-}$ ions. All of the enthalpies of formation are known, and the lattice energy, U, can be computed. Hence the ligation energy which is $-\Delta H_{lig}$, can be calculated. Actually, the value of U depends on how the total charge of -2 is taken to be distributed over the $[CoCl_4]^{2-}$ ion. For a reasonable

[2] H. F. Halliwell and S. C. Nyburg, *Trans. Faraday Soc.*, **59**, 1126 (1963).
[3] A. B. Blake and F. A. Cotton, *Inorg. Chem.*, **2**, 906 (1963).

choice, the value of E_{lig} is about 500 kcal/mole, although values in the range of 488 to 550 kcal/mole are possible.

2-5. Ionic Radii

It is already apparent from the nature of the wave functions for atoms and ions that they have no definite size. The only way we can assign a radius to an atom or ion is to measure in one way or another how close two atoms or ions can approach one another under the influence of forces of the magnitude encountered in chemical processes. For the ions in a crystal we can do this by considering the distance between the centers of two adjacent ions to be the sum of their ionic radii. Two questions then arise:

1. Are the radii, so defined, truly constant?

2. How do we apportion a given internuclear distance between the radii of the two ions?

The answer to the first question is that the radii are not exactly constant, but nearly enough so as to be useful. For example:

$$r_{\text{K}^+} - r_{\text{Na}^+} = a_{\text{KF}} - a_{\text{NaF}} = 0.35 \text{ A.}$$
$$r_{\text{K}^+} - r_{\text{Na}^+} = a_{\text{KCl}} - a_{\text{NaCl}} = 0.33 \text{ A.}$$
$$r_{\text{K}^+} - r_{\text{Na}^+} = a_{\text{KBr}} - a_{\text{NaBr}} = 0.32 \text{ A.}$$
$$r_{\text{K}^+} - r_{\text{Na}^+} = a_{\text{KI}} - a_{\text{NaI}} = 0.30 \text{ A.}$$

where a_{KF} is the K^+—F^- distance in KF, etc. We assume that if $r_{\text{K}^+} - r_{\text{Na}^+}$ is substantially constant, then r_{K^+} and r_{Na^+} are individually reasonably constant. From X-ray measurements of the interionic distances in a large number of ionic solids, extensive tables of the average sums and differences of ionic radii can be compiled. A table of individual ionic radii can then be prepared if the radius of one or perhaps several of the ions can be determined independently.

One simple method for estimating the radius of a single ion may be mentioned, with the qualification that values so obtained are in many cases subject to further small corrections in order to obtain the most useful set of radii. This method is based on the proposal that for a pair of isoelectronic ions, say Na^+ and F^-, the radii will be inversely proportional to the effective nuclear charge to which the outer electrons are subject. Such a proposal follows directly from the expression (page 4) for the radius of one of Bohr's circular orbits—which has a wave mechanical analog in the most probable radius derived from the wave function (page 11). Now, as discussed elsewhere (pages 23–24), electrons in the same or adjacent principal shells shield one another imperfectly, and by empirical correlations the fractional shielding factors can be estimated. When this is done according to the procedure of Slater, one obtains for the shielding of an outer ($2s$ or $2p$) electron in the neon configuration the value 4.15. For Na^+ ($Z = 11$),

Z^*, the effective nuclear charge felt by the outer shell electrons, is $11 - 4.15 = 6.85$ while for F^-, $Z^* = 9 - 4.15 = 4.85$. Thus, the ratio of the radii $r_{F^-}/r_{Na^+} = 4.85/6.85 = 0.71$. If now the sum of these radii is taken as the Na—F distance in NaF, viz., 2.31 A, the individual radii must be

$$r_{F^-} = 1.35 \text{ A}$$
$$r_{Na^+} = 0.96 \text{ A}$$

The method just outlined has been used by Pauling, with certain refinements, to estimate individual ionic radii. V. M. Goldschmidt, using a somewhat more empirical method has also estimated ionic radii. The ionic radii for a number of important ions, obtained by the two procedures, are given in Table 2-4. The differences are not large except in a few cases.

TABLE 2-4
Goldschmidt (G) and Pauling (P) Ionic Radii
(In Angstroms)

Ion	G	P[a]	Ion	G	P[a]
H^-	1.54	2.08	Pb^{2+}	1.17	1.21
F^-	1.33	1.36			
Cl^-	1.81	1.81	Mn^{2+}	0.80	0.80
Br^-	1.96	1.95	Fe^{2+}	0.76	0.75
I^-	2.19	2.16	Co^{2+}	0.70	0.72
			Ni^{2+}	0.68	0.69
O^{2-}	1.45	1.40	Cu^{2+}	0.92	—
S^{2-}	1.90	1.84			
Se^{2-}	2.02	1.98	B^{3+}	0.2	0.20
Te^{2-}	2.22	2.21	Al^{3+}	0.45	0.50
			Sc^{3+}	0.68	0.81
Li^+	0.68	0.60	Y^{3+}	0.90	0.93
Na^+	0.98	0.95	La^{3+}	1.04	1.15
K^+	1.33	1.33	Ga^{3+}	0.60	0.62
Rb^+	1.48	1.48	In^{3+}	0.81	0.81
Cs^+	1.67	1.69	Tl^{3+}	0.91	0.95
Cu^+	0.95	0.96			
Ag^+	1.13	1.26	Fe^{3+}	0.53	—
Au^+	—	1.37	Cr^{3+}	0.55	—
Tl^+	1.51	1.44			
			C^{4+}	0.15	0.15
Be^{2+}	0.30	0.31	Si^{4+}	0.38	0.41
Mg^{2+}	0.65	0.65	Ti^{4+}	0.60	0.68
Ca^{2+}	0.94	0.99	Zr^{4+}	0.77	0.80
Sr^{2+}	1.10	1.13	Ce^{4+}	0.87	1.01
Ba^{2+}	1.29	1.35	Ge^{4+}	0.54	0.53
Zn^{2+}	0.69	0.74	Sn^{4+}	0.71	0.71
Cd^{2+}	0.92	0.97	Pb^{4+}	0.81	0.84
Hg^{2+}	0.93	1.10			

[a] These radii are obtained using the *rock salt type of structure* as standard (i.e., six coordination); for other structures with different values of the Madelung constant, A, and the Born coefficient, B, small corrections can be made.

The large disagreement for H⁻ is discussed in Chapter 6 (page 201). It must be emphasized that although radii can be *estimated*, some of the ions, for example, C^{4+} or Pb^{4+}, are strictly hypothetical.

2-6. Some Important Types of Ionic Crystal Lattices

A great many ionic compounds of the type M^+X^- occur with one of three structures: the *sodium chloride* (see Fig. 2-1), the *cesium chloride* (Fig. 2-5a) or the *zinc blende* (ZnS) (Fig. 2-5b) structure. In an ionic lattice

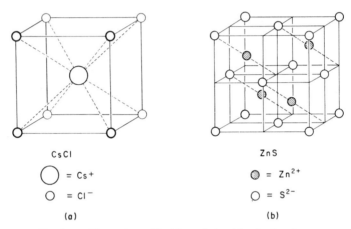

CsCl

◯ = Cs⁺

◯ = Cl⁻

(a)

ZnS

◍ = Zn^{2+}

◯ = S^{2-}

(b)

Fig. 2-5. The cesium chloride and zinc blende structures.

each ion is surrounded by a certain number of ions of the opposite sign; this number is called the *coordination number* of the ion. In the three structures mentioned the cations have the coordination numbers 6, 8 and 4, respectively. The question now arises as to why a particular compound crystallizes with one or another of these structures.

To answer this question, we first recognize that, ignoring the possibility of metastability, which seldom arises, the compound will adopt the arrangement providing the greatest stability, that is, the lowest energy. The factors which contribute to the energy are the attractive force between oppositely charged ions, which will increase with increasing coordination number, and the forces of repulsion, which will increase very rapidly if ions of the same charge are "squeezed" together. Thus the optimum arrangement in any crystal should be the one allowing the greatest number of oppositely charged ions to "touch" without requiring any squeezing together of ions with the same charge. The ability of a given structure to meet these requirements will depend on the relative sizes of the ions.

Again using the hard sphere model as a first approximation, let us analyze the situation for the CsCl structure. Let us place eight negative ions of radius r^- around a positive ion with radius r^+ so that the M^+—X^- distance is $r^+ + r^-$ and the adjacent X^- ions are just touching. Then the X^- to X^- distance, a, is given by

$$a = \frac{2}{\sqrt{3}} (r^+ + r^-) = 2r^-$$

or

$$\frac{r^-}{r^+} = 1.37$$

Now, if the ratio r^-/r^+ is greater than 1.37, the only way we can have all eight X^- ions touching the M^+ ion is to squeeze the X^- ions together. Alternatively, if $r^-/r^+ > 1.37$, and we do not squeeze the X^- ions, then they cannot touch the M^+ ion, and a certain amount of electrostatic stabilization energy will be unattainable. Thus when r^-/r^+ becomes equal to 1.37 the competition between attractive and repulsive coulomb forces is balanced, and any increase in the ratio may make the CsCl structure unfavorable relative to a structure with a lower coordination number, such as the NaCl structure.

In the NaCl structure, in order to have all ions just touching but not squeezed, with radius r^- for X^- and r^+ for M^+ we have

$$2r^- = \sqrt{2}(r^+ + r^-)$$

which gives for the critical radius ratio

$$r^-/r^+ = 2.44$$

If the ratio r^-/r^+ exceeds 2.44, then the NaCl structure becomes disfavored, and the zinc blende structure, for which the critical value of r^-/r^+ is 4.55, may become more favorable. To summarize, packing considerations, in the hard-sphere approximation, would lead us to expect the various structures to have the following ranges of stability in terms of the r^-/r^+ ratio:

CsCl structure:	$1 < r^-/r^+ < 1.37$
NaCl structure:	$1.37 < r^-/r^+ < 2.44$
ZnS structure:	$2.44 < r^-/r^+ < 4.44$

Obviously, similar reasoning may be applied to other structures and other types of ionic compounds. In view of the fact that the hard sphere model is a rather crude approximation, we must not expect these calculations to be more than a rough guide. We can certainly expect that in compounds where $r^- \sim r^+$ the CsCl structure will be found, whereas when $r^- \gg r^+$

the zinc blende structure is expected.   Table 2-5 gives some representative data.

TABLE 2-5
Structures and Radius Ratios for Some Ionic Salts

CsCl structure		NaCl structure		Zinc blende structure	
Salt	r^-/r^+	Salt	r^-/r^+	Salt	r^-/r^+
CsCl	1.1	NaCl	1.9	ZnS	2.1
CsBr	1.2	NaI	2.3	ZnSe	2.3
CsI	1.3	KCl	1.4	CuCl	1.9
TlCl	1.2	RbI	1.5	CuBr	2.0
TlBr	1.3	RbF	0.92	CuI	2.3
TlI	1.5			BeS	5.1
				BeSe	5.6

The three structures we have mentioned for compounds of the M^+X^- type are not, of course, the only ones, but they are probably the most common.   Ionic compounds with different stoichiometries crystallize in other types of lattice.   Many of these will be mentioned at appropriate places in the text, but we shall also describe here two structures which are quite common for compounds of the type $M^{2+}X^-_2$ or $M^+_2X^{2-}$.   One of these is the structure of the mineral fluorite, CaF_2, shown in Figure 2-6.

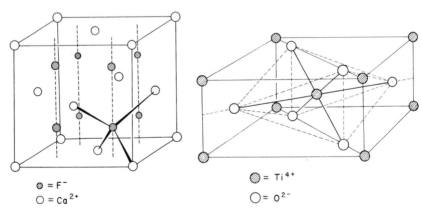

$\bigcirc$ = F^-
$\bigcirc$ = Ca^{2+}

$\bigcirc$ = Ti^{4+}
$\bigcirc$ = O^{2-}

Fig. 2-6.   The calcium fluoride (fluorite) structure.

Fig. 2-7.   The rutile structure.

When a compound of the type $M^{2+}X^-_2$ crystallizes in this same way, it is said to have the *fluorite structure*; when a compound of the type $M^+_2X^{2-}$ crystallizes in the analogous way, with X^{2-} ions at the Ca^{2+} positions and

M^+ ions at the F^- positions, it is said to have the *antifluorite structure*. The second structure frequently found for 1:2 compounds is the structure of the mineral rutile, TiO_2, and is called the *rutile structure*, shown in Figure 2-7. Some $M^+_2X^{2-}$ also crystallize in an antirutile structure.

In the fluorite structure the cations form a face-centered cube, and there are eight anions occupying the eight tetrahedral interstices in this cube. Note that each cation is surrounded by eight such interstices and therefore attains a coordination number of 8. In the rutile structure the unit cell is not cubic, and the cations have a coordination number of 6. Thus, roughly speaking, packing considerations favor the fluorite structure when the radius ratio r^-/r^+ is less than ~ 1.37, and the rutile structure when it is greater than ~ 1.37.

Structures with Close Packing of Anions. A considerable number of chalconide and halide structures can be described or thought of as close-packed arrays of the large anions with the smaller cations occupying interstices in these arrays. There are two principal types of close packing of isometric spheres: hexagonal and cubic. Both of these are built up by stacking two-dimensional close-packed sheets (Fig. 2-8a) in definite ways. When one such sheet is placed upon another as shown in Figure 2-8b, which is the arrangement occupying least volume, it will be seen that both tetrahedral interstices, A, A', and octahedral ones, B, are formed.

When we come to place a third sheet upon the second, there are two ways to do so, both giving minimum volume. Sheet 3 can be placed so that spheres lie directly over those of sheet 1 (i.e., over A positions in Figure 2-8b). If then a fourth layer is added with its spheres directly over those of sheet 2, a fifth directly over sheet 3, etc., giving a stacking sequence which can be symbolized as 12121212..., we have *hexagonal close packing* (*hcp*).

Alternatively, sheet 3 can be placed so that its spheres are not over the spheres of sheet 1 but are instead over the B positions, Figure 2-8b. If then the fourth sheet is placed with its spheres over those of the first sheet, the fifth sheet over sheet 2 and so on, giving a stacking sequence which can be symbolized 123123123..., we have *cubic close packing* (*ccp*). Such an array is actually identical with a face-centered cubic lattice as shown in Figure 2-8c; the face diagonals of the cube define the close-packed sheets, one of which is shown in Figure 2-8c.

Some examples of structures involving close-packed anions are the following. NaCl has *ccp* Cl^- ions with all octahedral interstices filled by Na^+ ions. $CdCl_2$ also has *ccp* Cl^- ions with every other octahedral hole occupied by Cd^{2+} while CdI_2 has *hcp* I^- ions with Cd^{2+} ions in half the octahedral holes. Corundum, the α form of Al_2O_3, has an *hcp* array of oxide ions with $\frac{2}{3}$ of the octahedral interstices occupied by cations. All of the

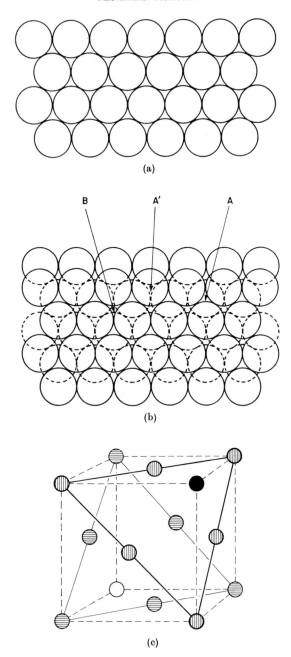

Fig. 2-8.   Close packing of spheres.   (a) One layer; (b) two layers showing tetrahedral
(A, A′) and octahedral (B) interstices; (c) cubic close packing.

structures just mentioned are adopted by *substances* other than those mentioned. The structures are usually named in reference to the above compounds. Thus we speak of the NaCl, $CdCl_2$, CdI_2 and corundum (or α-Al_2O_3) structures.

Some Mixed Oxide Structures. There are a vast number of oxides (and also some stoichiometrically related halides) having two or more different kinds of cations. Most of them occur in one of a few basic structural types, the names of which are derived from the first or principal compound shown to have that type of structure. Three of the most important such structures will now be described.

1. *The Spinel Structure.* The compound $MgAl_2O_4$, which occurs in nature as the mineral spinel, has a structure based on a *ccp* array of oxide ions. One-eighth of the tetrahedral holes (of which there are 2 per anion) are occupied by Mg^{2+} ions and one half of the octahedral holes (of which there is 1 per anion) are occupied by Al^{3+} ions. This structure, or a modification of the type to be discussed below, is adopted by many other mixed metal oxides of the type $M^{II}M^{III}_2O_4$ (e.g., $FeCr_2O_4$, $ZnAl_2O_4$, $Co^{II}Co^{III}_2O_4$), by some of the type $M^{IV}M^{II}_2O_4$ (e.g., $TiZn_2O_4$ and $SnCo_2O_4$) and by some of the type $M^I_2M^{VI}O_4$ (e.g., Na_2MoO_4 and Ag_2MoO_4). This structure is often symbolized as $A[B_2]O_4$, where square brackets enclose the ions in the octahedral interstices. An important variant is the *inverse spinel structure*, $B[AB]O_4$, in which half of the B ions are in tetrahedral interstices and the A ions are in octahedral ones along with the other half of the B ions. This often happens when the A ions have a stronger preference for octahedral coordination than do the B ions. So far as is known, all $M^{IV}M^{II}_2O_4$ spinels are inverse, e.g., $Zn[ZnTi]O_4$, and many of the $M^{II}M^{III}_2O_4$ ones are also, e.g., $Fe^{III}[Co^{II}Fe^{III}]O_4$, $Fe^{III}[Fe^{II}Fe^{III}]O_4$ and $Fe[NiFe]O_4$.

There are also many compounds with *disordered spinel structures* in which only a fraction of the A ions are in tetrahedral sites (and a corresponding fraction in octahedral ones). This occurs when the preferences of both A and B ions for octahedral *vs* tetrahedral sites do not differ markedly.

2. *The Ilmenite Structure.* This is the structure of the mineral ilmenite, $Fe^{II}Ti^{IV}O_3$. It is closely related to the corundum structure except that the cations are of two different types. It is adopted by ABO_3 oxides when the two cations, A and B, are of about the same size, but they need not be of the same charge so long as their total charge is +6. Thus in ilmenite itself and in $MgTiO_3$ and $CoTiO_3$ the cations have charges +2 and +4 while in α-$NaSbO_3$ the cations have charges of +1 and +5.

3. *The Perovskite Structure.* The mineral perovskite, $CaTiO_3$, has a structure in which the oxide ions and the large cation (Ca^{2+}) form a *ccp* array with the smaller cation (Ti^{4+}) occupying those octahedral holes formed exclusively by oxide ions, as shown in Figure 2-9. This structure is

often slightly distorted (in $CaTiO_3$ itself, for example). It is adopted by a great many ABO_3 oxides in which one cation is comparable in size to O^{2-} and the other much smaller, with the cation charges variable so long as their sum is $+6$. It is found in $Sr^{II}Ti^{IV}O_3$, $Ba^{II}Ti^{IV}O_3$, $La^{III}Ga^{III}O_3$, $Na^{I}Nb^{V}O_3$ and $K^{I}Nb^{V}O_3$, and also in some mixed fluorides, e.g., $KZnF_3$ and $KNiF_3$.

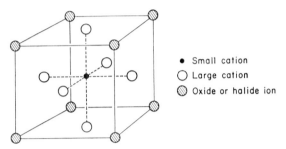

●   Small cation

○   Large cation

◎   Oxide or halide ion

Fig. 2-9.   The perovskite structure.

2-7. Other Electrostatic Interactions

In addition to the electrostatic interactions already discussed, which we may call ion–ion interactions, there are several other kinds, all much weaker but nevertheless often of great importance. These are ion–dipole, dipole–dipole, ion–induced dipole, dipole–induced dipole and finally, induced dipole–induced dipole interactions. The hydrogen bond, which owes most if not all of its strength to electrostatic forces, is of immense importance, and will be discussed at length in Chapter 6. It may be thought of as a combination of several of the above types of interactions, principally dipole–induced dipole, ion–induced dipole and ion–dipole, depending on circumstances.

The induced dipole–induced dipole interaction is the well-known van der Waals attraction (an indication of its magnitude relative to the magnitudes of ion–ion forces is given on page 39). Van der Waals forces will be mentioned in other connections throughout the text, particularly to explain the liquefaction and solidification of the noble gases, for which, owing to their spherical, closed-shell electron distributions, no other forces of attraction are possible. The energies of attraction due to van der Waals forces generally run around a few kcal/mole. It should also be noted that they are always present, irrespective of and more or less independent of any other forces; they are inherent in the nature of matter. They are proportional to the polarizabilities and inversely proportional to the ionization potentials of the molecules, atoms or ions concerned, and they are short range, being proportional to about the inverse sixth power of the distance.

Ion–dipole and ion–induced dipole interactions play an important role in solution chemistry, accounting for all or part of the solvation energies of electrolytes in solvents of varying polarities. For example, the interaction of an ion such as the sodium ion with the (presumably six) water molecules surrounding it in aqueous solution is at least partly and very likely largely an electrostatic attraction between the positive sodium ion and the dipole of the water molecule, oriented as shown in Figure 2-10. The dipole of the

Fig. 2-10. The combined ion–dipole and ion–induced dipole attraction of sodium ion for water molecules in aqueous solution.

water molecule here will be larger than that of the free water molecule because the positive charge on the sodium ion will cause additional polarization. Thus we have a superposition of ion–dipole and ion–induced dipole attractions. In the case of a species containing an ion and a neutral molecule lacking a dipole (e.g., the silver benzene complex, $AgC_6H_6{}^+$), the force of attraction may be considered as at least partially due to an ion–induced dipole attraction. There is, however, no rigorous way to distinguish between this and a genuine covalence resulting from overlap of orbitals; indeed, the two are to a certain extent merely different ways of looking at the same thing.

Dipole–dipole and dipole–induced dipole interactions are of very common occurrence, for practically all molecules either are polar in their entirety or contain polar bonds. Forces of this kind are probably of major importance in supplying the lattice energy of molecular compounds.

Polarization. When two ions, A^+ and B^-, are juxtaposed, there will be an interaction over and above their coulombic attraction, namely, an interaction due to mutual *polarization*. The smaller and more highly charged a cation is, the more it will tend to distort the charge distribution in a neighboring anion. A reasonably quantitative measure of this polarizing power of the cation is its charge/radius ratio. At the same time the polarizability of an anion will increase with its size and charge. Other things being equal, the larger of two anions will be more polarizable because the outer electrons are farther from the nucleus. At the same time, the more negative of two isoelectronic anions (e.g., O^{2-}, F^-) will be larger and more polarizable because the extra electron–electron repulsion expands the electron cloud. Since cations are usually small and compact relative to anions, the polarization of the cation by the anion is considered to be relatively negligible in most cases (CsF is probably an exception). We may therefore expect the shapes of the free ions and of closely juxtaposed ions to be somewhat as represented in Figure 2-11.

Covalent bonding can be considered as a case of ionic bonding in which the polarization of the anions is so extreme as to give an appreciable increase in electron density between the nuclei. Although this view is severely

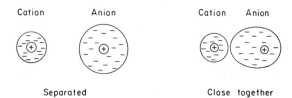

Fig. 2-11.   Schematic diagram showing how a small cation polarizes the electron cloud of a large anion.

limited insofar as quantitative treatment is concerned, and is not in general a substitute for the quantum mechanical treatment of covalent bonding, it has certain merits as a conceptual approach to bonds which are mainly ionic, with a little covalence.

As an example consider the melting points of some "ionic" halides of the alkaline earths (Table 2-6). The melting points of chlorides rise steadily as

TABLE 2-6

Melting Points and Ionic Radii of Some Alkaline Earth Halides; radii in A.

Compound	Cation	Anion	Melting point, °C
$BeCl_2$	0.31	1.81	405
$MgCl_2$	0.65	1.81	712
CaF_2	0.99	1.36	1392
$CaCl_2$	0.99	1.81	772
$CaBr_2$	0.99	1.95	730
CaI_2	0.99	2.16	575
$SrCl_2$	1.13	1.81	872
$BaCl_2$	1.35	1.81	960
$RaCl_2$	1.50 (est.)	1.81	~1000

the cation size increases, whereas those of the calcium halides decline steadily as the anion size increases. In other words, in general, the melting points vary inversely with the amount of polarization of the anion by the cation. It is also found that the greater the possibility of polarization, the lower is the heat of sublimation (to aggregates of ions) and the greater is the solubility in nonpolar solvents. LiCl, for example, is soluble in numerous organic liquids, whereas NaCl and other alkali chlorides are not. The reason for this kind of behavior is as follows. In the solid, where each anion is symmetrically surrounded by cations, polarization of the anions is not important because the various pulls in different directions by the cations balance out by symmetry. Thus the polarizability of the anion and the polarizing power of the cation have little effect on the lattice energy. However, for the ion pairs or other aggregates (e.g., $(LiI)_n$) in the gas phase, in solution, or in the melt, the polarizations contribute appreciably to the stability; hence, these phases have an "extra" stability relative to the crystals, with resultant higher solubilities and lower melting points and sublimation energies.

As will be seen in subsequent discussions, the first row elements, especially Li, Be and B, have certain chemical resemblances to the second members of the next groups. Thus, for example, when the properties of lithium compounds differ from those of the corresponding compounds of the other alkali metals, they frequently resemble those of magnesium compounds. Although Na^+ and Mg^{2+} are isoelectronic and Li^+ and Na^+ have the same charge, the resemblances between Li^+ and Mg^{2+} are also great because both are much more polarizing than Na^+. However, this type of relationship is perhaps best not overemphasized. For example, the charge/radius ratio of Li^+ (1.47) differs less from that of Na^+ (1.05) than from that of Mg^{2+} (3.08). Also, the basic idea that covalent bonds are due only to distortion of ions is a vast oversimplification.

References

Dunitz, J. D., and L. E. Orgel, *Adv. Inorg. Chem. Radiochem.*, **2**, 1 (1960). Although concerned mainly with stereochemistry of transition metal compounds, much useful data and discussion is included and many references given.

Gehman, W. G., *J. Chem. Educ.*, **40**, 54 (1963). Ionic crystals.

Ketelaar, J. A. A., *Chemical Constitution*, Elsevier, New York, 1958.

Ladd, M. F. C., and W. H. Lee in H. Reiss, ed., *Progr. Solid State. Chem.*, Vol I., Pergamon Press, London, 1964. Catalog of lattice energies.

Moody, G. J., and J. D. R. Thomas, *J. Chem. Educ.*, **42**, 204 (1965). Use of Born-Haber cycles: data on halides with examples.

Parker, A. J., *Quart. Rev.*, **16**, 163 (1962). Effects of solvation on properties and reactions of anions in aprotic solvents. Contains much unusual and useful information.

Pauling, L., *Nature of the Chemical Bond*, 3rd ed., Cornell University Press, Ithaca, New York, 1960.

Rice, O. K., *Electronic Structures and Chemical Binding*, McGraw-Hill, New York, 1940. This useful book is concerned only with inorganic compounds and has a good section on ionic compounds.

Roselaar, L. C., *Educ. in Chem.*, **2**, 135 (1965). Discussion of solubility of salts; thermodynamic data.

Slater, J. C., *J. Chem. Phys.*, **41**, 3199 (1964).   Discussion of atomic and ionic radii and set of empirical atomic radii.

Stern, K. H., and E. S. Amis, *Chem. Rev.*, **59**, 1 (1959).   A comprehensive review of ionic size in crystals and in solution.

van Arkel, A. E., *Molecules and Crystals in Inorganic Chemistry*, 2nd ed., Interscience, New York, 1957.   A small, general, readable book on bonding with good sections on ionic compounds.

Waddington, T. C., *Adv. Inorg. Chem. Radiochem.*, **1**, 157 (1959).   An authoritative treatment of the Born-Haber cycle, lattice energies and their significance in inorganic chemistry, with copious data and information.

Ward, R., *Progr. Inorg. Chem.*, **1**, 465 (1959).   Structure and properties of mixed metal oxides (see also references for Chap. 13).

3

The Nature of Chemical Bonding

THE VALENCE BOND (VB) THEORY OF BONDING

3-1. Introduction; Lewis' Electron Pair Bond

In this chapter we shall make a general survey of the types of forces which hold atoms together in chemical compounds. We have already considered the very simple case of crystalline ionic compounds where, typically, a metal atom having a few loosely bound outer electrons will lose them completely, one or more nonmetallic atoms having configurations just short of a noble gas configuration will accept these electrons, and the ions so formed will fall together into an ionic lattice. In such a case there are no chemical bonds in the usual sense of the word.

Normally, we use the word bond to describe the linkage between a particular pair of atoms as, for example, the H and Cl atoms in HCl or the N and one of the H atoms in NH_3. The student should already be familiar with the Lewis electron dot symbols for atoms and molecules whereby we would represent the HCl and NH_3 molecules by 3-I and 3-II. The basic

$$\text{H} : \overset{\cdot\cdot}{\underset{\cdot\cdot}{\text{Cl}}} : \qquad\qquad \overset{\text{H}}{\underset{\text{H}}{: \overset{\cdot\cdot}{\text{N}} : \text{H}}}$$

$$\text{(3-I)} \qquad\qquad \text{(3-II)}$$

idea of the Lewis theory is that chemical bonds are due to the sharing of one or more pairs of electrons between two atoms. Thus the bond in HCl results from the sharing of one hydrogen electron and one chlorine electron (eq. 3-1).

$$\text{H}\cdot + \cdot\overset{\cdot\cdot}{\underset{\cdot\cdot}{\text{Cl}}} : \rightarrow \text{H} : \overset{\cdot\cdot}{\underset{\cdot\cdot}{\text{Cl}}} : \qquad\qquad \text{(3-1)}$$

In other cases, though less commonly, two or three pairs may be shared (eq. 3-2).

$$: \overset{\cdot}{\underset{\cdot}{N}} \cdot + \cdot \overset{\cdot}{\underset{\cdot}{N}} : \; \rightarrow \; : N : \; : \; : N : \tag{3-2}$$

Furthermore, it is not necessary that the electrons constituting the bond be contributed equally by the two atoms. For example, there is the *coordinate bond*, illustrated by equation 3-3.

$$
\begin{array}{cccc}
F & C_2H_5 & F & C_2H_5 \\
 & \diagup & & \diagup \\
F : \overset{\cdot\cdot}{B} + : O & & \rightarrow \;\; F : \overset{\cdot\cdot}{B} : O & \\
 & \diagdown & & \diagdown \\
F & C_2H_5 & F & C_2H_5
\end{array}
\tag{3-3}
$$

All of these various bonds, whether single or multiple, are called *covalent bonds*. However, it is possible even in this simple approach to recognize the difference between nonpolar covalent bonding and polar covalent bonding. In a homonuclear diatomic molecule, the shared electron pair or pairs must be equally shared and hence there is no polarity in the system nucleus–electrons–nucleus. In a heteronuclear diatomic molecule, however, one of the atoms will, in general, have a greater affinity for the electrons than the other, and the bond will therefore be polar as in 3-III.

$$
\overset{\delta+}{H} \;\; \overset{\overset{\delta-}{\cdot\cdot}}{\underset{\cdot\cdot}{: Cl :}}
$$
$$(\text{3-III})$$

The intrinsic polarity of the bond should not be confused with the polarity that the molecule as a whole may have for other reasons which are discussed in Section 4-4.

These simple ideas were formulated before the advent of wave mechanics. It has been found that quantum theory not only justifies their use but enables us to refine and extend them. The great difficulty with applying wave mechanics to chemical problems is that the equations are far too complicated to be solved in any analytical and exact way. Therefore, the main function of molecular quantum mechanics has been to find approximate solutions to the equations and from these approximate solutions to gain an understanding of the factors which come into play and their relative importance, without attempting quantitative computations.

3-2. The Electron Pair Bond According to Quantum Mechanics

If we have two atoms—for simplicity, two hydrogen atoms—infinitely far apart, the wave function of this system is

$$\psi = \psi_A \psi_B \tag{3-4}$$

where ψ_A is the wave function for the first hydrogen atom, ψ_B is the wave function for the second hydrogen atom and ψ is the joint wave function for the system. Equation 3-4 implies that neither atom disturbs the other, which is, of course, to be expected if they are far apart. We can also see that the total energy of the system ought to be

$$E^0 = E_A + E_B = 2E_H \qquad (3\text{-}5)$$

This result can easily be shown to follow by putting equation 3-4 into the wave equation.

$$\mathcal{H}\psi = E\psi$$
$$\mathcal{H}(\psi_A\psi_B) = \psi_A\mathcal{H}\psi_B + \psi_B\mathcal{H}\psi_A$$
$$= \psi_A E_B\psi_B + \psi_B E_A\psi_A$$
$$= (E_A + E_B)(\psi_A\psi_B) = E^0\psi \qquad (3\text{-}6)$$

What we have done so far is completely rigorous but also rather useless since we are interested in calculating the energy of the system when the two hydrogen atoms approach one another closely and form a bond. The energy of the system is then E', which is less than E^0 by an amount we call the *bond energy*. However, our first attempt to calculate the bond energy makes use of the above considerations regarding the wave function.

We begin by assuming that the wave function in equation 3-4 remains a reasonably good approximation, even when the atoms approach one another closely. We shall rewrite it in the following more explicit form:

$$\psi_1 = \psi_A(1)\psi_B(2) \qquad (3\text{-}7)$$

where we have specifically assigned electron 1 to atom A and electron 2 to atom B. Now in order to calculate the energy of the molecule we must solve the wave equation for small values of the internuclear distance. To do so we first rearrange it in the following way:

$$\mathcal{H}\psi = E\psi$$
$$\psi^*\mathcal{H}\psi = \psi^*E\psi = E\psi^*\psi$$
$$\int \psi^*\mathcal{H}\psi\, d\tau = E \int \psi^*\psi\, d\tau$$

or
$$E = \frac{\int \psi^*\mathcal{H}\psi\, d\tau}{\int \psi^*\psi\, d\tau} \qquad (3\text{-}8)$$

Note that in these arrangements we have written $\psi^*E\psi = E\psi^*\psi$ because E is simply a numerical factor, whereas $\psi^*\mathcal{H}\psi$ cannot be so rearranged because $\mathcal{H}$ is not simply a number but a symbol for an operation to be performed on whatever function follows it.

At close distances our Hamiltonian contains terms involving the reciprocals of the distance of electron 1 from nucleus B, the distance of electron 2
from nucleus A and r_{12}, the distance between the two electrons. Now
when the atoms are far apart these reciprocal distances are so small that
these terms are negligible, but as the atoms move together they become
progressively more important. Thus the numerator on the right hand side
of equation 3-8 is a function of the internuclear distance, r. If we compute
the energy as a function of the internuclear distance, which can be done
by laboriously solving equation 3-8, we obtain the results shown in curve
a of Figure 3-1. Thus we find that the energy of the system does decrease

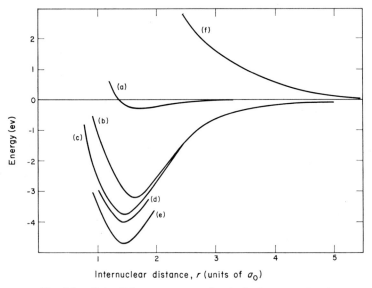

Fig. 3-1.   Potential energy curves for the hydrogen molecule.

(by $\sim 1/4$ ev at the minimum) as the atoms approach, giving a minimum
at $r = 1.7a_0$. Curve e is the actual potential energy function for H_2, and it
can be seen that our calculated results are qualitatively right but quantitatively rather disappointing.

We can make a dramatic improvement in our results by correcting an
error in our wave function. Equation 3-7 states that we know that electron
1 is associated with atom A and electron 2 is associated with atom B. But
in fact we do not and cannot know this. The electrons are not labeled so
we cannot tell them apart to begin with, and, more important, we cannot
attempt to follow any one electron in a system containing several. This is
because wave mechanics does not tell us where any particular electron is
but only the probability of finding an electron at a given place. Thus we

are no more entitled to use ψ_1 as an approximate wave function than to use ψ_2.

$$\psi_2 = \psi_A(2)\psi_B(1) \qquad (3\text{-}9)$$

Thus if either one is equally likely to be right, we use both, namely,

$$\psi_{cov} = (\psi_1 + \psi_2) \qquad (3\text{-}10)$$

If now we solve for the energy as a function of r using equation 3-10 we obtain curve b of Figure 3-1, which is obviously a vast improvement and indicates that provided we allow for the indistinguishability of electrons, the basic approach we have taken is not unrealistic.

Further improvement in the results can be made by modifying ψ_{cov} in accord with the dictates of physical intuition. ψ_{cov} is only a combination of the hydrogenic wave functions. Although we are correct in assuming that one electron does not affect the other one at large distances, we may well expect that when they are close together the forms of ψ_A and ψ_B will differ at least quantitatively from that of the unperturbed hydrogen orbital. Just as in a multielectron atom we use hydrogenic wave functions, but recognize that the electrons mutually shield one another to varying degrees from the nuclear charge, so we can allow for the existence of shielding in the H_2 molecule. We can do this again by using a number, Z^*, rather than $Z = 1$ for the effective nuclear charge. When this is done, curve c (Fig. 3-1) is obtained. We now have a binding energy of 3.76 ev, which is a reasonably good approximation to the experimental value of 4.72 ev. There is another refinement which can be made fairly straightforwardly, and a consideration of this introduces the concept of *resonance*.

Any wave function of the type 3-10, however we modify the exact forms of ψ_A and ψ_B, still states that we consider only the possibility that one electron is associated with one atom and the other electron is associated with the other atom. But there is, of course, some finite chance that both electrons will occasionally be in the same atomic orbital. Wave functions describing such a state would be $\psi_A(1)\psi_A(2)$ and $\psi_B(1)\psi_B(2)$, and, because ψ_A and ψ_B are identical in form, we have no reason to prefer one over the other. We therefore use both as follows:

$$\psi_{ion} = \psi_A(1)\psi_A(2) + \psi_B(1)\psi_B(2) \qquad (3\text{-}11)$$

We have called the wave function 3-10 ψ_{cov} because it states that the electrons are shared (in this case shared *exactly equally* because the two atoms are identical); similarly, we call the wave function 3-11 ψ_{ion} since it represents a state to which ionic forms contribute. The way in which we combine equations 3-10 and 3-11 is to write

$$\psi = (1 - 2\lambda + 2\lambda^2)^{-1/2}[(1 - \lambda)\psi_{cov} + \lambda\psi_{ion}] \qquad (3\text{-}12)$$

in which λ is a *mixing coefficient*, which tells how much of the ionic wave function is mixed in with the covalent wave function. We have also introduced a normalizing factor. It is necessary to do a considerable amount of tedious calculation to determine what value of λ gives the best (that is, lowest) value of the energy. It turns out to be $\sim 1/5$, and the new value of the minimum energy is 4.10 ev. Curve d (Fig. 3-1) shows part of the potential energy function obtained with a wave function of the type 3-12.

The formulation we have described for the bond in H_2 is, in essence, the following. We have selected an orbital on each atom, ψ_A and ψ_B, each containing one electron, and combined the wave functions of these orbitals into a wave function for the two electrons together, namely, $\psi_A(1)\psi_B(2) + \psi_A(2)\psi_B(1)$. This process is called pairing the electrons, and the valence bond (VB) method is sometimes called the method of electron pairs. There is another important feature of the process which we have not as yet mentioned explicitly. The wave function for the bonding electrons can, like a single atomic wave function, be described by a set of quantum numbers. Whatever these quantum numbers may be, it is clear that both electrons in the bond have the same set, since by the nature of equation 3-12 their distributions in space are identical. They must therefore differ in their m_s values in order to satisfy the exclusion principle. We shall call this adoption of different m_s values by two electrons *spin pairing*, or just *pairing*. We can in fact state the general rule that only when spin pairing occurs does there result an attractive force and hence an electron pair bond. Curve f (Fig. 3-1) shows the potential energy curve when two hydrogen atoms approach in such a way that their spins remain unpaired, that is, with the same quantum number or direction. It is seen that the net force of interaction is strongly repulsive, and this state is called a *repulsive state*.

It is obvious that these principles can be extended to describe many chemical bonds and that they represent a rationalization in terms of wave mechanics of G. N. Lewis' idea of the electron pair bond. Whenever we have two atoms, each with at least one unpaired electron, they may unite to form a bond in which these two electrons are paired. For example, two lithium atoms, each with the configuration $1s^2 2s$, combine to form Li_2 by pairing their $2s$ electrons, and two chlorine atoms, each with the configuration $[Ne] 3s^2 3p_x^2 3p_y^2 3p_z$, combine by pairing their odd $3p_z$ electrons.

Multiple bonding may also be treated in this way. For example, two nitrogen atoms, each with the configuration $1s^2 2s^2 2p_x 2p_y 2p_z$, unite and form a triple bond by pairing electrons in corresponding p orbitals. Similarly, we can consider a methylene radical, $H_2C:$, to have two unpaired electrons, so that two of them unite to give ethylene with a double bond. There is one case in which the simple VB method leads to a qualitatively incorrect prediction concerning electronic structure, and that is O_2. An oxygen atom has the ground state configuration $1s^2 2s^2 2p_x^2 2p_y 2p_z$, and we should therefore expect two of them to unite forming two electron pair bonds. Actually the O_2 molecule has a bond energy indicative of a double bond, but it also has two unpaired electrons, a combination which is awkward to rationalize, much less predict in simple VB terms. This failure is due not to any fundamental error in the VB method, but to our use of too rough an approximation. However, the molecular orbital (MO) method, even in a very crude approximation, gives the correct result for O_2, as will be seen presently.

3-3. Resonance

The wave function (eq. 3-12) has an interpretation in terms of simple electron dot pictures. The three *canonical forms*, 3-IVa, b and c corre-

$$\text{H:H} \leftrightarrow \text{H}^+ \quad \text{:H}^- \leftrightarrow \text{H:}^- \quad \text{H}^+$$

(3-IVa)   (3-IVb)   (3-IVc)

spond, respectively, to the wave functions $\psi_A(1)\psi_B(2) + \psi_A(2)\psi_B(1)$, $\psi_A(1)\psi_A(2)$ and $\psi_B(1)\psi_B(2)$. The double-pointed arrows between them indicate that they are in *resonance* with one another, or, to put it another way, that the actual electronic state of the molecule is a *resonance hybrid* of these three structures. This concept of resonance is a useful one provided it is not misinterpreted. H_2 *never has, at any time in its normal ground state life*, any one of the three structures shown. Taken one at a time they are only figments of our imagination, but as shown in the preceding section, we obtain a satisfactory description of the molecule by supposing it to be in a state which is a hybrid of all three in certain proportions.

Before proceeding to consider further examples of resonance, a few remarks about the mathematical justification for the concept should be made. We have already seen that for H_2 when we used the normalized function $(1 - \lambda)\psi_{\text{cov}} + \lambda\psi_{\text{ion}}$ instead of just ψ_{cov}, we calculated a lower and more nearly correct energy for the system. If we had used ψ_{ion} alone, we would have obtained an extremely high energy. Yet, the *linear combination* of the two gives us an energy which is lower than that for either one separately. The amount by which the energy of the mixed state lies below the energy of the more stable of the two single states is called the *resonance energy*. It would be simpler to see how it comes naturally out of the solution of the wave equation if we take an example in which the two canonical forms are equivalent. We can write for NO_2^-, the nitrite ion, the two canonical forms 3-Va and 3-Vb. Each of these forms can be described by a

$$\text{(3-Va)} \qquad \text{(3-Vb)}$$

wave function, namely, ψ_{Va} and ψ_{Vb}, and each of these wave functions would give the same energy, E^0, if used in the wave equation with the appropriate Hamiltonian, $\mathscr{H}$:

$$E^0 = \frac{\int \psi_{Va}^* \mathscr{H} \psi_{Va}\, d\tau}{\int \psi_{Va}^* \psi_{Va}\, d\tau} = \int \psi_{Va}^* \mathscr{H} \psi_{Va}\, d\tau$$

$$= \int \psi_{Vb}^* \mathscr{H} \psi_{Vb}\, d\tau = \frac{\int \psi_{Vb}^* \mathscr{H} \psi_{Vb}\, d\tau}{\int \psi_{Vb}^* \psi_{Vb}\, d\tau} \tag{3-13}$$

where we have assumed that ψ_{Va} and ψ_{Vb} are each already normalized. If we wish to take account, mathematically, of the resonance depicted above, we must solve the wave equation, using the same Hamiltonian but with a linear combination of ψ_{Va} and ψ_{Vb}. From the symmetry it is obvious that this must be the symmetrical combination $(\psi_{Va} + \psi_{Vb})$ where the two are given equal weights. Let us now see what happens when we solve for the energy, E', using this wave function.

$$E' = \frac{\int (\psi_{Va}^* + \psi_{Vb}^*)\mathscr{H}(\psi_{Va} + \psi_{Vb})\, d\tau}{\int (\psi_{Va}^* + \psi_{Vb}^*)(\psi_{Va} + \psi_{Vb})\, d\tau}$$

$$= \frac{\int \psi_{Va}^* \mathscr{H} \psi_{Va}\, d\tau + \int \psi_{Va}^* \mathscr{H} \psi_{Vb}\, d\tau + \int \psi_{Vb}^* \mathscr{H} \psi_{Va}\, d\tau + \int \psi_{Vb}^* \mathscr{H} \psi_{Vb}\, d\tau}{\int \psi_{Va}^* \psi_{Va}\, d\tau + \int \psi_{Va}^* \psi_{Vb}\, d\tau + \int \psi_{Vb}^* \psi_{Va}\, d\tau + \int \psi_{Vb}^* \psi_{Vb}\, d\tau} \tag{3-14}$$

Taking account of the normalization, using the following definitions

$$\int \psi_{Va}^* \psi_{Vb}\, d\tau = \int \psi_{Vb}^* \psi_{Va}\, d\tau = S$$

$$\int \psi_{Va}^* \mathscr{H} \psi_{Vb}\, d\tau = \int \psi_{Vb}^* \mathscr{H} \psi_{Va}\, d\tau = E_R$$

and remembering equation 3-13, we can rewrite equation 3-14 as

$$E' = \frac{E^0 + E_R}{1 + S} \approx E^0 + E_R \qquad (3\text{-}15)$$

since S, called the overlap integral, is usually small compared to 1. Thus we see that E' is lower than E^0 by E_R, the resonance energy.*

The equality of the two integrals called E_R is only true so long as ψ_{Va} and ψ_{Vb} are wave functions giving the same energy. Moreover, the value of such an integral diminishes rapidly the greater the difference in the energies given by ψ_{Va} and ψ_{Vb} separately in case the two wave functions are not equivalent. Thus stabilization of a molecule by resonance is greatest when the canonical forms contributing to the hybrid are close in energy, and best of all, identical. We might, for example, have taken the trouble to make our calculations using a wave function $(\psi_{Va} + \psi_{Vb} + \lambda\psi_{Vc})$ where ψ_{Vc} describes structure 3-Vc. For various reasons (for example, the

(3-Vc)

O—O distance is too great to permit the formation of a strong O—O bond, whereas we are at the same time giving up a rather strong N—O bond), 3-Vc would have a far higher energy than 3-Va or 3-Vb, and this calculation using $(\psi_{Va} + \psi_{Vb} + \lambda\psi_{Vc})$ will not give us a significantly lower energy than we can obtain using just $(\psi_{Va} + \psi_{Vb})$.

The hydrogen molecule has provided an example of *covalent–ionic resonance* in a particular bond. Because structures 3-IVb and 3-IVc are of importance in an accurate description of the bond from the VB point of view, we say that the bond has some ionic character. However, the polarity which 3-Vb introduces is exactly balanced by the polarity which 3-Vc introduces so that the bond has no net polarity. It is therefore called a *nonpolar covalent* bond. It is important not to confuse polarity and ionic character, although, unfortunately, the literature contains many instances of such confusion. When we turn to a heteronuclear diatomic molecule, we necessarily have bonds which have both ionic and polar character. Even for the pure covalent canonical structure of HCl (3-Ia) there is bond polarity

(3-Ia)   (3-Ib)   (3-Ic)

* It is *lower* because all three are intrinsically negative.

3 + A.I.C.

because the two different atoms necessarily have different affinities for the electron pair. It is thus shared but not equally shared. It is also to be expected that the ionic structures 3-Ib and 3-Ic make some contribution. Owing to the facts that (a) hydrogen and chlorine have about equal first ionization potentials, but (b) chlorine has a far higher electron affinity than hydrogen, 3-Ic is much less energetically favorable and hence contributes much less to the resonance hybrid than 3-Ib. Since the whole scheme we are using here is essentially qualitative, we normally ignore 3-Ic and consider the ionic-covalent resonance in HCl to be adequately described by 3-Ia ↔ 3-Ib.

Two other examples of the resonance description may be cited to round out the discussion. There is the classic case of benzene (3-VI) for which at least five canonical structures are of some importance. 3-VIa and 3-VIb

(3-VIa)   (3-VIb)   (3-VIc)   (3-VId)   (3-VIe)

are the well-known Kekulé structures and contribute most to the hybrid, while 3-VIc, d and e are the Dewar structures, which are much less important. An estimate of the resonance stabilization energy can be made in the following way. From empirical knowledge of the average energies of C=C, C—C and C—H bonds, the energy of the most stable canonical form, 3-VIa (or 3-VIb), can be estimated. Thermochemical studies show that the actual energy of benzene is some 35–40 kcal/mole lower. Actually, a correction to the resonance energy so computed should be made if we recall that the benzene molecule is a regular hexagon, and hence the hypothetical structures 3-VIa and 3-VIb should be also. When we estimate the energy for 3-VIa or 3-VIb using empirical bond energies, we get a result which applies to a molecule in which the double bonds are ∼1.35 A and the single bonds are ∼1.54 A. Thus in order to estimate the energy of a structure such as 3-VIa or 3-VIb with equal bond lengths, we must raise the energy previously estimated by the amount of energy necessary to stretch and contract the various bonds, thus increasing our estimate of the resonance energy.

The CO molecule can be considered as a resonance hybrid of the following canonical structures:

(3-VIIa)   (3-VIIb)   (3-VIIc)

Pauling has estimated that all three are of comparable importance, which is in accord with the low (0.1 D) dipole moment of the molecule, although the very short bond distance (1.13 A) would suggest that 3-VIIc is predominant. The low dipole moment can be perhaps explained on the basis of smaller contributions from 3-VIIa and 3-VIIb if polarity due to lone pair moments (see Chapter 4) is taken into account.

One final comment should be made here concerning the error of attributing any physical reality to a particular canonical form. The two or more wave functions we combine to make the total wave function must represent only differences in the distribution of electrons about a *fixed and constant* nuclear framework. Now, if such a molecule as is represented by 3-Va or 3-Vb for NO_2^- really existed, we should expect that the N=O distance would be appreciably shorter than the N—O distance. Thus 3-Vb could not be obtained from 3-Va simply by redistributing electrons. We should also have to shift the nuclear framework, and it is just that which is foreign to the whole concept of resonance. Thus the structures 3-Va and 3-Vb cannot represent real molecules, but only hypothetical ones. In our subsequent discussion of molecular orbital theory we shall examine an alternative, and perhaps to some tastes more realistic, method of getting the same results.

3-4. Promotion Energies and Valence States

The ground state of the carbon atom is $1s^2 2s^2 2p_x 2p_y$, and it thus has only two unpaired electrons. It would therefore seem to follow that its most stable compounds with atoms, X, having a single unpaired electron—H, F, Cl, etc.—would be of the type CX_2. This, of course, is contrary to fact, its most stable compounds with such atoms being of the type CX_4, for example, CH_4 and CCl_4. In order to explain these facts, we must assume that the electronic configuration of carbon is altered so as to give it four unpaired electrons before it combines with four X's. The lowest configuration we can write for such a four-spin state is $1s^2 2s 2p_x 2p_y 2p_z$, and it lies some 97 kcal above the $1s^2 2s^2 2p^2$ state. In order to understand why the carbon atom makes this initial sacrifice in stability, consider the energy level diagram for methane (Fig. 3-2)

The enthalpy of formation of CH_4(g) from C(s) and $2H_2$(g) is -18 kcal/mole. The various steps into which we analyze this over-all process are shown on the right side of the figure. First, four hydrogen atoms, each with an unpaired electron, must be formed from $2H_2$. Next, the graphite must be vaporized to carbon atoms in their ground states, which requires the input of energy, L. The gaseous carbon atoms must now be promoted to the state sp^3 (abbreviation for $1s^2 2s 2p_x 2p_y 2p_z$), which requires $E_1 = 97$ kcal, as mentioned already. The carbon atom in this state is not actually ready to form bonds yet, however; it must still be promoted to its tetravalent valence state, denoted V_4. (We shall discuss the reason for this in detail later when we take up the subject of hybridization.) It then forms four bonds to the hydrogen atoms releasing four times the mean C—H bond energy. Despite all of the various energies required to dissociate $2H_2$ and to promote C(s) to C[V_4], ~ 560 kcal, the net energy is favorable since four strong bonds are formed. Now let us consider the formation of the hypothetical CH_2. To do this, one H_2 must be dissociated into 2H and the carbon must be vaporized only to ground state atoms, C $(1s^2 2s^2 2p^2)$, so the

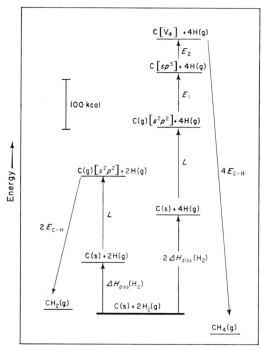

Fig. 3-2. Diagram showing various promotion energies in the formation of CH_4 and CH_2.

total promotion energy is only ~ 275 kcal. However, even if we assume the energy of a C—H bond in CH_2 to be the same as in CH_4 (and there are good reasons to believe it is weaker), we regain only ~ 289 kcal or less on forming the bonds. Thus the reaction C(s) + H_2(g) = CH_2(g) is less favorable than C(s) + $2H_2$(g) = CH_4(g) despite the much larger promotion energy required in the latter case.

Before leaving this subject a few more words must be said about the valence state. It is not a true stationary state of the atom which can be directly observed by experiment, but, rather, a hypothetical state whose energy can be calculated from sufficient information on true stationary states. It is a useful concept, however, and its use will be given further justification when we discuss hybridization.

3-5. The Overlap Criterion of Bond Strength

The best theoretical criterion we have for the strength of a given electron pair bond is, of course, the energy we calculate to be released when the bond is formed. We have seen, however, that even in the simple, prototype case of H_2 lengthy and tedious calculations are required to obtain even an approximate value for this energy. Obviously a simpler, if less fundamentally correct criterion is desirable, and such a criterion does exist. Pauling and Mulliken have pointed out that there is a qualitative and, under some well-defined conditions, even a semiquantitative relation between bond energies and the overlap of the atomic orbitals used in forming the bonds. It is not difficult to see qualitatively why good overlap makes for strong bonding. The more the two bonding orbitals overlap, the more the bonding electrons are concentrated between the nuclei where they can minimize the nuclear repulsion and maximize the attractive forces between themselves and both nuclei jointly.

The overlap between a pair of atomic orbitals, S, is given by the equation

$$S = \int \psi_A \psi_B \, d\tau \tag{3-16}$$

and S is called the overlap integral. This integral may have a value which is positive, negative or exactly zero. When its value is positive, there is a build-up of electronic charge between the nuclei and a bond can be formed. When the overlap integral is negative, there is reduction in the electron density between the nuclei. This increases the repulsion between them and they tend to move apart. When the overlap is zero, there is no net interaction, attractive or repulsive. Thus, in the use of the overlap criterion there are two stages. First, there is the qualitative question of whether the overlap will be positive, negative or zero. Second, when a positive overlap occurs, we may wish to know its magnitude in order to estimate the strength of the bond.

The qualitative nature of overlaps can generally be determined by examination of simple pictures of the orbitals involved.

Examples are presented in Figure 3-3. The overlaps shown in (a)–(d) are all positive, while those in (e)–(h) are negative. It should be noted that in each of these examples the magnitude and sign of the overlap depends on the internuclear distance and on the relative sizes of the orbitals. The situations depicted are those in which the orbitals are of comparable size with internuclear distances chosen relative to the sizes so as to correspond to conditions typical of an actual molecule. For example, in (a), if one orbital were much larger than the other, in the sense of having the maximum in its radial distribution (see Fig. 1-6) much further out from the nucleus,

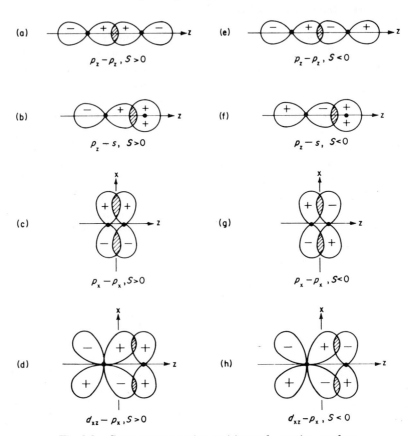

Fig. 3-3.   Some representative positive and negative overlaps.

its positive lobe could overlap the negative lobe of the other orbital more than the positive lobe, thus giving a net negative overlap. Also, as the internuclear distance decreases, beyond a certain point the net overlap tends to *decrease*, eventually becoming negative.

There are many cases in which the prediction of precisely zero overlap can be made, irrespective of the relative sizes of the orbitals or the internuclear distance. These predictions follow from the *symmetry properties* of the orbitals and are thus independent of scale factors, because there must always be *exactly* equal areas (volumes) of positive and negative overlap. It should now become obvious why it is important to remember not only the shapes but also the *signs* of the lobes of orbitals.

Figure 3-4 shows four examples in which the net overlap must be zero on symmetry grounds alone.

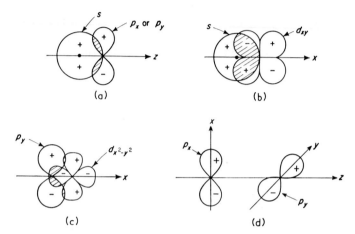

Fig. 3-4. Diagrammatic representation of some overlaps which are required by symmetry to be zero.

When non-zero overlaps are expected, it is often desirable to estimate their magnitudes. This can be done by expressing ψ_A and ψ_B in equation 3-16 as functions of the spacial coordinates about the nuclei A and B and then carrying out the integration. Algebraically, this is tedious, but there are now extensive tables of numerical values[1] of overlaps over the useful ranges of parameters. The parameters are the sizes of the orbitals (which depend on the effective nuclear charges) and the internuclear distance. These tables have been computed using simple exponential expressions (3-17) for the radial factors, $R(r)$, of the orbitals (see page 11), which were

$$R(r) = Nr^{n-1} e^{-\mu r/a_H} \qquad (3\text{-}17)$$

proposed many years ago by Slater. Orbitals which use the usual angular factors obtained by solving the wave equation for hydrogen together with these simple radial functions are called *Slater-Type Orbitals* (STO's).

In the expression for the radial part of an STO (Eq. 3-17) N is a normalizing factor, n is the principal quantum number, a_H is the Bohr radius

[1] R. S. Mulliken, C. A. Rieke, D. Orloff and H. Orloff, *J. Chem. Phys.*, **17**, 1248 (1949); H. H. Jaffe and G. O. Doak, *J. Chem. Phys.*, **21**, 196 (1963); H. H. Jaffe, *J. Chem. Phys.*, **21**, 258 (1963).

(0.529A) and μ is a function of the effective nuclear charge for an electron in the orbital concerned. Slater proposed rules for adjusting the value of μ so as to make the energy of the orbitals agree well with experiment. For overlap calculations, however, it is more important that the shape of the orbital in its outer region (where overlaps occur) match as closely as possible the true shape of the orbital. In general, STO's are only a fair approximation in the latter respect, as shown in Figure 3-5 where a Hartree–Fock $3d$ orbital for the Cr^{3+} ion is compared with the STO. Thus overlaps computed using single STO's are rough approximations. However, it is

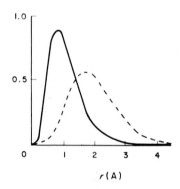

Fig. 3-5.   A comparison of a Hartree–Fock $3d$ wave function for the Cr^{3+} ion (———) with a Slater type wave function (– – –).

possible to take linear combinations of a few STO's so as to approximate very closely the true shape of an orbital.[2] The overlap between two orbitals each expressed as a combination of several (say, p and q) STO's can be evaluated by looking up the necessary number ($p \times q$ in general) of overlaps in the tables mentioned above. Thus, in summary, with the aid of existing tables, overlaps of accurate (i.e., Hartree–Fock) orbitals for atoms may be computed without excessive labor.

In order to estimate actual bond energies using the overlap criterion one usually uses the molecular orbital method. Hence, we shall return to this matter again after the molecular orbital method has been introduced.

3-6. Hybridization

In discussing the promotion energy required to transform the carbon atom from its divalent s^2p^2 ground state configuration to the tetravalent

---

[2] J. W. Richardson, W. C. Nieupoort, R. R. Powell and W. F. Edgell, *J. Chem. Phys.*, **36**, 1057 (1962).

state necessary to form its normal compounds (e.g., CH_4), we mentioned but did not properly explain the energy, E_2 in Figure 3-2, required to promote the atom from an observable, stationary state based on the configuration sp^3, to what we called its valence state, V_4. The sp^3 configuration referred to is, more specifically, the configuration $2s2p_x2p_y2p_z$. Now, according to the preceding discussion, if one atom, say A, with an orbital ψ_A containing one electron, is to form the strongest bond with another atom, B, then the A—B axis should be along the direction in which ψ_A has its maximum value. Thus if atom A is to use its p_x orbital, we should expect the A—B axis to be collinear with the x axis. For an s orbital, of course, all directions are equivalent. Thus if the valence state of the carbon atom were really the $2s2p_x2p_y2p_z$ stationary state, we should expect three hydrogen atoms to form bonds to the p_x, p_y and p_z orbitals, and thus lie along the x, y and z axes. The fourth hydrogen atom would bond to the s orbital and probably take up a position equidistant from the other three.

This hypothetical state of affairs is depicted in Figure 3-6. It is easily

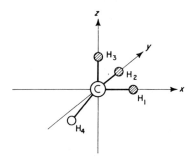

Fig. 3-6.   Geometric structure methane would have if the carbon atom used pure hydrogenic orbitals, $2s$, $2p_x$, $2p_y$ and $2p_z$ to form C—H bonds.

seen that the three angles H_1—C—H_2, H_1—C—H_3 and H_2—C—H_3 are 90°, and the three equivalent angles such as H_1—C—H_4 are $\sim 125°$. Moreover, since H_1, H_2 and H_3 are bonded to carbon through its p orbitals, all of these bonds should be equivalent and hence of equal length, whereas the C—H_4 bond is formed using a carbon s orbital and would not be expected to have the same length. It is known with complete certainty, however, that methane does not have such a structure. Actually all C—H distances and H—C—H angles are equal, and the molecule is a regular tetrahedron. From this we infer that the valence state of the carbon atom is one in which its four valence electrons are in four equivalent orbitals which have their lobes directed toward the apices of a tetrahedron. It is this valence state which we have denoted as V_4. Our next question, then, is how can we

3*

express such a set of equivalent orbitals in terms of the basic set of hydrogenic orbitals $2s$, $2p_x$, $2p_y$ and $2p_z$?

If we are to have four completely equivalent orbitals, they must each have the same fraction of s *character*, namely, one-fourth, and the same fraction of p *character*, namely, three-fourths, and the resulting orbitals must be normalized. We can pick the direction for the first one arbitrarily, so let us put it along the z axis. Neither p_x nor p_y can contribute to this one since they have precisely the value zero along the z axis, so this first one will consist entirely of s and p_z. Its general form must therefore be

$$N(s + kp_z)$$

where k is a mixing coefficient yet to be evaluated, and N is a normalizing factor. k can be shown to be $\sqrt{3}$ since the probability of the electron having p_z character must be three times greater than its having s character, and these probabilities are proportional to the squares of the wave functions, namely,

$$\frac{\int (kp_z)^2 \, d\tau}{\int (s)^2 \, d\tau} = 3$$

and since p_z and s are separately normalized, $k = \sqrt{3}$. The value of N is then easily found by normalizing $(s + \sqrt{3}p_z)$, namely,

$$\int [N(s + \sqrt{3}p_z)]^2 \, d\tau = 1$$

$$N^2 = \left[\int s^2 \, d\tau + 3 \int p_z^2 \, d\tau\right]^{-1}$$

$$= [1 + 3]^{-1}$$

$$N = 1/2$$

where we have also made use of the orthogonality of the s and p_z orbitals.

The expressions for the other three orbitals, equivalent to this one and having their lobes lying along directions 109° from the z axis, can be derived by similar reasoning, but trigonometric complications make it impractical to carry out the derivation here. (A complete derivation of all orbitals in a set is given later for simpler cases.) This set of four equivalently directed orbitals is one example of a set of *hybrid orbitals*; these four are commonly called sp^3 hybrids to indicate their composition in terms of hydrogenic atomic orbitals. In common—though somewhat loose—parlance it is said that the carbon atom "has sp^3 hybridization."

Before proceeding to further discussion of hybridization, we may complete our explanation of the difference between the valence state V_4 and the sp^3 stationary state. In order to promote the carbon atom from the sp^3 stationary state to the valence state, two things are done: (1) the s and the three p orbitals are hybridized to produce four sp^3 hybrids which are each occupied by one electron, and (2) any preferred orientations of the spins of these electrons due to interactions of their spins with one another or with their orbital motions are destroyed, leaving them completely free, random and ready to be paired with electron spins of other atoms. Both of these processes require input of energy, the total in this case being ~ 65 kcal/g-atom. Let us emphasize again that the valence state is in general not identical with any observable stationary state of the atom, and the idea of "promotion to the valence state" is only a mental construction which is useful in thinking about the bonding.

We return now to systematic consideration of hybridization, beginning with the simplest common type, namely, sp hybridization. Beryllium in its ground state has the configuration $1s^2 2s^2$, and without promotion to a higher state could form no electron pair bonds. Normally, it forms compounds such as $BeCl_2$, $BeBr_2$ and $Be(CH_3)_2$, which, as free gaseous molecules, are linear. To explain this we assume that the atom is first promoted to the state $2s2p$ followed by promotion to a valence state involving sp hybridization. The physical reasoning behind the construction of these hybrids can be understood with reference to Figure 3-7; the algebraic details in this case are quite simple. Since the two hybrid orbitals are to be equivalent, they must have equal fractions of s and p character, that is, the s orbital must contribute equally to both and the p_z orbital must contribute equally to both. Thus they must be of the forms $N(s + p)$ and $N'(s - p)$, where N and N' are normalizing factors. It is easily shown that these two orbitals are orthogonal:

$$\int N(s + p)N'(s - p)\, d\tau = NN' \int s^2\, d\tau - NN' \int p^2\, d\tau$$

$$= NN'(1 - 1) = 0$$

and that $N = N' = \sqrt{1/2}$:

$$N^2 \int (s + p)^2\, d\tau = N^2 \int s^2\, d\tau + N^2 \int p^2\, d\tau = 2N^2 = 1$$

An atom, X, using a pair of such sp or digonal hybrid orbitals, will form two equivalent bonds to two other atoms or univalent groups, Y, giving a linear YXY molecule. The gaseous halides (though not the solid compounds) of all of the group II elements have linear structures which may be attributed to the sp hybridization of the metal atoms. Of course, a completely ionic molecule $Y^-X^{2+}Y^-$ would tend to be linear for electrostatic reasons, so linearity does not, by itself, demonstrate that the bonds are covalent; in many cases, however, there are various kinds of evidence

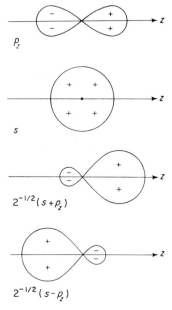

Fig. 3-7.   Schematic illustration of the formation of sp digonal hybrid orbitals by combination of an s and a p orbital.

suggesting appreciable covalent character in the bonds.   Mercuric halides and pseudo halides (e.g., $Hg(CN)_2$) are doubtless predominantly covalent. In these linear molecules we postulate that mercury with a configuration $[Xe]5d^{10}6s^2$, uses $6s6p$ hybrid orbitals.

The elements of group III which have ground state configurations ns^2np form many molecules of the type MX_3 where M is B, Al, Ga, In or Tl, and X is a halogen or an organic radical, CH_3, C_6H_5, etc.   In all of these the monomeric molecules (some dimerize; e.g., Al_2Cl_6) are known or presumed to have the shape of a planar equilateral triangle.   Thus we assume that the metal atoms, B, for example, must first be excited to a stationary state based on the configuration sp_xp_y and then further promoted to a valence state in which there is a set of equivalent sp^2 hybrid orbitals. The correct algebraic expressions and schematic "balloon" picture of a set of sp^2 or trigonal hybrids are shown in Figure 3-8.   Each one has its maximum along one of a set of three axes, lying in the same plane making angles of 120° with one another. Moreover, the orbitals are equivalent in shape. Each one, if rotated 120°, would be exactly superposed on the orbital already on that axis.

We can easily work out the expressions for these orbitals by invoking the requirements that they be equivalent, meaning that the proportion of s character to p character be the same in all of them, and that they be normalized. We shall see that in this particular case the orthogonality takes care of itself, but not all cases are as overdetermined as this one.

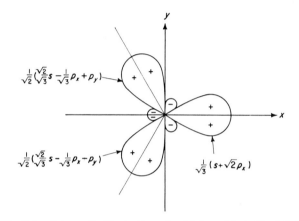

Fig. 3-8. Schematic illustration of sp^2 trigonal hybrid orbitals.

Let us choose to direct the first hybrid along the x axis (see Fig. 3-8), and make the coefficient of p_x $\sqrt{2}$ times that of s since the orbital must have twice as much p character as s character. This gives us

$$\psi_1 = N(s + \sqrt{2}p_x)$$

and the normalization factor is easily shown to have the value of $1/\sqrt{3}$. In order to work out the expressions for the other two orbitals to which s, p_x and p_y will all contribute, we make use of the fact that orbitals behave like vectors in the sense that if an orbital makes a contribution χ in a certain direction it makes a contribution $\chi \cos \theta$ in a direction θ from the first. Thus, considering ψ_2 to be the orbital lying in the second quadrant (Fig. 3-8) and ψ_3 to be the one in the third quadrant, we proceed as follows. The contribution of the s orbital is isotropic and the three hybrid orbitals are all to have the same amount of s character. Moreover, by virtue of the vectorial properties of the atomic and hybrid orbitals, p_y and p_x must contribute to ψ_2 in the proportions $\cos 30°(\sqrt{3}/2)$ and $\cos 120°(-1/2)$ and to ψ_3 in the proportions $-\cos 30°(-\sqrt{3}/2)$ and $\cos 240°(-1/2)$. Thus we can write

$$\psi_2 = (1/\sqrt{3})s + \alpha[(-1/2)p_x + (\sqrt{3}/2)p_y]$$
$$\psi_3 = (1/\sqrt{3})s + \beta[(-1/2)p_x - (\sqrt{3}/2)p_y]$$

It is now necessary to adjust α and β so that each of these orbitals is normalized. For α:

$$\int \psi_2\psi_2 \, d\tau = \tfrac{1}{3}\int ss d\tau + \tfrac{1}{4}\alpha^2 \int p_x p_x \, d\tau + \tfrac{3}{4}\alpha^2 \int p_z p_z \, d\tau$$
$$= \tfrac{1}{3} + \alpha^2 = 1$$

whence, α equals $\sqrt{2}/\sqrt{3}$. The same value is obtained for β and the final expressions for the three trigonal hybrid orbitals are therefore:

$$\psi_1 = (1/\sqrt{3})s + (\sqrt{2}/\sqrt{3})p_x$$
$$\psi_2 = (1/\sqrt{3})s - (1/\sqrt{6})p_x + (1/\sqrt{2})p_y$$
$$\psi_3 = (1/\sqrt{3})s - (1/\sqrt{6})p_x - (1/\sqrt{2})p_y$$

It is now easily shown that these orbitals are mutually orthogonal. For example:

$$\int \psi_1\psi_2 \, d\tau = \int [(1/\sqrt{3})s]^2 \, d\tau - \int [(\sqrt{2}/\sqrt{3})p_x][(1/\sqrt{6})p_x] \, d\tau$$
$$= 1/3 - 1/3 = 0$$

It is also easy to show that the ratio of p to s character is 2:1 in ψ_2 and ψ_3 as well as in ψ_1:

$$\frac{(-1/\sqrt{6})^2 + (\pm 1/\sqrt{2})^2}{(1/\sqrt{3})^2} = \frac{1/6 + 1/2}{1/3} = \frac{2}{1}$$

It can be seen from examination of Figures 3-7 and 3-8 that hybrid orbitals provide much greater concentrations of the electron cloud in particular directions than do the simple hydrogenic orbitals of which they are constructed. Thus hybrid orbitals can provide better overlap with orbitals of other atoms along these preferred directions, and they consequently make certain configurations of the molecule preferred. In general, the increased overlap means that the bonds are stronger, and this more than compensates for the promotion energy required to attain the hybridized valence state.

Hybridization is not limited to s and p orbitals, but may, in general, involve the mixing of all types of atomic orbitals. Hybrids involving d orbitals occur quite commonly among the heavier elements and are particularly important in complexes of the transition elements. We shall mention five of the most important hybridizations involving one or more d orbitals, each of which is illustrated in Figure 3-9.

1. d^2sp^3, *octahedral hybridization.* When the $d_{x^2-y^2}$ and d_{z^2} orbitals are combined with an s orbital and a set of p_x, p_y and p_z orbitals, a set of equivalent orbitals with lobes directed to the apices of an octahedron can be formed.

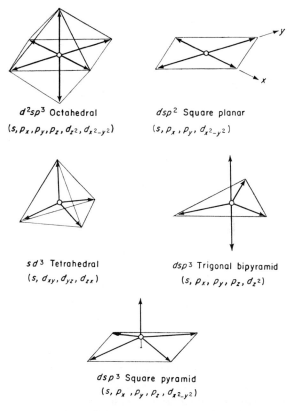

d^2sp^3 Octahedral
$(s, p_x, p_y, p_z, d_{z^2}, d_{x^2-y^2})$

dsp^2 Square planar
$(s, p_x, p_y, d_{x^2-y^2})$

sd^3 Tetrahedral
$(s, d_{xy}, d_{yz}, d_{zx})$

dsp^3 Trigonal bipyramid
$(s, p_x, p_y, p_z, d_{z^2})$

dsp^3 Square pyramid
$(s, p_x, p_y, p_z, d_{x^2-y^2})$

Fig. 3-9. Five important hybridization schemes involving d orbitals. Heavy arrows show the directions in which the lobes point.

2. dsp^2, *square planar hybridization.* A $d_{x^2-y^2}$ orbital, an s orbital and p_x and p_y orbitals can be combined to give a set of equivalent hybrid orbitals with lobes directed to the corners of a square in the xy plane.

3. sd^3, *tetrahedral hybridization.* An s orbital and the set d_{xy}, d_{xz}, d_{yz} may be combined to give a tetrahedrally directed set of orbitals.

4. dsp^3, *trigonal bipyramidal hybridization.* The orbitals s, p_x, p_y, p_z

and d_{z^2} may be combined to give a nonequivalent (see below) set of five hybrid orbitals directed to the apices of a trigonal bipyramid.

5. dsp^3, *square pyramidal hybridization*. The orbitals s, p_x, p_y, p_z and $d_{x^2-y^2}$ may be combined to give a nonequivalent (see below) set of five hybrid orbitals directed to the apices of a square pyramid.

We have now examined some hybridization schemes from the point of view of the kinds of atomic orbitals required to construct them. So long as the required orbitals are available, the existence of a particular set of hybrids is possible from this point of view. However, there are some energy considerations which are also important. If one or more of the orbitals required in the hybridization lie at a much higher energy than the others, it may not be energetically possible for the atom actually to achieve full hybridization. For example, referring again to methane and Figure 3-2, if the promotion energy E_1 were very much higher, say, >115 kcal/g-atom, instead of ~ 96 kcal/g-atom, CH_2 would be more stable than CH_4. As another example, sulfur, though it has six electrons in its valence shell, forms only a few compounds in which six d^2sp^3 hybrid orbitals are used because the energy required to promote the sulfur atom from its $[Ne]3s^23p^4$ ground state to a $[Ne]3s3p^33d^2$ state is too great to be offset by the energy of formation of the six bonds except in a few instances. It is also possible to have a mixture of hybrid states for energetic reasons. The two hybridization schemes giving a set of tetrahedrally directed orbitals, namely, sp^3 and sd^3, are only extremes, and it is possible to have a set of tetrahedral hybrids using one s orbital and portions of each of the two sets $d_{xy}d_{xz}d_{yz}$ and $p_xp_yp_z$. For carbon, the amount of d character is doubtless negligible since the lowest available d orbitals, the $3d$'s, are so far above the $2p$'s that their use could only be a great energetic disadvantage. In the tetrahedral ions MnO_4^-, CrO_4^{2-}, etc., however, the $3d$ orbitals are of about the same energy as the $4s$ orbitals, and the $4p$ orbitals are somewhat higher. The hybridization of the Mn and Cr atoms in these cases is thus probably a mixture of sd^3 and sp^3, with d character greater than p character.

Sets of hybrid orbitals have been described above as equivalent and nonequivalent. The orbitals in an equivalent set are all identical in every respect except for their direction in space. Their fractions of s, p, d, etc., character are identical. For an atom using sp^3, sd^3 or dsp^2 hybrid orbitals to form bonds to four identical atoms, sp hybrids to bond two identical atoms, sp^2 orbitals to bond three identical atoms or d^2sp^3 hybrids to bond six identical atoms, all of the orbitals in the set are equivalent. However, in CH_3Cl the four hybrid orbitals used by the carbon atom are not equivalent, for surely the carbon atom will form its best bond to chlorine using a more or less different orbital from the ones it uses to bond the hydrogen atoms. The three orbitals used to bond the hydrogens are equivalent. As evidence of this, it is found that the three H—C—H angles are equal and the three H—C—Cl angles are equal, but the H—C—H angles are not exactly the same as the H—C—Cl angles. All of the angles are, however, very close to the tetrahedral angle, and it is a good approximation to regard the four hybrid orbitals used by carbon as approximately sp^3 hybrids. It should be remembered, however, that in this or any analogous situation all the hybrid orbitals in the set are not *exactly* the same; that is, they are not an equivalent set.

The two dsp^3 sets, giving either trigonal bipyramid or square pyramid arrangements, depending upon the d orbital used, are sets which are intrinsically nonequivalent, even if the five atoms bonded—as in PF_5, for example, which has a trigonal bipyramidal structure—are identical. In the trigonal bipyramid there are two equivalent orbitals called axial orbitals and three equivalent orbitals called equatorial orbitals, but those in different sets are not equivalent. Two p orbitals, p_x and p_y, contribute to the three equatorial hybrid orbitals, whereas only one p orbital, p_z, contributes to the two axial hybrid orbitals, so that an axial orbital could not possibly be identical in composition with an equatorial orbital. Similarly, in the square pyramid, the four basal orbitals form an equivalent set, but no one of these is equivalent to the unique axial orbital.

THE MOLECULAR ORBITAL (MO) THEORY OF BONDING

3-7. Introduction

In the preceding section we have discussed the valence bond (VB) or electron pair theory of bonding. The basic qualitative idea in this theory is essentially Lewis' idea that each bonded atom pair in a molecule is held together by an electron pair or perhaps several electron pairs. These electron pairs are *localized* between particular pairs of nuclei. Moreover, it is assumed that the wave functions for these electrons are just the products of atomic wave functions. The MO theory starts with a qualitatively different assumption.

In building up a multielectron atom we started with a nucleus and a set of *one-center orbitals* about that nucleus and fed the required number of electrons into these orbitals in increasing order of orbital energy. We discovered the forms of these orbitals by solving exactly the problem with only one electron and then assumed that when many electrons are present the orbitals have the same form but that their relative energies are affected by the shielding of one electron by another. In other words, we treat each electron as if it moves in the effective field produced by the nucleus and all of the other electrons. In its essentials, the molecular orbital theory treats a molecule in the same way. We start with several nuclei, arranged as they are in the complete molecule. We then determine the various orbitals which *one* electron would have in the field of this set of nuclei. These *multicenter orbitals* are taken as the set to be filled with as many electrons as are required in the molecule under consideration. Again it is understood that the mutual shielding of the electrons and other interactions between them will have an important effect on the relative energies of the various molecular orbitals.

Although this scheme is just as good in principle for molecules as for atoms, it has a severe limitation in practice. As we have seen, we can get our basic set of atomic orbitals readily by exact solution of the wave equation of the hydrogen atom. In general, the problem of an electron moving in the field of several nuclei cannot be solved exactly. Therefore, we must begin by using only an approximate form for our one-electron MO's.

3-8. Linear Combination of Atomic Orbitals (LCAO) Approximation

The LCAO method is a simple and qualitatively useful approximation. It is based on the very reasonable idea that as the electron moves around in the nuclear framework it will at any given time be close to one nucleus and relatively far from others, and that when near a given nucleus it will behave more or less as though it were in an atomic orbital belonging to that nucleus. To develop this idea more concretely we shall use the hydrogen molecule ion H_2^+. This is a prototype for homonuclear diatomic molecules just as the hydrogen atom is for atoms in general.

If the electron belonged to either of the hydrogen nuclei A or B alone, its behavior in the ground state would be described by ϕ_A or ϕ_B alone. When it is in some general position with reference to the nuclear framework it can be approximately described by a superposition of both, that is, by $\phi_A \pm \phi_B$. Such an algebraic sum of functions is called a linear combination. The two normalized LCAO wave functions written out fully, are

$$\left. \begin{array}{l} \psi_b = N_b(\phi_A + \phi_B) \\ \psi_a = N_a(\phi_A - \phi_B) \end{array} \right\} (3\text{-}18)$$

The two normalization constants are readily shown to have the following values:

$$N_b = \frac{1}{\sqrt{2 + 2S}} = 0.56$$

$$N_a = \frac{1}{\sqrt{2 - 2S}} = 1.11$$

The numerical values were obtained by inserting the correct numerical value (0.59) of the overlap integral, S. Generally, the overlap integrals are not this great, but rather around 0.25. For $S = 0.25$ the two normalization constants would have been 0.63 and 0.82, whereas, neglecting S altogether, both normalization constants would be 0.71. The small errors thus introduced by neglect of S in the normalization constants are usually tolerable in simple LCAO–MO theory, and overlap is neglected.

In order to understand the physical meaning of the two LCAO–MO's, let us first examine Figure 3-10. The solid lines show ψ_a^2 and ψ_b^2, the

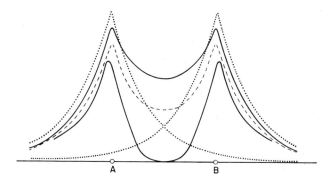

Fig. 3-10. A plot of the atomic orbital electron probabilities, ϕ_A^2 and ϕ_B^2 (. . . . .), the molecular orbital electron probabilities, ψ_a^2 and ψ_b^2 (———), and the probability distribution of a single electron equally distributed over ϕ_A and ϕ_B (– – – –) along the internuclear line for H_2^+, according to LCAO–MO theory, including overlap.

squares being used because we are at the moment chiefly interested in how the electron density is distributed along the internuclear line. The dotted lines show the electron density in the individual atomic orbitals, that is, they show ϕ_A^2 and ϕ_B^2. It is evident that an electron in ψ_b has a high distribution between the nuclei, while one in ψ_a has a very low distribution in this region. ψ_a^2 actually goes to zero at the midpoint. As a further indication of the significance of ψ_a^2 and ψ_b^2, they may also be compared with the dashed line, which is a plot of $\sqrt{1/2}\phi_A^2 + \sqrt{1/2}\phi_B^2$. This function gives the distribution of one electron spending its time equally in ϕ_A and in ϕ_B, these remaining, however, as separate atomic orbitals. The factors of $\sqrt{1/2}$ normalize the total electron density in each ϕ to 1/2. It is clear that ψ_b and ψ_a put more and less electron density, respectively, between the nuclei than does the simple sum of non-interacting atomic orbitals. This explains why one MO is given the subscript b, meaning *bonding*, and the other the subscript a, meaning *antibonding*.

In order to estimate the energies of the LCAO–MO's, ψ_a and ψ_b, we insert the expressions (3-18) into the wave equation. For ψ_b we have

$$E_b = \frac{\int \psi_b \mathscr{H} \psi_b \, d\tau}{\int \psi_b \psi_b \, d\tau} = \frac{N_b{}^2 \int (\phi_A + \phi_B)\mathscr{H}(\phi_A + \phi_B) \, d\tau}{1}$$

$$= N_b{}^2 \left[\int \phi_A \mathscr{H} \phi_A \, d\tau + \int \phi_A \mathscr{H} \phi_B \, d\tau + \int \phi_B \mathscr{H} \phi_A \, d\tau \right.$$
$$\left. + \int \phi_B \mathscr{H} \phi_B \, d\tau \right] \tag{3-19}$$

We do not immediately attempt to evaluate the four integrals in equation 3-19. Instead, we give them the following symbols:

$$Q_A = \int \phi_A \mathscr{H} \phi_A \, d\tau$$

$$Q_B = \int \phi_B \mathscr{H} \phi_B \, d\tau$$

$$\beta = \int \phi_A \mathscr{H} \phi_B \, d\tau = \int \phi_B \mathscr{H} \phi_A \, d\tau$$

Since atoms A and B here are identical, $Q_A = Q_B = Q$ and equation 3-19 takes the following simple form:

$$E_b = 2N_b{}^2(Q + \beta) \tag{3-20}$$

It follows, similarly, that

$$E_a = 2N_a{}^2(Q - \beta) \tag{3-21}$$

Now the integral Q is obviously just the energy of an electron in the orbital ϕ_A or ϕ_B, that is, it is equal to the ground state energy of the hydrogen atom. The integral β represents the energy of interaction between the orbitals ϕ_A and ϕ_B. It is called an exchange integral or resonance integral, and it can be shown that it is inherently negative. Thus an electron occupying the bonding MO, ψ_b, is more stable and an electron in ψ_a is less stable than one in a pure atomic orbital, ϕ_A or ϕ_B. The actual energies of stabilization and destabilization can be obtained in units of β by inserting the normalization coefficients into (3-20) and (3-21). If we make the approximation that overlap can be ignored, so that $N_a{}^2 = N_b{}^2 = 1/2$, we find that:

$$E_a = Q + \beta$$
$$E_b = Q - \beta$$

These results are expressed in the energy level diagram, Figure 3-11.

Its qualitative features are common to all energy level diagrams showing the energies of MO's formed between two atoms, each supplying one orbital. If the two atomic orbitals do not have the same energy, then ψ_a and ψ_b will be placed approximately equal distances above and below the mean energy of the two atomic orbitals. Figure 3-11 is also a typical energy level diagram in its arrangement. The atomic orbitals of the constituent atoms are placed on each side, and the resulting MO's are placed in the center. It is to be noted that when the overlap is included in the normalization coefficients, the problem becomes more complicated algebraically and the energy level diagram no longer possesses the simple, symmetrical form of Figure 3-11. We shall not, however, go into this matter further here since all applications of LCAO–MO theory in this book will utilize the approximation of neglecting overlap.

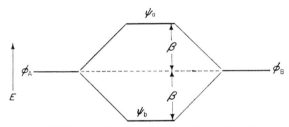

Fig. 3-11.   Energy level diagram showing the formation of bonding and antibonding MO's from two equivalent atomic orbitals in a homonuclear diatomic molecule.

In discussing the valence bond theory the overlap integral, S, was introduced and discussed. It was noted that, in general, the larger the value of S for two orbitals ϕ_A and ϕ_B, on two atoms, the stronger would be the bond which is formed using these orbitals. In terms of simple LCAO–MO theory, this idea may be given a more quantitative form, following a suggestion originally made by Mulliken. In essence, Mulliken proposed that integrals of the type β should be roughly proportional to the corresponding overlap integrals. It is also necessary to build into the relation expressing this proportionality a dependence on the average value of the energies of the orbitals which are forming the bond. Thus the following general equation is written:

$$\int \phi_A \mathscr{H} \phi_B \, d\tau = \beta = CQ_{av}S = CQ_{av} \int \phi_A \phi_B \, d\tau$$

in which C is a numerical constant, and Q_{av} is sometimes taken to be the arithmetic average,

$$Q_{av} = (Q_A + Q_B)/2$$

and by other workers as the geometrical average, viz.,

$$Q_{av} = (Q_A Q_B)^{1/2}$$

The proportionality constant, C, is expected to be approximately 2.0 and is often assigned exactly this value. Molecular orbital calculations made with this approximation are now quite common, especially for transition metal complexes and will be discussed further in Chapter 26.

We can now proceed to build up the electronic structures of some other molecules just as we used the aufbau principle to build up the electron configurations of atoms. If we add an additional electron to H_2^+ we have, of course, the hydrogen molecule H_2. This second electron will enter ψ_b along with the first, since ψ_b is the lowest energy orbital with a vacancy in it. In order to satisfy the exclusion principle, the spins of the two electrons must be paired. Thus we can write the electron configuration of H_2, from the MO viewpoint, as $(\psi_b)^2$. The binding energy will be approximately -2β with some correction for the mutual shielding effect. Thus in this simple case MO theory gives us a physical description of the bond in H_2 which is rather similar to what we obtain from VB theory, namely, that there are two electrons with spins paired which are concentrated between the nuclei. In more complicated cases we shall presently see more clearly how the two theories differ.

Let us continue applying the aufbau principle in the present situation. Suppose we bring together a helium atom and a hydrogen atom, so that again we have a bonding orbital, $\psi_b = \phi_{He} + \phi_H$, and an antibonding orbital, $\psi_a = \phi_{He} - \phi_H$. Again ψ_b will be more stable than the mean energy of the He $1s$ and H $1s$ orbitals, and ψ_a will be less stable, by roughly equal amounts. Because the exclusion principle prevents us from placing more than two electrons in one MO, the three electrons must occupy the two MO's in the following way: $(\psi_b)^2(\psi_a)^1$. Thus the molecule HeH should be stable by about the energy β. Such a molecule is known in the vapor phase.

Finally, let us suppose we bring together two helium atoms. Then we have four electrons to be housed in two MO's of the sort shown in Figure 3-11. Clearly, two must be placed in the bonding orbital and two in the antibonding orbital so that, according to the LCAO approximation, the binding energy of He_2 is precisely zero. A similar argument may be framed for all of the inert gases, and this explains why they are all monatomic.

Bond Orders. The bond order is defined in MO theory as the number of electron pairs occupying bonding MO's minus the number of electron pairs occupying antibonding MO's. Thus the bond orders in H_2^+, H_2, HHe and He_2 would be 1/2, 1, 1/2 and 0 respectively.

3-9. Homonuclear Diatomic Molecules

So far we have considered only cases in which the only important MO's are formed by overlap of an s orbital on each of the two atoms. MO's of this type are called σ (*sigma*) *MO's* and the property which so classifies them is their cylindrical symmetry about the internuclear axis. That such symmetry must exist should be clear from the fact that each of the two s orbitals composing them is symmetrical about this axis.

We must next consider how p orbitals may combine, in terms of the LCAO approximation, to form MO's in a homonuclear diatomic molecule. Suppose we define the internuclear axis as the z axis. If each atom has available a p_z orbital, they may be combined into a bonding MO, $p_z(1) + p_z(2)$ (Fig. 3-12a), and an antibonding MO, $p_z(1) - p_z(2)$. These MO's are

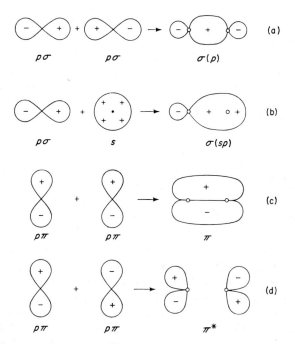

Fig. 3-12. Diagrams illustrating the formation of some simple two-center MO's from atomic orbitals.

also σ MO's. Note that a p_z orbital on one atom may also combine with an s orbital on the other to produce bonding (Fig. 3-12b) and anti bonding MO's. In general, any kind of s–p_z hybrid orbitals on the two atoms may combine to give σ MO's. Because of its ability to contribute to a σ MO, a p orbital (in this case, the p_z orbital, since we have chosen to identify the internuclear axis with the z axis of our coordinate system) lying along the molecular axis is called a $p\sigma$ orbital. An s orbital is simply understood to be of σ character and is not so denoted.

If the p_z orbital is a $p\sigma$ orbital, then the p_x and p_y orbitals are not. They are $p\pi$ orbitals. A π-type orbital is one whose nodal plane includes the molecular axis. It is not therefore cylindrically symmetric about this axis, but has equal electron density on either side of a plane containing the axis, while the wave function itself is of opposite sign on the two sides. Two such $p\pi$ orbitals can be combined into a bonding π MO, $p\pi(1) + p\pi(2)$ and an antibonding π MO, $p\pi(1) - p\pi(2)$. These two are simply denoted π and π^*, respectively. Their formation is illustrated in Figures 3-12c and 3-12d.

Let us consider an element in the first short period which has $2s$ and $2p$ orbitals in its valence shell. When two such atoms are combined into a homonuclear diatomic molecule, the two sets of atomic orbitals may combine into various MO's. Before we can apply the aufbau principle to determine the electronic structures of the diatomic molecules of these elements, we must know the relative energies of these MO's.

We may begin by treating the three types of orbitals, s, $p\sigma$ and $p\pi$ entirely separately. Thus the s orbitals give rise to σ_s and σ_s^*, bonding and antibonding MO's, respectively, just as in the case of H_2^+ and H_2. Similarly, the two $p\sigma$ orbitals combine to give σ_p and σ_p^* MO's. The two p_x orbitals combine to give bonding and antibonding MO's and so also do the two p_y orbitals. We note, however, that since the p_x and p_y orbitals on each atom are of the same energy, and entirely equivalent to one another except that one is rotated 90° from the other about the internuclear axis, the two π-type bonding MO's are equivalent to one another and of equal energy and so are the two π-type antibonding MO's. The two MO's of each pair are said to be *degenerate*. It is found that the magnitudes of the three sorts of overlaps decrease in the order s–$s \approx p\sigma$–$p\sigma > p\pi$–$p\pi$, and therefore, according to the overlap criterion of bond strength, the corresponding values of β should also decrease in the same order. On the basis of these considerations, together with the knowledge that for the elements of the first short period the p orbitals have higher energies than the s orbitals, the energy level diagram shown in Figure 3-13a can be drawn.

However, this diagram ignores one factor in the problem and is therefore not entirely correct. We have assumed that the s orbitals interact only with one another and the $p\sigma$ orbitals only with one another. While it is true that the greatest interactions should occur between the orbitals closest in energy (in this instance, those identical in energy) it is wrong to neglect entirely the other interactions permitted by symmetry. Actually, there are interactions between s and $p\sigma$ orbitals (see Fig. 3-12b). In order to examine these in detail and work out their consequences for the energies of the MO's, we should have to devote several pages to the problem. We shall instead simply state the results. First, the MO's we have called σ_s and σ_s^* now no longer have pure s character, and similarly, the orbitals we have called σ_p and σ_p^* no longer have pure p character. We shall therefore replace the subscripts s and p by others which do not carry an

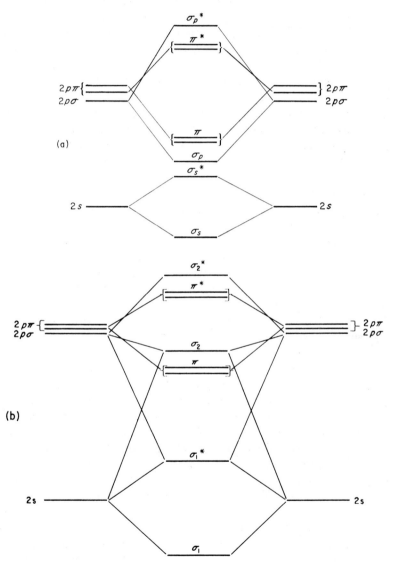

Fig. 3-13. Schematic energy level diagrams showing how atomic orbitals of two (identical) atoms of the first short period combine to form molecular orbitals.

inaccurate implication. Second, as a result of the mixing of s and p character in all the σ MO's, their energies are shifted such that the lower two become more stable while the upper two become less stable. Now referring to Figure 3-13a we see that if these shifts are sufficiently large, there may be a change in the qualitative order of the levels, namely, the 3rd lowest orbital may be a π orbital instead of a σ orbital as shown in Figure 3-13b. The extent of the energy shifts will be greatest when the energy difference between the s and p orbitals is least, because then they can interact most. The s–p energy difference is relatively small for Li (~ 2 ev) and increases steadily until it is about 27 ev for Ne. Thus, while we might definitely expect the pattern shown in Figure 3-13b at the beginning of the period, the pattern in Figure 3-13a *might* be correct at the end (i.e., for F_2). Whether this is so, we do not know for certain, but on the basis of experimental data, the pattern in Figure 3-13b does appear to persist as far, at least, as N_2.

We shall now consider the electron configurations of each of the homonuclear diatomic molecules of the elements in the first short period on the basis of the LCAO–MO theory outlined above.

Li$_2$. The two valence electrons should enter the MO σ_1. The configuration is thus $(\sigma_1)^2$, the bond order is 1 and the molecule should be diamagnetic. The situation is, of course, quite analogous to that in H_2, but there are quantitative differences. The bond in Li_2 is much longer (2.67 A *vs* 0.74 A) and weaker (25 kcal/mole *vs* 103 kcal/mole) than in H_2. Two factors account for these differences. First, the $2s$ and $2p$ orbitals of Li are much larger and more diffuse than the $1s$ orbital of hydrogen. Thus they tend to overlap less effectively and with maximum overlap at a greater internuclear distance than in the case of the hydrogen $1s$ orbitals. Second, the electrons occupying the $1s$ shells of the Li atoms cause a repulsion between the atoms, which lessens the net energy of interaction and prevents closer approach of the atoms.

Be$_2$. For this molecule, the four electrons would be expected to give the MO configuration $(\sigma_1)^2(\sigma_1{}^*)^2$. The bond order would thus be 0. Consistent with this, Be_2 has not been observed.

B$_2$. The six electrons should give the electron configuration $(\sigma_1)^2(\sigma_1{}^*)^2(\pi)^2$ on the basis of Figure 3-13b. The two electrons in the π orbital should have their spins unpaired in accord with Hund's first rule (page 30), which applies to the filling of MO's as well as to atomic orbitals. On the other hand, according to Figure 3-13a, the configuration would be $(\sigma_1)^2(\sigma_1{}^*)^2(\sigma_2)^2$, with no unpaired electrons. Experiment shows that B_2 has two unpaired electrons in a π orbital; thus, Figure 3-13b is still correct at B_2. The bond order is 1 (one net π bond, since the σ interactions cancel). This is consistent with the bond energy of 69 kcal/mole.

C_2. For this molecule, the level order in Figure 3-13b predicts a configuration $(\sigma_1)^2(\sigma_1{}^*)^2(\pi)^4$, while that in Figure 3-13a predicts $(\sigma_1)^2(\sigma_1{}^*)^2(\sigma_2)^2(\pi)^2$. In the event that the σ_2 and π levels are very close, a $(\sigma_1)^2(\sigma_1{}^*)^2(\sigma_2)^1(\pi)^3$ configuration is also possible. For a long time the ground state of C_2 was not certain, but the latest experimental results[3] indicate that the ground state is derived from the $(\sigma_1)^2(\sigma_1{}^*)^2(\pi)^4$ configuration although a state derived from the $(\sigma_1)^2(\sigma_1{}^*)^2(\sigma_2)^1(\pi)^3$ configuration lies only ~ 610 cm^{-1} higher. A bond order of 2 is expected, and this is consistent with the observed bond energy of 150 kcal/mole.

N_2. For N_2, with a very high bond energy (225 kcal/mole) and no unpaired electrons, either of the configurations $(\sigma_1)^2(\sigma_1{}^*)^2(\pi)^4(\sigma_2)^2$ or $(\sigma_1)^2(\sigma_1{}^*)^2(\sigma_2)^2(\pi)^4$ would be acceptable, each giving a bond order of 3. That the former is actually correct is strongly implied by the fact that the odd electron in $N_2{}^+$ is in a sigma orbital according to spectroscopic evidence.

O_2. For this molecule the electron configuration might be either $(\sigma_1)^2(\sigma_1{}^*)^2(\sigma_2)^2(\pi)^4(\pi^*)^2$ or $(\sigma_1)^2(\sigma_1{}^*)^2(\pi)^4(\sigma_2)^2(\pi^*)^2$. Either way, the bond order is predicted to be 2 and two unpaired electrons are expected. Both these predictions are in good accord with experiment, the experimental bond energy being 118 kcal/mole. It is also interesting to note that the addition of electrons to O_2 causes the bond length to *increase* ($d_{O_2} = 1.21$A; $d_{O_2}{}^- = 1.26$A; $d_{O_2}{}^{2-} = 1.49$A) while the loss of an electron causes the bond to shorten ($d_{O_2}{}^+ = 1.12$A). As we shall later (page 111) explain in detail, bond length varies inversely with bond strength. These results are therefore in excellent accord with the MO electron configuration, since the orbital to or from which electrons are added or removed is an antibonding one. Hence, contrary to the usual situation, removal of an electron strengthens the bond (the bond order in $O_2{}^+$ is 2.5), while addition of electrons weakens the bond (the bond orders in $O_2{}^-$ and $O_2{}^{2-}$ are 1.5 and 1.0).

F_2. On adding two more electrons to the O_2 configuration we fill all orbitals except $\sigma_2{}^*$. The molecule should have no unpaired electrons and a low bond energy corresponding to the bond order of 1. F_2 is diamagnetic with a bond energy of 36 kcal/mole.

Ne_2. This molecule has not been observed. Since the electron configuration would involve filling of all the MO's, the predicted bond order is 0, in accord with nonexistence of Ne_2.

To conclude this section we shall compare the results given by the VB and MO theories regarding bond orders in the diatomic molecules Li_2 to Ne_2. As Table 3-2 shows, the MO theory appears to be generally superior to the VB approach in this field.

[3] E. A. Ballik and D. A. Ramsey, *Astrophys. J.*, **137**, 61, 84 (1963).

TABLE 3-2

Bond Orders in Some Simple Homonuclear Diatomic Molecules

Molecule	VB theory	MO theory	Experiment[a]
Li_2	1	1	1
Be_2	0 (or 2)	0	0 (?)
B_2	1 (or 3)[b]	1	1
C_2	2	2	2
N_2	3	3	3
O_2	$\left\{\begin{matrix} 2 \text{ (diamagnetic)} \\ 1 \text{ (paramagnetic)} \end{matrix}\right\}$	2 (paramagnetic)	2 (paramagnetic)
F_2	1	1	1
Ne_2	0	0	0

[a] Assuming that single, double and triple bonds have energies of 25–75, 100–200 and > 200 kcal/mole, respectively.

[b] However, VB theory would predict that all electron spins are paired, whereas they are not.

3-10. Heteronuclear Diatomic Molecules

The treatment of heteronuclear diatomic molecules by LCAO–MO theory is not fundamentally different from the treatment of homonuclear diatomics, except that the MO's are not symmetric with respect to a plane perpendicular to and bisecting the internuclear axis. The MO's are still constructed by forming linear combinations of atomic orbitals on the two atoms, but since the atoms are now different we must write them $\phi_A + \lambda\phi_B$, where λ is not in general equal to ± 1. Thus these MO's will not in general represent nonpolar bonding. As examples let us consider HCl, CO and NO.

In treating HCl we find it necessary to mention explicitly another factor influencing the stability of a bonding MO. Even if two atomic orbitals are capable of combining from the point of view of symmetry, the extent to which they will actually mix—that is, lose their individuality and merge to form a bonding and an antibonding MO—will depend upon whether their energies are comparable to begin with. If their energies are vastly different, they will scarcely mix at all. Mathematically, the two unnormalized MO's would be

$$\psi_b = \phi_A + \lambda\phi_B$$
$$\psi_a = \phi_B - \lambda\phi_A$$

where λ would be very small so that $\psi_b \approx \phi_A$ and $\psi_a \approx \phi_B$. In other words, when the energies are not similar, we can treat ϕ_A and ϕ_B as though they do not mix at all. This is more or less what occurs in HCl. The H $1s$ orbital and the Cl $3p\sigma$ orbital mix fairly effectively to form a bonding and an antibonding MO, but the Cl $3p\pi$ and $3s$ orbitals are so much lower in energy than any other hydrogen orbitals such as $2s$ or $2p\pi$ that no significant mixing occurs. Thus we call the $3p\pi$ and $3s$ orbitals of Cl in this case nonbonding because they neither help nor hinder the bonding to a significant extent.

The heteronuclear molecule CO may be regarded as a perturbed nitrogen molecule. C and O, differing in atomic number by only two, have atomic orbitals which are quite similar; the formation of MO's will therefore be almost the same as shown in Figure 3-13 for a homonuclear diatomic, although the energies of the two sets of atomic orbitals will not now match exactly. In fact, the oxygen orbitals will be somewhat more stable, so that they will contribute more to the bonding MO's than will the carbon orbitals, whereas the carbon orbitals will contribute more to the antibonding MO's. Thus, although the ten electrons are comprised of six from oxygen and four from carbon, we can explain the low polarity of the molecule because eight of them are in bonding orbitals where they are held closer to O than to C, thus tending to neutralize the greater nuclear charge of the oxygen core. As for N_2, a bond order of 3 is predicted and is in accord with the experimental bond energy of 256 kcal/mole.

The electron configuration of NO might be derived by either removing one electron from O_2 or adding one to N_2. Actually it has an unpaired electron in the π^* orbitals. NO readily loses this electron to form the NO^+ ion, which is found to have a stronger bond than does NO (cf. the earlier discussion of the ions derived from O_2). In VB theory the electronic structure of NO can only be accounted for by Pauling's special postulate of a three-electron bond (3-VIII) and the corollary postulate

$$: N \overset{...}{=} O :$$

(3-VIII)

that a three-electron bond is half as strong as a two-electron bond. This second postulate can be rationalized in MO theory since if we have a bonding and an antibonding MO as in Figure 3-10, the binding energy which results from placing two electrons in the bonding MO is about halved when we place a third electron in the antibonding MO. The NO molecule is a good example of cases in which MO theory seems to give a good qualitative picture of the bonding more straightforwardly than does VB theory, although there are other cases where the reverse is true.

3-11. Polyatomic Molecules

MO theory is chiefly used for those polyatomic molecules in which multiple bonding occurs. We have already considered how NO_2^- is formulated in VB theory as a resonance hybrid (3-V). In MO theory it can be treated in the following way. We first assume that a set of σ bonds is formed using four electrons and that several other electron pairs are nonbonding. Thus we write a framework of nuclei and σ electrons (3-IX).

$$
\begin{array}{ccc}
& \overset{\displaystyle\cdot\cdot}{N} & \\
\diagup & & \diagdown \\
:O & & O: \\
\cdot\cdot & & \cdot\cdot
\end{array}
$$

(3-IX)

There are still four electrons to be assigned and each of the three atoms has an empty $p\pi$ orbital (one whose nodal plane coincides with the molecular plane). If we start with three atomic orbitals it must be possible to combine them into three molecular orbitals. A discussion of the methods by which the correct combinations are derived would be beyond the scope of this text, but their approximate forms are illustrated for the present case in Figure 3-14. ψ_b is bonding, having the lowest energy, ψ_n is nonbonding and

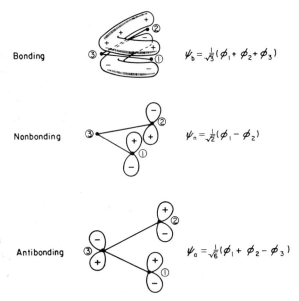

Bonding $\psi_b = \frac{1}{\sqrt{3}}(\phi_1 + \phi_2 + \phi_3)$

Nonbonding $\psi_n = \frac{1}{\sqrt{2}}(\phi_1 - \phi_2)$

Antibonding $\psi_a = \frac{1}{\sqrt{6}}(\phi_1 + \phi_2 - \phi_3)$

Fig. 3-14. Approximate shapes of the π MO's in nitrite ion, NO_2^-.

ψ_a is antibonding. If we place our four remaining electrons in this set of π MO's, the configuration will be $(\psi_b)^2(\psi_n)^2(\psi_a)^0$. The net energy is thus favorable to bonding. Note that in general these MO's are linear combinations of all three atomic orbitals, and this description of the bonding does not therefore refer to *localized* electron pair bonds, but to *delocalized* electrons moving in MO's which extend over the entire molecule. Moreover, from the nature of the occupied MO's, ψ_b and ψ_n, it is obvious that the distribution of the four π electrons is symmetric in the two NO links. This description is sometimes symbolized by 3-X, where the dashed line indicates bonding due to delocalized electrons in molecular orbitals.

(3-X)   (3-XI)   (3-XII)

Benzene is described in VB theory as a resonance hybrid of the Kekulé, Dewar and other canonical structures as we have seen. In MO theory, it is treated by assuming the formation of extensive π MO's. Each carbon atom is assumed to use its s, p_x and p_y orbitals and three of its electrons to form the σ-bonded framework (3-XI). Each carbon atom still has a p_z orbital (which is a $p\pi$-type orbital) containing an electron. These $p\pi$ orbitals will merge into various MO's and the electrons in them will thus not be localized in definite double bonds, but will be free to wander around the circular π MO's. This view can be rendered symbolically with a dotted line (3-XII).

References

Ballhausen, C. J., and H. B. Gray, *Molecular Orbital Theory*, Benjamin, New York, 1964. An introduction to the qualitative aspects of LCAO–MO theory directed particularly to inorganic chemists.

Cartmell, E., and G. W. A. Fowles, *Valency and Molecular Structure*, 2nd ed., Butterworths, London, 1961. A well-written introductory text.

Coulson, C. A., *Valence*, 2nd ed., Oxford University Press, 1961. Perhaps the best supplementary reference; it is lucidly written on a high but not too mathematical level. It leans to organic chemistry, but this will not do the student harm.

Eyring, H., J. Walter and G. E. Kimball, *Quantum Chemistry*, Wiley, New York, 1960. More advanced and rigorous mathematical text.

Gray, H. B., *Electrons and Chemical Bonding*, Benjamin, New York, 1964. An excellent introduction to the MO approach. On about the same level as this chapter but more extensive.

Kauzman, W., *Quantum Chemistry*, Academic Press, New York, 1957. More advanced and rigorous mathematical text.

Linnett, J. W., *The Electronic Structure of Molecules*, Methuen, London, 1964. Introduction to valence theory.

Murrell, J. N., S. F. A. Kettle and J. M. Tedder, *Valence Theory*, Wiley, London, 1965. A good introductory text with both inorganic and organic examples. Intermediate between Coulson and Eyring, Walter and Kimble.

Pauling, L., *The Nature of the Chemical Bond*, 3rd ed., Cornell University Press, Ithaca, N. Y., 1960. This famous book is a mine of information and a Bible to the advocates of the valence bond approach. It must be remembered that it creates the impression that there is no other approach to chemical bonding and fails to indicate the many defects of this approach.

Pauling, L., and E. B. Wilson, *Introduction to Quantum Mechanics*, McGraw-Hill, New York, 1935. More advanced and rigorous mathematical text.

4

Further Properties of Atoms, Molecules and Chemical Bonds

4-1. Bond Energies

We have already used the term bond energy several times, assuming that the reader's previous knowledge and/or the context would make the meaning sufficiently clear. In this section, the subject is examined more closely. For a diatomic molecule the bond energy, D, is equal to the enthalpy of the reaction

$$\text{XY(g)} = \text{X(g)} + \text{Y(g)} \qquad \Delta H = D \qquad (4\text{-}1)$$

where the molecule and the atoms are all in their ground states. To be exact, this bond energy is a function of temperature, and the best value to use would be that for the hypothetical reaction at $0°\text{K}$. The differences between the values at $0°\text{K}$ (properly denoted $D_0{}^0$, to indicate that the temperature is $0°$ and that the diatomic molecule is in its lowest, that is, 0, vibrational state) and those at room temperature, denoted D_{300} are always small. They cannot exceed ~ 2.4 kcal and must always be such that $D_{300} > D_0{}^0$. For example, $D_0{}^0$ for H_2 is 103.24, while D_{300} is 104.18 kcal/mole. For our purposes here, the differences between D_{300} and $D_0{}^0$ values are not important, and we shall simply speak of bond dissociation energies as though they were independent of temperature and use the symbol D.

Although the bond energy of a diatomic molecule is actually an experimental datum, bond energies in polyatomic molecules must be carefully defined to be meaningful. Let us consider the simplest case, that of an AB_n type molecule where all B's are equivalently bonded to A and not to one another. BF_3 is an example. Since all of the B—F bonds are equivalent, all B—F bond energies, D_{B-F}, must be equal and the relation

$$\text{BF}_3(\text{g}) = \text{B(g)} + 3\text{F(g)} \qquad \Delta H = 3D_{B-F} \qquad (4\text{-}2)$$

is obvious. Thus if we know the heats of formation of $BF_3(g)$, $B(g)$ and $F(g)$, we can readily calculate D_{B-F}. This value is called the *mean thermochemical bond energy*. However, it is *not* the energy, ΔH_1, of the process

$$BF_3(g) = BF_2(g) + F(g) \qquad \Delta H_1 \qquad\qquad (4\text{-}3)$$

since when the first bond is broken, the nature of the remaining two will necessarily be altered to some extent. Also ΔH_2 and ΔH_3

$$BF_2(g) = BF(g) + F(g) \qquad \Delta H_2 \qquad\qquad (4\text{-}4)$$
$$BF(g) = B(g) + F(g) \qquad \Delta H_3 \qquad\qquad (4\text{-}5)$$

are not likely to be equal to one another, or to ΔH_1 (eq. 4-3), or to D_{B-F}. It is, of course, true that $\Delta H_1 + \Delta H_2 + \Delta H_3 = 3D_{B-F}$, since the sum of equations 4-3, 4-4 and 4-5 is equal to equation 4-2 and Hess' law can be applied. The question of how much ΔH_1, ΔH_2, ΔH_3 and D_{B-F} will differ cannot be answered since there are not sufficient data available to calculate them all.

It is probable that the differences between successive dissociation energies and between any one of them and the mean will be fairly small so long as no one step involves a unique change in hybridization of the central atom. For example, the following data are available for H_2O:

$$H_2O(g) = 2H(g) + O(g) \qquad \tfrac{1}{2}\Delta H = D_{O-H} = 109.5$$
$$H_2O(g) = H(g) + OH(g) \qquad \Delta H_1 \qquad\quad = \sim 117$$
$$HO(g) = H(g) + O(g) \qquad \Delta H_2 \qquad\quad = \sim 103$$

Since the oxygen atom in its ground state has the two unpaired electrons required to form the two O—H bonds in H_2O, there will be only relatively small changes in valence states in the different processes and no one of them will have any particularly large promotion energy peculiar to itself. In the case of the mercuric halides, however, we have a quite different situation as the following data show:

$$HgCl_2(g) = Hg(g) + 2Cl(g) \qquad \tfrac{1}{2}\Delta H = D_{Hg-Cl} = 53$$
$$HgCl_2(g) = HgCl(g) + Cl(g) \qquad \Delta H_1 = 81$$
$$HgCl(g) = Hg(g) + Cl(g) \qquad \Delta H_2 = 25$$

Whereas breaking the first ClHg—Cl bond results in only a small change in the state of the Hg atom, when the second bond, Hg—Cl, is broken the mercury atom drops from some sort of sp state into its s^2 ground state, releasing considerable energy which partially offset the energy required to break the second bond. Hence, $\Delta H_2 \ll \Delta H_1$. Another good example is CO_2 in which the mean thermochemical bond energy is 192 kcal/mole, whereas the energies of breaking the bonds successively are 127 and 256 kcal/mole. This is because removal of the first oxygen atom causes the remaining bond to go from about a double bond to about a triple bond in CO.

The type of molecule in which the concept of a bond energy is rather loosely defined is the commonest type, namely, one in which two or more different kinds of bonds exist. This may be obvious, as in ethane, where there are six bonds of one kind (C—H bonds) and one of another kind (the C—C bond), or it may be a little subtler, as in PCl_5, which has the structure shown in 4-I. The two axial P—Cl bonds are not symmetrically

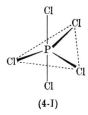

(4-I)

equivalent to the three equatorial P—Cl bonds, and so there is no reason to suppose that they have the same strength and energy. In cases such as this there is no unique way of assigning bond energy values. In C_2H_6, for example, we can only be sure that $6D_{C-H} + D_{C-C}$ must equal the energy of atomization of C_2H_6, that is,

$$C_2H_6(g) = 2C(g) + 6H(g)   \Delta H = 6D_{C-H} + D_{C-C}$$

but this gives us one equation in two unknowns so that we know only that

$$D_{C-C} = \Delta H - 6D_{C-H} \qquad (4\text{-}6)$$

but not the absolute values of D_{C-C} and D_{C-H}. Indeed, it is important to recognize that no such absolute values are defined, if by defined we mean experimentally measurable. However, meaningful and useful magnitudes have been deduced for these quantities in roughly the following way, in which we keep in touch with reality by demanding internal consistency in our values. We may evaluate a mean C—H bond energy in methane since there are enough experimental data to tell us the energy of the process

$$CH_4(g) = C(g) + 4H(g) \qquad \tfrac{1}{4}\Delta H = D_{C-H}$$

If we now assume the same value of D_{C-H} in C_2H_6, we can calculate D_{C-C} from equation 4-6. Now it has also proved possible to measure the energy of the process

$$C_2H_6(g) = 2CH_3(g)$$

and we must expect this energy to agree fairly well with the value of D_{C-C} we have calculated. In fact, it does within a few per cent. If we then consider processes such as

$$CH_3(CH_2)_nCH_3(g) = (n + 2)C(g) + (2n + 6)H(g)$$

we should expect their energies to be calculable by summing up the appropriate number of D_{C-C}'s and D_{C-H}'s. In fact, we can even refine our treatment by allowing D_{C-H} for a methylene group to differ slightly from D_{C-H} for a methyl group if we wish to be fancy. It turns out that by taking a large body of data and judiciously juggling the magnitudes of the various bond energies a set of average values which reproduce experimental energies of atomization to within a few per cent can be deduced. Similar procedures can be carried out with molecules other than hydrocarbons, although the supply of data is generally more restricted. In this way, the average bond energies in Table 4-1 were obtained.

TABLE 4-1

Some Representative Average Bond Energy Values at 25°. (In kcal/mole of bonds.)

A. Single Bond Energies[a]

H	C[a]	N	O	F	Si	P	S	Cl	Br	I	
104	99	93	111	135	70	76	81	103	88	71	H
	83	70	82	116	69	63	62	79	66	57	C[a]
		38	48	65	—	50*	—	48	58(?)	—	N
			33	44	88	84*	—	49	—	48	O
				37	129	117	68	61	57	—	F
					42	51*	54	86	69	51	Si
						41	55*	76	65	51	P
							63	66	51	—	S
								58	52	50	Cl
									46	43	Br
										36	I

B. Multiple Bond Energies

C=C	148	C=N	147	C=O	169	N=N	100
C≡C	194	C≡N	210	C≡O	256	N≡N	226

[a] Energies of all bonds involving carbon are based on a value of 170.89 kcal/mole as the heat of sublimation of graphite. Starred values are estimated using electronegativity differences.

It should be noted that the energies of multiple bonds are generally higher than those for single bonds, as we would expect, but that a double bond is not, in general, exactly twice as strong as a comparable single bond or a triple bond exactly three times as strong.

4-2. Electronegativities

The qualitative concept of electronegativity is one to which most chemists subscribe, but precise definition is elusive. The original qualitative definition of Pauling is: "Electronegativity is the power of an atom *in a molecule* to attract electrons to itself." It is not, however, the same as electron affinity, as will be seen.

Suppose we consider a bond A—B between dissimilar atoms A and B. From the viewpoint of VB theory this will be a resonance hybrid (4-II).

$$A\text{—}B \leftrightarrow A^-B^+ \leftrightarrow A^+B^-$$

$$\text{(4-IIa)} \qquad \text{(4-IIb)} \qquad \text{(4-IIc)}$$

If A is considerably more electronegative than B, then 4-IIc probably contributes negligibly and may be ignored. The contribution of 4-IIb may be expected to bear a relation to the magnitude of the difference in the electronegativities so that if the contribution and the relation were known we could calculate electronegativity differences. Pauling has proposed the following procedure for doing this.

TABLE 4-2

Use of Bond Energy Data (in kcal/mole) to Estimate Electronegativities
(Pauling's Method)

A	B	D_{A-A}	D_{B-B}	$\sqrt{D_{A-A}D_{B-B}}$	D_{A-B}	Δ^a	$\Delta^{1/2}$
F	Br	37	46	41	57	16	4.0
Si	F	42	37	40	129	89	9.3
Si	Br	42	46	44	69	25	5.0

$^a\Delta = D_{A-B} - \sqrt{D_{A-A}D_{B-B}}$.

Consider the data in Table 4-2. The various bond dissociation energies are the values estimated as described above from thermodynamic data for F_2, Br_2, FBr, SiF_4 and $SiBr_4$. The treatment of these data is dictated by the following argument. Note that in each case D_{A-B} is greater than the geometric mean of D_{A-A} and D_{B-B}. This mean energy is taken as the (hypothetical) A—B bond energy if the A—B bond were purely covalent, that is, represented only by canonical form 4-IIa. The differences, Δ's, are identified as "ionic resonance energies" due to resonance of 4-IIa with 4-IIb. It is assumed that the greater the electronegativity difference the more ionic resonance there will be, and hence the larger will be the value of Δ. However, Δ is not proportional to the electronegativity differences $x_A - x_B$. Thus

$$(x_F - x_{Si}) - (x_{Br} - x_{Si}) = (x_F - x_{Br})$$

but

$$89 - 25 \neq 16$$

However, in general, the quantities $\Delta^{1/2}$ do seem to be additive or approximately so. Thus, in the present case

$$9.3 - 5.0 = 4.3 \approx 4.0$$

Therefore, Pauling set up a table of relative electronegativities using the relation

$$x_A - x_B = K\Delta^{1/2}$$

The constant K was taken as $23^{-1/2}$ (that is, the Δ's were expressed in ev), since this gives numbers in the convenient range of 0 to ~ 4 for the differences. As with electrode potentials, where only differences can be measured it is necessary to fix one point arbitrarily. The data were considered so that the best agreement would be obtained giving the elements C to F the values 2.5 to 4.0. Of course, since Pauling worked out the first electronegativity scale in this way, bond energy values have been revised and electronegativities recalculated. The values listed in Table 4-3 as "Pauling electronegativities" were calculated by Pauling's method but are not, in general, his exact original values.

Among the dozens of other methods proposed for estimating experimentally or calculating electronegativity values, we shall mention only two. Mulliken showed by theoretical arguments that the tendency of an atom *in a molecule* to compete with another atom to which it is bound in attracting the shared electrons should be proportional to $(I + A)/2$, that is, to the average of its ionization potential and its electron affinity. Physically this is quite reasonable since we should expect that the over-all ability of an atom to attract shared electrons might be the average of quantities related to the tendencies of the free atom to hold its own electrons and to attract additional electrons. It is found that when the I and A values are expressed in electron volts the Mulliken electronegativity values can be adjusted to give the least mean deviation from Pauling's by dividing them by 3.15. Representative Mulliken electronegativities are listed in Table 4-3.

The empirical method of Allred and Rochow seems to have certain advantages stemming precisely from its complete and strict empiricism. Pauling's qualitative definition of electronegativity is interpreted in the following way. An electron in a bond is assumed to be attracted by one of the two nuclei according to Coulomb's law

$$\text{Force} = \frac{Z^* e^2}{r^2}$$

where Z^* is the effective nuclear charge which the electron feels and r is its mean distance from the nucleus. Z^* is estimated using a set of shielding

TABLE 4-3
Electronegativities of the Elements

(Values in bold type are calculated using the Allred-Rochow formula; those in italics are estimated by Pauling's method and those in Roman type are calculated by Mulliken's method.)[a]

I	II	III	IV	II	II	II	II	II	II	II	II	III	IV	III	II	I[b]	
H **2.20**																	He
Li **0.97** *0.98*	Be **1.47** *1.57*											B **2.01** *2.04, 2.01*	C **2.50** *2.55, 2.63*	N **3.07** *3.04, 2.33*	O **3.50** *3.44, 3.17*	F **4.10** *3.98, 3.91*	Ne
Na **1.01** *0.93*	Mg **1.23** *1.31, 1.32*											Al **1.47** *1.61, 1.81*	Si **1.74** *1.90, 2.44*	P **2.06** *2.19, 1.81*	S **2.44** *2.58, 2.41*	Cl **2.83** *3.16, 3.00*	Ar
K **0.91** *0.82, 0.80*	Ca **1.04** *1.00*	Sc **1.20** *1.36*	Ti **1.32** *1.54*	V **1.45** *1.63*	Cr **1.56** *1.66*	Mn **1.60** *1.55*	Fe **1.64** *1.83*	Co **1.70** *1.88*	Ni **1.75** *1.91*	Cu **1.75** *1.90, 1.36*	Zn **1.66** *1.65, 1.49*	Ga **1.82** *1.81, 1.95*	Ge **2.02** *2.01*	As **2.20** *2.18, 1.75*	Se **2.48** *2.55, 2.23*	Br **2.74** *2.96, 2.76*	Kr
Rb **0.89** *0.82*	Sr **0.99** *0.95*	Y **1.11** *1.22*	Zr **1.22** *1.33*	Nb **1.23**	Mo **1.30** *2.16*	Tc **1.36**	Ru **1.42**	Rh **1.45** *2.28*	Pd **1.35** *2.20*	Ag **1.42** *1.93, 1.36*	Cd **1.46** *1.69, 1.4*	In **1.49** *1.78, 1.80*	Sn **1.72** *1.96*	Sb **1.82** *2.05, 1.65*	Te **2.01**	I **2.21** *2.66, 2.56*	Xe
Cs **0.86** *0.79*	Ba **0.97** *0.89*	*La *1.08* *1.10*	Hf **1.23**	Ta **1.33**	W **1.40** *2.36*	Re **1.46**	Os **1.52** *2.20*	Ir **1.55** *2.20*	Pt **1.44** *2.28*	Au **1.42** *2.54*	Hg **1.44** *2.00*	Tl **1.44** *2.04*	Pb **1.55** *2.33*	Bi **1.67** *2.02*	Po **2.10** **1.76**	At **1.96**	Rn
Fr **0.86**	Ra **0.97**	**															

Lanthanides (*La)

La **1.08** *1.10*	Ce **1.06** *1.12*	Pr **1.07** *1.13*	Nd **1.07** *1.14*	Pm **1.07**	Sm **1.07** *1.17*	Eu **1.01**	Gd **1.11** *1.20*	Tb **1.10**	Dy **1.10** *1.22*	Ho **1.10** *1.23*	Er **1.11** *1.24*	Tm **1.11** *1.25*	Yb **1.06**	Lu **1.14** *1.27*

Actinides (**Ac)

Ac **1.00**	Th **1.11**	Pa **1.14**	U **1.22** *1.38*	Np **1.22** *1.36*	Pu **1.22** *1.28*	Am	Cm	Bk	Cf	Es	Fm	Md

⟵ ~1.2 (estimated) ⟶

[a] Allred-Rochow values from *J. Inorg. Nucl. Chem.*, **5**, 264 (1958); Pauling-type values from A. L. Allred, *J. Inorg. Nucl. Chem.*, **17**, 215 (1961); Mulliken-type values from H. O. Pritchard and H. A. Skinner, *Chem. Rev.*, **55**, 745 (1955).

[b] Roman numerals at the top give the oxidation states used for the Pauling-type values.

parameters derived many years ago by Slater, and r is taken as the covalent radius of the atom, which for a homonuclear diatomic molecule is half the internuclear distance. (Covalent radii are discussed below.) In order to relate the calculated forces, which are "absolute electronegativities," to Pauling's arbitrary and relative value, the forces are plotted against Pauling's electronegativities, the best straight line is drawn through the points, and from the slope and intercept of this line the following equation for Allred and Rochow's electronegativities is obtained:

$$x_{AR} = 0.359 \frac{Z^*}{r^2} + 0.744$$

A complete set of Allred-Rochow values is given in Table 4-3.

It is important to note that there must be a variation of the electronegativity of an element from one compound or bonding situation to another depending on its valence state. This may be best appreciated by considering Mulliken's definition. For rigorous application of Mulliken's definition, one should take, not the I and A values applying to the ground state atom but those applying to the *valence state* (see page 67) of the atom in a particular compound, and these will vary with the nature of the valence state. For example, if nitrogen is in the valence state s^2p^3 its Mulliken electronegativity is 2.33, whereas if it is in the state sp^4 the x_M value is 2.55. The former is given in Table 4-3 since the valence state for N in its common trivalent compounds is probably nearest to s^2p^3. It is clearly absurd to assume that the electronegativity of an element is independent of its valence, for S in SCl_2 must surely have a different electronegativity from S in SF_6. Clearly, an atom will have a greater attraction for electrons when it is in a high oxidation state than when it is in a low one. Thus, the numbers in Table 4-3 should not be taken as exact measures of electronegativities but only as rough guides, perhaps as the median numbers in a range for each element.

4-3. Bond Lengths and Covalent Radii

The lengths of bonds, that is, the internuclear distances in molecules, can be measured in many ways, and a considerable body of such data is available. If we consider a homonuclear diatomic molecule with a single bond, such as F_2 or Cl_2, we can assign to the atoms F and Cl *covalent single bond* radii equal to one-half of the internuclear distances in the respective molecules. It is then gratifying to find that very often the sums of these covalent radii are equal to the internuclear distances in the interhalogens such as Cl—Br (calculated 2.13, found 2.14). For elements which do not form diatomic molecules with single bonds, other methods of estimating the radii are used. For example, the C—C distance in diamond and a host of organic molecules is found to be 1.54 ± 0.01 A, so the covalent radius of C is taken as 0.77. To obtain the covalent radius of nitrogen, 0.77 is subtracted from the C—N distance in H_3C—NH_2, yielding 0.70. In this fashion a table of single bond covalent radii can be compiled (Table 4-4).

TABLE 4-4

Some Single Bond Covalent Radii.   (In Angstrom units.)

H[a]	0.28	O	0.66
C	0.77	S	1.04
Si	1.17	Se	1.17
Ge	1.22	Te	1.37
Sn	1.40	F	0.64
N	0.70	Cl	0.99
P	1.10	Br	1.14
As	1.21	I	1.33
Sb	1.41		

[a] One-half the bond length of H_2 is 0.375, but this value does not apply when H is bonded to other atoms.   0.28 was obtained by subtracting the radius of X from various H—X bond lengths.

Multiple bond radii can also be obtained. For example, the triple bond radii of carbon and nitrogen can be calculated from the bond lengths in HC≡CH and N≡N, as 0.60 and 0.55, giving 1.15 for —C≡N as compared to experimental values of ∼1.16. It may be stated, as a general rule, that the higher the order of a bond between two atoms, the shorter it is. Thus, for carbon–carbon bonds the following are typical lengths: C—C, 1.54; C=C, 1.33; C≡C, 1.21.

It is also true, however, that hybridization effects are important. Thus, strictly, the C—C distance of 1.54 refers to a bond between two sp^3 hybridized carbon atoms, and the C=C distance usually refers to a bond between two sp^2 hybridized carbon atoms, whereas the C≡C bond generally occurs between two sp hybridized carbon atoms. Since the $2s$ orbital of carbon has a smaller mean radius than the $2p$ orbitals, it would be expected that the greater the s character in the hybrid orbitals used, the shorter would be the internuclear distance at which the best balance of overlap and repulsion would occur in the σ bonds. Hence, at least part of the decreases in the bond lengths cited is attributable to this effect rather than to the π bonding. It has been estimated that the single bond radii for the carbon atom in the several states of hybridization are: sp^3, 0.77; sp^2, 0.74; sp, 0.70. When this effect is taken into account, certain previously accepted conclusions about the importance of single bond–multiple bond resonance become questionable. For example, the CC bond in cyanogen is only 1.37 A. If the carbon–carbon single bond distance is taken to be 2 × 0.77 =

4*

1.54 A, then there is evidently a large shortening and one assumes that in addition to 4-IIIa, the canonical forms 4-IIIb and 4-IIIc are of major

$$: N\equiv C\!-\!C\equiv N: \;\leftrightarrow\; : \overset{+}{N}\!=\!C\!=\!\overset{..}{\underset{..}{C}}\!\overset{-}{=}\!N: \;\leftrightarrow\; : \overset{..}{\underset{..}{N}}\overset{-}{=}C\!=\!C\!=\!\overset{+}{N}:$$

   (4-IIIa)   (4-IIIb)   (4-IIIc)

importance in a VB description of the electronic structure. However, if one notes that the carbon atoms have *sp* hybridization, the "expected" length of the CC bond in 4-IIIa is only $2 \times 0.70 = 1.40$ A, and the importance of 4-IIIb and 4-IIIc appears to be slight.

This subject is unfortunately not as tidy as might be imagined from the above examples, which were especially chosen to illustrate how the system works *when it works*. There are many cases in which it leaves much to be desired. The reader might have wondered why the radius of nitrogen (0.70) was obtained from the C—N bond in methylamine instead of from the N—N bond in H_2N—NH_2, which would be more analogous to the procedure used for the halogens. The answer is simply that one-half of the N—N distance in hydrazine is 0.73 and this does not fit as consistently with the bulk of data on X—N bond lengths as does 0.70. (The long bond in N_2H_4 is best attributed to repulsion between lone pairs of electrons on the N atoms.) Even more striking, however, are cases such as SiF_4, for which an Si—F distance of 1.81 would be calculated while the actual distance is ~ 1.54. Again, for BF_3 the calculated distance would be ~ 1.5 (the covalent radius of B is not easy to evaluate unambiguously), whereas the measured value is 1.30. Schomaker and Stevenson proposed that since these "shrinkages" generally occur in bonds between atoms of disparate electronegativities they may be due to bond strengthening and hence shortening due to ionic–covalent resonance 4-IVa $\leftrightarrow$ 4-IVb (three similar

  (4-IVa) (4-IVb)   (4-Va)   (4-Vb)

ionic forms) and 4-Va $\leftrightarrow$ 4-Vb (two similar ionic forms). They therefore proposed an equation known as the Schomaker-Stevenson relationship which takes account of this by making the bond distance depend on the electronegativity difference, which is an index of the ionic character of the bond. The equation they suggested is:

$$r_{A-B} = r_A + r_B - 0.09 \left| x_A - x_B \right|$$

where r_A is the covalent radius of atom A. This relationship is not really very satisfactory except qualitatively, since it predicts too little shortening for some bonds, for example, Si—O and Si—F, and too much for others, for example, C—Cl.   In the case of BF_3 the bond shortening can also be attributed to B—F double bonding since boron has a vacant p_z orbital and the fluorine atoms have filled p_z orbitals (4-VIa $\leftrightarrow$ 4-VIb and two other similar

(4-VIa)   (4-VIb)

forms).   In SiF_4 π bonding, using F $2p$ orbitals and Si $3d$ orbitals, could contribute to the shortening.   It is probable that *both* ionic–covalent resonance and multiple bonding contribute significantly.

In conclusion, we may say that the concept of atomic covalent radii is useful, but we cannot expect close correspondence between experimental interatomic distances and sums of these radii when the environment of either or both of the corresponding atoms differs appreciably from that of the atoms in the classes of substances used to derive the radii.   Whether or not the ionicity of a bond can be related quantitatively to deviations from covalent radius sums, it does seem logical that covalent radii cannot be expected to describe appreciably ionic bonds very exactly.

4-4. Bond and Molecular Polarity

The electrical polarity of a molecule is expressed as its *dipole moment*. A system consisting of a positive charge, $+x$, and a negative charge, $-x$, separated by a distance, d, possesses a dipole moment of magnitude xd. If x is equal to the electronic charge (4.80×10^{-10} e.s.u.) and d is 1 A, $xd = 4.80$ D (Debye) units.   It is important to recognize that a dipole moment is a vector quantity since it has a definite direction as well as magnitude.   We shall adopt here the arbitrary convention of having the vector point in the direction of the negative end of the dipole.

The dipole moment of a molecule can be thought of as the vector sum of moments due to various parts of the molecule.   These several contributions are, of course, interdependent, and no one of them can be altered without there being at least a second-order effect on the others.   Let us consider first a heteronuclear diatomic molecule, such as HCl.   Any such molecule must have a dipole moment since its two ends are different and only by a complex of unlikely coincidences could the various factors causing polarity cancel one another out exactly.   The electronic structure of HCl can be expressed in a very simple way by writing it as an ionic–covalent resonance hybrid of two Lewis structures (4-VII).

$$\text{H}:\ddot{\text{C}}\text{l}: \leftrightarrow \overset{+}{\text{H}} \quad :\ddot{\ddot{\text{C}}}\text{l}:$$

(4-VIIa)   (4-VIIb)

We may use equation 3-12, viz.,

$$\psi = (1 - 2\lambda + 2\lambda^2)^{-1/2}[(1 - \lambda)\psi_{\text{cov}} + \lambda\psi_{\text{ion}}]$$

and define the percent ionic character as 100λ.

The internuclear distance in HCl is 1.27 A. If λ were unity, the dipole moment would be 6.1 D. If we assume that ψ_{cov} is non-polar (an assumption which will presently be shown to be erroneous), we may say that since the measured dipole moment is only 1.03 D, we must then conclude that the percent ionic character is only 100 (1.03/6.1 D) = 17%, i.e., $\lambda = 0.17$. By the same procedure we could calculate percentages of ionic character of 43, 11 and 5 for HF, HBr and HI, respectively. This procedure was proposed by Pauling in order to obtain a relation between electronegativity difference and percent ionic character. By plotting the various percentages obtained above against $x_{\text{X}} - x_{\text{H}}$, where x_{X} is the electronegativity of the halogen atom, he obtained a smooth curve given by the equation

$$\text{percent ionic character} = 18(x_{\text{X}} - x_{\text{H}})^{1.4}$$

and assumed that this equation is valid for other classes of compounds as well. For some, such as the alkali halides, however, it has been recognized to be inapplicable.

This procedure is now known to be full of dangers and is probably unreliable for other than qualitative work. The main source of error is the assumption that ψ_{cov} is nonpolar. Actually it is polar because of (a) the intrinsically polar nature of the covalent bond and (b) the contribution of orbital moments of unshared electrons to the total dipole moment, both of which we shall now consider in more detail.

1. *Polar nature of a heteronuclear bond.* If we place a proton and a Cl^+ ion—the latter being assumed, for the moment, to have spherical symmetry (hence no dipole within itself)—1.27 A apart and then introduce the two bonding electrons between them, the system as a whole is neutral. If we place the centroid of charge of these two bonding electrons exactly half way between the nuclei, then the system will have no dipole moment. However, since the hydrogen orbital is much smaller than the chlorine

orbital, the centroid of charge for the bonding electrons must be closer to H than to Cl and a dipole will result, namely,

$$\overset{\longleftarrow}{\text{H—Cl}}$$

This moment has been estimated to be ~ 1.0 D.

2. *Orbital moments of unshared electrons.* Let us consider the internuclear axis to be the z axis of a coordinate system with the chlorine atom at the origin. If the chlorine atom uses a pure p_z orbital to form the bond, then the configuration of the remaining, unshared or nonbonding, electrons will be $s^2 p_x^2 p_y^2$, and they will contribute nothing to the polarity of the system. The s electrons are spherically distributed about the chlorine nucleus, and the p_x and p_y electrons lie in a disc perpendicular to the z axis with the Cl nucleus at its center. Now let us suppose instead that the chlorine atom has full sp^3 hybridization and uses one of these hybrid orbitals to form the bond. The remaining three pairs of electrons will lie in the three equivalent hybrid orbitals, which have approximately the shape shown in Figure 4-1. It is easily seen that electrons in such an

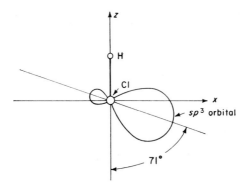

Fig. 4-1.   Diagram illustrating the electrical asymmetry of electrons in an sp^3 hybrid orbital of chlorine in HCl.

orbital are much more concentrated below the xy plane than above it, and hence there will be an *orbital dipole moment* which can be represented by a vector of magnitude $\mathbf{v}$ pointing along the axis of the orbital. There is, then, a dipole moment contribution in the bond direction of $-\mathbf{v}\cos 71°$, or a total from the three such orbitals of $-3\mathbf{v}\cos 71°$, namely,

$$\overset{-3\mathbf{v}\cos 71°}{\longrightarrow}_{\text{H—Cl}}$$

(The vector sum in the xy plane is, of course, zero.) Now, we do not expect the chlorine atom to have full sp^3 hybridization and the unshared pairs to make this maximal contribution; rather, we expect some lesser degree of hybridization and hence some smaller contribution from the nonbonding electrons. There are various reasons for believing that there must be *some* hybridization, however.

We might follow these lines of argument further, but we shall stop here and consider what general conclusion can be drawn about the relation between molecular dipole moment and the various contributions to it, of which three principal ones have been discussed. We see first that unless we assume the intrinsic bond polarity and the orbital moments of unshared electrons to balance one another out exactly—and it is hardly likely that they will do so in all of the hydrogen halides, even if they should do so by chance in one—there is not, in general, any *a priori* relation between molecular dipole moment and percent ionic character as had been thought. In fact, if bond polarity makes the largest contribution, then the moment *could* be in a direction opposite to that presumed in the simple argument which attributes the whole moment to resonance of 4-VIIa with 4-VIIb. It is perhaps worthwhile to point out that it is extremely difficult to determine the *direction* of the dipole in HCl or any similar molecule from experimental measurements, although it has been shown that in HI, H is positive relative to I. Although this discussion may have been a little disheartening in its inexorable regression from a state of tidy simplicity to uncertain complexity, there is, after all, nothing to be gained by pretending that things are simple when they are not.

We conclude this section by considering how the net dipole moment of a polyatomic molecule can be considered to be the vector sum of various contributing dipoles. Suppose we have a regular pyramidal molecule, AB_3. Because of its symmetry, its dipole moment must lie along the threefold axis of symmetry. If each A—B bond axis makes an angle, θ, with this symmetry axis, we might say the net molecular dipole moment, μ, is the vector sum of three equal bond moments, each of magnitude $(\mu/3)$ cos θ. Unfortunately, this picture is too simple to be satisfactory, as the following example will show.

The two pyramidal molecules NH_3 and NF_3 have dipole moments of 1.5 and 0.2 D, respectively. Knowing the bond angles ($\angle HNH = 106.75°$; $\angle FNF = 102.5°$), we would easily calculate the N—H bond moment to be ~ 1.33 D and the N—F bond moment to be ~ 0.15 D. Now the trouble is that these results do not appear to be credible. In the first place, we should expect an $\overrightarrow{N—F}$ bond moment much larger than 0.15 D. Secondly, if we assume that only the electronegativity difference is responsible for the bond dipole, the $\overrightarrow{N—H}$ dipole should be still smaller than the $\overrightarrow{N—F}$ dipole. If we treat the N—H bond as we did the H—Cl bond and consider that despite the tendency of electronegativity to produce a moment, $\overleftarrow{N—H}$, the difference in size of the overlapping orbitals will tend to produce the opposite polarity, $\overrightarrow{\text{N—H}}$, it is still difficult to believe that the net N—H moment is ~ 9 times the N—F moment. A satisfactory explanation of the molecular dipole moments can be developed, however, if we take account of the hybridization of the nitrogen atom and of the consequent orbital moment of the unshared electron pair on the nitrogen atom in each molecule. The observed bond angles are much larger than 90°, though not so large as 109°, and may be taken to mean that the nitrogen atom in each case is bonding the three atoms by s–p hybrid orbitals with slightly less than the amount of s character which occurs in regular sp^3 hybrids. Consequently, the unshared electrons do not occupy a pure s orbital, in which case they would be distributed spherically around the nitrogen atom and contribute nothing to the polarity of the molecules. Instead, they are in an s–p_z hybrid, so that they are more concentrated above than below the nitrogen atom. Thus, assuming the direction of the N—H bond moments to be as shown, the net polarity of each molecule may be accounted for as the vector sum of bond moments and the lone pair moment as shown in Figure 4-2. In general, bond moments are not directly relatable to the

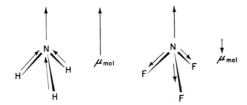

Fig. 4-2.   Diagram illustrating how the molecular dipole moment, μ_{mol}, can be regarded as a vector sum of bond moments and the lone pair moment in NH_3 and NF_3. -

molecular moment by geometry alone, but hybridization and consequent orbital moments of unshared pairs must also be considered. Once again, however, caution is necessary, for the assumption that the hybridization can be inferred from the bond angles lacks rigorous justification. It is possible that the orbitals are not directed *exactly* along the internuclear lines. That is, the bonds may be a little *bent*. There is evidence that bent bonds actually occur, though they are only slightly bent.[1] However, even slight bending can throw a calculation of the above kind off appreciably.

4-5. Some Relations between Bond Properties

We have already discussed bond lengths and bond energies, and noted that both of these observable properties vary—the first inversely and the

[1] H. Flygare, *Science*, **140**, 1179 (1964).

second directly—with the bond order.   Another measurable bond property whose magnitude is directly related to the bond order is the *force constant* of the bond.   The force constant of a bond between atoms A and B is given by equation 4-7

$$\nu \ (\text{cm}^{-1}) = \frac{1}{c} \ \sqrt{\frac{f}{4\pi^2 \mu}} \tag{4-7}$$

where the ν is vibration frequency of the bond expressed in wave numbers, cm^{-1} (see Appendix I), c is the velocity of light and μ is the reduced mass of the A–B oscillator in grams.   When values of the constants are put into equation 4-7, along with a numerical factor to permit inserting the atomic masses in the usual chemical atomic weight units (i.e., for C, a mass of 12.00), we obtain

$$\nu^2 = 17.0 \times \frac{f}{\mu} \tag{4-8}$$

Thus when the vibrational frequency, ν, of a bond has been measured, most commonly by observation of the infrared or Raman spectrum, the force constant can be calculated.   In polyatomic molecules there are often strong interactions between the vibrations of different bonds, so that the calculation of the force constant for a particular bond cannot be made directly from any one of the observed frequencies.   However, there are well-established methods for dealing with this problem.

The qualitative relationships between the three bond properties, length, dissociation energy and force constant are often useful in predicting or interpreting physical and chemical properties.   Since we know how each of them depends on the bond order, we can infer the dependence of any one of them on another.   Specifically, we have the following:

(1)   As bond order increases:
      length decreases
      energy increases
      force constant increases
(2)   As bond length increases:
      energy decreases
      force constant decreases
(3)   As energy increases:
      length decreases
      force constant increases
(4)   As force constant increases:
      length decreases
      energy increases

Generally, over any appreciable range, none of these relations is linear. Figures 4-3 to 4-5 show some representative plots of one bond parameter

against another. The shapes of the curves are easily understood in terms
of simple physical ideas. Consider, for example, Figure 4-5 which is a plot
of bond lengths against force constants for molybdenum–oxygen bonds.
The curve asymptotically approaches the horizontal axis, because as bond
length tends to infinity, the force of attraction between the atoms tends to
zero. The curve also asymptotically approaches a vertical line at some small

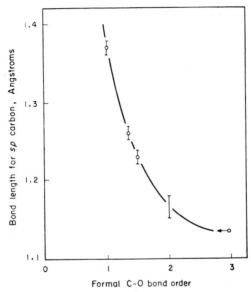

Formal C-O bond order

Fig. 4-3. A plot of bond length against bond order for CO bonds (from F. A. Cotton
and R. M. Wing, *Inorg. Chem.*, **4**, 314 (1965)).

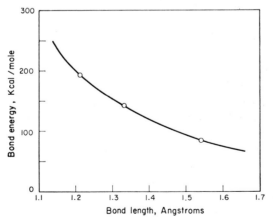

Bond length, Angstroms

Fig. 4-4. A plot of bond length against bond energies for CC bonds (from data in Table
4-1 and Sec. 4-3).

value of the bond length. As the force between the atoms increases the bond length decreases, but eventually the repulsive forces, due mainly to repulsion between the inner shell electrons of the two atoms, must become so great that further increases in attractive force can do little to shorten

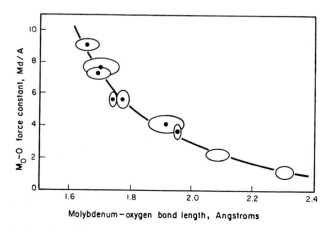

Fig. 4-5. A plot of bond lengths against force constant for Mo–O bonds (from F. A. Cotton and R. M. Wing, *Inorg. Chem.*, **4**, 867 (1965)).

the bond any further. These repulsive forces have an inverse dependence on the bond length, l, with a very high exponent in the neighborhood of 10–12, viz.,

$$\text{Repulsive force is proportional to } \frac{1}{l^{10-12}}$$

These relationships will be utilized in several places subsequently.

4-6. Van der Waals Radii

We have discussed the distances between ions in ionic solids and pointed out that they may be considered as approximately equal to the sums of appropriate ionic radii. We have also discussed the assignment of covalent radii whose sums approximate the separations of bonded atoms in covalent molecules. There remain to be considered the distances between atoms in liquids and solids when these atoms are not bonded to one another either ionically or covalently.

Let us consider, for example, the noble gases. The fact that they can be liquefied and solidified at all proves that there are *some* forces of attraction between the atoms; at the same time the exceedingly low temperatures required to condense them proves that these forces are extremely weak. These forces are usually called van der Waals forces, after the Dutch physicist who first emphasized their importance by taking account of them in his equation of state for imperfect gases, although sometimes they are also called London forces, since their nature was first explained using wave mechanics by Fritz London. We have mentioned them before as minor contributors to the total attractive force in ionic crystals. In crystals of the noble gases, however, there are no electrostatic forces, and these van der Waals forces are the only attractive forces. Again, as in ionic crystals, the equilibrium separation of neighboring atoms is that distance at which the attractive force is balanced by the repulsive force due to overlap of the outer portions of the electron clouds. Since this repulsive force rises very steeply and becomes important only at very short distances, the ionic radius of Br⁻ and one-half the distance of closest approach of two krypton atoms in solid krypton do not differ very much despite the differences in the nature of the attractive forces. This latter quantity—one half the Kr—Kr separation in solid krypton—is called the van der Waals radius of krypton. The van der Waals radii are much larger than covalent radii, however. Thus, the ionic radius of Br⁻ is 1.95 A, the covalent radius of Br is 1.15 A and the van der Waals radius of Kr is 2.00 A.

Van der Waals radii for all elements may be estimated if the distances of closest approach of their atoms to other atoms when no chemical bond exists between them are known from structural studies. For instance, in solid bromine the closest approach of nonbonded bromine atoms is 3.90 A, giving a van der Waals radius of 1.95 A. If we consider crystals consisting of molecules with permanent dipole moments, then the dipole–dipole attractions will contribute to the stability of the crystals, but the closest distance of approach of two nonbonded atoms can still be taken as the sum of their van der Waals radii. As with ionic and covalent radii, deviations from additivity occur since the basic idea is something of an oversimplification, but a set of radii has been assigned to commonly occurring non-metallic atoms which gives the best over-all agreement with a large number of experimental data. A set of van der Waals radii computed by Pauling is given in Table 4-5.

TABLE 4-5
Van der Waals Radii of Nonmetallic Atoms.   (In Angstroms.)

H	1.2				
N	1.5	O	1.40	F	1.35
P	1.9	S	1.85	Cl	1.80
As	2.0	Se	2.00	Br	1.95
Sb	2.2	Te	2.20	I	2.15

Radius of a methyl group, 2.0 A
Half thickness of an aromatic ring, 1.85 A

4-7. Molecular Symmetry

When we say that a molecule has symmetry, we mean that certain parts of it can be interchanged with others without altering the appearance of the molecule. The interchangeable parts are said to be equivalent to one another by symmetry. While a thorough study of the rules and relationships which have been devised for analyzing and representing the symmetry properties of molecules is beyond the scope of this book, a brief discussion, mainly covering nomenclature, will be given. In recent years, the inorganic research literature has become increasingly filled with references to molecular symmetry, so that it is now necessary to be familiar at least with the interpretation of the symbols, in order to read it with comprehension.

There are four ways, called *symmetry operations*, of interchanging equivalent parts of a molecule. Others might also be considered, but these four are sufficient and are the ones conventionally used.

1. Simple rotation about an axis passing through the molecule by an angle $2\pi/n$. This operation is called a *proper rotation* and is symbolized C_n. If it is repeated n times, of course the molecule comes all the way back to the original orientation.

2. Reflection of all atoms through a plane which passes through the molecule. This operation is called *reflection* and is symbolized σ.

3. Reflection of all atoms through a point in the molecule. This operation is called *inversion* and is symbolized i.

4. The combination, in either order, of rotating the molecule about an axis passing through it by $2\pi/n$ and reflecting all atoms through a plane which is perpendicular to the axis of rotation is called *improper rotation* and is symbolized S_n.

These operations are *symmetry operations if, and only if*, the appearance of the molecule is *exactly* the same after one of them is carried out as it was before. For instance, consider rotation of the molecule H_2S by $2\pi/2$ about an axis passing through S and bisecting the line between the H atoms. As shown in Figure 4-6, this operation interchanges the H atoms and interchanges the S—H bonds. Since these atoms and bonds are equivalent, there is no physical (i.e., physically meaningful or detectable) difference after the operation. For HSD, however, the corresponding operation replaces the S—H bond by the S—D bond, and vice versa, and one can see that a change has occurred. Therefore, for H_2S, the operation C_2 is a symmetry operation, while for HSD it is not.

Let us now examine some representative symmetry operations. The molecule BF_3 will serve to illustrate quite a few. Referring to Figure 4-7 we see first that the operation C_3 can be performed about an axis perpendicular to the molecular plane. There are also three different C_2

operations which can be performed about axes which are coincident with the three B—F bonds. Furthermore, there are three planes, each containing a B—F bond and perpendicular to the plane of the molecule through which reflections, σ, may be performed. It is also possible to

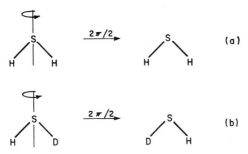

(a)

(b)

Fig. 4-6. Sketches showing that the operation C_2 carries H_2S into an orientation indistinguishable from the original, but HSD into an observably different orientation.

reflect through the molecular plane itself, though none of the atoms actually move because they all lie in this plane. Finally, it is possible to carry out the rotation C_3 followed by reflection in the molecular plane (or vice versa), so that there is an operation S_3. The only type of symmetry

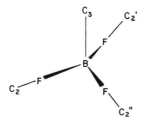

Fig. 4-7. Sketch showing the axes of rotational symmetry operations for BF_3.

operation which cannot be performed on BF_3 is the inversion operation, i. It is interesting to compare the symmetry of a planar AB_3 molecule, such as BF_3, with that of a pyramidal one, such as NF_3. The latter has less symmetry, that is, there are fewer symmetry operations which can be performed upon it. Thus, for NF_3 the operation C_3 and the reflections in the three planes which are defined by the axis of C_3 rotation together with each of the three N—F bonds are still possible, but the two-fold rotations, C_2, the reflection in the molecular plane (which now does not exist) and the S_3 operation have all been lost.

Examples of molecules upon which the inversion operation, i, may be performed are XeF_4, which is square, and benzene, which is a regular hexagon. In the first case, there is an atom at the *center of symmetry*, that is, at the point through which all atoms are to be reflected. In the case of benzene, there is no atom at the center of symmetry. It should be noted that if a molecule has a center of symmetry, it must contain even numbers of all atoms save, possibly, one, which can be at the center. Thus BF_3, with odd numbers of two different kinds of atoms cannot have a center of symmetry.

We have seen that for BF_3 the operation S_3 exists, but so do the operations C_3 and σ (through a plane perpendicular to the axis of C_3). Improper rotations, S_n, can be performed on some molecules for which C_n and the appropriate σ are not possible, however, as separate operations. An example is provided by the ethane molecule in its staggered configuration. As Figure 4-8 shows, if we rotate by $2\pi/6$ about the C—C axis, we do *not* perform a symmetry operation, because all six H atoms are moved to places where there were no H atoms before. That is, we do not leave the molecule in a condition indistinguishable from its original condition by performing such an operation. Similarly, if we reflect all atoms through a plane perpendicular to the C—C bond and cutting it at its center, we also move hydrogen atoms to places where there were none before, as also shown in Figure 4-8. However, if we perform a rotation by $2\pi/6$ and then reflect, or reflect and then rotate by $2\pi/6$, the molecule goes into a configuration which is physically identical with the original one. It is *essential* to realize that the numbers which have been put on the atoms in Figure 4-8 are only aids to visualizing the operations. Real atoms do not carry serial numbers, and thus there is no *physical* significance to these labels.

Having now defined and illustrated the symmetry operations, we turn to another concept, that of a *symmetry element*. A symmetry element is the axis, plane or point, about which or through which the symmetry operation is performed. Thus, when it is possible to perform an operation C_n, we say that the molecule possesses an *n-fold axis of symmetry*. We use symbol C_n to represent this axis. Similarly, the axis about which an improper rotation, S_n, is performed is an S_n axis. It is possible for one line to be several kinds of symmetry axis simultaneously.

The plane used to perform a reflection operation, σ, is a symmetry element, σ. Subscripts are often appended to σ in order to distinguish between different types which may occur in the same molecule. When a molecule has one symmetry axis of uniquely high *order* (the order is given by the subscript, n), this axis is regarded as being vertical. Any plane which includes the vertical axis is called a vertical plane, σ_v; if there is a plane perpendicular to the vertical axis it is called the horizontal plane, σ_h. Thus, in BF_3 there are three σ_v's and a σ_h; in NF_3 there are only the three σ_v's.

As already implied, the point through which the inversion operation is carried out is called the center of symmetry. It is represented by i.

We are now in a position to explain the main rules by which the symmetry of a molecule is expressed using a symbol. We shall adopt the Schönflies

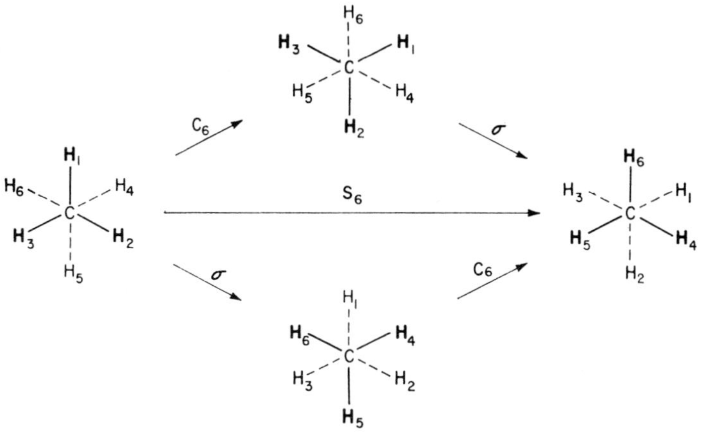

Fig. 4-8. Sketch showing that neither C_6 nor σ_h is a symmetry operation for ethane (viewed down the CC axis) whereas, the successive application of both, represented by S_6, is a symmetry operation.

symbols,* since these are most often used for molecules by spectroscopists, chemists and physicists. Crystallographers usually use a different set† (based on an improper rotation which is differently defined).

1. We turn first to molecules which possess only one symmetry element. This may be i, σ, C_n or one of the S_n of even order. For reasons beyond the scope of this discussion, the presence of an odd order S_n necessarily means that certain other symmetry elements are present, and the molecule then belongs to one of the more elaborate symmetry classes discussed below. The symmetry classes based on the presence of a single symmetry element are described in Table 4-6.

2. When a molecule possesses not only a proper axis, C_n, but a set of n vertical planes, σ_v, it belongs to the symmetry class C_{nv}. Common examples are: C_{2v}, H_2O, $BClF_2$; C_{3v}, NH_3, PF_3, $C_6H_6Cr(CO)_3$; C_{4v}, IF_5, B_5H_9, $SClF_5$, $S_4N_4H_4$ (see page 533); C_{5v}, TlC_5H_5, C_5H_5NiNO; C_{6v}, C_6H_6CoNO.

---

* These symbols usually are said to stand for *point groups*. Since we shall not attempt here to explain the meaning or significance of the term point group, we shall regard them as symbols for *classes or types* of symmetry.

† See the reference list, especially the book by Brand and Speakman, for further information.

TABLE 4-6

Symmetry Classes Based on a Single Symmetry Element

Symbol for symmetry class	Symmetry element present	Examples and remarks
C	i	This symmetry type is rarely found. A real example is:
C_s	σ	Not very common.
C_n	C_n	Not common. C_2: H_2O_2 (see page 373 for sketch); N_2H_4 (see page 338 for sketch) cis-[Coen$_2$X$_2$]$^+$ (see page 128). C_3: H_3NBF_3 (except when in exactly eclipsed configuration; then C_{3v})
S_n	S_n	Not common. S_4: $S_4N_4F_4$ (see page 533 for sketch)

3. When a molecule possesses a proper axis, C_n, and a horizontal plane, σ_h, it belongs to the symmetry class C_{nh}. Examples are relatively rare: C_{2h}, trans-N_2F_2, trans-$C_2H_2Cl_2$; C_{3h}, B(OH)$_3$ when planar. It should be noted that the combination of C_n and σ_h necessarily means that S_n is also present. Moreover, when n is even, there is also, necessarily a center of symmetry. However, C_n together with σ_h constitute the defining elements of C_{nh}, the existence of the other elements being logical consequences of the existence of these two.

4. When a molecule possesses a proper axis, C_n, and a set of n C_2 axes perpendicular to C_n, it belongs to the symmetry class D_n. Only relatively complicated molecules can have this type of symmetry, and it is rarely encountered. Perhaps the only common examples, but they are quite important ones, are tris-chelated octahedral complexes in which the chelates are themselves symmetrical, e.g., [Coen$_3$]$^{3+}$, Fe(acac)$_3$, which belong to the class D_3.

5. When, in addition to C_n and the n C_2's, there is a horizontal plane, σ_h, the symmetry class is D_{nh}. This type of symmetry is quite common, and some examples are: D_{2h}, all planar bis-chelated complexes with symmetrical ligands, such as Pd(acac)$_2$, [Cuen$_2$]$^{2+}$, etc., and trans planar molecules such as Pt(NH$_3$)$_2$Cl$_2$, ignoring the H's; D_{3h}, all planar AB$_3$ molecules, e.g., BF$_3$, and trigonal bipyramid molecules, e.g., PCl$_5$, PF$_2$Cl$_3$; D_{4h}, XeF$_4$, AuCl$_4^-$, PtCl$_4^{2-}$ and numerous other square AB$_4$ species; D_{5h}, C$_5$H$_5^-$, Ru(C$_5$H$_5$)$_2$ (a pentagonal prism); D_{6h}, C$_6$H$_6$. It is to be noted that D_{nh} symmetry also necessarily includes the presence of n

vertical planes, σ_v, which *contain* the C_2 axes, and an S_n collinear with the C_n, but these are simply necessary consequences of the presence of C_n, $n\, C_2$ and σ_h.

6. When, in addition to C_n and $n\, C_2$, there are n vertical planes which lie *between* the C_2's, the symmetry class is D_{nd}. These vertical planes are called *dihedral planes* and represented by σ_d. D_{nd} symmetry is also fairly common. Examples are: D_{2d}, allene, tetrahedron flattened or elongated along a C_2 axis, as in $CuCl_4{}^{2-}$; D_{3d}, ethane; D_{4d}, $Mn_2(CO)_{10}$, $B_{10}H_{10}{}^{2-}$; D_{5d}, $Fe(C_5H_5)_2$.

7. All linear molecules belong to one of two special groups, $C_{\infty v}$ or $D_{\infty h}$. Unsymmetrical molecules such as CO, HCl, N_2O, OCS, HCN, ClCCH, etc., belong to the class $C_{\infty v}$, while symmetrical ones such as Cl_2, OCO, $HgCl_2$, XeF_2, HCCH, OCCCO, etc., belong to the class $D_{\infty h}$.

8. Finally, there are three classes of extremely symmetrical molecules. These have the symmetry of a regular tetrahedron, T_d, the symmetry possessed by both the cube and the regular octahedron, O_h, or the symmetry possessed by both the regular (pentagonal) dodecahedron and the regular icosahedron, I. The characteristic symmetry elements for T_d are a set of four C_3 axes, a set of three S_4 axes and a set of six planes, σ_d. Figure 4-9

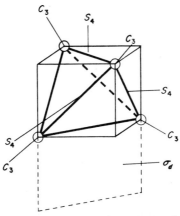

Fig. 4-9.   Sketch showing some of the essential symmetry elements of a tetrahedron, which has symmetry T_d. All of the C_3 and S_4 axes are shown, but only one of the six dihedral planes, σ_d.

illustrates these. The characteristic symmetry elements of O_h are a set of four C_3 axes, a set of three C_4 axes, a set of three planes, σ_h, each of which contains two of the C_4's and a set of six planes, σ_d, each of which contains one of the C_4's and bisects two of the angles between the other two C_4's. These elements are illustrated in Figure 4-10. From combinations of these, there are also S_4, S_6, C_2 and i symmetry elements. One important difference to be noted between T_d and O_h is that only the latter has a center of symmetry. The symmetry class I arises when there are six C_5 axes, as well as other symmetry elements. At present it is represented among real molecules only by the icosahedra found in various forms of elemental boron and in $B_{12}H_{12}{}^{2-}$, $B_{12}Cl_{12}{}^{2-}$, etc. (see page 284 for a sketch).

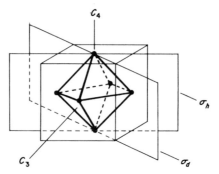

Fig. 4-10.   A sketch showing one of each of the four essential types of symmetry element in symmetry class O_h, in relation to a cube and an octahedron.

In this book, we shall describe molecular symmetry in terms of Schönflies symbols only when there is some distinct advantage in precision or clarity to be gained. This will be true almost only in connection with the application of the crystal field, ligand field and MO theories to transition metal complexes. However, we shall often state the symmetry class of a molecule so that the student may then use it as a worked example in deriving the symbols according to the above outline.

More commonly, we shall use some words descriptive of certain aspects of symmetry. A molecule with a C_3 axis will be said to have trigonal symmetry. Analogously, the terms tetragonal, pentagonal and hexagonal will be used when there are C_4, C_5 and C_6 axes, respectively. The terms tetrahedral and octahedral are commonly used by chemists to indicate the symmetry, or approximate symmetry, of the essential bond structure of a molecule, even when the molecule does not have actual T_d or O_h symmetry. For example, $[Co(NH_3)_4Cl_2]^+$ is called an "octahedral" complex. The term *centrosymmetric* is used to mean that a center of inversion or center of symmetry is present.

References*

Allred, A. L., *J. Inorg. Nucl. Chem.*, **17**, 215 (1961). Electronegativity.
—— and A. L. Hensly, *J. Inorg. Nucl. Chem.*, **17**, 43 (1961).
—— and E. G. Rochow, *J. Inorg. Nucl. Chem.*, **5**, 264, 269 (1958).

* The references given for Chapter 3 apply here also.

Brand, J. C. D., and J. C. Speakman, *Molecular Structure*, Arnold, London, 1960. An excellent presentation of all phases of molecular structure determination, including molecular and crystallographic symmetry.

Cotton, F. A., *Chemical Applications of Group Theory*, Wiley–Interscience, New York, 1963. A chemist's introduction to molecular symmetry.

Cottrell, T. L., *The Strengths of Chemical Bonds*, 2nd ed., Butterworths, London, 1958. An excellent, authoritative book dealing with methods of determination of bond energies and containing much detailed information and numerical data.

Gaydon, A. G., *Bond Dissociation Energies*, Chapman and Hall, London, 1953.

Jaffé, H. H., and M. Orchin, *Symmetry in Chemistry*, Wiley, New York, 1965. Another chemist's introduction to molecular symmetry and group theory.

Pritchard, H. O., and H. A. Skinner, *Chem. Rev.*, **55**, 745 (1955). A review on electronegativity.

Schonland, D. S., *Molecular Symmetry: An Introduction to Group Theory and Its Uses in Chemistry*, Van Nostrand, London, 1965.

Swarc, M., *Chem. Rev.*, **47**, 75 (1950). The determination of bond dissociation energies by pyrolytic methods.

Tables of Interatomic Distance and Configuration in Molecules and Ions, Special Publication No. 11; No. 18, Supplement 1956–1959, Chemical Society, London. An extensive compilation of structural information.

Wheatley, P. J., *The Determination of Molecular Structure*, Clarendon Press, Oxford, 1960. An excellent introduction to methods of structure determination such as X-ray diffraction, molecular spectroscopy and nuclear resonance methods.

5

Coordination Compounds

5-1. Introductory Remarks

Although coordination compounds are of particular importance in the chemistry of transition elements, they play a significant role in the chemistry of all elements having electropositive natures, that is, elements which form ions or compounds in which they are electrophilic and hence capable of binding donor molecules. Indeed, in a purely *formal* sense all— or nearly all—chemical compounds might be treated as coordination compounds. The point at which the *formalism* becomes realistic, and hence useful in a practical sense, is a matter of subjective judgement to a degree, although there is surely general agreement as to where the extremes lie.

To illustrate this, we first introduce a rather general definition of a *complex*, or coordination compound: a complex is formed when a central atom or ion, M, unites with one or more ligands, L, L', etc., to form a species of the type $ML_lL'_{l'}L''_{l''}$. M, the ligands and the resulting complex may all bear charges. This definition is so general that methane could be considered a coordination compound formed from C^{4+} and $4H^-$. In practice, of course, we do not regard methane as a coordination compound because there is no practical utility or theoretical value in thinking in terms of the combining of ions, which are not themselves stable, in a reaction which does not actually occur under ordinary chemical conditions. From this example we can infer some practical qualifications which ought to be added to our definition: (1) that the central atom and the ion should be capable of existence under chemically significant circumstances and (2) that the reaction involved in forming the complex from the central atom or ion and the ligands actually occur under chemically significant conditions. With these qualifications we rule out CH_4, PF_5, ClO_4^- and many other molecules or polyatomic ions from consideration, while leaving such species as AlF_6^{3-}, $CoCl_4^{2-}$, TlI_4^-, $[Cr(NH_3)_6]^{3+}$ within the scope of the definition.

The definition is still not perfect, cumbersome as it has already become. Normally we would call $SiF_6{}^{2-}$ a complex, and yet the reaction

$$Si^{4+} + 6F^- = SiF_6{}^{2-}$$

violates both of our qualifications. However, the reaction

$$SiF_4 + 2F^- = SiF_6{}^{2-}$$

does occur, and thus $SiF_6{}^{2-}$ will come within the scope of the definition if we allow further that a complex may be formed by adding ligands to a *molecule* in which the initial atom has not *already* attained its maximum coordination number. Other examples of this sort are

$$BF_3 + F^- = BF_4{}^-$$
$$BF_3 + NH_3 = BF_3NH_3$$

In the second of these, the resulting complex might also be called an *adduct*, a term which has more recently come into use for complexes formed when two neutral molecules, one a donor (nucleophile) and the other an acceptor (electrophile), unite to form a neutral complex.

This brief discussion is intended to show that the terms *coordination compound* and *complex* are somewhat flexible, their meanings having evolved and changed with the development of inorganic chemistry. The sensible way to convey their meaning is to abandon the attempt to formulate a perfect definition and to proceed instead to an account of the behavior and properties of some compounds representative of those normally considered to be complexes.

In this chapter, the majority of the examples will involve transition metal ions, for reasons which will be apparent as the discussion proceeds. Thus the students of this book may prefer to defer study of this chapter until the chemistry of transition elements is reached. However, the fact that complexes are far more important and numerous among transition metals should not be permitted to obscure the fact that they do play a role in the chemistry of all electropositive elements. Indeed most of the aqueous chemistry of elements such as cadmium and mercury is one of complexes, and even for very highly electropositive elements such as the alkalies or lanthanides, the formation of complex compounds or ions is of considerable importance.

5-2. Early Development of Coordination Chemistry

Very early in the development of chemical science, substances were prepared which appeared to consist of stoichiometric mixtures of two or more compounds, each of which is capable of independent existence. Some of these were the so-called double salts, of which $AlF_3 \cdot 3KF$,

$KCl \cdot MgCl_2 \cdot 6H_2O$, $Fe(CN)_2 \cdot 4KCN$, $ZnCl_2 \cdot 2CsCl$, $Al_2(SO_4)_3 \cdot K_2SO_4 \cdot 24H_2O$ and many others are well-known examples. The other general class of these substances included the molecular compounds or addition compounds, in which one metal salt was combined with one or more neutral molecules, rather than another salt. Of these, the ones containing ammonia, which came to be called *ammines*, were among the earliest and best known. For example, over 140 years ago, it was found that the addition of aqueous NH_3 to a green solution of $NiCl_2$ caused an instant change in color to purple, and that from this solution purple crystals of the composition $NiCl_2 \cdot 6NH_3$ could be obtained. In a similar way, Cu^{II} afforded the ammine $CuSO_4 \cdot 4NH_3$. Of special importance, however, were the ammines of Co^{III}, Pt^{IV} and Pt^{II}; whereas the ammines of most metal ions, such as Ni^{II} and Cu^{II}, are both limited in number and very labile with respect to acids and bases, those of Co^{III}, Pt^{IV} and Pt^{II} (and also those of Cr^{III}, Pd^{II} and several other metal ions) are numerous and varied and exhibit considerable stability. Thus, research directed at the understanding of the nature of "addition compounds" centered around the Co^{III}, Pt^{IV} and Pt^{II} compounds and, toward the end of the nineteenth century, came to be dominated by the Danish chemist S. M. Jørgenson and the Swiss Alfred Werner. These two men, as well as others, prepared hundreds of coordination compounds, mainly ammines, of these ions and examined their transformations, the occurrence of isomers, their degrees of ionization, etc. It was Werner, however, who had the imagination to deduce from these results his *coordination theory* for which he received the Nobel Prize in chemistry. In the following paragraphs, a few of the salient facts and Werner's deductions from them will be summarized. The intention is to be didactic rather than historically scrupulous.

Experiments showed that five ammines of Pt^{IV} (Table 5-1) could be isolated and that their electrolytic conductances had the values listed. These conductances, when compared with values for simpler electrolytes, indicate the number of ions produced by electrolytic dissociation, and these numbers are given in the table for convenience. In addition to the conductance data, it was also known that on addition of Ag^+ ion to solutions

TABLE 5-1

Some Pt^{IV} Ammines and Their Degrees of Ionization

	Λ, ohm^{-1}	No. of ions	No. of Cl$^-$ ions
(1) $PtCl_4 \cdot 6NH_3$	523	5	4
(2) $PtCl_4 \cdot 5NH_3$	404	4	3
(3) $PtCl_4 \cdot 4NH_3$	229	3	2
(4) $PtCl_4 \cdot 3NH_3$	97	2	1
(5) $PtCl_4 \cdot 2NH_3$	0	0	0

of the tabulated compounds no immediate precipitate was obtained with (5), whereas in each of the others the number of chloride ions immediately precipitated per molecule of the ammine addition compound are those listed in the last column of the table. This means that in (1) all chlorine is present in solution as chloride ions, which are immediately precipitated as AgCl, whereas in compounds (2), (3) and (4) only three, two and one, respectively, of the chlorine atoms are present in solution as Cl^- ions. Werner proposed the following explanation for these facts. He assumed that for Pt^{IV}, in addition to its electrovalence of $+4$, which determines the total number of negative charges which may be carried by the anions present, there is another property of the Pt^{IV} ion called its *coordination number*, which is the total number of anions or molecules which may be directly associated with the cation. For Pt^{IV} this coordination number must be assumed to be 6. The five compounds of Table 5-1 can then be formulated

$$[Pt(NH_3)_6]Cl_4 = [Pt(NH_3)_6]^{4+} + 4Cl^-$$
$$[Pt(NH_3)_5Cl]Cl_3 = [Pt(NH_3)_5Cl]^{3+} + 3Cl^-$$
$$[Pt(NH_3)_4Cl_2]Cl_2 = [Pt(NH_3)_4Cl_2]^{2+} + 2Cl^-$$
$$[Pt(NH_3)_3Cl_3]Cl = [Pt(NH_3)_3Cl_3]^+ + Cl^-$$
$$[Pt(NH_3)_2Cl_4] \text{ (not dissociated)}$$

where all *coordinated* groups are written inside of the square bracket. It will be seen that this simple postulate—that Pt^{IV} always has six groups in its *coordination shell*—nicely explains the conductances and chloride ion numbers in all of the compounds. These formulations imply that two additional members of the series, the anions $[Pt(NH_3)Cl_5]^-$ and $[PtCl_6]^{2-}$, might be capable of existence and, indeed, both are now known. Their potassium salts are found to be 1:1 and 2:1 electrolytes, respectively, on the basis of conductance measurements. On the basis of similar data, Co^{III} and Cr^{III} were also shown to have a coordination number of 6, and Pt^{II} and Pd^{II} were shown to have a coordination number of 4.

Once coordination numbers are established, the next question that naturally arises concerns the geometrical arrangement of the coordinated groups around the cation. Werner was able to postulate the correct arrangements on the basis of the numbers of isomers and optical activity, especially for the Co^{III} compounds. For example, there are just two known isomers of $[Co(NH_3)_4Cl_2]Cl$, one lavender, the other green. There are also two known isomers of the analogous complex in which two molecules of ethylenediamine, $H_2NCH_2CH_2NH_2$ (abbreviated en), are substituted for the four NH_3 molecules, namely, $[Co(en)_2Cl_2]Cl$, and one of them can be resolved into optical isomers. These and many other facts led Werner to propose that the geometrical arrangement of the coordinated groups for the coordination number 6 is that of an octahedron. On this basis the isomers of $[Co(en)_2Cl_2]Cl$ would be formulated as 5-I. Similarly, on the basis of such facts as the occurrence of $[Pt(NH_3)_2Cl_2]$ in two isomeric forms, Werner proposed that the four-fold coordination sphere of Pt^{II}

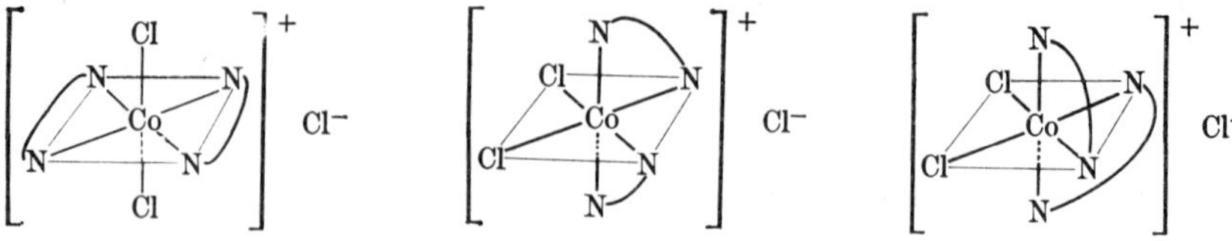

The *trans* isomer
(Symmetry D_{2h})

Optical isomers of the *cis* structure
(Symmetry C_2)

(5-I)

must be square. The two isomers mentioned are then formulated as *cis* (5-IIa) and *trans* (5-IIb).

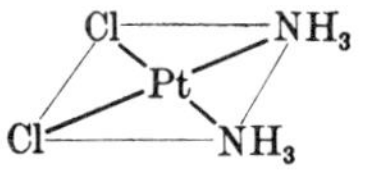

cis (C_{2v})   *trans* (D_{2h})

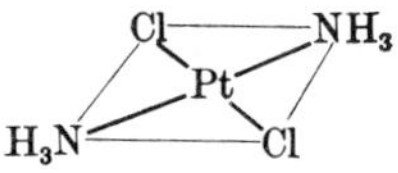

(5-IIa)   (5-IIb)

Once Werner's views about coordination numbers and the geometrical arrangements in the coordination shells became accepted, there still remained the intriguing question of the nature of the bonds which held the ligands to the metal ions. This is a question which even today is not settled in a definitive way. Werner simply attributed them to "secondary valences" of the metals. With the advent of the electronic theories of Lewis, Langmuir and Sidgwick, emphasizing the importance of electron pairs in binding atoms together, the notion developed that ligands are of necessity ions or molecules which contain unshared pairs of electrons, as in $[:\overset{..}{\underset{..}{Cl}}:]^-$ or $H_3N:$, which could be used to form dative (i.e., donating) bonds, also called coordinate bonds, to the metal ions.

We shall now consider in detail the various aspects of the behavior of coordination compounds which have been touched on in this short introduction, but from an entirely contemporary point of view.

5-3. Coordination Numbers and Symmetries

As outlined in the preceding section, the assumption that certain metal ions have characteristic coordination numbers and their coordination polyhedra certain definite shapes or symmetries provided Werner and those of his contemporaries who followed his lead with an extremely fruitful basis for the interpretation of many otherwise puzzling facts. As we shall see, the assumptions that the coordination spheres of Cr^{III}, Co^{III} and Pt^{IV} are consistently octahedral and those of Pt^{II} and Pd^{II} consistently square planar were confirmed by a wealth of experimental data. In this section we will discuss the subject of coordination numbers and the shapes of coordination shells in a more general and comprehensive way. We shall discuss coordination numbers of 2 to 9, describing for each the various geometrical structures known and citing examples of their occurrence. The infrequent occurrence of still higher coordination numbers will also be noted. It should be noted that we now possess an enormous amount of direct evidence, via X-ray diffraction studies, and indirect evidence, via dipole moments, magnetic properties and electronic spectra concerning coordination numbers and geometries, so that these ideas are no longer mere hypotheses but well-established facts.

It is also important to realize that a given metal ion does not necessarily have *one* characteristic coordination number and geometry. Some, such as Co^{III}, apparently do. There does not appear to be any complex of Co^{III} in which its coordination sphere is other than octahedral. Of course, the Co^{III} ion can be forced into other environments, a tetrahedral one, for instance, in certain solid compounds with extended, rigid structures, but few coordination chemists would quarrel with the statement that six octahedrally arranged ligand atoms constitute *the* characteristic coordination shell of Co^{III}. If we turn to Ni^{II}, however, we have quite the opposite situation. There are many well-established Ni^{II} complexes in each of the following classes: octahedral, six coordinate; planar, four coordinate; and tetrahedral, four coordinate. Zinc(II) and cobalt(II) also adopt all three of these coordination shells, and many other ions adopt at least two different coordination shells, depending on the conditions, types of ligands, etc. For example, Al^{3+} has tetrahedral coordination in $AlCl_4^-$ but octahedral coordination in AlF_6^{3-}.

Two Coordination. Coordination number 2 is not very common. It is best exemplified by some complexes of Cu^I, Ag^I, Au^I and Hg^{II}. Such complexes have linear arrangements of the metal ion and the two ligand atoms, and typical ones are $[ClCuCl]^-$, $[H_3NAgNH_3]^+$, $[ClAuCl]^-$ and $[NCHgCN]$. The metal atoms in cations such as $[UO_2]^{2+}$, $[UO_2]^+$, $[MoO_2]^{2+}$ and $[PuO_2]^{2+}$ which are linear may also be said to have coordination number 2, but these oxo cations interact fairly strongly with additional ligands and their true coordination numbers are much higher. It is true, however, that they have a specially strong affinity for the two oxygen atoms.

Three Coordination. Outside of a few discrete molecules of lighter elements, where the cationic nature of the central atom is slight, e.g., the

5+ A.I.C.

boron halides, this coordination number is of very infrequent occurrence. Thus, most of the halides of the trivalent metals crystallize in lattices containing metal ions in octahedral interstices, while $FeCl_3$, which is relatively volatile for a transition metal halide, vaporizes to Fe_2Cl_6 molecules consisting of two $FeCl_4$ tetrahedra sharing an edge, and $AuCl_3$ is a dimer consisting of two planar $AuCl_4$ units sharing an edge. Many complexes of the type $M^IM^{II}X_3$, for example, $CsCuCl_3$, contain not discrete MX_3^- anions but infinite chains $—(MX_2)—X—(MX_2)—X—$ in which each M^{II} ion is surrounded by four X atoms; and others of the stoichiometry LMX_2, such as $(C_2H_5)_3PPtCl_2$ (5-III), are dimeric with X atom bridges.

(5-III)

Of course, complexes in solution, which we may for simplicity write as ML_3, are almost certainly further coordinated by solvent molecules, for example, $M(H_2O)_3L_3$ or $M(H_2O)L_3$.

Some coordination compounds formed by tridentate ligands of particular steric requirements were postulated to have 3-coordinated metal ions, but X-ray studies have shown that they are polymeric.[1]

An authentic instance of 3-coordination is found in the HgI_3^- ion, which occurs in $[(CH_3)_3S]^+[HgI_3]^-$ as an approximately equilateral triangle of I atoms with Hg in the center.[2]

Tetrahedral Four Coordination. It is well established that there are many complexes with this geometry, though it is not as common as octahedral coordination among the transition elements. It occurs fairly commonly for complexes of nontransition ions where its stability can be attributed partly to the covalence in the bonds, achieved by the use of metal sp^3 hybrid orbitals, and partly to the fact that the tetrahedral configuration is the most stable one for four coordination from an electrostatic point of view. Thus, there are such tetrahedral complexes as BeF_4^{2-}, BF_4^-, BCl_4^-, BBr_4^-, $ZnCl_4^{2-}$, $ZnBr_4^{2-}$, $Zn(CN)_4^{2-}$, $Cd(CN)_4^{2-}$ and $Hg(CN)_4^{2-}$, as well as the many BX_3L adducts and complexes of Be and B with bidentate ligands (pages 246 and 256).

Among the transition metal ions (i.e., those with d shell vacancies) tetrahedral complexes are usually stable only under certain conditions. Notable exceptions to this are the ions $FeCl_4^-$, $CoCl_4^{2-}$, $CoBr_4^{2-}$, CoI_4^{2-}, $Co(NCS)_4^{2-}$ and a few other CoX_4^{2-} and $[CoX_3(H_2O)]^-$ species. All of these form in aqueous solution despite the fact that water molecules are

[1] G. A. Barclay, C. M. Harris, B. F. Hoskins and E. Kokot, *Proc. Chem. Soc.*, **1961**, 264.
[2] R. H. Fenn, J. W. H. Oldham and D. C. Phillips, *Nature*, **198**, 381 (1963).

present in abundance which could serve to increase the coordination number to 6. The factors governing the stability of the tetrahedral configuration relative to the planar one and the octahedral one which could be obtained by addition of two solvent molecules are not fully understood.

Other transition metal ions have been shown to form tetrahedral complexes under special conditions, for example, in crystalline form where the tetrahedral anions are combined with large cations or in solvents of low coordinating power. Thus with cations such as $[(C_nH_{2n+1})_4N]^+$, $[(C_6H_5)_4As]^+$, $[(C_6H_5)_3(CH_3)P]^+$, etc., the tetrahedral complex anions $[VX_4]^-$, $[MnX_4]^{2-}$, $[NiX_4]^{2-}$ and $[CuX_4]^{2-}$ (where X is Cl, Br or I) have been obtained. None of them persist in solution in coordinating solvents such as water or alcohols, but many retain their structures in solvents such as nitrobenzene, acetone or dichloromethane.

Most of the known tetrahedral complexes are anionic, either $[M^{II}X_4]^{2-}$ or $[M^{II}LX_3]^-$ (where L is a neutral ligand), or neutral, $[ML_2X_2]$. Among the latter are, for example, those of Mn^{II}, Co^{II} and Ni^{II} on which L is a phosphine oxide or an arsine oxide. There are very few known cationic tetrahedral complexes, such as $[ML_4]^{2+}$ or $[ML_3X]^+$, as well as a very few neutral ones (e.g., of Co^{II}, see Sect. 29-F-3). Some cations such as Cr^{III} and Co^{III} have never been found with tetrahedral coordination in simple complexes.

Planar Four Coordination. This form of coordination is especially characteristic of certain elements and otherwise uncommon. For Rh^I, Ir^I, Pt^{II}, Pd^{II} and Au^{III} it is the form of coordination usually found, and for Ni^{II} and Cu^{II} it is very common and important. For most other ions it is seldom or never observed.

With Pt^{II} and, to a lesser extent, Pd^{II} extensive investigations beginning in the late nineteenth century have led to the preparation of an enormous number of complexes illustrating essentially all of the possible types and their isomers. The latter will be discussed on page 144. With regard to charge types, all five possibilities are known, and are represented by the following:

2+ cation	$[Pt(NH_3)_4]^{2+}$
1+ cation	$[Pt(NH_3)_3Cl]^+$
Neutral	$[Pt(Ph_3P)_2Cl_2]$
1− anion	$[Pt(py)Cl_3]^-$
2− anion	$[PtCl_4]^{2-}$

Cationic, anionic and neutral chelated complexes of both Ni^{II} and Cu^{II} are known, though not of all of the above five types.

Five Coordination. Though far more common than coordination number 3, this one is also relatively rare, and in various instances where stoichiometry might suggest its occurrence, the true coordination number is different, being either higher or lower. For instance, the crystalline compound

Cs_3CoCl_5 contains tetrahedral $CoCl_4^{2-}$ ions and separate Cl^- ions in its lattice, whereas the crystalline compounds $NbCl_5$, $NbBr_5$, $TaCl_5$ and $MoCl_5$ all contain dimeric M_2X_{10} molecules consisting of two octahedral MX_6 groups sharing an edge.

There are two fairly regular forms of five-fold coordination. In one (5-IV), the ligands lie at the vertices of a trigonal bipyramid (TBP) while in the other (5-V), they lie at the vertices of a square pyramid (SP). In

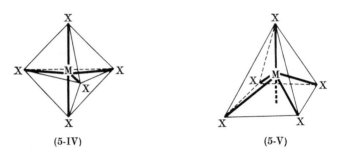

(5-IV)　　　　　　　　　(5-V)

many real cases, however, the arrangement of ligands is not exactly either of these. For example in $Zn(acac)_2 \cdot H_2O$, the arrangement is intermediate, although it is somewhat closer to SP than to TBP.[3] Another important aspect of five-coordinate species is concerned with the *relative ease with which the TBP and SP configurations can be interconverted*. As illustrated in Figure 5-1, a slight deformation of the bond angles is all that is required, and such processes might be expected to have relatively low energies.

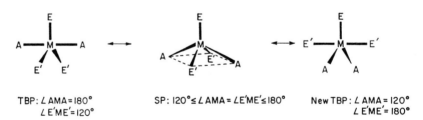

TBP: ∠AMA=180°　　SP: 120°≤∠AMA=∠E'ME'≤180°　　New TBP: ∠AMA=120°
∠E'ME'=120°　　　　　　　　　　　　　　　　　　　∠E'ME'=180°

Fig. 5-1. The interconversion of the trigonal bipyramid (TBP) and square pyramid (SP) configurations is shown so as to indicate how axial (A) and equatorial (E) positions of the TBP may be interchanged. As shown, the E' ligands become axial and the A ligands become equatorial. Starting with the new TBP (right) the E' ligands could be exchanged with E and one of the A's, etc.

Thus, for example, even if the TBP configuration is the more stable for a given compound, the SP configuration may not be very much less stable.

[3] H. Montgomery and E. C. Lingafelter, *Acta. Cryst.*, **16**, 748 (1963).

This has the important consequence that one of these may provide a path by which the two types of ligands in the other (more stable one) may change places.[4a,b] Thus, a scrambling of the axial (A) and equatorial (E) ligands in a TBP may occur as in Figure 5-1. Nuclear resonance studies have shown that such scrambling actually occurs in $Fe(CO)_5$,[5] and in PF_5 and numerous derivatives thereof.[4b] Similar phenomena, involving interconversion of alternative coordination polyhedra for other coordination numbers, can also occur and are of interest.[5a] However, they are as yet less well understood than is the TBP–SP situation.

We now give a few further examples of five-coordinate complexes. Those dimeric pentahalides mentioned earlier vaporize to pentacoordinate monomers which are apparently trigonal bipyramids. Iron carbonyl, $Fe(CO)_5$, and the isoelectronic ions such as $Mn(CO)_5{}^-$ and $[Co(C\equiv NR)_5]^+$ also have trigonal bipyramidal configurations[6] and so also do substituted iron carbonyls such as $R_3PFe(CO)_4$ and $(R_3P)_2Fe(CO)_3$. There are then a number of five-coordinate derivatives of Ni, Co, Pd and several other metals toward the right side of the transition block which are believed to have a square pyramid configuration, although only a little conclusive evidence for this has yet been produced. These compounds are exemplified by $NiBr_3$-$[(C_2H_5)_3P]_2$, $CoI_2 \cdot$triarsine and $NiI_2 \cdot$triarsine (triarsine represents a tridentate ligand of the type $R_2As(CH_2)_2As(R)(CH_2)_2AsR_2$), and $[Pd(diarsine)_2Cl]ClO_4$. X-ray study has shown recently that the square pyramidal configuration exists in bis(salicylaldehydeethylenediimine)zinc monohydrate (5-VI) and in 5-VII, a complex of Ni^{II} with the triarsine

(5-VI)   (5-VII)

noted above having R equal to CH_3. One bromide ion is appreciably

[4a] R. S. Berry, J. Chem. Phys., **32**, 933 (1960).

[4b] E. L. Muetterties, W. Mahler and R. Schmutzler, Inorg. Chem., **2**, 613 (1963).

[5] F. A. Cotton, A. Danti, J. S. Waugh and R. W. Fessenden, J. Chem. Phys., **29**, 1427 (1958).

[5a] E. L. Muetterties, Inorg. Chem., **4**, 769 (1965).

[6] F. A. Cotton, T. G. Dunne and J. S. Wood, Inorg. Chem., **4**, 318 (1965).

($\sim 20°$) out of the basal plane, presumably because of steric pressure by two of the methyl groups.

With certain polydentate arsines, five-coordinate species are obtained[7a] presumably because of the steric preference of the ligands. There are quite a number of other transition metal complexes in which five-coordination is known or reasonably certain to be involved, as well as certain compounds of As^{III} and Sb^{III} (see page 494), though in the latter a sixth coordination position is "occupied" by a pair of nonbonding electrons (see Chapter 15); examples are given in tables of stereochemistries throughout the text.

Six Coordination. This is very common and is found mainly in one regular geometrical arrangement, the octahedron, although large distortions are often found. Some of the reasons for such distortions are discussed in Section 26-6.

The octahedron is a figure of very high symmetry. It is important to note that although octahedral complexes are often drawn as in (5-VIII),

$$
\begin{array}{c}
\text{Cl} \\
\text{Cl} \!-\!\!\!\!-\!\!\!\!-\!\!\!\!- \text{Cl} \\
\text{Pt} \\
\text{Cl} \!-\!\!\!\!-\!\!\!\!-\!\!\!\!- \text{Cl} \\
\text{Cl}
\end{array}
$$

(5-VIII)

so that two of the chloride ions might *look* different from the other four, all six are completely equivalent in an undistorted octahedron (see Sec. 4-6) which has symmetry O_h.

Two forms of distortion commonly occur in complexes we might loosely call octahedral. The first is a *trigonal distortion,* in which the octahedron is extended or compressed along one of its three-fold axes. A trigonally distorted octahedron is, of course, a trigonal antiprism (5-IX) belonging to symmetry class D_{3d}. The second important form of distortion is the

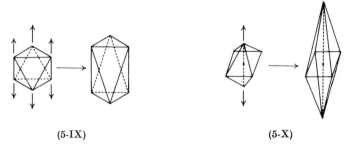

(5-IX)   (5-X)

[7a] See L. M. Venanzi, *Angew. Chem. (Internat.),* **3,** 453 (1964).

tetragonal distortion, in which the octahedron is elongated or flattened along a four-fold axis as in (5-X), whence its symmetry is reduced to D_{4h}. Obviously, in the limit, a tetragonally distorted octahedral complex (by elongation) completely loses two *trans* ligands and becomes a four-coordinated, square complex. There is no definite answer to the question of how long the two metal-ligand bonds must become, relative to the other four, before we cease to regard these two ligands as truly coordinated. Thus, we must take the view that the octahedral and square planar forms of coordination merge into one another.

Another fairly regular polyhedron, the *trigonal prism*, is occasionally found, for example in MoS_2 and WS_2 and in the rhenium complex of the rigid, bidentate ligand *cis*-1,2-diphenylethene-1,2-ditholate.[7b]

Coordination Numbers Greater Than Six. Coordination numbers 7, 8 and 9 are known to occur, though with few exceptions they are confined to compounds of the elements in the second and third transition series, the lanthanides and the actinides. This is attributable in part to the larger size of these ions and also to the availability of orbitals. Of these, coordination number 8 has been by far the most frequently observed and is, in fact, a rather common coordination number for the ions of the heavier metals.

Seven Coordination. Three geometrical arrangements are known. The most regular is the pentagonal bipyramid (symmetry D_{5h}), which is found in $[UO_2F_5]^{3-}$, as shown in 5-XI, and in $[UF_7]^{3-}$, $[ZrF_7]^{3-}$ and $[HfF_7]^{3-}$. A second arrangement, which can be considered to result from addition of a seventh atom at the center of one face of an octahedron (giving symmetry C_{3v}), which is distorted mainly by the spreading apart of the three atoms defining this face, has been found in one modification of the lanthanide oxides, M_2O_3, and in $[NbOF_6]^{3-}$. The third arrangement, which occurs in $[NbF_7]^{2-}$ and $[TaF_7]^{2-}$ ions, is derived by inserting a seventh atom above the center of one of the rectangular faces of a trigonal prism, as shown in 5-XII.

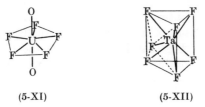

(5-XI) (5-XII)

Eight Coordination. The most symmetrical arrangement possible is the cube (which has O_h symmetry), but this seems to occur only in a few

[7b] R. Eisenberg and J. A. Ibers, *J. Amer. Chem. Soc.*, **87**, 3776 (1965).

solid compounds where the anions form continuous arrays, as in the CsCl structure. It is not known for any discrete MX_8 groups. This is presumably because there are several ways in which the cube may be distorted so as to lessen repulsions between the X atoms while maintaining good M–X interactions.[8]

The two principal ways in which the cube may become distorted are shown in Figure 5-2. The first of these, rotation of one square face by 45° relative to the one opposite to it, clearly lessens repulsions between

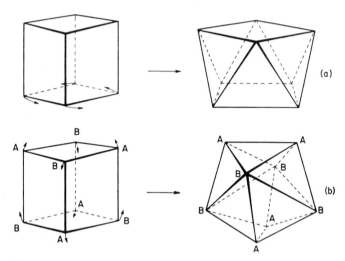

Fig. 5-2.   The two most important ways of distorting the cube: (a) to produce a square antiprism; (b) to produce a dodecahedron.

non-bonded atoms while leaving M–X distances unaltered. The resulting polyhedron is the square antiprism (symmetry D_{4d}). It has square top and bottom and eight isosceles triangles for its vertical faces. The second distortion shown can be best comprehended by recognizing that the cube is composed of two interpenetrating tetrahedra. The distortion occurs when the vertices of one of these tetrahedra are displaced so as to decrease the two vertical angles, that is, to elongate the tetrahedron, while the vertices of the other one are displaced to produce a flattened tetrahedron. Tetrahedra which are distorted in either of these ways are called bisphenoids (symmetry D_{2d}) and the resulting polyhedron of eight vertices formed by the two interpenetrating bisphenoids is sometimes called a bisbisphenoid (also of symmetry D_{2d}). A commoner (and more graceful) name is dodecahedron. As indicated in Figure 5-2, the eight vertices of this dodecahedron

[8] J. L. Hoard and J. V. Silverton, *Inorg. Chem.*, **2**, 235 (1963).

are not all equivalent, but are divided into two bisphenoidal sets, those within each set being equivalent.

A close analysis[8] of the energetics of M–X and X–X interactions suggests that there will in general be little difference between the energies of the square antiprism and dodecahedral arrangements, unless other factors, such as the existence of chelate rings, energies of partially filled inner shells, exceptional opportunities for orbital hybridization or the like come into play. In fact both arrangements occur quite commonly.

The square antiprismatic arrangement is found in the $[ReF_8]^{2-}$ ion,[9] in the $[TaF_8]^{3-}$ ion, in zirconium(IV) acetylacetonate,[10] around Ce^{IV} in $Ce(IO_3)_4$ and around Th^{IV} in the ThI_4.[11] Examples of the dodecahedral arrangement are found in K_2ZrF_6 (through sharing of F atoms), in $[TiCl_4(diars)_2]$ and several analogous Ti and Zr compounds, and in $[Zr(C_2O_4)_4]^{4-}$. The $[Mo(CN)_8]^{4-}$ ion also has dodecahedral symmetry in the crystalline potassium salt, but there are conflicting claims regarding its structure in solution. A change to square antiprismatic symmetry in solution cannot be ruled out. Still other examples of these two forms of eight-coordination will be found in Chapter 30.

A form of eight-coordination closely related to that represented by the more or less equidimensional dodecahedron shown in Figure 5-2 is found in two compounds which contain bidentate ligands, wherein the two donor atoms are held much closer together than would normally be permitted by their van der Waals radii. Thus, in the compound K_3CrO_8[12] there are Cr atoms formally in the oxidation state V surrounded by four peroxide ions, so disposed that one atom of each peroxide ion lies at a vertex of an elongated bisphenoid (the A vertices, Fig. 5-2b) with the vertical angles being 87°, while the other atom of each peroxide lies at one of the vertices of an extremely flattened bisphenoid (vertical angles, 174°). The latter is scarcely different from a planar, square array. The oxygen atoms of the elongated bisphenoid lie ca 0.1A closer to Cr than those in the nearly square bisphenoid.

Somewhat the same arrangement is found in the $[Co(NO_3)_4]^{2-}$ ion,[13] where each NO_3^- is bidentate. The vertical angles in the elongated bisphenoid are about 95°, while those in the flattened one are about 158°; here, however, the bond lengths in the two bisphenoids differ markedly, being 2.04 A in the elongated one and 2.41 and 2.70 A in the less regular flattened one. Essentially the same structure, except for

[9] P. A. Kozmin, *Zhur. Struk. Khim.*, **5**, 70 (1964).
[10] J. V. Silverton and J. L. Hoard, *Inorg. Chem.*, **2**, 243 (1963).
[11] A. Zalkin, J. D. Forrester and D. H. Templeton, *Inorg. Chem.*, **3**, 639 (1964).
[12] J. D. Swalen and J. A. Ibers, *J. Chem. Phys.*, **37**, 17 (1962).
[13] J. G. Bergman and F. A. Cotton, *J. Amer. Chem. Soc.*, **86**, 2941 (1964).

5*

the occurrence of practically equal metal–oxygen bonds, occurs[14a] also in $Ti(NO_3)_4$.

Another eight-coordinate structure is found in the $[UO_2(O_2CCH_3)_3]^-$ ion (Fig. 32-3); this is somewhat outside of the pattern of structures discussed above because of the special requirement that the UO_2 group be linear.

Nine Coordination. Only one regular arrangement is known for this coordination number, which occurs quite frequently. It is derived from a trigonal prism by placing the three additional atoms outside the centers of the three vertical faces, as shown in Figure 5-3; it retains the D_{3h}

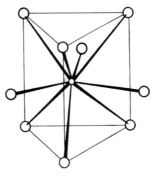

Fig. 5-3.   The structure of many 9-coordinate complexes.

symmetry of the trigonal prism. Among the compounds in which this arrangement occurs are $La(OH)_3$, UCl_3, $PbCl_2$, hydrated lanthanide compounds such as $Nd(BrO_3)_3 \cdot 9H_2O$, certain hydrated salts of Sr^{2+} and the $[ReH_9]^{2-}$ ion.

Higher Coordination Numbers. These occur relatively infrequently[14b], and mainly with the largest spherical cations, i.e., the heaviest alkali and alkaline earth ions. Generally the geometry is irregular and the assignment of a coordination number, 10, 11, 12, ..., is often somewhat arbitrary since the cation–anion distances cover a range from those short enough to imply clearly that there is strong interaction to those long enough to be regarded as beyond the limits of true coordination. When, as in certain mixed metal oxides (e.g., $BaTiO_3$), the large cations and the oxide ions form a heterogeneous, close-packed array, the large cations have a coordination number of twelve. The set of coordinated oxide ions consists of an equatorial band of six oxygen ions at the vertices of a hexagon and an equilateral triangle of oxide ions above, and another below this plane (symmetry D_{3h}).

[14a] C. C. Addison, et al., Proc. Chem. Soc., **1964**, 367.
[14b] J. L. Hoard, et al., J. Amer. Chem. Soc., **87**, 1610, 1611, 1612 (1965).

5-4. Types of Ligands

The most general definition of a ligand might be that it is any atom, ion or molecule capable of functioning as the donor partner in one or more coordinate bonds. There may be cases—for example, among the metal carbonyls—where the partner we call the ligand, namely CO, does approximately as much accepting as donating, but in general the above definition will serve our purposes here.

At present there is no evidence that any single uncharged atom functions as a ligand. However, monatomic ions, especially the halogens, do so. Thus, there are numerous complexes containing only halide ions as ligands, such as $[PF_6]^-$, $[FeCl_4]^-$, $[CoBr_4]^{2-}$ and $[TlI_4]^{2-}$, as well as many containing halide ions along with other ligands, such as $[Co(NH_3)_5Cl]^{2+}$, $[Pt(Et_3P)_2Br_2]$, $[CopyCl_3]^-$ and $[Cr(H_2O)_4Cl_2]^+$.

Monatomic ions necessarily belong to the general class of ligands known as *uni-* or *monodentate* (literally, one-toothed) ligands. Monodentate ligands use only one atom at a time as a donor atom, and hence they fill only one coordination position of a given cation. Of course, many polyatomic ions and molecules are also monodentate ligands. Some representative and important ones are: halide ions—F^-, Cl^-, Br^-, I^-; other ions—H^-, CN^-, SCN^-, NO_3^-, NO_2^-, N_3^-, $RCOO^-$, SO_4^{2-}; molecules—R_3N, R_3P, CO, R_2S, R_3PO, R_2SO, pyridine, H_2O. It should be noted that a monodentate ligand may simultaneously fill coordination positions in two or even three *different* metal ions; that is, it may function as a bridge. The kinds of

(5-XIII)   (5-XIV)   (5-XV)   (5-XVI)

(5-XVII)   (5-XVIII)   (5-XIX)

bridging illustrated in 5-XIII through 5-XIX are well known and illustrative. In 5-XIII through 5-XVI the bridging ligand is still strictly monodentate in the sense that only one atom in it is functioning as a donor atom. In 5-XVII, 5-XVIII and 5-XIX different metal ions are coordinated by different atoms of the ligand. In the thiocyanate ion only one of the two potential donor atoms, S and N, can be bonded to one metal ion for geometric reasons, but both ends may be simultaneously bound to different cations. In the carboxylate anions and in the sulfate, carbonate and nitrate ions, two atoms could be coordinated to the same metal ion, and there are cases known in which this happens with all of them.

Ligands having two or more atoms which can simultaneously serve as donors are called *polydentate* ligands. Those with two donor sites are called bidentate, those with three, four, five and six donor sites are called tri(or ter)-, tetra(or quadri)-, penta- and hexa(or sexi)dentate ligands, respectively. Polydentate ligands whose structures permit the attachment of two or more donor sites to the same metal ion simultaneously, thus closing one or more rings, are called *chelate* (from the Greek for claw) ligands, and are by far the most important class of polydentate ligands. Thus, both of the diamines 5-XX and 5-XXI are bidentate ligands, but only ethylene-

(5-XX)   (5-XXI)

diamine is a chelate. Examples of various polydentate chelate ligands are given in Table 5-2.

TABLE 5-2

Some Polydentate Chelate Ligands

Name	Formula
Some Bidentate Ligands	
Acetylacetonato ion (acac⁻)	
N,N-Diethylthiocarbamate ion	
2,2′-Dipyridyl (dipy)	
o-Phenylenebisdimethylarsine (diars)	

TABLE 5-2 (*continued*)

Name	Formula

Some Tridentate Ligands

Diethylenetriamine (dien)

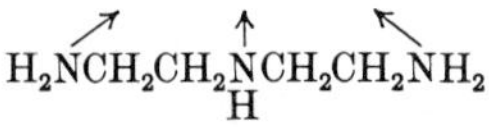

$$H_2NCH_2CH_2NCH_2CH_2NH_2$$
$$H$$

Iminodiacetic acid anion

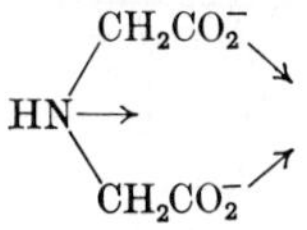

$$CH_2CO_2^-$$
$$HN{\longrightarrow}$$
$$CH_2CO_2^-$$

Some Tetradentate Ligands

Triethylenetetramine (trien)

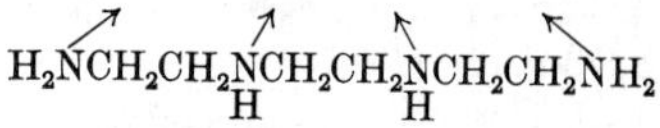

$$H_2NCH_2CH_2NCH_2CH_2NCH_2CH_2NH_2$$
$$H \qquad H$$

Anion of nitrilotriacetic acid

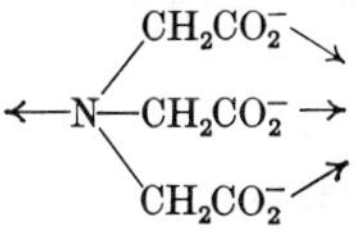

$$CH_2CO_2^-$$
$$\longleftarrow N{\longrightarrow}CH_2CO_2^- \rightarrow$$
$$CH_2CO_2^-$$

Pentadentate Ligand

Anion of ethylenediaminetriacetic acid

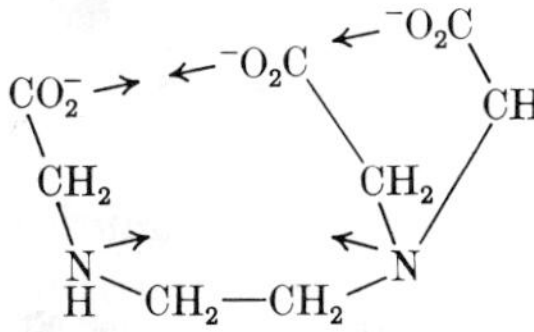

$$CO_2^- \rightarrow \quad \leftarrow {}^-O_2C \quad \leftarrow {}^-O_2C$$
$$CH_2 \qquad CH_2 \qquad CH_2$$
$$\underset{H}{N} \quad CH_2{-}CH_2 \quad N$$

Some Hexadentate Ligands

1,8-Bis(salicylideneamino)-3,6-dithiaoctane

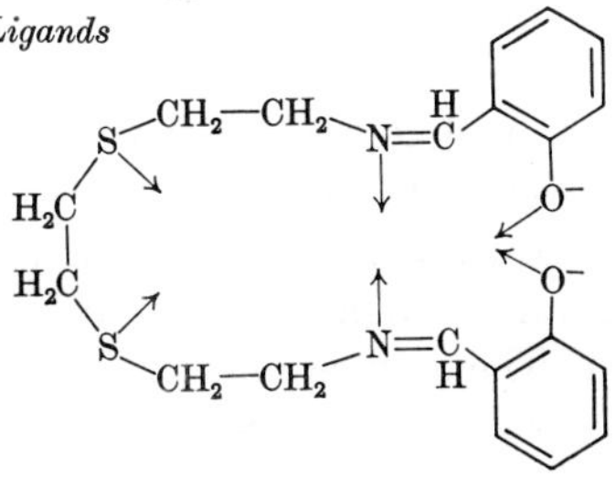

$$S{-}CH_2{-}CH_2{-}N\overset{H}{=}C$$
$$H_2C \qquad O^-$$
$$H_2C \qquad O^-$$
$$S{-}CH_2{-}CH_2{-}N{=}\underset{H}{C}$$

Anion of ethylenediaminetetraacetic acid (EDTA)

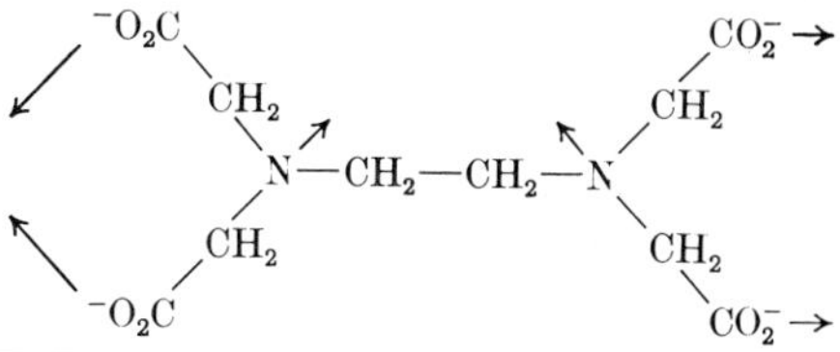

$$^-O_2C \qquad\qquad CO_2^- \rightarrow$$
$$CH_2 \qquad\qquad CH_2$$
$$N{-}CH_2{-}CH_2{-}N$$
$$CH_2 \qquad\qquad CH_2$$
$$^-O_2C \qquad\qquad CO_2^- \rightarrow$$

STRUCTURE, ISOMERISM AND NOMENCLATURE
OF COMPLEX COMPOUNDS

5-5. Elements of Nomenclature

Coordination compounds can be sufficiently complicated and intricate structurally that a certain minimum discussion of formal rules of nomenclature is necessary in even an elementary account of their chemistry. Therefore, before discussing isomerism, we shall state and illustrate some of the more important and indispensable rules selected from a considerably larger body of rules proposed by the International Union of Chemistry.

1. *Naming of ligands.*

a. Negative (anionic) ligands have names ending in *o*, derived, usually, by adding *o* to the stem name of the group. For example, Cl^- (chloro), Br^- (bromo), SCN^- (thiocyanato), CN^- (cyano), SO_4^{2-} (sulfato), OH^- (hydroxo), O^{2-} (oxo), O_2H^- (perhydroxo), O_2^{2-} (peroxo), NH_2^- (amido) and NH^{2-} (imido). Note the following special points. Since SCN^- may coordinate through either S or N, the distinction, when known, is made using the terms thiocyanato-*S* and thiocyanato-*N*. The ion NO_2^- may coordinate via nitrogen, and is then called nitro, or through oxygen, when it is called nitrito.

b. For neutral ligands, the names are not systematic. For less common ones, the name of the free molecule is used as such. For some of the common ones, special names are used. The more important ones are H_2O (aquo), NH_3 (ammine), CO (carbonyl) and NO (nitrosyl).

2. *Naming of mononuclear complex ions.*

a. If the compound is ionic, the cation(s) are mentioned first (whether complex or not).

b. In naming the complex, whether it is cationic or neutral, the ligands are listed beginning with the negative ones, then the central metal is mentioned, followed by a roman numeral in parentheses giving its oxidation number. (0) is used for an oxidation state of zero.

c. If the complex is an anion, the suffix -*ate* is attached to the name of the central metal, and this suffix is followed by the oxidation number.

d. The number of each kind of ligand is specified using the Greek prefixes di-, tri-, tetra-, penta- and hexa-. The examples below illustrate these rules.

$[Co(NH_3)_6]Cl_3$	Hexaamminecobalt(III) chloride
$K_3[Al(C_2O_4)_3]$	Potassium trioxalatoaluminate(III)
$[Cr(H_2O)_4Cl_2]Cl$	Dichlorotetraaquochromium(III) chloride
$[Co(NH_3)_4(NO_2)Cl]NO_3$	Chloronitrotetramminecobalt(III) nitrate
$K_3[Co(CN)_5NO]$	Potassium pentacyanonitrosylcobaltate(III)
$K[PtCl_3(NH_3)]$	Potassium trichloroammineplatinate(II)
$[(CH_3)_4N]_2[Co(NCS)_4]$	Tetramethylammonium tetrathiocyanato-*N*-cobaltate(II)

3. *Dealing with complicated ligands.* When ligands themselves have polysyllabic names, perhaps containing numerical prefixes, they are closed in parentheses, and the number present is indicated by the prefixes bis, tris, tetrakis, pentakis, hexakis:

[Coen$_3$]Cl$_3$ — Tris(ethylenediamine)cobalt(III) chloride

[Co(H$_2$NCH$_2$CH$_2$NHCH$_2$CH$_2$HN$_2$)$_2$](NO$_3$)$_3$ — Bis(diethylenetriamine)cobalt(III) nitrate

Ni(PF$_3$)$_4$ — Tetrakis(phosphorus(III) fluoride)nickel(0)

[Fe(CN)(CNCH$_2$C$_6$H$_5$)$_5$]Cl — Cyanopentakis(benzylisocyanide)iron(II) chloride

4. *Bridged polynuclear complexes.* A bridging ligand is indicated by placing μ- before its name. The μ should be repeated before the name of each different bridging group. Some examples are

K$_3$[Cl$_3$TlCl$_3$TlCl$_3$] — Potassium trichlorothallium(III)-μ-trichlorotrichlorothallium(III), *or* Potassium hexachloro-μ-trichlorodithallium(III).

$$\left[(en)_2Co \underset{H}{\overset{NH}{\diagdown \diagup}} \underset{}{\overset{}{O}} Co(en)_2 \right]^{3+}$$ — Bis(ethylenediamine)cobalt(III)-μ-imido-μ-hydroxobis(ethylenediamine)cobalt(III)

[(H$_3$N)$_3$Co(OH)$_3$Co(NH$_3$)$_3$]$^{3+}$ — Triamminecobalt(III)-μ-trihydroxotriamminecobalt(III)

$$\left[(C_6H_5)_3P \underset{Cl}{\overset{Cl}{\diagup}} Pd \underset{Cl}{\overset{Cl}{\diagdown}} Pd \underset{P(C_6H_5)_3}{\overset{Cl}{\diagup}} \right]$$ — Chlorotriphenylphosphinepalladium(II)-μ-dichlorochlorotriphenylphosphinepalladium(II)

5. *Geometrical and optical isomerism.* In several of the examples used above, the names given are not quite complete, since no specification is made regarding the particular structural isomer. The kinds of isomers which can occur will be described next, at which time the necessary nomenclature will be introduced.

5-6. Stereoisomerism

Both geometrical and optical isomerism are encountered among coordination complexes. In the following outline, we shall restrict our attention to tetrahedral, square and octahedral complexes only.

Geometrical Isomers. Geometrical isomerism with respect to the metal has not been found among tetrahedral complexes, nor can it be expected except perhaps when some very complex and esoteric ligands might be involved.

In square complexes, several types of geometrical isomerism are of frequent occurrence.

1. Any complex of the type MA_2B_2 can exist in *cis* or *trans* forms:

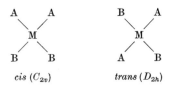

cis (C_{2v}) *trans* (D_{2h})

In a complex of the type MA_2BC, there are also *cis* and *trans* isomers. For a complex of the type MABCD, three isomers are possible, all of symmetry C_s, and all three have been isolated in several cases, such as in 5-XXII.

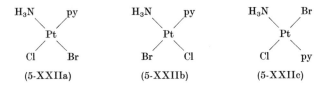

(5-XXIIa)   (5-XXIIb)   (5-XXIIc)

2. A chelate complex with substituents on the ring atoms can be expected to afford geometrical isomers which are *cis* (5-XXIIIa) and *trans* (5-XXIIIb) with respect to the median plane of the molecule.

cis (C_{2v}) *trans* (C_{2h})

(5-XXIIIa)   (5-XXIIIb)

3. In bridged binuclear planar complexes, *cis* (C_{2v}) (5-XXIVa) and *trans* (C_{2h}) (5-XXIVb) isomers as well as the "unsymmetrical" isomer

(5-XXIVa)   (5-XXIVb)   (5-XXIVc)

(C_{2v}) (5-XXIVc) are possible, although in the example cited, and in all other cases, only the first two have been found.

In octahedral complexes, several kinds of *cis–trans* isomerism are known, the most important ones being the *cis* (C_{2v}) (5-XXVa) and *trans* (D_{4h})

(5-XXVb) isomers in MA_4B_2 and the *cis* (C_{3v}) (5-XXVIa) and *trans* (C_{2v}) (5-XXVIb) isomers in MA_3B_3.

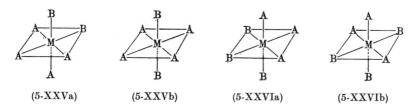

| (5-XXVa) | (5-XXVb) | (5-XXVIa) | (5-XXVIb) |

In naming compounds capable of existing in *cis* and *trans* isomers, the isomer intended is specified by placing the prefix with a hyphen before the name of the compound, for example, *cis*-dichlorotetraamminecobalt(III) chloride.

An alternative system of nomenclature* for octahedral complexes utilizes a numbering scheme, as shown in 5-XXVIIa. For the simpler

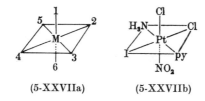

(5-XXVIIa)   (5-XXVIIb)

situations, e.g., those in 5-XXV and 5-XXVI, this is scarcely necessary, but in more complicated cases, e.g., 5-XXXIb, it is quite useful. For example, 5-XXVIIb is called 1,2-dichloro-4-iodo-6-nitro-3-pyridineammine-platinum(IV).

Optical Isomers. Of various conceivable types of optical isomers obtainable with tetrahedral complexes, only the kind which occurs in bis chelates with unsymmetrical ligands have been detected. These are of the general type 5-XXVIIIa and 5-XXVIIIb. The bis(salicylaldehydo)boron(III) anion, page 257, presents a case where resolution has been accomplished.

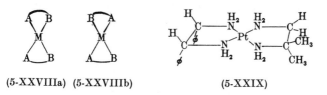

(5-XXVIIIa) (5-XXVIIIb)   (5-XXIX)

---

* For a more detailed and precise nomenclature, see R. F. Pasternak and P. M. McDonnell, *Inorg. Chem.*, **4**, 600 (1965).

Optical isomers occur only rarely among square complexes, the known cases involving rather unusual chelate ligands which are unsymmetrical. For example, the Pt^{II} complex (5-XXIX) was resolved, thus proving that the coordination is planar, for the tetrahedral form would have a plane of symmetry and therefore no optical isomerism. It has been shown that EDTA forms an anionic complex with Pd^{II} which can be resolved into optical isomers. These must be the antimers of 5-XXXa (symmetry C_2); the *cis* (C_s) isomer, 5-XXXb, was not detected.

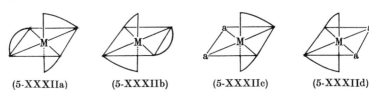

(5-XXXa)   (5-XXXb)

The most important cases of optical isomerism occur among octahedral complexes. Optical isomers can occur in nonchelate complexes with three or more different kinds of ligands and no more than two of any one kind, namely, in the cases $[Ma_2b_2c_2]$, $[Ma_2b_2cd]$, $[Ma_2bcde]$ and $[Mabcdef]$. For the $[Ma_2b_2c_2]$ case there are five geometrical isomers and 5-XXXI exists in optical isomers. 5-XXVIIb also exists in optical isomers. No resolution

(5-XXXIa)   (5-XXXIb)

of a complex containing only monodentate ligands has as yet been reported, however.

A great deal of work on optical isomerism has been done with octahedral complexes containing chelate ligands. The most common types are those containing three bidentate ligands or two bidentate and two monodentate ligands. The enantiomorphs in these cases are 5-XXXIIa (symmetry D_3) through 5-XXXIId (symmetry C_2). There are a vast number of complexes

(5-XXXIIa)   (5-XXXIIb)   (5-XXXIIc)   (5-XXXIId)

of these types, and many have been resolved. Resolution is usually achieved using cationic (e.g., $[Cr(en)_3]^{3+}$ or cis-$[Co(en)_2Cl_2]^+$) or anionic (e.g., $[Co(oxalato)_3]^{3-}$) species by fractional crystallization of the diastereoisomeric salts with optically active organic anions or cations. For example, a racemic mixture of cis-$[Coen_2Cl_2]Cl$ can be treated with ammonium d-α-bromocamphor-π-sulfonate to yield a mixture of diastereoisomers as indicated by the following equation:

$$\left\{\begin{matrix} \text{D-}[Coen_2Cl_2]Cl \\ \text{L-}[Coen_2Cl_2]Cl \end{matrix}\right\} + 2NH_4(d\text{-}C_{10}H_{14}BrO_4S) \rightarrow$$

$$\text{D-}[Coen_2Cl_2](d\text{-}C_{10}H_{14}BrO_4S) + \text{L-}[Coen_2Cl_2](d\text{-}C_{10}H_{14}BrO_4S) + 2NH_4Cl$$

The diastereoisomers, once separated, may then be treated with hydrochloric acid and the acid of the organic anion removed to allow recovery of the two optical isomers of $[Coen_2Cl_2]Cl$. Of course, resolution is not always possible for kinetic reasons. For example, there is scarcely any doubt that $[Znen_3]^{2+}$ and $[Nien_3]^{2+}$ have octahedral structures and exist as DL mixtures even though their antimers have never been separated. It is well known that the rates of reaction and rearrangement, as judged from tracer exchange experiments, are relatively fast for Ni^{II} and Zn^{II} complexes in general, and thus, an isolated antimer would racemize so quickly that its initial presence would be undetectable. With Cr^{III} and Co^{III} complexes, reaction rates are in general slow, requiring hours and even days for rearrangements to occur, so that isolated optical antimers are stable for hours and even days, but they do, of course, eventually racemize. We may also note that by a special X-ray diffraction technique, whereby X-rays of the same wavelength as an X-ray absorption edge of the metal ion are used (the technique of "anomalous dispersion"), the absolute configurations of the $[Coen_3]^{3+}$ ions have been determined.

Optical activity in complexes with hexadentate ligands has also been rather extensively studied. For example, the first of the hexadentate ligands shown in Table 5-2, which we will here represent simply as O—N—S—S—N—O, can arrange itself in four geometrically different ways (5-XXXIIIa–d) around an octahedral ion, and each of these geometrical isomers can exist in optical antimers. Detailed steric considerations, best appreciated by inspection of models, indicate that 5-XXXIIIa is much less strained than the others, and the green cation obtained with Co^{III}

(5-XXXIIIa)

(5-XXXIIIb)

(5-XXXIIIc)

(5-XXXIIId)

is assumed to have this structure. This cation has been resolved using an optically active anion, and the resulting optical antimers have the highest molecular rotations so far reported among complex compounds.

Complexes of ethylenediaminetetraacetic acid should also exist in optical antimers, and resolution of the cobalt(III) anions (5-XXXIV) has been accomplished.

(5-XXXIVa)   (5-XXXIVb)   (5-XXXVa)   (5-XXXVb)

When complexes in which the metal atoms themselves lie at centers of asymmetry (e.g., $[Coen_3]^{3+}$ and cis-$[Coen_2X_2]^+$ mentioned above) are made using ligands which contain centers of asymmetry, various diastereoisomers may be formed. For example, the ligand propylenediamine, pn, exists in optical antimers (5-XXXV). In $[Copn_3]^{3+}$ these may be grouped in eight ways. If we use D and L to indicate the configuration of the entire octahedral unit, and d and l to indicate the configurations of the ligand molecules (this being the standard nomenclature), the eight diastereoisomers may be specified as:

1. D-$[Co(l\text{-pn})_3]^{3+}$
2. D-$[Co(l\text{-pn})_2(d\text{-pn})]^{3+}$
3. D-$[Co(l\text{-pn})(d\text{-pn})_2]^{3+}$
4. D-$[Co(d\text{-pn})_3]^{3+}$
5. L-$[Co(l\text{-pn})_3]^{3+}$
6. L-$[Co(l\text{-pn})_2(d\text{-pn})]^{3+}$
7. L-$[Co(l\text{-pn})(d\text{-pn})_2]^{3+}$
8. L-$[Co(d\text{-pn})_3]^{3+}$

It has long been known that in systems of this kind the various diastereoisomers are not formed in statistically expected proportions, but instead certain ones are distinctly favored. For example, in the $[Co(l\text{-pn})_3]^{3+}$ system, the L complex is present in great excess over the D isomer, and when $[Co(l\text{-pn})_2Cl_2]^+$ is treated with d-pn, there is obtained a mixture of L-$[Co(l\text{-pn})_3]^{3+}$ and D-$[Co(d\text{-pn})_3]^{3+}$ rather than either of the diastereoisomers of the mixed complex $[Co(l\text{-pn})_2(d\text{-pn})]^{3+}$. The stereospecificities observed here and in similar equilibria can be understood by detailed consideration of the configurations and conformations of the ligands and the relative amounts of steric hindrance resulting in the several diastereoisomers.[15] In fact, the absolute configuration of D-$[Co(d\text{-pn})_3]^{3+}$ has been deduced and shown to agree with that found for D-$[Coen_3]^{3+}$ by the anomalous dispersion X-ray method mentioned above.

[15] E. J. Corey and J. C. Bailar, *J. Amer. Chem. Soc.*, **81**, 2620 (1959); see also R. D. Gillard and G. Wilkinson, *J. Chem. Soc.*, **1964**, 1368.

When the metal atom of a complex is a center of asymmetry the electronic transitions of the metal exhibit optical rotatory dispersion effects. These are discussed in Sections 25-11 and 25-12.

5-7. Other Types of Isomerism

1. *Ionization isomerism.* Compounds which have the same composition but yield different ions in solution are called ionization isomers. Some representative examples are: $[Co(NH_3)_4Cl_2]NO_2$ and $[Co(NH_3)_4(Cl)(NO_2)]Cl$; $[Coen_2(NO_2)Cl]SCN$, $[Coen_2(NO_2)(SCN)]Cl$ and $[Coen_2(SCN)Cl]NO_2$; $[Pt(NH_3)_4Cl_2]Br_2$ and $[Pt(NH_3)_4Br_2]Cl_2$.

A special case of this, often called hydrate isomerism, is sometimes encountered, as in the three isomers of $CrCl_3 \cdot 6H_2O$, which are correctly formulated as (1) $[Cr(H_2O)_6]Cl_3$—violet; does not lose water over H_2SO_4; all Cl^- immediately precipitated by Ag^+. (2) $[Cr(H_2O)_5Cl]Cl_2 \cdot H_2O$—green; loses one H_2O over H_2SO_4; two Cl^- immediately precipitated by Ag^+. (3) $[Cr(H_2O)_4Cl_2]Cl \cdot 2H_2O$—green; loses two H_2O over H_2SO_4; one Cl^- immediately precipitated by Ag^+. Additional evidence for these formulations is obtained from molar conductances which show them to be uni-tri-, uni-di- and uni-univalent electrolytes in the above order. An example involving both ionization and hydrate isomerism is provided by the compounds $[Co(NH_3)_4(H_2O)Cl]Br_2$ and $[Co(NH_3)_4Br_2]Cl \cdot H_2O$.

2. *Ligand isomerism.* Some ligands themselves can exist as isomers and be so incorporated into complexes. Thus there are both 1,2-diaminopropane (pn) and 1,3-diaminopropane, also called trimethylenediamine (tn) and the isomeric complexes $[Co(pn)_2Cl_2]Cl$ and $[Co(tn)_2Cl_2]Cl$.

3. *Linkage isomerism.* This occurs with ligands capable of coordinating in more than one way. The best-known simple cases are those involving nitro–nitrito isomerism, for example, the nitro isomer $[Co(NH_3)_5NO_2]^{2+}$ and the nitrito isomer $[Co(NH_3)_5ONO]^+$. The thiocyanate ion provides the only other known case, e.g., in the compounds $[Pddipy(SCN)_2]$ and $[Pddipy(NCS)_2]$.[16] Several other ligands (as well as NO_2^- and SCN^-), for instance $(NH_2)_2CO$ and $(CH_3)_2SO$, which are capable of coordinating at either of two different atoms are known to form the two types of bonds, but actual isomeric compounds have not yet been found. Such isomers are, of course, to be expected only for metal ions forming *inert* (see page 158) complexes.

4. *Coordination isomerism.* In compounds where both anion and cation are complex, the distribution of ligands between the two coordination spheres can vary, giving rise to isomers. This is illustrated by $[Co(NH_3)_6]$-

[16] F. Basolo, J. L. Burmeister and A. J. Poë, *J. Amer. Chem. Soc.*, **85**, 1700 (1963).

$[Cr(CN)_6]$ and $[Cr(NH_3)_6][Co(CN)_6]$; $[Co(NH_3)_6][Cr(C_2O_4)_3]$ and $[Cr(NH_3)_6]$-$[Co(C_2O_4)_3]$; $[Cu(NH_3)_4][PtCl_4]$ and $[Pt(NH_3)_4][CuCl_4]$; $[Co(en)_3]$-$[Cr(C_2O_4)_3]$, $[Co(en)_2(C_2O_4)][Cr(en)(C_2O_4)_2]$, $[Co(en)(C_2O_4)_2][Cr(en)_2(C_2O_4)]$ and $[Co(C_2O_4)_3][Cr(en)_3]$. Such isomerism may also occur even when the same metal atom occurs in cation and anion, for example, $[Cr(NH_3)_6]$-$[Cr(SCN)_6]$ and $[Cr(NH_3)_4(SCN)_2][Cr(NH_3)_2(SCN)_4]$; and $[Pt^{II}(NH_3)_4]$-$[Pt^{IV}Cl_6]$ and $[Pt^{IV}(NH_3)_4Cl_2][Pt^{II}Cl_4]$.

5. *Polymerization isomers.* These are not truly isomers, but they have classically been considered so. They are not isomers because they differ in size of the smallest representative unit, but they do have the same empirical composition. Some examples are $[Pt(NH_3)_2Cl_2]$ and $[Pt(NH_3)_4][PtCl_4]$; $[Co(NH_3)_3(NO_2)_3]$, $[Co(NH_3)_6][Co(NO_2)_6]$, $[Co(NH_3)_4(NO_2)_2][Co(NH_3)_2$-$(NO_2)_4]$, $[Co(NH_3)_5NO_2][Co(NH_3)_2(NO_2)_4]_2$, $[Co(NH_3)_6][Co(NH_3)_2$-$(NO_2)_4]_3$, $[Co(NH_3)_4(NO_2)_2]_3[Co(NO_2)_6]$ and $[Co(NH_3)_5(NO_2)]_3[Co(NO_2)_6]_2$-

STABILITY OF COMPLEX IONS IN SOLUTION

5-8. Introduction

When we speak of the stability of a compound, we should be careful to specify what kind of stability we mean. In studying the formation of coordination complexes in solution, two kinds of stability come into question, namely, thermodynamic stability and kinetic stability. The thermodynamic stability of a species is a measure of the extent to which this species will form from or be transformed into other species under certain conditions *when the system has reached equilibrium.* The kinetic stability of a species refers to the speed with which transformations leading to the attainment of equilibrium will occur. In this and the next several sections we will consider problems of thermodynamic stability, that is, the nature of equilibria once they are established. Kinetic problems are discussed on page 158.

Suppose we put a metal ion, M, and some monodentate ligand, L, together in solution. Assuming that no insoluble products are formed, nor any species containing more than one metal ion, equilibrium expressions of the following sort will describe the system:

$$M + L = ML \qquad K_1 = \frac{[ML]}{[M][L]}$$

$$ML + L = ML_2 \qquad K_2 = \frac{[ML_2]}{[ML][L]}$$

$$ML_2 + L = ML_3 \qquad K_3 = \frac{[ML_3]}{[ML_2][L]}$$

$$\cdot \qquad \cdot \qquad \cdot \qquad \cdot$$
$$\cdot \qquad \cdot \qquad \cdot \qquad \cdot$$

$$ML_{N-1} + L = ML_N \qquad K_N = \frac{[ML_N]}{[ML_{N-1}][L]}$$

There will be N such equilibria, where N represents the maximum co-ordination number of the metal ion M for the ligand L. N may vary from one ligand to another. For instance, Al^{3+} forms $AlCl_4^-$ and AlF_6^{3-}, and Co^{2+} forms $CoCl_4^-$ and $Co(NH_3)_6^{2+}$, as the highest complexes with the ligands indicated.

Another way of expressing the equilibrium relations is the following:

$$M + L = ML \qquad \beta_1 = \frac{[ML]}{[M][L]}$$

$$M + 2L = ML_2 \qquad \beta_2 = \frac{[ML_2]}{[M][L]^2}$$

$$M + 3L = ML_3 \qquad \beta_3 = \frac{[ML_3]}{[M][L]^3}$$

$$\cdot \qquad \cdot \qquad \cdot \qquad \cdot$$
$$\cdot \qquad \cdot \qquad \cdot \qquad \cdot$$
$$\cdot \qquad \cdot \qquad \cdot \qquad \cdot$$

$$M + NL = ML_N \qquad \beta_N = \frac{[ML_N]}{[M][L]^N}$$

Since there can be only N independent equilibria in such a system, it is clear that the K_i's and the β_i's must be related. The relationship is indeed rather obvious. Consider, for example, the expression for β_3. Let us multiply both numerator and denominator by $[ML][ML_2]$ and then re-arrange slightly:

$$\beta_3 = \frac{[ML_3]}{[M][L]^3} \cdot \frac{[ML][ML_2]}{[ML][ML_2]}$$

$$= \frac{[ML]}{[M][L]} \cdot \frac{[ML_2]}{[ML][L]} \cdot \frac{[ML_3]}{[ML_2][L]}$$

$$= K_1 K_2 K_3$$

It is not difficult to see that this kind of relationship is perfectly general, namely:

$$\beta_k = K_1 K_2 K_3 \ldots K_k = \prod_{i=1}^{i=k} K_i$$

The K_i's are called the *stepwise formation constants* (or stepwise stability constants), and the β_i's are called the *over-all formation constants* (or over-all stability constants); each type has its special convenience in certain cases.

In all of the above equilibria we have written the metal ion without specifying charge or degree of solvation. The former omission is obviously of no importance, for the equilibria may be expressed as above whatever the charges. It is also true that the equilibria may be treated as written without taking any explicit account of solvation of the ions, but the latter point is nonetheless of significance, and we shall therefore digress briefly to summarize some basic facts about aquo ions.

5-9. Condition of Ions in Aqueous Solution

We know that ions in solution interact with and in some sense bind the solvent molecules. From thermodynamic cycles the enthalpies of plunging gaseous metal ions into water can be estimated and the results, 10^2–10^3 kcal/mole (see Table 2-3), show that these interactions are very strong indeed. It is of importance in understanding the behavior of metal ions in aqueous solution to know how many water molecules each of these ions binds by direct metal–oxygen bonds. To put it another way, if we regard the ion as being an aquo complex, $[M(H_2O)_x]^{n+}$, which is then further and more loosely solvated, we wish to know the coordination number x and also the manner in which the x water molecules are arranged around the metal ion. Classical measurements of various types—for example, ion mobilities, apparent hydrated radii, entropies of hydration, etc.,—fail to give such detailed information because they cannot make any explicit distinction between those water molecules directly bonded to the metal—the x water molecules in the inner coordination sphere—and additional molecules which are held less strongly by hydrogen bonds to the water molecules of the inner coordination sphere. There are, however, ways of answering the question in many instances, ways depending, for the most part, on modern physical and theoretical developments. A few illustrative examples will be considered here.

For the transition metal ions, the spectral and, to a lesser degree, magnetic properties depend upon the constitution and symmetry of their surroundings. As a favorable but not essentially a typical example, the Co^{II} ion is known to form both octahedral and tetrahedral complexes. Thus, we might suppose that the aquo ion could be either $[Co(H_2O)_6]^{2+}$ with octahedral symmetry, or $[Co(H_2O)_4]^{2+}$ with tetrahedral symmetry. It is found that the spectrum and magnetism of Co^{II} in pink aqueous solutions of its salts with noncoordinating anions such as ClO_4^- or NO_3^- are very similar to the corresponding properties of octahedrally coordinated Co^{II} in general, and virtually identical with those of Co^{II} in such hydrated salts as $Co(ClO_4)_2 \cdot 6H_2O$ or $CoSO_4 \cdot 7H_2O$ where octahedral $[Co(H_2O)_6]^{2+}$ ions are known from X-ray studies definitely to exist. Complementing this, we have the fact that the spectral and magnetic properties of the many known tetrahedral Co^{II} complexes, such as $[CoCl_4]^{2-}$, $[CoBr_4]^{2-}$, $[Co(NCS)_4]^{2-}$ and $[(pyridine)_2CoCl_2]$, which have intense green, blue or purple colors, are completely different from those of Co^{II} in aqueous solution. Thus, there can scarely be any doubt that aqueous solutions of otherwise uncomplexed Co^{II} contain predominantly[17] well-defined, octahedral

---

[17] However, there are also *small* quantities of tetrahedral $[Co(H_2O)_4]^{2+}$. See **T. J. Swift**, *Inorg. Chem.*, **3**, 526 (1964).

$[Co(H_2O)_6]^{2+}$ ions, further hydrated, of course. Evidence of similar character can be adduced for many of the other transition metal ions. For all of the di- and tripositive ions of the first transition series, it is certain that the aquo ions are octahedral $[M(H_2O)_6]^{2(\text{or }3)+}$ species, although in those of Cr^{II}, Mn^{III} and Cu^{II} there are definite distortions of the octahedra because of the Jahn–Teller effect (see Section 26-6). Information on aquo ions of the second and third transition series, of which there are only a few, however, is not so certain. It is probable that the coordination is octahedral in many, but higher coordination numbers may occur.

For ions which do not have partly filled d shells, evidence of the kind mentioned is lacking, since such ions do not have spectral or magnetic properties related in a straightforward way to the nature of their coordination spheres. We are therefore not entirely sure about the state of aquation of many such ions, although nmr and other relaxation techniques have now supplied some such information. It should be noted that even when the existence of a well-defined aquo ion is certain, there are vast differences in the average length of time which a water molecule spends in the coordination sphere, the so-called mean residence time. For Cr^{III} and Rh^{III} this time is so long that on mixing a solution of $[Cr(H_2O)_6]^{3+}$ in ordinary water with water enriched in ^{18}O, many hours are required for complete equilibration of the enriched solvent water with the coordinated water. From a measurement of how many molecules of H_2O in the Cr^{III} and Rh^{III} solutions fail immediately to exchange with the enriched water added, the coordination numbers of these ions by water were shown to be 6. These cases are exceptional, however, Most other aquo ions are far more labile, and a similar equilibration would occur too rapidly to permit the same type of measurement. This particular rate problem is only one of several which will be discussed more fully in Section 5-14.

Aquo ions are all more or less acidic; that is, they dissociate in a manner represented by the equation:

$$[M(H_2O)_x]^{n+} = [M(H_2O)_{x-1}(OH)]^{(n-1)+} + H^+ \qquad K_A = \frac{[H^+][M(H_2O)_{x-1}(OH)]}{[M(H_2O)_x]}$$

The acidities vary widely, as the following K_A values show.

M in $[M(H_2O)_6]^{n+}$	K_A
Al^{III}	1.12×10^{-5}
Cr^{III}	1.26×10^{-4}
Fe^{III}	6.3×10^{-3}

Coordinated water molecules in other complexes also dissociate in the same way, for example,

$$[Co(NH_3)_5(H_2O)]^{3+} = [Co(NH_3)_5(OH)]^{2+} + H^+ \qquad K \approx 10^{-5.7}$$
$$[Pt(NH_3)_4(H_2O)_2]^{4+} = [Pt(NH_3)_4(H_2O)(OH)]^{3+} + H^+ \qquad K \approx 10^{-2}$$

5-10. The "Stepwise" Formation of Complexes

The series of stepwise formation constants, K_i's, have been described. These imply that all complexes in the series $ML \ldots ML_N$ can exist in the system; their proportions will depend, of course, on the concentrations [M] and [L] and on the relative values of the K_i's. With only a few exceptions, there is generally a slowly descending progression in the values of the K_i's in any particular system. This is illustrated by the data* for the Cd^{II}–NH_3 system where the ligands are uncharged and by the Cd^{II}–CN^- system where the ligands are charged.

$$Cd^{2+} + NH_3 = [Cd(NH_3)]^{2+} \qquad K = 10^{2.65}$$
$$[Cd(NH_3)]^{2+} + NH_3 = [Cd(NH_3)_2]^{2+} \qquad K = 10^{2.10}$$
$$[Cd(NH_3)_2]^{2+} + NH_3 = [Cd(NH_3)_3]^{2+} \qquad K = 10^{1.44}$$
$$[Cd(NH_3)_3]^{2+} + NH_3 = [Cd(NH_3)_4]^{2+} \qquad K = 10^{0.93} \ (\beta_4 = 10^{7.12})$$

$$Cd^{2+} + CN^- = [Cd(CN)]^+ \qquad K = 10^{5.48}$$
$$[Cd(CN)]^+ + CN^- = [Cd(CN)_2] \qquad K = 10^{5.12}$$
$$[Cd(CN)_2] + CN^- = [Cd(CN)_3]^- \qquad K = 10^{4.63}$$
$$[Cd(CN)_3]^- + CN^- = [Cd(CN)_4]^{2-} \qquad K = 10^{3.55} \ (\beta_4 = 10^{18.8})$$

Thus, typically, as ligand is added to the solution of metal ion, ML first forms more rapidly than any other complexes in the series. As addition of ligand is continued, the ML_2 concentration rises rapidly, while the ML concentration drops, then ML_3 becomes dominant, ML and ML_2 becoming unimportant, and so forth until the highest complex, ML_N, is formed to the nearly complete exclusion of all others at very high ligand concentrations. From the formation constants given above for the Cd–CN system, graphical pictures of these relations may be drawn, as shown in Figure 5-4.

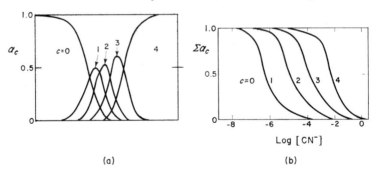

(a)   (b)

Fig. 5-4. Plots of the proportions of the various complexes $[Cd(CN)_c]^{(2-c)+}$ as a function of the ligand concentration:

$$\alpha_c = [Cd(CN)_c]/\text{total Cd} \qquad \sum \alpha_c = \sum_{c=0}^{4} [Cd(CN)_c]$$

(Reproduced by permission from F. J. C. Rossotti in J. Lewis and R. G. Wilkins, eds., *Modern Coordination Chemistry*, Interscience, New York–London, 1960, p. 10.)

* Cd–NH_3 constants determined in $2M$ NH_4NO_3; Cd–CN constants determined in $3M$ $NaClO_4$.

A steady decrease in K_i values with increasing i is to be expected provided there are only slight changes in the metal–ligand bond energies as a function of i, which is usually the case. For example, in the Ni^{2+}–NH_3 system to be discussed below, the enthalpies of the successive reactions $Ni(NH_3)_{i-1} + NH_3 = Ni(NH_3)_i$ are all within the range of 4.0–4.3 kcal/mole.

There are several reasons for a steady decrease in K_i values as the number of ligands increases: (1) statistical factors; (2) increased steric hindrance as the number of ligands increases if they are bulkier than the H_2O molecules they replace; (3) coulombic factors, mainly in complexes with charged ligands. The statistical factors may be treated in the following way. Suppose, as is almost certainly the case for Ni^{2+}, that the coordination number remains the same throughout the series $[M(H_2O)_N] \ldots$ $[M(H_2O)_{N-n}L_n] \ldots [ML_N]$. The $[M(H_2O)_{N-n}L_n]$ species has n sites from which to lose a ligand, whereas the species $[M(H_2O)_{N-n+1}L_{n-1}]$ has $(N - n + 1)$ sites at which to gain a ligand. Thus the relative probability of passing from $[M(H_2O)_{N-n+1}L_{n-1}]$ to $[M(H_2O)_{N-n}L_n]$ is proportional to $(N - n + 1)/n$. Similarly, the relative probability of passing from $[M(H_2O)_{N-n}L_n]$ to $[M(H_2O)_{N-n-1}L_{n+1}]$ is proportional to $(N - n)/(n + 1)$. Hence, on the basis of these statistical considerations alone, we expect

$$K_{n+1}/K_n = \frac{(N - n)}{n + 1} \div \frac{N - n + 1}{n} = \frac{n(N - n)}{(n + 1)(N - n + 1)}$$

In the Ni^{2+}–NH_3 system $(N = 6)$, we find the comparison between experimental ratios of successive constants and those calculated from the above formula to be as shown in Table 5-3. The experimental ratios are consistently smaller than the statistically expected ones, which is typical and shows that other factors are also of importance.

There are cases where the experimental ratios of the constants do not remain constant or change monotonically; instead, one of them is singularly large or small. There are several reasons for this: (1) an abrupt change in coordination number and hybridization at some stage of the sequence of complexes, (2) special steric effects which become operative only at a certain stage of coordination and (3) an abrupt change in electronic structure of the metal ion at a certain stage of complexation. Each of these will now be illustrated.

TABLE 5-3

	Experimental	Statistical
K_2/K_1	0.28	0.417
K_3/K_2	0.31	0.533
K_4/K_3	0.29	0.562
K_5/K_4	0.36	0.533
K_6/K_5	0.2	0.417

Values of K_3/K_2 are anomalously low for the halogeno complexes of mercury(II); HgX_2 species are linear, whereas $[HgX_4]^{2-}$ species are tetrahedral. Presumably the change from sp to sp^3 hybridization occurs on going from HgX_2 to $[HgX_3]^-$. K_3/K_2 is anomalously small for the ethylenediamine complexes of Zn^{II}, and this is believed to be due to the change from sp^3 to sp^3d^2 hybridization if it is assumed that $[Znen_2]^{2+}$ is tetrahedral. For the Ag^+-NH_3 system $K_2 > K_1$, indicating that the linear, sp-hybridized structure probably is attained with $[Ag(NH_3)_2]^+$ but not with $[Ag(NH_3)(H_2O)_{3(or\ 5)}]^+$.

(5-XXXVI)

With 6,6'-dimethyl-2,2'-dipyridyl (5-XXXVI), many metal ions which form tris-2,2'-dipyridyl complexes form only bis or mono complexes, or, in some cases, no isolable complexes at all, because of the steric hindrance between the methyl groups and other ligands attached to the ion.

In the series of complexes of Fe^{II} with 1,10-phenanthroline (and also with 2,2'-dipyridyl), K_3 is greater than K_2. This is because the tris complex is diamagnetic (i.e., the ferrous ion has the low-spin state* t_{2g}^6), whereas in the mono and bis complexes, as in the aquo ion, there are four unpaired electrons. This change from the $t_{2g}^4e_g^2$ to the t_{2g}^6 causes the enthalpy change for addition of the third ligand to be anomalously large because the e_g electrons are antibonding.

5-11. The Chelate Effect

This term refers to the enhanced stability of a complex system containing one or more chelate rings as compared to the stability of a system which is as similar as possible without containing the rings. As an example, consider the equilibrium constants for the following three systems of nickel–amine complexes:

$$Ni^{2+} + 2NH_3 = [Ni(NH_3)_2]^{2+} \qquad \log \beta = 5.00$$
$$Ni^{2+} + 4NH_3 = [Ni(NH_3)_4]^{2+} \qquad \log \beta = 7.87$$
$$Ni^{2+} + 6NH_3 = [Ni(NH_3)_6]^{2+} \qquad \log \beta = 8.61$$
$$Ni^{2+} + en = [Nien]^{2+} \qquad \log \beta = 7.51$$
$$Ni^{2+} + 2en = [Nien_2]^{2+} \qquad \log \beta = 13.86$$
$$Ni^{2+} + 3en = [Nien_3]^{2+} \qquad \log \beta = 18.28$$

$$Ni^{2+} + (NH_2CH_2CH_2)_2NCH_2CH_2N(CH_2CH_2NH_2)_2$$
$$= complex \qquad \log \beta = 19.3$$

* The nomenclature t_{2g}^6, $t_{2g}^4e_g^2$ is described in Chapter 26.

The overall stability constants for forming complexes with six Ni—N bonds, 8.6, 18.3, 19.3, show that the formation of chelate rings has a considerable stabilizing influence, which increases as the number of rings increases. It should be noted, however, that part of the great increase in stability from $[Ni(NH_3)_6]^{2+}$ to $[Nien_3]^{2+}$ is due to the formation of stronger Ni—N bonds by the aliphatic amine, according to direct calorimetric measurements of the enthalpies of reaction.

It has also been established that five-membered rings are more stable than comparable six-membered rings, providing no special resonance effects are involved, as shown, for example, by data for Cu^{II} complexes of en, $H_2N(CH_2)_2NH_2$, and tn, $H_2N(CH_2)_3NH_2$.

$$Cu^{2+} + en = [Cuen]^{2+} \qquad \log \beta = 10.72$$
$$Cu^{2+} + 2en = [Cuen_2]^{2+} \qquad \log \beta = 20.03$$
$$Cu^{2+} + tn = [Cutn]^{2+} \qquad \log \beta = 9.98$$
$$Cu^{2+} + 2tn = [Cutn_2]^{2+} \qquad \log \beta = 17.17$$

This decreasing stability with increasing ring size continues so that there are few complexes known with seven-membered rings and none with larger rings.

In order to understand the chelate effect properly, we must consider in more detail the thermodynamic significance of the stability constants. First of all, we note that an equilibrium constant is a measure of the standard free energy of the reaction, that is,

$$\Delta G^0 = -RT \ln K$$

There is also the following relation between the free energy change and the enthalpy and entropy changes:

$$\Delta G^0 = \Delta H^0 - T\Delta S^0$$

Thus an increase in an equilibrium constant may arise because ΔH^0 becomes more negative, because ΔS^0 becomes more positive, or both.

In the formation of a complex, ΔH^0 is attributable mainly to the difference in bond energies of the metal–oxygen bonds broken and the new metal–ligand bonds formed. Experimental studies of the enthalpy changes for the various reactions mentioned above, as well as for a number of others, have shown that enthalpy differences between chelated and nonchelated systems cannot in general account for the chelate effect. Hence, the chelate effect must be mainly an entropy effect, and, from the measured values of the equilibrium constants and enthalpies, the ΔS^0 values may be calculated. The general result is, as it must be, that increasing chelation corresponds to increasingly positive values of ΔS^0 in the formation of the complexes.

The physical reason for the favorable entropies of chelation reactions is not difficult to appreciate in a qualitative way. To do so, we must recognize that when atoms of the ligand enter the coordination sphere, water molecules are necessarily displaced. Now, one contribution to an increase in the entropy or disorder of the system is an increase in the number of free molecules. Thus, in a nonchelate system, each water molecule is displaced by one ligand molecule, and the total number of molecules in the system remains constant. In chelation reactions, one ligand molecule displaces two or more water molecules, so that the net number of more or less independent molecules increases. Another more pictorial way to look at the problem is to visualize a chelate ligand with one end attached to the metal ion. The other end cannot then get very far away, and the probability of it, too, becoming attached to the metal atom is greater than if this other end were instead another independent molecule which would then have access to a much larger volume of the solution. This latter view provides an explanation for the decreasing magnitude of the chelate effect with increasing ring size. If the ring which must be formed becomes sufficiently large (seven-membered or more), it becomes more probable that the other end of the chelate molecule will contact another metal ion than that it will come around to the first one and complete the ring.

An interesting but easily understood exception to the considerations outlined above is the Ag^I ion, which has a characteristic coordination number of 2 for amine ligands, with the two Ag–ligand bonds lying collinearly. For five- and six-membered rings, the requirement that one angle be 180° prevents closure, and, for rings sufficiently large to close despite the 180° angle, the probability of ring closure becomes negligible irrespective of the angles. Thus, bicoordinate Ag^I forms no chelated complexes. There are some ligands such as diphosphines which form tetrahedral complexes with Ag^I, and in this case of course chelate rings can be stable.

KINETICS AND MECHANISMS IN REACTIONS OF COMPLEX IONS

5-12. Introduction

There are many reactions of complexes in which the composition of the coordination sphere changes. Included in this category are those in which complexes are formed from the metal ions and the ligands, since the "uncomplexed" metal ions are actually aquo complexes. The ability of a particular complex ion to engage in reactions which result in replacing one or more ligands in its coordination sphere by others is called its *lability*. Those complexes for which reactions of this type are very rapid are called *labile*, whereas those for which such reactions proceed only slowly or not at all are called *inert*. It is important to emphasize that these two terms refer to rates of reactions and should not be confused with the terms stable and unstable which refer to the thermodynamic tendency of species to exist under equilibrium conditions. A simple example of this distinction is provided by the $[Co(NH_3)_6]^{3+}$ ion which will persist for days in an acid medium because of its kinetic inertness or lack of lability despite the fact that it is thermodynamically unstable, as the following equilibrium constant shows:

$$[Co(NH_3)_6]^{3+} + 6H_3O^+ = [Co(H_2O)_6]^{3+} + 6NH_4^+ \qquad K \sim 10^{25}$$

In contrast, the stability of $Ni(CN)_4^{2-}$ is extremely high,

$$[Ni(CN)_4]^{2-} = Ni^{2+} + 4CN^- \qquad K \sim 10^{-22}$$

but the rate of exchange of CN^- ions with isotopically labeled CN^- added to the solution is immeasurably fast by ordinary techniques. Of course this lack of any necessary relation between thermodynamic stability and kinetic lability is to be found generally in chemistry, but its appreciation here is especially important.

In the first transition series, virtually all octahedral complexes save those of Cr^{III} and Co^{III} are normally labile; that is, ordinary complexes come to equilibrium with additional ligands, including H_2O, so rapidly that the reactions appear instantaneous by ordinary techniques of kinetic measurement. Complexes of Cr^{III} and Co^{III} ordinarily undergo ligand replacement reactions with half-times of the order of hours, days or even weeks at 25°, thus making them convenient systems for detailed kinetic and mechanistic study. Some of the factors responsible for the great range of reaction rates will be discussed later (sec. 5-14, page 163).

In recent years increasing attention has been devoted to detailed kinetic studies of ligand replacement reactions with the objective of learning details of the mechanisms by which such reactions take place. Although a great deal remains to be done, some important advances have been made. The range of systems accessible to study depends on the experimental techniques available. At present the techniques can be classified into three broad categories; reaction rates for which they are generally used are indicated by the half times:

1. Static methods ($t_{\frac{1}{2}} \geq 1$ min)
2. Flow or rapid-mixing techniques (1 min $\geq t_{\frac{1}{2}} \geq 10^{-3}$ sec)
3. Relaxation methods ($t_{\frac{1}{2}} \leq 0.1$ sec)

As a more explicit definition of the terms inert and labile, we may adopt an operational definition (due in a slightly different form to Taube) which says that complexes whose reactions may be studied by static methods are inert and the faster ones labile. The static methods are the classical ones in which reactants are mixed simply by pouring them both into one vessel and the progress of the reaction then followed by observation of the time variation of some physical or chemical observable (e.g., light absorption, gas evolution, pH, isotopic exchange). Flow and rapid-mixing techniques differ mainly in achieving rapid mixing (in $\sim 10^{-3}$ sec) of the reactants, but use many of the same observational techniques as in static measurements. Relaxation methods are relatively new and have enormously increased the field accessible to study. They depend either (a) on creating a single disturbance in a state of equilibrium in a very short period of time (usually by a temperature or pressure jump) and following the process of relaxation to an equilibrium state by a combination of spectrophotometric and fast electronic recording devices, or (b) upon continuous disturbances by ultrasonic waves or radiofrequency signals in presence of a magnetic field (i.e., nmr). The latter methods are capable of following the very fastest reactions, and in many cases rate constants up to the limit ($\sim 10^{10}$ sec^{-1}) set by diffusion processes have been measured by ultrasonic methods.

The *direct* result of a kinetic study can at best be a *rate law*, that is, an equation showing how the velocity, v, of a reaction at a given temperature and in a given medium, varies as a function of the concentration of the reactants. Certain constants, k_i, called *rate constants*, will appear in the rate law. For example, a rate law for the reaction

$$A + B = C + D$$

might be

$$v = k_a[A] + k_{ab}[A][B] + k'_{ab}[A][B][H^+]^{-1}$$

This would mean that the reaction occurs by three detectable paths, one influenced only by [A], a second influenced by [A] and [B] and a third which depends also on pH. The third term shows that not only A and B, but also [OH$^-$] (since this is related inversely to [H$^+$]), participate in the activated complex when this path is followed.

The ultimate purpose of a rate and mechanism study is usually to *interpret* the rate law correctly so as to determine the correct *mechanism* for the reaction. By mechanism, we mean a specification of what species actually combine to produce activated complexes, and what steps occur before and/or after the formation of the activated complex.*

---

* We do not attempt here to explain or justify most of the reaction rate theory which must underlie any discussion of kinetics and mechanisms. The few brief definitions have been given only as reminders, or where the concepts are particularly important in the following discussion. Readers lacking the necessary elementary understanding of chemical kinetics are referred to standard physical chemistry texts or to several of the books cited in the reference list, especially those of Edwards and King.

5-13. Possible Mechanisms for Ligand Replacement Reactions

Two extreme mechanistic possibilities may be considered for such reactions. First, there is the S_N1 mechanism, in which the complex dissociates, losing the ligand to be replaced, the vacancy in the coordination shell then being taken by the new ligand. This path may be represented as follows

$$[L_5MX]^{n+} \xrightarrow{\text{slow}} X^- + \underset{\substack{\text{Five-coordinated}\\\text{intermediate}}}{[L_5M]^{(n+1)+}} \xrightarrow[\text{fast}]{+Y^-} [L_5MY]^{n+} \qquad (5\text{-}1)$$

The important feature here is that the first step, in which X^- is lost, proceeds *relatively* slowly and thus determines the rate at which the complete process can proceed. In other words, once it is formed, the intermediate complex, which is only five coordinated, will react with the new ligand, Y^-, almost instantly. The rate law for such a process is:

$$v = k[L_5MX] \qquad (5\text{-}2)$$

When this mechanism is operative, the rate of the reaction necessarily is directly proportional to the concentration of $[L_5MX]^{n+}$ but independent of the concentration of the new ligand, Y^-. The symbol S_N1 stands for *substitution, nucleophilic, unimolecular*. The other extreme pathway for a ligand exchange is the S_N2 mechanism. In this case the new ligand attacks the original complex directly to form a seven-coordinated activated complex which then ejects the displaced ligand, as indicated in the following scheme:

$$[L_5MX]^{n+} + Y^- \xrightarrow{\text{slow}} \left\{ \left[L_5M \underset{Y}{\overset{X}{\diagup}} \right]^{(n-1)+} \right\} \xrightarrow{\text{fast}} [L_5MY]^{n+} + X^- \qquad (5\text{-}3)$$

When this mechanism is operative, the rate of the reaction will be proportional to the concentration of $[L_5MX]^{n+}$ times that of Y^-, the rate law being

$$v = k[L_5MX][Y^-] \qquad (5\text{-}4)$$

The symbol S_N2 stands for *substitution, nucleophilic, bimolecular*.

Unfortunately, these two extreme mechanisms are just that—extremes—and real mechanisms are seldom so simple. It is more realistic to recognize that it is likely that some degree of bond formation will occur before bond breaking is complete, that is, that the transition state may not be either the truly 5-coordinate species or the one in which the *leaving* and *entering* groups are both strongly bound at once. Subsequently, we shall use the terms S_N1 and S_N2 not to imply necessarily the extremes, but to describe mechanisms which may only approximate to these extremes.

6 + A.I.C.

To complicate matters further, a rate law of type (5-2) or (5-4) does not *prove* that the reaction proceeds by an S_N1 or S_N2 mechanism, even approximately. The three most important cases in illustration of this are (1) solvent intervention, (2) ion pair formation and (3) conjugate base formation.

(1) *Solvent intervention.* Most reactions of complexes have been studied in water, which is itself a ligand and which is present in high and effectively constant concentration ($\sim 55.5M$). Thus, the rate law (5-2) might be observed even if the actual course of the reaction were

$$[L_5MX] + H_2O \longrightarrow [L_5MH_2O] + X \quad \text{slow} \qquad (5\text{-}5a)$$
$$[L_5MH_2O] + Y \longrightarrow [L_5MY] + H_2O \quad \text{fast} \qquad (5\text{-}5b)$$

Moreover, we would not be able to tell from the rate law alone whether either (5-5a) or (5-5b) proceeded by S_N1 or S_N2 type processes.

(2) *Ion pair formation.* When the reacting complex is a cation and the entering group is an anion, especially when one or both have high charges, ion pairs (or *outer sphere complexes,* as they are also called) will form to some extent,

$$[L_5MX]^{n+} + Y^{m-} = \{[L_5MX]Y\}^{n-m} \qquad (5\text{-}6)$$

with an equilibrium constant K. These equilibrium constants can be estimated from theory or by comparison with measurements on systems where no subsequent reaction occurs, and they are generally in the range of 0.1–20. Now if the only path by which $[L_5MX]^{n+}$ and Y^{m-} can react with significant velocity involves preliminary formation of the ion pair, then the rate law might* be

$$v = k'K[L_5MX][Y] = k''[L_5MX][Y] \qquad (5\text{-}7)$$

But the only *kinetic* observation will be a rate law of type (5-4) and only by additional experiments can we learn whether the reaction is truly an S_N2 type in the sense of equation (5-3) or whether the ion pair is involved. Even if it can be shown that the ion pair is involved (and this is frequently determinable) the question of how the ion pair transforms itself into the products remains unanswered, because S_N1, S_N2 or solvent participation processes might all occur.

---

* Rigorously, the velocity for such a process is given by the equation

$$v = \frac{k'K[L_5MX][Y]}{1 + K[Y]}$$

which reduces to equation (5-7) when $K[Y] \ll 1$. Thus, if [Y] can be made sufficiently large (say $\sim 1M$) and if K exceeds ~ 0.1, careful measurements can provide kinetic evidence against a simple bimolecular mechanism. Such experiments are not often possible in aqueous solution, but in some non-aqueous solvents, where K values can become large, they are generally feasible.

(3) *Conjugate base formation.* Whenever a rate law involving $[OH^-]$ is found, there is the question whether OH^- actually attacks the metal giving an S_N2 reaction in the sense of (5-3), or whether it appears in the rate law because it first reacts rapidly to remove a proton from a ligand, forming the conjugate base (CB), which then reacts, as in the following sequence

$$[Co(NH_3)_5Cl]^{2+} + OH^- = [Co(NH_3)_4(NH_2)Cl]^+ + H_2O \quad \text{fast} \qquad (5\text{-}8a)$$

$$[Co(NH_3)_4(NH_2)Cl]^+ \xrightarrow[\text{then } H^+]{+ Y^-} [Co(NH_3)_5Y]^{2+} + Cl^- \qquad \text{slow} \qquad (5\text{-}8b)$$

In cases where 5-8b proceeds by an S_N1 mechanism, the overall mechanism represented by 5-8a and 5-8b is called an S_N1CB mechanism. Of course, in cases where there are no protonic hydrogen atoms available (or if it is known that a process like (5-8a) is too slow) the appearance of $[OH^-]$ in the rate law probably does indicate an authentic S_N2 process.

It may be noted here that rate laws are often written with terms $[H^+]^{-n}$, like the third term in the law for the hypothetic reaction $A + B = C + D$ above. It should be recognized that this is equivalent to using $[OH^-]^n$, since

$$k[H^+]^{-n} = k'K_w^n[OH^-]^n$$

5-14. Water Exchange and Formation of Complexes from Aquo Ions

Our knowledge of this subject depends almost entirely upon the results of relaxation measurements, since nearly all the reactions are very fast. As an important special case, we will first consider the rates at which aquo ions exchange water molecules with solvent water. Except for $Cr(H_2O)_6^{3+}$, with a half time of $\sim 3.5 \times 10^5$ sec and an activation energy of 27 kcal/mole and $[Rh(H_2O)_6]^{3+}$, which is still slower ($E_{act} \approx 33$ kcal/mole), these reactions are all fast as shown in Figure 5-5. It will be seen that though they are all "fast" a range of some 10 orders of magnitude is spanned. These data therefore provide a good base for tackling the question of what factors influence the rates of reaction of similar complexes of different metal ions.

First, by considering the alkali and alkaline earth ions, the influence of size and charge may be seen. Within each group the rate of exchange increases with size, and for M^+ and M^{2+} ions of similar size, the one of lower charge exchanges most rapidly. Since M—OH_2 bond strength should increase with charge and decrease with size of the metal ion, these correlations suggest that the transition state for the exchange reaction is attained by breaking an existing M—OH_2 bond to a much greater extent than a new one is formed; that is, that the mechanism lies toward the

S_N1 extreme. It may be noted that there is a similar decrease in lability with increasing formal charge in the series $AlF_6^{3-} > SiF_6^{2-} > PF_6^- > SF_6$. Again the supposition is that exchange (and other) reactions of these species occur by an S_N1 mechanism.

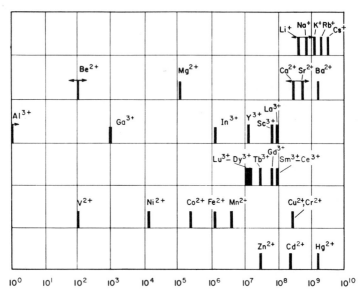

Fig. 5-5. Characteristic rate constants (sec^{-1}) for substitutions of inner sphere H_2O of various aquo ions. (Adapted from M. Eigen, *Pure Appl. Chem.*, **6**, 105 (1963), with revised data kindly provided by M. Eigen.)

Referring again to Figure 5-5 it will be seen that other series, i.e., (Al^{3+}, Ga^{3+}, In^{3+}), (Sc^{3+}, Y^{3+}) and (Zn^{2+}, Cd^{2+}, Hg^{2+}) also obey the radius rule. There are, however, several cases in which two ions of about the same size disobey the charge rule, i.e., the more highly charged ion exchanges faster. Such exceptions are thought to be due to differences in coordination numbers, but this is not quite certain.

It will also be noted that the divalent transition metal ions do not follow the charge and radius rules very well. There are at least two additional factors involved here. With Cu^{2+}, the coordination polyhedron is not a regular octahedron, but rather, two bonds are very much longer and weaker than the other four (see Sect. 29-H-3). By way of these, the rate of exchange is thus increased. Secondly, for most transition metal ions the rates of ligand exchange reactions are influenced by the changes in d-electron energies as the coordination changes from that in the reactant to that in the transition state. This will always increase the activation energy and hence decrease the rate, but the magnitude of the effect is not monotonically related to the atomic number; rather, it varies irregularly from ion to ion. The nature of this will be explained in detail later when electronic structures of transition metal complexes are discussed (Chapter 26).

Extensive studies of the rates at which an aquo ion combines with a ligand to form a complex have revealed the following remarkable general rules.

(1) The rates for a given ion show little or no dependence (less than a factor of 10) on the identity of the ligand.

(2) The rates for each ion are practically the same as the rate of water exchange for that ion, usually ~ 10 times slower.

It is believed that the only reasonable explanation for these observations is that the formation reactions proceed in two steps, the first being formation of the aquo ion-ligand or outer sphere complex, followed by elimination of H_2O from the aquo ion in the same manner as in the water exchange process. When the observed rate constants are divided by estimated ion pair formation constants, numbers very close to the water exchange rate constants are obtained, generally to within the uncertainties in the estimated ion pair formation constants. It is even found that activation energies and entropies, where available, are essentially the same for the two processes.

One slow complex formation reaction which has been studied in detail is that of equation 5-9.

$$Cr(H_2O)_6^{3+} + NCS^- = Cr(H_2O)_5NCS^{2+} + H_2O \qquad (5\text{-}9)$$

The rate law was found to be

$$v = [Cr(H_2O)_6^{3+}][NCS^-](k_1 + k_2[H^+]^{-1} + k_3[H^+]^{-2}) \qquad (5\text{-}10)$$

From this it is concluded that there are three important paths, involving $Cr(H_2O)_6^{3+}$, $Cr(H_2O)_5(OH)^{2+}$ and $Cr(H_2O)_4(OH)_2^+$ as reactants. The dependence on $[NCS^-]$ does not by itself prove that the mechanism is S_N2, since the following path

$$Cr(H_2O)_6^{3+} \underset{k_{-a}}{\overset{k_a}{\rightleftharpoons}} Cr(H_2O)_5^{3+} + H_2O \qquad (5\text{-}11a)$$

$$Cr(H_2O)_5^{3+} + NCS^- \overset{k_b}{\rightleftharpoons} Cr(H_2O)_5NCS^{2+} \qquad (5\text{-}11b)$$

will also lead to the same rate law (using the appropriate hydroxo complexes for the second and third terms) provided that* $k_{-a} \gg k_b[NCS^-]$. In fact, this is true since the rate of water exchange is about 25 times faster than the rate of reaction (5-9). Thus the rate law does not, from a purely

* This well-known result for this type of reaction sequence is proved in textbooks on chemical kinetics.

algebraic point of view, distinguish between S_N1 and S_N2 mechanisms. However, it is also found that the relative values of the rate constants in (5-10) is $k_3 > k_2 > k_1$. This order is consistent with an S_N1 process, but inconsistent with an S_N2 process.

The metal ion–water exchange (or elimination) process must also be the principal rate determining feature in the early stages of hydrolytic polymerization of many metal ions. For instance, the following reaction

$$2Fe(OH)^{2+} = Fe_2(OH)_2^{4+}$$

has a rate constant of $4.5 \times 10^2 M^{-1} \sec^{-1}$ at $25°$, and considering the adverse effect of the like charges of the combining species, this is in reasonable accord with the water exchange rate for $Fe(OH)^{2+}$, namely $\sim 3 \times 10^4 \sec^{-1}$ at $25°$.

5-15. Ligand Displacement Reactions in Octahedral Complexes

A general equation for a ligand displacement reaction is

$$[L_nMX] + Y = [L_nMY] + X$$

In aqueous solution the special case in which Y is H_2O (or OH^-) is of overwhelming importance. It appears that there are few, if any, reactions in which X is not first replaced by H_2O, and only then does the other ligand, Y, enter the complex by displacing H_2O. Thus our discussion will be restricted almost entirely to the subject of the *aquation* or *hydrolysis* reaction.

The rates of hydrolyses of cobalt(III) ammine complexes are pH dependent and generally follow the rate law

$$v = k_A[L_5CoX] + k_B[L_5CoX][OH^-] \tag{5-12}$$

In general, k_B (for *base hydrolysis*) is some 10^5–10^6 times k_A (for *acid hydrolysis*). The interpretation of this rate law has occasioned an enormous amount of experimental study and discussion, but as yet there is nothing approaching a complete and generally accepted interpretation. Here, we can but touch on a few main aspects of the problem.

Acid Hydrolysis. We turn first to the term $k_A[L_5CoX]$. Since the entering ligand is H_2O, which is present in high ($\sim 55.5M$) and effectively constant concentration, the rate law tells us *nothing* as to the order in H_2O; the means for deciding whether this is an S_N1 or an S_N2 process must be sought elsewhere.

Among the most thoroughly studied systems are those involving

$[Co(NH_3)_5X]$. There are various kinds of data, some of which favor a predominantly S_N1 mechanism, but the question can perhaps most safely be described as unresolved. To illustrate the work which has been done, the following points may be mentioned.

(1) The variation of rates with the identity of X correlates well with the variation in thermodynamic stability of the complexes. This indicates that breaking the Co—X bond is at least important in reaching the transition state.

(2) In a series of complexes where X is a carboxylate ion, there is not only the correlation of higher rates with lower basicity of the $RCOO^-$ group, but an *absence* of any slowing down due to increased size of R, after due allowance for the basicity effect. For an S_N2 mechanism, increased size of R should decrease the rate, at least if the attack were on the same side as X, although an attack on the *opposite* side is not excluded by these data.

(3) In the case where X is H_2O, that is, for the water exchange reaction, the pressure dependence of the rate has been measured and the volume of activation found to be $+1.2$ ml per mole. This result definitely excludes a predominantly S_N2 mechanism, but it does not agree satisfactorily with an extreme S_N1 mechanism either. It is most consistent with a transition state in which the initial Co—OH_2 bond is stretched quite far while formation of a new Co—*OH_2 bond is only beginning to occur, that is, a predominantly S_N1 mechanism.

(4) For an extreme S_N1 mechanism, the five coordinate intermediate $Co(NH_3)_5^{3+}$ would be generated and the behavior of this would be independent of its source. In studies where the ions Hg^{2+}, Ag^+ and Tl^{3+} were used to assist in removal of Cl^-, Br^- and I^- because of their high affinity for these halide ions, the ratio H_2O^{18}/H_2O^{16} in the product was studied. For a genuine $Co(NH_3)_5^{3+}$ intermediate this ratio should be >1 and constant regardless of the identity of X. When the assisting cation was Hg^{2+} the ratio 1.012 was observed for all three $[Co(NH_3)_5X]^{3+}$ ions, indicating the existence of $Co(NH_3)_5^{3+}$ as an intermediate. However, with Ag^+ the ratio varied (1.009, 1.007, 1.010) indicating that $Co(NH_3)_5^{3+}$ does not have a completely independent existence in this case. For Tl^{3+} the ratios were 0.996, 0.993 and 1.003, showing considerable deviation from a pure dissociative mechanism. If one assumes that with no assisting cation present bond breaking would proceed less far in the transition state, it could then be argued that these experiments favor an S_N2 mechanism, but there is also the unresolved question as to whether the entering water molecule in the assisted aquations comes from the bulk of the solvent or from the coordination sphere of the assisting metal ion. Thus, like many another mechanistic study, this one is tricky to interpret.

(5) A means of generating $Co(NH_3)_5^{3+}$ has been found[18] using the reaction (5-13) where azide is the sixth ligand:

$$Co(NH_3)_5N_3^{2+} + HNO_2 = [Co(NH_3)_5N_3NO]^{3+} = Co(NH_3)_5^{3+} + N_2 + N_2O \quad (5\text{-}13)$$

The relative rates of reaction of this with various anions, e.g., Cl^-, Br^-, SCN^-, F^-, HSO_4^-, $H_2PO_4^-$ and with H_2O were studied. The agreement between these results and those in the reaction (5-14)

$$Co(NH_3)_5(H_2O)^{3+} + X^- = Co(NH_3)_5X^{2+} + H_2O \quad (5\text{-}14)$$

was close, thus indicating that (5-14) also involves the intermediate $Co(NH_3)_5^{3+}$ or something of similar reactivity. By the principle of microscopic reversibility, this intermediate must also participate in the reverse of (5-14), that is, in the hydrolysis reaction itself. However, there are other experiments which are considered[19] to show that the usual aquation reactions (e.g., that of $[Co(NH_3)_5NO_3]^{2+}$) *cannot* proceed through the same intermediate as that generated by oxidation of $[Co(NH_3)_5N_3]^{2+}$.

For the reaction (5-15), where L–L represents a bidentate amine, it has

$$[Co(L-L)_2Cl_2]^+ + H_2O = [Co(L-L)_2Cl(H_2O)]^{2+} + Cl^- \quad (5\text{-}15)$$

been found that the rate is increased by increasing bulk of the ligands, a result not in agreement with an S_N2 mechanism, but consistent with an S_N1 mechanism.

Another class of hydrolyses which have been extensively studied are those of *trans* $Co^{III}en_2AX$ species, in which the leaving group is X^-. The variation in rates and stereochemistry (*cis* or *trans*) of products as functions of the nature of A have been examined, and certain informative correlations established. When A is NH_3 or NO_2^- the data indicate that the mechanism is S_N2, whereas for $A = OH^-$, Cl^-, N_3^- and NCS^- an S_N1 mechanism is postulated. The assignments of mechanism in these cases depends heavily upon detailed consideration of the stereochemical possibilities for the intermediates or activated complexes and are thus of an indirect though apparently reliable nature.

Base Hydrolysis. The interpretation of the second term in, e.g., (5-12) has also provoked much controversy. It could, of course, be interpreted as representing a genuine S_N2 process, OH^- making a nucleophilic attack on Co^{III}. However, the possibility of an S_N1CB mechanism, discussed above, must also be considered. Again, there are arguments on both sides and the distinct possibility that the mechanism may vary for different complexes, but the S_N1CB mechanism seems generally the more likely.

In some cases the S_N1CB mechanism seems reasonably certain on the

[18] A. Haim and H. Taube, *Inorg. Chem.*, **2**, 1199 (1963).
[19] R. G. Pearson and J. W. Moore, *Inorg. Chem.*, **3**, 1334 (1964).

basis of steric effects, and from the dependence of rates on the nucleophilicity of the leaving group. Another argument, used to defend the S_N1CB mechanism *in general*, is that there is no reason to expect OH^- to be uniquely capable of electrophilic attack on the metal, since in the reactions of square complexes (see below) it turns out to be a distinctly inferior nucleophile toward Pt^{II}.

The S_N1CB mechanism, of course, requires that the reacting complex have at least one protonic hydrogen atom on a non-leaving ligand, and that the rate of reaction of this hydrogen be fast compared to the rate of ligand displacement. It has been found that the rates of proton exchange in many complexes subject to rapid base hydrolysis are in fact some 10^5 times faster than the hydrolysis itself (e.g., in $Co(NH_3)_5Cl^{2+}$ and $Coen_2NH_3Cl^{2+}$).

The fact that base hydrolysis is faster than acid hydrolysis (i.e., simple aquation) is explained in terms of the S_N1CB mechanism, because the NH_2^- group in the conjugate base can donate its electron pair to a metal orbital thus enabling the coordinately unsatisfied metal ion in the activated complex (or intermediate, depending on what lifetime it is assumed to have) to partially satisfy its deficiency of electrons. There are, however, some cases, such as $Cr(NH_3)_6^{3+}$, where OH^- does not significantly accelerate hydrolysis, but the significance of this is not clear.

It should also be noted that some results obtained in non-aqueous solvents also support the S_N1CB mechanism. Thus, in dimethylsulfoxide, reactions of the type

$$Coen_2NO_2Cl^+ + Y^- = Coen_2NO_2Y^+ + Cl^- \tag{5-16}$$
$$(Y = N_3^-, NO_2^- \text{ or } SCN^-)$$

are slow, with half times in hours, but when trace amounts of OH^- or piperidine are added the half times are reduced to minutes. Since it was also shown that reaction of $Coen_2NO_2OH^+$ with Y^- is slow, an S_N2 mechanism with this as an intermediate is ruled out, and a genuine conjugate base mechanism must prevail here.

Further interesting evidence for the conjugate base (though it does not bear on whether the actual aquation is S_N1 or S_N2) comes from a study[20] of the activity of OOH^- in base hydrolysis. Since OOH^- is a weaker base but a better nucleophile toward metal ions than OH^-, base hydrolysis by OOH^- compared to OH^- should proceed more slowly if its function is to form the conjugate base by removing a proton, but faster if it attacks the metal in a genuine S_N2 process. Experimental data are in agreement with the former.

Finally, in complexes having no protonic hydrogen, acceleration by base should not be observed according to the S_N1CB mechanism. This is in

[20] R. G. Pearson and D. N. Edgington, *J. Amer. Chem. Soc.*, **84**, 4607 (1962).

general true (as for 2,2'-dipyridyl complexes, for instance), but there are a few cases in which a reaction first order in OH^- is observed nonetheless. One of these is the hydrolysis of $Co(EDTA)^-$ by OH^-. The formation of the 7-coordinate intermediate (5-XXXVII) has been proposed, since it is also found that the complex racemizes with a first order dependence on OH^-, but with a rate faster than that of hydrolysis. The 7-coordinate species could revert to $Co(EDTA)^-$ again without hydrolysis occurring, but with concomitant racemization.

(5-XXXVII)

Anation Reactions. These are reactions in which an anion displaces H_2O from the coordination sphere. In general, attempts to distinguish between S_N1 and S_N2 mechanisms have been unsuccessful because of complications such as ion pairing or the slow rate of anation compared to water exchange. In order to avoid the ion pairing problem, an anionic complex may be used, and $Co(CN)_5H_2O^{2-}$ has proved very suitable. In a classic study[21] it was shown that the reaction (5-17) proceeds by an essentially limiting S_N1 mechanism with the intermediate, $Co(CN)_5^{2-}$, having a long enough lifetime to discriminate between various ligands present in the solution.

$$Co(CN)_5H_2O^{2-} = Co(CN)_5^{2-} + H_2O \qquad (5\text{-}17a)$$

$$Co(CN)_5^{2-} + X^- = Co(CN)_5X^{3-} \qquad (5\text{-}17b)$$

5-16. Some Additional Topics

Some Reactions of Chelate Complexes. A number of reactions of the trisoxalatochromium(III) ion, $[Cr(C_2O_4)_3]^{3-}$, have been studied and an interesting and rather detailed picture of the reaction mechanisms has emerged. The aquation reaction (5-18) has been found to obey the rate law (5-19) where trisoxalatochromium(III) is represented by TOC.

$$[Cr(C_2O_4)_3]^{3-} + 2H_2O = [Cr(C_2O_4)_2(H_2O)_2]^- + C_2O_4^{2-} \qquad (5\text{-}18)$$

$$v = k_1[H^+][TOC] + k_2[H^+]^2[TOC] \qquad (5\text{-}19)$$

[21] A. Haim and W. K. Wilmarth, *Inorg. Chem.*, 1, 573 (1962).

This rate law is consistent with (though it does not prove) the following sequence of steps:

$$[Cr(C_2O_4)_3]^{3-} + H_3O^+ = [Cr(C_2O_4)_2(OC_2O_3H)(H_2O)]^{2-} \qquad (5\text{-}20)$$

$$[Cr(C_2O_4)_2(OC_2O_3H)(H_2O)]^{2-} + H_2O = [Cr(C_2O_4)_2(H_2O)_2]^- + HC_2O_4^- \qquad (5\text{-}21)$$

$$[Cr(C_2O_4)_2(OC_2O_3H)(H_2O)]^{2-} + H_3O^+ = [Cr(C_2O_4)_2(H_2O)_2]^- + H_2C_2O_4 \qquad (5\text{-}22)$$

(5-20) is assumed to be a rapid equilibrium and accounts for the presence of $[H^+]$ in both terms of the rate law. (5-21) and (5-22) are then alternative, competitive paths for completion of the reaction. k_1 and k_2 are thus both the products of the equilibrium constant for (5-20) with the specific rate constants for (5-21) and (5-22).

The reverse of (5-18) has also been studied and the rate law observed is:

$$v = k_3[Cr(C_2O_4)_2(H_2O)_2]^- \qquad (5\text{-}23)$$

A mechanism consistent with this involves a rapid addition of $C_2O_4^{2-}$, (5-24), followed by a slow, rate-determining step in which the chelate ring is closed (5-25):

$$[Cr(C_2O_4)(H_2O)_2]^- + C_2O_4^{2-} = [Cr(C_2O_4)_2(OC_2O_3)(H_2O)]^{3-} + H_2O \qquad (5\text{-}24)$$

$$[Cr(C_2O_4)_2(OC_2O_3)(H_2O)]^{3-} = [Cr(C_2O_4)_3]^{3-} + H_2O \qquad (5\text{-}25)$$

The two intermediates with one opened ring which have been postulated above, are also postulated in the mechanism of ligand exchange, which has been studied using C^{14}-labeled oxalate, $C_2{}^*O_4^{2-}$. The rate law for exchange, from pH 2 to pH 6, and 65–85° is (5-26).

$$v = k_4[TOC] + k_5[TOC][HC_2O_4^-] + k_6[TOC][H^+] + k_7[TOC][H^+][HC_2O_4^-] \qquad (5\text{-}26)$$

To explain this, two rapid equilibria (5-27) and (5-28) and four slow, competitive, rate-determining steps, (5-29) to (5-32), have been invoked:

$$[Cr(C_2O_4)_3]^{3-} + H_2O = [Cr(C_2O_4)_2(OC_2O_3)(H_2O)]^{3-} \qquad (5\text{-}27)$$

$$[Cr(C_2O_4)_3]^{3-} + H_3O^+ = [Cr(C_2O_4)_2(OC_2O_3H)(H_2O)]^{2-} \qquad (5\text{-}28)$$

$$[Cr(C_2O_4)_2(OC_2O_3)(H_2O)]^{3-} + H_2O = [Cr(C_2O_4)_2(H_2O)_2]^- + C_2O_4^{2-} \qquad (5\text{-}29)$$

$$[Cr(C_2O_4)_2(OC_2O_3)(H_2O)]^{3-} + HC_2{}^*O_4^- = [Cr(C_2O_4)_2(OC_2{}^*O_3)(H_2O)]^{3-} + HC_2O_4^- \qquad (5\text{-}30)$$

$$[Cr(C_2O_4)_2(OC_2O_3H)(H_2O)]^{2-} + H_2O = [Cr(C_2O_4)_2(H_2O)_2]^- + HC_2O_4^- \qquad (5\text{-}31)$$

$$[Cr(C_2O_4)_2(OC_2O_3H)(H_2O)]^{2-} + HC_2{}^*O_4^- = [Cr(C_2O_4)_2(OC_2{}^*O_3H)(H_2O)]^{2-} + HC_2O_4^- (5\text{-}32)$$

Rate steps (5-29) and (5-31) are each followed by the reverse reactions, which proceed rapidly (the equilibrium constant for reaction (5-18) being $\sim 10^{-6}$ at 32°). It will be noted that the step (5-31) is identical to (5-21) and support for both postulated mechanisms is provided by the fact that the experimental values of k_1 and k_6 are identical within experimental error.

Still another reaction of $[Cr(C_2O_4)_3]^{3-}$ is racemization of one of the optical isomers. It has been found that this occurs more rapidly than does oxalate exchange, since complete racemization occurs under conditions in which no significant exchange can be detected. Thus the racemization must occur without liberation of oxalate ligands. This aspect of $[Cr(C_2O_4)_3]^{3-}$ chemistry will be considered further within the following general discussion of racemization of tris chelate complexes.

The Racemization of tris Chelate Complexes. There are numerous other cases besides $[Cr(C_2O_4)_3]^{3-}$ in which it is known that racemization of a tris chelate complex occurs without complete detachment of any ligand. Several possible mechanisms have been envisioned for these processes, of which the chief ones are (1) the trigonal shift, (2) the tetragonal shift, and (3) a mechanism with a five coordinate intermediate. The first two involve no bond breaking. These mechanisms are depicted in Figure 5-6.

From nmr studies[22] of rearrangements of various tris β-ketoenolate complexes, it has been inferred that racemization and other isomerization reactions most likely occur by way of a 5-coordinate intermediate. Both of the twist mechanisms would appear to have relatively high activation energies for the transition metal complexes studied. It is not impossible, however, that for a complex of a non-transition element (where d orbital stabilization energies would not be involved) with strong metal–ligand bonds, one of the twist mechanisms would be preferred.

Although the only ring opening mechanism which appears to have been discussed in the literature is the one shown in Figure 5-6(c), it would appear that the one shown as (d) has some merits. It avoids both loss of d orbital stabilization energy and loss of bond energy provided the solvent has some donor ability. Actually it differs from the first three in that the intermediate might have a definite lifetime, that is, it might be a true chemical species, and correspond to a saddle point rather than the maximum in the energy along the reaction coordinate. The other three intermediates seem more likely to represent true activated complexes, that is, to lie at the maximum of energy on the reaction coordinate.

For the $[Cr(C_2O_4)_3]^{3-}$ racemization, it is likely that the mechanism is of a ring-opening type since it has been shown that *all* oxalate oxygen atoms exchange with solvent water at a rate faster than that for oxalate exchange but almost equal to that of racemization. While the path (c) has been suggested for this, path (d) seems also to be a good possibility, involving perhaps the same intermediate as in (5-27) and taking advantage of the ligand properties of H_2O.

Tris chelate complexes sometimes racemize at a measurable rate in the

---

[22] R. C. Fay and T. S. Piper, *Inorg. Chem.*, **3**, 348 (1964).

solid state. In the case of $K_3[Co(C_2O_4)_3]$ the effect of pressure on the rate has been studied.[23] The rate was found to *increase* with pressure and a volume of activation of *ca.* -1.5 ml/mole was reported. Since it seems unlikely, though not necessarily impossible, that the intermediate in mechanism (c) of Figure 5-6 could give such a result, it was proposed that in this case a process such as (a) or (b) is operative.

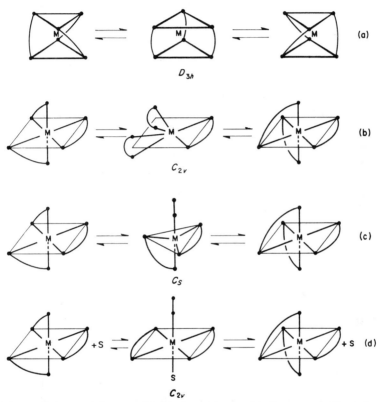

Fig. 5-6. Diagrams of four possible modes of intramolecular racemization of a tris chelate complex. (a) The trigonal shift, (b) the "tetragonal" shift, (c) a ring opening path with a trigonal bipyramid intermediate, (d) a ring opening path with an octahedral, solvent-coordinated intermediate.

Electrophilic Attack on Ligands. There are some reactions known where ligand exchange does not involve the breaking of metal–ligand bonds, but instead bonds within the ligands themselves are broken and re-formed. One well-known case is the aquation of carbonato complexes.

[23] J. Brady, F. Dachille and C. D. Schmulbach, *Inorg. Chem.*, **2**, 803 (1963).

When isotopically labeled water, $H_2{*}O$, is used, it is found that no ${*}O$ gets into the coordination sphere of the ion during aquation,

$$[Co(NH_3)_5OCO_2]^+ + 2H_3{*}O^+ \rightarrow [Co(NH_3)_5(H_2O)]^{3+} + 2H_2{*}O + CO_2$$

The most likely path for this reaction involves proton attack on the oxygen atom bonded to Co followed by expulsion of CO_2 and then protonation of the hydroxo complex (eq. 5-33). Similarly, in the reaction of

$$\left\{ \begin{array}{c} Co(NH_3)_5\!-\!O\cdots C \diagup^{O}_{\diagdown O} \\ \quad\quad H^+ \\ \quad\quad \vdots \\ \quad\quad O \\ H \diagup \diagdown H \end{array} \right\} \longrightarrow [Co(NH_3)_5\!-\!O]^{2+} \underset{\displaystyle H}{\overset{+H^+}{\longrightarrow}} [Co(NH_3)_5(H_2O)]^{3+} \qquad (5\text{-}33)$$

Transition state

NO_2^- with pentaammineaquocobalt(III) ion, isotopic labeling studies show that the oxygen originally in the bound H_2O turns up in the bound NO_2^-. This remarkable result is explained by the reaction sequence 5-34.

$$2NO_2^- + 2H^+ = N_2O_3 + H_2O \qquad (5\text{-}34a)$$

$$[Co(NH_3)_5{*}OH]^{2+} + N_2O_3 \longrightarrow \left\{ \begin{array}{c} (NH_3)_5CO\!-\!\overset{*}{O}\cdots H \\ \quad\quad \vdots \quad\quad \vdots \\ O\dot{N}\cdots \dot{O}NO \end{array} \right\} \overset{fast}{\longrightarrow}$$

Transition state

$$HNO_2 + [Co(NH_3)_5{*}ONO]^{2+} \overset{slow}{\longrightarrow} [Co(NH_3)_5(NO{*}O)]^{2+} \qquad (5\text{-}34b)$$

5-17. Square Complexes

Mechanism of Ligand Displacement Reactions. For square complexes, the mechanistic problem is more straightforward and hence better understood. One might expect that four-coordinate complexes would be more likely than octahedral ones to react by an S_N2 mechanism, and extensive studies of Pt^{II} complexes have shown that this is so.

For reactions in aqueous solution of the type (5-35) the rate law takes the general form (5-36). It is believed that the second term corresponds to

$$PtL_nCl_{4-n} + Y = PtL_nCl_{3-n}Y + Cl^- \qquad (5\text{-}35)$$

$$v = k[PtL_nCl_{4-n}] + k'[PtL_nCl_{4-n}][Y] \qquad (5\text{-}36)$$

a genuine S_N2 reaction of Y with the complex, while the first term represents a two step path in which one Cl^- is first replaced by H_2O (probably also by an S_N2 mechanism) as the rate-determining step followed by relatively fast replacement of H_2O by Y.

It has been found that the rates of reaction (5-35) for the series of four complexes in which L = NH_3, and Y = H_2O varies by only a factor of 2. This is a remarkably small variation since the charge on the complex changes from -2 to $+1$ as n goes from 0 to 3. Since Pt—Cl bond breaking should become more difficult in this series, while the attraction of Pt for a nucleophile should increase in the same order, the virtual constancy in the rate argues for an S_N2 process in which both Pt—Cl bond breaking and Pt····OH_2 bond formation are of comparable importance.

The question of whether the five-coordinate $PtL_nCl_{4-n}Y$ species is to be regarded as a chemical intermediate or merely as the activated complex remains unanswered. Since the starting complex possesses an empty valence shell orbital with which a fifth Pt–ligand bond could be formed (see Sect. 30-H-1 for a discussion of isolable 5- and 6-coordinated Pt^{II} complexes) the first alternative requires consideration.

It is interesting that the rates of reaction of the series of complexes $[MCl(o\text{-tolyl})(PtEt_3)_2]$ with pyridine vary enormously with change in the metal, M. The relative rates for Ni, Pd and Pt are $5 \times 10^6 : 10^5 : 1$, which seems to be in accord with the relative ease with which these metal ions increase their coordination numbers from 4 to 6, as this is inferred from their general chemical behavior.

While there is as yet little in the way of direct evidence, it is considered likely that the S_N2 mechanism is valid for the reactions of square complexes other than those of Pt^{II}, such as those of Ni^{II}, Pd^{II}, Rh^{I}, Ir^{I} and Au^{III}.

The order of nucleophilic strength of entering ligands (i.e., the order of the rate constants k' in equation 5-36) for substitution reactions on Pt^{II} is:

$$F^- \sim H_2O \sim OH^- < Cl^- < Br^- \sim NH_3 \sim \text{olefins} < C_6H_5NH_2 < C_5H_5N$$
$$< NO_2^- < N_3^- < I^- \sim SCN^- \sim R_3P$$

This order of nucleophilicity toward Pt^{II} has been the subject of much discussion. It is clearly not at all related to the order of basicity toward protons nor does it reflect simple electrostatic effects. It also differs from the order found in certain processes which take place by nucleophilic attack upon other species. It appears that the ligand properties most faithfully reflected by this sequence are polarizability and oxidizability.

The *trans* Effect. This is a particular feature of ligand replacement reactions in square complexes which is of less importance in reactions of octahedral complexes except in some special cases where CO (or NO) is present as a ligand, or where M=O or M≡N bonds are present (see e.g. Sect. 30-D-9). Most work has been done with Pt^{II} complexes, which are numerous and varied and have fairly convenient rates of reaction. Consider the general reaction 5-37,

$$[PtLX_3]^- + Y^- \rightarrow [PtLX_2Y]^- + X^- \qquad (5\text{-}37)$$

Sterically, there are two possible reaction products, with *cis* and *trans* orientation of Y with respect to L. It has been observed that the relative proportions of the *cis* and *trans* products vary appreciably with the ligand L. Moreover, in reactions of the type 5-38 either or both of the indicated

$$
\begin{bmatrix} L & X \\ & \diagup Pt \diagdown \\ L' & X \end{bmatrix} + Y^- \rightarrow X^- + \begin{bmatrix} L & X \\ & \diagup Pt \diagdown \\ L' & Y \end{bmatrix} \quad or \quad \begin{bmatrix} L & Y \\ & \diagup Pt \diagdown \\ L' & X \end{bmatrix} \tag{5-38}
$$

isomers may be produced. It is found that in both these types of reaction and in others, a fairly extensive series of ligands may be arranged in the same order with respect to their ability to facilitate substitution in the position *trans* to themselves. This phenomenon is known as the *trans effect*, and the order of ligands is, in part: $H_2O < OH^- < NH_3 < Cl^- < Br^- < I^- \sim NO_2^- \sim PR_3 \ll CO \sim C_2H_4 \sim CN^-$.

The *trans* effect series has proved very useful in rationalizing known synthetic procedures and in devising new ones. As an example we may consider the synthesis of the *cis* and *trans* isomers of $[Pt(NH_3)_2Cl_2]$. The synthesis of the *cis* isomer is accomplished by treatment of the $[PtCl_4]^{2-}$ ion with ammonia (eq. 5-39). Since Cl^- has a greater *trans*-directing

$$
\begin{array}{ccc}
\begin{matrix} Cl & Cl \\ \diagup Pt \diagdown \\ Cl & Cl \end{matrix} & \xrightarrow{NH_3} & \begin{matrix} Cl & NH_3 \\ \diagup Pt \diagdown \\ Cl & Cl \end{matrix} & \xrightarrow{NH_3} & \begin{matrix} Cl & NH_3 \\ \diagup Pt \diagdown \\ Cl & NH_3 \end{matrix}
\end{array} \tag{5-39}
$$

influence than does NH_3, substitution of NH_3 into $[Pt(NH_3)Cl_3]^-$ is least likely to occur in the position *trans* to the NH_3 already present and thus the *cis* isomer is favored. The *trans* isomer is made by treating $[Pt(NH_3)_4]^{2+}$ with Cl^- (eq. 5-40). Here the superior *trans*-directing influence of Cl^-

$$
\begin{array}{ccc}
\begin{matrix} H_3N & NH_3 \\ \diagup Pt \diagdown \\ H_3N & NH_3 \end{matrix} & \xrightarrow{Cl^-} & \begin{matrix} H_3N & NH_3 \\ \diagup Pt \diagdown \\ H_3N & Cl \end{matrix} & \xrightarrow{Cl^-} & \begin{matrix} Cl & NH_3 \\ \diagup Pt \diagdown \\ H_3N & Cl \end{matrix}
\end{array} \tag{5-40}
$$

causes the second Cl^- to enter *trans* to the first one, producing *trans*-$[Pt(NH_3)_2Cl_2]$.

Efforts to develop a theory of the *trans* effect have been made over many years, during which time the chief handicap has been a lack of knowledge of the mechanism of the substitution reactions. Now that the S_N2 nature of the rate determining step has been established, the theoretical picture has been greatly clarified. The earliest idea was that the *trans*-directing ability of a ligand reflected its tendency to weaken the bond *trans* to itself. More recently it has been shown that the ability of a ligand to accept $d\pi$ electrons from the metal would enhance the tendency of an incoming nucleophile to approach in the *trans* position and would also stabilize the five-coordinate activated complex, thus lowering the activation energy. Since the S_N2 process involves both bond formation to the incoming ligand and weakening of the bond to the ligand being displaced, both of these ideas now find a place in the complete theoretical picture.

At present it appears that the second factor is dominant in most cases where the *trans* effect is large. It should be noted explicitly that there is in general a lack of correlation between the thermodynamic stability of the products of substitution reactions and the rates at which they are formed, which means that the bond weakening and nucleophile-attracting factors exert their effect in the activated complex or transition state.

The ligands at the weak end of the *trans* effect series are in very nearly the same order as in the series relating to nucleophilic strength of attacking ligands, which is in accord with the idea that polarizability is important in both cases. A definitive picture of how this polarizability effect is translated into a bond weakening effect toward the *trans* ligand is difficult to devise with rigor. In very simple terms, it has been argued that if, in a complex MX_3Y, Y has greater polarizability than X, the distribution of induced charges will be as shown 5-XXXVIII, thus causing that X which is *trans* to Y to experience an extra repulsive, i.e., bond weakening, force.

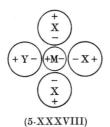

(5-XXXVIII)

The argument regarding the π-bonding ability of the ligands can be formulated in somewhat more detailed terms. If a particular ligand in a square complex has a strong tendency to accept electrons originally occupying a d_{xz} or d_{yz} orbital on the metal atom into a π orbital of its own, then the electron density above and below the bond between the metal ion and the ligand *trans* to the particular ligand is lessened. This in turn makes this region of space more attractive to an attacking nucleophilic ligand. This is illustrated in Figure 5-7. Furthermore, the five-coordinate activated complex is actually stabilized by the fact that the ligand L is taking electron density from a d orbital. The d orbital has two of its lobes directed more or less directly toward the entering ligand Y and the leaving ligand X.' As electron density is withdrawn from the d orbital the bonds to these two ligands are strengthened. Thus the stability of the activated complex is enhanced and the activation energy is therefore diminished for this path. There is no such effect if Y approaches so as to displace one of the X's *cis* to L.

For discussion of some recent studies on ^{19}F nmr spectra of *m*- and *p*-fluorophenyl complexes of Pt^{II} which have provided additional insight into the π-bonding and polarization contributions to the *trans* effect, see Sect. 30-H-1.

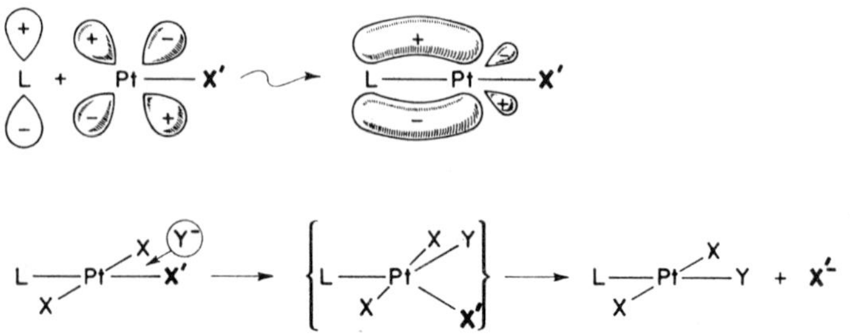

Fig. 5-7. Diagram showing how the presence of a strongly accepting π orbital on L withdraws electron density in the $d\pi$ orbital which it has in common with the ligand *trans* to it, thus making the region near this *trans* ligand more accessible to the nucleophilic group, and then reducing the repulsive effect of d electrons upon the ligands X' and Y in the transition state.

Evidence for *trans* effects in octahedral complexes is scant. In those containing strongly π-accepting ligands such as CO, there is a tendency for reaction products to have the CO groups *cis* rather than *trans* to one another, so that each can obtain the maximum share in the available metal $d\pi$ electrons (Sect. 27-1). Whether this is a truly kinetic effect has not been established, however.

Some experimental data concerning a *trans* effect in more common types of complexes has been obtained,[24] but detailed studies and interpretations comparable to those for planar complexes are lacking.

5-18. Electron Transfer Reactions

These can be divided into two main classes: (1) those in which the electron transfer effects no net chemical change, and (2) those in which there is a chemical change. The former, called *electron exchange* processes, can be followed only indirectly, as by isotopic labelling or by nmr. The latter are the usual oxidation–reduction reactions and can be followed by many standard chemical and physical methods. The electron exchange processes are of interest because of their particular suitability for theoretical study.

There are two well-established general mechanisms for electron transfer

---

[24] F. Basolo, E. J. Bounsall and A. J. Pöe, *Proc. Chem. Soc.*, **1963**, 366.

processes. In one, each complex maintains its own complete coordination shell in the activated complex, and the electron must tunnel through both of these shells. Naturally we do not imply by this statement that the "same" electron leaves one metal ion and arrives at the other. In the second mechanism, there is at least one atom common to both coordination shells in the activated complex and usually the bridging atom (or atoms) is transferred along with the electron. These mechanisms are called respectively the *tunnelling* or *outer sphere* and the *bridging* or *inner sphere* mechanism.

Tunnelling or Outer Sphere Processes. This mechanism is certain to be the correct one when *both* species participating in the reaction undergo ligand exchange reactions more slowly than they undergo electron transfer. In many cases the reactions are of the electron exchange type, that is, they take place between species which are converted one into the other by the electron transfer. For such a process, a sketch of the energy *vs* reaction coordinate takes the symmetrical form shown in Figure 5-8. The energy

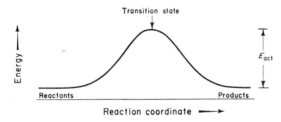

Fig. 5-8.   Graph of the energy versus reaction coordinate for an electron exchange reaction in which reactants and products are identical.

of activation, E_{act}, is made up of three parts: (1) the electrostatic energy (repulsive for species of like charge), (2) the energy required to distort the coordination shells of both species and (3) the energy required to modify the solvent structure about each species. There have been various attempts to compute each of these terms accurately and thus to provide a quantitative theory of electron exchange reactions, and reasonable success has been achieved in some instances. In this discussion, however, we shall take only a qualitative approach.

Table 5-3 lists some electron exchange reactions believed to proceed by the tunnelling mechanism, though for the Co^{II}–Co^{III} reactions this might not be correct since one of the reactants (i.e., the Co^{II} partner) undergoes ligand substitution rapidly. The range covered by the rate constants is very large, extending from $\sim 10^{-4}$ up to perhaps nearly the limit of diffusion control ($\sim 10^9$). It is possible to account qualitatively for the observed variation in rates in terms of the second contribution mentioned to the

TABLE 5-3

Rates of Some Electron Exchange Reactions
with Outer Sphere or Tunnelling Mechanisms

Reactants	Rate constants (liter mole^{-1} sec^{-1})
$[Fe(dipy)_3]^{2+}, [Fe(dipy)_3]^{3+}$ $[Mn(CN)_6]^{3-}, [Mn(CN)_6]^{4-}$ $[Mo(CN)_8]^{3-}, [Mo(CN)_8]^{4-}$ $[W(CN)_8]^{3-}, [W(CN)_8]^{4-}$ $[IrCl_6]^{2-}, [IrCl_6]^{3-}$ $[Os(dipy)_3]^{2+}, [Os(dipy)_3]^{3+}$	$> 10^6$ at 25°
$[Fe(CN)_6]^{3-}, [Fe(CN)_6]^{4-}$	Second order, $\sim 10^5$ at 25°
$[MnO_4]^-, [MnO_4]^{2-}$	Second order, $\sim 10^3$ at 0°
$[Coen_3]^{2+}, [Coen_3]^{3+}$ $[Co(NH_3)_6]^{2+}, [Co(NH_3)_6]^{3+}$ $[Co(C_2O_4)_3]^{3-}, [Co(C_2O_4)_3]^{4-}$	Second order, $\sim 10^{-4}$ at 25°

activation energy. The transition state for electron exchange will be one in which each species has the same dimensions. This is so because a transition state for a process in which there is no adjustment of bond lengths prior to the electron jump would necessarily have a much higher energy. Suppose for a $Co^{II}-Co^{III}$ exchange the electron jumped while both ions were in their normal configurations. This would produce a Co^{II} complex with bonds compressed *all the way* to the length appropriate to a Co^{III} complex and a Co^{III} complex with the bonds lengthened *all the way* to the length of those in the Co^{II} complex. This would be the zenith of energy, and, as the bonds readjusted, the energy of the exchanging pair would drop to the initial energy of the systems. However, this zenith of energy is obviously higher than it would be if the reacting ions first adjusted their configurations so that each met the other one *only halfway* and then exchanged the electron. Still, the more the two reacting species differ initially in their sizes the higher will be the activation energy.

In the seven cases at the top of Table 5-3, the two species differ by only one electron in an orbital which is approximately non-bonding with respect to the metal–ligand interaction (see Chapter 26 for further discussion). Therefore the lengths of the metal–ligand bonds should be practically the same in the two participating species and the contribution to the activation energy of stretching and contracting bonds should be small. For the $MnO_4^- - MnO_4^{2-}$ case, the electron concerned is not in a strictly non-bonding orbital. In the three cases of slow electron exchange, there is a considerable difference in the metal–ligand bond lengths. However, there is also a change in the extent of electron spin pairing among the non-exchanging electrons on each metal ion. Since it is possible that this could effect the rate of the process either through the activation energy or by influencing the frequency factor (the transmission coefficient, in terms of the absolute theory of rate processes), the significance of the Co^{II}–Co^{III} results is not entirely clear.

In several cases the rate constants for reactions in Table 5-3 have been found to depend on the identity and concentration of cations present in the solution. The general effect is an increase in rate with an increase in concentration of the cations, but certain cations are particularly effective. The general effect can be attributed to the formation of ion pairs which then decrease the electrostatic contribution to the activation energy. Certain specific effects found for example in the MnO_4^-–MnO_4^{2-} and $[Fe(CN)_6]^{4-}$–$[Fe(CN)_6]^{3-}$ systems[25] are less easily interpreted with certainty. The effect of $[Co(NH_3)_6]^{3+}$ on the former is thought to be due to ion pairing, greatly enhanced by the high charge. It appears that the large effect of the Cs^+ ion in both cases is perhaps due to its acting as a bridge for conducting the electron, in addition to lessening the repulsion between anions.

Ligand-bridged or Inner Sphere Processes. Ligand-bridged transition states have been shown to occur in a number of reactions, mainly through the elegant experiments devised and executed by H. Taube and his school. He has demonstrated that the following general reaction occurs:

$$[Co(NH_3)_5X]^{2+} + Cr^{2+}(aq) + 5H^+ = [Cr(H_2O)_5X]^{2+} + Co^{2+}(aq) + 5NH_4^+$$
$$(X = F^-, Cl^-, Br^-, I^-, SO_4^{2-}, NCS^-, N_3^-, PO_4^{3-}, P_2O_7^{4-}, CH_3COO^-, \quad\quad (5\text{-}41)$$
$$C_3H_7COO^-, \text{crotonate, succinate, oxalate, maleate})$$

The significance and success of these experiments rest on the following facts. The Co^{III} complex is not labile while the Cr^{II} aquo ion is, whereas, in the products, the $[Cr(H_2O)_5X]^{2+}$ ion is not labile while the Co^{II} aquo ion is. It is found that the transfer of X from $[Co(NH_3)_5X]^{2+}$ to $[Cr(H_2O)_5X]^{2+}$ is quantitative. The only reasonable explanation for these facts is the postulation of the transition state $(H_3N)_5Co$—X—$Cr(H_2O)_5$ and the assumption that when the electron is transferred from Cr^{II} to Co^{III} the Co—X bond becomes labile (the Co now being Co^{II}) while the Cr—X bond becomes nonlabile (the Cr now being Cr^{III}). It is also significant that, of

Oxalate   Maleate

the organic anions in the above list of X groups, the two (oxalate and maleate) which provide a continuous pathway of conjugated π bonds between the metal ions allow electron exchange to occur about 100 times faster than do the others.

[25] M. Shporer, G. Ron, A. Loewenstein and G. Navon. *Inorg. Chem.*, **4**, 361 (1965).

It is noteworthy that in reactions where a bridge mechanism is certain the order of effectiveness of several common anions as bridges is $N_3^- \gg I^- > Br^- > Cl^- > F^-$. This may perhaps be considered diagnostic of the mechanism.

In an extensive study[26] of reaction (5-41) in which the ligand X was an aromatic ring connected to the Co^{III} through a carboxyl group and bearing also another functional group, one interesting observation was that when the additional group contained a carbonyl group, the rate was greatly enhanced. It is believed that in these cases the Cr^{II} attaches itself to the "remote" carbonyl group and that the electron is transferred through the π system of the aromatic ring, while in other cases the Cr^{II} must attack at the second oxygen atom of the coordinated carboxyl group which is sterically hindered and hence less favorable.

Reactions 5-42, which are catalyzed by a trace of Cr^{2+}, must occur as

$$[Cr(NH_3)_5X]^{2+} + 5H^+ = [Cr(H_2O)_5X]^{2+} + 5NH_4^+ \qquad (5\text{-}42)$$
$$(X = F^-, Cl^-, Br^-, I^-)$$

shown in equation 5-43, in view of the complete retention of X by Cr^{III} while the NH_3's are completely lost.

$$[Cr(NH_3)_5X]^{2+} + {}^*Cr^{2+}(aq) \rightarrow$$

$$\{[(H_3N)_5Cr\text{—}X\text{—}{}^*Cr(H_2O)_5]^{4+}\} \rightarrow [{}^*Cr(H_2O)_5X]^{2+} + \{Cr(NH_3)_5{}^{2+}\} \qquad (5\text{-}43)$$
$$\text{Transition state} \qquad\qquad\qquad \begin{array}{c}\text{rapidly}\\ +5H^+\end{array}$$

$$5NH_4^+ + Cr^{2+}(aq)$$

There are various other cases, especially the $[Cr(H_2O)_5X]^{2+}$–$[Cr(H_2O)_6]^{2+}$ exchanges, in which retention of the X groups shows that they must be bridges in the activated complex. Also when Fe^{3+} is reduced by Cr^{2+} in the presence of halide ions, the chromium(III) is produced as $[Cr(H_2O)_5X]^{2+}$

The possibility that there might be reactions in which multiple bridges are formed has long been recognized but only recently confirmed. The reaction of cis-$[Cr(H_2O)_4(NH_3)_2]^+$ with Cr^{II} was the first proved example. More recently,[27] several other examples have been found, including the following:

$$cis\text{-}[Co(NH_3)_4(OCOR)_2]^+ + Cr^{2+} = cis\text{-}[Cr(H_2O)_4(OCOR)_2]^+ + Co^{2+}$$
$$[Co(EDTA)]^- + Cr^{2+} = Co^{2+} + [Cr(H_2O)_3(EDTA)]^-$$

In the latter, three oxygen atoms of EDTA evidently serve as bridges.

There is one system known in which both the tunnelling and the bridging mechanisms operate, namely, $[Co(NH_3)_5X]^{2+}$–$[Co(CN)_5]^{3-}$. The rate via

[26] E. S. Gould and H. Taube, J. Amer. Chem. Soc., **86**, 1318 (1964).
[27] P. B. Wood and W. C. E. Higginson, Proc. Chem. Soc., **1964**, 109.

the bridging mechanism depends markedly upon the identity of X whereas the outer sphere path has a rate practically independent of X.

Iron(II)–Iron(III) Exchange. This system has been extensively studied under a variety of conditions, but many uncertainties still remain concerning mechanism. Both the Fe^{II} and Fe^{III} aquo ions and the complexes to be considered are labile so that, while bridge processes must be considered, there is no simple way to prove them as when Cr^{II} is the reductant. For the reactions of Fe^{II} with a series of Fe^{III} species the results in Table 5-4 have been reported.

TABLE 5-4

Rates of Electron Exchange between Fe^{II} and Various Fe^{III} Species

Fe^{III} species	Rate constant at $0°$ (liter mole^{-1} sec^{-1})
$Fe^{3+}(aq)$	0.87
FeF^{2+}	9.7
$FeCl^{2+}$	9.7
$FeBr^{2+}$	4.9
FeN_3^{2+}	1.8×10^3
$FeOH^{2+}$	1.0×10^3
$FeC_2O_4^+$	7.0×10^3

The fact that all complexes react faster than the aquo ion must be due in part to the reduction of net charge and is not qualitatively diagnostic of mechanism. However, since the rates for the monohalo complexes are all practically the same, contrary to the results for the CrX^{2+} species, a bridge mechanism seems unlikely for these. For the N_3^-, OH^- and $C_2O_4^{2-}$ complexes, on the other hand, the great enhancement of rate reflects more than a simple electrostatic effect and is considered indicative of a bridge mechanism, though this is not entirely certain.

It has been proposed that for the aquo ion exchange may proceed through the $FeOH^{2+}$ ion via the symmetrical transition state 5-XXXIX.

$$\left[(H_2O)_5Fe-O\cdots H\cdots O-Fe(H_2O)_5\right]^{4+}$$
$$\qquad\qquad\quad H\qquad H$$

(5-XXXIX)

If this is so the reaction can be considered as a proton transfer in one direction rather than an electron transfer in the other. It is of course impossible to distinguish between the two possibilities on the basis of the rate law, and the only evidence adduced for the proton transfer process is an isotope effect (slower by a factor of 2 in D_2O than in H_2O). However, it has been shown that the isotope effect is not necessarily inconsistent with an ordinary tunnelling mechanism.

Two-Electron Transfers and Non-complementary Reactions. There are some elements which have stable oxidation states differing by two electrons, without a stable state in between. It has been shown that in several such cases, if not in all, two-electron transfers occur. The Pt^{II}–Pt^{IV} system (to be discussed briefly below) and the Tl^{I}–Tl^{III} system have been studied in some detail. For the latter in aqueous perchlorate solution the rate law is:

$$v = k_1[Tl^+][Tl^{3+}] + k_2[Tl^+][TlOH^{2+}]$$

In presence of other anions, more complicated rate laws are found indicating that two-electron transfers occur through various Tl^{3+} complexes.

All of the reactions discussed here so far have been *complementary*, that is, oxidant and reductant have changed oxidation state by the same number of electrons. For non-complementary reactions, e.g.,

$$2Fe^{2+} + Tl^{3+} = 2Fe^{3+} + Tl^+$$

the mechanistic possibilities, in the sense of series of electron transfer steps which may occur, are more numerous, but the individual electron transfers are subject to the same considerations as in complementary reactions.

Ligand Exchange via Electron Exchange. When a metal atom forms cations in two oxidation states, one giving labile complexes and the other inert complexes, substitution reactions of the latter can be accelerated by the presence of trace quantities of the former. An example of this has already been cited in equation (5-42) where Cr^{II} labilizes Cr^{III} complexes. This phenomenon is found also in the Co^{II}–Co^{III} aquo system and fairly generally in Pt^{II}–Pt^{IV} systems.

Pt^{II} catalyzes the exchange of chloride ion with $[Pt(NH_3)_4Cl_2]^{2+}$, the rate law being:

$$v = k[Pt^{II}][Pt^{IV}][Cl^-]$$

The mechanism proposed to explain this is the following:

$Pt(NH_3)_4{}^{2+} + {}^*Cl^- = Pt(NH_3)_4{}^*Cl^+$ (fast pre-equilibrium)

$$Pt(NH_3)_4Cl_2{}^{2+} + Pt(NH_3)_4{}^*Cl^+ = \left[\begin{array}{c} H_3N \quad NH_3 \ H_3N \quad NH_3 \\ Cl\text{------}Pt\text{·······}Cl\text{·········}Pt\text{------}{}^*Cl \\ H_3N \quad NH_3 \ H_3N \quad NH_3 \end{array}\right]^{3+}$$

$$= Pt(NH_3)_4Cl^+ + Pt(NH_3)_4{}^*ClCl^{2+}$$

The structure of the proposed activated complex, or intermediate, is very plausible, being quite comparable to the structures found in crystals of several compounds containing equal molar quantities of Pt^{II} and Pt^{IV}

(see Sect. 30-H-1). There is also considerable kinetic evidence corroborating this mechanism.[28] It is likely that traces of Pt^{II} generated by adventitious reducing agents (traces of other metal ions, organic matter, etc.) or photochemically play a role in many reactions of Pt^{IV} complexes. It is also known that traces of other metals, notably Ir, which have several oxidation states can catalyze Pt^{IV} reactions.

5-19. Reactions of Coordinated Ligands

In previous sections we have dealt at length with the structures of complexes and with certain reactions of complexes involving substitution of ligands, isomerizations and oxidation–reduction reactions of the metal atom. We now consider briefly the matter of chemical reactions involving the coordinated ligand. In some cases the reactions of coordinated ligands are quantitatively similar to reactions which the free ligands can undergo except that the rates are enhanced or the equilibrium shifted. However, in other instances the presence of the metal ion so alters the electronic and/or geometric structure of the ligand that it engages in qualitatively new reactions. It should be noted, also, that in some cases it is not easy to prove directly and positively that the ligand reacts while coordinated. It is in general *possible* that the function of the metal ion is to stabilize the product of reaction rather than to activate the ligand. For nearly all of the examples cited below it seems certain that the ligand reacts while coordinated, however.

Reactions Involving Hydrogen or its Ions. One of the simplest reactions, which we have already discussed, is the loss of a proton from coordinated water—or conversely the protonation of a hydroxo complex, e.g.,

$$[Al(H_2O)_6]^{3+} \rightleftarrows [Al(H_2O)_5OH]^{2+} + H^+$$

In this case the metal ion simply enhances a reaction characteristic of the free ligand. Ligand protonation reactions are fairly common, another example being the protonation of cyanide ligands, e.g.,

$$Fephen_2(CN)_2 + H^+ \rightleftarrows Fephen_2(CN)(CNH)^+$$

In the free cyanide acids, such as $H_4[Fe(CN)_6]$, the proton is hydrogen bonded to the nitrogen atom of the CN ligand.

Just as H_2O can lose a proton, coordinated amines such as NH_3 or ethylenediamine also undergo deprotonation reactions, generally

$$ML_nNH_3 \rightleftarrows [ML_nNH_2]^- + H^+$$
$$ML_n(NH_2CH_2CH_2NH_2) \rightleftarrows [ML_n(NHCH_2CH_2NH_2)]^- + H^+$$

Complexes of en which have lost a proton are commonly designated as complexes of (en − H). The acidity of coordinated en is not high,

[28] R. R. Rettew and R. C. Johnson, *Inorg. Chem.*, **4**, 1965 (1965).

however, so that quite strongly basic conditions are usually required. For example, treatment of $[Iren_3]I_3$ with KNH_2 in liquid ammonia at low temperature gives sequential removal of protons; the complexes $[Ir(en - H)_2en]I$ and $K_2[Ir(en - 2H)_2(en - H)]$ have been characterized.[29]

Although the above types of reaction are in general reversible, the breakdown of many complexes by acids probably proceeds through protonation of ligands. There are a number of cases where the central metal atom may be protonated but these are discussed elsewhere (Chap. 27).

There are a number of other reactions in which a coordinated ligand may be involved in reversible proton or hydride ion transfer reactions. These reactions, which are usually those of complexes with olefin, cyclopentadienyl or arene ligands are discussed in detail in Chapter 28, but one example can be quoted, viz.,

$$(\pi\text{-}C_5H_5)_2Co^+ \underset{acid}{\overset{H^-(BH_4^-)}{\rightleftarrows}} (\pi\text{-}C_5H_5)CoC_5H_6$$

where a delocalized $\pi\text{-}C_5H_5$ ring is converted by H^- to a bound cyclopentadiene.

Substitution Reactions. There are several cases in which a ligand when coordinated has properties comparable to those of an aromatic system because of delocalization of electron density, so that substitution reactions are possible.

One of the most extensive series of such substitution reactions involves the organoiron compound ferrocene, $(\pi\text{-}C_5H_5)_2Fe$, and related complexes (Chap. 28) where a number of organic reactions typical of aromatic ring systems can be carried out, for example, Friedel–Crafts acylations:

$$(\pi\text{-}C_5H_5)_2Fe + CH_3COCl \xrightarrow{AlCl_3} (\pi\text{-}C_5H_5)Fe(\pi\text{-}C_5H_4COCH_3)$$

Of the more conventional complexes, neutral acetylacetonates, $M(acac)_3$, have been most extensively studied; here the chelate ring forms a quasi-aromatic system and reactions such as halogenation, nitration and acylation may be performed, e.g.,

[29] G. W. Watt, L. E. Sharif and E. P. Helvenston, *Inorg. Chem.*, **1**, 6 (1962).

Addition and Condensation Reactions. Alkyl groups can often be added to the sulfur atoms of bound thiol groups as, for example, when $[Ni(NH_2CH_2CH_2S)_2]$ is treated with an alkyl halide, RX, transforming the coordinated mercapto group into a bound thioether group in the octahedral product complex, $[Ni(NH_2CH_2CH_2SR)_2X_2]$. This type of addition reaction can be used to form macrocyclic ligands,[30] as illustrated in equation (5-44):

$$(5\text{-}44)$$

The formation of complexes of Schiff bases (i.e., compounds containing the $-N{=}C\diagup^{\diagdown}$ group) is often carried out by first forming the metal complex of the ketone or aldehyde and treating this with the primary amine, or vice versa, e.g.,

In these reactions there is, however, the possibility that Schiff base formation takes place by reaction of the uncoordinated ligand, the metal ion merely serving to stabilize the product against hydrolytic decomposition.

There are some very interesting reactions which begin with Schiff base formation but lead to new macrocyclic polydentate ring systems.[31] A representative reaction is shown in equation (5-45):

$$(5\text{-}45)$$

---

[30] D. H. Busch, *et al.*, *J. Amer. Chem. Soc.*, **86**, 3642, 3651 (1964).
[31] D. A. House and N. F. Curtis, *J. Amer. Chem. Soc.*, **86**, 223, 1331 (1964).

The products of the type shown may be catalytically hydrogenated to give cyclic aliphatic tetraamines.

Perhaps one of the most striking examples of a synthetic process in which mediation by a metal ion is critical is that of a nickel corrin complex.[32] This is important since corrin is the name given to the hypothetical parent compound of the porphin-like system which immediately surrounds the Co atom in the Vitamin B_{12} structure. The two starting components can be converted by a series of reactions to the complex (5-46).

$$(5\text{-}46)$$

Other Reactions. There are innumerable examples of other types of reactions of coordinated ligands, several of which will be noted later in the text. Many of these reactions are important intermediate steps in catalytic processes. A particularly important type of reaction is the *insertion reaction* where a small molecule, CO, C_2F_4 or SO_2, can be inserted between a metal atom and a ligand, usually an alkyl, e.g.,

$$L_nM\text{---}CH_3 + CO \rightleftarrows L_nM\text{---}\underset{\underset{O}{\|}}{C}\text{---}CH_3$$

Some of these reactions are discussed in Chapter 28.

The catalytic effect of metal ions on many organic and inorganic reactions is due to changes in the reactivity of the ligand produced by coordination. Many of the reactions catalyzed by enzymes, in which the presence of metal atoms such as Mg^{2+}, Zn^{2+}, Cu^{2+}, etc., is essential, fall into this category. An important example is the metal ion-catalyzed decarboxylation of carboxylic acids. For dimethyloxaloacetic acid, a possible mechanism is shown in equation (5-47)

We have also discussed (page 181) the fact that ligands may act as

[32] A. Eschenmoser, *et al.*, *Angew. Chem.* (*Internat.*), **3**, 490 (1964).

bridges in transition states and that electronic effects may be transmitted from the metal atom through a ligand via the π system.

$$(5\text{-}47)$$

References

Advances in Chemistry Series, No. 37, "Reactions of Coordinated Ligands and Homogeneous Catalysis," A.C.S., Washington, D.C., 1963. A symposium collection including articles on reactions of ligands in complexes, metal ion catalysis, ring substitution reactions of cyclopentadienyls, effects of coordination on reactivity of aromatic ligands, etc.

Bailar, J. C., ed., *The Chemistry of Coordination Compounds*, A.C.S. Monograph No. 131., Reinhold, New York, 1956. General survey; many references.

Basolo, F., *Survey Progr. Chem.*, **2**, 1 (1964). A general introductory survey of substitution mechanisms of complexes.

Basolo, F., and R. G. Pearson, *Mechanisms of Inorganic Reactions*, Wiley, New York, 1958. A comprehensive text on substitution and other reaction mechanisms of complexes. Somewhat dated—see recent reviews by these authors.

————, *Adv. Inorg. Chem. Radiochem.*, **3**, 1 (1961). Review on substitution reactions of complexes.

————, *Prog. Inorg. Chem.*, **4**, 381 (1962). A review and discussion of the *trans* effect.

Berghoff, G., *Angew. Chem. (Internat.)*, **3**, 686 (1964). Review on complexes with anionic central atom surrounded by cationic ligands such as $[SAg_3]^+$, $[OBe_4]^{6+}$, etc.

Caldin, E. F., *Fast Reactions in Solution*, Wiley, New York, 1964. Includes redox and complex forming reactions and describes in detail perturbation, nmr and other methods.

Chaberek, S., and A. E. Martell, *Sequestering Agents*, Wiley–Interscience, New York, 1959.

Clifford, A. F., *Inorganic Chemistry of Qualitative Analysis*, Prentice-Hall, London, 1961. Contains much general information on complex formation and equilibria.

Collman, J. P., *Angew. Chem. (Internat.)*, **4**, 132 (1965). Substitution reactions of metal acetylacetonates.

Crow, R. D., and J. V. Westwood, *Quart. Rev.*, **19**, 57 (1965). Study of complexes by polarography.

Dwyer, F. P. and D. P. Mellor, eds., *Chelating Agents and Metal Chelates*, Academic Press, New York, 1964. Contains articles on chelates, nature of metal–ligand bond, redox potentials, chelates in biochemistry, etc.

Edwards, J. O., *Inorganic Reaction Mechanisms*, Benjamin, New York, 1964. An excellent introduction to basic kinetic theory and applications to substitution, electron transfer, free radical and other inorganic reactions.

Eigen, M., and R. G. Wilkins, in *Mechanisms of Inorganic Reactions*, Adv. in Chem. Series, No 49, p. 55, American Chemical Society, Washington, D.C. A recent survey of complex formation studies, with extensive references to literature on these and other fast reactions of complexes.

Fronaeus, S., in *Technique of Inorganic Chemistry*, Vol. I, Interscience–Wiley, New York, 1963. Methods for determination of stability constants.

Grinberg, A. A., *The Chemistry of Complex Compounds*, Pergamon Press, Oxford, 1962. A translation of a Russian text which is good on classical complex chemistry and the historical background.

Halpern, J., *Quart. Rev.*, **15**, 207 (1961). Electron transfer mechanisms in solution.

Hunt, J. P., *Metal Ions in Aqueous Solution*, Benjamin, New York, 1963. Structures of water and ionic solutions, equilibria involving complex ions, rates and mechanisms and redox reactions.

King, E. L., *How Chemical Reactions Occur*, Benjamin, New York, 1963. Introduction to chemical kinetics.

Kirschner, S., ed., *Advances in the Chemistry of the Coordination Compounds*, McMillan, New York, 1961. The plenary lectures are recommended, and also the paper by M. Eigen on water exchange and fast kinetics.

Lewis, J., and R. G. Wilkins, eds., *Modern Coordination Chemistry, Principles and Methods*, Interscience, 1960, A collection of authoritative reviews on stereochemistry, stability constants, reaction mechanisms etc.

Martell, A. E., and M. Calvin, *Chemistry of Metal Chelates*, Prentice-Hall, New York, 1952. General survey; many references.

Pearson, R. G., and M. M. Anderson, *Angew. Chem. (Internat.)*, **4**, 281 (1965). Principles and applications of nmr line broadening to exchange rates in complexes.

Perrin, D. D., *Organic Complexing Reagents*, Interscience–Wiley, New York, 1964. A useful survey of organic ligands and their applications in analysis.

Ringbom, A., *Complexation in Analytical Chemistry*, Vol. 16, *Chemical Analysis*, Interscience–Wiley, New York, 1963. Critical guide for selection of analytical methods based on complexes.

Rossotti, F. J. C., and H. Rossotti, *The Determination of Stability Constants*, McGraw-Hill, New York, 1961. Very thorough treatment.

Stability Constants of Metal Ion Complexes, Special Publication No. 17, Chemical Society, London, 1964. Authoritative and critical compilation of stability constants of metal complexes for both inorganic and organic ligands. Includes useful definitions and examples.

Strehlow, H., *Ann. Rev. Phys. Chem.*, **16**, 167 (1965). Fast reactions in solution.

Walton, R. A., *Quart. Rev.*, **19**, 126 (1965). Complexes of metal halides with alkyl cyanides.

Wells, A. F., *Structural Inorganic Chemistry*, 3rd ed., Oxford University Press, 1962. Authoritative book with references on structural aspects including complexes.

Wilkins, R. G., *Quart. Rev.*, **16**, 316 (1962). A review of kinetic and mechanistic studies.

Woldbye, F., in *Technique of Inorganic Chemistry*, Vol. IV, Interscience–Wiley, New York, 1965. Optical activity of metal complexes.

PART TWO

Chemistry of the Nontransition Elements

6

Hydrogen

6-1. Introduction

The hydrogen atom has the simplest structure of all atoms. It consists of a nucleus of charge $+1$ with a single extranuclear electron. Three isotopes are known: ^1H, ^2H (deuterium or D) and ^3H (tritium or T). Although isotope effects are greatest for hydrogen, justifying the use of distinctive names for the two heavier isotopes, the chemical properties of H, D and T are essentially identical except in matters such as rates and equilibrium constants of reactions. These effects are discussed later (Section 6-10). The normal form of the element is the diatomic molecule; various possibilities are H_2, D_2, T_2, HD, HT, DT.

Although the abundance on earth of molecular hydrogen is trivial, hydrogen in its compounds has one of the highest of abundances. Hydrogen compounds of all the elements other than the noble gases are known, and many of these are of transcendental importance. Water is the most important hydrogen compound; others of great significance are hydrocarbons, carbohydrates and other organic compounds, ammonia and its derivatives, sulfuric acid, sodium hydroxide, etc. Hydrogen forms more compounds than any other element.

Hydrogen forms the lightest of all gaseous molecules. It is a colorless, odorless gas, virtually insoluble in water. It is most easily prepared by the action of dilute acids on metals such as Zn or Fe and by electrolysis of water; industrially hydrogen may be obtained by thermal cracking of hydrocarbons, by the reduction of water by carbon (water gas reaction) and in other ways.

Hydrogen is not exceptionally reactive. It burns in air to form water and will react with oxygen and the halogens explosively under certain conditions. The gas at high temperatures will reduce many oxides either to lower oxides or to the metal. At elevated temperatures in the presence of suitable catalysts, it will react with N_2 to form NH_3. With electropositive metals and most nonmetals it forms hydrides. In the presence of platinum or platinum oxide catalysts it is able to reduce, in solution in certain organic solvents (e.g., alcohol, acetic acid), a great many organic compounds; unsaturated compounds may be reduced to saturated ones, aldehydes to alcohols, certain nitrogen compounds to ammonia or amines, etc. Although these hydrogenation reactions are heterogeneous, certain transition metal salts and complexes can react homogeneously with hydrogen at room temperature. Thus cupric acetate in quinoline and $(Ph_3P)_3RhCl$ in ethanol–benzene can function as hydrogenation catalysts, while Ag^+, MnO_4^- and other ions can be homogeneously reduced by molecular hydrogen. These low temperature reactions are believed to involve the formation of a reactive bond between the transition metal and hydrogen (see also page 203).

The dissociation of hydrogen is highly endothermic, and this accounts in part for its rather low reactivity at low temperatures:

$$H_2 = 2H \qquad \Delta H_0^0 = 103.2 \text{ kcal/mole}$$

In its low temperature reactions with transition metal species heterolytic splitting to give H^-, bound to the metal, and H^+ may occur; the energy involved here is much lower, probably ~ 30 kcal/mole. At high temperature, in arcs at high current density, in discharge tubes at low hydrogen pressure, or by ultraviolet irradiation of hydrogen, atomic hydrogen can be produced. It has a short half-life (~ 0.3 sec). The heat of recombination is sufficient to produce exceedingly high temperatures, and atomic hydrogen has been used for welding metals. Atomic hydrogen is exceedingly reactive chemically, being a strong reducing agent.

6-2. The Bonding of Hydrogen

The chemistry of hydrogen depends mainly on three electronic processes:

1. *Loss of the valence electron.* The $1s$ valence electron may be lost to give the hydrogen ion, H^+. This ion is merely the proton. Its small size ($r \sim 1.5 \times 10^{-13}$ cm) relative to atomic sizes ($r \sim 10^{-8}$ cm) and charge result in the proton having a unique ability to distort the electron cloud surrounding other atoms; the proton accordingly never exists as such, except in gaseous ion beams, and is invariably associated with other atoms or molecules in condensed phases, for example, at the H_3O^+ ion.

2. *Acquisition of an electron.* The hydrogen atom can acquire an electron, attaining the $1s^2$ structure of He, to form the hydride ion, H^-. This ion

surely exists essentially as such in the saline hydrides (e.g., KH and CaH_2), which are formed by the most electropositive metals. There are also many hydride complexes of both transition and nontransition elements. In many of these, however, the more so as the electropositive character of the metal is lowered, there is a considerable degree of covalence in the metal–hydrogen bond. Thus, there is no sharp line of demarcation between hydride complexes and the covalent hydrides mentioned in the next paragraph.

3. *Formation of an electron pair bond.* The hydrogen atom again attains the $1s^2$ structure by formation of an electron pair bond. This bond may be homopolar, as in the H_2 molecule, but in other cases has a heteropolar nature, as, for example, in HCl.

The ways in which hydrogen can bond with other elements are discussed in more detail below. The nature of the proton and the complete absence of any shielding of the nuclear charge by electron shells allow other forms of chemical activity which are either unique to hydrogen or particularly characteristic of it. Some of these are the following, which are discussed in some detail subsequently:

1. The formation of numerous compounds, often nonstoichiometric, with metallic elements. They are generally called *hydrides*, but cannot be regarded as simple saline hydrides as they almost certainly do not contain hydride ions.

2. Formation of the *hydrogen bridge bond* in electron-deficient compounds, as in 6-I.

(6-I)

3. Formation of the *hydrogen bond.*

6-3. The Hydrogen Ion

For the reaction

$$H(g) = H^+(g) + e \qquad (6\text{-}1)$$

the ionization potential is 13.595 ev ($\Delta H = 313$ kcal/mole), which is very high by comparison with other unipositive elements such as the alkali metals and indeed many other elements; it is higher even than the first ionization potential of Xe. It can therefore be shown that, with the possible exception of HF, bonds from hydrogen to other elements must be mainly covalent. For HF the bond energy is 5.9 ev. For a purely ionic bond the energy can be estimated as the sum of (1) 13.6 ev to ionize H, (2) -3.5 ev to place the electron on F and (3) -15.6 ev as an upper limit on the electrostatic energy of the ion pair H^+F^- at the observed internuclear distance in HF. The sum of these terms is -5.5 ev as an upper limit, which is not too far below the actual bond energy. For HCl, on the other hand, the experimental bond energy is 4.5 ev, whereas for a purely ionic situation we would have the sum $+13.6 - 3.6 - 11.3 = -1.5$ ev as an upper limit. Thus purely electrostatic bonding cannot nearly explain the stability of HCl.

Hydrogen can form the hydrogen ion *only* when its compounds are dissolved in media which *solvate* protons. The solvation process thus provides the energy required for bond rupture; a necessary corollary of this process is that the proton, H^+, never exists in condensed phases, but occurs always as solvates—H_3O^+, R_2OH^+, etc. The order of magnitude of these solvation energies can be appreciated by considering the solvation reaction in water

$$H^+(g) + xH_2O = H^+(aq) \qquad \Delta H = -268 \text{ kcal/mole}$$

Compounds which furnish solvated hydrogen ions in suitable solvents, such as water, are *acids*, or more particularly, *protonic acids*.

Since the most important aspect of the chemistry of the hydrogen ion is that in aqueous media, this case will be considered in more detail.

The nature of the hydrogen ion in water, which should more correctly be called the hydroxonium ion, H_3O^+, is discussed below. The hydrogen ion in water is customarily referred to as "the hydrogen ion," implying H_3O^+. The use of other terms, such as hydroxonium, is somewhat pedantic except in special cases. As a matter of convenience we shall usually write H^+ for the hydrogen ion and assume it to be understood that the ion is aquated, since in a similar manner many other cations, Na^+, Fe^{2+}, Zn^{2+}, etc., are customarily written as such, although there also it is understood that the actual species present in water are aquated species, for example, $[Fe(H_2O)_6]^{2+}$.

Water itself is weakly ionized:

$$2H_2O = H_3O^+ + OH^-$$

or

$$H_2O = H^+ + OH^-$$

Other cases of such *self-ionization* of a compound where one molecule solvates a proton originating from another are known; for example, in pure sulfuric acid

$$2H_2SO_4 = H_3SO_4^+ + HSO_4^-$$

and in liquid ammonia

$$2NH_3 = NH_4^+ + NH_2^-$$

In aqueous solutions, the hydrogen ion concentration is often given in terms of pH, defined as $-\log_{10}[H^+]$, where $[H^+]$ is the hydrogen ion activity, which may be considered to approximate to the molar concentration of H^+ ions in very dilute solutions.

At 25° the ionic product of water is

$$K_w = [H^+][OH^-] = 1 \times 10^{-14}M^2$$

This value is significantly temperature dependent. When $[H^+] = [OH^-]$, the solution is said to be neutral and $[H^+] = 1 \times 10^{-7}M$; that is, pH = 7.0. Solutions of lower pH are acid; those of higher pH, alkaline.

The standard hydrogen electrode provides the reference for all other oxidation–reduction systems. The hydrogen half-cell or hydrogen electrode is

$$H^+(aq) + e = \tfrac{1}{2}H_2(g)$$

By definition, the potential of this system is zero ($E^0 = 0.000$ v) at all temperatures when an inert metallic electrode dips into a solution of hydrogen ions of unit activity (i.e., pH = 0) in equilibrium with H_2 gas at 1 atm pressure. The potentials of all other electrodes are then referred to this defined zero. However, the absolute potentials of other electrodes may be either greater or smaller, and thus some must have positive and others negative potentials relative to the standard hydrogen electrode. While this subject is not properly an aspect of the chemistry of hydrogen, it will be briefly discussed here as a matter of convenience.

The difficulties which are sometimes caused by the so-called electrochemical sign conventions have arisen largely because the term "electrode potential" has been used to mean two distinct things:

(1) *The potential of an actual electrode.* For example, a zinc rod in an aqueous solution of zinc ions at unit activity ($a = 1$) at 25° has a potential of -0.7627 v relative to the standard hydrogen electrode. There is no ambiguity about the sign because if this electrode and a hydrogen electrode were connected with a salt bridge, it would be necessary to connect the zinc rod to the negative terminal of a potentiometer and the hydrogen electrode to the positive terminal in order to measure the potential between them. Physically, the zinc electrode is richer in electrons then the hydrogen electrode.

(2) *The potential of a half reaction.* Using the same chemical system as an example, and remembering also that the Gibbs free energy of the standard hydrogen electrode is also defined as zero, we can write:

$$
\begin{array}{ll}
Zn + 2H^+(a = 1) \to Zn^{2+}(a = 1) + H_2(g) \\
Zn \qquad\qquad\quad \to Zn^{2+}(a = 1) + 2e^-
\end{array}
\left.\begin{array}{l}\\\\\end{array}\right\}
\begin{array}{l}
\Delta G^0 = -35.18 \text{ kcal} \\
E^0 = -\Delta G^0/nF = +0.7627 \text{ v}
\end{array}
$$

$$
\begin{array}{ll}
Zn^{2+}(a = 1) + H_2(g) \to Zn + 2H^+(a = 1) \\
Zn^{2+}(a = 1) + 2e^- \quad \to Zn
\end{array}
\left.\begin{array}{l}\\\\\end{array}\right\}
\begin{array}{l}
\Delta G^0 = +35.18 \text{ kcal} \\
E^0 = -\Delta G^0/nF = -0.7627 \text{ v}
\end{array}
$$

Since metallic zinc does actually dissolve in acid solutions, under conditions specified in the definition of a standard electrode, the standard change in Gibbs free energy must be negative for the first pair of reactions and positive for the second pair. The potential of the zinc couple, defined by $\Delta G^0 = -nFE^0$ (n = number of electrons = 2, F = the Faraday), has to change sign accordingly. The half-reaction

$$Zn \rightarrow Zn^{2+} + 2e^-$$

involves oxidation and its potential is an *oxidation potential* whose sign is that of the so-called American or Latimer sign convention. The half-reaction

$$Zn^{2+} + 2e^- \rightarrow Zn$$

involves reduction and its potential is a *reduction potential* associated with the name of the European sign convention. There is no doubt about which potential is relevant provided the half-reaction to which it refers is written out in full.

Inspection shows that the reduction potential has the same sign as the potential of the actual electrode. For this reason the International Union of Pure and Applied Chemistry (IUPAC) recommended at the Stockholm meeting in 1953 that *only reduction potentials should be called electrode potentials*; this recommendation is adopted in the present edition of this text. Every half-reaction is therefore written in the form

$$Ox + ne^- \rightleftharpoons Red$$

and the Nernst equation for the electrode potential, E, is

$$E = E^0 + \frac{2.3026\,RT}{nF} \log_{10} \frac{\text{activity of oxidant}}{\text{activity of reductant}} \qquad (6\text{-}2)$$

where E^0 is the standard electrode potential, R the gas constant and T the absolute temperature. Alternatively, we may sometimes speak of the electrode potential of a couple, e.g., Fe^{3+}/Fe^{2+}, giving it the sign appropriate to the half reaction written as a reduction.

For pure water, in which the H^+ activity is only 10^{-7} the electrode potential, according to equation (6-2) is more negative than the standard potential, that is, hydrogen becomes a better reductant:

$$H^+(aq)(10^{-7}M) + e = \tfrac{1}{2}H_2 \qquad E_{298}^0 = -0.414 \text{ v}$$

In a basic solution, where the OH^- activity is $1M$, the potential is -0.83 v. In the absence of overvoltage (a certain lack of reversibility at certain metal surfaces), hydrogen is liberated from pure water by reagents whose electrode potentials are more negative than -0.414 v. Similarly, certain ions, for example the U^{3+} ion, for which the U^{4+}/U^{3+} standard potential is -0.61 v, will be oxidized by water, liberating hydrogen.

Many electropositive metals or ions, even if they do not liberate H_2 from water, will be oxidized by a greater concentration of hydrogen ions—thus the reactions of Zn or Fe are normally used to prepare H_2 from dilute acids.

The Hydroxonium Ion, H_3O^+. The lifetime of an individual H_3O^+ ion in water is exceedingly short, $\sim 10^{-13}$ second, since all of the protons are undergoing rapid migration from one O atom to another. Evidence for H_3O^+ in lattices has been obtained by nmr, infrared and Raman studies of solid hydrates of a number of acids. In these, the proton cannot occupy a lattice site on account of its negligible size and must hence (a) be present as H_3O^+ or (b) remain attached to some atom in the acid molecule as in acids such as $H_4[Fe(CN)_6]$ (page 212). Ten acids that have been shown to contain H_3O^+ are listed in Table 6-1; in oxalic and some other acids, the

TABLE 6-1
Constitution of Some Solid Acid Hydrates

Ordinary formula	Species actually present
$HF \cdot H_2O$	H_3O^+, F^-
$HCl \cdot H_2O$	H_3O^+, Cl^-
$HBr \cdot H_2O$	H_3O^+, Br^-
$HI \cdot H_2O$	H_3O^+, I^-
$HClO_4 \cdot H_2O$	H_3O^+, ClO_4^-
$HNO_3 \cdot H_2O$	H_3O^+, NO_3^-
$H_2PtCl_6 \cdot 2H_2O$	$2H_3O^+$, $PtCl_6^{2-}$
$H_2SO_4 \cdot H_2O$	H_3O^+, HSO_4^-
$H_2SO_4 \cdot 2H_2O$	$2H_3O^+$, SO_4^{2-}
$H_2SeO_4 \cdot H_2O$	H_3O^+, $HSeO_4^-$
$C_2O_4H_2 \cdot 2H_2O$	$C_2O_4H_2 \cdot 2H_2O$

proton or protons have been shown to remain attached to the acid molecule. The behavior of H_3O^+ in a crystal lattice closely resembles that of NH_4^+. Thus $[H_3O][ClO_4]$ and $[NH_4][ClO_4]$ form isomorphous crystals. An important difference between H_3O^+ and NH_4^+ compounds lies in the uniformly lower melting points of the former, which results in their being of less practical importance. The structure of the H_3O^+ ion appears to be that of a rather flat triangular pyramid with the HOH angle about 115°. There is evidence that in solution H_3O^+ binds other water molecules fairly strongly, presumably attracting an oxygen atom to each of its rather positive hydrogen atoms, so that aqueous "hydrogen ions," have the kind of structure shown in 6-II.

Another hydroxonium ion for which there is some evidence in crystals is $[H_5O_2]^+$. Infrared spectra of the hydrochloric acid adducts of *trans*-dichlorobisethylenediamine complexes of Cr, Co and Rh, such as $[Coen_2Cl_2] \cdot Cl \cdot HCl \cdot 2H_2O$, indicate that H_2O and H_3O^+ are absent and that the best formulation[1] is $[M^{III}en_2Cl_2]^+$, $[H_5O_2]^+$, $2Cl^-$.

(6-II)

HYDRIDES AND HYDRIDE COMPLEXES

6-4. The Hydride Ion, H^-; Saline Hydrides

The formation of the unipositive ion H^+ (or H_3O^+, etc.) suggests that hydrogen should be classed with the alkali metals in the periodic table. On the other hand, the formation of the hydride ion might suggest an analogy with the halogens. Such attempts at classification of hydrogen with other elements can be misleading. Hydrogen has a very low electron affinity and the tendency to form the negative ion is much lower than for the more electronegative halogen elements. This may be seen by comparing the energetics of the formation reactions:

$$\frac{1}{2}H_2(g) \rightarrow H(g) \, \Delta H = \quad 52 \text{ kcal/mole} \qquad \frac{1}{2}Br_2(g) \rightarrow Br(g) \quad \Delta H = \quad 27 \text{ kcal/mole}$$
$$H(g) + e \rightarrow H^-(g) \, \Delta H = -16 \text{ kcal/mole} \qquad Br(g) + e \rightarrow Br^-(g) \quad \Delta H = -78 \text{ kcal/mole}$$
$$\frac{1}{2}H_2(g) + e \rightarrow H^-(g) \, \Delta H = +36 \text{ kcal/mole} \qquad \frac{1}{2}Br_2(g) + e \rightarrow Br^-(g) \quad \Delta H = -51 \text{ kcal/mole}$$

Thus, owing to the endothermic character of the H^- ion, only the most electropositive metals—the alkalies and alkaline earths—form saline or salt-like hydrides, such as NaH and CaH_2. The ionic nature of the compounds is shown by their high conductivity just below or at the melting point and by the fact that on electrolysis of solutions in molten alkali halides hydrogen is liberated at the *anode*.

X-ray and neutron diffraction studies show that in these hydrides the H^- ion has a crystallographic radius between those of F^- and Cl^-. Thus the electrostatic lattice energies of the hydride and the fluoride and chloride of a given metal will be similar. These facts and a consideration of the Born–Haber cycles leads us to conclude that *only* the most electropositive metals *can* form ionic hydrides, since in these cases relatively little energy is required to form the metal ion.

[1] R. D. Gillard and G. Wilkinson, *J. Chem. Soc.*, **1964**, 1640; D. Dollimore, R. D. Gillard and E. D. McKenzie, *J. Chem. Soc.*, **1965**, 4479.

The known saline hydrides and some of their physical properties are given in Table 6-2. The heats of formation of the saline hydrides, com-

TABLE 6-2
The Saline Hydrides and Some of Their Properties

Salt	Heat of formation, kcal/mole	M—H distance, A	Apparent radius of H⁻, A[a]
NaCl type crystal structure			
LiH	21.7	2.04	1.35
NaH	14.4	2.44	1.47
KH	14.2	2.85	1.53
RbH	20.3	3.02	1.53
CsH	19.9	3.19	1.50
Orthorhombic crystal structure			
CaH_2	46.6	—[b]	—
SrH_2	42.2	—	—
BaH_2	41.0	—	—

[a] See text.
[b] There are two different sets of M—H neighbors in this lattice with separations differing by ~ 0.3 A.

pared with those of the alkali halides, which are about 100 kcal/mole, reflect the inherently small stability of the hydride ion.

For the relatively simple two-electron system in the H^- ion, it is possible to calculate an effective radius for the free ion, the value 2.08 A having been obtained. It is of interest to compare this with some other values, specifically, 0.93 A for the He atom, ~ 0.5 A for the H atom, 1.95 A for the crystallographic radius of Br^- and 0.30 A for the covalent radius of hydrogen, as well as with the values of the "apparent" crystallographic radius of H^- given in Table 6-2. The latter are obtained by subtracting the Goldschmidt radii of the metal ions from the experimental M—X distances. The value 2.08 A for the radius of free H^- is at first sight surprisingly large, being more than twice as large as that for He. This results from the facts that the H^- nuclear charge is only half that in He and that the electrons repel each other and screen each other ($\sim 30\%$) from the pull of the nucleus. It will be seen in Table 6-2 that the apparent radius of H^- in the alkali hydrides never attains the value 2.08 A and also that it decreases markedly with decreasing electropositive character of the metal. The generally small size is probably attributable in part to the easy compressibility of the rather diffuse H^- ion and partly to a certain degree of covalence in the bonds.

A crystal radius for H^- of about 1.53 A appears to be collatable with Pauling's crystal radii and is appropriate to distances in ionic crystals where the polarization is minimal.[2a]

[2a] D. F. C. Morris and G. L. Reed, *J. Inorg. Nucl. Chem.*, **27**, 1717 (1965).

7*

Chemical Properties of Saline Hydrides.   The saline hydrides are white crystalline substances of generally high reactivity, best prepared by direct reaction of the metal with hydrogen gas at temperatures up to $\sim 700°$. They can be dissolved in molten alkali halides and on electrolysis of such a solution, for example, CaH_2 dissolved in LiCl + KCl at $360°$, hydrogen is released at the anode.   LiH alone can be melted without decomposition.

A key to the reactivity of these hydrides lies in the formalism of regarding H—H as the exceedingly weak parent acid (an extrapolation back from HCl, strong, and HF, weak) of the MH salts.   Thus H^- and its salts react instantly and completely with any substance affording even the minutest traces of H^+, such as water, according to the reaction

$$NaH + H^+ = Na^+ + H_2$$

The standard potential of the H_2/H^- couple has been estimated to be -2.25 v, making H^- one of the most powerful reducing agents known.

As would be expected from the above, the saline hydrides are excellent reducing agents.   LiH and CaH_2 are often used in preparative chemistry for this purpose, and CaH_2 also serves as a drying agent, although the complex hydrides like $LiAlH_4$ or $NaBH_4$ (see below) are most generally useful.   Several of the saline hydrides ignite spontaneously in ordinary air, perhaps owing to initial exothermic hydrolysis by traces of water vapor. Thermal decomposition at high temperatures gives the metal and hydrogen.[2b]

6-5. Hydride Complexes

Hydride complexes are compounds which can be regarded, at least formally if not literally, as containing H^- ions coordinated to metal ions. In many cases such a description is very formal indeed but nonetheless often useful in interpreting chemical behavior.

1. *Nontransition elements.*   The most important hydride complexes of nontransition elements are formed by boron, aluminum and gallium, for example, $Na[BH_4]$, $Li[AlH_4]$, $Li[GaH_4]$, $U(BH_4)_4$, $Al(BH_4)_3$ and $Na[BH(OCH_3)_3]$.   All of these XH_4^- *ions* are believed to be tetrahedral since this structure has been established for the BH_4^- ion.   The discovery and study of this class of compound ($LiAlH_4$ in particular) by H. I. Schlesinger, H. C. Brown and others rank among the most important developments in inorganic chemistry in view of the broad usefulness of these hydrides as reductants and sources of the H^- ion.

The chemistry of these substances may be understood through considera-

---

[2b] For NaH, see C. C. Addison, R. J. **Pulham** and R. J. **Roy**, *J. Chem. Soc.*, **1964,** 4895.

tion of a hypothetical equilibrium representing their formation (eq. 6-3).

$$\text{H:}^- + \overset{\text{H}}{\underset{\text{H}}{\overset{..}{\text{X}}}}\text{:H} = \left[\overset{\text{H}}{\underset{\text{H}}{\text{H:}\overset{..}{\underset{..}{\text{X}}}\text{:H}}}\right]^- \qquad \text{(X = B, Al, Ga)} \qquad (6\text{-}3)$$

The XH_3 group behaves as an electron acceptor and the hydride ion as an electron donor. It might then be expected that the thermal and chemical stabilities of the three anions should then vary according to the Lewis acid behavior of XH_3. This order is B > Al > Ga. The experimental facts bear this out in general. For example, the hydrolysis of the XH_4^- ions

$$4H_2O + XH_4^- \rightarrow 4H_2 + X(OH)_3 + OH^-$$

is probably initiated by reaction of XH_4^- with H^+ to form H_2 and XH_3, the latter then reacting further. In effect, XH_3 is competing with the acceptor H^+ for the hydride ion. Thus, sodium borohydride is quite soluble in water, undergoing only a slight initial decomposition which renders the solution basic and prevents further hydrolysis. It is, of course, completely hydrolyzed in acid, but Na salts of AlH_4^- and GaH_4^- are rapidly and often explosively hydrolyzed by water alone.

The stability and other properties of a given XH_4^- salt depend also on the *nature of the cation*. While $NaBH_4$ is completely ionic, most other borohydrides and the salts of AlH_4^- and GaH_4^- show considerable covalent character. If the cation, as in $Be(BH_4)_2$ or $Al(BH_4)_3$, has considerable acceptor power, it will tend to distort the XH_4^- groups, especially AlH_4^- and GaH_4^-, where the central metal is of somewhat lower acceptor ability. Thus, as an admittedly extreme example, $Al(BH_4)_3$ is a very reactive, unstable liquid (m $-64.5°$), very soluble in organic solvents. $Be(BH_4)_3$ is a solid, but sublimes at $90°$ and is insoluble in nonpolar media. The more covalent complex hydrides are rapidly, often explosively, hydrolyzed by water and ignite in air. Structural studies required to specify clearly the nature of the bonding in these covalent compounds are lacking, but it is believed that there is hydrogen bridging between XH_4 groups and the cations similar perhaps to that postulated in BeH_2 and MgH_2 and known to exist in the boron hydrides.

The principal use of these complex hydrides is as reducing agents in both organic and inorganic chemistry. The most generally used materials are $LiAlH_4$ and $Na(K)BH_4$, which are soluble in certain ethers like diethylene glycol dimethyl ether (see pages 446 and 281).

2. *Transition elements.* These hydride complexes are for the most part very new and still rather novel compounds.[3] They are most commonly prepared by the action of BH_4^- on a halo complex though numerous

[3] M. L. Green, *Adv. Inorg. Chem. Radiochem.*, **7**, 215 (1965); A. Ginsberg, *Prog. Transition Metal Chem.*, **1**, 111 (1965).

other methods are used in particular cases. Some representative complexes are the following:

$$ReH_9^{2-}, [Rhen_2ClH]^+, [Rhen_2H_2]^+$$
$$Mn(CO)_5H, Fe(CO)_4H_2, Fe(CO)_4H^-, Co(CO)_4H$$
$$Re(C_5H_5)_2H, W(C_5H_5)_2H_2, Ta(C_5H_5)_2H_3$$
$$[M(R_2PCH_2CH_2PR_2)_2Cl_{2-x}H_x]; \quad x \leq 2; M = Fe, Ru, Os$$
$$[Ir(PR_3)_2Cl_{3-x}H_x]; \quad x \leq 3$$
$$[Pt(PR_3)_2XH]; \quad X = Cl, Br, I, SCN, NO_2, NO_3, CN$$

Particular compounds will be discussed in detail at appropriate places in the text. However, a few observations about these compounds as a class can be made here.

(a) In all cases where structural data are available,[4a] the hydrogen appears to be acting as an ordinary monatomic, uninegative ligand, viz., as H^-. Previous views that the hydrogen was sometimes bonded so that it failed to make the normal contribution to the coordination group about the metal ion have proved incorrect whenever structural data have been forthcoming.

(b) In the structural and stoichiometric senses H^- is interchangeable with ligands such as Cl^-, Br^-, I^-, SCN^-, etc., although there are some hydrido complexes which have no analogs containing these other ligands, such as ReH_9^{2-} and $Co(CO)_4H$.

(c) Hydrido complexes are usually most stable when the other ligands are of the π-acid type (see Chap. 27).

(d) It is characteristic of the coordinated H^- ion in transition metal complexes to have its nuclear resonance absorption at very high magnetic fields, namely at τ values of 15–40 compared to values of $\tau < 10$ for most hydrogen compounds. While chemical shift values of this magnitude and direction might be naively attributed to high electron density about the proton, it is now believed[4b] that more subtle electronic factors are responsible.

(e) The complexes exhibit M—H stretching bands in the infrared in the range 1700–2250 cm^{-1}.

(f) The hydride ion appears to lie between H_2O and NH_3 in the spectrochemical series[5] (see Section 26-5), but the position may depend on the nature of other ligands present on the metal atom.

6-6. Covalent Compounds of Hydrogen

The most numerous of hydrogen compounds are those in which it forms electron pair bonds with other elements; the number of carbon compounds

---

[4a] See, e.g., R. Eisenberg and J. A. Ibers, *Inorg. Chem.*, **4**, 773 (1965).

[4b] L. L. Lohr and W. N. Lipscomb, *Inorg. Chem.*, **3**, 77 (1964); A. D. Buckingham and P. J. Stephens, *J. Chem. Soc.*, **1964**, 2747.

[5] J. A. Osborn, R. D. Gillard and G. Wilkinson, *J. Chem. Soc.*, **1964**, 3168.

of hydrogen is legion, and most of the less metallic elements form numerous hydrogen derivatives. Many of these compounds are volatile, being either gases or liquids.

The chemistry of many of these compounds is highly dependent upon the nature of the element to which hydrogen is bonded; particularly dependent is the degree to which the compounds behave as acids under various conditions (see later). A few general remarks about covalent hydrogen compounds are pertinent here.

Except in H_2 itself, where the electronegativity difference is zero and the resonance structures $H^+H^- \leftrightarrow H^-H^+$ are of equal weight and contribute a few percent, all H—X bonds will possess some polar character. As will be seen subsequently, important chemical differences arise from reversal of orientation of the H—X bond dipole. In spite of the heteropolar nature of H—X bonds and in spite of the possibility of ionization and acid behavior on dissolution in a polar solvent, many compounds in this class are properly called covalent hydrides. Thus, although HCl behaves as a strong acid on dissolution in water, in nonpolar solvents, for example, in benzene, it is not dissociated and it is itself a gas. In condensed phases of such covalent hydrides there are only dipole–dipole attractions and van der Waals forces between the molecules (in some special cases hydrogen bonding occurs).

The strength of H—X bonds and the thermal stability of covalent hydrides seem to depend on the electronegativities and size of the element X. The variation in bond strength in some binary hydrides is shown in Figure 6-1. There is a fairly smooth *decrease* in bond strength with

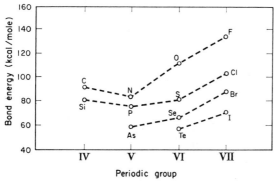

Fig. 6-1. Variation in mean H—X bond energies.

increasing Z in a periodic group and a general *increase across* any period. Thermal stability is only a crude guide to bond strength, but is useful where precise bond energies are unknown. Thermal stability, in the sense of resistance to the reaction

$$H_nX \rightarrow \tfrac{n}{2}H_2 + \tfrac{1}{x}X_x$$

invariably decreases with increasing Z. Generally, for two elements of about equal electronegativity, the *heavier* element forms the less stable hydride. Thus the stability orders $CH_4 > H_2S$ and $PH_3 > TeH_2$.

The relation of H—X bond strength to acidity in aqueous solution will be discussed on page 222.

The volatile boron hydrides (e.g., B_2H_6, B_4H_{10}) are unusual in that they are electron-deficient hydrides possessing hydrogen bridges (see Chapter 10).

6-7. Other Hydrides

We have so far discussed compounds in which the state of the hydrogen is rather definitely known. Hydrogen does, in fact, form some sort of "compound" with nearly every other element, but with those to be discussed here the nature of the substance is not always well understood. A rough attempt to classify the various types of hydrogen compounds, which are all loosely called "hydrides," is shown in Figure 6-2. The hydrides of

H																	He
Li	Be											B	C	N	O	F	Ne
Na	Mg											Al	Si	P	S	Cl	Ar
K	Ca	Sc	Ti*	V*	Cr*	Mn*	Fe*	Co*	Ni*	Cu	Zn	Ga	Ge	As	Se	Br	Kr
Rb	Sr	Y	Zr	Nb	Mo*	Tc*	Ru*	Rh*	Pd*	Ag	Cd	In	Sn	Sb	Te	I	Xe
Cs	Ba	La-Lu	Hf	Ta*	W*	Re*	Os*	Ir*	Pt*	Au	Hg	Tl	Pb	Bi	Po	At	Rn
Fr	Ra	Ac		U	Pu												

Saline hydrides | Transition metal hydrides | Borderline hydrides | Covalent hydrides

Fig. 6-2. A classification of the hydrides. The starred elements are the transition elements for which complex molecules or ions containing M—H bonds are known.

beryllium and *magnesium*, BeH_2 and MgH_2, seem to represent a transition between the ionic and covalent hydrides. Both are white nonvolatile solids, insoluble in organic media. They appear to be polymerized, and it has been suggested that this is effected by hydrogen bridging (6-III)

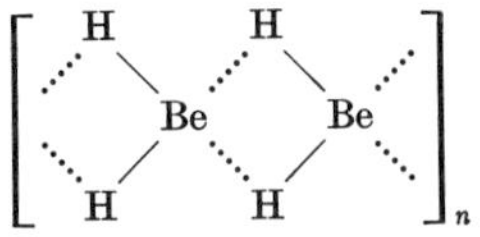

(6-III)

similar to that in the boranes. Both react violently with water, alcohols and active hydrogen in general, and both, like the saline hydrides, are powerful reducing agents.

The larger group of borderline hydrides are mostly of a very uncertain nature. Copper hydride, CuH, seems to be a definite compound, but hydrides of the other elements are certainly unstable and difficult to prepare and perhaps nonexistent. CuH is a red-brown solid with some reducing properties, insoluble in and apparently stable toward water, although decomposed by acids to liberate hydrogen.

The *transition metal binary hydrides*, also called simply *metallic hydrides*, are commonly grouped as a class for convenience rather than because of any uniformity in properties. In fact, a very wide range of behavior toward hydrogen is shown by the various elements in this group. Metal–hydrogen systems involving scandium, yttrium, some of the lanthanides, thorium uranium and plutonium have been well studied, and the behavior seems well established.

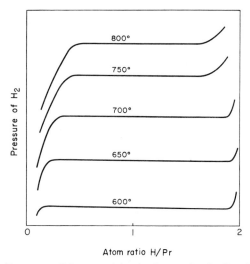

Fig. 6-3. Pressure–solid composition isotherms for the Pr—H system.

The data shown in Figure 6-3 for the Pr—H system are typical. The plateaus represent regions in which two phases, Pr and PrH_2, coexist, the latter having the fluorite structure. In the regions to the extreme left, hydrogen merely dissolves in the metal. Failure of the plateaus to reach the full H/Pr ratio of 2.00 probably means that there is a short range, between H/Pr of about 1.8 and H/Pr of 2.00, in which the PrH_2 phase can exist in a hydrogen deficient condition. Further absorption of hydrogen seems to involve the solution of hydrogen in the PrH_2 phase. With Gd and Pr the behavior in the M to MH_2 range is the same, but between GdH_2 and GdH_3 a third hexagonal MH_3 phase appears. Although it is true that, in general, specimens of these hydrides containing only one phase and having a perfectly stoichiometric composition are not isolated, perfectly well-defined hydride phases, MH_2 and MH_3, do exist. The MH_2 phases are grey solids which react with water and acids to produce hydrogen. They have metallic properties, presumably because there is still one unused valence electron per metal atom which may occupy electronic conduction bands in the solid. The heats of formation of the MH_2 phases are of the order of 40–50 kcal/mole. *Uranium hydride*, UH_3, which is a black pyrophoric powder, is formed by direct action of hydrogen on the metal. The phase relations in the U—H system show no UH_2 phase (*plutonium*, on the other hand, does also show a PuH_2 phase). UH_3 is stoichiometric with a rather complex structure, and is formed quite exothermically, $\Delta H_f{}^0 = -30.8$ kcal/mole.

Titanium, zirconium and presumably *hafnium* absorb hydrogen exothermically, giving nonstoichiometric materials with compositions such as $TiH_{1.7}$ and $ZrH_{1.9}$. The lattice changes on uptake of such quantities of hydrogen, but the phase relations have not been extensively studied. TiH_x and ZrH_x have industrial utility as reducing agents. The remaining metals in the transition group seem to have little affinity for hydrogen and do not form any well-defined binary hydrides. Several, including Fe, Co and Ni, were reported to give black pyrophoric hydrides, such as NiH_2, when suspensions of their salts in Grignard reagents were treated with hydrogen, but more recent work indicates that there are probably no such compounds. *Palladium*, alone of the group VIII metals, absorbs appreciable amounts of hydrogen gas, but H/Pd ratios do not exceed ~ 0.7 at room temperature. There is some evidence to suggest that a disordered, nonstoichiometric phase of ideal composition PdH is formed, but the exact nature of "palladium hydride" still remains uncertain.

THE HYDROGEN BOND

6-8. Experimental Evidence

Substances containing hydrogen bound to the most electronegative elements frequently exhibit properties best explained by assuming that the hydrogen atom has a small but significant affinity for other electronegative atoms while remaining strongly bonded to the first one. This relatively weak secondary bond is called the *hydrogen bond*. We shall employ the following notation for a hydrogen bond between an H atom bonded initially to atom X and another atom Y which has one or more lone pairs of electrons:

$$X—H\cdots\cdots Y$$

Some of the main lines of experimental evidence showing the existence of and defining the properties of the hydrogen bond are:

1. *Molecular association.* If the boiling points of the covalent hydrides (along with those of the noble gases and the group IV hydrides for comparison) are plotted against molecular weight as in Figure 6-4, it is at once obvious that the boiling points of H_2O, HF and NH_3 are out of line in a

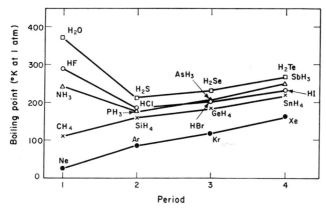

Fig. 6-4. Boiling points of some molecular hydrides.

direction indicating some additional intermolecular attraction not significantly operative in the other substances. In Figure 6-5 are shown the

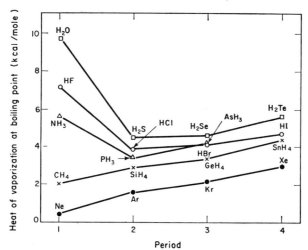

Fig. 6-5. Heats of vaporization of some molecular hydrides.

heats of vaporization of the same substances plotted against position in the periodic table. In both plots it is evident that only the hydrides of F, O and N have significant intermolecular attraction owing to the existence of strong hydrogen bonds, with HCl showing evidence of slight deviation.

Suffice it to say that all experimental evidence indicates that hydrogen bonds are most important when the elements X and Y are F, O, N or Cl. As Figures 6-4 and 6-5 indicate, methane exhibits no significant hydrogen bonding. However, if the carbon to which hydrogen is bound is also bonded to sufficiently electronegative groups, as in $HCCl_3$ and HCN, then intermolecular hydrogen bonding can occur. Figure 6-5 also shows the order of magnitude of the forces with which we are dealing, namely, energies of 1–10 kcal/mole, as compared to the range 30–100 kcal/mole for ordinary chemical bonds.

We have not yet shown proof that the above effects are indeed due to the type of hydrogen bond symbolized above. Another well-known and clear-cut case of molecular association which throws considerably more light on the details is the dimerization of carboxylic acids. For instance the acetic acid dimer has the configuration shown in Figure 6-6, and an enthalpy of dissociation of 13.8 kcal/mole of dimer.

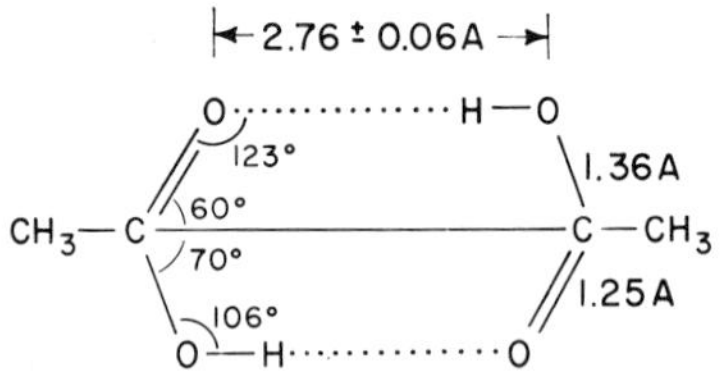

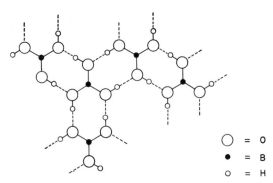

Fig. 6-6.   Structure of the acetic acid dimer.

2. *X-ray and neutron diffraction studies.* Even though the position of hydrogen atoms themselves cannot generally be determined directly by X-rays, X-ray diffraction studies have provided much knowledge about hydrogen bonds. As an example, the structure (Fig. 6-7) of orthoboric acid, H_3BO_3, was found to consist of loosely bound parallel sheets with the

Fig. 6-7.   Structure of boric acid showing hydrogen bonds

indicated geometry. The study of H_3BO_3 is exceptional in giving any indication of the hydrogen positions. Generally only the over-all X to Y distance is measured. Thus structural studies do not generally answer the question of where the proton is placed along the XY axis, or even whether the X—H····Y grouping is indeed linear. Nevertheless, the XY distances alone are significant, since they are shorter than would be found for adjacent but non-hydrogen-bonded XY pairs. Thus in crystalline $NaHCO_3$, there are four kinds of O—O distances (between O's of different bicarbonate anions) having the values 2.55, 3.12, 3.15 and 3.19 A. The last three are all approximately equal to twice the van der Waals radius of oxygen, but the first, 2.55 A, corresponds to the hydrogen-bonded pair, O—H····O. Neutron diffraction measurements can locate the hydrogen atoms because the scattering of neutrons of thermal energies (~ 0.1 ev) is roughly similar for all nuclei regardless of atomic number. Such studies have now been made on several dozen compounds.

3. *Entropy data.* We shall begin directly with a particular example, namely, ice. The structure of ice is such that each oxygen atom is surrounded tetrahedrally by four hydrogen atoms, two of which are covalently bonded to it, the other two being bonded to other oxygens but forming hydrogen bonds to the oxygen atom under consideration. Because of the existence of an extended, three-dimensional structure, it is possible for each oxygen to have the four hydrogen atoms around it paired off into two near and two far neighbors in several ways, two of which are illustrated in Figure 6-8. Now, entropy is defined, statistically, by the equation

$$S = -R \ln W$$

where R is the gas constant (~ 2.0 cal/deg) and W is the probability of the state of the system. As the temperature of a system approaches

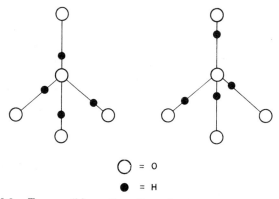

$\bigcirc$ = O

$\bullet$ = H

Fig. 6-8. Two possible configurations about an oxygen atom in ice.

absolute zero, it tends to assume the state of lowest energy, and if there is only one state, of lower energy than all others, the probability of the system being in that state at $0°K$ will be 1. Hence $S_0{}^0 = -R \ln 1 = 0$, which is the substance of the third law of thermodynamics. If, however, the above model of ice is correct—that is, if hydrogen bonds are, in fact, unsymmetrical—then there will be more than one way of arranging the H atoms to give each oxygen atom two near and two far neighbors, so that the probability of any one arrangement being frozen in as the temperature is lowered will be less than 1 and the entropy of the crystal of ice will be greater than 0. By an argument which will not be given here, it can be shown that the probability of any particular arrangement (in the sense required by the above equation) is $\frac{2}{3}$, giving the frozen-in entropy the value 0.81. Experimentally, from a comparison of thermodynamic and spectroscopic entropies, the value 0.81 ± 0.05 is obtained, giving excellent confirmation of the unsymmetrical model. It should be clear that if the OHO groups were symmetrical, then no zero point configuration entropy could occur.

Similar confirmation of the consequences of an unsymmetrical hydrogen bond has been obtained for other crystals, for example, KH_2PO_4 and $Ag_2H_3IO_6$.

Notably, there is no residual entropy found for KHF_2 which contains the ions K^+ and $(FHF)^-$. Moreover, nuclear resonance studies confirm the symmetrical arrangement in the FHF^- ion. Because of the paucity of data on hydrogen atom positions, other confirmed cases of symmetrical hydrogen bonds are few. It is generally agreed that as the $O \cdots O$ (or, in general, $X \cdots X$) distance decreases the bonds become more nearly symmetrical, but the distance (if any) at which there exists a single potential energy minimum exactly in the middle of the $O \cdots O$ line is unknown. Some authors have suggested that this may occur at a distance of ~ 2.45 A but others argue that it is unlikely to occur, if it does at all, at a distance greater than ~ 2.30 A. For potassium hydrogen maleate and a few other compounds diffraction studies indicate symmetrical bonding although it is difficult to be sure whether this is true or only statistical centering of the hydrogen atom.[6] Broad infrared bands (see below) occur in these compounds and also in some cyanide acids, e.g., $H_3Ir(CN)_6$, where symmetrical bonding N—H—N may be present.[7]

4. *Infrared evidence.* When the grouping X—H enters into hydrogen bond formation with the atom Y, the X—H stretching frequency (cm^{-1}) is

[6] G. E. Bacon and N. A. Curry, *Acta Cryst.*, **13**, 717 (1960); S. W. Peterson and H. A. Levy, *J. Chem. Phys.*, **29**, 948 (1958).

[7] D. F. Evans, D. Jones and G. Wilkinson, *J. Chem. Soc.*, **1964**, 3164; A. P. Ginsberg and E. Koubek, *Inorg. Chem.*, **4**, 1186 (1965).

lowered. Thus infrared studies provide a convenient diagnostic test for hydrogen bonding. There is a fairly smooth relation between the XY distance and the X—H stretching frequency but the relationship between frequency shifts and the energies of hydrogen bonds appears to be only a rough and qualitative one.

Depression of the X—H stretching frequency shows the existence of hydrogen bonding in many cases where it seems likely that a bent X—H$\cdots$Y grouping may exist. An example of this type is *o*-nitrophenol (6-IV). Another case, of importance in the following theoretical discussion,

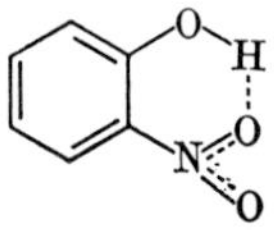

(6-IV) 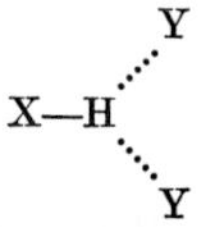   (6-V)

is that of the $(HF)_n$ polymer, which has the zigzag arrangement shown in Figure 6-9. Bifurcated hydrogen bonds, that is, the arrangement 6-V, are

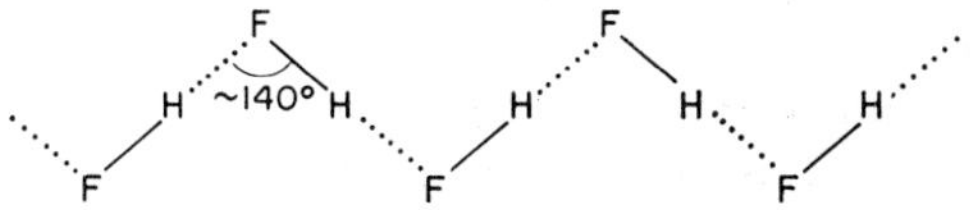

Fig. 6-9.   Structure of the hydrogen-bonded polymer of HF.

quite rare but have been found in a few instances.

Some examples of the parameters involved in H bond formation are given in Table 6-3. It will be noted that with decreasing X$\cdots$Y distance both $\Delta\nu$ and the bond energy increase.

TABLE 6-3

Some Parameters of Hydrogen Bonds

Bond	Compound	Bond energy, kcal/mole	Depression of str. freq., cm^{-1}	Bond length,[a] A	X—H distance, A
F—H—F	KHF_2	~ 27	~ 2700	2.26	1.13
F—H$\cdots$F	HF(g)	~ 6.8	700	2.55	
O—H$\cdots$O	$(HCOOH)_2$	7.1	~ 600	2.67	
O—H$\cdots$O	$H_2O(s)$	~ 5	~ 400	2.76	0.97
O—H$\cdots$O	$B(OH)_3$			2.74	1.03
N—H$\cdots$N	Melamine	~ 6	~ 120	3.00	
N—H$\cdots$Cl	N_2H_5Cl		~ 460	3.12	

[a] The distance between the hydrogen-bonded atoms X and Y.

6-9. Theory of Hydrogen Bonding

In order to account for the existence of hydrogen bonds we must consider the possible contributions of covalent bonding, resonance and electrostatic attraction and attempt to assess the importance of each. In short, we must ask how much each of the possible canonical structures 6-VI, 6-VII and 6-VIII contributes to the bond energy. It is certain that

$$\overset{\delta^-}{X}\text{—}\overset{\delta^+}{H}\text{——}\overset{\delta^-}{Y} \qquad X\text{—}H \quad :Y \leftrightarrow X\overset{-}{:} \quad H\text{——}\overset{+}{Y} \qquad \overset{\delta^-}{X}\text{—}\overset{\delta^+}{H}\cdots\overset{\delta^-}{Y}$$

| (6-VI) | (6-VIIa) | (6-VIIb) | (6-VIII) |

Covalence   Resonance   Electrostatic attraction

structure 6-VI, involving the coexistence of two covalent bonds to hydrogen is completely negligible, since it would require the use of the $2s$ or $2p$ orbitals of hydrogen, and these are of such high energy as to be essentially useless for bonding.

Theoretical work is concerned with the relative contributions of 6-VII and 6-VIII and leads to the conclusion that the resonance represented by 6-VII is of importance *only* for the *strongest, shortest bonds*. It has been estimated, for example, that in an O—H····O bond with the O—O distance 2.78 A, and the O—H distance 1.0 A (fairly typical parameters), structure 6-VIIb appears in the over-all wave function to the extent of only about 4%. Thus, it is believed that most hydrogen bonds are *basically electrostatic*; but this then raises another question. If unshared electron pairs are concentrated along the direction of hybrid orbitals, will the proton approach the atom Y preferentially along these directions? In other words, does the proton see the atom Y as a structureless concentration of negative charge or as an atomic dipole? The answer to this question is not entirely clear cut, because in most cases where the angle θ in 6-IX is in accord with

$$\overset{Y\cdots\cdots\cdots H\text{—}X}{\underset{Z}{\diagup \theta}}$$

(6-IX)

the latter idea, it is possible to attribute this to steric requirements, as in carboxylic acid dimers or o-nitrophenol, or it can be equally well explained on the simpler theory as in the case of HCN polymers which are linear. However, the case of the $(HF)_n$ polymer (and a few others) seems to lend strong support to the hypothesis of preferred directions, since there appears to be no other reason why the structure should not be linear.

For the FHF⁻ ion with its symmetrical structure a molecular orbital treatment has been proposed. The situation is formally somewhat similar to that in some other F—X—F molecules (see page 407). Thus, using a p or sp hybrid orbital on each F atom directed toward H and the $1s$ orbital of H, it is possible to form three 3-center MO's, viz., a bonding orbital, a non-bonding orbital and an antibonding orbital. The two electron pairs originally occupying the F orbitals then occupy the bonding and the nonbonding MO's, giving the equivalent of two H—F bonds each of order 0.5. This approach can, in principle, be generalized to deal with unsymmetrical hydrogen bonds as well, but it has not as yet been subjected to detailed study.

Recent infrared studies have shown that hydrogen bonding can also occur between any polar X⁻—H⁺ group and a highly polarizable atom or molecule. Thus, although pure HBr and HI show no significant tendency to associate by hydrogen bonding because there is too little electronegative character to the halogen atoms in these molecules, a strongly positive hydrogen, such as that found, for example, in a phenol OH group, will form strong hydrogen bonds to the polarizable Br and I atoms in many compounds. Hence, instead of the initial attraction between H(δ^+) and Y(δ^-) there is attraction between H(δ^+) and the negative end of a dipole induced in the polarizable atom, Y, viz.,

$$\overset{\delta^-}{X}—\overset{\delta^+}{H}\cdots\overset{(\delta^- - \delta^+)}{Y}—$$

Other interesting examples of this dipole–induced dipole type of hydrogen bond are those formed between very polar $\overset{\delta^-}{X}$—$\overset{\delta^+}{H}$ groups, especially O—H groups, and polarizable multiple bonds such as isolated double bonds and benzene rings[8] (Fig. 6-10), and, in a few cases, transition metal atoms.

Fig. 6-10.   Examples of intramolecular hydrogen bonding of OH groups to polarizable π electron clouds.

---

[8] For X-ray study see A. T. McPhail and G. A. Sim, *Chem. Comm.*, **1965**, 124; M. R. Basila, E. L. Saier and L. R. Cousins, *J. Amer. Chem. Soc.*, **87**, 1665 (1965), contains many references.

SPECIAL PROPERTIES OF THE HYDROGEN ATOM
AND THE HYDROGEN MOLECULE

6-10. The Isotopes of Hydrogen: Deuterium and Tritium

Naturally occurring hydrogen contains 0.0156% deuterium, while tritium occurs naturally in only minute amounts believed to be of the order of 1 in 10^{17}.

Tritium is formed continuously in the upper atmosphere by cosmic ray-induced nuclear reactions. Thus, fast neutrons arising from cosmic ray reactions can produce tritium by the reaction $^{14}N(n, {}^3H)^{12}C$. Tritium is radioactive (β^-, 12.4 years) and is believed to be the main source of the minute traces of ^3He found in the atmosphere. It can be made artificially in nuclear reactors, for example, by the reaction of thermal neutrons with lithium, $^6Li(n,\alpha)^3H$. It is available commercially for use as a tracer in reaction mechanism studies.

Deuterium as D_2O is separated from water by fractional distillation or electrolysis and by utilization of very small differences in the free energies of the H and D forms of different compounds, the H_2O–H_2S system being particularly favorable in large scale use:

$$HOH(l) + HSD(g) = HOD(l) + HSH(g) \qquad K \approx 1.01$$

Deuterium oxide is commercially available in ton quantities and is used as a moderator in nuclear reactors both because it is effective in reducing the energies of fast fission neutrons to thermal energies and because deuterium has a much lower capture cross section for neutrons than has hydrogen and hence does not reduce appreciably the neutron flux. Deuterium is also widely used in the study of reaction mechanisms and in spectroscopic studies.

Isotope Effects. For many years deuterium and more recently tritium have found wide application as tracers. Usually the value of a tracer arises from the fact that, although its difference in mass or its radioactivity permits its detection, it is chemically identical with the ordinary atoms of the element. For most elements a change of one or several mass units in the nucleus is such a small percentage change that, owing to the very indirect way in which nuclear mass can affect chemical behavior, the chemical differences between isotopes are not detectable. However, for the lightest elements, B, C, N and especially H, reactions involving different isotopes do proceed at slightly but measurably different rates. This is often turned to good purpose in detailed studies of reaction mechanisms. In biological systems the substitution of deuterium for hydrogen can alter the delicately balanced processes substantially. In the case of deuterium the difference is not so great as to detract from its use as a tracer, although occasionally caution is necessary in the interpretation of data. Tritium, however, is so much heavier than H that one cannot assume *as a matter of course* that any given tritium compound will react by exactly the same path as its hydrogen analog. However, it is fair to say that even for hydrogen the chemistry of all isotopes is basically the same.

6-11. Ortho and Para Hydrogen

Molecular hydrogen exhibits the phenomenon of ortho and para forms to a marked degree. This is not peculiar to hydrogen, but will occur with all homonuclear diatomic molecules in which the nuclei have spin. In ortho hydrogen the nuclear spins are aligned, and in para hydrogen they are opposed. The equilibrium between the two forms as a function of temperature is shown in Figure 6-11. The interconversion of the two forms

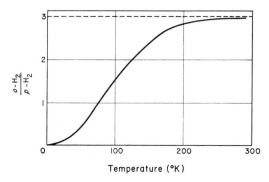

Temperature (°K)

Fig. 6-11. Equilibrium ratio o-H_2/p-H_2 as a function of temperature.

is not thermally activated to any appreciable extent until temperatures high enough to cause dissociation and recombination are reached. Hence, if hydrogen is prepared at any given temperature, the equilibrium ortho/para ratio characteristic of that temperature persists at other temperatures indefinitely unless the interconversion is catalyzed. This may be done by adsorption on activated charcoal or through the influence of very strong magnetic fields such as those encountered by hydrogen adsorbed on the surface of a paramagnetic material. In fact, the latter process has been utilized for the measurement of paramagnetism. It will be noted from Figure 6-11 that by equilibrating on a catalyst at a very low temperature essentially pure para hydrogen can be made, but that it is not possible in this way to obtain pure ortho hydrogen. However, ortho and para hydrogen have been separated by gas chromatography. The two forms differ very slightly in certain physical properties such as thermal conductivity, which provides a method of analysis. They are chemically equivalent, however.

The reason why the existence of ortho and para forms is of greater importance for hydrogen than for other diatomic molecules arises because of the very low mass in the following way. The total molecular wave function can be written

$$\psi_T = \psi_e\psi_t\psi_v\psi_r\psi_{ns}$$

where ψ_T must, according to Pauli's principle, be antisymmetric. The ψ's are respectively the electronic, translational, vibrational, rotational and nuclear spin wave functions. Now the product $\psi_e\psi_t\psi_v$, if the molecules are in electronic and vibrational ground states, is symmetric so that for ψ_{ns} symmetric (o-H_2) ψ_r is antisymmetric, and vice versa, since there must be an odd number of antisymmetric ψ_i's to make ψ_T antisymmetric. Furthermore, only those rotational states having j even are symmetric, only those having j odd are antisymmetric. For most molecules the moment of inertia is so large that the separation of rotational states is small relative to kT even at low temperatures; thus both ortho and para molecules populate a host of rotational states in an almost classical distribution, and there is then practically no difference in their energy or specific heat. For H_2, however, with its uniquely small moment of inertia, only the lowest few states are populated even at room temperature, so that at and below 300°K the differences in energy and heat capacity of para and ortho hydrogen molecules (i.e., those in the states $J = 0, 2$ and $J = 1, 3$, respectively) are uniquely large.

For D_2, on account of the different spin of the nucleus, the ortho–para relationship is the *opposite* of that in H_2. The ortho form is the more stable and can be obtained pure at low temperatures.

STRENGTHS OF PROTONIC ACIDS IN WATER

Protonic acids are substances which ionize to give an anion and a proton solvated by the solvent, which is to say in water, $[H_{2n+1}O_n]^+$. This discussion will be explicitly limited to strengths of acids in water. The strength of an acid is dependent not only on the nature of the acid itself, but also on the medium in which it is dissolved; as an extreme example, nitric acid is an acid in water

$$HNO_3 + nH_2O = [H_{2n+1}O_n]^+ + NO_3^-$$

whereas in liquid hydrogen fluoride it functions quite differently, behaving as a base (H^+ acceptor):

$$HNO_3 + nHF = [H_2NO_3]^+ + [F_nH_{n-1}]^-$$

Protonic acids may be broadly classed into two groups. There are *oxo acids* in which the acidic protons are bound to oxygen, which in turn is bound to a central atom, that is, X—O—H, and *binary acids* in which protons are directly bound to a central atom, X—H.

TABLE 6-4

Strengths of Oxo Acids, H_nXO_m, in Water

$(m - n)$	Examples	$-\text{Log } K_1$ (pK_1)	$-\text{Log } K_2$ (pK_2)	$-\text{Log } K_3$ (pK_3)
0	HClO	7.50	—	—
	HBrO	8.68	—	—
	H_3AsO_3	9.22	?	?
	H_4GeO_4	8.59	13	?
	H_6TeO_6	8.80	?	?
	[H_3PO_3	1.8	6.15	—]
	H_3BO_3	9.22	?	?
1	H_3PO_4	2.12	7.2	12
	H_3AsO_4	3.5	7.2	12.5
	H_5IO_6	3.29	6.7	~ 15
	H_2SO_3	1.90	7.25	—
	H_2SeO_3	2.57	6.60	—
	$HClO_2$	1.94	—	—
	HNO_2	3.3	—	—
	[H_2CO_3	6.38 (3.58)	10.32	—]
2	HNO_3	Large neg. value	—	—
	H_2SO_4	Large neg. value	1.92	—
	H_2SeO_4	Large neg. value	2.05	—
3	$HClO_4$	Very large neg. value	—	—
	$HMnO_4$	Very large neg. value	—	—
[-1(?)]	H_3PO_2	2	?	?]

6-12. Oxo Acids

For oxo acids certain useful generalizations may be made concerning (a) the magnitude of K_1 and (b) the ratios of successive constants, K_1/K_2, K_2/K_3, etc. The value of K_1 seems to depend upon the charge on the central atom. Qualitatively it is very reasonable to suppose that the greater the positive charge, the more will the process of proton loss be favored on electrostatic grounds. It has been found that if this positive charge is taken to be the so-called formal charge, semiquantitative correlations are possible. The formal charge in an oxo acid, H_nXO_m, is computed in the following way, assuming the structure of the acid to be $O_{m-n}X(OH)_n$. Each X—(OH) bond is formed by sharing one X electron and one OH electron and is thus *formally* nonpolar. Each X—O bond is formed using two X electrons and thus represents a net loss of one electron by X. Therefore, the formal positive charge on X is equal to the number of X—O bonds, hence equal to $(m - n)$. It may be seen from the data in Table 6-4 that, with the exception of the acids listed in brackets, which are special cases to be discussed presently, the following relations between $(m - n)$ (or formal positive charge on X) and the values of K_1 hold:

For $m - n = 0$,
$$pK_1 \sim 8.5 \pm 1.0 \ (K \sim 10^{-8} \text{ to } 10^{-9})$$
For $m - n = 1$,
$$pK_1 \sim 2.8 \pm 0.9 \ (K \sim 10^{-2} \text{ to } 10^{-4})$$
For $m - n \gtrsim 2$,
$$pK_1 \ll 0 \text{ (the acid is very strong)}$$

It will also be noted that the difference between successive pK's is 4–5 with very few exceptions.

H_3PO_3 obviously is out of line with the other acids having $m - n = 0$ and seems to fit fairly well in the group with $m - n = 1$. This is, in fact, where it belongs, since there is independent evidence (page 512) that its structure is $OPH^*(OH)_2$ with H^* bonded directly to P. Similarly, H_3PO_2 has a pK_1 which would class it with the $m - n = 1$ acids where it, too, belongs since its structure is $OP(H^*)_2(OH)$, with the two H^* hydrogen atoms directly bound to P.

Carbonic acid is exceptional in that the directly measured pK_1, 6.38, does not refer to the process

$$H_2CO_3 = H^+ + HCO_3^-$$

since carbon dioxide in solution is only partly in the form of H_2CO_3, but largely present as more loosely hydrated species, $CO_2(aq)$. When a correction is made for the equilibrium

$$CO_2(aq) + H_2O = H_2CO_3(aq)$$

the pK_1 value of 3.58 is obtained which falls in the range for other $m - n = 1$ acids (see also page 308).

Before leaving the subject of oxo acids, we may note that many metal ions whose solutions are acidic may be regarded as oxo acids. Thus, although the hydrolysis of metal ions is often written as shown here for Fe^{3+}

$$Fe^{3+} + H_2O = Fe(OH)^{2+} + H^+$$

it is just as valid thermodynamically and much nearer to physical reality to recognize that the ferric ion is coordinated by water molecules, very likely six, and write

$$[Fe(H_2O)_6]^{3+} = [Fe(H_2O)_5(OH)]^{2+} + H^+ \qquad K_{Fe^{3+}} \approx 10^{-3}$$

From this formulation it becomes clear why the ferrous ion, with a lower positive charge, is less acidic or, in alternative terms, less hydrolyzed than the ferric ion

$$[Fe(H_2O)_6]^{2+} = [Fe(H_2O)_5(OH)]^+ + H^+ \qquad K_{Fe^{2+}} \ll K_{Fe^{3+}}$$

It should be noted that one cannot necessarily compare the acidity of the divalent ion of one metal with that of the trivalent ion of *another* metal in this way, however. There appears to be no good general rule concerning the acidities of hydrated metal ions at the present time, although some attempts have been made at correlations.

6-13. General Theory of Ratios of Successive Constants

It was pointed out many years ago by Niels Bjerrum that the ratios of successive acid dissociation constants could be accounted for in a nearly quantitative way by electrostatic considerations. Consider any bifunctional acid, HXH,

$$HXH = HX^- + H^+ \qquad K_1$$
$$HX^- = X^- + H^+ \qquad K_2$$

There is a purely statistical effect which can be considered in the following way. For the first process, dissociation can occur in two ways (i.e., there are two protons, either of which may dissociate), but recombination in only one; whereas in the second process, dissociation can occur in only one way, but recombination in two (i.e., the proton has two sites to which it may return and hence twice the probability of recombining). Thus, on purely statistical grounds one would expect $K_1 = 4K_2$. Bjerrum observed that for the dicarboxylic acids, $HOOC(CH_2)_nCOOH$, the ratio K_1/K_2 was always greater than four, but decreased rapidly as n increased (see Table 6-5). He suggested the following explanation. When the two

TABLE 6-5

K_1/K_2 Ratio for Dicarboxylic Acids,
$HOOC(CH_2)_nCOOH$

n	K_1/K_2
1	1120
2	29.5
3	17.4
4	12.3
5	11.2
6	10.0
7	9.5
8	9.3

points of attachment of protons are close together in the molecule, the negative charge left at one site when the first proton leaves strongly restrains the second one from leaving by electrostatic attraction. As the separation between the sites increases, this interaction should diminish.

By making calculations using the Coulomb law,* Bjerrum was able to obtain rough agreement with experimental data. The principal difficulty in obtaining quantitative agreement lies in a choice of dielectric constant since some of the lines of electrostatic force run through the molecule ($D \sim 1$–10), others through neighboring water molecules (D uncertain), and still others through water having the dielectric constant (~ 82) of pure bulk water. More recently, Kirkwood and Westheimer were able to get nearly quantitative agreement with the data by making very elaborate calculations which take into account the variability of the dielectric constant. The important point here for our purposes is to recognize the physical principles involved without necessarily trying to obtain quantitative results.

Thus, the large separations in successive pK's for the oxo acids are attributable to the electrostatic effects of the negative charge left by the dissociation of one proton upon the remaining ones. In bifunctional binary acids, where the negative charge due to the removal of one proton is concentrated on the very atom to which the second proton is bound, the separation of the constants is extraordinarily great. K_1 and K_2 for H_2S are $\sim 10^{-7}$ and $\sim 10^{-14}$, respectively, whereas for water we have

$$H_2O = H^+ + OH^- \qquad K_1 = 10^{-14}$$
$$OH^- = H^+ + O^{2-} \qquad K_2 < 10^{-36} \text{ (est.)}$$

6-14. Binary Acids

Factors determining the strengths of binary acids may best be discussed in terms of a thermodynamic cycle. Consider an acid, HX, which dissociates in solution according to the equation

$$HX(aq) = H^+(aq) + X^-(aq)$$

The dissociation constant, K, is related to the change in Gibbs free energy by the relation

$$\Delta G^0 = -RT \ln K \qquad (6\text{-}4)$$

and the free energy change is in turn related to the changes in enthalpy and entropy via the relation

$$\Delta G = \Delta H - T\Delta S \qquad (6\text{-}5)$$

---

* $F \propto q_1 q_2 / D r^2$, where F is the force; q_1 and q_2 the charges, separated by r; and D is the dielectric constant of the medium between them.

in which R is the gas constant and T is the absolute temperature, which we shall take to be 298° in the following discussion. The dissociation process may be considered as the sum of several other reactions (that is, as one step in a thermodynamic cycle). Table 6-6 summarizes the Gibbs free

TABLE 6-6

Free Energy Changes for Dissociation of HX Molecules in Water
at 298°, kcal/mole

Process	HF	HCl	HBr	HI
$HX(aq) = HX(g)$	5.7	-1	-1	-1
$HX(g) = H(g) + X(g)$	127.8	96.5	81.0	65.0
$H(g) = H^+(g) + e$	315.3	315.3	315.3	315.3
$X(g) + e = X^-(g)$	-83.0	-87.6	-82.5	-75.3
$H^+(g) + X^-(g) = H^+(aq) + X^-(aq)$	-361.5	-332.8	-325.7	-317.7
$HX(aq) = H^+(aq) + X^-(aq)$	4.3	-10	-13	-14
$pK_a(= \Delta G^0/1.36)$	3.2	-7.4	-9.5	-10

energy changes for these several steps. It can be seen that HF is out of line with the other three HX acids principally in two respects. (1) It has an exceptionally high free energy of bond breaking, and (2) the F^- ion has an exceptionally high hydration energy. The first of these disfavors acid dissociation while the second favors it. However the first factor is larger and predominates.

It is further to be noted that the entropies of bond breaking are nearly the same for all the HX molecules (21.2 cal mol^{-1} deg^{-1} for HI, increasing smoothly to 23.8 for HF) so that one can say, on the basis of equation 6-5, that the main cause of the weakness of HF as an acid in aqueous solution is the strength of the HF bond. It is also worth noting that relatively small changes in enthalpies or free energies make large changes in equilibrium constants, as shown by equation 6-4. A change of 1.36 kcal/mole at 298° in the bond energy would change K by a factor of 10. Thus a decrease of only about 6 kcal/mole in the H—F bond energy would make K_a about 10 and HF, therefore, a strong acid.

The foregoing discussion of the hydrogen halides exemplifies the principles necessary in understanding the strengths of binary acids generally.

6-15. Clathrates, Gas Hydrates and Other Enclosure Compounds

There are certain substances formed by combining one stable compound with another or with an atomic or molecular element without the existence of any chemical bonds between the two components. This occurs when one of the compounds can crystallize in a very open structure containing cavities, holes or channels in which atoms or molecules of the other can be trapped. Those compounds in which the *host* lattice contains cavities like cages are the most important type; they are called *clathrate* compounds, from the Latin *clathratus*, meaning "enclosed or protected by cross bars or grating." Since most of these, and the important ones certainly, involve hydrogen-bonding it is convenient to discuss them in this chapter.

One of the first clathrate systems to be investigated in detail, and still one of the best understood, are the substances in which the host is β-quinol. Quinol clathrates have been prepared enclosing O_2, NO, CH_4, SO_2,* HCl, HBr, Ar, Kr, Xe, HCOOH, HCN, H_2S, CH_3OH and CH_3CN.

Crystallization of solutions of quinol (p-dihydroxybenzene, p-$C_6H_4(OH)_2$) in water or alcohol under pressure of 10–40 atm of, say, krypton, produces crystals, often up to 1 cm in length, which are readily distinguishable from the crystals of ordinary quinol† (α-quinol), even visually. These crystals contain the noble gas trapped in the lattice of β-quinol. On dissolving the crystals in water, or on heating, the gas is released. The crystals are stable and can be kept for years.

Such trapping of the gases is made possible by the occurrence of cavities in the crystal lattices of certain compounds. X-ray analysis indicates that in β-quinol, three quinol molecules form an approximately spherical cage of free diameter ~4 A with the quinol molecules being bound together by hydrogen bonds (see 6-X, in which the circles represent oxygen atoms,

(6-X)

* It may be noted that the SO_2 quinol clathrate was discovered by Wohler in 1848, although the nature of the solid was not elucidated until the work of Powell.

† o-Quinol exists in three crystalline modifications, the ordinary form being α-quinol. One of the other modifications is the β form which gives the lattice cages in clathrate compounds. The pure form can be obtained by crystallization from n-propyl alcohol by addition of a seed crystal of the argon clathrate; the seed can be removed subsequently from the mass by inspection. The pure β form has empty cages; it transforms spontaneously into the thermodynamically more stable α-quinol on standing.

the lines hydrogen bonds between them, and the benzene rings are omitted for clarity). The free volumes are in the form of isolated cavities, and the apertures leading from one cage to another through the crystal are very small in diameter. Molecules trapped within these cavities during formation of the crystal are unable to escape. As a molecule approaches the cage walls, it will experience repulsive forces.

Since three quinol molecules are required to form each cavity, the limiting ratio of quinol to trapped atom or molecule for the composition of clathrates is $3:1$. This ratio is reached for acetonitrile, but for the noble gases various composition ranges may be obtained depending on conditions—for example, $C_6H_4(OH)_2/Kr$, $3:0.74$; $C_6H_4(OH)_2/Xe$, $3:0.88$—and normally the cages are incompletely filled.

Since the free diameter of the quinol cage in a clathrate compound is ~ 4 A, only molecules of appropriate size may be expected to be trapped. Thus, although CH_3OH forms quinol clathrates, C_2H_5OH is too large and does not. On the other hand, not all small molecules may form clathrates. Helium does not, the explanation being that the He atom is too small and can escape between the atoms of the quinol molecules which form the cage. Similarly, neon has not been obtained in a quinol clathrate as yet. Water, although of a suitable size, also does not form a clathrate; in this case the explanation cannot be a size factor, but may lie in the ability of water molecules to form hydrogen bonds which enables them to approach the cage walls and thus escape through gaps in the walls.

A second very important class of clathrates are the *gas hydrates*. When water is solidified in the presence of certain atomic or small molecular gases, as well as some substances such as $CHCl_3$ which are volatile liquids at room temperature, it forms one of several types[9] of very open structure in which there are cages occupied by the gas or other guest molecules. These structures are far less dense than the normal form of ice and are unstable with respect to the latter in the absence of the guest molecules. There are two common gas hydrate structures, both cubic. In one the unit cell contains 46 molecules of H_2O connected to form six medium size and two small cages. This structure is adopted when atoms (Ar, Kr, Xe) or relatively small molecules (e.g., Cl_2, SO_2, CH_3Cl) are used, generally at pressures greater than one atmosphere for the gases. Complete filling of only the medium cages by atoms or molecules, X, would give a composition $X \cdot 7.67H_2O$, while complete filling of all cages (8) would lead to $X \cdot 5.76H_2O$. In practice, complete filling of all cages of one or both types is seldom attained and these formulas therefore represent limiting rather than observed compositions. For instance, the usual formula for chlorine

[9] M. V. Stackelberg and B. Muethen, *Z. Elektrochem.*, **62**, 130 (1958), and earlier papers cited therein.

hydrate (see page 561) is $Cl_2 \cdot 7.3H_2O$. The second structure, often formed
in the presence of larger molecules of liquid substances (and thus sometimes
called the liquid hydrate structure) such as chloroform and ethyl chloride,
has a unit cell containing 136 water molecules with eight large cages and
sixteen smaller ones. It has been suggested[10] that the anesthetic effects
of substances such as chloroform is due to the formation of liquid hydrate
crystals in brain tissue.

It may also be noted here that the large negative entropy of solution of
argon in water may be due to the formation of an orientated water sheath
around the dissolved atoms. Addition of small quantities of dioxan leads
to a rapid increase in the entropy of solution, presumably destroying the
water structure around the argon atoms.[11]

A third notable class of clathrate compounds is formed when salts of
tetraalkylammonium ions or sulfonium ions crystallize from aqueous solu-
tion with high water content,[12] for example, $[(n\text{-}C_4H_9)_4N]C_6H_5CO_2 \cdot 39.5H_2O$
or $[(n\text{-}C_4H_9)_3S]F \cdot 20H_2O$. It has been shown that the structures of
these substances are very similar to the gas and liquid hydrate structures
in a general way though different in detail. Some compounds are, in fact,
practically isostructural with the first of the cubic structures described
above, whereas there are others which have tetragonal, orthorhombic or
monoclinic structures. These *salt hydrate* structures consist of clathrate
frameworks constructed mainly of hydrogen bonded water molecules but
apparently including also the anions (e.g., F^-) or parts of the anions
(e.g., the O atoms of the benzoate ion). The cations and parts of the
anions (e.g., the C_6H_5C part of the benzoate ion) occupy cavities in an incomplete and random way.

An additional relationship between the gas hydrate and salt hydrate
structures has been recently indicated by the discovery that bromine
hydrate, $Br_2 \cdot \sim 8.5H_2O$, crystallizes in neither of the cubic gas hydrate
structures but rather is nearly isostructural with the tetragonal tetra-*n*-
butylammonium salt hydrates. Its ideal, limiting composition would be
$Br_2 \cdot 8.6H_2O$.

The formation of enclosure compounds has a number of useful applications. Argon can be separated from neon by clathrate formation, and
enrichment of Xe over Kr can be obtained.

Clathrate compounds can be utilized to study the physical properties of
isolated molecules under conditions where measurements could not nor-

[10] L. Pauling, *Science*, **134**, 15 (1961); S. L. Miller, *Proc. Nat. Acad. Sci. (U.S.A.)*, **47**,
    1515 (1961).
[11] A. Ben-Naim and G. Moran, *Trans. Faraday Soc.*, **61**, 861 (1965).
[12] G. A. Jeffrey, *et al., J. Chem. Phys.*, **31**, 1231 (1959); **35**, 1863 (1961); **37**, 2219, 2231
    (1962).

mally be made. Thus the magnetic susceptibility of the oxygen molecule in β-quinol has been measured at temperatures from 1 to 20°K. Nitric oxide can be studied similarly.

Nickel cyanide in ammonium hydroxide solution crystallizes with enclosed benzene and similar substances. In one crystallization of $Ni(CN)_2NH_3 \cdot C_6H_6$, benzene of $99.992 \pm 0.002\%$ purity can be obtained.

The compound trithymotide, $C_{33}H_{36}O_6$ (6-XI), has been resolved into its d and l forms by formation of clathrates of formula $2C_{33}H_{36}O_6R$, where R can be benzene, chloroform or numerous hydrocarbons. If d- or l-trithymotide

(6-XI)

is crystallized with some solvent, R, which is itself a dl mixture, cavities of the d or l crystal enclose preferentially the d or l form of the solvent molecule. sec-Butyl bromide has been resolved in this way.

Although not classifiable as clathrate compounds, many other crystalline substances have holes, channels or honeycomb structures which allow inclusion of foreign molecules, and many studies have been made in this field. Urea is an example of an organic compound which in the crystal has parallel continuous uniform capillaries; it may be utilized to separate straight chain hydrocarbons from branched chain ones, the latter being unable to fit into the capillaries.

Among inorganic lattices which can trap molecules, the best known are the crystalline zeolites, which are aluminosilicates. These are the so-called "molecular sieves" which are discussed on page 473.

References

Advances in Chemistry Series, No. 39, "Non-stoichiometric Compounds," A.C.S., Washington, D.C. Contains several contributions on metallic hydrides and an article on clathrate compounds.

Bell, R. P., *The Proton in Chemistry*, Cornell University Press, Ithaca, New York, 1960. A lucid account of hydrogen ions in solution and acid–base behavior.

Britton, H. S., *Hydrogen Ions*, 4th ed., Chapman Hall, London, 1955.

Brodowski, H., *Z. Physik. Chem.* (*Frankfurt*), **44**, 129 (1965). The Pd–H system.

Emmett, P. H., ed., *Catalysis*, Vols. III–V, Reinhold, New York, 1955–57. These volumes cover various aspects of hydrogenation and other reactions involving hydrogen.

Frankenberg, W. G., V. I. Komarewsky and E. K. Rideal, eds., *Advances in Catalysis*, Academic Press, New York, annually from 1948. These volumes discuss various aspects of hydrogenation and other reactions involving hydrogen.

Gibb, T. R. P., *Progr. Inorg. Chem.*, **3**, 315 (1962). An extensive discussion of the nature of metallic hydrides.

Gillespie, R. J., in G. A. Olah, ed., *Friedel–Crafts and Related Reactions*, Vol. I, Interscience, Wiley, 1963. Discussion of protonic acids.

Gold, V., *pH Measurement*, Methuen, London, 1950.

Gold, V., and D. P. N. Satchell, *Quart. Rev.*, **9**, 51 (1955). Isotope effects.

Hadzi, D., ed., *Hydrogen Bonding*, Pergamon Press, New York, 1959.

Hagen, Sister M., *Clathrate Inclusion Compounds*, Reinhold, New York, 1962.

Halpern, J., *Advan. in Catalysis*, **11**, 301 (1959); *3rd Internat. Congress on Catalysis*, Vol. I, p. 146, North Holland Publ. Co., Amsterdam, 1965. Reactions of hydrogen in homogeneous solutions.

Hurd, D. T., *Introduction to the Chemistry of the Hydrides*, Wiley, New York, 1952. A general survey.

Janz, G. J., and S. S. Danyluk, *Chem. Rev.*, **60**, 209 (1960). Conductivities of hydrogen halides in anhydrous polar organic solvents.

Katz, J. J., in *Chemical and Biological Studies with Deuterium*, Pennsylvania State Univ., 1965. Physical properties and isotope effects including biological effects.

Libowitz, G. G., *Solid State Chemistry of Binary Metal Hydrides*, Benjamin, New York, 1965.

Mandelcorn, L., *Chem. Rev.*, **59**, 827 (1959). A comprehensive review on clathrate compounds.

Mikheeva, V. I., *Hydrides of the Transition Elements*, U.S. Atomic Energy Commission, A.E.C.-tr-5224, (1962). Office of Technical Service, Dept. of Commerce, Washington, D.C. A review with 678 references.

Murphy, G. M., ed., *Production of Heavy Water*, National Nuclear Energy Series, Vol. VIII-4F, McGraw-Hill, New York, 1955.

Pimentel, G. C., and A. L. McClellan, *The Hydrogen Bond*, Freeman and Co., San Francisco, 1960. A thorough, readable book with extensive tables of data and bibliography.

Siegel, B., *J. Chem. Educ.*, **38**, 484 (1961). A review of the reactions of atomic hydrogen.

Sokolskii, D. V., *Hydrogenation in Solutions*, Oldbourne Press, London, 1965. Comprehensive Russian source book.

Steacie, F. W. R., *Atomic and Free Radical Reactions*, 2nd ed., American Chemical Society Monograph, No. 125, Reinhold, New York, 1954. Chemistry of atomic hydrogen.

Westheimer, F. H., *Chem. Rev.*, **61**, 265 (1961). Hydrogen and deuterium isotope effects.

Wiberg, K. B., *Chem. Rev.*, **55**, 713 (1955). Isotope effects.

7

The Elements of the First Short Period

7-1. General Nature of the Elements

At He, $Z = 2$, the $1s$ shell is filled, and the next element, Li, $Z = 3$, has a single electron in the $2s$ orbital. With increasing Z, in Be, B, C, N, O and F, the electrons successively fill the $2s$ and $2p$ levels until the next closed configuration, $1s^22s^22p^6$, is reached at neon. The seven elements Li–F are often referred to as the elements of the *first short period* of the periodic table. They constitute the first members of the *groups* of elements in the table.

Although these elements have some properties in common with the heavier elements of their respective groups—which is, of course, to be expected in view of the similarity in the outer electronic structures of the gaseous atoms (e.g., N, $2s^22p^3$; P, $3s^23p^3$)—they nevertheless show highly individual behavior in many important respects. For example, the normal state of nitrogen is as gaseous N_2 molecules, whereas P, As and Sb form tetraatomic molecules, such as P_4, and are solids at room temperature. There are, in several cases, sufficiently striking differences between the first and succeeding members of a group to detract considerably from the usefulness of regarding these first members as prototypes for their *congeners*. Whereas Li, Be, O and F show, on the whole, more important similarities than important differences with respect to their congeners, B, C and especially N have chemical resemblances to their congeners which, aside from parallel oxidation states, are more formal than real. For example, stoichiometrically analogous halides, oxides and oxo acids of N and P are otherwise almost completely unrelated, whereas those of P are fairly similar to those of As and Sb. Hence we treat the first short period separately, proceeding thereafter to consider the remaining elements by groups.

The increase in nuclear charge and the consequent changes in the extra-nuclear arrangement of electrons in going from Li to F result in extremes

229

of physical and chemical character. Some important physical properties of the elements are given in Table 7-1. The range of chemical properties can be briefly indicated as follows:

Lithium is a low-melting, highly electropositive metal, and its chemistry is mainly that of the Li^+ ion in the solid state and in solution.

Beryllium is also metallic, but is less electropositive and reactive than Li; the discrete Be^{2+} ion does not exist in solution or lattices even in BeF_2 or BeO, there being a great tendency for Be to form at least partially covalent bonds.

Boron is essentially nonmetallic in the elemental state; it does not form simple B^{3+} cations, and its compounds contain predominantly covalent bonds. It has an extensive chemistry in combination with oxygen (borates) and with carbon in organoboron compounds and forms a unique series of hydrides.

TABLE 7-1

Some Physical Properties of Elements in the First Short Period

Element	Normal state	Melting point, °C	Boiling point, °C
Li	Silvery white, soft metal[a]	179	1340
Be	Grey, fairly hard metal[b]	1285	2970
B	Crystalline solid[c] or brownish amorphous powder	~2200	?
C	Colorless, hard crystals (diamond) grey, unctuous solid (graphite)	3850	?
N	Colorless, diatomic gas	−201.5	−195.8
O	Colorless, diatomic gas	−218.9	−182.96
F	Very pale, yellow diatomic gas	−223	−187

[a] Body-centered cubic lattice; atomic radius, 1.56 A.

[b] Hexagonal close-packed lattice; atomic radius, 1.05 A.

[c] Boron has at least four polymorphic forms; at least three are built mainly or entirely of boron icosahedra.

Carbon is completely nonmetallic. Its chemistry is dominated by the formation of four covalent bonds, by formation of carbon–carbon bonds (catenation), and by ready formation of multiple bonds to itself, nitrogen and oxygen.

Nitrogen exists normally as the diatomic gas N_2, which is very unreactive because of the great strength of the N≡N triple bond. Its compounds are covalent, usually involving three single bonds, although multiple bonds also occur. Under special circumstances the nitride ion, N^{3-}, can exist.

Oxygen normally exists as a paramagnetic, diatomic gas. It forms well-defined oxide ions, O^{2-}, in many crystals and OH^- ions in crystals and in solution (where they are doubtless hydrated via hydrogen bonds). Oxides may also be covalent, for example, SO_3.

Fluorine is a diatomic gas and is extremely reactive. It forms both ionic compounds containing F^- ions and covalent compounds containing X—F bonds; owing to the high electronegativity of fluorine, these bonds generally have considerable ionic character.

7-2. Ionization Potentials, Electron Affinities and Electronegativities

The first ionization potentials of the gaseous atoms increase, though not monotonically, from Li to F as shown in Figure 7-1 and Table 7-2. The low ionization potential of Li is in accord with the fact that its chemistry is dominated by electron loss to form the Li^+ ion. The first (9.32 ev) and second (18.21 ev) ionization potentials of Be are sufficiently high that total

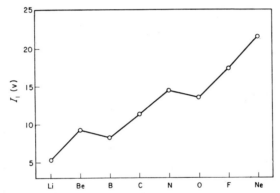

Fig. 7-1.   First ionization potentials of the elements Li–Ne.

loss of both electrons to give Be^{2+} ions does not occur; BeX bonds (even Be—F) therefore have appreciable covalent character, and "Be^{2+} ions" in solution are strongly aquated to give $[Be(OH_2)_4]^{2+}$ and more complicated hydrolyzed species. For the succeeding elements, the absence of any simple cations under any conditions is to be expected from the high ionization potentials.

The I's of the elements B, C, N increase regularly, but they are all lower than the values which would be predicted by extrapolation from Li and Be. This is because p electrons are less penetrating than s electrons; they are therefore shielded by the s electrons and are more easily removed. Another discontinuity occurs between N and O. This one is due to the fact that the $2p$ shell is half full (i.e., is $p_x p_y p_z$) at N, and the p electrons added in O, F and Ne are all going into p orbitals already singly occupied. Hence, they are partly repelled by the p electron already present in the same orbital and are thus less tightly bound.

TABLE 7-2
Electronic Properties of the Elements Li–Ne

	Li	Be	B	C	N	O	F	Ne
Electronic structure								
1s	↑↓	↑↓	↑↓	↑↓	↑↓	↑↓	↑↓	↑↓
2s	↑	↑↓	↑↓	↑↓	↑↓	↑↓	↑↓	↑↓
2p			↑	↑ ↑	↑ ↑ ↑	↑↓ ↑ ↑	↑↓ ↑↓ ↑	↑↓ ↑↓ ↑↓
First ionization potential, ev	5.390	9.320	8.296	11.264	14.54	13.614	17.42	21.559
Electron affinity,[a] ev	0.54	~ −0.6	~0.2	1.25	N^-: ~0.0; N^{3-}: −10 to −20	O^-: 1.47; O^{2-}: ~ −6.8	3.45	—
Electronegativities	1.0	1.5	2.0	2.6	3.1	3.5	4.0	
Unpaired electrons	1	0	1	2	3	2	1	0
Normal valence	1	2	3	4	3	2	1	0
Typical compounds	$LiCl$ LiC_3H_7	$BeCl_2$ $BeSO_4$	BCl_3 $B(OH)_3$ B_2H_6	C_2H_6 CCl_4 $HC{\equiv}CH$	NH_3 NF_3 Li_3N	H_2O $NaOH$ $(CH_3)_2O$	ClF KF CF_4	

[a] Many of these numbers are estimates with rather wide and indefinite uncertainties and should not be taken too literally.

Like the ionization potentials, the electron affinities rise from Li to F, and the atoms become more electronegative, as indicated in Table 7-2. The consequent tendency toward anion formation becomes noticeable at carbon, which forms $C_2{}^{2-}$ and other polyatomic anions, although the existence of C^{4-} ions is uncertain. N^{3-} ions are stable in some ionic nitrides, whereas O^{2-} and F^- ions are common and important. F^- is relatively stable in water, whereas O^{2-} is completely hydrolyzed:

$$O^{2-} + H_2O = 2OH^- \qquad K \gtrsim 10^{22}$$

$$F^- + H_2O = HF + OH^- \qquad K \approx 10^{-11}$$

7-3. Formation of Electron Pair Bonds

Single Bonds. Table 7-2 recapitulates the previously discussed (Chapter 3) fact that the elements Be, B and C have fewer unpaired electrons in their ground state atoms than the number of electron pair bonds they normally form. This has been explained in terms of promotion to valence states having the requisite numbers of unpaired electrons. Similar promotions are, of course, also required for the congeners of these elements.

There is an important empirical rule, which has a theoretical basis, concerning the valence of these elements. This is the *octet rule*. It states that these atoms tend to be surrounded by eight electrons in their compounds and, more rigorously true, are never surrounded by more than eight electrons (in the valence shell).

Let us consider the idea that eight valence shell electrons are a maximum. This means that the maximum number of electron pair bonds is four. In the first row atoms, only the orbitals of the second principal shell can be used for bond formation because any other free orbitals are of far too high energies to be useful. For example, phosphorus, with the configuration $3s^23p^33d^0$, can be excited to a valence state of configuration $3s^13p^33d^1$ with an expenditure of energy so modest that the heat of formation of the two additional bonds will more than compensate for it. On the other hand, promotion of nitrogen, $2s^22p^3$, to any state with five unpaired electrons, such as $2s^12p^33d^1$, would require such an enormous promotion energy that it could not be offset by the additional bond formation energy. The same type of argument can be made for all of the elements of the first short period. Thus all of them have only four orbitals energetically suitable for bond formation, cannot form more than four electron pair bonds, and can be surrounded by no more than eight electrons in the valence shell.

In the case of carbon the valence of four can be attained by promotion from the $2s^22p^2$ state to the $2s2p^3$ state. For nitrogen, only three of the five electrons can possibly be unpaired, in oxygen only two, and in fluorine

8*

only one, so that these elements are limited to valences of 3, 2 and 1, respectively. On the other side of carbon, namely, in Li, Be and B, the valences are less than four, not for lack of four low energy orbitals but for lack of electrons to occupy those orbitals. Thus by electron sharing, these elements can exhibit valences of only 1, 2 and 3, respectively.

However, the atoms with four energetically useful orbitals and fewer electrons have a strong drive to use their unoccupied orbitals. Also, atoms with too many electrons have a tendency to utilize these electrons. Thus compounds of boron, such as BCl_3, BF_3 and $B(CH_3)_3$, readily form adducts with nitrogen compounds such as NH_3, $N(CH_3)_3$, etc., as illustrated in Figure 7-2; boron makes use of an available but empty orbital, and nitrogen

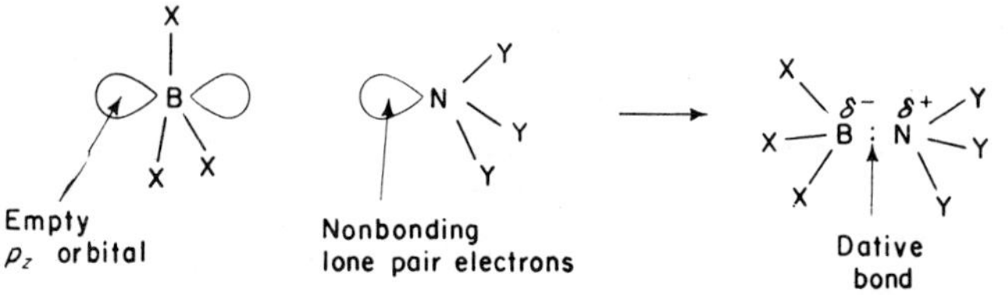

Fig. 7-2. The formation of a dative bond between boron in a BX_3 acceptor and nitrogen in an NY_3 donor.

makes use of an "idle" pair of electrons. Oxygen compounds, ethers, for example, which have unshared electron pairs also function as *donors* with boron compounds in which boron functions as an *acceptor*. The bond formed is called a *dative bond* (dative meaning "giving"). The number of atoms surrounding a given atom, X, is called the *coordination number* of X. The maximum coordination number of first row elements is four. Carbon attains this by forming four bonds since its valence is also four. Boron frequently attains maximum coordination by functioning as an acceptor, nitrogen by functioning as a donor. Oxygen *tends* to increase its coordination number from two to as high as four, but there are not a great many instances in which it gets beyond three. Beryllium, however, usually achieves four coordination by binding two donor atoms in addition to forming two ordinary covalent bonds. Boron also uses its orbitals in 3-center and multicenter bonds in the boron hydrides and other electron deficient compounds.

The reason why some atoms succeed in increasing their coordination numbers from three to four, but seldom from two to four, can be understood if we consider the polar nature of the dative bond. The donor molecule and the acceptor molecule are both electrically neutral. When the dative bond is formed, the donor atom has, in effect, lost an electron charge, rendering it positive, since it then has only half ownership of an electron pair which formerly belonged entirely to it. The acceptor atom, conversely, now has an extra negative charge. This would be true for complete sharing of the electron pair (7-I); lesser polarity is introduced if the electron pair is still more the property of the donor atom than the acceptor (7-II), in which case we indicate only charges δ^+ and δ^- on the atoms.

$$\overset{-e \quad +e}{\text{B : N}}\qquad\qquad \overset{\delta^- \qquad\quad \delta^+}{\text{B....: N}}\qquad\qquad \overset{\overset{\delta^+}{\cdot\cdot} \quad \delta^-}{\text{R—O: BX}_3}$$

$$\text{(7-I)}\qquad\qquad\qquad \text{(7-II)}\qquad\qquad\qquad \underset{\underset{\text{(7-III)}}{\text{R}}}{|}$$

This charge separation can only be accomplished by doing work against coulomb forces, which we must assume is more than compensated by the bond energy when a stable system results. However, if we take a case where one donor bond has already been formed (7-III), we see that the other unshared pair on oxygen is further restrained by the positive charge on O arising in the dative bond already formed. There is thus much more coulombic work to be done in forming a second dative bond and apparently enough to make this process energetically unfavorable. Of course, steric hindrance between the first acceptor and a second would also militate against addition of a second. It will be noted that this electrostatic argument is basically the same as that used by Niels Bjerrum to explain the relative values of dissociation constants in a polyfunctional acid (Chapter 6). Be^{2+} probably achieves four-fold coordination in aqueous solution, as $[Be(H_2O)_4]^{2+}$. In this case it is likely that the forces between Be^{2+} and H_2O are more in the nature of ion–dipole coulomb forces than $Be{\leftarrow}O$ dative bonding forces. There are many other beryllium compounds in which the metal atom becomes four coordinate.

Multiple Bonds. The elements C, N and O characteristically form multiple bonds with themselves and with one another. Their congeners do not, however (or at least only to a minor degree and by different mechanisms as in P=O, S=C and S=O). We have seen that a multiple bond can be viewed, in MO theory, as a σ bond plus one or two π bonds, and we have seen how the π orbitals of two atoms can overlap to give π bonding MO's. The reasons why Si, P and S do not characteristically form double bonds, in contrast to C, N and O, have not been fully elucidated. The most probable reason is that in order to approach closely enough to get good overlap of $p\pi$ atomic orbitals, the heavier atoms would encounter large repulsive forces due to overlapping of their filled inner shells, whereas the small compact inner shell of the first row elements (i.e., just $1s^2$) does not produce this repulsion. At any rate, multiple bond formation is an important feature of the elements of the first short period but not, significantly, of their congeners.

Reference

Bent, H. A., *Chem. Rev.*, **61**, 275 (1961).   A review on the structure of, and hybridization in, compounds of the first row elements.

8

Lithium

GENERAL REMARKS

8-1. Valence and Bonding

The lithium atom has a single valence electron, and lithium is the first member of the closely allied group I or alkali metals, Li, Na, K, Rb, Cs, (Fr), all of which have a single electron in an s orbital outside a noble gas core (distinction from Cu, Ag, Au). The chemistry of these elements is accordingly the simplest of any group. Here also, the similarity between the first member and its congeners is rather great, although the uniquely small size of the lithium atom and ion does lead to some notable differences in chemical behavior which will be detailed below. The low ionization potential (5.39 ev) results in the ready formation of the Li^+ ion, which exists as such in crystalline salts, for example, LiCl. In solutions the ion is heavily solvated and may be written $Li^+(aq)$ in water. Lithium can also form covalent bonds, Li—X. The vapor of the metal, although predominantly monatomic, contains about 1% of the diatomic molecule, Li_2, near the boiling point. These molecules are detected by their characteristic band spectrum. Although to a first approximation the Li—Li bond might be considered as due to s–s overlap, more detailed study indicates that there is some s–p hybridization, which gives a bond with $\sim 14\%$ p character. The Li—Li bond energy, 27 kcal/mole, is rather low and the Li—Li distance is 2.67 A. There are lithium compounds, such as C_2H_5Li and C_3H_7Li, which behave like typical covalent compounds, being quite volatile and soluble in nonpolar solvents. There is no evidence for oxidation states other than $+1$, nor would they be expected in view of the noble gas configuration of Li^+ and the very high second ionization potential (75.2 ev).

237

Some typical lithium compounds are listed in Table 8-1.

TABLE 8-1

Some Typical Lithium Compounds and Their Properties

Compound	Color and form	Melting point, °C	Solubility
Li	Silvery white, soft metal	179	Liquid NH_3 and certain amines
Li_2O	White solid (CaF_2 structure)	1700	Reacts with H_2O to give LiOH
LiOH	White, tetragonal crystals	450	12.8 g/100 g of H_2O at 20°
LiF	White, cubic crystals	842	Sp. sol. H_2O (0.27 g/100 g at 18°)
LiCl	White, cubic crystals	614	V. sol. H_2O, methanol
Li_2CO_3	White, monoclinic crystals	723	1.5 g/100 g of H_2O at 0°
$LiNO_3$	White, trigonal crystals	264	55.7 g/100 g of H_2O at 0°; pyridine
$LiClO_4$	White, rhombic crystals	236	V. sol. H_2O; sol. alcohols, ethers
LiH	White, crystalline (NaCl structure)	688	Insol. ethers, hydrocarbons
$LiCH_3$	White, crystalline	—	Insol. benzene, ligroin
LiC_2H_5	Colorless crystals	90	Sol. benzene, ligroin
LiC_6H_5	Colorless powder	—	Sl. sol. benzene

8-2. Comparison of Lithium and its Congeners

Although, as stated above, Li in most ways has properties typical of all group I metals, there are some differences which also provide resemblances to the chemistry of Mg. The anomalies of Li result mainly from the small size of the atom and the ion; the polarizing power of Li^+ is the greatest of all the alkali ions and leads to a singularly great tendency toward solvation and covalent bond formation.

1. The reactivity of the group I metals toward all chemical reagents except nitrogen increases with increasing electropositive nature (Li → Cs). Li is usually the least reactive. Li is only rather slowly attacked by water at 25°, whereas Na reacts vigorously, K inflames, and Rb and Cs react explosively. With liquid Br_2, Li and Na barely react, whereas the others do so violently. Lithium will not liberate the weakly acidic hydrogen in $C_6H_5C \equiv CH$, whereas the other alkali metals do so. However, with N_2, it is uniquely reactive to give Li_3N (Mg also reacts to give Mg_3N_2). At 25° the reaction is slow, but is rapid on heating. Both Li and Mg can be used to remove nitrogen from other gases. Finally, metallic lithium is harder and higher melting than the other group I metals.

2. Lithium hydride, LiH, is far more stable than the other group I hydrides and can be melted without decomposition; it is unaffected by oxygen below red heat, by chlorine or by HCl. The heat of formation of LiH is greater than those of the other alkali metal hydrides (cf. Chapter

6). These facts have led to some confusion because in some places it is stated that Li is more reactive toward hydrogen (and also carbon) than the other alkalies. This is not ·so, since Li reacts with H_2 at 600–700°, whereas the others react at 350–400°. For carbon, the statement is more nearly correct—both Li and Na react directly with carbon on heating to form the *acetylides* Li_2C_2 and Na_2C_2. The heavier alkalies also react with carbon, but give nonstoichiometric interstitial compounds where the metal atoms enter between the planes of carbon atoms in the lamellar graphite structure. This difference may be attributed to size requirements for the metal both in the ionic acetylides (M^+, C_2^{2-}) and in the penetration of the graphite.

3. Only lithium oxide, Li_2O (with a trace of Li_2O_2), is formed on burning the metal in air or oxygen. The other alkali oxides, M_2O, react further giving peroxides, M_2O_2, and (with K, Rb and Cs) superoxides, MO_2. This difference may again be attributed to the small size of Li^+ which makes it unable to stabilize the larger anions relative to the O^{2-} ion.

4. Lithium hydroxide, LiOH, unlike the other hydroxides, MOH, decomposes at red heat to Li_2O (cf. Mg, Ca, etc.); NaOH, KOH, etc., sublime unchanged, mainly as dimers. LiOH is also considerably less soluble in water (4 moles/liter at 10°) than NaOH (12 moles/liter at 10°) or other alkali hydroxides.

5. Lithium hydrosulfide, LiSH, is not stable under ordinary conditions, whereas other MSH compounds are.

6. Lithium carbonate, Li_2CO_3, is relatively thermally unstable with respect to Li_2O and CO_2 compared to the other alkali carbonates (cf. $MgCO_3$). This is because the small Li^+ ion makes the Li_2O lattice more stable compared with the Li_2CO_3 lattice than are the other M_2O lattices compared to the M_2CO_3 lattices.

7. Lithium is the only alkali metal to form an imide, Li_2NH. This is a very reactive substance formed by heating the amide, $LiNH_2$.

$$2LiNH_2 = Li_2NH + NH_3$$

8. Lithium alkyls and aryls are usually liquids or low-melting solids soluble in hydrocarbons. Methyllithium, CH_3Li, is less fusible and soluble and thus resembles the alkyls and aryls of the other alkalies.

9. The solubilities of various lithium salts resemble those of Mg salts and often differ noticeably from those of the other group I elements. Thus, while LiCl, LiBr and LiI are highly soluble in H_2O, LiF is relatively insoluble and can be precipitated by ammoniacal ammonium fluoride (like Mg^{2+}). LiCl, LiBr and particularly LiI are quite soluble in oxygenated organic solvents (like Mg^{2+}); also, $LiClO_4$ (like Mg^{2+}, Ca^{2+}, Sr^{2+} and Ba^{2+} perchlorates) is remarkably soluble in oxygenated organic solvents

such as alcohol, acetone or ethyl acetate. $NaClO_4$ is less soluble by factors of 3–12, whereas $KClO_4$, $RbClO_4$ and $CsClO_4$ have solubilities only 10^{-3} of these. Since the spherical ClO_4^- ion is virtually nonpolarizable and the alkali metal perchlorates form ionic crystals, the high solubility of $LiClO_4$ is most likely attributable to strong solvation of the Li^+ ion. Magnesium perchlorate, $Mg(ClO_4)_2$, which has solubility properties similar to $LiClO_4$, is a very effective drying agent, also because of strong solvation of the cation. LiBr in hot concentrated solution has the unusual property of dissolving cellulose. LiBr and also $LiClO_4$ form ammoniates with ammonia or amines.

10. Lithium *sulfate*, Li_2SO_4, in contrast to the other M_2SO_4 salts, does not form alums. It is also not isomorphous with the other sulfates. Lithium *sulfite*, Li_2SO_3, is also unusual in that it oxidizes in moist air or when moist, with evolution of heat.

THE ELEMENT

8-3. Occurrence, Isolation and Properties

The most important lithium minerals are *lepidolite*, $Li_2(F, OH)_2Al_2$-$(SiO_3)_3$, and *spodumene*, $LiAl(SiO_3)_2$. Two isotopes of Li occur in nature: ^6Li, 7.30% and ^7Li, 92.7%.

In view of the high standard potential

$$Li^+(aq) + e = Li \qquad E^0 = -3.045 \text{ v}$$

the metal cannot be made by electrolysis of aqueous solutions of lithium salts; this produces the hydroxide. The metal can be obtained by electrolysis of a fused salt, usually LiCl, or by electrolysis of LiCl in pyridine, ethanol or acetone. It is soft, silver white, and much less reactive than the other alkali metals. Freshly cut surfaces tarnish in air owing to oxide and nitride formation, but the reaction with water is not so vigorous as to inflame the hydrogen.

The metal is relatively light, the density being 0.53 g/cm^3. It has the highest melting and boiling points, 179 and 1317°, and also the longest liquid range of all the alkali metals. It also has an extraordinarily high specific heat (0.784 cal/g °C at 0°). These properties make it an excellent coolant in heat exchangers, but it is also very corrosive—more so than other liquid alkalies—which is a great practical disadvantage. It is also used to deoxidize, desulfurize and generally degas copper and copper alloys. It is extensively used in the preparation of organolithium compounds, as well as LiH and $LiAlH_4$.

Like other electropositive metals, lithium dissolves in liquid ammonia and in various amines (e.g., ethylamine) to give blue solutions which conduct electricity. The nature of such solutions is discussed in more detail elsewhere (page 417), but we may state here that their properties are consistent with the existence of solvated Li^+ ions and solvated electrons. Solutions of lithium in amines, particularly in ethylenediamine, $H_2NCH_2CH_2NH_2$, are powerful reducing agents used in organic chemistry. The reactions of lithium metal are summarized in Table 8-2.

TABLE 8-2

Some Reactions of Lithium Metal

Reagent	Products
Water, slow at 25°	LiOH, H_2
Oxygen, 100°	Li_2O
Hydrogen, 700–800°	LiH
Nitrogen, 25–200°	Li_3N
Ammonia (liquid) and certain amines	Blue solutions catalytically (Fe) decomposed to amide, $LiNH_2$, which on heating gives imide, Li_2NH
Alkyl, aryl halides in petrol or ether	Organolithium compounds, RLi
Alcohols	Alkoxides, ROLi, $+H_2$
Nonmetals, heating	Li_2C_2, Li_2S, Li_3P, etc.
Isoprene, butadiene, styrene	Polymers

LITHIUM COMPOUNDS

8-4. Ionic Salts; the Hydrated Li^+ Ion

The stoichiometries and general properties are mostly similar to those of the other alkali metals, with the exceptions already discussed above.

Salts with common anions such as Cl^-, SO_4^{2-} are highly ionic under all conditions. Thus the fused salts conduct electricity. Owing to its small size, the Li^+ ion has a large hydration energy, and it is often hydrated in its solid salts when the same salts of other alkalies are unhydrated, viz., $LiClO_4 \cdot 3H_2O$. For salts of *strong* acids, the lithium salt is usually the *most* soluble in water of the alkali metal salts, whereas for *weak* acids the lithium salts are usually *less* soluble than those of the other alkalies.

Lithium fluoride is a white crystalline solid, only slightly soluble in water (0.27 g/100 g at 18°) and insoluble in alcohol. It is used in welding fluxes and as massive crystals in infrared spectrometers because of its excellent dispersion in the range 4000–1600 cm^{-1}. Lithium chloride is the most common lithium salt. It is very soluble in water and moderately soluble in oxygenated or basic organic liquids, such as alcohols, ketones, esters and pyridine. Such substances doubtless strongly solvate the lithium ion, thus overcoming the lattice forces.

The vapors of the halides contain polymeric species—mainly dimers and trimers; for $(LiF)_2$ and $(LiF)_3$, the dissociation energies are 58.9 and 38.3 kcal/mole, respectively. $(LiCl)_2$ has been shown to be a planar, diamond-shaped molecule in the gas phase.

The *hydrated ion*, Li^+(aq), occurs both in solution and in some hydrous salts. Although the number of water molecules strongly bound to Li^+ in water cannot be estimated very exactly, it is certain that an ion with a very small crystallographic radius has a very large hydrated radius because it binds dipolar water molecules very effectively. Thus the Li^+(aq) ion in water doubtless has a larger effective radius than Cs^+(aq) (3.40 A *vs* 2.28 A, estimated). In spite of the strong solvation in solution, crystalline hydrates seldom have more than four H_2O molecules per Li^+ ion, and exceptions are very likely owing to hydration of anions. Lithium salts in solution generally deviate from ideal solution behavior, yielding solutions of abnormal colligative properties such as very low vapor pressure, freezing point, etc.

Lithium hydroxide formed in solution from Li_2O or directly from Li is a strong base like all alkali hydroxides. It absorbs CO_2 from the air, either in solution or in the solid state, to form Li_2CO_3. Since LiOH is a strong base, lithium salts of weak acids ($LiCO_3$, Li_2S, etc.) are hydrolyzed in solution and give pH's > 7. LiOH is less soluble (4 moles/liter, at 0°) than NaOH (12 moles/liter, at 0°).

The metal reacts directly with most nonmetallic and some metallic elements, but the products are of no special interest. The nitrogen compounds $LiNH_2$, Li_2NH and Li_3N are known; they are hydrolyzed to ammonia by water. The hydride and borohydride have been discussed in Chapter 6; the latter is soluble not only in water but in ethers such as tetrahydrofuran and is a very useful reducing agent. The borohydride also forms ammonia solvates.

8-5. Organolithium Compounds

One of the largest uses of metallic lithium, industrially and in the laboratory, is for the preparation of organolithium compounds. These are of great importance and utility; in their reactions they generally resemble the well-known Grignard reagents, although they are usually more reactive. The preparation is best accomplished using an alkyl or aryl

$$C_2H_5Cl + 2Li = C_2H_5Li + LiCl \qquad (8\text{-}1)$$

chloride (eq. 8-1) in benzene or petroleum; ether solutions can be used, but these solvents are attacked slowly by the lithium compounds. Metal–hydrogen exchange (eq. 8-2), metal–halogen exchange (eq. 8-3) and metal–metal exchange (eq. 8-4) may also be used.

$$n\text{-}C_4H_9Li \; + \quad\quad\quad = \quad\quad\quad + \; n\text{-}C_4H_{10} \tag{8-2}$$

$$n\text{-}C_4H_9Li \; + \quad\quad\quad = \quad\quad\quad + \; n\text{-}C_4H_9Br \tag{8-3}$$

$$2Li + R_2Hg = 2RLi + Hg \tag{8-4}$$

Organolithium compounds all react rapidly with oxygen, being usually spontaneously inflammable in air, with liquid water and with water vapor. However, lithium bromide and iodide form solid complexes of stoichiometry $RLi(LiX)_{1-6}$ with the alkyls, and these solids are stable in air.

Organolithium compounds are among the very few alkali metal compounds which have properties—solubility in hydrocarbons or other non-polar liquids and high volatility—typical of covalent substances. They are generally liquids or low-melting solids, and molecular association is evidently an important structural feature. The crystal structure of ethyllithium[1] exemplifies this. As indicated in Figure 8-1, it consists of nearly regular tetrahedra of Li atoms surrounded by ethyl groups. Two opposite Li—Li bonds are 2.25 A while the other four are nearly equal at ~2.63 A. The α-carbon atom of each ethyl group is most closely bonded to one Li (Li—C = 2.19 A) and then more weakly bonded (Li—C ≈ 2.50 A) to the two other Li atoms on the same face of the tetrahedron of Li atoms. The bridge bonding by these α-carbon atoms is of the delocalized, electron-deficient multi-center bond type found in the beryllium and aluminum alkyls (page 318), but it is less symmetrical and hence more difficult to describe simply. The structure of methyllithium is similar; the Li atoms form tetrahedra with a methyl group above the center of each face and forming four-center bonds with three adjacent Li atoms. The electronic structure of the tetramers has been discussed by MO theory; the 2s and 2p orbitals of Li can give rise to four strongly bonding MO's which can accommodate the eight available electrons.[2]

[1] H. Dietrich, Acta Cryst., 16, 681 (1963).
[2] E. Weiss and E. A. C. Lucken, J. Organometal. Chem., 2, 197 (1964).

Methyllithium is insoluble in organic solvents and has low volatility. The ethyl and higher alkyl compounds are polymers both in solution and vapor phases; the exact degree of polymerization is sometimes uncertain. C_2H_5Li and $n\text{-}C_3H_7Li$ have been reported to be hexameric and $i\text{-}C_3H_7Li$, tetrameric

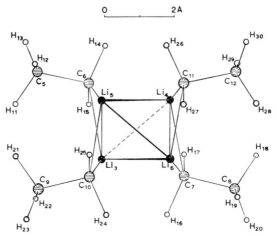

Fig. 8-1. The tetrameric unit $(C_2H_5Li)_4$ in crystalline ethyllithium. Small filled circles are Li, large shaded circles are C and small open circles are H.

in hydrocarbons, while in diethyl ether nmr studies suggest that $n\text{-}C_3H_7Li$ is a solvated dimer.

Lithium alkyls act as stereospecific catalysts for the polymerization of olefins, notably isoprene, which gives up to 90% of 1,4-*cis*-polybutadiene.

References*

Braude, E. A., in J. W. Cook, ed., *Progress in Organic Chemistry*, Vol. III, Butterworths, London, 1955, p. 172. A review of organolithium compounds in organic chemistry.

Brown, T. L., *Adv. Organomet. Chem.*, Vol. 3 (1965). Structures of organolithium compounds.

Foote Mineral Co., Philadelphia 4, Pa. Various bulletins containing physical and chemical data on lithium and its compounds.

Laidler, D. S., *Lithium and Its Compounds* (Royal Institute of Chemistry, Monograph No. 6), London, 1957. Describes the occurrence, manufacture, uses, alloys and compounds.

Lithium Corp. of America, Minneapolis 2, Minn. Various bulletins containing physical and chemical data on lithium and its compounds.

Mellor's Comprehensive Treatise on Inorganic and Theoretical Chemistry, Vol. I, Supplement 2, "Lithium and Sodium," Longmans Green, London.

Sinn, H., and F. Patat, *Angew. Chem.* (*Internat.*), **3**, 93 (1964). A review on the mechanism of catalysis by lithium alkyls.

* See also references for Chapter 16.

9

Beryllium

9-1. Covalent Bond Formation; Stereochemistry; Coordination Number

The electron configuration of the gaseous beryllium atom is $1s^2 2s^2$. The increased nuclear charge over that in lithium, coupled with the fact that the $2s$ electrons only partially shield one another, has two effects. (1) The Be atom has a metallic radius of only 0.89 A, much smaller than metallic Li's 1.22 A. (2) The ionization potentials of Be, 9.32 and 18.21 ev, are much higher than that of Li (5.39 ev), making Be far less electropositive in all its chemical behavior than Li. In fact, there are no crystalline compounds or solutions in which Be^{2+} ions exist as such. All compounds whose structures have been determined, even those with the most electronegative elements, such as BeO and BeF_2, have at least partial covalent bonding. Atoms of the other elements of group II, Mg, Ca, Sr, Ba and Ra, have electronic structures similar to that of Be. However, the greater size of these atoms reduces the effect of the nuclear charge on the valence electrons. Thus their ionization potentials are lower than those of Be; they are, in general, more electropositive, and the ionic nature of their compounds steadily increases in descending the group. Though some Mg compounds show covalent character, compounds of Ca, Ba, Sr and Ra are all essentially ionic.

Some typical beryllium compounds and their properties are listed in Table 9-1.

As a result of the small size, high ionization potentials, and high sublimation energy of beryllium, the lattice or hydration energies are insufficient for essentially complete charge separation and the formation of

TABLE 9-1

Some Representative Beryllium Compounds and Their Properties

Compound	Color and form	Melting point, °C	Solubility
Be	Fairly hard, grey metal	1285	Dil. acids and alkalies
BeO	White refractory powder	2570	Slowly in fused acid salts
$Be(OH)_2$	White solid	—	Acids and bases
BeF_2	Transparent, glassy solid	803	H_2O
$BeCl_2$	White solid; sublimable	405	Hydrolyzed by H_2O
$[Be(H_2O)_4]SO_4$	Colorless octahedra	$-H_2O$ at ~ 200	H_2O
$Be(C_2H_5)_2$	Colorless liquid	—	Many organic solvents
BeH_2	White nonvolatile solid	—	Insol. organic solvents; reacts with H_2O
$Be_4O(OCOCH_3)_6$	White crystalline solid	283	Nonpolar organic solvents, e.g., CCl_4

simple Be^{2+} ions. On the other hand, to allow the formation of two covalent bonds, —Be—, it is clear that unpairing of the two $2s$ electrons is required. Where free BeX_2 molecules occur, the Be atom is promoted to a state in which the two valence electrons occupy two equivalent sp hybrid orbitals and the X—Be—X system is linear. However, in such a linear molecule the Be atom has a coordination number of only two and there is a strong tendency for Be to achieve maximum (four-fold) coordination, or at least three-fold coordination. Maximum coordination is achieved in several ways:

1. Polymerization may occur through bridging, as in solid $BeCl_2$ (Fig. 9-1). The coordination of Be is not exactly tetrahedral since the Cl—Be—Cl

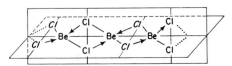

Fig. 9-1.   The structure of polymeric $BeCl_2$ in the crystal.

angles are only 98°, which means that the $BeCl_2Be$ units are somewhat elongated in the direction of the chain axis. In such a situation steric factors are very important in determining the exact sizes of the angles. Presumably, if the angle were opened to 109°, any improvement in bond strength would be insufficient to counterbalance the increase in Be—Be repulsion energy. Beryllium chloride readily sublimes; at high temperatures ($\sim 750°$) it consists of essentially all monomeric, linear $BeCl_2$ molecules, but at lower temperatures there are appreciable amounts ($\sim 20\%$ at 560°) of the dimer, in which Be is three-coordinate.

2. By functioning as acceptors, many beryllium compounds attain maximum coordination of the metal atom. Thus the chloride forms etherates, $Cl_2Be(OR_2)_2$, and complex ions such as BeF_4^{2-} and $[Be(H_2O)_4]^{2+}$ exist.

3. In chelate compounds, such as the acetylacetonate (9-I), four approximately tetrahedral bonds are formed. Actually, resonance makes all of the C—O and Be—O bonds equivalent, and we cannot really speak of the two dative and the two ordinary covalent bonds implied by structure 9-I.

(9-I)

4. It has been found from X-ray structural studies that the packing in crystals is almost invariably such as to give Be a coordination number of four with a tetrahedral (or nearly so) configuration. Thus, in BeO there are BeO_4 tetrahedra. Be_2SiO_4 is exceptional among the orthosilicates of the alkaline earths, the rest of which have structures giving the metal ion octahedral coordination, in having the Be atoms tetrahedrally surrounded by oxygen atoms. It may be noted in passing that Be with F gives compounds often isomorphous with oxygen compounds of silicon; thus BeF_2 is isomorphous with cristobalite, SiO_2, $BaBeF_4$ with $BaSiO_4$, and $NaBeF_3$ with $CaSiO_3$, and there are five different corresponding forms of Na_2BeF_4 and Ca_2SiO_4.

Three-coordinate Be occurs in some cases, for example, the gaseous dimers Be_2Cl_4, Be_2Br_4 and $Be_2(CH_3)_4$. In Be phthalocyanin, the metal is perforce surrounded by four nitrogen atoms in a plane. However, no more than three electron pairs from the N atoms can be truly coordinated to the Be atom since there are only three atomic orbitals available (the s and two p orbitals) in any given plane. This compound constitutes an example of a *forced configuration* since the Be atom is held strongly in a rigid environment.

9-2. Resemblances between Beryllium and Aluminum

Although, as seen, most simple beryllium salts are mainly covalent, it is possible to estimate an ionic radius for Be^{2+} of ~ 0.31 A. With this value the charge/radius ratio is ~ 6.5, greater than for any other cation (except H^+, which does not occur in crystals, and B^{3+}, which is wholly hypothetical). Al^{3+} has nearly as high a charge/radius ratio, namely, ~ 6.0, and, considering polarization effects, some chemical similarities between the two may be expected. Such similarities do in fact exist, and this is probably the best example of the "diagonal relationship." Among the striking similarities are:

1. Metallic Be, like Al, is rather resistant to acids unless finely divided or amalgamated owing to the formation of an inert and impervious oxide film on the surface. Thus, although the potential

$$Be^{2+}(aq) + 2e = Be \qquad E^0 \text{ (calc.)} = -1.85$$

would indicate rapid reaction with dilute acids (and even H_2O; cf. Chapter 6), the rate of attack depends greatly also on the source and fabrication of the metal. For very pure metal the relative dissolution rates are $HF > H_2SO_4 \sim HCl > HNO_3$. The metal dissolves rapidly in $3M$ H_2SO_4 and in $5M$ NH_4F, but very slowly in HNO_3.

It may be noted that the Be potential is considerably below those of the other alkaline earth metals, showing that the high heat of sublimation and ionization potentials of Be are not as fully compensated by the hydration energy of the ion as with the other metals.

2. The metal dissolves in strong bases to give what is called the "beryllate" ion:

$$Be + 2OH^- = BeO_2^{2-} + H_2$$

Aluminum dissolves similarly to give "aluminate" ions, AlO_2^-. Neither of these formulas for the ions is representative of the true species, which are probably four and six coordinated, respectively. There is also evidence that "beryllate" solutions contain polymeric anions such as $Be_2O_3^{2-}$ as well as hydrated and hydroxo-bridged species. Both Be and Al oxides and hydroxides are amphoteric, dissolving readily in sodium hydroxide solutions.

3. BeO resembles Al_2O_3 in being extraordinarily high melting and nonvolatile as well as extremely hard. BeO is polymorphic and converts into a second form above $\sim 800°$. This high temperature form is virtually insoluble in aqueous acids or bases and is only difficulty soluble in fused salts such as $KHSO_4$ or KOH. Curiously, it dissolves rather readily in a hot sirup of concentrated sulfuric acid and ammonium sulfate. The low temperature form of BeO has the Be atoms tetrahedrally coordinated by O (wurtzite structure), whereas the other alkaline earth oxides all have the NaCl structure. In Al_2O_3 aluminum is six coordinate.

Beryllium and its compounds are exceedingly poisonous, especially if inhaled, and great precautions must be taken in handling them.

THE ELEMENT

9-3. Occurrence, Isolation and Properties

The most important beryllium mineral is *beryl*, $Be_3Al_2(SiO_3)_6$, which often occurs as large hexagonal prisms. Beryllium, like lithium, is made by electrolysis of the fused chloride, but the extraction from ores is complicated.[1] However, since $BeCl_2$ is covalent and has a very low electrical conductivity, about 10^{-3} that of NaCl, the latter salt is added to the melt. Beryllium amalgam, a very air-sensitive liquid or paste, depending on the concentration, can be obtained by electrolysis of fused NaCl and $BeCl_2$ with a mercury cathode in an argon atmosphere.

The grey metal is rather light (1.86 g/cm³) and quite hard and brittle. Since the absorption of electromagnetic radiation, X-rays, for example, depends on the electron density in matter, beryllium has the lowest stopping power per unit mass thickness of all suitable construction materials and is used for "windows" in X-ray apparatus. It is also added as an antioxidant to copper and phosphor bronzes and as a hardener to copper.

Beryllium has a much lower chemical reactivity than lithium. Some of its reactions are given in Figure 9-2.

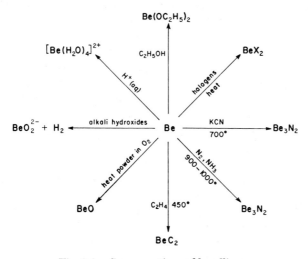

Fig. 9-2. Some reactions of beryllium.

BERYLLIUM COMPOUNDS

9-4. Halides, Oxo Salts and Binary Compounds of Beryllium

Beryllium *fluoride* is obtained as a glassy hygroscopic mass by heating $(NH_4)_2BeF_4$. The melt is a poor conductor of electricity. It is glassy in form like silica, having randomly oriented chains of $\cdots F_2BeF_2Be\cdots$ with F bridges. Thus the structure is similar to those of $BeCl_2$ and $BeBr_2$ except

[1] *Chem. and Eng. News*, April 19th, 1965, p. 70.

that the packing of the chains is disordered. BeF_2 is readily soluble in water.

Fluoroberyllates can be made by dissolving BeO in concentrated solutions of acid fluorides or fusing it with an acid fluoride such as NH_4HF_2, and they contain tetrahedral BeF_4^{2-} ions. This ion has a crystal chemistry much like that of SO_4^{2-} and corresponding salts, for example, $PbSO_4$ and $PbBeF_4$, usually have similar structures and solubilities. The ion is partially hydrolyzed in solution unless a large excess of F^- is present. In addition to K_2BeF_4, the $KF-BeF_2$ system has K_3BeF_5, $KBeF_3$ and KBe_2F_5 phases.

Beryllium *chloride* is prepared by passing CCl_4 over BeO at 800°. It dissolves in water very exothermically, and a hydrate, $[Be(H_2O)_4]Cl_2$, can be crystallized from HCl solutions of the salt. It also dissolves in many donor solvents (R_2O, ROH, RCOOH) as noted previously. There is evidence of chloroberyllate ions, for example, in Na_2BeCl_4, from study of the phase diagrams of alkali chloride-$BeCl_2$ systems, but this ion is rather unstable and does not exist in solution.

Salts of *oxo acids* are known. $[Be(H_2O)_4]SO_4$ can be dehydrated at 400° to $BeSO_4$, which is very stable and does not decompose below 580°. The nitrate, $[Be(H_2O)_4](NO_3)_2$, melts in its own water at 60.5°.

Other noteworthy compounds are: the *sulfide*, BeS, which has the zinc blende structure and is insoluble in water (although all other alkaline earth sulfides and Al_2S_3 are rapidly hydrolyzed by water); Be_3N_2, a white crystalline powder or colorless crystals hydrolyzed by water; $BeCO_3$, which is unstable and can be kept only in an atmosphere of CO_2. The addition of soluble carbonates to aqueous solutions of beryllium salts gives basic carbonates of unknown structures.

Beryllium *hydride*, BeH_2, not obtainable by direct reaction, may be made in other ways, for example, by action of $LiAlH_4$ on $(CH_3)_2Be$ or by thermal decomposition of $[(CH_3)_3C]_2Be$. The latter method appears to give the purest product ($\sim 96\%$) which is stable to $\sim 240°$ and reacts only slowly and incompletely with water at 50°; the less pure products react vigorously. The general properties of BeH_2 suggest that it is polymeric with hydrogen bridging (see page 206).

9-5. Aqueous Chemistry of Beryllium

In concentrated acid solutions beryllium appears to exist as $[Be(H_2O)_4]^{2+}$ ions, and these occur (or probably occur) in several salts which have been mentioned above. The water in such salts is rather firmly bound; $[Be(H_2O)_4]Cl_2$, for example, loses no water over P_2O_5.

Solutions of all beryllium salts are acid owing to hydrolysis of the beryllium ion. It has also long been known that solutions of beryllium salts can dissolve considerable amounts of beryllium oxide or hydroxide. The reason for this appears to be that beryllium readily forms oxo and hydroxo complexes with Be—O—Be and Be—OH—Be bridges. In the precipitation of $Be(OH)_2$ some interesting effects have been observed. If n is the number of OH^- ions added per Be^{2+} ion, solutions remain clear up to $n = 1$. When $n > 1$, precipitation commences. With halide solutions precipitation is complete at $n = 2$, but with other ions precipitation is complete at $n = 1.8$–1.9, indicating that such precipitates of beryllium "hydroxide" contain SO_4^{2-}, NO_3^- or ClO_4^- ions.

That precipitation occurs *only* when $n > 1$ suggests that there are $[Be(OH)^+]_n$ species which are soluble. Electrometric titration studies have, in fact, shown that in dilute solutions ($< 0.050M$) the main species is $[Be(OH)]_3^{3+}$, and an equilibrium constant has been estimated

$$3Be^{2+} + 3H_2O = [Be(OH)]_3^{3+} + 3H^+ \qquad pK = -8.66$$

At very low concentrations of beryllium there is some evidence for Be_2OH^{3+} and $Be(OH)_2$, but none for $[Be(OH)]_2^{2+}$ or $[Be(OH)]_4^{4+}$. All the equilibria appear to be established rapidly. In view of the propensity of beryllium for four coordination, the structure of the $[Be(OH)]_3^{3+}$ species is thought to be (9-II). An open structure seems less likely in view of the stability of

$$
(H_2O)_2Be
\begin{array}{c}
\overset{\displaystyle H}{O}\text{—Be}(OH_2)_2 \\
OH \\
\underset{\displaystyle H}{O}\text{—Be}(OH_2)_2
\end{array}
\qquad
(H_2O)_3Be\text{—O—Be}(H_2O)_3
\qquad
(H_2O)_2Be(OH)_2
$$

(9-II)	(9-III)	(9-IV)

the trimer. The other hydroxo species may be formulated as 9-III and 9-IV. It is possible that the beryllate ion with only one Be atom in solution is actually $[Be(OH)_4]^{2-}$, but this has not been proved.[2]

9-6. Beryllium Complexes

Some of these have been mentioned already such as the BeF_4^{2-} and $[Be(H_2O)_4]^{2+}$ ions, the etherates, alcoholates and similar complexes with oxygenated organic compounds (e.g., $(R_2O)_2BeCl_2$). The tetrahedral chelate complex with acetylacetone (page 247) is only one example of many electrically neutral complexes formed with β-keto enols and β-keto esters.

Beryllium also forms some nitrogen complexes. The tetraammine, $[Be(NH_3)_4]Cl_2$, is very stable thermally, but is rapidly decomposed by

[2] D. A. Everest, *et al.*, *J. Inorg. Nucl. Chem.*, **24**, 525 (1962).

water, an indication that oxygen is a stronger donor to beryllium than is nitrogen. Dimethylamine reacts with BeH_2 to give a trimer, $\{[(CH_3)_2N]_2Be\}_3$, which probably contains a six-membered ring with alternating Be and N atoms.

One of the most interesting types of beryllium complex is that of general formula $Be_4O(OOCR)_6$, formed by refluxing $Be(OH)_2$ with carboxylic acids. The resulting compounds are volatile crystalline substances, soluble in nonpolar solvents—even alkanes—and in many polar solvents other than water and lower alcohols. They are inert to water, but hydrolyzed by dilute acids. In solution they are un-ionized and monomeric. X-ray study has shown that they have the structures illustrated in Figure 9-3. The cen-

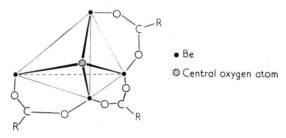

Fig. 9-3. The structure of the carboxylate complexes $Be_4O(OOCR)_6$. Only three RCOO groups are shown.

tral oxygen atom is tetrahedrally surrounded by the four beryllium atoms (this being one of the few cases, excepting solid oxides, in which oxygen is four coordinate), and each beryllium atom is tetrahedrally surrounded by four oxygen atoms. Zinc also forms such complexes as does the ZrO^{2+} ion with benzoic acid. The zinc complexes are rapidly hydrolyzed by water in contrast to those of beryllium. The acetate complex has been utilized as a means of purifying beryllium by solvent extraction from an aqueous solution into an organic layer. It has also been shown that when $BeCl_2$ is dissolved in N_2O_4 in ethyl acetate, crystalline $Be(NO_3)_2 \cdot 2N_2O_4$ is obtained. On heating at 50° this gives $Be(NO_3)_2$, which at 125° decomposes to N_2O_4 and volatile $Be_4O(NO_3)_6$.[3] The structure of the latter appears to be similar to that of the acetate but with bridging nitrate groups. The basic nitrate is insoluble in nonpolar solvents.

9-7. Organoberyllium Compounds

These are obtained by reaction of beryllium halides with Grignard reagents or with lithium alkyls or aryls. They are mostly liquids or low-

[3] C. C. Addison and A. Walker, *J. Chem. Soc.*, **1963**, 1220.

melting solids of high reactivity, being spontaneously inflammable in air and violently hydrolyzed by water.

The methyl compound, $(CH_3)_2Be$, is polymerized in a manner (9-V) reminiscent of the $BeCl_2$ polymer, although the bridge bonding is rather

$$\left[\begin{array}{c} \diagdown \; CH_3 \;\; CH_3 \\ Be \;\;\; Be \\ \diagup \; CH_3 \;\; CH_3 \end{array} \right]_n \qquad\qquad CH_3{-}Be \begin{array}{c} CH_3 \\ \diagdown \\ \diagup \\ CH_3 \end{array} Be{-}CH_3$$

$$(9\text{-}V) \qquad\qquad\qquad\qquad (9\text{-}VI)$$

different and will be discussed later (page 318). In the vapor phase dimethylberyllium is mostly dimeric (9-VI); again there is a geometrical similarity to the chloride dimer. The higher alkyls are less highly polymerized, the diethyl being less polymerized than $(CH_3)_2Be$, and the diisopropyl compound being definitely a dimer in benzene. This lower degree of polymerization has been attributed to the more electropositive character of substituted carbon atoms and may also be due to steric hindrance. Since these compounds are not coordinately saturated, the polymeric structures can be split by strong donors and, for example, the methyl compound gives with $(CH_3)_3N$, $[(CH_3)_3\overset{+}{N}{-}\overset{-}{Be}(CH_3)_2]_2$ which is stable even as a vapor.

Pyrolysis of diisopropylberyllium gives a polymeric alkyl-beryllium hydride, a colorless, nonvolatile oil.

$$n(i\text{-}C_3H_7)_2Be \xrightarrow{200°} [(i\text{-}C_3H_7)BeH]_n + nC_3H_6$$

Pyrolysis of di-t-butylberyllium at $> 100°$ gives essentially pure BeH_2 and isobutene.

Beryllium alkyls give colored complexes with 2,2′-dipyridyl, for example, $dipyBe(C_2H_5)_2$, which is bright red; the colors of these and similar complexes with aromatic amines given by beryllium, zinc, cadmium, aluminum and gallium alkyls are believed to be due to electron transfer from the M—C bond to the lowest unoccupied orbital of the amine. Thus Be—C bonds appear to be acting as donors to the excited state of the complex. The green paramagnetic complex obtained from the lithium salt of 2,2′-dipyridyl with $BeCl_2$ is regarded as a complex between Be^{2+} and the dipyridyl negative ion[4] (see discussion Section 27-8).

9-8. Unipositive Beryllium

The difference between the first and second ionization potentials might suggest that there is a possibility of obtaining univalent beryllium. It has

---

[4] G. E. Coates and S. I. E. Green, *J. Chem. Soc.*, **1962**, 3340.

been claimed that the dissolution of beryllium anodes provides evidence for Be$^+$ as an intermediate.   However, further studies have shown that disintegration of the metal occurs during dissolution so that the apparent effect is one of the metal going into solution in the $+1$ state—too much metal is lost for the amount of current passed.   The anode sludge, a mixture of Be and Be(OH)$_2$, had been considered to be due to disproportionation of Be$^+$, but photomicrography indicates that the beryllium in the sludge is due merely to spallation of the anode.

There is some evidence for Be^{I} in fused chloride melts, for example,

$$\text{Be} + \text{Be}^{\text{II}} = 2\text{Be}^{\text{I}}$$

but no compound has yet been isolated.

References

Bellamy, R. G., and N. A. Hall, *Extraction and Metallurgy of Uranium, Thorium and Beryllium*, Pergamon Press, New York, 1965.

Darwin, F. E., and J. H. Buddery, *Beryllium* (No. 7 of *Metallurgy of the Rarer Metals*), Butterworths, London, 1960.

Everest, D. A., *The Chemistry of Beryllium*, Elsevier, New York, 1964.   A comprehensive treatise with many references.

10

Boron

GENERAL REMARKS

10-1. Electronic Structure and Bonding

The first ionization potential of boron, 8.296 ev, is rather high, and the next two are much higher. Thus the total energy required to produce B^{3+} ions is far more than would be compensated by lattice energies of ionic compounds or by hydration of such ions in solution. Consequently, simple electron loss to form a cation plays no part in boron chemistry. Instead, covalent bond formation is of major importance, and boron compounds usually resemble those of other nonmetals, notably silicon, in their properties and reactions.

Despite the $2s^2 2p$ electronic structure, boron is always trivalent and never monovalent. This is because the total energy released in formation of three bonds in a BX_3 compound exceeds the energy of formation of one bond in a BX compound by more than enough to provide for promotion of boron to a hybridized valence state of the sp^2 type. This matter has been treated at length in Chapter 3, where it has also been shown that the three sp^2 hybrid orbitals lie in one plane at angles of 120°. It would therefore be expected, and is indeed found, without exception, that all monomeric, three-covalent boron compounds (trihalides, trialkyls, etc.) are planar with X—B—X bond angles of 120°.

It has proved troublesome to determine the covalent radius for trigonally hybridized boron very exactly, but estimates place it between 0.85 and 0.90 A. On this basis, there are apparently substantial shortenings of many B—X bonds, and this has occasioned much discussion. For example, the estimated B—F, B—Cl and B—Br distances would be ~ 1.52, ~ 1.87 and ~ 1.99, whereas the actual distances in the respective trihalides are 1.30, 1.75 and 1.87 A. Three factors appear to be responsible for the shortness of the bonds.

255

1. Formation of $p\pi$–$p\pi$ bonds using filled $p\pi$ orbitals of the halogens and the vacant $p\pi$ orbital of boron. This is probably most important in BF_3, but of some significance in BCl_3 and BBr_3 as well.

2. Strengthening and hence shortening of the B—X bonds by ionic–covalent resonance. It is certainly in BF_3 that this will be of greatest importance, because of the large electronegativity difference. Evidence that this is important, in addition to the dative $p\pi$–$p\pi$ bonding, is afforded by the fact that even in BF_3 complexes such as $(CH_3)_3\overset{+}{N}\overset{-}{B}F_3$ and $BF_4{}^-$, where the $p\pi$–$p\pi$ bond must be largely or totally absent, the B—F bonds are still apparently shortened (1.41–1.43 A).

3. It is also possible that because of the incomplete octet in boron, repulsions between nonbonding electrons are somewhat less than normal, permitting closer approach of the bonded atoms.

10-2. Acceptor Behavior

In BX_3 compounds the boron octet is incomplete; boron has a low-lying orbital which it does not use in bonding owing to a shortage of electrons, although partial use is made of it in the boron halides through B—X multiple bonding. The alkyls and halides of aluminum make up this insufficiency of electrons by forming dimers with alkyl or halogen bridges, but the boron compounds do not. The reason or reasons for this difference are not known with certainty. The size factor may be important for BCl_3 and BBr_3, since the small boron atom may be unable to coordinate strongly to four atoms as large as Cl and Br. The fact that $BCl_4{}^-$ and $BBr_4{}^-$ ions are stable only in crystalline salts of large cations such as Cs^+ or $(CH_3)_4N^+$ might suggest this. The fact that a certain amount of B—X $p\pi$–$p\pi$ bond energy would have to be sacrificed would also detract from the stability of dimers relative to monomers. The size factor cannot be controlling for BF_3, however, since $BF_4{}^-$ is quite stable. Here, the donor power of the fluorine already bonded to another boron atom may be so low that the energy of the bridge bonds would not be sufficient to counterbalance the energy required to break the B—F π bonding in the monomer. Phenomena of this nature are often difficult to explain with certainty.

An important consequence of the incomplete octet in BX_3 compounds is their ability to behave as acceptors (Lewis acids), in which boron achieves its maximum coordination with approximately sp^3 hybridization. Thus, various Lewis bases, such as amines, phosphines, ethers and sulfides, form 1:1 complexes with BX_3 compounds. The following are representative of the addition compounds formed: $(CH_3)_3NBCl_3$, $(CH_3)_3PBH_3$, $(C_2H_5)_2OBF_3$.

There is good evidence that the relative strengths of the boron halides as Lewis acids are in the order $BBr_3 \geqslant BCl_3 > BF_3$. This order is the opposite of what would be expected both on steric grounds and from electronegativity considerations. It can be explained, at least partially, in terms of the boron–halogen π bonding. In an addition compound this π bonding is largely or completely lost so that addition compounds of the trihalide with the strongest π bonding will be the most destabilized by loss of the energy of π bonding. Calculations indicate that the π bonding energies of the trihalides are in the order $BF_3 \gg BCl_3 > BBr_3$. However, certain properties of the BX_3 adducts with donor molecules suggest that the donor to boron bonds may themselves increase in strength in the order $BF_3 < BCl_3 < BBr_3$. No satisfactory explanation has been given for this.

Boron also completes its octet by forming anions such as $BF_4{}^-$, $BH_4{}^-$, $[HB(OR)_3]^-$ and $[B(C_6H_5)_4]^-$ and chelate complexes such as 10-I. It has

(10-I) (10-II)

been proven that the four bonds to boron in such chelates are approximately tetrahedral (and certainly not planar) since, with ligands which themselves are sufficiently unsymmetrical, the complex ions may be resolved into optical isomers. Thus the borosalicylaldehydo complex (10-II) has been resolved by fractional crystallization of the diastereoisomeric salts formed with optically active strychnine.

10-3. Comparison with Silicon and Aluminum

Elemental boron has properties which place it on the borderline between metals and nonmetals. It is a semiconductor, not a metallic conductor. Chemically, boron must be classed as a nonmetal, and in general its chemistry resembles that of silicon much more closely than that of aluminum or its other congeners, Ga, In and Tl. The main resemblances to Si and differences from Al are the following:

1. The similarity and complexity of the boric and silicic acids is notable. Boric acid, $B(OH)_3$, is weak but definitely an acid. It has no amphoteric properties, whereas $Al(OH)_3$ is mainly basic with some amphoteric behavior.

2. The hydrides of B and Si are volatile, spontaneously inflammable, and readily hydrolyzed, whereas the only binary hydride of Al is a solid,

9+A.I.C.

polymeric material of uncertain structure. However, structurally, the boron hydrides are unique, having unusual stoichiometries and configurations and unusual bonding because of their *electron-deficient* nature.

3. The ready hydrolysis of the boron halides (not BF_3) gives $B(OH)_3$, just as the silicon halides readily hydrolyze to silicic acid. The aluminum halides are only partially hydrolyzed in water.

4. B_2O_3 and SiO_2 are similar in their acidic nature, as evidenced by their facility in dissolving metallic oxides to form borates and silicates, and both readily form glasses which are difficult to crystallize. Certain oxo salts of B and Si are structurally similar, specifically the linear $(BO_2)_x$ and $(SiO_3)_x$ ions in metaborates and pyroxene silicates, respectively.

5. However, despite dimerization of the halides of Al and Ga and of the alkyls of Al, they behave as acceptors and form adducts similar to those given by boron halides and alkyls, for example, $Cl_3\overset{-}{Al}\overset{+}{N}(CH_3)_3$. Aluminum, like boron, also forms volatile alkoxides such as $Al(OC_2H_5)_3$, which are similar to borate esters, $B(OR)_3$.

THE ELEMENT

10-4. Occurrence, Isolation and Properties

Boron occurs in quite substantial deposits of soluble borates such as *borax*, $Na_2B_4O_7 \cdot 10H_2O$, particularly in desert areas of India and California. Boric acid is present in volcanic steam and can be recovered.

Natural boron consists of two isotopes, ^{10}B (18.83%) and ^{11}B (81.17%). Both these nuclides have spin, and nuclear magnetic resonance studies have proved quite fruitful in elucidating structures of boron compounds. ^{10}B can be enriched by reactions such as

$$^{11}BF_3 \cdot O(C_2H_5)_2(l) + {}^{10}BF_3(g) = {}^{10}BF_3 \cdot O(C_2H_5)_2(l) + {}^{11}BF_3(g)$$
$$^{11}BF_3 \cdot anisole(l) + {}^{10}BF_3(g) = {}^{10}BF_3 \cdot anisole(l) + {}^{11}BF_3(g)$$

It is exceedingly difficult to prepare elemental boron in a high state of purity because of its high melting point and the corrosive nature of the liquid. It can be prepared in quantity but low purity (95–98%) in an amorphous form by reduction of B_2O_3 with Mg followed by vigorous washing of the material so obtained with alkali, hydrochloric acid and hydrofluoric acid. This amorphous boron is a dark powder which may contain some microcrystalline boron, but also contains oxides and borides.

The preparation of pure boron in crystalline form is a matter of considerable complexity and difficulty even when only small research scale quantities are required. Details will be found in an article by Newkirk (see Adams, R. M., in reference list).

There are three allotropic forms whose structures are known in detail, at least one other allotrope which is well established though its structure is not yet worked out and, in all probability, other allotropes not as yet identified with certainty.

α-Rhombohedral boron has been obtained by pyrolysis of BI_3 on tantalum, tungsten and boron nitride surfaces at 800–1000°, by pyrolysis of boron hydrides and by crystallization from boron–platinum melts at 800–1200°. It is the most dense allotrope, and its structure consists entirely of B_{12} icosahedra (cf. Fig. 10-18), which are packed together in a manner similar to cubic closest packing of spheres. There are bonds between the icosahedra which are, however, weaker than those within the icosahedra.

A tetragonal form of boron, which can be obtained by reduction of BBr_3 with H_2 on a tantalum filament at 1300°, is the form longest known and most extensively studied. Its rather complicated structure still has certain puzzling features. It consists of layers of B_{12} icosahedra interleaved with layers of single boron atoms. The latter tie the layers of icosahedra together.

β-Rhombohedral boron is invariably obtained by crystallization of fused boron and may be the thermodynamically stable form above about 1500°. It is built entirely of B_{12} icosahedra packed together, with B—B bonds between them, in a more complicated way than in the case of α-rhombohedral boron.

It has not yet been possible to learn with certainty the stability ranges of the various modifications of boron, with the possible exception of the β-rhombohedral one. The whole problem is complicated by the probable predominance of kinetic rather than thermodynamic factors in the various preparation and deposition processes. Even the melting point is uncertain; the best estimate is 2200 ± 100°.

Crystalline boron is extremely inert chemically. It is unaffected by boiling HCl or HF, only slowly oxidized by hot, concentrated nitric acid when finely powdered, and either not attacked or only very slowly attacked by many other hot concentrated oxidizing agents.

BORON COMPOUNDS

10-5. Borides

Compounds of boron with elements less electronegative than itself (i.e., metals) are called borides. Often compounds of boron with rather less metallic or metalloidal elements (e.g., P, As) are also termed borides. Borides of most but not all elements are known. They are generally hard, refractory substances, fairly inert chemically, and they often possess very unusual physical and chemical properties. For example, the electrical and thermal conductivities of ZrB_2 and TiB_2 are about ten times greater than those of the metals themselves, and the melting points are more than 1000° higher. Some of the lanthanide hexaborides are among the best thermionic emitters known. The monoborides of phosphorus and arsenic are promising high-temperature semiconductors and higher borides of some metalloids, e.g., AsB_6, are remarkably inert to chemical attack.

Industrially, borides are prepared in various ways including reduction of metal oxides using mixtures of carbon and boron carbide, electrolysis in fused salts and direct combination of the elements. For research purposes, the last method is usually used.

The borides do not conform to the ordinary concepts of valence either in their stoichiometries or in their structures. With only a few exceptions, borides are of one of the following main types:

1. Borides with isolated boron atoms. These include most of the ones with low B to M ratios such as M_4B, M_3B, M_2B, M_5B_2 and M_7B_3. In the M_4B and M_2B structures, boron atoms lie in triangular prismatic or square antiprismatic holes between multiple layers of metal atoms. In the others, the metal atoms are arranged in approximately close-packed arrays, with the boron atoms in triangular prismatic interstices.

2. Borides with single and double chains of boron atoms. As the proportion of boron atoms increases, so do the possibilities for boron–boron linkages. In V_3B_2 there are pairs of boron atoms. In one modification of Ni_4B_3, two-thirds of the boron atoms form infinite, zigzag chains, while one-third are isolated from other boron atoms, while in another all boron atoms are members of chains. MB compounds all have structures with single chains, while in many M_3B_4 compounds there are double chains.

3. Borides with two-dimensional nets. These are represented by MB_2 and M_2B_5 compounds, and include some of the best electrically conducting, hardest and highest melting of all borides. The crystal structures of the MB_2 compounds are unusually simple, consisting of alternating layers of close-packed metal atoms and "chicken wire" sheets of boron atoms, as shown in Figure 10-1.

4. Borides with three-dimensional boron networks. The major types have formulas MB_4, MB_6 and MB_{12}. MB_4 compounds may be of several types insofar as structural details are concerned. ThB_4 and CeB_4 contain rather open networks of boron atoms interpenetrating a network of metal atoms. Perhaps as many as twenty other MB_4 compounds have the same structure. The MB_6 structure is fairly easy to visualize with the help of

Figure 10-2. It can be thought of as a CsCl structure, with B_6 octahedra in place of the Cl^- ions. However, the B_6 octahedra are closely linked along the cube edges so that the boron atoms constitute an infinite three-dimensional network. The MB_{12} compounds also have cubic structures

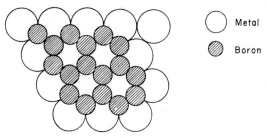

○ Metal

◎ Boron

Fig. 10-1. Parallel layers of metal atoms and boron atoms in MB_2 compounds.

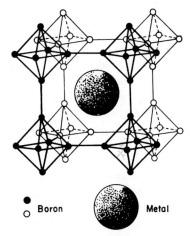

● ○ Boron   Metal

Fig. 10-2. Atomic arrangement in many MB_6 compounds.

consisting of M atoms and B_{12} cubo-octahedra (10-III) packed in the manner of NaCl. Again, the B_{12} polyhedra are closely linked to one another.

(10-III)

Boron nitride, which can be obtained by interaction of boron with ammonia at white heat, is a slippery white solid with a layer structure very similar to that of graphite (page 297). The units, instead of being hexagonal carbon rings, have alternate B and N atoms 1.45 A apart with angles of 120° (sp^2 at B). The distance between the sheets is 3.34 A. The analogy of C—C and B—N further discussed below is heightened by the conversion of graphite-like BN under high temperature and pressure to a cubic form with a diamond-like structure. This form is extremely hard and will scratch diamond. The nitride is stable in air but slowly hydrolyzed by water.

10-6. Oxo Compounds of Boron

Boron compounds with oxygen are very important; with the possible exception of fluorine, boron seems to have its greatest affinity for oxygen. Boron always occurs oxygenated in nature, mainly as borates, and most boron compounds on burning or hydrolysis are converted to oxide, boric acid or borates.

The structures of oxo compounds of boron are based on either a planar BO_3 unit with 120° angles or, less commonly, a tetrahedral BO_4 unit.

Boron Oxides. The principal oxide, B_2O_3, is obtained by fusing boric acid. It usually forms a glass and is one of the most difficult substances to crystallize. Its most important chemical feature is its acidity. With water it gives boric acid, and it readily dissolves many metal oxides when fused to give borate glasses. In glassy B_2O_3 there exist randomly oriented three-dimensional networks of BO_3 groups, each oxygen being bonded to two boron atoms. The crystal is quite different. Here there are BO_4 tetrahedra, two sets of which form two types of interconnected spiral chains; three B—O bonds are equivalent, but the fourth is somewhat longer. The reluctance of B_2O_3 to crystallize is probably due to the difficulty of transforming one three-dimensional network into another.

Boron also forms a well-established lower oxide, $(BO)_x$. The structure of the solid compound is unknown, but it seems certain that it contains B—B bonds and B—O—B bonds. At 1300–1500° it vaporizes to B_2O_2 molecules. It is obtained by heating $B_2(OH)_4$ at 250° and 0.5 mm pressure. $B_2(OH)_4$ is itself obtained in fair yield by the following reactions:

$$2(Me_2N)_2BCl \xrightarrow{\text{Na dispersion}} (Me_2N)_2BB(NMe_2)_2$$

$$(Me_2N)_2BB(NMe_2)_2 \xrightarrow{\text{H}_3\text{O}^+} (HO)_2BB(OH)_2 + 4\ Me_2NH_2^+$$

It is also obtained in essentially quantitative yield by reaction of neutral water with $(RO)_2BB(OR)_2$ (R = C_2H_5 or i-C_3H_7). $(BO)_x$ reacts with BCl_3 at 200° to give B_2Cl_4. Since B_2Cl_4 is definitely known to have the Cl_2BBCl_2 structure (page 271), and the substances hydrolyzed are virtually certain to have B—B bonds, it seems extremely likely that the intermediate compounds, $B_2(OH)_4$ and $(BO)_x$, also have B—B linkages.

Boric Acid. The acid, $B(OH)_3$, or its salts are formed by hydrolysis of boron halides, hydrides, etc.; the acid forms white needle-like crystals in which there are $B(OH)_3$ units linked together by hydrogen bonds to form layers of nearly hexagonal symmetry (see page 211). It was at one time believed that the hydrogen atoms were midway between the oxygen atoms, but recent work has shown that the hydrogen bonds are unsymmetrical. The layers in the crystal are 3.18 A apart, which accounts for the pronounced basal cleavage.

Some reactions of boric acid are given in Figure 10-3.

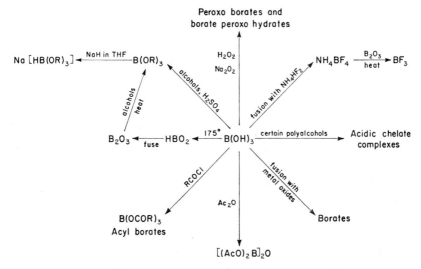

Fig. 10-3.   Some reactions of boric acid.

Boric acid is moderately soluble in water with a large negative heat of solution so that the solubility increases markedly with temperature. It is a very weak and exclusively monobasic acid which acts not as a proton donor but as a Lewis acid, accepting OH^-:

$$B(OH)_3 + H_2O = B(OH)_4^- + H^+ \qquad pK = 9.00$$

At concentrations $\leqslant 0.025M$, essentially only mononuclear species $B(OH)_3$ and $B(OH)_4^-$ are present; but at higher concentrations the acidity increases, and pH measurements are consistent with the formation of polymeric species such as

$$3B(OH)_3 = B_3O_3(OH)_4^- + H^+ + 2H_2O \qquad pK = 6.84$$

There is also good evidence that polymers are present in mixed solutions of boric acid and borates:

$$2B(OH)_3 + B(OH)_4^- = B_3O_3(OH)_4^- + 3H_2O \qquad K = 110$$

There are probably some other polymers of similar type present, but the predominant species appears to be the ring polymer 10-IV. Rings of this

(10-IV)   (10-V)

sort have been characterized in crystalline borates such as $Cs_2O \cdot 2B_2O_3$. The equilibria in solution are rapidly established as shown, for example, by rapid exchange between boric acid labeled with ^{18}O and borates.

The strength of boric acid can be greatly increased by the addition of polyhydroxo compounds to the solutions. Glycerol and mannitol are used for analytical purposes, the boric acid being then titratable with strong bases. This effect is due to the formation of complexes of type 10-V and others. Steric considerations are very critical in the formation of these complexes. Thus 1,2- and 1,3-diols in the *cis* form only, such as *cis*-cyclo-pentane-1,2-diol, are active, and only *o*-quinols react. Indeed, the ability of a diol to affect the acidity of boric acid is a useful criterion of the configuration where *cis–trans* isomers are possible.

Borates. Many borates occur naturally, usually in hydrated form. Anhydrous borates can be made by fusion of boric acid and metal oxides, and hydrated borates can be crystallized from aqueous solutions. The stoichiometry of borates, for example, $KB_5O_8 \cdot 4H_2O$, $Na_2B_4O_7 \cdot 10H_2O$, CaB_2O_4 and $Mg_7Cl_2B_{16}O_{30}$, gives little idea of the structures of the anions, which are cyclic or linear polymers formed by linking together of BO_3 and/or BO_4 units by sharing oxygen atoms. The main principles for determining these structures are similar to those for silicates, to which the borates are structurally and often physically similar in forming glasses. It is interesting to note that in contrast to the borates, the carbonate ion of superficially similar structure forms no polymeric species; this is probably attributable to the formation of strong C—O π bonds.

Examples of complex anhydrous borate anions are the ring anion (10-VI) in $K_3B_3O_6$ and the infinite chain anion (10-VII) in CaB_2O_4.

Hydrated borates also contain polyanions in the crystal, but not all the known polyanions exist as such in solutions; only those containing one or

(10-VI)   (10-VII)

more BO_4 groups appear to be stable. The structures are best correlated by the following assumptions:

1. Both trigonal BO_3 and tetrahedral BO_4 groups are present, the ratio of BO_4 to total B being equivalent to the ratio of the charge on the anion to total boron. Thus $KB_5O_8 \cdot 4H_2O$ has one BO_4 and four BO_3, whereas $Ca_2B_6O_{11} \cdot 7H_2O$ has four BO_4 and two BO_3 groups.

2. The basic structure is a six-atom ring whose stability depends on the presence of one or two BO_4 groups. Anions which do not have BO_4 groups, such as metaborate, $B_3O_6{}^{3-}$, or metaboric acid, $B_3O_3(OH)_3$, hydrate rapidly and lose their original structures. The fact that certain complex borates can be precipitated or crystallized from solution does not constitute evidence for the existence of such anions in solution, since other less complex anions can readily recombine during the crystallization process. ^{11}B nuclear resonance and other evidence has shown that both BO_3 and BO_4 groups are present in a variety of hydrated crystalline borates.

3. Other discrete and chain polymer anions can be formed by linking of two or more rings by shared tetrahedral boron atoms, in some cases with dehydration (cf. metaborate below).

Some known structures are $KB_5O_8 \cdot 4H_2O$ (10-VIII) and borax, $Na_2B_4O_7 \cdot 10H_2O$ (10-IX).

(10-VIII)   (10-IX)

Simple sharing of one oxygen by two BO_3 units would give $[O_2BOBO_2]^{4-}$; this so-called pyroborate anion has been shown to exist in $Co_2B_2O_5$. Also, the compound referred to as boron acetate, prepared by the reaction

$$2B(OH)_3 + 5(CH_3CO)_2O = (CH_3COO)_2BOB(OOCCH_3)_2 + 6CH_3COOH$$

9*

has a pyroborate-like structure. Boron phosphate, BPO_4, obtained by the reaction of boric and phosphoric acids, has tetrahedrally coordinated boron with B—O—P bonds.

Treatment of borates with hydrogen peroxide or of boric acid with sodium peroxide leads to products variously formulated as $NaBO_3 \cdot 4H_2O$ or $NaBO_2 \cdot H_2O_2 \cdot 3H_2O$, which are extensively used in washing powders because they afford H_2O_2 in solution. The crystal structure has been found to contain $[B_2(O_2)_2(OH)_4]^{2-}$ units with two peroxo groups bridging the tetrahedral boron atoms. Esr studies have shown the presence of free radicals in peroxoborates, but their nature is not yet certain.

Metaborates. On heating, boric acid loses water stepwise:

$$B(OH)_3 \underset{H_2O}{\overset{heat}{\rightleftarrows}} HBO_2 \underset{H_2O}{\overset{heat}{\rightleftarrows}} B_2O_3$$

Metaboric acid, HBO_2, exists in three modifications, the one obtained depending on the conditions of preparation; metaborate anions of at least two types exist in crystals. Orthorhombic HBO_2-I has cyclic, trimeric units (10-X) which are bound together by hydrogen bonds; monoclinic-II contains chains with both three- and four-coordinated boron.

(10-X)

10-7. Trihalides of Boron

Compounds of the type BX_3 exist for all of the halogens. On mixing any two of the halides, BF_3, BCl_3, BBr_3, at room temperature, a redistribution of halogen atoms occurs rather rapidly to produce a mixture of the original pure halides with the mixed halides in about statistical proportions. Thus, for example, we have the equilibrium

$$BF_3 + BCl_3 = BFCl_2 + BF_2Cl$$

Nuclear resonance studies of mixtures of three halides have established the existence of BFClBr and BClBrI. There is some reason to believe that these redistribution reactions take place via the transitory formation of dimers

(10-XI), although the concentration of dimers in any simple or mixed

(10-XI)   (10-XII)

halide system must be exceedingly low.   No mixed halides have been isolated, however.

Some reactions of the halides are summarized in Figure 10-4.

Boron trifluoride is the most important of the halides.   It is a pungent, colorless gas (b $-101°$) prepared by heating B_2O_3 with NH_4BF_4 or with CaF_2 and concentrated H_2SO_4.

BF_3 reacts with water to form two "hydrates," which may be written $BF_3 \cdot H_2O$ and $BF_3 \cdot 2H_2O$, melting at 10.18 and 6.36°, respectively.   It has been shown by nuclear resonance studies that they are un-ionized in the solid state.   For the monohydrate, we may assume that the structure is that of a normal adduct (10-XII).   This species presumably also exists in the solid dihydrate, but the manner in which the second H_2O is held is at present unknown.   Both of these hydrates are partially dissociated into ions in their liquid phases, presumably as follows:

$$2(BF_3 \cdot H_2O) = [H_3O-BF_3]^+ + [BF_3OH]^-$$
$$BF_3 \cdot 2H_2O = H_3O^+ + [BF_3OH]^-$$

Above about 20° they decompose extensively, giving off BF_3.   The mode of dissociation of the monohydrate is similar to the autoprotolysis of pure H_2SO_4, that is,

$$2H_2SO_4 = H_3SO_4^+ + HSO_4^-$$

When relatively small amounts of BF_3 are passed into water, a solution of fluoroboric acid (not isolable as a pure substance) is obtained.

$$4BF_3 + 6H_2O = 3H_3O^+ + 3BF_4^- + B(OH)_3$$

There is also some hydrolysis of the fluoroborate ion to produce HF and hydroxofluoroborate ion.

$$BF_4^- + H_2O = [BF_3OH]^- + HF \qquad K = 2.3 \times 10^{-3}$$

Boron trifluoride is one of the most avid acceptors—that is, strongest Lewis acids—known, and readily unites with water, ethers, alcohols, amines, phosphines, etc., to form adducts. BF_3 is commonly available as its diethyl etherate, $(C_2H_5)_2\overset{+}{O}\overset{-}{B}F_3$.   Because of its potency as a Lewis acid and its greater resistance to hydrolysis compared with BCl_3 and BBr_3,

BF$_3$ is widely used to promote various organic reactions, such as (*a*) ethers or alcohols + acids → esters + H$_2$O or ROH; (*b*) alcohols + benzene → alkyl benzenes + H$_2$O; (*c*) polymerization of olefins and olefin oxides; and (*d*) Friedel–Crafts-like acylations and alkylations. In the first two cases, the effectiveness of BF$_3$ must depend on its ability to form an adduct with one or both of the reactants, thus lowering the activation energy of the

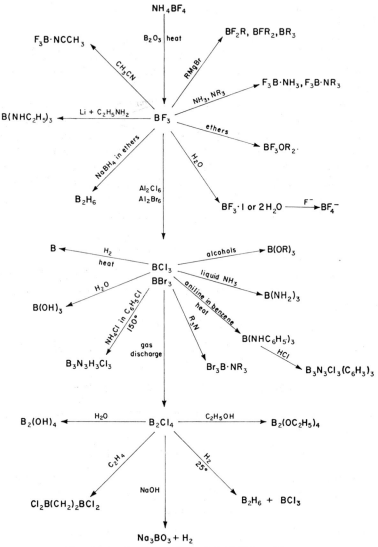

Fig. 10-4.   Some reactions of the halides of boron.

rate-determining step in which H_2O or ROH is eliminated by breaking of C—O bonds. However, the exact mechanisms of these reactions are not at present known, nor are those of the olefin and olefin oxide polymerizations.

In the case of the Friedel–Crafts-like reactions, isolation of certain intermediates at low temperatures has provided a fairly definite idea of the function of the BF_3. Thus, the ethylation of benzene by ethyl fluoride proceeds as in equation 10-1. With benzene, HF and BF_3, compound

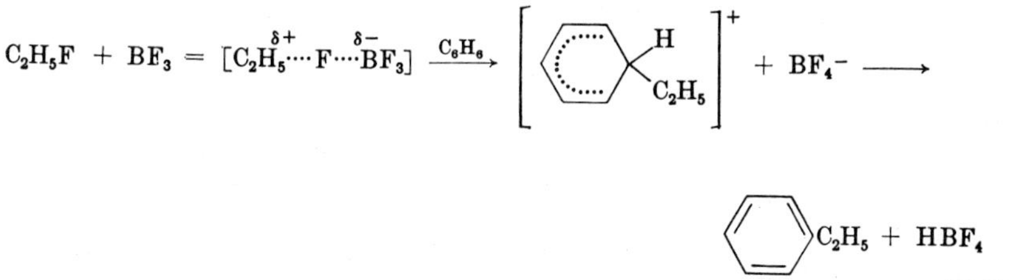

$$C_2H_5F \;+\; BF_3 \;=\; [C_2H_5^{\delta+}\cdots F\cdots \overset{\delta-}{B}F_3] \;\xrightarrow{C_6H_6}\; \left[\raisebox{-0.5em}{\includegraphics{}} \begin{array}{c} H \\ C_2H_5 \end{array} \right]^{+} \;+\; BF_4^{-} \;\longrightarrow$$

$$\left\langle \right\rangle C_2H_5 \;+\; HBF_4$$

(10-1)

10-XIII can be isolated at low temperatures. It will be seen that the BF_3 is not really "catalytic," but must be present in the stoichiometric amount since it is consumed in the process of tying up the HF as HBF_4.

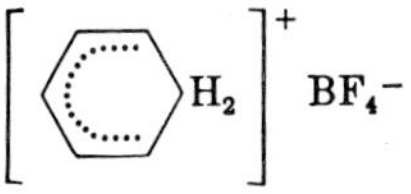

$$\left[\raisebox{-0.5em}{\includegraphics{}} H_2 \right]^{+} \; BF_4^{-}$$

(10-XIII)

Solid salts of tetrafluoroboric acid are readily isolated, those of NH_4^+ and many metals such as the alkalies and alkaline earths being commercially available. Ammonium fluoroborate may be prepared in a dry way by fusing NH_4HF_2 with B_2O_3. $B(OH)_3$ also readily dissolves in HF to form solutions of fluoroboric acid:

$$B(OH)_3 + 4HF = H_3O^+ + BF_4^- + 2H_2O$$

Fluoroboric acid is a strong acid. The fluoroborate ion has a tetrahedral structure, and fluoroborates closely resemble the corresponding perchlorates in their crystal structures and solubilities.

Boron trichloride is a liquid at room temperature under slight pressure (b 12.5°), whereas the *bromide* boils at 90°. Both fume in moist air and are completely hydrolyzed by water,

$$BCl_3 + 3H_2O = B(OH)_3 + 3HCl$$

The compounds are prepared by direct interaction of the elements at elevated temperatures.

The rapid hydrolysis by water could indicate that these halides are stronger Lewis acids than BF_3. In fact, the molar heats of solution of the trihalides in nitrobenzene and the heats of reaction with pyridine in nitrobenzene show that under these conditions the electron acceptor strength decreases $BBr_3 > BCl_3 > BF_3$.

The *iodide* is a white solid (m 43°). It is explosively hydrolyzed by water. It is prepared by the action of iodine on $NaBH_4$ or of HI on BCl_3 at red heat.

Tetrachloroborates are obtained by addition of BCl_3 to alkali chlorides at high pressures, by cold milling at room temperatures, or by the reaction

$$[(C_2H_5)_4N]^+Cl^- + BCl_3 \xrightarrow{CHCl_3} [(C_2H_5)_4N]^+BCl_4^-$$

The stability of these salts and the corresponding tetrabromoborates and tetraiodoborates is greatest with the largest cations. With a given cation, the stability order is $MBCl_4 > MBBr_4 > MBI_4$, tetraiodoborates occurring only with the largest cations. Mixed ions such as BF_3Cl^- also exist.

The reaction of BCl_3 with anhydrous $HClO_4$ at $-78°$ has been reported to yield $BCl_2(ClO_4)$, $BCl(ClO_4)_2$ and $B(ClO_4)_3$, the product depending on the mole ratio of the reactants.[1] There is as yet no structural information or other indication of how the perchlorate groups are bound to the boron atoms.

10-8. Lower Halides of Boron

Diboron tetrachloride, B_2Cl_4, is prepared by passing a discharge through BCl_3 vapor between mercury electrodes or, better, by the reaction of $(BO)_x$ with BCl_3. It is a colorless liquid which ignites in air and decomposes above 0° forming B_4Cl_4, B_8Cl_8, a red, paramagnetic solid of unknown structure which is probably $B_{12}Cl_{11}$ and a dark purple solid of approximate composition $(BCl_{0.9-1.1})_x$. X-ray study of solid B_2Cl_4 has shown that the molecule has the *planar* structure shown in Figure 10-5a. By contrast, spectroscopic study of the vapor indicates that the molecule is not planar and an electron diffraction study[2] has shown that in the vapor one BCl_2 group lies on a plane perpendicular to that of the other.

B_2F_4 is a gas which may be solidified at $-56°$. It reacts violently with oxygen and with metal oxides.[3] The structure of the molecule in the crystal

---

[1] R. A. Mosher, E. K. Ives and E. F. Morello, *J. Amer. Chem. Soc.*, **85**, 3037 (1963).

[2] K. Hedberg and R. Ryan, Jr., *J. Chem. Phys.*, **41**, 2215 (1964).

[3] A. K. Holliday and F. B. Taylor, *J. Chem. Soc.*, **1964**, 2731.

is analogous to that of B_2Cl_4, the molecule being planar. The F—B—F angles are 120 ± 2.5°, the B—F distance is 1.32 ± 0.03 A, and the B—B distance is 1.67 ± 0.05 A. Owing to the errors in the B—B distance measurements in both molecules, it is not certain that this distance in B_2F_4 is significantly shorter than in B_2Cl_4. If it really is, there is uncertainty as to the reason.

Tetraboron tetrachloride, B_4Cl_4, is a pale yellow, fairly volatile solid. It has a novel structure (Fig. 10-5b). The B_4 arrangement is tetrahedral,

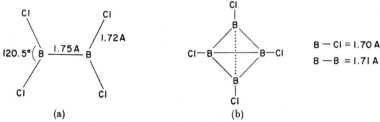

Fig. 10-5. Structures of (a) B_2Cl_4 and (b) B_4Cl_4.

and the B—Cl axes are collinear with the axes of the tetrahedron. This molecule is an example of an electron-deficient molecule. There are insufficient electrons for all of the B—B bonds and the B—Cl bonds to be two-electron bonds. It is assumed that the B—Cl bonds are normal electron pair bonds, whereas the tetrahedral boron skeleton is held together by multicenter bonds (see pages 276–280).

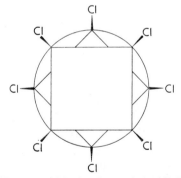

Fig. 10-6. Idealized structure of B_8Cl_8.

A compound to which the formula $(BCl_{0.9})_n$ had been assigned in the literature has been shown to be B_8Cl_8. The boron atoms are at the vertices of a distorted square antiprism with a chlorine atom bonded to each one (Fig. 10-6). Because of the distortion, twelve B—B distances are 1.78–1.85 A while four are 2.07 A.

10-9. The Boron Hydrides and Related Compounds

In a remarkable series of papers from 1912 to 1936, Alfred Stock and his coworkers prepared and chemically characterized the following hydrides of boron: B_2H_6, B_4H_{10}, B_5H_9, B_5H_{11}, B_6H_{10} and $B_{10}H_{14}$. With the exception of diborane, B_2H_6, which was prepared by thermal decomposition of higher boranes, Stock prepared these hydrides by the action of acid on magnesium boride, MgB_2, obtaining in this way a mixture of volatile, reactive and air-sensitive (some spontaneously inflammable) compounds. In order to handle compounds with these properties, Stock developed the glass vacuum line and techniques for using it. More recently, the additional boranes B_6H_{12},[4] B_8H_{12},[5] B_8H_{18},[5a] B_9H_{15}, $B_{10}H_{16}$, $B_{18}H_{22}$, iso-$B_{18}H_{22}$ and $B_{20}H_{16}$[6] have been prepared and characterized. Table 10-1 lists the principal boron hydrides and summarizes some of their important properties.

For preparation of boron hydrides, the Stock method is now seldom used. Diborane is now the starting material for most of the higher hydrides. All boron hydrides participate in a series of complex, reversible reactions at 100–250° which are similar to the cracking and reforming reactions in hydrocarbon systems except that they take place at lower temperatures and without catalysts. BH_3 is thought to be an important intermediate in these reactions. Figure 10-7 illustrates the general nature of these processes. For some boranes special preparative procedures are used. B_6H_{10}

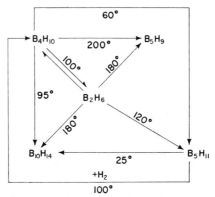

Fig. 10-7. Interconversion of boranes.

[4] D. F. Gaines and R. Schaeffer, *Inorg. Chem.*, **3**, 438 (1964); C. A. Lutz, D. A. Phillips and D. M. Ritter, *Inorg. Chem.*, **3**, 1191 (1964).

[5] R. E. Enrione, F. P. Boer and W. N. Lipscomb, *Inorg. Chem.*, **3**, 1659 (1964).

[5a] R. Schaeffer and D. F. Gaines, *Chem. and Eng. News*, April 12, 1965, p. 46.

[6] B. Friedman, R. D. Dobrott and W. N. Lipscomb, *J. Amer. Chem. Soc.*, **85**, 3505 (1963); N. E. Miller, J. A. Forstner and E. L. Muetterties, *Inorg. Chem.*, **3**, 1690 (1964).

TABLE 10-1

Important Properties of Boranes

Formula	Name	Melting point, °C	Boiling point, °C	Reaction with air at 25°C	Thermal stability	Reaction with water
B_2H_6	Diborane	−165.6	−92.5	Spontaneously inflammable	Fairly stable at 25°	Instant hydrolysis
B_4H_{10}	Tetraborane	−120	18	Not spontaneously inflammable if pure	Decomposes fairly rapidly at 25°	Hydrolysis in 24 hours
B_5H_9	Pentaborane-9	−46.6	48	Spontaneously inflammable	Stable 25°; slow decomposition 150°	Hydrolyzed only on heating
B_5H_{11}	Pentaborane-11	−123	63	Spontaneously inflammable	Decomposes very rapidly at 25°	Rapid hydrolysis
B_6H_{10}	Hexaborane-10	−62.3	—[b]	Stable	Slow decomposition at 25°	Hydrolyzed only on heating
B_6H_{12}	Hexaborane-12	−82.3	80–90	—[b]	Liquid decomposes rapidly	Quantitative, to give B_4H_{10}, $B(OH)_3$, H_2
B_8H_{12}	Octaborane-12	−20°	—[b]	—[b]	Decomposes above −20°	—[b]
B_8H_{18}	Octaborane-18	—[b]	—[b]	—[b]	Unstable	—[b]
B_9H_{15}	Enneaborane[c]	2.6	—[b]	Stable	—[b]	—[b]
$B_{10}H_{14}$	Decaborane	99.7	213(extrap.)	Very stable	Stable at 150°	Slow hydrolysis
$B_{10}H_{16}$	—[a]	—[b]	—[b]	—[b]	—[b]	—[b]
$B_{18}H_{22}$	—[a]	—[b]	—[b]	—[b]	—[b]	Monoprotic acid
iso-$B_{18}H_{22}$	—[a]	—[b]	—[b]	—[b]	—[b]	—[b]
$B_{20}H_{16}$	Icosaborane-16	196–199	—[b]	Stable	Stable at 25°	Irreversibly gives $B_{20}H_{16}(OH)_2^{2-}$ and $2H^+$

[a] No common name. [b] Not reported. [c] Unstable iso-B_9H_{15} exists also.

is still best prepared by the hydrolysis of magnesium boride,[7] though other methods are known. B_9H_{15} is obtained by heating B_5H_{11} in presence of solid hexamethylene tetramine, and $B_{10}H_{16}$ by passing B_5H_9 and H_2 through a glow discharge. $B_{18}H_{22}$ and $iso\text{-}B_{18}H_{22}$ are major and minor products, respectively, of the partial hydrolysis of an ether solution of the conjugate acid of $B_{20}H_{18}{}^{2-}$. $B_{20}H_{16}$, the only boron hydride with fewer H atoms than B atoms, has been prepared in two ways, viz., by passing $B_{10}H_{14}$ together with H_2 through a 1700 volt AC discharge or by pyrolyzing $B_{10}H_{14}$ at 350° and <1 mm pressure in the presence of $CH_3NHB(CH_3)_2$ as a catalyst.

Diborane, B_2H_6, is of special interest because it is the starting material for preparation of various other boron hydrides and for other reasons. It can be prepared in essentially quantitative yields by reaction of metal hydrides with boron trifluoride, a convenient method being to drop boron trifluoride etherate into a solution of sodium borohydride in diglyme:

$$3NaBH_4 + 4BF_3 = 3NaBF_4 + 2B_2H_6$$

It can also be prepared by the reaction

$$2NaBH_4 + H_2SO_4 = B_2H_6 + 2H_2 + Na_2SO_4$$

by the reaction of BCl_3 with hydrogen over a Cu–Al catalyst at 450°, and also directly from B_2O_3 by hydrogenation of the oxide in presence of Al and $AlCl_3$, a reaction in which an aluminum chlorohydride is probably an intermediate.[8] In presence of amines, amine boranes and borazines (see below) can also be directly synthesized. These direct procedures are a most important development. Some important reactions of diborane are collected in Figure 10-8.

Borane (or borine), BH_3, cannot be isolated but it has been detected by physical means,[9] and its occurrence as a reaction intermediate is generally accepted. Many adducts of BH_3 with donors are well known, for example, H_3BCO, $H_3BN(CH_3)_3$ and H_3BPF_3. Thermodynamic quantities pertaining to the reaction

$$B_2H_6 = 2BH_3$$

have been estimated indirectly,[10a] viz., $K_p \approx 10^{-5}$ atm at 25° and $\Delta H = 32\text{–}38$ kcal/mole. The bond dissociation energy of B_2H_6 has also been estimated as 37.1 ± 4 kcal/mole.[10b]

[7] P. L. Timms and C. S. G. Phillips, *Inorg. Chem.*, **3**, 297 (1964).
[8] T. H. Ford, G. M. Kalb, A. L. McClelland, E. L. Muetterties, *Inorg. Chem.*, **3**, 1032 (1964).
[9] T. P. Fehlner and W. S. Koski, *J. Amer. Chem. Soc.*, **86**, 2733 (1964).
[10a] M. E. Garabedian and S. W. Benson, *J. Amer. Chem. Soc.*, **86**, 176 (1964).
[10b] T. P. Fehlner and W. S. Koski, *J. Amer. Chem. Soc.*, **87**, 409 (1965).

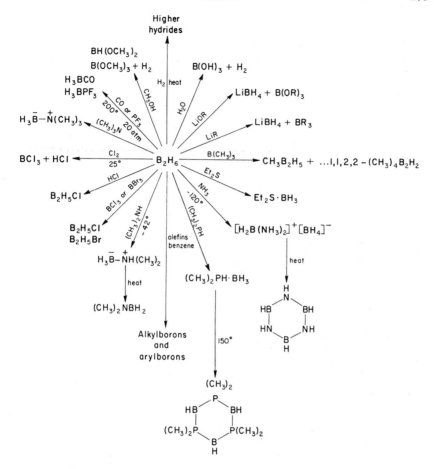

Fig. 10-8. Some reactions of diborane.

10-10. Configuration and Bonding in the Boranes

The unusual stoichiometries of the boranes are inexplicable on the basis of "normal" ideas of bond formation. These compounds, in fact, are one of the most important classes of *electron-deficient* compounds, which means that there are more adjacent pairs of atoms, close enough together that they must be regarded as bonded, than there are electrons necessary to provide an electron-pair bond for each pair of atoms. Before discussing the theory of valence necessary here, the molecular structures of several of the hydrides will be examined.

Although it was long the subject of uncertainty and controversy, the molecular structure of diborane is now firmly established. As shown in

Figure 10-9, it consists essentially of two irregular BH_4 tetrahedra sharing an edge. Thus the boron atoms and the four *terminal* hydrogen atoms lie in one plane while the two *bridging* hydrogen atoms lie above and below this plane. The structures of some other hydrides are shown in Figure 10-10.

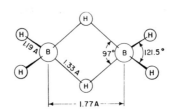

Fig. 10-9.   Structure of diborane.

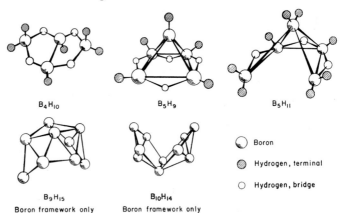

Fig. 10-10.   Structures of some higher boranes.

Bonding in the Boranes.   In order to account for the bonding in these compounds, chemists were compelled to broaden their views of chemical bonding. Thus these compounds—along with certain other electron-deficient compounds—have had a very important influence upon the development of valence theory. From the MO viewpoint (see page 81) an ordinary, electron-pair covalent bond between two atoms is formed when one orbital on each atom is used. These orbitals combine to form a bonding orbital, ψ_b, which provides increased electron density between the two atoms, and an antibonding orbital, ψ_a, which has a nodal surface and thus decreased electron density between the atoms.

Now suppose we have three atoms, each with an available orbital. From the three atomic orbitals it is possible to form three molecular orbitals, as shown in Figure 10-11. In the first of these, ψ_b, the three atomic orbitals combine so as to give positive overlap throughout and hence a continuous distribution of electron density around and between the nuclei. Electrons in such an orbital have a bonding effect; they act to hold the *three* nuclei together just as electrons occupying the two-center bonding MO act to hold two nuclei together. The second MO, ψ_a, is formed from the three atomic orbitals in such a way that nodal surfaces exist

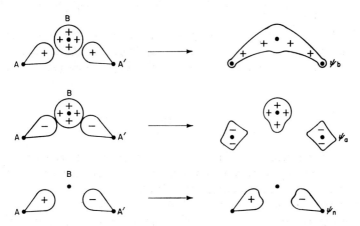

Fig. 10-11. Combination of atomic orbitals to give molecular orbitals.

between adjacent nuclei; therefore, electron density between them is diminished and such an MO is antibonding. Finally, there is an MO, ψ_n, formed only from the orbitals of the outer two atoms; since these have an almost negligible negative overlap, this MO is very slightly antibonding, but is conveniently taken as nonbonding. The set of 3-center MO energies is set out in an energy level diagram in Figure 10-12. It will be seen that

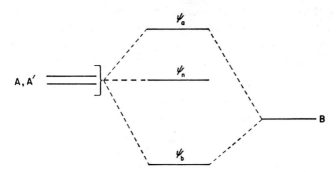

Fig. 10-12. Energy level diagram for 3-center molecular orbitals.

the maximum bond energy can be attained using just two electrons, since these are sufficient to fill only the bonding orbital. Another pair of electrons would have little effect, since they would occupy the nonbonding orbital.

Indeed if this second pair of electrons were available, the system would probably be unstable relative to one with two classical two-center, two-electron bonds. Thus, the three-center bonding situation is especially suited to the case where there are three nuclei but only two electrons. Let us now see how this concept enables us to explain the structure and bonding of B_2H_6.

In B_2H_6 we have two BH_2 fragments united by hydrogen bridges. Let us begin by supposing that in each BH_2 fragment there exist ordinary two-center, two-electron B—H bonds (10-XIV). Thus each boron atom

$$H$$
$$\cdot \overset{\cdot\cdot}{\underset{\cdot\cdot}{B}} \colon$$
$$H$$

(10-XIV)

has only one electron left. Let us now consider the bridging arrangement, BHB. The hydrogen atom has one electron and one useful orbital, namely, its $1s$ orbital. Each boron atom will also have an orbital available (to be specified in more detail presently). We may envision the formation of a three-center bonding MO as shown in Figure 10-11. An identical three-center bonding MO will be formed in the other bridging system, BHB. We now have two three-center bonding MO's. Altogether we have four electrons: one from each BH_2 group and one from each hydrogen atom. These four electrons now occupy the two bonding MO's, and the bridge bonding system is complete.

We may now discuss the nature of the s–p hybrid orbitals* contributed by boron to the bridging system in more detail. From the measured H—B—H angle of 122° we can infer that boron is using some sort of s–p hybrid orbitals. It is then possible, by assuming that these two hybrid orbitals point *exactly* in the directions of the hydrogen atoms, to calculate that the boron atom has two more s–p hybrids, which would make an angle of 101 ± 7° (Fig. 10-13). Note that this calculated angle agrees

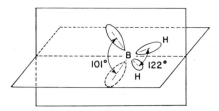

Fig. 10-13.   The orbitals used by a boron atom in B_2H_6.

* We use s–p to mean *some* form of hybrid made up of s and p orbitals, reserving sp to denote the linear, equivalent hybrids formed by equal s and p contributions. Thus sp, sp^2, sp^3 and all intermediate schemes are s–p hybrids.

within the errors of experiment and calculation with the observed H(bridge) —B—H(bridge) angle of 97 ± 3°.

In some of the higher boranes a somewhat different three-center bond exists, namely, between three boron atoms. The type discussed above has been called an "open" three-center bond, and this second type may be called a "closed" three-center bond. Figure 10-14 is a rough physical picture of its formation.

Both two-center and three-center bonds are merely simple special cases

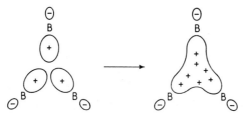

Fig. 10-14.   Sketch showing overlap of orbitals to form a closed, three-center BBB bond.

of *multicenter bonds* which may be four-, five- and, in general, n-centered; the MO's may be considered as linear combinations of the atomic orbitals of all the atoms involved, and they may be visualized in the same manner as has been illustrated for the three-center bonds above. Multicenter bonds may be expected to exist only in electron-deficient molecules, that is, where there are more usable atomic orbitals than there are electrons to use them all in forming two-center bonds. In general, where we have n atomic orbitals and m electrons, the following cases arise:

1. $m = n$, as in the hydrocarbons. In C_2H_6, for example, there are fourteen atomic orbitals, which are combined to produce seven bonding orbitals. There are also fourteen electrons, or seven pairs, to occupy these seven bonding orbitals, and we can thus write the usual description of ethane, with seven two-center, two-electron bonds (10-XV).

H   H
H : C : C : H
H   H
(10-XV)

H
: N : H
H
(10-XVI)

2. $m > n$, as in NH_3 or H_2O. In NH_3 we have seven orbitals and four electron pairs. Six of the orbitals combine to form three bonding orbitals (and three antibonding orbitals), while a fourth orbital remains unused in bonding. Thus there are three pairs of bonding electrons and a pair of "lone" or nonbonding electrons, in accordance with our usual picture of the electronic structure of NH_3 (10-XVI).

3. $m < n$. In these cases, where energetically possible, multicenter orbitals will be formed. Thus, to recapitulate the case of B_2H_6, there are altogether fourteen atomic orbitals and twelve electrons. Eight orbitals (two from each boron and the orbitals from the four terminal hydrogen atoms) are combined to form four bonding orbitals of the two-center type in which eight of the electrons are housed. The remaining six orbitals are combined into two three-center bonding orbitals (and four three-center non- or antibonding MO's) which are occupied by the remaining four electrons.

A useful and elaborate though essentially empirical scheme for formulating the bonding in the majority of boranes has been developed by Lipscomb. This "semitopological" description makes use of the following types of bonds and symbols:

B—H   terminal, 2-center, 2-electron boron–hydrogen bond

$\overset{\displaystyle H}{B\diagup\diagdown B}$ 3-center, 2-electron hydrogen bridge bond

B—B   2-center, 2-electron boron–boron bond

$B\diagup^{B}\diagdown B$ "open" 3-center, 2-electron boron bridge bond

$\overset{\displaystyle B}{\underset{B\diagup\diagdown B}{|}}$ "closed" 3-center, 2-electron boron bond

Figure 10-15 shows how the bonding in B_2H_6 and in two of the boron hydrides whose geometrical structures appear in Figure 10-10 can be

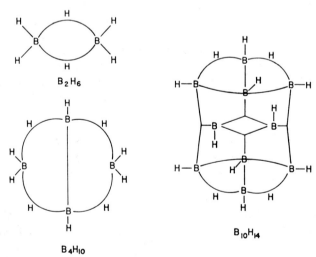

Fig. 10-15.   Valence descriptions of boron hydrides in terms of the "semi-topological" scheme of Lipscomb.

depicted in this way. Extensions of such descriptions have allowed the prediction of stabilities and structures of possible new boranes.[11]

10-11. Compounds Closely Related to the Boranes

We shall discuss here three classes of compounds which are closely related to the boron hydrides not only in the empirical sense of being obtained from them by chemical reactions, but also in having molecular and electronic structures which are qualitatively similar. These are the boron hydride anions, the coordination derivatives of boron hydrides and the carboranes.

Anions and Equivalent Coordination Derivatives. Some of the boron hydride anions can be treated, at least formally, as though they owe their negative charges to the presence of coordinated hydride ions, H^-. Consequently, neutral compounds which contain donor molecules (amines acetonitrile, phosphines, etc.) in place of H^- should be structurally similar to the anions, and in many cases they are. They are then considered as "equivalent" to the anions, and vice versa. Actually, there are some coordination compounds known for which no analogous hydride anions are yet known[12] (e.g., $B_4H_{10}{}^{2-}$ and $B_5H_{11}{}^{2-}$).

The simplest and commonest boron hydride anion is $BH_4{}^-$, the borohydride ion (see also page 202). A variety of substituted borohydride ions, for example, $[BH(OCH_3)_3]^-$, are also known. Borohydrides of a great many metallic elements—the alkali metals, Be, Mg, Al, Ti, Zr, Th, U, etc.—have been made.[13] Typical preparative reactions are

$$4NaH + B(OCH_3)_3 \xrightarrow{\sim 250°} NaBH_4 + 3NaOCH_3$$
$$NaH + B(OCH_3)_3 \xrightarrow{THF} NaBH(OCH_3)_3$$
$$2LiH + B_2H_6 \xrightarrow{ether} 2LiBH_4$$
$$AlCl_3 + 3NaBH_4 \xrightarrow{heat} Al(BH_4)_3 + 3NaCl$$
$$UF_4 + 2Al(BH_4)_3 \longrightarrow U(BH_4)_4 + 2AlF_2BH_4$$

$NaBH_4$ is representative of the alkali borohydrides and it is the most common one. It is a white crystalline substance, stable in dry air and non-volatile. While insoluble in diethyl ether, it dissolves in water, tetrahydrofuran and glymes to give solutions widely useful in synthetic chemistry as reducing agents and sources of hydride ions. Treatment of $NaBH_4$, with protonic acids (e.g., HCl) or Lewis acids (e.g., BCl_3, $AlCl_3$) generates

[11] W. N. Lipscomb, *Inorg. Chem.*, **3**, 1683 (1964).
[12] N. E. Miller, H. C. Miller and E. L. Muetterties, *Inorg. Chem.*, **3**, 866 (1964).
[13] For references see N. F. Curtis, *J. Chem. Soc.*, **1965**, 924.

diborane; when this is done in presence of olefinic hydrocarbons the so-called hydroboration reaction, an anti-Markownikoff, *cis* hydrogenation or hydration can be effected:

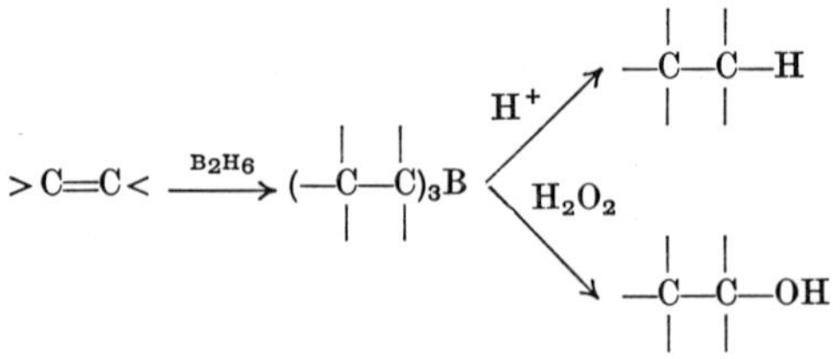

$$> C{=}C < \xrightarrow{\mathrm{B_2H_6}} (-\overset{|}{\underset{|}{C}}{-}\overset{|}{\underset{|}{C}})_3B \begin{cases} \xrightarrow{\mathrm{H^+}} -\overset{|}{\underset{|}{C}}{-}\overset{|}{\underset{|}{C}}{-}H \\ \\ \xrightarrow{\mathrm{H_2O_2}} -\overset{|}{\underset{|}{C}}{-}\overset{|}{\underset{|}{C}}{-}OH \end{cases}$$

Ionic borohydrides (e.g., $NaBH_4$) contain discrete BH_4^- ions, which are tetrahedral, and structures of MBH_4 compounds are often the same as that of NH_4Cl since NH_4^+ and BH_4^- are isoelectronic and isosteric. In $LiBH_4$ the BH_4 tetrahedron is distorted by the attraction of the small, positive Li ion for the hydrogen atoms closest to it. This tendency toward distortion increases with increasing charge-to-radius ratio of the cation. In $Al(BH_4)_3$ each BH_4 shares two H atoms with Al and the bonding in the Al—H—B groups can be described by three-center MO's similar to those in diborane.

Coordination derivatives equivalent to BH_4^- are numerous. They have the general formula LBH_3, in which L may be a tertiary amine, a phosphine, CO, etc. Amines containing N—H bonds presumably also form similar adducts initially but these quickly lose H_2.

$$B_2H_6 + 2(CH_3)_3N = 2(CH_3)_3NBH_3$$
$$B_2H_6 + 2(CH_3)_2NH = [2(CH_3)_2NHBH_3] = 2(CH_3)_2NBH_2 + 2H_2$$

The next most complicated boron hydride anion is $B_3H_8^-$, obtained, for example, by reaction of NaH with B_4H_{10}, or by the reaction[14]

$$NaBH_4 + B_2H_6 \xrightarrow{25-60°, \ 1-2 \ atm} NaB_3H_8 + H_2$$

Other polyhedral borane anions such as $B_{12}H_{12}^{2-}$ and $B_{11}H_{14}^-$ are also made by similar reactions. In view of the direct preparation of B_2H_6 from B_2O_3 referred to above, direct synthesis of these anions is thus now quite straightforward. $B_3H_8^-$ has the structure shown in Figure 10-16. The equivalent coordination compound, $B_3H_7NH_3$, has a structure which is similar but not exactly analogous. Other equivalent compounds are also known.

The most novel and interesting of the boron hydride anions are $B_{10}H_{10}^{2-}$

[14] H. C. Miller, N. E. Miller and E. L. Muetterties, *Inorg. Chem.*, **3**, 1456 (1964).

and $B_{12}H_{12}{}^{2-}$, which are best prepared in yields of 80–100% by the following reactions:

$$B_{10}H_{14} + 2(CH_3)_2S \longrightarrow B_{10}H_{12} \cdot 2(CH_3)_2S + H_2$$

$$\xrightarrow{2NH_3} (NH_4)_2B_{10}H_{10} + 2(CH_3)_2S$$

$$2NaBH_4 + 5B_2H_6 \xrightarrow[100-180°]{(C_2H_5)_3N} Na_2B_{12}H_{12} + 13H_2$$

$$2(C_2H_5)_3NBH_3 + 5B_2H_6 \xrightarrow{100-80°} [(C_2H_5)_3NH]_2B_{12}H_{12} + 11H_2$$

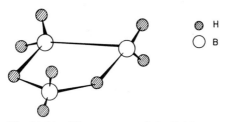

H
B

Fig. 10-16.   The structure of the $B_3H_8{}^-$ ion.

These ions are remarkably stable toward acids, bases and oxidizing agents, and aqueous solutions are resistant to thermal decomposition.[15,16] Since both ions are thermodynamically unstable, kinetic inertness must account for their resistance to these reagents and conditions. Both anions react with F_2, Cl_2, Br_2, I_2, HF, HCl and some other halogenating agents to give halosubstituted ions, $[B_{10}H_{10-n}X_n]^{2-}$ and $[B_{12}H_{12-n}X_n]^{2-}$, including the limiting species $[B_{10}X_{10}]^{2-}$ and $[B_{12}X_{12}]^{2-}$ where X is Cl, Br and I; the perfluoro compounds have not yet been made. For the intermediate species many isomers are possible (see next paragraph) and studies of isomerism are still to be made. Like the $[B_{10}H_{10}]^{2-}$ and $[B_{12}H_{12}]^{2-}$ ions, the partially and fully halogenated ones are extremely stable toward acids, bases and heat. Besides these halogenation reactions,[15] other substitution reactions have been found[16] and it appears likely that these two anions will have a very extensive derivative chemistry.[17] Oxidation of $B_{10}H_{10}{}^{2-}$ and of its substituted derivatives such as $B_{10}H_9SMe_2{}^-$ lead to coupled species $B_{20}H_{16}L_2$ which can be regarded as derivatives of the known $B_{20}H_{18}{}^{2-}$ ion.[18]

[15] E. L. Muetterties, W. Knoth, et al., Inorg. Chem., **3**, 159, 444 (1964).

[16] E. L. Muetterties, et al., J. Amer. Chem. Soc., **86**, 3973 (1964); M. F. Hawthorne and F. P. Olsen, J. Amer. Chem. Soc., **86**, 4219 (1964); W. R. Hertler and M. S. Raasch, J. Amer. Chem. Soc., **86**, 3361 (1964).

[17] For references see W. H. Knoth, W. R. Hertler and E. L. Muetterties, Inorg. Chem., **4**, 280 (1965).

[18] B. L. Chamberlain and E. L. Muetterties, Inorg. Chem., **3**, 1450 (1964).

The $B_{10}H_{10}^{2-}$ ion has the structure shown in Figure 10-17.   It consists of two square pyramids connected with their bases 45° out of coincidence. There are two kinds of boron atoms: the two apical ones and the eight equatorial ones.   This structure for the B_{10} framework allows the existence

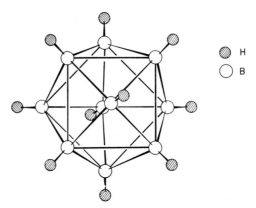

Fig. 10-17.   The structure of the $B_{10}H_{10}^{2-}$ ion.

of two isomers of $B_{10}H_9X$, six isomers of $B_{10}H_8X_2$, thirteen of $B_{10}H_7X_3$, and so on.   It is not impossible, however, that certain pairs of isomers may be interconvertible by rearrangements of the B_{10} framework which can be accomplished without extensive bond breaking.   Again, this is something which still awaits investigation.

The $[B_{12}H_{12}]^{2-}$ anion has the shape of the icosahedron, one of the Pythagorean regular polyhedra, in which all vertices are equivalent.   Again, in the partially substituted derivatives, $[B_{12}H_{12-n}X_n]^{2-}$, a number of isomers are possible.   Figure 10-18 shows the three isomers of $[B_{12}H_{10}X_2]^{2-}$ or $[B_{12}H_2X_{10}]^{2-}$.

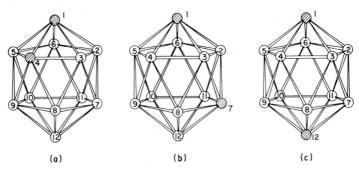

(a)   (b)   (c)

Fig. 10-18.   Three isomers of $[B_{12}H_{10}X_2]^{2-}$ or $[B_{12}H_2X_{10}]^{2-}$.   This basic icosahedral structure also exists in $B_{10}C_2$ units of carboranes such as $B_{10}Cl_8H_2C_2H_2$.

Carboranes. A *carborane* may be defined, at least tentatively, as a polyhedral-type molecule containing both B and C atoms in the polyhedral framework. It may be derivable, in principle though not in a preparative sense, from a known boron hydride anion by replacing B—H$^-$ with C—H, or from a boron hydride by replacing B—H plus a bridging H with C—H. These replacements lead to isoelectronic molecules. For example, $B_{10}C_2H_{12}$ is analogous to $[B_{12}H_{12}]^{2-}$ in the sense of the first type of substitution while $B_4C_2H_8$ is analogous to B_6H_{10} in the sense of the second type. The existence of analogous boron hydride molecules or anions is not a necessity; for instance, $B_3C_2H_5$ has no analogous boron hydride (B_5H_7) nor boron hydride anion ($B_5H_5{}^{2-}$) though theory suggests that $B_5H_5{}^{2-}$ should be quite stable.

Carboranes have generally been prepared by reactions of acetylene or substituted acetylenes with boron hydrides, as in the following examples:

$$B_5H_9 + RC \equiv CR' + \underset{N}{\bigcirc} \longrightarrow B_4H_6C_2RR' + \underset{N:BH_3}{\bigcirc}$$

$$B_5H_9 + C_2H_2 \xrightarrow[\text{discharge}]{\text{silent elect.}} B_3C_2H_5,\ B_4C_2H_6,\ B_5C_2H_7,\ \text{etc.}$$

$$B_{10}H_{14} + 2(C_2H_5)_2S \xrightarrow{40°} B_{10}H_{12} \cdot 2(C_2H_5)_2S + H_2$$

$$B_{10}H_{12} \cdot 2(C_2H_5)_2S + HC \equiv CH \xrightarrow{90°} B_{10}C_2H_{12} + 2(C_2H_5)_2S + H_2$$

The last two reactions, which together constitute a preparative procedure for $B_{10}C_2H_{12}$, may be run in sequence in the same vessel without isolating the intermediate, $B_{10}H_{12} \cdot 2(C_2H_5)_2S$. Also, bases other than $(C_2H_5)_2S$ and various substituted acetylenes may be used.

The most thoroughly studied carborane system[19] is that of $B_{10}C_2H_{12}$ (o-carborane or 1,2-dicarbaclovododecaborane), including its many C-substituted derivatives and its isomers. From the structure of decaborane (Fig. 10-10) it might be expected that the direct product of the addition of an acetylene would be a 12 atom cage having essentially the shape of an icosahedron with the C atoms *ortho* to one another (Fig. 10-18a). Nmr and X-ray evidence on derivatives shows that this is the case.[20,21] o-$B_{10}C_2H_{12}$ is an extremely stable molecule with the $B_{10}H_{10}C_2$ part resisting attack by acids, alkalies and oxidizing agents while a great variety of reactions can be carried out upon the groups bound to the carbon atoms. It is also possible to chlorinate $B_{10}C_2H_{12}$ to varying degrees by direct action of

[19] See a series of papers in *Inorganic Chemistry*, **2**, 1087–1133 (1963).
[20] J. A. Potenza and W. N. Lipscomb, *Inorg. Chem.*, **3**, 1673 (1964); D. Voet and W. N. Lipscomb, *Inorg. Chem.*, **3**, 1679 (1964).
[21] H. Schroeder and G. D. Vickers, *Inorg. Chem.*, **2**, 1317 (1964).

chlorine. H atoms attached to B atoms are replaced first and representative products are $B_{10}H_8Cl_2C_2H_2$, $B_{10}H_4Cl_6C_2H_2$, $B_{10}Cl_{10}C_2H_2$ and $B_{10}Cl_{10}C_2HCl$. Perchlorocarborane, $B_{10}C_2Cl_{12}$, and perchloroneocarborane (see below) are also known.[22]

Upon heating $o\text{-}B_{10}C_2H_{12}$ at 460–500° in an inert atmosphere, it isomerizes to a compound which has been called *neocarborane*. Nmr evidence[21] shows that this is *meta*-$B_{10}C_2H_{12}$ (Fig. 10-18b). The greater stability of the *meta* isomer had been anticipated from molecular orbital calculations.[23] The $B_{10}C_2$ skeleton of $m\text{-}B_{10}C_2H_{12}$ shows the same high resistance to acidic, basic and oxidative attack as that of the o-isomer and, again, there is a considerable chemistry based on reactions at the carbon atoms. The *para* isomer (Fig. 10-18c), also predicted by MO theory to be more stable than $o\text{-}B_{10}C_2H_{12}$, has been obtained in small quantities by thermal rearrangement of $o\text{-}B_{10}C_2H_{12}$.

The $B_4C_2H_8$-type carborane (2,3-dicarbahexaborane-8) is best known in the form of derivatives with two hydrogen atoms replaced by alkyl groups.[24] X-ray diffraction work[25] has shown that the structures of $B_4H_6C_2H_2$ and $B_4H_6C_2Me_2$ are similar to that of B_6H_{10}; thus in the methyl compound a CH_3—C—C—CH_3 group replaces the H_b—BH—BH—H_b group in the basal plane of the pentagonal pyramid. 2,3-Dicarbahexaborane-8, $B_4C_2H_8$, derivatives are made by action of acetylenes on B_5H_9 using 2,6-lutidine as catalyst.[26]

The series of carboranes obtained by reaction of B_5H_9 and C_2H_2 in a silent electric discharge[27] include the following three which are reasonably well characterized structurally though not chemically: $B_3C_2H_5$ (m $-126.4°$; b $-3.7°$), stable at 25° for long periods; $sym\text{-}B_4C_2H_6$ (m $-30°$; b 22.7°), stable at 25° for at least 6 months and not very reactive; $unsym\text{-}B_4C_2H_6$, probably unstable relative to sym isomer; $B_5C_2H_7$ of which several C-sub-stituted derivatives are also known. Structural information for these molecules comes mainly from nmr spectra. Thus, $B_3C_2H_5$ appears to contain a trigonal bipyramidal B_3C_2 skeleton with the C atoms at the axial apices, while the $B_4C_2H_6$ isomers have distorted octahedral skeletons[28] with the C atoms in *trans* positions in $sym\text{-}B_4C_2H_6$ and in *cis* positions in $unsym\text{-}B_4C_2H_6$. Finally, from both nmr and microwave spectra,[29] $B_5C_2H_7$

[22] H. Schroeder, J. Reiner, R. P. Alexander and T. L. Heying, *Inorg. Chem.*, **3**, 1464 (1964).
[23] R. H. Hoffman and W. N. Lipscomb, *Inorg. Chem.*, **2**, 231 (1963).
[24] T. P. Onak, R. E. Williams and H. G. Weiss, *J. Amer. Chem. Soc.*, **84**, 2830 (1962).
[25] F. P. Boer, W. E. Streib and W. N. Lipscomb, *Inorg. Chem.*, **3**, 1666 (1964).
[26] T. Onak, R. P. Pake and G. B. Dunks, *Inorg. Chem.*, **3**, 1686 (1964).
[27] I. Shapiro, C. D. Good and R. E. Williams, *J. Amer. Chem. Soc.*, **84**, 3837 (1962).
[28] I. Shapiro, B. Keilin, R. E. Williams and C. D. Good, *J. Amer Chem. Soc.*, **85**, 3167 (1963).
[29] R. A. Beaudet and R. B. Poynter, *J. Amer. Chem. Soc.*, **86**, 1258 (1964).

appears to have a pentagonal bipyramidal B_5C_2 skeleton with the C atoms in non-adjacent positions in the equatorial plane.

It would seem that the carborane field is now only in its infancy, with a great many new compounds and reactions to be discovered and studied. Since silicon-containing carboranes[30] are now known and the possibility of binding to other elements exists, the field is potentially very wide indeed.

10-12. Compounds with Boron Bonded to Other Elements

Diborane has proved to be a useful starting material for the preparation of compounds containing boron bound to N, As, P, O, S, C, etc. Here, again, the chemistry is extensive and complex, and only a selection of important types of compounds will be presented.

There are some very interesting compounds of boron with the group V elements, especially nitrogen. Of particular interest are certain boron–nitrogen compounds which are isoelectronic and isostructural with carbon

(10-XVII)   (10-XVIIIa)   ⟷   (10-XVIIIb)

compounds. As examples, consider benzene (10-XVII) and borazine (10-XVIII), isobutene (10-XIX) and B,B'-dimethylaminoborine (10-XX).

$$(CH_3)_2C\!=\!CH_2 \qquad (CH_3)_2B\!-\!\ddot{N}H_2 \leftrightarrow (CH_3)_2\bar{B}\!=\!\overset{+}{N}H_2$$

(10-XIX)   (10-XXa)   (10-XXb)

Borazine, or *borazole*, $B_3N_3H_6$ (b 55°), has the superficial resemblance to benzene which is indicated, and does resemble it in some of its physical and chemical properties. However, in benzene the C⋯C bonds are non-polar and the nucleus is very resistant to addition reactions, whereas the borazine nucleus, because of its polarities, is fairly reactive. Thus it readily adds three molecules of H_2O, CH_3OH, CH_3I or HCl, the more negative group generally attaching itself to the boron atoms.

$$B_3N_3H_6 + 3HCl =$$

---

[30] S. Papetti, B. B. Schaeffer, H. J. Troscianiec and T. L. Heying, *Inorg. Chem.*, **3**, 1445 (1964); S. Papetti and T. L. Heying, *Inorg. Chem.*, **3**, 1448 (1964).

Borazine also decomposes slowly on standing and is hydrolyzed at high temperatures to $B(OH)_3$ and NH_3. It may be conveniently prepared by heating together ammonium chloride and BCl_3, the initial product being the B-chloroborazine, which is then reduced with sodium borohydride in a polyether:

$$3NH_4Cl + 3BCl_3 \xrightarrow[140-150°]{C_6H_5Cl} \text{[B-chloroborazine ring]} \xrightarrow{NaBH_4} B_3N_3H_6$$
$$\xrightarrow{CH_3MgBr} B_3N_3H_3(CH_3)_3$$

N-Alkylated borazines may also be obtained by starting with alkyl-ammonium halides:

$$CH_3NH_2 + BCl_3 \xrightarrow[C_6H_5Cl]{\text{boiling}} Cl_3B\cdot NH_2CH_3$$
$$(m\ 126-128°)$$

$$3Cl_3B\cdot NH_2CH_3 + 6(CH_3)_3N \xrightarrow{\text{toluene}} 6(CH_3)_3NHCl + \text{[substituted borazine ring]}$$

$$(m\ 153-156°)$$

Borazine and substituted borazines can also be made by treating sodium borohydride with ammonium or alkylammonium chlorides in triethylene glycol dimethyl ether. The B—Cl bonds can often be subsequently alkylated by Grignard reagents.

Diborane and ammonia under the proper conditions react to produce the so-called diammoniate of diborane which has been shown to be $[H_2B(NH_3)_2]^+[BH_4]^-$. This, on heating, produces borazine. On heating mixtures of ammonia and diborane, a compound, B_2H_7N or $B_2H_5NH_2$, can be obtained, and by using mono- and disubstituted (but not trisubstituted) amines similar compounds such as $B_2H_5(CH_3NH)$, $B_2H_5(CH_3NSiH_3)$, etc., are produced. These compounds, called aminodiboranes, have been shown to have the 10-XXI type of structure.

(10-XXI)   (10-XXII)

In view of the extensive aminoboron chemistry, studies have been made of boron–phosphorus and boron–arsenic chemistry. One of the notable B—P compounds is $[(CH_3)_2PBH_2]_3$, which has the cyclic structure 10-XXII. The arsenic analog is also known. This compound and its arsenic analog are extraordinarily stable and inert, a fact which has been attributed to a drift of electron density from the BH_2 groups into the d orbitals of P or As. This has the effect of reducing the hydridic nature of the hydrogen atoms, making them less susceptible to reaction with protonic reagents, and also of offsetting the $\overset{-}{B}$—$\overset{+}{P}$, $\overset{-}{B}$—$\overset{+}{As}$ polar character, which the σ bonding alone tends to produce. These cyclic compounds are inorganic analogs of cyclohexanes such as $C_6(CH_3)_{12}$.

Organoboron Compounds. Some organoboron compounds, $(CH_3)_3B$, $(CH_3O)_3B$, etc., have already been mentioned in passing. Hundreds of boron compounds containing organic groups bonded either directly to boron or indirectly via other atoms such as O and N are known. One important series of compounds is the alkyl and aryl orthoborates, $B(OR)_3$, and their complexes such as $Na[HB(OR)_3]$, the trialkoxo borohydrides. These may be thought of as derived from $B(OH)_3$. There are, then, also the *boronic* and *boronous* acids, $RB(OH)_2$ and $R_2B(OH)$, their esters and anhydrides, and finally the trialkyl or triaryl borons, R_3B. The lower alkyl borons are very reactive substances which will inflame in air. Aryls and hydroxo derivatives are stable in air. Sulfur analogs of many of the oxo compounds also exist. The boronic acids can be made in various ways, for example,

$$BF_3 \cdot O(C_2H_5)_2 + C_6H_5MgBr \longrightarrow C_6H_5BF_2 \xrightarrow{H_2O} C_6H_5B(OH)_2$$

and are quite stable and water soluble. Their acidities depend upon the nature of the alkyl or aryl group. Dehydration of a boronic acid by heating yields a boronic anhydride:

$$3RB(OH)_2 = (RBO)_3 + 3H_2O$$

These boronic anhydrides, also called *boroxines*, have been shown to have trimeric, cyclic structures with planar rings of alternating boron and oxygen atoms. The alkyl groups are also in the plane of the ring.

Salts of boronium ions[31] such as $[Ph_2Bdipy]^+$ which can be obtained by action of 2,2′-dipyridyl on Ph_2BCl are quite stable to hydrolysis; with some anions, such as I^-, the salts are yellow due to charge-transfer absorption.

Lastly, we may mention that if boron halides are reacted with four moles of a Grignard reagent or other metal alkyl or aryl, the trialkyl or triaryl

---

[31] L. Banford and G. E. Coates, *J. Chem. Soc.*, **1964**, 3564; N. E. Miller and E. L. Muetterties, *J. Amer. Chem. Soc.*, **86**, 1033 (1964).

10 + A.I.C.

boron first produced will add another alkyl or aryl group forming an anion of the type BR_4^-.

$$3RM + BX_3 = R_3B + 3MX$$
$$R_3B + RM = (M^+)(BR_4^-)$$

Perhaps the most important such compound is sodium tetraphenylborate, $Na[B(C_6H_5)_4]$. The sodium compound is moderately soluble in water, but tetraphenylborates of larger cations such as K^+, Rb^+, Cs^+ or $(CH_3)_4N^+$ are insoluble and suitable for gravimetric analysis.

References

Adams, R. M., ed., *Boron, Metallo-Boron Compounds and Boranes*, Interscience–Wiley, New York, 1964. Chapters of particular interest are those on "Inorganic Boron–Oxygen Chemistry" by N. P. Nies and G. W. Campbell, "Elemental Boron" by A. E. Newkirk, "Refractory Binary Borides" by B. Post, "The Hydroboron Ions" by R. M. Adams and A. R. Siedle, and "The Boron Hydrides" by R. M. Adams.

Advances in Chemistry Series, No. 42. "Boron–Nitrogen Chemistry". American Chemical Society, Washington, D.C. Papers and reviews on aminoboranes, aromatic B—N compounds, etc.

Aronsson, B., T. Lundstrom and S. Rundqvist, *Borides, Silicides and Phosphides*, Methuen, London, 1965. Concise account.

Booth, H. S., and L. Audrieth, *Boron Trifluoride and Its Derivatives*, Wiley, New York, 1949.

Bradley, D. C., in *Progress in Stereochemistry*, Butterworths, London, 1962. A review of B and Group III stereochemistry.

Brown, H. C., *Hydroboronation*, W. A. Benjamin, New York, 1962.

Gerrard, W., *The Organic Chemistry of Boron*, Academic Press, New York, 1961.

Hawthorne, M. F., *Adv. Inorg. Chem. Radiochem.*, **5**, 308 (1963). A review of the chemistry of decaborane-14.

Holliday, A. K., and A. G. Massey, *Chem. Rev.*, **62**, 303 (1962). Boron sub-halides and compounds with B—B bonds.

Köster, R., *Adv. Organometal. Chem.*, **2**, 257 (1965). Heterocyclic organoboranes.

Lipscomb, W. N., *Boron Hydrides*, Benjamin, New York, 1963. The definitive work on structure and bonding in compounds containing polyhedral boron skeletons.

Martin, D. R., and J. M. Canon, in *Friedel–Crafts and Related Reactions*, Vol. I, G. A. Olah, ed., Interscience–Wiley, New York and London, 1963, p. 399. A comprehensive review of coordination compounds of boron halides, with 589 references. (Cf. also p. 226 for data on BF_3, BCl_3 and $BrBr_3$ and their catalytic activity.)

Mellon, E. K., Jr., and J. J. Lagowski, *Adv. Inorg. Chem. Radiochem.*, **5**, 259 (1963). Review on borazines.

Niedenzu, K., *Angew. Chem. (Internat.)*, **3**, 86 (1964). Chemistry of aminoboranes.

Onak, T., *Adv. Organomet. Chem.*, Vol. 3 (1965). Carboranes and organo substituted boron hydrides.

Sharp, D. W. A., *Adv. Fluorine Chem.*, **1**, 68 (1960). Fluoroboric acids and their derivatives.

Sheldon, J. C., and B. C. Smith, *Quart. Rev.*, **14**, 200 (1960).   Borazole and related compounds.

Steinberg, H., *Organoboron Chemistry*, Vol. I, Wiley, New York, 1963.   B—O and B—S compounds.   Comprehensive reference book.

Steinberg, H., and A. L. McCloskey, eds., *Progress in Boron Chemistry*, Vol. I, Macmillan, New York, 1964.   Review series.   Vol. I has Monographs on B—B bonds, co-ordination chemistry, boron hydride structures, organoboron heterocycles, nmr data, boronic and borinic acids, etc.

Topschiev, A. V., S. V. Zavgorodnii and Y. M. Paushkin (Trans. J. Greaves), *Boron Fluoride and its Compounds as Catalysts in Organic Chemistry*, Pergamon Press, London, 1959.

11

Carbon

There are more known compounds of carbon than of any other element except hydrogen. Indeed the chemistry of carbon is so extensive and so important that it constitutes, in itself, that branch of the whole field of chemistry known as organic chemistry.

The electronic structure of the carbon atom in its ground state is $1s^2 2s^2 2p^2$, with the two $2p$ electrons unpaired following Hund's rule. In order to account for the normal four covalence of carbon, we must consider that it is promoted to a valence state based on the configuration $2s 2p_x 2p_y 2p_z$. This has been discussed in detail in Chapter 3. The ion C^{4+} does not arise in any normal chemical processes; the C^{4-} ion may possibly exist in some carbides. In general, however, carbon forms covalent bonds.

Some cations, anions and radicals of moderate stability can occur, and there is abundant evidence from the study of organic reaction mechanisms for transient species of these types. Cations of the type $R_1 R_2 R_3 C^+$ are called *carbonium* ions. The triphenylmethyl carbonium ion was one of the first to be discovered and is a fairly typical example. It doubtless owes its stability primarily to the fact that the positive charge is highly delocalized, as indicated by canonical structures of the type 11-Ia–d. It behaves in

(11-Ia)   (11-Ib)   (11-Ic)   (11-Id)

some respects like other large univalent cations (Cs^+, $R_4 N^+$, $R_4 As^+$, etc.) and forms insoluble salts with large anions, such as BF_4^-, $GaCl_4^-$. There is good evidence that the cation has a propeller-like arrangement for the phenyl groups which are bound to the central atom by coplanar sp^2 trigonal bonds.

Anions of the type $R_1R_2R_3C^-$ are called *carbanions*. Like carbonium ions they generally have no permanent existence, except in cases where the negative charge can be effectively delocalized. The triphenylmethyl

(11-IIa)   (11-IIb)   (11-IIc)   (11-IId)

carbanion (11-II) is a good example, as is also the cyclopentadienyl anion (11-III). In fact, since the negative charge in this case is equally delocal-

(11-IIIa)   (11-IIIb)   (11-IIIc)   (11-IV)

ized on all of the carbon atoms, the anion is a regular plane pentagon and the π-electron density distribution can be well represented by 11-IV.

There are also a number of radicals which are fairly long-lived, such as the triphenylmethyl radical. Here again the stability is due mainly to delocalization—in this case of the odd electron—as in the representative canonical structures 11-V. Note that in both of the ions and in the

(11-Va)   (11-Vb)   (11-Vc)   (11-Vd)

radical this resonance stabilization is possible only because of the ability of the unique carbon atom to form strong double bonds with the carbon atoms in the phenyl groups. If it is indeed the resonance effect which causes $(C_6H_5)_3C^+$ and $(C_6H_5)_3C\cdot$ to be stable, then we should not expect other Group IV species such as $(C_6H_5)_3Si^+$ or $(C_6H_5)_3Pb$ to be stable since Si, Ge, Sn and Pb are unable, according to independent evidence, to form the required double bonds. In point of fact $(C_6H_5)_6Si_2$, $(C_6H_5)_6Ge_2$,

$(C_6H_5)_6Sn_2$ and $(C_6H_5)_6Pb_2$ do not dissociate to form $(C_6H_5)_3M$ radicals, and compounds such as $(C_6H_5)_3MCl$ are only partially or negligibly ionic.

Divalent carbon compounds, or carbenes, $:CR_1R_2$, are intermediates in a number of organic reaction mechanisms.[1] In some cases, e.g., difluoro-methylene, CF_2, the life-time in gas reactions is sufficiently long to allow detection by spectroscopy (see also Chap. 19).

Carbon is one of the few elements for which *catenation* is a key feature in its chemistry. By catenation is meant the formation of chains of identical atoms. Such chains may also be closed into rings. Obviously, only an element with a valence of at least two which forms rather strong bonds with itself will do this. Carbon forms chains and rings not only with

$$R\text{—}(C\text{=}C\text{—})_nR$$
(11-VI)

$$R\text{—}(C\text{≡}C\text{—})_nR$$
(11-VII)

(11-VIII)

carbon–carbon single bonds but also with multiple bonds (11-VI, 11-VII and 11-VIII). Sulfur is probably the element with the next greatest tendency to catenation; it forms rings and chains in the elemental state and in the class of compounds known as sulfanes: $Y\text{—}S_n\text{—}Y$ ($n = 1\text{-}15$; Y = halogen, H, SO_3, etc.). However, the sulfanes are relatively unstable toward heat and oxidation. Silicon also has some tendency to catenation, the silanes $H(SiH_2)_nH$ with n from 1 to 6 being known. However, the stability of these compounds is very low compared to their carbon analogs.

The unusual stability of catenated carbon compounds, compared with those of Si and S, can be appreciated by considering the bond energy data shown in Table 11-1. (See also Table 19-2, and discussion, page 457.)

TABLE 11-1
Bond Energies of Carbon, Silicon and Sulfur

Bond	Energy, kcal/mole	Bond	Energy, kcal/mole
C—C	83	C—O	84
Si—Si	52	Si—O	88
S—S	51	S—O	~80

Thus the simple *thermal* stability of C—C—C—... chains is high because of the intrinsic strength of C—C bonds. The relative stabilities toward oxidation follow from the fact that for carbon C—C and C—O bonds

---

[1] For extensive reviews see E. Chinoporos, *Chem. Rev.*, **63**, 235 (1963) and W. Kirmse, *Progr. Org. Chem.*, **6**, 164 (1964).

are of comparable stability, whereas for Si, and probably also S, the bond to oxygen is considerably stronger. Thus, given the necessary activation energy, compounds with a number of Si—Si links are converted very exothermically to compounds with Si—O bonds.

THE ELEMENT

Naturally occurring carbon has the isotopic composition ^{12}C, 98.89%; ^{13}C, 1.11%. In addition, traces of ^{14}C exist, and this radioisotope provides the basis for the radiocarbon dating technique. ^{14}C is produced in the upper atmosphere by slow neutron capture by nitrogen atoms—$^{14}N(n,p)^{14}C$— and it decays by β^- emission with a half-life of 5570 years. Before the nuclear age this upper atmosphere process was presumably the only source of ^{14}C, and it was probably present in the atmosphere (as CO_2) at a constant, steady-state concentration determined by the relative values of the rate of production and the total rate of removal (e.g., by consumption of the CO_2 by plants, by radioactive decay, etc.). The half-life is sufficiently long that ^{14}C in atmospheric CO_2 will become thoroughly mixed into all carbon-containing systems which are in equilibrium with atmospheric CO_2, namely, carbonic acid and dissolved carbonates and, of special importance, living organisms. When the organisms die they are no longer able to take up further ^{14}C, and that which is present diminishes by radioactive decay. Thus from a knowledge of the concentration now present in objects of organic origin (estimated from β counting) and the steady-state concentration of ^{14}C when they lived one can estimate when the organism lived (or, more precisely, died). The method has been well calibrated using objects of known ages, and the uncertainties are of the order of 5% of the age.

11-1. Allotropy of Carbon: Diamond; Graphite

The two best-known forms of carbon, diamond and graphite, differ in their physical and chemical properties because of differences in the arrangement and bonding of the atoms. Diamond is denser than graphite (diamond: 3.51 g/cm³; graphite: 2.22 g/cm³), but graphite is the more stable, by 0.69 kcal/mole at 300°K and 1 atm pressure. From the densities it follows that in order to transform graphite into diamond, pressure must be applied, and from the known thermodynamic properties of the two allotropes it can be estimated that they would be in equilibrium at 300° under a pressure of ~15,000 atm. Of course, equilibrium is attained extremely slowly at this temperature, and it is this which allows the diamond structure to persist under ordinary conditions.

The energy required to vaporize graphite to a monatomic gas is an important quantity, since it enters into the estimation of the energies of all bonds involving carbon. It is not easy to measure directly because, even at very high temperatures, the vapor contains appreciable fractions of C_2, C_3, etc. Spectroscopic studies established that the value had to be either ~ 124, ~ 137 or 171.7 kcal/mole depending on the actual nature of the process measured spectroscopically. The composition of vapors has been determined mass spectrographically with sufficient accuracy to show that the low values are unacceptable, hence it is now certain that the exact value is 171.7 kcal/mole at 300°K. In using older tables of bond energies, attention should be paid to what value was used for the heat of sublimation of graphite.

Diamond. The diamond is one of the hardest solids known. This and the higher density are explicable in terms of the structure, which was one of the first to be determined by X-ray diffraction study. In the diamond lattice, each carbon atom is tetrahedrally surrounded by four other carbon atoms at a distance of 1.54 A. This reticulated structure extends throughout each entire crystal so that each one is in effect a giant "molecule." This structure also accounts for many other properties of diamond. Its melting and boiling points are unknown but presumably extraordinarily high. It is also a nonconductor of electricity, since all of the electrons are firmly held in the carbon–carbon bonds.

The diamond structure can be produced from graphite carbon only by the application of high pressures. Furthermore, in order to get an appreciable rate of conversion, high temperatures are necessary. Naturally occurring diamonds must have been formed when such conditions were provided by geological processes. Since at least 1880, recognition of these requirements has led many workers to attempt the production of synthetic diamonds. Until 1955 all such attempts ended in failure, inadequately proved claims, and even in a bogus report of success. Modern knowledge of the thermodynamics of the process indicates that none of the conditions of temperature and pressure reported could have been sufficient for success.

The present knowledge, some of it tentative, of the phase diagram for carbon is summarized in Figure 11-1. Although graphite can be directly converted to diamond at temperatures of *ca* 3000°K and pressures above 125 kbar, in order to obtain useful rates of conversion, transition metal catalysts such as Cr, Fe or Pt are used. It appears that a thin film of molten metal forms on the graphite, dissolving some and reprecipitating it as diamond, which is less soluble. So far, diamonds up to 0.1 carat of high industrial but not gem quality have been produced.

The chemical reactivity of diamond is much lower than that of carbon in the form of macrocrystalline graphite or the various amorphous forms. Diamond can be made to burn in air by heating to 600–800°.

Graphite.   Graphite has a layer structure as indicated in Figure 11-2. The separation of the layers is 3.35 A, which is about equal to the sum of van der Waals radii and indicates that the forces between layers should be relatively slight.   Thus the observed softness and particularly the lubricity

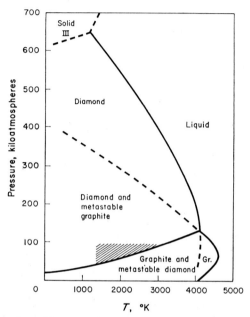

Fig. 11-1.   Carbon phase diagram [adapted from F. P. Bundy, *J. Chem. Phys.*, **38**, 618, 631 (1963)].   Shaded area is that in which catalyzed graphite–diamond conversion has been studied.

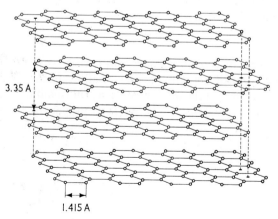

Fig. 11-2.   The normal structure of graphite.

10*

of graphite can be attributed to the easy slippage of these layers over one another. It will be noted that within each layer each carbon atom is surrounded by only three others. After forming one σ bond with each neighbor, each carbon atom would still have one electron and these are paired up into a system of π bonds (11-IX). Resonance with other structures having different but equivalent arrangements of the double bonds makes all C—C distances equal at 1.415 A. This is a little longer

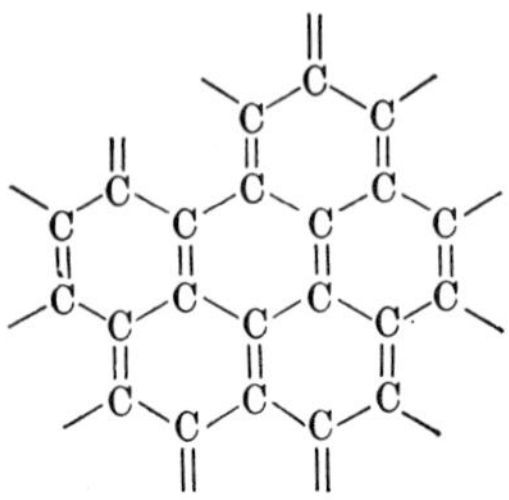

(11-IX)

than the C—C distance in benzene, where the bond order is 1.5, and agrees with the assumption that the bond order in graphite is ~1.33.

Actually two modifications of graphite exist, differing in the ordering of the layers. In no case do all the carbon atoms of one layer lie directly over those in the next layer, but, in the structure shown in Figure 11-2, carbon atoms in every other layer are superposed. This type of stacking, which may be designated (ABAB . . .), is apparently the most stable and exists in the commonly occurring hexagonal form of graphite. There is also a rhombic form, frequently present in naturally occurring graphite, in which the stacking order is (ABCABC . . .); that is, every third layer is super-posed. It seems that local areas of rhombic structure can be formed by mechanical deformation of hexagonal crystals and can be removed by heat treatment.

The many forms of so-called amorphous carbon, such as charcoals, soot and lampblack, are all actually microcrystalline forms of graphite. In some soots the microcrystals are so small that they contain only a few unit cells of the graphite structure. The physical properties of such materials are mainly determined by the nature and magnitude of their surface areas. The finely divided forms, which present relatively vast surfaces with only partially saturated attractive forces, readily absorb large amounts of gases and solutes from solution.

Although Si, Ge and Sn also occur with the diamond structure, the graphite structure is peculiar to carbon, presumably because only carbon has marked ability to form double bonds.

It has been reported[2] that at 150 kiloatmospheres and 300°K, single crystals of graphite are partially transformed to a new form of carbon which seems to be cubic and have a density of 2.8 g/cm³. Little more is known about it and its place in the phase diagram, Figure 11-1, is unknown.

11-2. Lamellar Compounds of Graphite

The very loose, layered structure of graphite makes it possible for many molecules and ions to penetrate between the layers. The resulting interstitial or lamellar compounds of graphite are of sufficient interest to merit extended discussion.

There are two basic types of lamellar compounds: those in which the graphite, which has good electrical conductivity, becomes nonconducting and those in which high electrical conductivity remains and is enhanced. Only two substances of the first type are known, namely, graphite oxide and graphite fluoride.

Graphite oxide is prepared by treating graphite with strong oxidizing agents such as mixtures of concentrated nitric and sulfuric acids or fuming nitric acid and potassium perchlorate or potassium permanganate. Graphite oxide is not obtained as a definite reproducible substance of fixed composition. Oxygen/carbon ratios approach but never exceed 1:2, and the material invariably contains hydrogen. The structure of graphite oxide is still rather uncertain, but the following are important features:

1. The presence of the oxygen causes the layer separation of the graphite to increase to 6–7 A in thoroughly dried samples. The product readily absorbs water, acetone, dioxane and alcohols with resultant swelling, the interlayer spacing increasing to as much as 19 A with some of the alcohols.

2. The oxygen atoms are believed to be bound in C—O—C ether-like bridges between meta positions of the hexagonal rings, in keto groups, and the corresponding enol forms, $\rangle C{=\!\!=}O$ and $\rangle C{-}OH$. These hydroxo groups are fairly acidic and may be esterified and methylated.

3. As a result of the formation of four covalent bonds by all or most of the carbon atoms, it is believed that the layers become buckled, although certain proof of this is lacking. Formation of four covalent bonds, thus tying up all of the electrons, and buckling of the layers would account for the loss of the electrical conductivity, which in graphite takes place by the ready movement of electrons through the delocalized π orbitals in the layers. Graphite oxide is thus an aliphatic compound.

[2] R. B. Anst and H. G. Drickamer, *Science*, **140**, 817 (1963).

Graphite fluoride is the only other nonconducting compound of graphite and is obtained by direct reaction, which is occasionally explosive, of fluorine and graphite. The reproducibility of the preparation is poor, but products with C/F ratios up to 1:0.99, white in color, have been obtained. More commonly it is grey with a lower fluorine content. As with graphite oxide, the layer spacing is increased, typically to ~ 8 A. This is about equal to the sum of two C—F bond lengths (1.4 A) plus two van der Waals radii of fluorine (~ 2.6 A), and it is believed that ideally the compound should have the composition $(CF)_n$ with each carbon atom forming a C—F bond (in accord with the infrared spectrum which shows only one C—F bond) and three C—C bonds. Although the layers should be buckled because of the tetrahedral carbon bonding, certain proof has not been obtained.

In the *electrically conducting lamellar compounds*, various atoms, molecules and ions are inserted or intercalated between the carbon sheets. A large number of the compounds form spontaneously on bringing graphite and the reactant into contact. Thus the heavier alkali metals K, Rb and Cs, the halogens Cl_2 and Br_2, and a great variety of halides, oxides and sulfides of metals, for example, $FeCl_3$, UCl_4, FeS_2 and MoO_3, form spontaneous lamellar compounds.

A smaller group of compounds are formed by electrolysis of the reactant using a graphite anode. For example, with sulfuric acid, the following reaction occurs:

$$C_m + 3H_2SO_4 = C_mHSO_4 \cdot 2H_2SO_4 + H^+ + e$$

the value of m depending on the amount of current passed. In these compounds the graphite layers remain planar. The gross composition of a compound does not necessarily fix its internal nature, since two factors relate this with the gross composition. First, the composition depends upon the concentration of invading reactant in the invaded layers; second, it depends upon what fraction of the layers are invaded. Definite stages of invasion have been observed; in many cases there is considerable long-range order, every nth layer being invaded, the intervening ones being untouched.

The manner in which the invading reactant species increase the conductivity of the graphite is not definitely settled, but apparently they do so by either adding electrons to or removing electrons from the conduction levels of graphite itself. They thus either increase the number of electrons or the number of positive holes which carry current by moving in these conduction levels. The alkali metals, for example, must add electrons, some of them therefore being present in the graphite as ions,

$$C_mK_n \qquad\qquad C_m^{z-}K_x^+K_{n-x}$$

Stoichiometry   Ionic nature

As another example, in a ternary compound in which both chlorine and $AlCl_3$ are present, the state of ionization may be represented by the following:

$C_mCl_n(AlCl_3)_p$ $C_m^{z+}(AlCl_4)_x^-Cl_{n-x}(AlCl_3)_{p-x}$
Stoichiometry   Ionic nature

In most cases, at least, the extent of ionization appears to be only fractional.

There is some evidence that compounds whose lattices, like that of graphite, can expand—BN, AlB_2 and $CrCl_3$—can also act as host lattices for oxides, sulfides and chlorides.

CARBIDES

The term carbide is applied to those compounds in which carbon is combined with elements of lower or about equal electronegativity. Thus compounds with oxygen, sulfur, phosphorus, nitrogen, halogens, etc., are not considered in this category, and by convention neither are those with hydrogen. The reasonableness of this division will become apparent as the nature of the carbides is discussed. They are usually considered to be of three types: (1) the salt-like carbides, formed chiefly by the elements of groups I, II and III; (2) the interstitial carbides formed by most transition metals, especially those in groups IV, V and VI, and (2a) a borderline type formed by a few of the transition metals with small atomic radii; and (3) covalent carbides, SiC and B_4C.

The general preparative methods for carbides of all three types include (a) direct union of the elements at high temperature (2200° and above); (b) heating a compound of the metal, particularly the oxide, with carbon; and (c) heating the metal in the vapor of a suitable hydrocarbon. Carbides of Cu, Ag, Au, Zn and Cd, also commonly called acetylides, are prepared by passing acetylene into solutions of the metal salts; with Cu, Ag and Au, ammoniacal solutions of salts of the unipositive ions are used to obtain Cu_2C_2, Ag_2C_2 and Au_2C_2 (uncertain), whereas with Zn and Cd, the acetylides ZnC_2 and CdC_2 are obtained by passing acetylene into petrol solutions of dialkyl compounds. The Cu and Ag acetylides are explosive, being sensitive to both heat and mechanical shock.

1. *Salt-like carbides.* The most electropositive metals form carbides having physical and chemical properties which indicate that they are essentially ionic. They form colorless, transparent crystals and are decomposed by water and/or dilute acids at ordinary temperatures. The liberated anions are immediately hydrolyzed too, and hydrocarbons are thus evolved. There are ionic carbides containing C^{4-} and C_2^{2-} ions and one which, it has been inferred, contains C_3^{4-} ions.

Carbides containing C^{4-} ions evolve methane on hydrolysis and can be called methanides. Be_2C and Al_4C_3 are of this type. Thus the hydrolysis of the latter may be written:

$$Al_4C_3 + 12H_2O = 4Al(OH)_3 + 3CH_4$$

The structure of Be_2C is rather simple, being the antifluorite structure (see Fig. 2-6, page 48) with the beryllium atoms replacing F^- in CaF_2 and carbon atoms replacing Ca^{2+}. The structure of Al_4C_3 is quite complicated; the details need not concern us except insofar as it is found that the carbon atoms occur singly.

There are a great many carbides which contain C_2^{2-} ions, or anions which can be so written to a first approximation. For the $M^I_2C_2$ compounds, where M^I may be one of the alkali metals or one of the coinage metals, and for the $M^{II}C_2$ compounds where M^{II} may be an alkaline earth metal, Zn or Cd, and for $M^{III}C_3$ (actually, $M^{III}_2(C_2)_3$) compounds in which M^{III} is Al, La, Pr or Tb, this description is probably a very good approximation. In these cases, the postulation of C_2^{2-} ions requires that the metal ions be in their normal oxidation states. In those instances where accurate structural parameters are known, the C—C distances lie in the range 1.19–1.24 A. The compounds react with water and the C_2^{2-} ions are hydrolyzed to give acetylene only, e.g.,

$$Ca^{2+}C_2^{2-} + 2H_2O = HCCH + Ca(OH)_2$$

There are, however, a number of carbides which have the same structures as those discussed above, meaning that the carbon atoms occur in discrete pairs, which cannot be satisfactorily described as C_2^{2-} compounds. These include YC_2, LaC_2, TbC_2, YbC_2, LuC_2, UC_2, Ce_2C_3, Pr_2C_3 and Tb_2C_3. For all of the MC_2 compounds in this list, neutron scattering experiments[3] show that (a) the metal atoms are essentially trivalent and (b) the C—C distances are 1.28–1.30 A for the lanthanide compounds and 1.34 A for UC_2. These facts and other details of the structures are consistent with the view that the metal atoms lose not only the electrons necessary to produce C_2^{2-} ions (which would make them M^{2+} ions) but a third electron, mainly to the antibonding orbitals of the C_2^{2-} groups, thus lengthening the C—C bonds (cf. C—C = 1.19 in CaC_2). There are actually other, more delocalized, interactions among the cations and anions in these compounds since they have metallic properties. The M_2C_3 compounds have the metals in their trivalent states, C—C distances of 1.24–1.28 A and also direct metal–metal interactions.[4] These carbides which cannot be represented simply as aggregates of C_2^{2-} ions and metal atoms in their normal oxidation

[3] M. Atoji, *J. Chem. Phys.*, **35**, 1950 (1961).
[4] M. Atoji and D. E. Williams, *J. Chem. Phys.*, **35**, 1960 (1961).

states are hydrolyzed by water to give only 50–70% HCCH, while C_2H_4, CH_4 and H_2 are also produced. Presumably reactions such as

$$2C_2{}^{3-} + 6H_2O = C_2H_2 + C_2H_4 + 6OH^-$$

and others more complicated take place, but there is no detailed understanding of these hydrolytic processes.

All of the acetylides so far examined structurally have sodium chloride-like lattices. Most have the CaC_2 structure in which the $[C—C]^{2-}$ ions lie lengthwise in the same direction along the cell axes, thus causing a distortion from cubic symmetry to tetragonal symmetry with one axis longer than the other two. In thorium carbide, the $C_2{}^{2-}$ ions are lying flat in parallel planes in such a way that two axes are equally lengthened with respect to the third. These structures are shown in Figure 11-3.

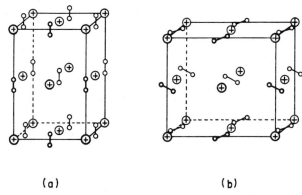

(a)   (b)

Fig. 11-3.   The CaC_2 (a) and ThC_2 (b) structures (the latter is somewhat simplified here).

2. *Interstitial carbides.* In interstitial carbides, carbon atoms occupy the octahedral holes in close-packed arrays of metal atoms. The characteristics of interstitial carbides, namely, very high melting points (3000–4800°), great hardness (7–10, mostly 9–10, on Mohs' scale) and metallic electrical conductivity, are thus easily explainable. The free electron structure and other characteristic properties of the pure metal are not fundamentally altered by insertion of the carbon atoms into some of the interstices of the metal lattice; at the same time, the carbon atoms further stabilize the lattice thus increasing hardness and raising the melting point. The ability of the carbon atoms to enter the interstices without appreciably distorting the metal structure requires that the interstices, and hence the metal atoms, be relatively large, and it can be estimated that a metal atom radius of ~1.3 A or greater is required.

The metals Cr, Mn, Fe, Co and Ni have radii somewhat smaller than 1.3 A, and they do not therefore form typical interstitial carbides. Instead, the metal lattices are appreciably distorted and the carbon atoms interact directly with one another. The structures can be roughly described as having carbon chains (with C—C distances ~ 1.65 A) running through very distorted metal lattices. The carbides Cr_3C_2 and M_3C (M = Mn, Fe, Co, Ni) are rather easily hydrolyzed by water and dilute acids to give a variety of hydrocarbons (even liquid and solid ones and, in the case of Fe_3C, free carbon) and hydrogen. They are thus transitional between the typical ionic and interstitial carbides.

3. *Covalent carbides.* Although other carbides, for example, Be_2C, are at least partially covalent, the two elements which approach carbon closely in size and electronegativity, namely, Si and B, give completely covalent compounds. Silicon carbide, SiC, technically known as carborundum, is an extemely hard, infusible and chemically stable material made by reducing SiO_2 with carbon in an electric furnace. It occurs in three structural modifications, in all of which there are infinite three-dimensional arrays of Si and C atoms, each tetrahedrally surrounded by four of the other kind. Interestingly, no evidence has ever been obtained for a germanium carbide of this or any other type.

Boron carbide, B_4C, also an extremely hard, infusible and inert substance, and made by reduction of B_2O_3 with carbon in an electric furnace, has a very unusual structure. The carbon atoms occur in linear chains of three, and the boron atoms in icosahedral groups of twelve (as in crystalline boron itself). These two units are then packed together in a sodium chloride-like array. There are, of course, covalent bonds between carbon atoms and boron atoms as well as between boron atoms in different icosahedra.

SIMPLE MOLECULAR COMPOUNDS

In this section we shall discuss a few simple compounds which are neither carbides, organometallic compounds, nor compounds of the kinds which are mainly if not exclusively in the province of organic chemistry. With the above restrictions, we are left only with the simpler compounds of carbon with the elements of groups V, VI and VII. Some important compounds and their principal properties are listed in Table 11-2.

11-3. Carbon Halides

Carbon tetrafluoride is an extraordinarily stable compound. It is the end product in the fluorination of any carbon-containing compound. A useful laboratory preparation, for example, involves the fluorination of

TABLE 11-2

Some Simple Compounds of Carbon

Compound	Melting point, °C	Boiling point, °C	Remarks
CF_4	-185	-128	Very stable
CCl_4	-23	76	Moderately stable
CBr_4	93	190	Decomposes slightly on boiling
CI_4	171	—	Decomposes before boiling; can be sublimed under low pressure
COF_2	-114	-83	Easily decomposed by H_2O
$COCl_2$	-118	8	"Phosgene"; highly toxic
$COBr_2$	—	65	Fumes in air; $COBr_2 + H_2O \rightarrow CO_2 + 2HBr$
$CO(NH_2)_2$	132	—	Decomposes on heating to $NH_4{}^+NCO^-$
CO	-205	-190	Odorless and toxic
CO_2	-57 (5.2 atm)	-79	
C_3O_2	—	7	Evil-smelling gas
COS	-138	-50	Inflammable; slowly decomposed by H_2O
CS_2	-109	46	Inflammable and toxic
$(CN)_2$	-28	-21	Very toxic; colorless; water soluble
HCN	-13.4	25.6	Very toxic; high dielectric constant (116 at 20°) for the associated liquid

silicon carbide. The SiF_4 also formed is removed easily by passing the mixture through 20% NaOH solution; the CF_4 is quite unaffected, whereas the SiF_4 is immediately hydrolyzed:

$$SiF_4 + 8OH^- = SiO_4{}^{4-} + 4F^- + 4H_2O$$

This phenomenon is a good illustration of the differences which frequently exist between a compound of an element in the first short period and seemingly analogous compounds of its congeners. The difference in this case is due to the fact that, in CF_4, carbon is coordinately saturated—that is, it has no orbitals with which to coordinate OH^- ions as a first step in the process of hydrolysis—whereas silicon in SiF_4 has $3d$ orbitals available, and by means of these is rapidly attacked.

Carbon tetrachloride is a commonly used solvent; it is fairly readily photochemically decomposed and also quite often readily transfers chloride ion to various substrates, CCl_3 radicals often being formed simultaneously at high temperatures (300–500°). It is often used to convert oxides to chlorides. Although it is thermodynamically unstable with respect to hydrolysis, the absence of any acceptor orbitals on carbon makes attack very difficult.

Carbon tetrabromide is a pale yellow solid at room temperature. It is insoluble in water and other polar solvents, soluble in some nonpolar solvents such as benzene.

Carbon tetraiodide is a bright red crystalline material possessing an odor like that of iodine. Both heat and light cause decomposition to iodine and tetraiodoethylene. It is insoluble in water and alcohol, though attacked by both at elevated temperatures, and soluble in benzene. It may be prepared by the following reaction

$$CCl_4 + 4C_2H_5I \xrightarrow{AlCl_3} CI_4 + 4C_2H_5Cl$$

The increasing instability, both thermal and photochemical, of the carbon tetrahalides with increasing weight of the halogen correlates with a steady decrease in the C—X bond energies:

C—F, 116;　　C—Cl, 81;　　C—Br, 68;　　C—I, 51 kcal/mole

The *carbonyl halides*, COX_2 (X = F, Cl and Br), are all hydrolytically unstable substances. Mixed carbonyl halides such as $COClBr$ are also known. The compound $CO(NH_2)_2$ is urea. In the molecular structures of both urea and $COCl_2$ the C—O bond length is somewhat longer than the expected value for a C=O double bond, whereas the N—C and Cl—C distances are somewhat shorter than expected for single bonds. These facts lead to the conclusion that these molecules should be viewed as resonance hybrids (11-X).

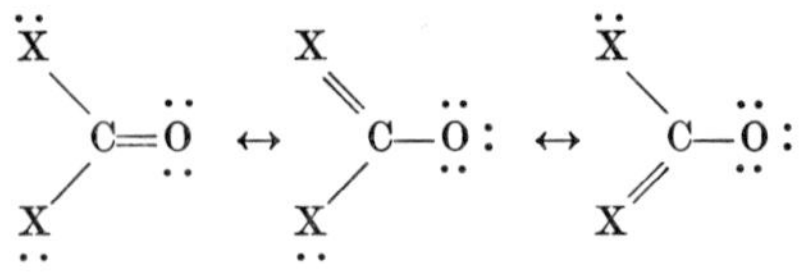

(11-X)

11-4. Carbon Oxides

There are five reported oxides of carbon: CO, CO_2, C_3O_2, C_5O_2 and $C_{12}O_9$. The last one is the anhydride of mellitic acid (11-XI) and will not be discussed further.

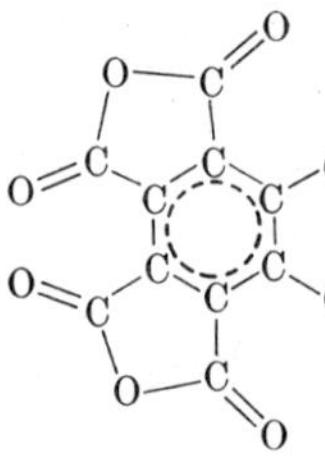

(11-XI)

Carbon monoxide is formed when carbon is burned with a deficiency of oxygen. At all temperatures, the following equilibrium exists, but is not rapidly attained at ordinary temperatures

$$2CO(g) = C(s) + CO_2(g)$$

The reaction

$$C + H_2O = CO + H_2$$

is important commercially, the equimolar mixture of CO and H_2 being called water gas. A convenient laboratory preparation of CO is by the action of concentrated sulfuric acid on formic acid,

$$HCOOH \xrightarrow{-H_2O} CO$$

Although CO is an exceedingly weak Lewis base, one of its most important properties is the ability to act as a donor ligand toward transition metals giving *metal carbonyls*. For example, nickel metal reacts with CO to form $Ni(CO)_4$, and iron reacts under more forcing conditions to give $Fe(CO)_5$; many carbonyl complexes are known (see Chapter 27). The ability of CO to form bonds to transition metal atoms is attributed to the fact that, in addition to a very weak dative bond, $O{\equiv}C \rightarrow M$, there exists "back-bonding" by the donation of electrons in metal d orbitals to the empty antibonding π orbitals of the CO.

Transition metal salts are used in a variety of catalytic reactions in which carbon monoxide is incorporated into organic compounds and carbonyl complexes are probably intermediates in these reactions.

CO reacts with alkali metals in liquid ammonia to give the so-called alkali metal "carbonyls"; these white solids contain the $[OCCO]^{2-}$ ion.[5]

Carbon dioxide is obtained by combustion of carbon in the presence of excess oxygen or by treating carbonates with dilute acids. Its important properties should already be familiar.

Carbon suboxide, C_3O_2, is an interesting but relatively uncommon substance which is formed by dehydrating malonic acid with P_2O_5 in vacuum at 140–150°. It is an evil-smelling gas (b 7°). It appears likely from various structural and spectral studies that the C_3O_2 molecule is completely linear.[6] The bond distances are C—C, 1.30 A (theory for C=C, 1.33), and C—O, 1.20 A (theory for C=O, 1.22). It is supposed that linearity of the molecule and the observed bond lengths are attributable to resonance among the canonical structures 11-XII.

$$O{=}C{=}C{=}C{=}O \leftrightarrow \overset{+}{O}{\equiv}C{-}C{\equiv}C{-}\overset{-}{O} \leftrightarrow \overset{-}{O}{-}C{\equiv}C{-}C{\equiv}\overset{+}{O}$$

(11-XII)

[5] E. Weiss and W. Büchner, *Helv. Chim. Acta*, **46**, 1121 (1963).
[6] W. J. Lafferty, A. G. Maki and E. K. Plyler, *J. Chem. Phys.*, **40**, 224 (1964).

Although indefinitely stable at $-78°$, C_3O_2 polymerizes at room temperature and above to yellow to violet materials believed to have polymeric structures containing 6-membered ring lactones whose principal resonance form is a pyrylium-like aromatic structure.[7]

C_5O_2 has been claimed, but others have disputed the claim and its existence must at present be considered uncertain. Note that if resonance of the above type is an important stabilizing factor, then oxides of the type C_nO_2 would be expected only for n odd, so that C_5O_2 would be theoretically possible, whereas C_2O_2 and C_4O_2, which are unknown, would not.

There also exist aromatic anions such as $C_4O_4^{2-}$ and $C_5O_5^{2-}$, the latter containing a planar carbon ring.[8]

"Carbonic Acids." Carbon monoxide is formally the anhydride of formic acid, but its solubility in water and bases is slight. On heating with alkalies, however, it will react to give the corresponding formate. C_3O_2 is the anhydride of malonic acid. It combines very vigorously with water to produce the acid and with ammonia and amines to produce malondiamides.

$$C_3O_2 + 2H_2O = HOOCCH_2COOH$$
$$C_3O_2 + 2NHR_2 = R_2NCOCH_2CONR_2$$

Carbon dioxide is the anhydride of the most important simple acid of carbon, "carbonic acid." For many purposes, the following acid dissociation constants are given for aqueous "carbonic acid":

$$\frac{[H^+][HCO_3^-]}{[H_2CO_3]} = 4.16 \times 10^{-7}$$

$$\frac{[H^+][CO_3^{2-}]}{[HCO_3^-]} = 4.84 \times 10^{-11}$$

The equilibrium quotient in the first equation above is not really correct. It assumes that all CO_2 dissolved and undissociated is present as H_2CO_3, which is not true. In actual fact, the greater part of the dissolved CO_2 is only loosely hydrated, so that the correct first dissociation constant, using the "true" activity of H_2CO_3, has a value of about 2×10^{-4}. As has been noted in Chapter 6, this value is more nearly in agreement with what one would expect for an acid with the structure $(HO)_2CO$.

The rate at which CO_2 comes into equilibrium with H_2CO_3 and its dissociation products when passed into water is measurably slow, and this indeed is what has made possible an analytical distinction between H_2CO_3 and the loosely hydrated $CO_2(aq)$. This slowness is of great importance physiologically and in biological, analytical and industrial chemistry. The slow reaction can easily be demonstrated by addition of a saturated

[7] A. R. Blake, *J. Chem. Soc.*, **1965**, 3866, and references therein.

[8] M. D. Glick, G. L. Downs and L. F. Dahl, *Inorg. Chem.*, **3**, 1712 (1964), and references therein.

aqueous solution of CO_2 on the one hand and of dilute acetic acid on the other to solutions of dilute NaOH containing phenolphthalein indicator. The acetic acid neutralization is instantaneous whereas with the CO_2 neutralization it takes several seconds for the color to fade.[9]

The neutralization of CO_2 occurs by two paths. For pH < 8 the principal mechanism is direct hydration of CO_2

$$CO_2 + H_2O = H_2CO_3 \qquad \text{(slow)} \qquad\qquad (11\text{-}1)$$
$$H_2CO_3 + OH^- = HCO_3^- + H_2O \qquad \text{(instantaneous)}$$

The rate law is pseudo first order,

$$-d(CO_2)/dt = k_{CO_2}(CO_2); \qquad k_{CO_2} = 0.03 \text{ sec}^{-1}$$

At pH > 10, the predominant reaction is direct reaction of CO_2 and OH^-

$$CO_2 + OH^- = HCO_3^- \qquad \text{(slow)} \qquad\qquad (11\text{-}2)$$
$$HCO_3^- + OH^- = CO_3^{2-} + H_2O \qquad \text{(instantaneous)}$$

where the rate law is

$$-d(CO_2)/dt = k_{OH}(OH^-)(CO_2); \qquad k_{OH} = 8500 \text{ sec}^{-1} \text{ (mol./l)}^{-1}$$

This can be interpreted, of course, merely as the base catalysis of (11-1). In the pH range 8–10 both mechanisms are important. For each hydration reaction (11-1, 11-2) there is a corresponding dehydration reaction

$$H_2CO_3 \rightarrow H_2O + CO_2 \qquad k_{H_2CO_3} = k_{CO_2} \times K = 20 \text{ sec}^{-1}$$
$$HCO_3^- \rightarrow CO_2 + OH^- \qquad k_{HCO_3^-} = k_{OH^-} \times K K_w/K_a = 2 \times 10^{-4} \text{ sec}^{-1}$$

Hence for the equilibrium

$$H_2CO_3 \rightleftharpoons CO_2 + H_2O \qquad\qquad (11\text{-}3)$$
$$K = (CO)_2/(H_2CO_3) = k_{H_2CO_3}/k_{CO_2} = ca\ 600$$

It follows from (11-3) that the true ionization constant of H_2CO_3, K_a, is greater than the apparent constant as noted above.

An etherate of H_2CO_3 is obtained[10] by interaction of HCl with Na_2CO_3 at low temperatures in dimethylether. The resultant white crystalline solid, m $-47°$, which decomposes about $5°$, is probably $OC(OH)_2 \cdot O(CH_3)_2$.

Carbamic acid, also called aminoformic acid, $O{=}C(OH)NH_2$, can be regarded as derived from carbonic acid by substitution of $-NH_2$ for $-OH$. This is only one example of the existence of compounds which are related in this way; $-NH_2$ and $-OH$ are isoelectronic and virtually isosteric and frequently give rise to isostructural compounds. If the second

[9] See, e.g., P. Jones, M. L. Haggett and J. L. Longridge, *J. Chem. Educ.*, **41**, 610 (1964).
[10] G. Gattow and U. Gerwath, *Angew. Chem. (Internat.)*, **4**, 149 (1965).

OH in carbonic acid is replaced by NH_2, we have urea. Carbamic acid is not known in the free state, but many salts are known, all of which, however, are unstable to water, because of hydrolysis:

$$H_2NCO_2^- + H_2O = NH_4^+ + CO_3^{2-}$$

11-5. Compounds with C—N Bonds; Cyanides and Related Compounds

An important area of "inorganic" carbon chemistry is that of compounds with C—N bonds. The most important species are the cyanide, cyanate and thiocyanate ions and their derivatives. We can regard many of these compounds as being pseudo-halogens or pseudo-halides (see page 560) but the analogies, although reasonably apt for cyanogen, $(CN)_2$, are not especially valid in other cases.

1. *Cyanogen.* This inflammable gas (Table 11-2) is stable despite the fact that it is unusually endothermic with an enthalpy of formation of $+71$ kcal/mole. Cyanogen can be obtained by direct oxidation of HCN in the gas phase by air over a silver catalyst, by Cl_2 over activated carbon or silica, or by NO_2 over calcium oxide-glass; the latter reaction allows the NO to be recycled.[11]

$$2HCN + NO_2 = (CN)_2 + NO + H_2O$$

It can also be obtained from the cyanide ion by aqueous oxidation using Cu^{2+} (cf. the Cu^{2+}–I^- reaction)

$$Cu^{2+} + 2CN^- = CuCN + \tfrac{1}{2}(CN)_2$$

or acidified peroxodisulfate. A better procedure for dry $(CN)_2$ is to heat a mixture:

$$Hg(CN)_2 + HgCl_2 = Hg_2Cl_2 + (CN)_2$$

This reaction also gives some paracyanogen, $(CN)_n$. Although pure $(CN)_2$ is stable,[12] the impure gas may polymerize at 300–500°. The solid polymer reverts to $(CN)_2$ at 800–850° but decomposes above this temperature. The structure of $(CN)_n$ has been inferred from infrared spectroscopy to be 11-XIII.

| (11-XIII) | (11-XIV) |

---

[11] W. F. Fierce and W. J. Sandner, *Ind. Eng. Chem.*, **53**, 985 (1961).
[12] C. F. Cullis and J. G. Yates, *J. Chem. Soc.*, **1964**, 2833.

Cyanogen is slowly hydrolyzed by water, in part giving 11-XIV, which indicates that the order of atoms must be NCCN. This is fully confirmed by physical studies, in particular by structural investigations which give the following data: the molecule is symmetrical and linear with the C—C distance equal to 1.37 A and the C—N distance equal to 1.13 A. The C—C distance is only slightly shorter than that expected (1.40) for a single bond between two carbon atoms using sp hybrid orbitals. The single canonical form: :N≡C—C≡N: therefore provides a reasonably good description of the electronic structure. Cyanogen dissociates into CN radicals. A further resemblance to the halogens is the disproportionation in basic solution:

$$(CN)_2 + 2OH^- = CN^- + OCN^- + H_2O$$

Thermodynamically this reaction can occur in acid solution but is rapid only in base. Cyanogen has a large number of reactions, some of which are shown in Figure 11-4. A stoichiometric mixture of O_2 and $(CN)_2$ burns producing one of the hottest flames (ca 5050°K) known from a chemical reaction.

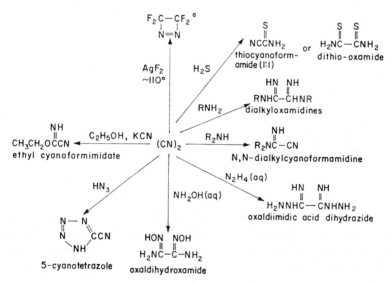

Fig. 11-4. Some reactions of cyanogen. [a] Other products may also be obtained by fluorination, e.g., $CF_3N{=}NCF_3$, see H. J. Eméléus and G. L. Hurst, *J. Chem. Soc.*, **1964**, 396.

2. *Hydrogen cyanide.* This compound, HCN, like the hydrogen halides, is a covalent, molecular substance, but capable of dissociation in aqueous solution. It is an extremely poisonous (though less so than H_2S), colorless

gas and is evolved when cyanides are treated with acids. It condenses at 25.6° to a liquid with a very high dielectric constant (107 at 25°). Here, as in similar cases, such as water, the high dielectric constant is due to association of intrinsically very polar molecules by hydrogen bonding. Liquid HCN is unstable and can polymerize violently in the absence of stabilizers. One solid polymer has been shown to be diaminomaleonitrile; with water and a trace of ammonia, HCN under pressure polymerizes to the biochemically important molecule, adenine. In aqueous solution HCN is a very weak acid ($K = 2.1 \times 10^{-9}$), even weaker than HF, so that aqueous solutions of soluble cyanides hydrolyze

$$CN^- + H_2O \rightleftharpoons HCN + OH^-$$

Although HCN was originally made by acidification of cyanides and by recovery from coke oven gas, it is made industrially from CH_4 and NH_3 by catalytic oxidation in a highly exothermic (113.3 kcal/mole) reaction[13]:

$$2CH_4 + 3O_2 + 2NH_3 \xrightarrow[>800°]{catalyst} 2HCN + 6H_2O$$

HCN is used to make adiponitrile (for Nylon), and in the synthesis of acrylonitrile by reaction with acetylene using an aqueous cuprous chloride–ammonium chloride catalyst.

3. *Cyanides.* Sodium cyanide is manufactured by fusion of calcium cyanamide with carbon and sodium carbonate

$$CaCN_2 + C + Na_2CO_3 = CaCO_3 + 2NaCN$$

The cyanide is leached with water. The calcium cyanamide is made in a rather impure form contaminated with CaO, CaC_2, C, etc., by the interaction

$$CaC_2 + N_2 \xrightarrow{ca\ 1100°} CaNCN + C$$

The linear cyanamide ion is isostructural and isoelectronic with CO_2. Cyanamide itself, H_2NCN, can be made by dehydrosulfurization of thiourea with HgO or by acidification of CaNCN. The commercial product is the dimer, $H_2N—C(=NH)NHCN$, which also contains a large component of the tautomer containing the substituted carbodiimide group, $H_2N—C(=NH)—N=C=NH$. Sodium cyanide can also be obtained by the reaction

$$NaNH_2 + C \xrightarrow{500-600°} NaCN + H_2$$

In crystalline alkali cyanides at normal temperatures, the CN^- ion is freely rotating and is thus effectively spherical with a radius of 1.92 A. Hence, for example, NaCN has the same structure as NaCl.

[13] P. W. Sherwood, *Petroleum Processing*, **9**, 384 (1954).

There are numerous salts of CN^- and those of Ag^I, Hg^I and Pb^{II} are very insoluble. Mercuric cyanide, $Hg(CN)_2$, is made by treating $HgSO_4$ with $NaCN$ and extracting the $Hg(CN)_2$ with ethanol; it is moderately soluble in water and is un-ionized. The cyanide ion is of great importance as a ligand and large numbers of cyano complexes are known of transition metals, Zn, Cd, Hg, etc.; some, like $Ag(CN)_2^-$ and $Au(CN)_2^-$, are of technical importance and cyano complexes are also employed analytically. The complexes sometimes resemble halogeno complexes, e.g., $Hg(CN)_4^{2-}$, and $HgCl_4^{-2}$ but other types exist; they are discussed in detail later (Sect. 27-7). One respect in which CN shows no close resemblance to halogen is in the relative scarcity of covalent compounds of nonmetals; this may be due to lack of efforts to prepare them rather than to inherent lack of stability.

4. *Cyanogen halides.* Compounds of CN with the halogens (halogen cyanides or cyanogen halides) are well known. FCN has only recently been characterized[14] by cracking cyanuric fluoride (from fluorination of cyanuric chloride):

$$(FCN)_3 \xrightarrow[50\text{ mm}]{1300°} FCN$$

It is stable for weeks in the gas (b $-46°$) but polymerizes in the liquid at $25°$ and can be exploded. ClCN and BrCN are prepared by treating aqueous solutions of CN^- with chlorine or bromine, while ICN is obtained by treating a dry cyanide, usually $Hg(CN)_2$, with iodine. ClCN, BrCN and ICN are all rather volatile compounds which behave like the halogens and like other halogenoids. The molecules are linear, and the important canonical forms, in a valence bond view of the electronic structures, are 11-XVa,b, with 11-XVb becoming more important as the electropositive

$$:\ddot{X}:C:::N: \leftrightarrow :\overset{+}{\ddot{X}}::C::\ddot{\underset{..}{N}}:$$

(11-XVa)   (11-XVb)

nature of the halogen increases. Like HCN, the halogen cyanides tend to polymerize forming the trimeric cyanuric halides, which have cyclic structures like 11-XVI.

(11-XVI)   (11-XVII)

[14] F. S. Fawcett and R. D. Lipscomb, *J. Amer. Chem. Soc.*, **86**, 2576 (1964).

The amide (11-XVII), melamine, can be obtained by polymerization of cyanamide.

Compounds between CN and other halogenoid radicals are known, such as NCN_3 formed by the reaction

$$BrCN + NaN_3 = NaBr + NCN_3$$

5. *Cyanate and its analogous S, Se and Te ions.* The *cyanate ion*, OCN^-, is obtained by mild oxidation of aqueous CN^-, e.g.,

$$PbO(s) + KCN(aq) = Pb(s) + KOCN(aq)$$

The cyanate ion is linear. The free acid, $K = 1.2 \times 10^{-4}$, decomposes in solution to NH_3, H_2O and CO_2. There is little evidence for $(OCN)_2$ but covalent compounds such as $P(NCO)_3$ and some metal complexes are known. The compounds are usually prepared from halides by interaction with AgOCN in benzene or NH_4OCN in acetonitrile or liquid SO_2. In such compounds or complexes, either the O or N atoms of OCN can be bound to other atoms and this possibility exists also for SCN. In general most nonmetallic elements seem to be N-bonded.

Thiocyanates are obtained by fusing alkali cyanides with sulfur; the reaction of S with KCN is rapid and quantitative and S in benzene or acetone can be titrated with KCN in isopropanol using bromothymol blue indicator. On oxidation of aqueous SCN^- by $Pb(O_2CMe)_4$ or MnO_2, thiocyanogen is obtained:

$$(SCN)_2 + 2e = 2\,SCN^- \qquad E^\circ\ = +0.77\ v$$

$(SCN)_2$ apparently exists in the dimeric state in certain solvents,[15] but in the free state it rapidly and irreversibly polymerizes to brick-red parathiocyanogen, $(SCN)_n$, the structure of which is unknown. Chemical evidence, of a rather inconclusive sort, suggests that the dimer may have structure 11-XVIIa rather than 11-XVIIb.

$$
\begin{array}{cc}
 & \overset{\displaystyle S}{\overset{\displaystyle \|}{}} \\
N{\equiv}C{-}S{-}S{-}C{\equiv}N & N{\equiv}C{-}S{-}C{\equiv}N \\
\text{(11-XVIIa)} & \text{(11-XVIIb)}
\end{array}
$$

The thiocyanate ion, SCN^-, is far more important than its parent pseudohalogen. It has been shown definitely to have the structure SCN, but the question of its linearity is not definitely settled. It is a good ligand, numerous thiocyanate complexes being known, which are usually stoichiometrically analogous to halide complexes.

Selenocyanogen is obtained as a yellow powder by oxidation of $SeCN^-$

---

[15] F. Séel, *Chem. Ber.*, **86**, 1107 (1953).

with I_2 or $Pb(O_2CMe)_4$. It is fairly stable when dry and in vacuum but otherwise polymerizes to a red material. $(SeCN)_2$ is dimeric in benzene solution. Ionic and covalent selenocyanates and a variety of metal complexes are known.

There appears to be no evidence[16] for the existence of a $TeCN^-$ ion although the compound $Te(CN)_2$ exists; the latter is made by a reaction typical for the preparation of cyanides, cyanates or thiocyanates of non-metallic elements, namely interaction of a halide with AgCN in benzene.

$$TeBr_4 + 3AgCN = Te(CN)_2 + 3AgBr + BrCN.$$

11-6. Compounds with C—S Bonds

Carbon disulfide is prepared on a large scale by direct interaction of the elements and is a pale yellow liquid which is extensively used as a solvent. It is also used to prepare carbon tetrachloride:

$$CS_2 + Cl_2 = CCl_4 + S_2Cl_2$$

A similar diselenide is obtained by the action of CH_2Cl_2 on molten selenium; it has a worse smell than CS_2, but, unlike it, is nonflammable.

The action of ammonium hydroxide on CS_2 gives red solutions from which orange and yellow crystals of $(NH_4)_2CS_3$ and $(NH_4)_2CS_4$ can be obtained. The action of alcoholic HCl on the thiocarbonate gives the acid H_2CS_3, a red liquid.

If CS_2 is treated with various primary or secondary amines in sodium hydroxide solution, dithiocarbamates of general formula 11-XVIII are obtained; these soluble salts form a large number of metal complexes and are of great industrial importance as catalysts in the vulcanization of rubber. If sodium alkoxides are used instead of amines, xanthates (11-XIX), which have similar properties, are obtained.

$$\begin{bmatrix} R_1 \\ \diagdown \\ R_2 \diagup \end{bmatrix} NC \diagup{}^S \diagdown{}_S$$

(11-XVIII)   (11-XIX)

When aqueous solutions of alkali metal alkyl or dialkyldithiocarbamates are treated with oxidizing agents such as Cl_2, I_2, $S_2O_8{}^{2-}$, $[Fe(CN)_6]^{3-}$ or H_2O_2, a *thiuram disulfide* is obtained

$$2R_2NCS_2{}^- + I_2 = R_2N-\underset{\overset{\|}{S}}{C}-S-S-\underset{\overset{\|}{S}}{C}-NR_2 + 2I^-$$

[16] N. N. Greenwood, R. Little and M. J. Sprague, *J. Chem. Soc.*, **1964**, 1292.

The commonest compound, tetramethylthiuram disulfide, is an oxidizing agent and also gives radicals on heating, acting as a polymerization initiator, as well as undergoing other unusual reactions.

ORGANOMETALLIC COMPOUNDS

11-7. General Survey of Types

Organometallic compounds are those in which the *carbon* atoms of organic groups are bound to metal atoms. Thus we do not include in this category compounds in which carbon-containing moieties are bound to a metal via some other atom such as oxygen, nitrogen or sulfur. For example, $(C_3H_7O)_4Ti$ is not considered to be an organometallic compound, whereas $C_6H_5Ti(OC_3H_7)_3$ is, because in the latter there is one direct linkage of the metal to carbon. Although organic groups can be bound through carbon, in one way or another, to virtually all the elements in the periodic table, excluding the noble gases, the term organometallic is usually rather loosely defined and organo compounds of decidedly non-metallic elements such as B, P and Si are often included in the category. Specific compounds are discussed in the sections on the chemistry of the individual elements since the organo derivatives are usually just as characteristic of any element as are, say, its halides or oxides. However, it is pertinent to make a few general comments here on the various types of compounds.

1. *Ionic Compounds of Electropositive Metals.* The organometallic compounds of highly electropositive metals are usually ionic in nature. Thus the alkali metal derivatives, with the exception of those of lithium (page 242) which are fairly covalent in nature, are insoluble in hydrocarbon solvents and are very reactive toward air, water, etc. The alkaline earth metals Ca, Sr and Ba give poorly characterized compounds which are even more reactive and unstable than the alkali salts. The stability and reactivity of ionic compounds are determined in part by the stability of the organic anion. Compounds containing unstable anions (e.g., $C_nH_{2n+1}^-$) are generally highly reactive and often unstable and difficult to isolate. However, where reasonably stable anions (see page 293) exist, the metal derivatives are more stable though still quite reactive (e.g., $(C_6H_5)_3C^-Na^+$ and $(C_5H_5^-)_2Ca^{2+}$). The only organo derivatives of such highly electropositive elements as scandium and the lanthanides are of this type, for example, with the cyclopentadienide ion, $(C_5H_5)_3Nd$.

2. *σ-Bonded Compounds.* Organo compounds in which the organic residue is bound to a metal by a normal two-electron covalent bond (albeit

in some cases with appreciable ionic character) are formed by most metals of lower electropositivity and, of course, by nonmetallic elements. The normal valence rules apply in these cases, and partial substitution of halides, hydroxides, etc., by organic groups is possible, as in $(CH_3)_3SnCl$, $(CH_3)SnCl_3$, etc. In most of these compounds, bonding is predominantly covalent and the chemistry is organic-like, although there are many differences in detail due to factors such as use of higher d orbitals or donor behavior as in R_4Si, R_3P, R_2S, etc., incomplete valence shells or coordinative unsaturation as in R_3B or R_2Zn, and effects of electronegativity differences between M—C and C—C bonds.

It was long believed that the transition metals of the d type could not, except in a few special cases, form σ bonds to carbon. This view is no longer held (see Chapter 28). Although it is true that few binary organo compounds (R_nM) have been characterized, it is now well established that σ-bonded compounds can be formed by the transition elements provided that other ligands, usually though not always π-bonding ligands, are present. The first-known extensive group of compounds of this type had π-C_5H_5 and CO groups present, for example, π-$C_5H_5Mo(CO)_3C_2H_5$, but several other types are now recognized.

3. *Nonclassically Bonded Compounds.* The organometallic field has presented some very challenging problems since there are several classes of compounds whose structures have been found to be unexpected and novel and which cannot be treated on normal valence considerations. The more important are the following:

Bridge-bonded alkyl compounds: This type of compound is exemplified by the polymeric alkyls of Li, Be and Al.

Sandwich-bonded compounds: These are compounds which have a delocalized "aromatic" ring system bound symmetrically to a transition metal so that all M—C distances are identical. They involve overlap of ring π electron density and certain d orbitals of the metal. The main classes are those with the cyclopentadienyl, benzene and tropylium entities bound to a metal. The name "sandwich" was first used in connection with the structure of the molecule now known as ferrocene, $C_{10}H_{10}Fe$, where the iron atom lies between two planar C_5H_5 rings. In the case of the cyclopentadienyl radical, the prefix π is used to denote symmetrical bonding and to make a distinction from σ-bonded C_5H_5 groups.

Olefin and acetylene compounds: These compounds, like those discussed in the preceding paragraph, are characteristic of the transition metals. They also involve interaction of π electron density of the hydrocarbon with d orbitals. Olefins of various types and acetylenes can be directly bound to a metal atom. In addition, acetylenes can undergo reactions with metal carbonyls in which the acetylene group is modified, for example, by linking to carbon monoxide to give quinone, cyclopentadienone or lactone groupings which are bound to the metal atom. Certain carbanions or carbonium ions derived from olefins, e.g., the allyl ion $H_2C\text{---}CH\text{---}CH_2^-$, form compounds with metal ions in which the bonding is delocalized.

Since the sandwich-bonded, olefin and acetylene types of compounds are specific to transition metals and the bonding results from the special properties of d orbitals, these types are discussed separately in Chapter 28. The *bridge-bonded compounds* are conveniently discussed here.

11-8. Electron-deficient Bridged Alkyls

The elements B, Al, Ga, In and Tl all form fairly stable but reactive alkyls and aryls. The most striking feature of the compounds of this series is the dimerization of the lower alkyls of aluminum.

The trialkyls of B, Ga, In and Tl are monomeric in the vapor and in solution.[17] Trimethylindium, though it is monomeric in solution, appears to be associated in the solid state only where its structure is complicated, tetrameric units being linked together by rather long bonds. Unlike the methyl bridges in $Be(CH_3)_2$ or $Al_2(CH_3)_6$, the $CH_3\text{---}In\text{---}CH_3$ bridges are unsymmetrical. The reasons for this exceptional behavior are not too clear.

Trimethylaluminum (a liquid) is a dimer, $Al_2(CH_3)_6$, in benzene solution and appreciably dimerized in the vapor phase. Triethylaluminum and tri-n-propylaluminum are also dimeric in benzene solution but much more highly dissociated in the vapor phase than is $Al(CH_3)_3$. Triisopropylaluminum is monomeric in benzene solution. Presumably in this last case steric hindrance prevents dimerization (or could, whatever the nature of the bridge bonding). The structures of $[Be(CH_3)_2]_n$ and $[Al(CH_3)_3]_2$ are shown in Figure 11-5. The important feature of these structures is the bridging by methyl groups.

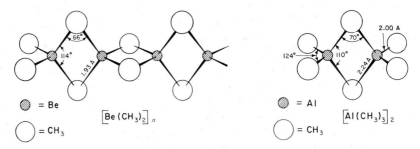

Fig. 11-5. Structures of $[Be(CH_3)_2]_n$ and $[Al(CH_3)_3]_2$ as found by X-ray diffraction.

[17] N. Muller and A. L. Otermat, *Inorg. Chem.*, **4**, 296 (1965).

It should first be emphasized that although these structures are geometrically similar to those of the corresponding chlorides, the nature of the bridge bonding must be essentially different. In the chlorides there is no deficiency of electrons, and we may consider that the equality of the bridge bonds is due to resonance of type 11-XX.

(11-XX)   (11-XXI)   (11-XXII)

In the case of the methyl-bridged compounds, there are insufficient electrons to form four electron pair bonds. In attempting to write classical Lewis structures we could get only as far as 11-XXI, where the question marks indicate that there is no way within the classical framework of valence theory, which recognizes only two-center bonds, to account for the additional metal–carbon bonds. At one time structures such as 11-XXII were discussed, but the meaning of the dotted lines—that is, the nature of the hydrogen–metal interaction they imply—was obscure. The structure data now available, of course, rule out any such idea since the M—C—M groupings are shown to be symmetrical.

The solution to this problem of methyl bridging lies in the recognition of multicenter bonding as in the case of the boranes (Chapter 10). In $[Al(CH_3)_3]_2$, for example, each aluminum atom is assumed to be hybridized in a manner approximating to, but not exactly, the tetrahedral sp^3 hybridization. It then uses two of these orbitals and two of its electrons to form two normal two-center bonds to the terminal methyl groups. The $Al(CH_3)_2$ fragments then have two hybrid orbitals and one electron each available for further bonding. The bridging methyl groups are normal methyl groups and therefore have one empty sp^3 (approximately) hybrid orbital and one electron available for further bonding. These fragments then combine in much the same way as the $2BH_2\cdot$ and $2H\cdot$ in B_2H_6. The methyl orbital and one orbital from each of the aluminum atoms overlap to form a three-center bonding orbital which is occupied by two electrons. A schematic representation of the overlap of these orbitals is given in Figure 11-6. Inspection of Figure 11-5 shows that the metal–carbon–metal angles are quite small, 70 and 66°. From Figure 11-6 the reason for this may be deduced. The hybrid orbital of carbon is directed and condensed rather strongly along the C—C axis. Consequently, in order for the aluminum orbitals to overlap well with it, the axes of their orbitals must not make too great an angle with the C—C axis. Hence the small Al—C—Al and Be—C—Be angles. In $[Be(CH_3)_2]_n$ all methyls are bridging, and the nature of this bonding is in principle exactly the same as in the trimethylaluminum dimer. It should be noted that the metal orbitals doubtless overlap one another to some extent, as indicated in Figure 11-6. This means, in effect, that there is some direct metal–metal bonding. According to present views, this is probably not the dominant factor in the bridge bonding.

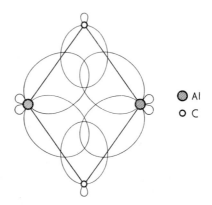

Fig. 11-6. Orbital overlaps in $[Al(CH_3)_3]_2$.

The curious fact that none of the alkyls of the group III elements except those of aluminum are dimerized (while $GaMe_3$ is certainly monomeric in the gas and pure liquid,[18] $GaEt_3$ and trivinylgallium appear to be dimers in solution) has not yet been satisfactorily explained. It has been proposed that for the heavier metals, the small M—C—M angles required to secure good overlap would introduce large repulsions between the bulky metal atoms, but this cannot explain why $B(CH_3)_3$ does not dimerize, especially since hydrogen bridging is quite important in the boranes.

Alkyl bridged species commonly occur as transition states in exchange reactions of certain metal alkyls; the exchange situation is thus similar to that involved in exchange reactions of halides where bridging halides are involved (cf. page 267). Thus according to nmr studies even Me_6Al_2 in alkane solutions undergoes exchange through dissociation at room temperature and two peaks, attributable to terminal and bridging methyl groups, are only seen at $-75°$. Similarly proton resonance spectra for alkyl

[18] G. E. Coates and A. J. Downs, *J. Chem. Soc.*, **1963**, 3353; J. R. Hull, L. A. Woodward and E. A. V. Ebsworth, *Spectrochim. Acta,* **20**, 1249 (1964).

exchanges of $ZnMe_2$ with $CdMe_2$ and of thallium alkyls also show rapid intermolecular exchange of methyl groups. In $TlMe_3$ this follows second order kinetics with an activation energy of 6.3 ± 0.5 kcal/mole; at $25°$ only a single resonance is observed but at low temperatures the line is resolved into two resonances, one due to the end and the other to the bridge methyl groups of the bridged intermediate (11-XXIII). For mixtures of

(11-XXIII)

$TlMe_3$ and $TlEt_3$ exchange also occurs but at low temperatures $TlMeEt_2$ and $TlMe_2Et$ exist independently. In a donor solvent, NMe_3, the exchange rate is slower, owing to formation of the weak complex Me_3TlNMe_3 and for $TlPh_3$ exchange is stopped by formation of the stable isolable complex Ph_3TlNMe_3.[19]

11-9. Carbon "Complexes"

There are a few organo carbon monoxide complexes of transition metals which appear to have C bound to four metal atoms. However, another unusual group of compounds are complex ions of the type $[CH_2 \text{ diars}]^{2+}$ and $[C \text{ diars}_2]^{4+}$, which can be obtained as white crystalline halides or as perchlorate salts.[20] They are made by direct interaction, e.g.,

$$CX_4 + 2 \text{ diars} \rightarrow [C \text{ diars}_2]^{4+} X_4^-$$

Although they could be regarded as carbonium C^{4+} ions stabilized by coordination $C \leftarrow As$, this seems a bit precious and the As—C bonds are probably much as they are in, say, $AsMe_3$; the complexes are stable presumably because of the large size and ability to distribute positive charge over a large surface. These carbon complexes are in principle similar to other first-row complexes such as $[H_2Bdipy]^+$ or $[H_2B-(AsMe_3)_2]^+$.[21]

[19] J. P. Maher and D. F. Evans, *J. Chem. Soc.*, **1963**, 5534.
[20] R. N. Zollinge, R. S. Nyholm and M. L. Tobe, *Nature*, **201**, 1322 (1964).
[21] N. E. Miller and E. L. Muetterties, *J. Amer. Chem. Soc.*, **86**, 1033 (1964).

References

Brotherton, T. K., and J. W. Lynn, *Chem. Revs.*, **59**, 841 (1959). Cyanogen and its chemistry.

Coates, G. E., *Organometallic Compounds*, 2nd ed., Methuen, London, 1960. An excellent general text, but silicon, phosphorus and arsenic compounds are not treated.

Croft, R. C., *Quart. Revs. (London)*, **14**, 1 (1960). Intercalation compounds of graphite.

Ford-Smith, M.H., *The Chemistry of Complex Cyanides*, H.M. Stationery Office, London, 1964. Literature survey.

Hall, H. Tracy, *J. Chem. Educ.*, **38**, 484 (1961). Review on the synthesis of diamonds.

Hennig, G. R., *Progr. Inorg. Chem.*, **1**, 125 (1959). Chemistry of graphite compounds.

Hine, J., *Divalent Carbon*, Ronald Press, New York, 1964. Methylene and other carbenes.

Kern, D. M., *J. Chem. Educ.*, **37**, 14 (1960). An excellent review on the hydration of CO_2, the CO_2–carbonate equilibrium and kinetics.

Kirmse, W., *Carbene Chemistry*, Academic Press, New York, 1964.

Metal-Organic Compounds (Advances in Chemistry Series, No. 23), American Chemical Society, Washington, D.C., 1959. A collection of papers on various aspects, technical and otherwise, such as preparation of organolithium compounds, organoboron compounds, organoaluminum compounds, etc.

Rochow, E. G., D. T. Hurd and R. N. Lewis, *The Chemistry of Organometallic Compounds*, Wiley, New York, 1957. A general survey.

Rüdorff, W., *Adv. Inorg. Chem. Radiochem.*, **2**, 224 (1959). Chemistry of graphite compounds.

———, *et al.*, *Angew. Chem. (Internat.)*, **2**, 67 (1963). A review of reactions of graphite with metal chlorides.

Seyfurth, D., and R. B. King, *Annual Surveys of Organometallic Chemistry*, 1964, *et. seq.*, Elsevier, New York. These volumes survey developments in both transition and nontransition metal compounds in a critical way.

Skinner, H. A., *Adv. Organometal. Chem.*, **2**, 49 (1965). Strengths of metal to carbon bonds; much data given.

Tee, P. A. H., and B. L. Tonge, *J. Chem. Educ.*, **40**, 117 (1963). An excellent short review on graphite and its compounds.

Thorn, G. D., and R. A. Ludwig, *The Dithiocarbamates and Related Compounds*, Elsevier, Amsterdam, 1962.

Tolansky, S., *History and Uses of Diamond*, Methuen, London, 1962.

Ubbelohde, A. R. J. P., and F. A. Lewis, *Graphite and Its Crystal Compounds*, Oxford University Press, 1961.

Williams, H. E., *Cyanogen Compounds*, 2nd ed., Arnold, London, 1948. A detailed account of most C—N compounds including cyanides.

Zeiss, H. H., ed., *Organometallic Chemistry*, ACS Monograph No. 147 Reinhold, New York, 1960. A collection of review articles on metal–carbon bonding, vinylmetallics, organoaluminum compounds, cyclopentadienyl metal compounds, transition metal alkyls and metal carbonyls.

12

Nitrogen

12-1. Introduction

The electronic structure of the nitrogen atom in its ground state is $1s^2 2s^2 2p^3$, with three $2p$ electrons distributed among the p_x, p_y and p_z orbitals with spins unpaired. Nitrogen forms an exceedingly large number of compounds, most of which are to be considered organic rather than inorganic. In its compounds, nitrogen is one of the most electronegative elements, only oxygen and fluorine exceeding it in this respect.

The nitrogen atom has five valence electrons, and the completed octet can be achieved in several ways:

1. *Electron gain to form the nitride ion*, N^{3-}. This ion occurs only in the salt-like nitrides of the most electropositive elements, for example, Li_3N. Many other nitrides exist, but they are not ionic and do not contain the nitride ion. Nitrides in general are discussed later in this chapter.

2. *Formation of electron pair bonds*. The octet can be completed either by the formation of three single bonds, as in NH_3 or NF_3, or by multiple bond formation as in nitrogen itself, $:N{\equiv}N:$, azo compounds, $-\ddot{N}{=}\ddot{N}-$, nitro compounds, $R-NO_2$, etc.

3. *Formation of electron pair bonds with electron gain*. The completed octet is achieved in this way in ions such as the amide ion, NH_2^-, and the imide ion, NH^{2-}.

4. *Formation of electron pair bonds with electron loss*. Nitrogen can form four bonds, provided an electron is lost, to give positively charged ions R_4N^+ such as NH_4^+, $N_2H_5^+$, and $(C_2H_5)_4N^+$. The ions may sometimes be regarded as being formed by the protonation of the lone pair,

$$H_3N: + H^+ = [NH_4]^+$$

or generally

$$R_3N: + R^+X^- = R_4N^+X^-$$

Failure to Achieve Octet. In NO and NO_2 there are an odd number of electrons. Consequently, it is impossible for all atoms to have complete octets. It is, of course, impossible to say that the odd electron is localized on one atom or another, but for the molecule as a whole there is at least one electron shell which is not closed; satisfactory valence descriptions are provided by molecular orbital theory.

Valence of Nitrogen. Compounds of nitrogen in all the possible formal oxidation states from -3 to $+5$ are known. In the chemistry of nitrogen, and in the chemistry of covalent compounds generally, the oxidation state concept is only a formalism, useful, for example, in balancing equations, but not to be taken literally. The various formal oxidation states arise *only* because of covalent bond formation by nitrogen, and there are no grounds whatever for considering nitrogen as a cation in the positive oxidation states or as an anion in the negative ones. The positive oxidation states are found only in oxygen and fluorine compounds (owing, of course, to the purely arbitrary convention that we allow only O and F to have negative oxidation states). Some examples are N_2O_5 ($+5$), NO_2 ($+4$), HNO_2 ($+3$), NO ($+2$), N_2O ($+1$), N_2 (0), NH_2OH (-1), N_2H_4 (-2) and NH_3 (-3).

12-2. Types of Covalence in Nitrogen; Stereochemistry

In common with other first row elements, nitrogen has only four orbitals available for bond formation, and a maximum of four bonds may be formed. However, since formation of three electron pair bonds completes the octet, $:N(:R)_3$, and the nitrogen atom then possesses a lone pair of electrons, four covalent bonds can only be formed by either (*a*) coordination, as in donor–acceptor complexes (e.g., $F_3\overset{-}{B}—\overset{+}{N}(CH_3)_3$) or in amine oxides (e.g., $(CH_3)_3\overset{+}{N}—\overset{-}{O}$), or (*b*) loss of an electron, as in ammonium ions. This loss of an electron gives a valence state configuration for nitrogen (as N^+) with four unpaired electrons in sp^3 hybrid orbitals analogous to that of neutral carbon, while, as noted above, gain of an electron (as in NH_2^-) leaves only two electrons for bond formation. In this case, the nitrogen atom (as N^-) is isoelectronic with the neutral oxygen atom, and angular bonds are formed. We can thus compare, sterically, the following isoelectronic species:

Tetrahedral				*Angular*	
NH_4^+	*and*	CH_4 (also BH_4^-)			*and*

It may be noted that the ions NH_2^-, OH^- and F^- are isoelectronic and have comparable sizes. The amide, imide and nitride ions, which can be considered as members of the isoelectronic series NH_4^+, NH_3, NH_2^-, NH^{2-}, N^{3-} occur as discrete ions only in salts of highly electropositive elements.

In all nitrogen compounds where the atom forms two or three bonds, there remain, respectively, two or one pair of nonbonding electrons, also called lone pairs. As will be discussed more generally in Chapter 15, these nonbonding electron pairs have a profound effect on the stereochemistry. Thus, the stereochemistry about an atom with a filled octet depends on the spatial distribution of *four* pairs of electrons, whether all four pairs are bonding electrons (as in CX_4) or not (as in NH_3, or NH_2^-, or H_2O). Furthermore, the lone pairs are responsible for the donor properties of the atom possessing them. To illustrate the important chemical consequences of nonbonding electron pairs in nitrogen chemistry, we shall consider one of the most important types of molecule, namely, NR_3, as exemplified by NH_3 and amines.

Three-covalent Nitrogen. With only two known exceptions—$N(SiH_3)_3$ and a closely related compound, to be discussed later—molecules of this general type are invariably pyramidal. The bond angles vary depending on the groups attached to the nitrogen atom.

It is to be noted that in a pyramidal R_3N compound of the kind $NRR'R''$ there should exist nonsuperposable mirror images, that is, optically active isomers. No such optical isomers have ever been isolated, however, because molecules of this type have a mode of vibration known as inversion, in which the nitrogen atom oscillates through the plane of the three R groups, much as an umbrella can turn inside out. Inversion has been shown not to occur in solid ammonia since the lone pair is involved in hydrogen bonding to other molecules. In order for the nitrogen atom to cross from one side of the plane to the other (to go from one equilibrium position, say, $+r_0$, to the other, $-r_0$, in Figure 12-1a), the molecule goes through a state of higher potential energy, as shown in the potential energy curve (Fig. 12-1b). However, this "potential energy barrier" to inversion

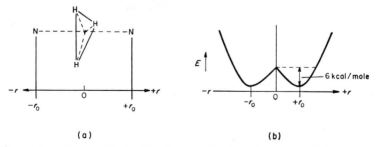

(a)   (b)

Fig. 12-1.   Diagrams illustrating the inversion in NR_3 compounds (see text).

is only 6 kcal/mole, and the frequency of the oscillation is 2.387013×10^{10} c.p.s. (cycles per second) in NH_3. A lower, but still very high, inversion frequency would be expected in any R_3N molecule, which explains why it is impossible to isolate any optical isomers. It has been estimated that a barrier of at least 20 kcal/mole would be necessary in order to make the rate of interconversion sufficiently slow.

Multiple Bonding in Nitrogen and its Compounds. Like its neighbors carbon and oxygen, nitrogen readily forms multiple bonds, differing in this respect from its heavier congeners, P, As, Sb and Bi. Nitrogen thus forms many compounds for which there are no analogs with the heavier elements. Thus, whereas phosphorus, arsenic and antimony form tetrahedral molecules, P_4, As_4, Sb_4, nitrogen forms the multiple-bonded diatomic molecule $:N{\equiv}N:$, with an extremely short internuclear distance (1.094 A) and very high bond strength. The multiple bonding in nitrogen has already been discussed in both the VB and MO approximations in Chapter 3. Nitrogen also forms triple bonds to carbon (in $-C{\equiv}N:$) and to oxygen (in $:\overset{\cdot}{N}{\equiv}O:$, the odd electron being in an antibonding orbital).

In compounds where nitrogen forms one single and one double bond, the grouping $X-\overset{..}{N}{=}Y$ is nonlinear. This can be explained by assuming that nitrogen uses a set of sp^2 orbitals, two of which are used to form σ bonds to X and Y, while the third houses the lone pair. A π bond to Y is then formed using the nitrogen p_z orbital. In certain cases, stereoisomers result from the nonlinearity, for example, cis- and trans-azobenzenes (12-Ia and

(12-Ia)   (12-Ib)   (12-IIa)   (12-IIb)

12-Ib) and the oximes 12-IIa and 12-IIb. These do not readily interconvert, although they do so more easily than do cis and trans olefins.

Multiple bonding occurs also in oxo compounds. For example, NO_2^- (12-III) and NO_3^- (12-IV) can be regarded as resonance hybrids in the

(12-IIIa)   (12-IIIb)

(12-IVa)   (12-IVb)   (12-IVc)

VB approach. From the MO viewpoint, one considers the existence of a π MO extending symmetrically over the entire ion and containing the two π electrons.

An unusual but significant case of multiple bonding occurs in trisilylamine, $N(SiH_3)_3$. This compound differs from trimethylamine (a) in being a very weak base (measured in terms of its ability to form donor–acceptor complexes; e.g., $(H_3Si)_3\overset{+}{N}$—$\overset{-}{B}F_3$ decomposes above $-40°$) and (b) in being *planar* rather than pyramidal. These observations can be explained by supposing that nitrogen forms dative π bonds to the silicon atoms. In the planar state of $N(SiH_3)_3$, the nonbonding electrons of nitrogen would occupy the $2p_z$ orbital, if we assume that the N—Si bonds are formed using sp_xp_y trigonal hybrid orbitals of nitrogen. Silicon has empty $3d$ orbitals, which are of low enough energy to be able to interact appreciably with the nitrogen $2p_z$ orbital. Thus, the N—Si π bonding is due to the kind of overlap indicated in Figure 12-2. It is the additional bond strength to be

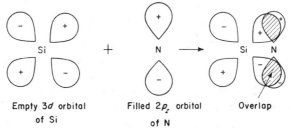

| Empty $3d$ orbital | Filled $2p_z$ orbital | Overlap |
| of Si | of N | |

Fig. 12-2.   Formation of $d\pi$–$p\pi$ bond between Si and N in trisilylamine.

gained by this $p\pi \rightarrow d\pi$ bonding which causes the NSi_3 skeleton to take up a planar configuration, whereas with $N(CH_3)_3$, where the carbon has no low energy d orbitals, the σ bonding alone determines the configuration, which is pyramidal as expected. A very similar situation occurs in the cyclic molecule 12-V in which the bonds to N are coplanar.[1] Yet another

$$(CH_3)_3Si\text{—}N\text{—}Si(CH_3)_2$$
$$(CH_3)_2Si\text{—}N\text{—}Si(CH_3)_3$$
$$(12\text{-}V)$$

case of N—Si $p\pi \rightarrow d\pi$ bonding occurs in silyl isothiocyanate H_3SiNCS, which has a linear Si—N—C—S grouping, whereas in H_3C—$\overset{..}{N}$=C=S the C—$\overset{..}{N}$=C linkage is bent as would normally be expected. Tetrasilylhydrazine has been shown to be much less effective a donor than $(CH_3)_4N_2$, but the structure is not yet known.

[1] P. J. Wheatley, *J. Chem. Soc.*, **1962**, 1721.

Donor Properties of Three-covalent Nitrogen; Four-covalent Nitrogen.
As noted above, the formation of tetrahedral sp^3 (or approximately)
bonds to nitrogen occurs in cations, R_4N^+, and in amine oxides, $R_3\overset{+}{N}—\overset{-}{O}$;
and the dipolar nature of NR_3 compounds has been discussed in terms of
the occupancy of a hybrid orbital by the unshared pair, which confers
donor properties on most R_3N: compounds. In donor–acceptor compounds,
for example, $R_3\overset{+}{N}—\overset{-}{B}X_3$, the N—B bond is polar as indicated; the degree
of polarity is influenced by the relative electronegativities of the donor
and acceptor atoms, but some polarity will always exist because of the
higher effective nuclear charge of the donor atom. Multiple bonds cannot
be formed between the acceptor atom and nitrogen (regardless of the
acceptor atom)—that is, no contribution of the form $X{=}N\!\!<$ is possible—
in view of the limit of four covalence for nitrogen. This situation contrasts
strongly with that for phosphorus and arsenic derivatives, for example,
R_3P: and R_3As:, because these elements possess low-lying d orbitals
that are capable of back acceptance from a suitable partner. Thus, the
amine oxides can only be written $R_3\overset{+}{N}—\overset{-}{O}$, whereas the phosphine oxides
have a considerable multiple bond character, and $R_3P{=}O$ represents a
good approximation to the electronic structure.

Catenation and N—N Single Bond Energies.   Unlike carbon and a few
other elements, nitrogen has little tendency for catenation, primarily due
to the weakness of the N—N single bond. If we compare the single bond
energies in $H_3C—CH_3$, $H_2N—NH_2$, H—O—O—H and F—F which are,
respectively, 83.1, 38.4, 33.2 and 36.6 kcal/mole, it is clear that there is a
profound drop between C and N. This difference is most likely attributable
to the effects of repulsion between nonbonding lone-pair electrons. The
strength of the N—N bond, and also the O—O bond, decreases
with increasing electronegativity of the attached groups; while increasing
electronegativity would perhaps have been expected to reduce repulsion
between lone-pairs, it obviously also will weaken any homonuclear σ bond.

There are a few types of compounds containing chains of three or more
nitrogen atoms with some multiple bonds such as $R_2N—N{=}NR_2$,
$R_2N—N{=}N—NR_2$, $RN{=}N—N(R)—NR_2$, $RN{=}N—N(R)—N{=}NR$ and
even $RN{=}N—N(R)—N{=}N—N(R)—N{=}NR$, where R represents an
organic radical (some R's may be H, but known compounds contain only
a few H's). There are also cyclic compounds containing rings with up to
five consecutive nitrogen atoms. Many of these compounds are not particularly stable, and all are traditionally in the realm of organic chemistry.

Hydrogen Bonding.   Since it is one of the most electronegative elements, nitrogen, along with oxygen, fluorine and, to a lesser extent,

chlorine, extensively enters into hydrogen bond formation in its hydrogen compounds.

THE ELEMENT

12-3. Occurrence and Properties

Nitrogen occurs in nature mainly as the inert diatomic gas N_2 (m 63.1°K, b 77.3°K), which comprises 78% by volume of the earth's atmosphere. Naturally occurring nitrogen consists of ^{14}N and ^{15}N with an absolute ratio $^{14}N/^{15}N = 272.0$. ^{15}N is often useful as an isotopic tracer, and it has been found possible to prepare nitric acid containing up to 99.8% ^{15}N by taking advantage of the preferential concentration of ^{15}N in HNO_3 in the system

$$^{15}NO(g) + H^{14}NO_3(aq) = {}^{14}NO(g) + H^{15}NO_3(aq)$$

The equilibrium distribution of ^{15}N favors HNO_3 by only a very minute fraction, owing to the extremely slight effect of the mass differences on the free energies of the two compounds. Thus, the exchange system operates so that the equilibration is carried automatically through thousands of stages in much the same way as two liquids with only a slight boiling point difference are separated by distillation through a fractionation column with thousands of theoretical plates. The $H^{15}NO_3$ produced can be used to prepare any desired ^{15}N-labeled nitrogen compound.

The heat of dissociation of nitrogen is extremely large:

$$N_2(g) = 2N(g) \quad \Delta H = 225.8 \text{ kcal/mole}; \; K_{25°} = 10^{-120}$$

Because the reaction is endothermic, the equilibrium constant increases with increasing temperature, but still, even at 3000° and ordinary pressures, there is no appreciable dissociation. The great strength of the N≡N bond is principally responsible for the chemical inertness of N_2 and for the fact that most simple nitrogen compounds are endothermic even though they may contain strong bonds. Thus $E(N≡N) \approx 6E(N—N)$ whereas $E(C≡C) \approx 2.5\,E(C—C)$. Nitrogen is notably unreactive when compared with other systems containing triple bonds, such as X—C≡C—X, :C≡O:, X—C≡N: and X—N≡C:. This is because N_2 has (a) no polarity and (b) an appreciably higher ionization potential than these other systems. Thus, both —C≡C— and —C≡N groups are known to serve as donors by using their π electrons, and :C≡O: functions as a donor (with reinforcement of the σ bond by back-bonding (see Chapter 27)) using the unshared electron

11*

pair on carbon. N_2 will do neither of these things, so far as is known (see below, however).

Nitrogen is obtained commercially by liquefaction and fractionation of air; when so prepared it usually contains some argon and, depending on the quality, upwards of ~ 30 p.p.m. of oxygen. The oxygen may be removed by admixing with a little hydrogen and treating with a platinum catalyst, by passing the gas over hot copper or other metal, or by bubbling it through aqueous solutions of Cr^{2+} or V^{2+} ions. Spectroscopically pure nitrogen is conveniently prepared by thermal decomposition of sodium or barium azides, for example,

$$2NaN_3 = 2Na + 3N_2$$

The only reactions of N_2 at room temperature are with metallic lithium to give Li_3N and with nitrogen-fixing bacteria, either free-living or symbiotic on root nodules of clover, peas, beans, etc. The mechanism by which these bacteria fix nitrogen is still completely unknown, although it is believed that the terminal reduction product is ammonia. The initial attack on nitrogen must surely involve the coordination of the molecule to some site, presumably a transition metal atom; there have been some claims that absorption spectra of certain enzyme systems show evidence for complex formation. However, the mechanism of biological nitrogen fixation remains one of the most conspicuously challenging unsolved problems in chemistry.

At elevated temperatures nitrogen becomes more reactive, especially when catalyzed, typical reactions being:

$$N_2(g) + 3H_2(g) = 2NH_3(g) \qquad K_{25^\circ} = 10^3 \text{ atm}^{-2}$$
$$N_2(g) + O_2(g) = 2NO(g) \qquad K_{25^\circ} = 5 \times 10^{-31}$$
$$N_2(g) + 3Mg(s) = Mg_3N_2(s)$$
$$N_2(g) + CaC_2(s) = C(s) + CaCN(s)$$

Active nitrogen has been known for many years to result from passing discharges through nitrogen. This gas has a persistent golden-yellow afterglow and is chemically very reactive. After years of study and discussion, during which such species as an ozone-like N_3 were considered, it has recently been established by mass spectroscopic and other studies that, in the main, active nitrogen consists of nitrogen atoms in their ground state (^4S). These recombine only relatively slowly, producing excited N_2 molecules in quintet spin states, which then emit the characteristic radiation as they drop to the ground state. The large change in electron spin when the two atoms in spin quartet states (total of six unpaired electrons) combine to produce a molecule in a quintet state (four unpaired electrons) accounts for the slowness of the recombination while the presence of atomic nitrogen explains the great chemical reactivity.

NITROGEN COMPOUNDS

12-4. Nitrides

As with carbides, there are three general classes, although the nitrides have not been as extensively studied structurally.

Ionic nitrides are formed by Mg, Ca, Ba, Sr, Zn, Cd, Li and Th. Their formulas correspond to what would result from combination of the normal metal ions with N^{3-} ions. So far as is known they are all essentially ionic compounds and are properly written as $Ca_3^{2+}N_2^{3-}$, $Li_3^{+}N^{3-}$, etc. Nitrides of the M_3N_2 type are often anti-isomorphous with M_2O_3-type oxides. This does not, however, necessarily mean that, like the oxides, they are ionic. However, their ready hydrolysis to ammonia and the metal hydroxides makes this seem likely. The ionic nitrides are prepared by direct union of the elements or by loss of ammonia from amides on heating, for example,

$$3Ba(NH_2)_2 \rightarrow Ba_3N_2 + 4NH_3$$

There are various covalent "nitrides"—BN, S_4N_4, P_3N_3, etc.—the properties of which vary greatly depending upon the element with which nitrogen is combined. Such substances are therefore discussed under the appropriate element.

The transition metals form interstitial nitrides that are analogous to the interstitial borides and carbides in their constitution and properties. The nitrogen atoms occupy interstices in the close-packed metal lattices. These nitrides are often not exactly stoichiometric (being nitrogen deficient), and they are metallic in appearance, hardness and electrical conductivity, since the electronic band structure of the metal persists. Like the interstitial borides and carbides, they are chemically very inert, extremely hard, and very high melting. A representative compound, VN, melts at 2570° and has a hardness between 9 and 10. Interstitial nitrides are usually prepared by heating the metal in ammonia at 1100–1200°.

12-5. Nitrogen Hydrides

Ammonia. On a laboratory scale, ammonia, NH_3, may be prepared by treatment of an ammonium salt with a base

$$NH_4X + OH^- = NH_3 + H_2O + X^-$$

Hydrolysis of an ionic nitride is a convenient way of preparing ND_3 (or NH_3)

$$Mg_3N_2 + 6D_2O = 3Mg(OD)_2 + 2ND_3$$

On the industrial scale ammonia is obtained by the Haber process in which the reaction

$$N_2(g) + 3H_2(g) = 2NH_3(g) \qquad \Delta H = -11 \text{ kcal/mole}; \ K_{25°} = 10^3 \text{ atm}^{-2}$$

is carried out in the presence of a catalyst at pressures of 10^2–10^3 atm and temperatures of 400–550°. Although the equilibrium is most favorable at low temperature, even with the best available catalysts elevated temperatures are required to obtain a satisfactory rate of conversion. The best catalyst is α-iron containing some oxide in order to widen the lattice and enlarge the active interface.

Ammonia is a colorless pungent gas with a normal boiling point of $-33.35°$ and a freezing point of $-77.8°$. The liquid has a large heat of evaporation (327 cal/g at the boiling point) and is therefore fairly easily handled in ordinary laboratory equipment. Liquid ammonia resembles water in its physical behavior, being highly associated because of the polar nature of the molecules and strong hydrogen bonding. Its dielectric constant (~ 22 at $-34°$; cf. 81 for H_2O at 25°) is sufficiently high to make it a fair ionizing solvent. A system of nitrogen chemistry with many analogies to the oxygen system based on water has been built up. Thus, we have the comparable self-ionization equilibria:

$$2NH_3 = NH_4^+ + NH_2^- \qquad K_{-50°} = [NH_4^+][NH_2^-] = \sim 10^{-30}$$
$$2H_2O = H_3O^+ + OH^- \qquad K_{25°} = [H_3O^+][OH^-] = 10^{-14}$$

Table 12-1 presents a comparison of the ammonia and water systems.

TABLE 12-1

	Ammonia system		Water system	
	Class of compound	Example	Class of compound	Example
Acids	$NH_4^+X^-$	$NH_4^+Cl^-$	$H_3O^+X^-$	$H_3O^+Cl^-$
Bases	Amides	$Na^+NH_2^-$	Hydroxides	Na^+OH^-
	Imides	$Li_2^+NH^{2-}$	Oxides	$Li_2^+O^{2-}, Mg^{2+}O^{2-}$
	Nitrides	$Mg_3^{2+}N_2^{3-}$		

Liquid ammonia has lower reactivity toward electropositive metals than H_2O, such metals reacting immediately with water to evolve hydrogen. Liquid ammonia, on the other hand, readily dissolves many electropositive metals (the alkali metals, Ca, Sr, Ba and some of the lanthanide metals) to give blue solutions containing metal ions and solvated electrons (see also page 417). Such solutions are stable for long periods and are useful as powerful reducing agents. However, they do react slowly—or rapidly in the presence of transition metal salts like $FeCl_2$ as catalysts:

$$Na + NH_3 = NaNH_2 + \tfrac{1}{2}H_2$$

This is a convenient laboratory preparation of sodium amide.

Chemical Reactions of Ammonia. Perhaps the two most important reactions of ammonia are those with oxygen and with water.

Ammonia will burn in pure oxygen but only under certain conditions. Normal combustion in air gives mainly water and nitrogen according to equation 12-1. However, ammonia can be made to react with oxygen as

$$4NH_3(g) + 3O_2(g) = 2N_2(g) + 6H_2O(g) \qquad K_{25°} = 10^{228} \qquad (12\text{-}1)$$

shown in equation 12-2, despite the fact that the process of equation 12-1 is thermodynamically much more favorable. This is accomplished by

$$4NH_3 + 5O_2 = 4NO + 6H_2O \qquad K_{25°} = 10^{168} \qquad (12\text{-}2)$$

carrying out the reaction at 750–900° in the presence of a platinum or platinum–rhodium catalyst which selectively catalyzes the second reaction. It can easily be demonstrated in the laboratory by introducing a piece of glowing platinum foil into a jar containing gaseous NH_3 and O_2; the foil will continue to glow because of the heat of reaction 12-2, which occurs only on the surface of the metal, and brown fumes will appear owing to the reaction of NO with excess oxygen to produce NO_2. Industrially, the mixed oxides of nitrogen are then absorbed in water to form nitric acid:

$$2NO + O_2 = 2NO_2$$
$$3NO_2 + H_2O = 2HNO_3 + NO, \text{ etc.}$$

Thus, the sequence in industrial utilization of atmospheric nitrogen is as follows:

$$N_2 \xrightarrow[\substack{\text{Haber} \\ \text{process}}]{H_2} NH_3 \xrightarrow[\substack{\text{Ostwald} \\ \text{process}}]{O_2} NO \xrightarrow{O_2 + H_2O} HNO_3(aq)$$

Ammonia is extremely soluble in water. It is possible to isolate two stable crystalline hydrates at low temperatures, $NH_3 \cdot H_2O$ (m 194.15°K) and $2NH_3 \cdot H_2O$ (m 194.32°K), in which the NH_3 and H_2O molecules are linked by hydrogen bonds. The substances contain neither $NH_4{}^+$ and OH^- ions nor discrete NH_4OH molecules. Thus, $NH_3 \cdot H_2O$ has chains of H_2O molecules linked by hydrogen bonds (2.76 A). These chains are cross linked by NH_3 into a three-dimensional lattice by OH····N (2.78 A) and O····H—N bonds (3.21–3.29 A). In aqueous solution ammonia is probably hydrated in a similar manner. Although aqueous solutions are commonly referred to as solutions of the weak base NH_4OH, called "ammonium hydroxide," this is to be discouraged, since there is no evidence that undissociated NH_4OH exists and there is reason to believe that it probably does not. Solutions of ammonia are best described as $NH_3(aq)$, with the equilibrium written as

$$NH_3(aq) + H_2O = NH_4^+ + OH^- \qquad K_{25°} = \frac{[NH_4^+][OH^-]}{[NH_3]} = 1.81 \times 10^{-5} \; (pK_b = 4.75)$$

In an odd sense NH_4OH might be considered a *strong* base since it is completely dissociated in water. A $1N$ solution of NH_3 is only $0.0042N$ in NH_4^+ and OH^-.

Nuclear magnetic resonance measurements show that the hydrogen atoms of NH_3 readily exchange with those of water by the process

$$H_2O + NH_3 = OH^- + NH_4^+$$

but there is no exchange between NH_3 molecules in the vapor phase or in the liquid if water is completely removed.

Ammonium Salts. There are many rather stable crystalline salts of the tetrahedral NH_4^+ ion; most of them are water soluble like alkali metal salts. Salts of strong acids are fully ionized, and the solutions are slightly acidic:

$$NH_4Cl = NH_4^+ + Cl^- \qquad K \approx \infty$$
$$NH_4^+ + H_2O = NH_3 + H_3O^+ \qquad K_{25°} = 5.5 \times 10^{-10}$$

Thus, a $1M$ solution will have a pH of ~ 4.7. The constant for the second reaction is sometimes called the hydrolysis constant; however, it may equally well be considered as the acidity constant of the cationic acid NH_4^+, and the system regarded as an acid–base system in the following sense:

$$NH_4^+ + H_2O = H_3O^+ + NH_3(aq)$$
$$\text{Acid} \quad \text{Base} \quad \text{Acid} \quad \text{Base}$$

Ammonium salts generally resemble those of potassium and rubidium in solubility and, except where hydrogen bonding effects are important, in structure, since the three ions are of comparable radii: $NH_4^+ = 1.43$ A, $K^+ = 1.33$ A, $Rb^+ = 1.48$ A.

Many ammonium salts volatilize with dissociation around 300°, for example,

$$NH_4Cl(s) = NH_3(g) + HCl(g) \qquad \Delta H = 42.3 \text{ kcal/mole}; \; K_{25°} = 10^{-16}$$
$$NH_4NO_3(s) = NH_3(g) + HNO_3(g) \qquad \Delta H = 40.9 \text{ kcal/mole}$$

Some salts which contain oxidizing anions decompose on heating, with oxidation of the ammonia to N_2O or N_2 or both. For example:

$$(NH_4)_2Cr_2O_7(s) = N_2(g) + 4H_2O(g) + Cr_2O_3(s) \qquad \Delta H = -75.4 \text{ kcal/mole}$$
$$NH_4NO_3(l) = N_2O(g) + 2H_2O(g) \qquad \Delta H = -5.5 \text{ kcal/mole}$$

Ammonium nitrate volatilizes reversibly at moderate temperatures; at higher temperatures, irreversible decomposition occurs exothermically, giving mainly N_2O. This is the reaction by which N_2O is prepared commercially. At still higher temperatures, the N_2O itself decomposes into nitrogen and oxygen. Ammonium nitrate can be caused to detonate when initiated by another high explosive, and mixtures of ammonium nitrate with TNT or other high explosives are used for bombs. The decomposition of liquid ammonium nitrate can also become explosively rapid, particularly when catalyzed by traces of acid and chloride; there are a number of instances of disastrous explosions following after fires of ammonium nitrate in bulk.

Derivatives of Ammonia. There are an enormous number of compounds which can be considered as derived from ammonia by replacement of hydrogen atoms with other organic and inorganic radicals. Most of them, such as amines and amides, are properly considered as organic compounds and will not concern us further here. We may note, however, that tetra-alkylammonium cations, R_4N^+, are often of use in inorganic chemistry where large, univalent cations are required. They are prepared generally by the following reaction:

$$R_3N + RI = R_4N^+I^-$$

and I^- may be replaced with the anion of interest in various metathetical reactions in a suitable solvent. Some important "inorganic" derivatives of ammonia are discussed in succeeding sections.

Hydrazine. Hydrazine, N_2H_4, may be thought of as derived from ammonia by replacement of a hydrogen atom by the $-NH_2$ group. It might therefore be expected to be a base, but somewhat weaker than NH_3, which is the case. Of course, it is a bifunctional base:

$$N_2H_4(aq) + H_2O = N_2H_5^+ + OH^- \qquad K_{25°} = 8.5 \times 10^{-7}$$
$$N_2H_5^+(aq) + H_2O = N_2H_6^{2+} + OH^- \qquad K_{25°} = 8.9 \times 10^{-16}$$

Anhydrous N_2H_4 (m $2°$, b $114°$) is a fuming colorless liquid with a high dielectric constant ($\epsilon = 52$ at $25°$). It is surprisingly stable in view of its endothermic nature:

$$N_2(g) + 2H_2(g) = N_2H_4(l) \qquad \Delta H_f° = 12.0 \text{ kcal/mole}$$

It will burn in air, however, with considerable evolution of heat

$$N_2H_4(l) + O_2(g) = N_2(g) + 2H_2O(l) \qquad \Delta H = 148.6 \text{ kcal/mole}$$

which accounts for interest in it and certain of its alkylated derivatives as potential rocket fuels.

Two series of hydrazinium salts are obtainable, those of $N_2H_5^+$ and those of $N_2H_6^{2+}$. The former are stable in aqueous solution, simply ionizing to $N_2H_5^+$ and X^-, whereas, owing to the low value of K_2 for N_2H_4, the latter are immediately hydrolyzed (cf. hydrolysis of sulfides, for example, Na_2S):

$$N_2H_6X_2 + H_2O = N_2H_5^+ + H_3O^+ + 2X^- \qquad K = 11$$

However, the diacid salts can be obtained by crystallization from aqueous solution containing a large excess of the acid, since they are usually less soluble than the monoacid salts.

As another consequence of its basicity, hydrazine, like NH_3, can form coordination complexes with both Lewis acids and metal ions. Just as with respect to the proton, electrostatic considerations (and in these cases, also steric considerations) militate against bifunctional behavior. Although some polymeric complexes having hydrazine bridges (12-VI) have been demonstrated, generally only one nitrogen atom is coordinated[2], e.g., as in $[Zn(N_2H_4)_2Cl_2]$.

(12-VI)

Aqueous hydrazine is a powerful reducing agent in basic solution; in many of such reactions, diimine (see below) is an intermediate. One reaction which is quantitative with some oxidants (e.g., I_2) is

$$N_2 + 4H_2O + 4e = 4OH^- + N_2H_4(aq) \qquad E^\circ = -1.16 \text{ v}$$

However, NH_3 and HN_3 are also obtained under various conditions. Air and oxygen, especially when catalyzed by polyvalent metal ions in basic solution, produce hydrogen peroxide:

$$2O_2 + N_2H_4(aq) = 2H_2O_2(aq) + N_2$$

but further reaction will occur in presence of metal ions:

$$N_2H_4 + 2H_2O_2 = N_2 + 4H_2O$$

In acid solution, hydrazine can reduce halogens:

$$N_2H_4(aq) + 2X_2 = 4HX + N_2$$

The *preparation* of hydrazine has been the subject of much study. Many reactions produce it in small amounts under certain conditions, for example,

$$N_2 + 2H_2 = N_2H_4$$
$$N_2O + 2NH_3 = N_2H_4 + H_2O + N_2$$
$$2NH_3(g) + \tfrac{1}{2}O_2 = N_2H_4 + H_2O$$
$$N_2O + 3H_2 = N_2H_4 + H_2O$$

[2] A. Ferrari, A. Braibanti and G. Bigliardi, *Acta Cryst.*, **16**, 498 (1963); *idem* and F. Dallavalle, *Zeit. Krist.*, **119**, 284 (1963).

However, none of these has ever been developed into a practical method because there are competing, and thermodynamically more favorable, reactions, such as

$$2NH_3 + \tfrac{3}{2}O_2 = N_2 + 3H_2O$$
$$2NH_3 + 3N_2O = 4N_2 + 3H_2O$$
$$N_2O + H_2 = N_2 + H_2O$$

These are good illustrations of the effect of the great stability of N_2 on nitrogen chemistry.

The only practical method until very recently for preparing hydrazine in quantity has been the Raschig synthesis, discovered in the first decade of this century. The over-all reaction, carried out in aqueous solution, is

$$2NH_3 + NaOCl = N_2H_4 + NaCl + H_2O$$

Actually, the reaction proceeds in two steps. The first one, which is fast, produces chloramine, NH_2Cl:

$$NH_3 + NaOCl = NaOH + NH_2Cl$$

The chloramine then reacts slowly with further ammonia:

$$NH_3 + NH_2Cl + NaOH = N_2H_4 + NaCl + H_2O \qquad (12\text{-}3)$$

However, there is a competing and parasitic reaction which is rather fast once some hydrazine has been formed:

$$2NH_2Cl + N_2H_4 = 2NH_4Cl + N_2 \qquad (12\text{-}4)$$

In order to obtain appreciable yields, it is necessary, as Raschig discovered, to add some gelatinous material, usually glue or gelatin, to the reaction mixture. It is now known that this serves two essential purposes. First, it sequesters heavy metal ions which catalyze reaction 12-4 at the expense of 12-3. Even the part per million or so of Cu^{2+} in ordinary water will almost completely prevent the formation of hydrazine if no catalyst is used. However, although addition of simple sequestering agents (e.g., ethylene-diaminetetraacetic acid), in the absence of glue or gelatin, was shown to be beneficial, it was found that the glue or gelatin must serve a second function, namely, to catalyze reaction 12-3 but not 12-4. Under proper conditions, yields of 60–70% are obtained. By distillation hydrazine is obtained as a dilute aqueous solution which may be concentrated to ~85% by further distillation. From this solution anhydrous hydrazine may be obtained by further distillation over NaOH or KOH. Alternatively, hydrazine sulfate, $N_2H_6SO_4$, may be precipitated from the dilute solution obtained in the Raschig process. On treating this with liquid ammonia, ammonium sulfate is almost quantitatively precipitated

$$N_2H_6SO_4 + 2NH_3 = N_2H_4 + (NH_4)_2SO_4$$

and the hydrazine is easily obtained by stripping the ammonia after filtration.

There are now competitive routes to hydrazine[2a] which are variants on the Raschig process. They involve the interaction of Cl_2 and NH_3 in a ketone to give a diazacyclopropane; this intermediate is converted to a ketazine by an acid catalyzed reaction with more ketone. The ketazine is then hydrolyzed by water under pressure to give hydrazine hydrate or by sulfuric acid to give hydrazine sulfate.

$$4NH_3 + Cl_2 + R_2CO \ = \quad R_2C\langle^{NH}_{NH} \quad + \ 2NH_4Cl + H_2O$$

diazacyclopropane

$$R_2C\langle^{NH}_{NH} \ + \ R_2CO \ = \quad R_2C{=}N{-}N{=}CR_2 \ + \ H_2O$$

ketazine

$$R_2C{=}N{-}N{=}CR_2 \ + \ 2H_2O \ = \ 2\ R_2C{=}O \ + \ N_2H_4$$

Structurally, hydrazine resembles hydrogen peroxide. From the fact that the molecule has a dipole moment of about 1.85 Debye units, the *trans* structure (Fig. 12-3a) must be ruled out. The equilibrium configuration is probably the *gauche* form (Fig. 12-3b); a completely eclipsed form seems

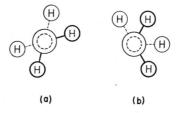

(a)   (b)

Fig. 12-3.   Structure of hydrazine (see text).

unlikely, although it has not been positively disproved. The N—N distance is 1.47 ± 0.02 A, the N—H distance ~ 1.04 A and the HNH and NNH angles $\sim 110°$.

[2a] *Chem. and Eng. News*, July 5, 1965, p. 38.

Diimine. Although the parent of azo compounds, diimine, $HN{=}NH$ cannot be isolated, there is good evidence for its existence in the gas phase and in solutions. Diimine can be obtained in a variety of ways but it is commonly found in oxidations of hydrazine by two electron oxidants, e.g., molecular oxygen, peroxides, chloramine-T, etc.

$$N_2H_4 \xrightarrow{-2e,-2H} N_2H_2$$

It is also formed in alkaline cleavage of chloramine,

$$H_2NCl \xrightarrow{OH^-} HNCl^-$$

$$HNCl^- + H_2NCl \xrightarrow{-Cl^-} \underset{\underset{Cl}{|}}{HN-NH_2} \xrightarrow{-HCl} HN{=}NH$$

The existence of N_2H_2 has been shown *inter alia* by the stereospecific *cis* hydrogenation of $C{=}C$ bonds using hydrazine and an oxidant. Diimine can either decompose to N_2 and H_2 or can disproportionate:

These two reactions appear to be competitive.

Hydrazoic Acid and Azides. Although hydrazoic acid, HN_3, is a hydride of nitrogen in a formal sense, it has no essential relationship to NH_3 and N_2H_4. The sodium salt is prepared by the reactions

$$3NaNH_2 + NaNO_3 \xrightarrow{175°} NaN_3 + 3NaOH + NH_3$$

$$2NaNH_2 + N_2O(g) \xrightarrow{190°} NaN_3 + NaOH + NH_3$$

while the free acid can be obtained in solution by the reaction

$$N_2H_5^+ + HNO_2 \xrightarrow{aq.\ soln.} HN_3 + H^+ + 2H_2O$$

Many other oxidizing agents attack hydrazine to form small amounts of HN_3 or azides. Free hydrazoic acid, obtainable by distillation from aqueous solutions, is a colorless liquid (b 37°), and dangerously explosive. In water it is a weak acid ($K_{25°} = 1.8 \times 10^{-5}$). Azides of many metals are known. Salts of heavy metals are generally explosive; those of Pb, Hg and Ba explode on being struck sharply and are used in detonation caps.

Azides of electropositive metals are not explosive and, in fact, decompose smoothly and quantitatively when heated to 300° or higher, for example,

$$2NaN_3(s) = 2Na(l) + 3N_2(g)$$

Azide ion also functions as a ligand in complexes of transition metals. In general, N_3^- behaves rather like a halide ion and is commonly considered as a pseudohalide, although the corresponding pseudohalogen $(N_3)_2$ is not known.

The azide ion itself is symmetrical and linear (N—N distance *ca* 1.15 A), and its electronic structure may be represented in valence bond theory as:

$$: \overset{-}{\underset{\cdot\cdot}{N}} = \overset{+}{N} = \overset{-}{\underset{\cdot\cdot}{N}} : \quad \leftrightarrow \quad : N \equiv \overset{+}{N} : \overset{2-}{\underset{\cdot\cdot}{N}} : \quad \leftrightarrow \quad : \overset{2-}{\underset{\cdot\cdot}{N}} : \overset{+}{N} \equiv N :$$

In covalent azides, on the other hand, the symmetry is lost as is evident in

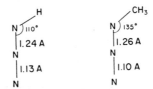

Fig. 12-4.   Structure of HN_3 and CH_3N_3.

HN_3 and CH_3N_3 (Fig. 12-4). In such covalent azides the electronic structure is a resonance hybrid

$$R : \overset{\cdot\cdot}{N} = \overset{+}{N} = \overset{-}{\underset{\cdot\cdot}{N}} : \quad \leftrightarrow \quad R : \overset{-}{\underset{\cdot\cdot}{N}} : \overset{+}{N} \equiv N :$$

Hydroxylamine. As hydrazine may be thought of as derived from ammonia by replacement of one hydrogen by NH_2, so hydroxylamine, NH_2OH, is obtained by replacement of H by OH. Like hydrazine, hydroxylamine is a weaker base than NH_3:

$$NH_2OH(aq) + H_2O = NH_3OH^+ + OH^- \qquad K_{25°} = 6.6 \times 10^{-9}$$

Hydroxylamine is prepared by reduction of nitrates or nitrites either electrolytically or with SO_2. In order to obtain good yields by either method, conditions of reaction must be very closely controlled. It is also made, in 70% yield, by H_2 reduction of NO_2 in HCl solution using platinized active charcoal as catalyst. Free hydroxylamine is a white solid (m 33°) which must be kept on ice to avoid decomposition. It is normally encountered as an aqueous solution and in the form of its salts, especially $[NH_3OH]Cl$, $[NH_3OH]NO_3$ and $[NH_3OH]_2SO_4$, which are stable, water-soluble, white solids. Although hydroxylamine can serve as either an oxidizing or a reducing agent, it is usually used as the latter. It has properties which, in many ways, lie between those of ammonia, H_2N—H, and water, H—OH, as its formula, H_2N—OH, might suggest. It can serve as a ligand in complexes (e.g., $Zn(NH_2OH)_2Cl_2$), probably coordinating through nitrogen.

12-6. Oxides of Nitrogen

The known oxides of nitrogen are listed in Table 12-2.

TABLE 12-2
Oxides of Nitrogen

Formula	Name	Color	Remarks
N_2O	Nitrous oxide	Colorless	Rather unreactive
NO	Nitric oxide	Gas, colorless; liquid and solid, blue	Moderately reactive
N_2O_3	Dinitrogen trioxide	Blue solid	Extensively dissociated as gas
NO_2	Nitrogen dioxide	Brown	Rather reactive
N_2O_4	Dinitrogen tetroxide	Colorless	Extensively dissociated to NO_2 as gas and partly as liquid
N_2O_5	Dinitrogen pentoxide	Colorless	Unstable as gas; ionic solid
NO_3; N_2O_6	—	—	Not well characterized and quite unstable

Nitrous Oxide. Nitrous oxide, N_2O, is obtained by thermal decomposition of ammonium nitrate in the melt at 250–$260°$:

$$NH_4NO_3 = N_2O + 2H_2O$$

The contaminants are NO, which can be removed by passage through ferrous sulfate solution and 1–2% nitrogen. The NH_4NO_3 must be free from Cl^- as this causes catalytic decomposition to N_2.[3] However, heating HNO_3 or H_2SO_4 solutions of NH_4NO_3 with small amounts of Cl^- gives almost pure N_2O. The gas is also produced in the reduction of nitrites and nitrates under certain conditions and by decomposition of hyponitrites.

Nitrous oxide is relatively unreactive, being inert to the halogens, alkali metals and ozone at room temperature. At higher temperatures it decomposes to nitrogen and oxygen, reacts with alkali metals and many organic compounds, and will support combustion. It has a moderate solubility in cream, and, apart from its anesthetic role, its chief commercial use is as the propellant gas in "whipped" cream bombs.

[3] J. van R. Smit, *Chem. and Ind.*, **1964**, 2019; C. I. Colvin, P. W. Fearnow and A. G. Keenan, *Inorg. Chem.*, **4**, 173 (1965).

Its structure is well established; it has a linear NNO grouping and can be considered as a resonance hybrid,

$$:\overset{-}{\text{N}}\!\!=\!\!\overset{+}{\text{N}}\!\!=\!\!\overset{\cdot\cdot}{\text{O}}: \;\;\leftrightarrow\;\; :\text{N}\!\!\equiv\!\!\overset{+}{\text{N}}\!\!-\!\!:\overset{-}{\overset{\cdot\cdot}{\text{O}}}:$$

Nitric Oxide. Nitric oxide, NO, is formed in many reactions involving reduction of nitric acid and solutions of nitrates and nitrites. For example, with $8N$ nitric acid:

$$8HNO_3 + 3Cu = 3Cu(NO_3)_2 + 4H_2O + 2NO$$

Reasonably pure NO is obtained by the aqueous reactions

$$2NaNO_2 + 2NaI + 4H_2SO_4 = I_2 + 4NaHSO_4 + 2H_2O + 2NO$$
$$2NaNO_2 + 2FeSO_4 + 3H_2SO_4 = Fe_2(SO_4)_3 + 2NaHSO_4 + 2H_2O + 2NO$$

or, dry,

$$3KNO_2(l) + KNO_3(l) + Cr_2O_3(s) = 2K_2CrO_4(s, l) + 4NO$$

Commercially it is obtained by catalytic oxidation of ammonia as already noted. Direct combination of the elements occurs only at very high temperatures, and in order to isolate the small amounts so formed (a few volume per cent at 3000°) the equilibrium mixture must be rapidly chilled. Although this reaction has been much studied, it has not been developed into a practical commercial synthesis.

Nitric oxide is an "odd molecule" in that it has an unpaired electron. However, its behavior is atypical for an odd molecule since it is not colored (although in the liquid and solid phases it has a blue color) and the molecules do not show a *marked* tendency to associate via electron pairing. The high Trouton constant (27) indicates that *some* association occurs in the liquid, and the solid has been found to consist of loose dimers with the structure shown in Figure 12-5.

Fig. 12-5. Structure of nitric oxide dimer.

Not unrelated to the fact that, for an odd molecule, NO is relatively stable and unreactive is its unusual magnetic behavior. This stems from a combination of factors not found in any other case. The odd electron has an orbital momentum of one unit about the molecular axis. The spin momentum of one-half may couple either with or against this orbital momentum, yielding a ground state which is diamagnetic or an excited state which is paramagnetic. It happens that the energy difference between these states is only 352 cal/mole, whereas kT at room temperature is

~ 600 cal/mole. In fact, down to quite low temperatures kT is greater than or comparable with this separation so that the distribution of molecules between the diamagnetic and paramagnetic states is markedly influenced by temperature, and the molecule *appears* to have a temperature dependent magnetic moment. The diamagnetism of the solid at low temperatures does not, therefore, imply the existence of strong *intermolecular* spin coupling.

Among the important chemical reactions of nitric oxide are those of oxidation and reduction. It reacts instantly with oxygen, forming brown NO_2:

$$2NO + O_2 = 2NO_2$$

Thus, it must be handled out of contact with air. It reacts with F_2, Cl_2 and Br_2 but not I_2 to give the nitrosyl halides XNO (see page 355) and with CF_3I to give CF_3NO and I_2. It is oxidized to nitric acid by several strong oxidizing agents; the reaction with permanganate is quantitative and provides a method of analysis. It is reduced to N_2O by SO_2 and to NH_2OH by chromous ion in acid solution.

Nitric oxide is thermodynamically unstable at 25° and 1 atm and at high pressures it readily decomposes[4a] in the range 30–50°:

$$3NO = N_2O + NO_2$$

Although the electronic structure of NO may be considered in the valence bond theory it is advantageous to use molecular orbital theory. NO contains one more electron than does N_2, and according to simple MO theory (pages 87–92) this extra electron occupies an antibonding π MO (cf. O_2, page 91). The consequences of this are (*a*) that the theoretical bond order is 2.5 (0.5 less than the 3 for nitrogen), which agrees fairly well with the observed bond distance of 1.14 A (estimated for double and triple bonds 1.18 and 1.06 A, respectively), (*b*) that removal of this electron ought not to be too difficult, and (*c*) that the NO^+ ion produced should have a stronger N—O bond than does NO itself. In fact, the ionization potential of 9.5 ev is appreciably lower than for similar molecules (e.g., N_2, CO), and the stronger N—O bond is evidenced by an N—O stretching frequency[4b] of 2150–2400 cm^{-1} in NO^+ salts as compared to 1840 cm^{-1} in NO.

The theoretical prediction that the *nitrosonium ion*, NO^+, should be readily formed is abundantly confirmed experimentally, and the ion has an extensive and interesting chemistry which can be only briefly summarized here. When N_2O_3 or N_2O_4 is dissolved in concentrated sulfuric acid, the ion is formed:

$$N_2O_3 + 3H_2SO_4 = 2NO^+ + 3HSO_4^- + H_3O^+$$
$$N_2O_4 + 3H_2SO_4 = NO^+ + NO_2^+ + 3HSO_4^- + H_3O^+$$

[4a] T. P. Melia, *J. Inorg. Nucl. Chem.*, **27**, 95 (1965).
[4b] D. W. A. Sharp and J. Thorley, *J. Chem. Soc.*, **1963**, 3557.

The compound $NO^+HSO_4^-$, nitrosonium bisulfate, is an isolable compound which is an important intermediate in the lead chamber process for manufacture of sulfuric acid. That it has the salt-like constitution indicated has been shown by electrolysis, conductivity studies and cryoscopic measurements. The compounds $NO^+ClO_4^-$ and $NO^+BF_4^-$, both isostructural with the corresponding ammonium and H_3O^+ compounds, are known; many others such as $(NO)_2PtCl_6$, $NOFeCl_4$, $NOAsF_6$, $NOSbF_6$ and $NOSbCl_6$ may be made in the following general ways:

$$NO + MoF_6 = NO^+MoF_6^-$$
$$ClNO + SbCl_5 = NO^+SbCl_6^+$$

All such salts are readily hydrolyzed

$$NO^+ + H_2O = H^+ + HNO_2$$

and must be prepared and handled under anhydrous conditions.

The NO^+ ion is isoelectronic with CO, and, like CO, but to a somewhat lesser extent and sometimes under somewhat different conditions, will form bonds to metals. Thus, for example, analogous to nickel carbonyl, $Ni(CO)_4$, there is the isoelectronic $Co(CO)_3NO$. These transition metal nitrosyl complexes are discussed in more detail later (Sec. 27-6), but we may note here that the compound responsible for the brown ring in the test for nitrates is a nitrosyl complex of iron(I) with the formula $[Fe^I(H_2O)_5NO]^{2+}$.

There are a number of reactions of NO that can best be considered as indicating Lewis acid behavior, where electron density is accepted into anti-bonding π^* orbitals to give radical intermediates; the end products contain N—N bonds.[5] Thus in alkaline solution at $0°$, SO_3^{2-} reacts with NO to give a white crystalline solid $K_2SO_3N_2O_2$:

$$O\dot{N} + :SO_3^{2-} = [O\dot{N} \leftarrow SO_3]^{2-}$$
$$[O\dot{N}SO_3]^{2-} + \dot{N}O = [O{=}N\diagdown{\diagup}SO_3]^{2-}$$
$$N$$
$$|$$
$$O$$

Other species with N_2O_2 groups are obtained by interaction of amines with NO; alcohol in base also gives $[O_2N_2CH_2N_2O_2]^{2-}$.

Dinitrogen Trioxide.[6] This oxide, N_2O_3, exists pure only in the solid state at low temperatures; in the liquid and vapor it is largely dissociated:

$$N_2O_3(g) = NO(g) + NO_2(g)$$

It is best obtained by interaction of stoichiometric quantities of NO and

[5] R. Longhi, R. O. Ragsdale and R. S. Drago, *Inorg. Chem.*, **1**, 768 (1962).
[6] I. R. Beattie, *Prog. Inorg. Chem.*, **5**, 1 (1963). A review.

O_2 or NO and NO_2. It is an intensely blue liquid (f ca $-100°$) and a very pale blue solid. The oxide is formally the anhydride of nitrous acid, and dissolution of an equimolar mixture of NO and NO_2 in alkalies gives virtually pure nitrite. Nitrogen tracer studies have shown rapid exchange between NO and NO_2 consistent with the above equilibrium. The solid is believed to have two forms, an unstable one of structure ONONO and the other with a long N—N bond similar to that in N_2O_4 discussed below.

Nitrogen Dioxide and Dinitrogen Tetroxide. These two oxides, NO_2 and N_2O_4, exist in a strongly temperature-dependent equilibrium:

$$2NO_2 \quad = \quad N_2O_4$$
Brown   Colorless
Paramagnetic Diamagnetic

In the solid state, the oxide is wholly N_2O_4. In the liquid, partial dissociation occurs; it is pale yellow at the freezing point ($-11.2°$) and contains 0.01% NO_2 which increases to 0.1% in the deep red-brown liquid at the boiling point, 21.15°. In the vapor at 100°, the composition is 90% NO_2, 10% N_2O_4 and dissociation is complete above 140°. The monomer, NO_2 (Fig. 12-6), is an "odd molecule" and the electron appears to be located mainly on the N atom; its properties, red-brown color and ready dimerization to colorless and diamagnetic N_2O_4, are what would be expected for an odd molecule. NO_2 can also lose its odd electron fairly readily (ionization potential, 9.91 ev) to give $NO_2{}^+$, the *nitronium ion*, discussed later.

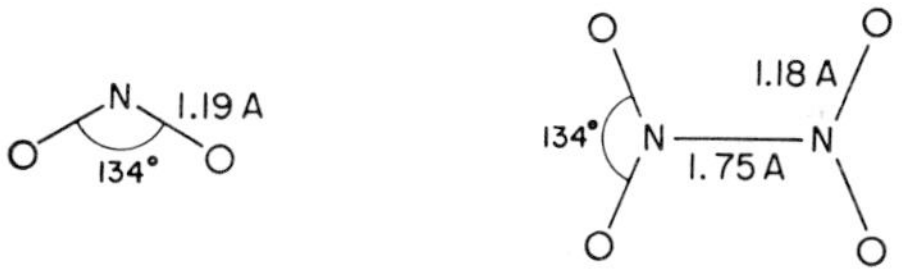

Fig. 12-6. The structure of nitrogen dioxide and of the most stable form of dinitrogen tetroxide. (P. Groth, *Nature*, **198**, 1081 (1963).)

The dimer of NO_2 is known to exist in three isomeric forms.[7] The most stable by far is the *planar* O_2N—NO_2 molecule (Fig. 12-6). At liquid nitrogen temperature a twisted or nonplanar form can be trapped in an inert matrix. At $\sim 4°K$ still a third species can be trapped which has an infrared spectrum suggesting that it is $ONONO_2$. While there is no doubt that the O_2NNO_2 molecule constitutes almost the entirety of the $(NO_2)_2$ molecules in the gas and liquid phases under the usual conditions of chemical reactions, it may well be that small amounts of the evanescent

[7] W. G. Fateley, H. A. Bent and B. Crawford, Jr., *J. Chem. Phys.*, **31**, 204 (1959); H. A. Bent, *Inorg. Chem.*, **2**, 747 (1963).

$ONONO_2$ play a key role in the reactions of $(NO_2)_2$. Thus, many reactions of the gas can be most reasonably explained assuming the presence or ready formation of $NO^{\cdot}$ and $NO_3^{\cdot}$ and these radicals would be plausible products of homolytic bond scission in ON—ONO_2. For liquid $(NO_2)_2$ most chemical evidence is consistent with the idea that NO^+ and NO_3^- are present or readily formed. These are plausible products of heterolytic dissociation of ON—ONO_2 in the moderately ionizing solvents $(NO_2)_2$ or $(NO_2)_2$ mixed with liquids such as ethyl acetate.[8] Thus, although its equilibrium concentration may be quite small, $ONONO_2$ may provide the pathway between NO_2, O_2NNO_2 and the actual reactive entities, $NO^{\cdot}$, NO^+, $NO_3^{\cdot}$ and NO_3^-. This hypothesis is *not* proved, but it is attractive and consistent with available evidence.

Several features of the planar O_2N—NO_2 molecule are unusual: (1) the greater stability of the planar form relative to a twisted one, since the former maximizes $O\cdots O$ repulsions; (2) the unusually long N—N bond, 1.75 A compared to 1.47 in H_2NNH_2. Many attempts[7] have been made to explain these features but none is entirely adequate.

The mixed oxides are obtained by heating metal nitrates, by oxidation of nitric oxide in air and by reduction of nitric acid and nitrates by metals and other reducing agents. The gases are highly toxic and attack metals rapidly. They react with water,

$$2NO_2 + H_2O = HNO_3 + HNO_2$$

the nitrous acid decomposing, particularly on warming

$$3HNO_2 = HNO_3 + 2NO + H_2O$$

The thermal decomposition

$$2NO_2 = 2NO + O_2$$

begins at 150° and is complete at 600°.

The oxides are fairly strong oxidizing agents in aqueous solution, comparable in strength to bromine:

$$N_2O_4 + 2H^+ + 2e = 2HNO_2 \qquad E^0 = +1.07 \text{ v}$$

The mixed oxides, "nitrous fumes," are used in organic chemistry as selective oxidizing agents; the first step is hydrogen abstraction

$$RH + NO_2 = R^{\cdot} + HONO$$

and the strength of the C—H bond generally determines the nature of the reaction.

Dinitrogen tetroxide has been extensively studied as a nonaqueous solvent. The electrical conductivity of the liquid is quite low. It forms

[8] See C. C. Addison, *Angew. Chem.*, **72**, 193 (1960).

molecular addition compounds with a great variety of nitrogen, oxygen and aromatic donor compounds. Systems involving liquid N_2O_4 mixed with an organic solvent are often very reactive; for example, they dissolve relatively noble metals to form nitrates, often solvated with N_2O_4. Thus copper reacts vigorously with N_2O_4 in ethyl acetate to give crystalline $Cu(NO_3)_2 \cdot N_2O_4$, from which anhydrous, volatile (at 150–200°) cupric nitrate is obtained (see Sec. 29-H-3). Some of the compounds obtained in this way may be formulated as nitrosonium salts, for example, $Zn(NO_3)_2 \cdot 2N_2O_4$ as $(NO^+)_2[Zn(NO_3)_4]^{2-}$, although conclusive proof of such structures is lacking.

In anhydrous acids, N_2O_4 dissociates ionically, as in H_2SO_4 above, and in anhydrous HNO_3 almost completely:

$$N_2O_4 = NO^+ + NO_3^-$$

The dissociation in H_2SO_4 is complete in dilute solution; at higher concentrations undissociated N_2O_4 is present, and at very high concentrations nitric acid is formed:

$$N_2O_4 + 3H_2SO_4 = NO^+HSO_4^- + HNO_3 + HSO_4^- + SO_3 + H_3O^+$$

The $NOHSO_4$ actually crystallizes out. The detailed mechanism and intermediates are undoubtedly complex, and the system is not yet completely unraveled.

Dinitrogen Pentoxide. This oxide, N_2O_5, which forms colorless crystals, is usually obtained by dehydration of nitric acid with P_2O_5; the oxide is not too stable (sometimes exploding) and is distilled in a current of ozonized oxygen.

$$2HNO_3 + P_2O_5 = 2HPO_3 + N_2O_5$$

It is, conversely, the anhydride of nitric acid:

$$N_2O_5 + H_2O = 2HNO_3$$

It is deliquescent, readily producing nitric acid by the above reaction. The gaseous compound appears[9] to have a structure of the type 12-VII

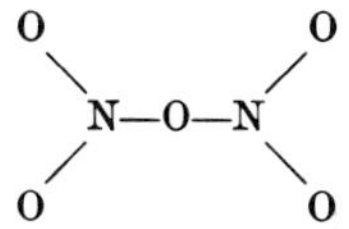

$$
\begin{array}{ccc}
O & & O \\
\diagdown & & \diagup \\
& N\!-\!O\!-\!N & \\
\diagup & & \diagdown \\
O & & O
\end{array}
$$

(12-VII)

with a bent N—O—N group, although this angle may be near 180°. Solid N_2O_5 in its stable form is nitronium nitrate, $NO_2^+NO_3^-$, but when the gas is condensed on a surface at $\sim 90°K$, the molecular form is obtained and persists for several hours. On warming to $\sim 200°K$, however, it

[9] I. C. Hisatsune, J. P. Devlin and Y. Wada, *Spectrochim. Acta.*, **18**, 1641 (1964).

rapidly rearranges to $NO_2^+NO_3^-$. In the latter it is found that the nitronium ion is linear and symmetrical with the N—O distance equal to 1.154 A (cf. CO_2 which is isoelectronic, linear and symmetrical, with C—O distance of 1.163 A). The nitrate ion, as in common nitrates, is symmetrical and planar.

As with N_2O_4, ionic dissociation occurs in anhydrous H_2SO_4, HNO_3 or H_3PO_4 to produce NO_2^+, for instance,

$$N_2O_5 + 3H_2SO_4 = 2NO_2^+ + 3HSO_4^- + H_3O^+$$

Many gas phase reactions of N_2O_5 depend on dissociation to NO_2 and NO_3, with the latter then reacting further as an oxidizing agent. These reactions are among the better understood complex inorganic reactions.[10] In the N_2O_5 catalyzed decomposition of ozone, the steady state concentration of NO_3 can be high enough to allow its absorption spectrum to be recorded.

12-7. Oxo Acids of Nitrogen

Hyponitrous Acid. Salts of hyponitrous acid, $H_2N_2O_2$, are formed by treating NH_2OH with amyl nitrite in ethanol containing $NaOC_2H_5$. Reduction of nitrites with sodium amalgam also gives hyponitrites. The silver salt is insoluble in water, and the ion is commonly isolated as the silver salt. The sodium salt and also the free acid can be obtained as white crystals, the latter from the silver salt on treatment with HCl in ether. The acid is weak, $pK = 7$, and is moderately stable in solution. Hyponitrites of the alkalies react with CO_2 to give N_2O.

Infrared spectra of the silver, sodium and mercury hyponitrites have shown that the anion has the *trans* configuration (12-VIII).

It has lately been shown that a "compound" made by the action of NO on Na in liquid NH_3, and long formulated NaNO is unlikely to contain NO^- ions nor does it contain the hyponitrite ion. It has been proposed that it may contain a *cis* hyponitrite ion, but there is no positive evidence for this.[11]

(12-VIII)   (12-IX)

[10] G. Schott and N. Davidson, *J. Amer. Chem. Soc.*, **80**, 1841 (1958).
[11] J. Goubeau and K. Laitenberger, *Z. anorg. Chem.*, **320**, 78 (1963).

Hyponitrites undergo various oxidation–reduction reactions in acid and alkaline solutions, depending on conditions;[12] they usually behave as reducing agents, however.

There is a compound called *nitramide*, which is also a weak acid ($K_{25°} = 2.6 \times 10^{-7}$) and is an isomer of hyponitrous acid. Its structure has been shown to be 12-IX.

Nitrous Acid. Solutions of nitrous acid, HNO_2, are easily made by acidifying solutions of nitrites. The aqueous solution can be obtained free of salts by the reaction

$$Ba(NO_2)_2 + H_2SO_4 = 2HNO_2 + BaSO_4(S)$$

Nitrous acid is a weak acid ($K_{25°} = 6.0 \times 10^{-6}$). The acid is unknown in the liquid state but it can be obtained in the vapor phase; the *trans* form has been shown to be more stable than the *cis* form by about 0.5 kcal/mole. In the gas phase the following equilibrium is rapidly established:

$$NO + NO_2 + H_2O = 2HNO_2 \qquad K_{20°} = 1.56 \text{ atm}^{-1}$$

Aqueous solutions of nitrous acid are unstable and decompose rapidly when heated, according to the equation:

$$3HNO_2 = HNO_3 + H_2O + 2NO$$

This reaction is reversible.

Nitrites of the alkali metals are best prepared by heating the nitrates with a reducing agent such as carbon, lead, iron, etc.

Nitrous acid is used in the well-known preparation of diazonium compounds in organic chemistry. Numerous organic derivatives of the NO_2 group are known. They are of two types: nitrites, R—ONO, and nitro compounds, R—NO_2. Similar tautomerism occurs in some inorganic complexes, in which either oxygen or nitrogen is the actual donor atom when NO_2^- is a ligand.

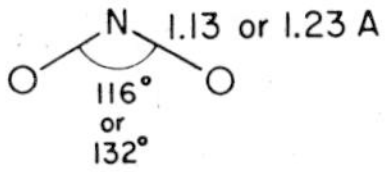

Fig. 12-7. Dimensions of NO_2^- reported in $AgNO_2$ and $NaNO_2$.

The NO_2^- ion in ionic nitrites has a bent structure (Fig. 12-7). Two surprisingly different dimensions have been reported by different workers and the discrepancy has not yet been resolved; in view of the large standard deviations for the $AgNO_2$ results the difference may not be significant.

[12] See, e.g., M. N. Hughes and G. Stedman, *J. Chem. Soc.*, **1963**, 1239, 4230.

The bent structure is readily explicable in terms of the resonance 12-X or, in MO theory, by assuming N forms three sp^2 hybrid orbitals, one

(12-Xa)   (12-Xb)

housing an unshared pair and the other two being used in σ bonding to the oxygens. The p_z orbitals of N and O are then used for π bond formation.

Nitric Acid. Nitric acid, HNO_3, and its salts are the most important oxo compounds of nitrogen. The acid is now almost invariably made by converting atmospheric nitrogen to ammonia, oxidizing ammonia catalytically to NO, and absorbing the NO in presence of oxygen in water.

Anhydrous nitric acid is a colorless liquid boiling at 84.1° and freezing to a crystalline solid at $-41.59°$. The pure acid auto-ionizes:

$$2HNO_3 = NO_2^+ + NO_3^- + H_2O$$

the molar concentration of each species being 0.51 at $-10°$. In dilute aqueous solution nitric acid is strong, being about 93% dissociated in $0.1M$ solution. The normal "concentrated" aqueous acid ($\sim 70\%$ by weight) is colorless, but often becomes yellow as a result of photochemical decomposition to give NO_2:

$$2HNO_3 \xrightarrow{hv} 2NO_2 + H_2O + \tfrac{1}{2}O_2$$

So-called "fuming" nitric acid contains dissolved NO_2 (in excess of the amount which can be hydrated to $HNO_3 + NO$). Concentrated nitric acid is a powerful oxidizing agent; of the metals, only Au, Pt, Rh and Ir are unattacked, although a few other metals such as Al, Fe and Cr are rendered "passive." The exact nature of this passivity is not known, but the formation of an impervious oxide film probably plays some part. Magnesium alone can liberate H_2 and only initially; the attack on metals generally involves reduction of nitrogen. Gold and the platinum metals are attacked by aqua regia (~ 3 parts conc. HCl + 1 part conc. HNO_3) which contains free chlorine and ClNO. The complexing action of the chloride ions is also important in making aqua regia more effective than nitric acid. Nonmetals are usually oxidized by concentrated nitric acid to oxides or oxo acids. The oxidizing power of nitric acid is, however, very dependent on concentration, and below about $2M$ the acid has virtually no oxidizing power.

The gaseous nitric acid molecule has a planar structure, although hindered rotation of OH relative to NO_2 probably occurs (Fig. 12-8).

Nitrates of practically all metallic elements are known. They are frequently hydrated and are mostly soluble in water. Many metal nitrates can be obtained anhydrous and a number of these will sublime without decomposition. Even alkali metal nitrates will sublime in vacuum at 350–500° but decomposition occurs at higher temperatures to nitrites or at very high temperatures to oxides or peroxides.[13] NH_4NO_3 gives N_2O

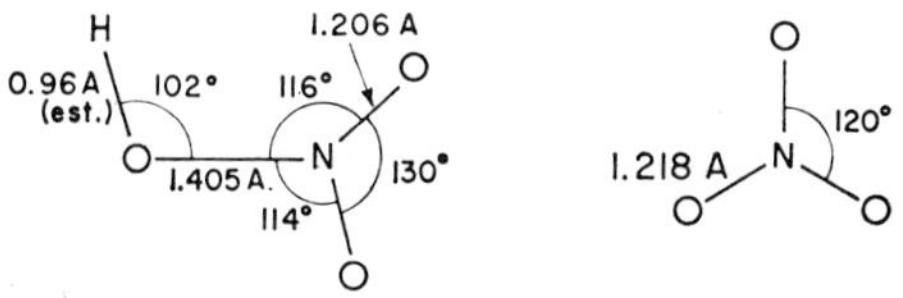

Fig. 12-8.   Structure of nitric acid in vapor and the nitrate ion

and H_2O. In neutral solution, nitrates can be reduced only with difficulty. The mechanism of the reduction is still obscure. Al or Zn in alkaline solution produce NH_3.

The nitrate ion is planar and symmetrical (Fig. 12-8). This structure may be explained in valence bond theory as a resonance hybrid (12-IV, page 326) or in molecular orbital theory by assuming that nitrogen forms three σ bonds using sp^2 hybrid orbitals and that the p_z orbitals of nitrogen and the three oxygen atoms combine to form a bonding π MO, housing two electrons.

Although older literature suggests that the nitrate ion is a poor ligand, recent studies show that in many instances it forms quite stable coordination compounds even in aqueous solutions. For example, the compounds $[(C_6H_5)_3PO]_2M(NO_3)_2$, M = Co, Ni, melt without decomposition at $\sim250°$ and are stable to at least 270°, while the known anhydrous transition metal nitrates volatilize without decomposition at temperatures of 100–200°. The nitrate ion may function as a monodentate ligand (e.g., in $[Co(NH_3)_5(NO_3)]^{2+}$) or, perhaps more commonly, as a bidentate ligand, for example in $Co(Me_3PO)_2(NO_3)_2$, $[Co(NO_3)_4]^{2-}$ and in $[Ce(NO_3)_6]^{3-}$. In the last two cases, the unusually high coordination numbers 8 and 12 are found.

Nitric acid has the ability to nitrate many organic compounds, especially in the presence of concentrated sulfuric acid. This property results from the dissociation of the acid to produce the nitronium ion, NO_2^+.

The Nitronium Ion. This ion, NO_2^+, is directly involved not only in the dissociation of nitric acid itself but in nitration reactions and in solutions of nitrogen oxides in nitric and other strong acids. Various early physical measurements by Hantzsch gave evidence for dissociation of HNO_3 in sulfuric acid. Thus "HNO_3" in H_2SO_4 shows no vapor pressure,

---

[13] C. J. Hardy and B. O. Field, *J. Chem. Soc.*, **1963**, 5130.

and cryoscopic studies gave a van't Hoff i factor of 3. Hantzsch proposed therefore:

$$HNO_3 + 2H_2SO_4 = H_3NO_3{}^{2+} + 2HSO_4{}^-$$

More recent work has shown that Hantzsch's suggestion is not correct in detail, but that ionic dissociation does occur. This work was undertaken by Hughes and Ingold and others to find an explanation for the enormous increases in the rate of nitration of aromatic compounds by HNO_3–H_2SO_4 mixtures as the concentration of the sulfuric acid is increased and to account for variations in rate in other media. For example, the rate of nitration of benzene increases by 10^3 on going from 80% H_2SO_4 to 90% H_2SO_4. Detailed kinetic data, in sulfuric acid, nitromethane and glacial acetic acid solutions, were explicable only by the postulate that the $NO_2{}^+$ ion was the attacking species. The origin of the $NO_2{}^+$ ion can be explained, for example, by ionizations of the following types:

$$2HNO_3 = NO_2{}^+ + NO_3{}^- + H_2O$$
$$HNO_3 + H_2SO_4 = NO_2{}^+ + HSO_4{}^- + H_2O$$

The importance of the first type is reflected in the fact that addition of ionized nitrate salts to the reaction mixture will retard the reaction. The actual nitration process can then be formulated as equation 12-5. The

dissociation of nitric acid in various media has been confirmed by cryoscopic studies, and nitrogen oxides have also been found to dissociate to produce nitronium ions as noted above. Spectroscopic studies have confirmed the presence of the various ions in such solutions. For example, the $NO_2{}^+$ ion can be identified by a Raman line at about 1400 cm^{-1}.

Final confirmation of the existence of nitronium ions has been obtained by isolation of nitronium salts which have a symmetrical N—O stretching frequency at $\sim$1400 cm^{-1} and a bond length of 1.10 A. Thus, from HNO_3 and $HClO_4$ in nitromethane a mixture of the perchlorates $NO_2{}^+ClO_4{}^-$ and $H_3O^+ClO_4{}^-$ can be obtained by crystallization. Other reactions leading to crystalline nitronium salts are:

$$N_2O_5 + HClO_4 = [NO_2{}^+ClO_4{}^-] + HNO_3 \qquad (12\text{-}6)$$
$$N_2O_5 + FSO_3H = [NO_2{}^+FSO_3{}^-] + HNO_3 \qquad (12\text{-}7)$$
$$HNO_3 + 2SO_3 = [NO_2{}^+HS_2O_7{}^-] \qquad (12\text{-}8)$$

Reactions 12-6 and 12-7 are really just metatheses, since N_2O_5 in the solid and in anhydrous acid solution is $NO_2{}^+NO_3{}^-$. Reaction 12-8 is that between an acid anhydride, SO_3, and a base(!), $NO_2{}^+OH^-$ (cf. $2NaOH + SO_3 = Na^+{}_2SO_4{}^{2-} + H_2O$).

Nitronium salts are crystalline and thermodynamically stable, but very reactive chemically. They are rapidly hydrolyzed by moisture; in addition $NO_2^+ClO_4^-$, for example, reacts violently with organic matter, but can actually be used to carry out nitrations in nitrobenzene solution.

12-8. Halogen Compounds of Nitrogen

Binary Halides. In addition to NF_3, NF_2Cl, $NFCl_2$ and NCl_3, we have N_2F_2, N_2F_4 and the halogen azides XN_3 (X = F, Cl, Br and I). With the exception of NF_3 the halides are reactive, potentially hazardous substances, some of them like $NFCl_2$ explosive, others not. Only the fluorides are important.[14]

Nitrogen trifluoride, together with small amounts of dinitrogen difluoride, is obtained by electrolysis of ammonium fluoride in anhydrous HF. Dinitrogen tetrafluoride, together with N_2F_2, is obtained by homogeneous reaction of NF_3 with mercury in an electric discharge or by heterogeneous reduction of NF_3 by hot metals. With copper reactor packing as catalyst, ammonia and fluorine diluted with nitrogen have been found to react smoothly and exothermically. Excess fluorine gives only NF_3, but with excess ammonia N_2F_2 and N_2F_4 are also formed; difluoroamine, NHF_2, can be obtained under certain conditions.

Nitrogen trifluoride (b $-129°$) is a very stable gas which is reactive only above 250–300° normally, but which reacts readily with $AlCl_3$ at 70°:

$$2NF_3 + 2AlCl_3 = N_2 + 3Cl_2 + 2AlF_3$$

It is not affected by water and most other reagents at room temperature and does not decompose on heating in the absence of reducing metals. On heating it in presence of fluorine acceptors such as copper, the metal is fluorinated and N_2F_4 is obtained. The NF_3 molecule has a pyramidal structure but a very low dipole moment (see page 110), and it appears to be totally devoid of donor properties.

Difluorodiazine, N_2F_2, is a gas which exists in *cis* and *trans* forms separable by gas chromatography. Both are reactive substances, but the *trans* is least reactive despite the fact that it is thermodynamically the least stable. The structures have been confirmed by nmr and microwave studies.[15a,b] Difluorodiazine is best made from difluoroamine, which is itself readily obtained from urea (see below), by the reaction[16a]

$$2HNF_2 + 2KF = 2KHF_2 + N_2F_2$$

[14] (a) C. J. Hoffman and R. G. Neville, *Chem. Rev.*, **62**, 1 (1962); (b) C. B. Colburn, *Adv. Fluorine Chem.*, **3**, 92 (1963). Extensive reviews of N—F compounds, especially of (a) organic, (b) inorganic derivatives. See also A. V. Pankratov, *Russ. Chem. Rev.*, **1963**, 157.

[15a] J. H. Noggle, J. D. Baldeschwieler and C. B. Colburn, *J. Chem. Phys.*, **37**, 182 (1962).

[15b] R. L. Kuczkowski and E. B. Wilson, Jr., *J. Chem. Phys.*, **39**, 1030 (1963).

[16a] E. A. Lawton, D. Pilipovitch and R. D. Wilson, *Inorg. Chem.*, **4**, 118 (1965).

The pure *trans* form can be obtained in about 45% yield under related conditions by the reaction[16b]

$$2N_2F_4 + 2AlCl_3 = N_2F_2 + 3Cl_2 + 2AlF_3 + N_2$$

Tetrafluorohydrazine, N_2F_4, also a gas (b $-73°$), is best prepared by the reaction of NF_3 with copper mentioned above. Microwave study has shown that its structure is similar to that of hydrazine. It is interesting that N_2F_4 dissociates readily in the gas and liquid phases according to the equation:

$$N_2F_4 = 2NF_2 \quad \Delta H_{298°K} = 20.3 \pm 1 \text{ kcal/mole}$$

which accounts for its high reactivity. The difluoroamino radical, NF_2, appears surprisingly stable. Its esr and electronic spectra indicate that it is bent (cf. OF_2, O_3^-, SO_2^-, ClO_2) with the odd electron in a relatively pure π MO. It must be added to the list of relatively stable "odd molecules."

Since N_2F_4 dissociates so readily, it can be expected to show reactions typical of free radicals.[14,17] Thus it abstracts hydrogen from thiols

$$2NF_2 + 2RSH = 2HNF_2 + RSSR$$

and undergoes other reactions such as:

$$N_2F_4 + Cl_2 \xrightarrow{h\nu} 2NF_2Cl \quad K_{25°} = 1 \times 10^{-3}$$
$$RI + NF_2 \xrightarrow{UV} RNF_2 + \tfrac{1}{2}I_2$$
$$RCHO + N_2F_4 \longrightarrow RCONF_2 + NHF_2$$
$$R_FSF_5 + N_2F_4 \longrightarrow R_FNF_2$$

It also reacts at $300°$ with NO and rapid chilling in liquid nitrogen gives the purple nitrosodifluoroamine[17] $ONNF_2$. This is unstable.

Nitrogen trichloride is formed in the chlorination of slightly acid ammonium chloride solutions as a pale yellow oil, b $\sim 71°$. It is an exceedingly explosive and treacherous compound above its boiling point, in light, or in the presence of organic compounds. Unlike NF_3 ($\Delta H_f^0 = -26$ kcal/mole), the chloride is endothermic ($\Delta H_f = 55.4$ kcal/mole) and is also different in being readily hydrolyzed to NH_3 and $HOCl$.

The interaction of Br_2 and ammonia in solutions more acid than pH 6 gives NBr_3 which can be extracted into $CHCl_3$; it decomposes quite rapidly; ultraviolet spectra of more alkaline solutions suggest the presence also of NH_2Br and $NHBr_2$.[18]

[16b] G. L. Hurst and S. I. Khayat, *J. Amer. Chem. Soc.*, **87**, 1620 (1965).

[17] C. B. Colburn, *et al.*, *Inorg. Chem.*, **2**, 24, 131 (1963); F. A. Johnson and J. P. Freeman in *Inorganic Free Radicals*, Advances in Chemistry Series No. 36, A.C.S. Washington, pp. 123, 128.

[18] H. Galal-Gorchev and J. C. Morris, *Inorg. Chem.*, **4**, 899 (1965).

The interaction of I_2 with concentrated ammonia at room temperature gives black explosive crystals of $NI_3 \cdot NH_3$. With liquid ammonia more complex reactions occur.[19]

Haloamines. These are compounds of the type H_2NX and HNX_2, where H may be replaced by an alkyl radical also. Only H_2NCl, chloramine, HNF_2 and H_2NF have been isolated; $HNCl_2$, H_2NBr and $HNBr_2$ probably exist but are quite unstable. It is believed that, on chlorination of aqueous ammonia, NH_2Cl forms at pH > 8.5, $NHCl_2$ at pH 4.5–5.0 and NCl_3 at pH < 4.4. Difluoroamine, a colorless, explosive liquid (b 23.6°) can be obtained as above or by H_2SO_4 acidification of fluorinated aqueous solutions of urea; the first product, $CO(NH_2)NF_2$, gives HNF_2 on hydrolysis.[16] It can be converted to chlorodifluoroamine, $ClNF_2$, by action of Cl_2 and KF.[20]

Oxo Halides.[21] There are two series of these which might be formally considered as salts of the nitronium and nitrosonium ions, but since they are, in fact, quite covalent compounds, they were not discussed under the chemistry of these ions. The known compounds and some of their properties are listed in Table 12-3.

TABLE 12-3

Physical Properties of Nitrosyl and Nitryl Halides

	FNO[a]	ClNO	BrNO	FNO₂[a]	ClNO₂[a]
Color of gas	Colorless	Orange-yellow	Red	Colorless	Colorless
Melting point, °C	-133	-62	-56	-166	-145
Boiling point, °C	-60	-6	~ 0	-72	-15
Structure	Bent	Bent	Bent	Planar[b]	Planar[b]
X—N distance, A	1.52	1.95 ± 0.01	2.14 ± 0.02	1.35	1.79
N—O distance, A	1.13	1.14 ± 0.02	1.15 ± 0.04	1.23	1.25
X—N—O angle, deg	110	116 ± 2	114		
O—N—O angle, deg				125 (assumed)	125 (assumed)

[a] Uncertainties in structure parameters not known.
[b] Molecular symmetry, C_{2v}.

The nitrosyl halides can all be obtained by direct union of the halogens with nitric oxide and also in other ways. They are increasingly unstable in the series FNO, ClNO, BrNO. ClNO is always slightly impure, decomposing (to Cl_2 and NO) to the extent of about 0.5% at room temperature, and BrNO is decomposed to $\sim 7\%$ at room temperature and 1 atm.

All three are reactive and are powerful oxidizing agents, able to attack many metals. All decompose on treatment with water producing HNO_3, HNO_2, NO and HX. Their structures indicate that they are covalent

[19] J. Jander and A. Engelhard, *Proc. I.C.C.C.* 8., **1964**, 330.
[20] W. C. Firth, *Inorg. Chem.*, **4**, 254 (1965).
[21] J. W. George, *Prog. Inorg. Chem.*, **2**, 33 (1960); C. J. Hoffman and R. G. Neville, *Chem. Rev.*, **62**, 1 (1962)—fluorides only.

molecules. From the MO viewpoint, nitrogen may be considered to have $sp_x p_y$ hybridization, forming σ bonds to X and O and having an unshared pair, and then a π bond, using its p_z orbital, to oxygen.

The only known nitryl halides are FNO_2 and $ClNO_2$. The former is conveniently prepared by the reaction:

$$N_2O_4 + 2CoF_3(s) \xrightarrow{300°} 2FNO_2 + 2CoF_2(s)$$

$ClNO_2$ is not obtainable by direct reaction of NO_2 and Cl_2, but is easily made in excellent yield by the reaction:

$$ClSO_3H + HNO_3(\text{anhydrous}) \xrightarrow{0°} ClNO_2 + H_2SO_4$$

Both compounds are quite reactive; both are decomposed by water:

$$XNO_2 + H_2O = HNO_3 + HX$$

Their structures are not fully known, but it has been established with certainty that they are planar, as valence considerations would suggest, and they can be considered as being derived from NO_3^- by replacement of O^- by F or Cl.

References

Addison, C. C., and J. Lewis, *Quart. Rev.*, **9**, 115 (1955). Chemistry of nitric oxide with particular reference to its metal complexes.

Addison, C. C., and N. Logan, *Adv. Inorg. Nucl. Chem.*, **6**, 72 (1964). Comprehensive review on anhydrous metal nitrates.

Addison, C. C., in *Free Radicals in Inorganic Chemistry*, Advances in Chemistry Series No. 36, p. 14. NO_2, reactions of N_2O_4 and metal nitrates. A review with references.

Audrieth, L. F., and J. Kleinberg, *Non-Aqueous Solvents: Application as Media for Chemical Reactions*, Wiley, New York, 1953. Use of liquid ammonia as a solvent system.

Audrieth, L. F., and B. J. A. Ogg, *The Chemistry of Hydrazine*, Wiley, New York, 1951.

Beckman, L. J., W. A. Fessler and M. Kise, *Chem. Rev.*, **51**, 319 (1951). Chemistry of nitrosyl chloride.

Brotherton, T. K., and J. W. Lynn, *Chem. Rev.*, **59**, 841 (1959). Synthesis and chemistry of cyanogen.

Clark, F., *Hydrazine*, Mathieson Chemical Company, 1953.

Closson, W. D., and H. B. Gray, *J. Amer. Chem. Soc.*, **85**, 290 (1963). Electronic structure of azide.

Evans, B. L., A. D. Yoffee and P. Gray, *Chem. Rev.*, **59**, 515 (1959). Gray, P., *Quart. Rev.*, **17**, 441 (1963). Chemistry of azides.

Evans, R. F., *Rev. Pure. Appl. Chem.*, **12**, 146 (1962). Organic chemistry of hydrazine.

Field, B. O., and C. J. Hardy, *Quart. Rev.*, **18**, 361 (1964). Inorganic nitrates and nitrato compounds.

Franklin, E. C., *The Nitrogen System of Compounds* (*American Chemical Society Monograph*, No. 68), Reinhold, New York, 1935. A classic volume containing much information on ammonia and related compounds.

Furst, A., R. C. Berlow and S. Hooton, *Chem. Rev.*, **65**, 51 (1965). The catalytic reduction of organic compounds by hydrazine; diimine intermediates.

Gray, P., *Royal Institute of Chemistry Monograph*, No. 4, London, 1958. Chemistry of N_2O_4.

Hünig, S., H. R. Muller and W. Thier, *Angew. Chem. (Internat.)*, **4**, 271 (1965). Chemistry of diimine, its sources and reactions.

Jennings, K. R., and J. W. Linnett, *Quart. Rev.*, **12**, 116 (1957). Spectroscopic and chemical properties of active nitrogen.

Jolly, W. L., *The Inorganic Chemistry of Nitrogen*, Benjamin, New York, 1964. A short text.

Jolly, W. L., and C. J. Hallada, in *Non-Aqueous Solvent Systems*, Academic Press, New York, 1965. Review on liquid ammonia.

Lewis, J., *Sci. Progr.*, **47**, 206 (1959). Chemistry of nitric oxide with particular reference to its metal complexes.

McLaren, A. C., *Rev. Pure Appl. Chem.*, **12**, 54 (1962). Thermal transformations in alkali metal nitrates.

Mannella, G. G., *Chem. Rev.*, **63**, 1 (1963). Active nitrogen. A comprehensive review especially of spectroscopic properties.

Mellor's Comprehensive Treatise on Inorganic and Theoretical Chemistry, Vol. VIII, Supplement 1, Nitrogen, Part 1, Longmans Green, London, 1964.

Miller, C. E., *J. Chem. Educ.*, **42**, 254 (1965). Hydrogenation with diimine.

Orville-Thomas, W. J., *Chem. Rev.*, **57**, 1179 (1957). Valence bonding in nitrogen compounds.

Reed, R. A., *Royal Institute of Chemistry Lectures*, No. 5, London, 1957. Hydrazine and its derivatives.

Smith, H., *Organic Reactions in Liquid Ammonia*, Wiley, New York, 1963.

Stern, S. A., J. T. Mullhaupt and W. B. Kay, *Chem. Rev.*, **60**, 185 (1960). An exhaustive review on the physical properties of nitric acid.

Symposium on Inorganic Chemistry of Nitrogen, *Chem. Soc. (London)*, *Spec. Publ.*, No. 10 (1957). Nitronium compounds, chemistry of N_2O_4, synthesis of H_2SO_4 by NO catalysis, halogen derivatives of ammonia.

Turney, T. A., and G. A. Wright, *Chem. Rev.*, **59**, 497 (1959). Nitrous acid and nitrosation.

Yost, D. M., and H. Russell, *Systematic Inorganic Chemistry (of the 5th and 6th Group Elements)*, Prentice-Hall, New York, 1946. Selected topics in nitrogen chemistry, brilliantly expounded.

13

Oxygen

13-1. Types of Oxides

The oxygen atom has the electronic structure $1s^2 2s^2 2p^4$. Oxygen forms compounds with all of the elements except He, Ne and possibly Ar, and it combines directly with all of the other elements except the halogens, a few noble metals and the noble gases, either at ordinary or at elevated temperatures. The earth's crust contains about 50% by weight of oxygen. Most inorganic chemistry is concerned with its compounds, if only in the sense that so much chemistry involves the most important oxygen compound—water.

As a first row element, oxygen follows the octet rule, and the closed shell configuration can be achieved in ways which are similar to those for nitrogen, namely, by (a) electron gain to form O^{2-}, (b) formation of two single covalent bonds (e.g., R—O—R) or a double bond (e.g., O=C=O), (c) gain of one electron and formation of one single bond (e.g., in OH^-) and (d) formation of three or four covalent bonds (e.g., R_2OH^+, etc.).

There are a variety of binary oxygen compounds of disparate natures. The range of physical properties is attributable to the range of bond types from essentially ionic to essentially covalent. Some representative oxides and their properties are listed in Table 13-1.

The formation of the oxide ion, O^{2-}, from molecular oxygen requires the expenditure of a considerable energy, 227 kcal/mole;

$$\tfrac{1}{2}O_2(g) = O(g) \qquad \Delta H = 59.2 \text{ kcal/mole}$$
$$O(g) + 2e = O^{2-}(g) \qquad \Delta H = 157 \text{ kcal/mole}$$

Moreover, in the formation of an ionic oxide, energy must be expended in vaporizing and ionizing the metal atoms. Nevertheless, many essentially ionic oxides exist and are very stable because the energies of lattices con-

TABLE 13-1

Some Representative Oxides

Compound	Nature	Properties
	Crystalline Oxides	
CaO	White solid; m 2580°	Ionic lattice; basic
SiO_2	Colorless crystals; m 1710° [a]	Infinite three-dimensional lattice; acidic
BeO	White solid; m 2570°	Semi-ionic; amphoteric
$Th_{0.7}Y_{0.3}O_{1.85}$	White crystalline solid	Fluorite lattice with some O^{2-} missing. Typical mixed metal oxide
$FeO_{0.95}$	Black solid	NaCl lattice with some Fe^{3+} ions and some cation vacancies
	Molecular Oxides	
CO	Colorless gas	Inert; no acid or basic properties
SO_2	Colorless gas	Acid anhydride
OsO_4	Pale yellow, volatile solid; m 41°	Readily reduced to Os
Cl_2O_7	Explosive, colorless oil	Anhydride of $HClO_4$

[a] β-Crystobalite; see page 468.

taining the relatively small (1.40 A), doubly charged oxide ion are quite high. In fact, the lattice energies are often sufficiently high to allow the ionization of metal atoms to unusually high oxidation states. Many metals form oxides in oxidation states not encountered in their other compounds, except perhaps in fluorides or some complexes. Examples of such higher oxides are MnO_2, AgO and PrO_2. Many of these higher ionic oxides are nonstoichiometric.

In some cases the lattice energy is still insufficient to permit complete ionization, and oxides having substantial covalent character, such as BeO or B_2O_3, are formed. Finally, at the other extreme there are numerous oxides, such as CO_2, the nitrogen and phosphorus oxides, SO_2, SO_3, etc., which are essentially covalent molecular compounds. Such compounds are gases or volatile solids or liquids. Even in "covalent" oxides, unusually high *formal* oxidation states are often found, as in OsO_4, CrO_3, SO_3, etc.

In terms of chemical behavior, it is convenient to classify oxides according to their acid or base character in the aqueous system.

Basic Oxides. Although X-ray studies show the existence of discrete oxide ions, O^{2-} (and also peroxide, O_2^{2-}, and superoxide, O_2^-, ions, to be discussed presently), these ions cannot exist in any appreciable concentrations in aqueous solution owing to the hydrolytic reaction:

$$O^{2-}(s) + H_2O = 2OH^-(aq) \qquad K > 10^{22}$$

We have also for the per- and superoxide ions:

$$O_2^{2-} + H_2O = HO_2^- + OH^-$$
$$2O_2^- + H_2O = O_2 + HO_2^- + OH^-$$

Thus only those ionic oxides which are insoluble in water are inert to water. Ionic oxides function, therefore, as *basic anhydrides*. When insoluble in water, they usually dissolve in dilute acids, for example,

$$MgO(s) + 2H^+(aq) = Mg^{2+}(aq) + H_2O$$

although in some cases, MgO being one, high temperature ignition produces a very inert material, quite resistant to acid attack.

Acidic Oxides. The covalent oxides of the nonmetals are usually acidic, dissolving in water to produce solutions of acids. They are termed *acid anhydrides*. Insoluble oxides of some less electropositive metals of this class will generally dissolve in bases. Thus,

$$N_2O_5(s) + H_2O = 2H^+(aq) + 2NO_3^-(aq)$$
$$Sb_2O_5(s) + 2OH^- + 5H_2O = 2Sb(OH)_6^-$$

Basic and acidic oxides will often combine directly to produce salts, such as

$$Na_2O + SiO_2 \xrightarrow{\text{fusion}} Na_2SiO_3$$

Amphoteric Oxides. These oxides behave acidically toward strong bases and as bases toward strong acids:

$$ZnO + 2H^+(aq) = Zn^{2+} + H_2O$$
$$ZnO + 2OH^- + H_2O = Zn(OH)_4^{2-}$$

Other Oxides. There are various other oxides, some of which are relatively inert, dissolving in neither acids nor bases, for instance, N_2O, CO and MnO_2; when MnO_2 (or PbO_2) does react with acids, e.g., concentrated HCl, it is a redox, not an acid–base, reaction.

There are also many oxides which are nonstoichiometric. These commonly consist of arrays of close-packed oxide ions with some of the interstices filled by metal ions. However, if there is variability in the oxidation state of the metal, nonstoichiometric materials result. Thus ferrous oxide probably never has the composition FeO, but is usually something in the range $FeO_{0.90}$–$FeO_{0.95}$, depending on the manner of preparation. There is an extensive chemistry of mixed metal oxides (see also page 51).

It may also be noted that when a given element forms several oxides, the oxide with the element in the highest formal oxidation state (usually meaning more covalent) is more acidic (cf. the rules for dependence of acid dissociation constants on formal charge in Chapter 6). Thus, for chromium we have: CrO, basic; Cr_2O_3, amphoteric; and CrO_3, fully acidic.

The Hydroxide Ion. Discrete hydroxide ions, OH^-, exist only in the hydroxides of the more electropositive elements such as the alkali metals and alkaline earths. For such an ionic material, dissolution in water results in formation of aquated metal ions and aquated hydroxide ions:

$$M^+OH^-(s) + nH_2O = M^+(aq) + OH^-(aq)$$

and the substance is a strong base. In the limit of an extremely covalent M—O bond, dissociation will occur to varying degrees as follows:

$$MOH + nH_2O = MO^-(aq) + H_3O^+(aq)$$

and the substance must be considered an acid. Amphoteric hydroxides are those in which there is the possibility of either kind of dissociation, the one being favored by the presence of a strong acid

$$M—O—H + H^+ = M^+ + H_2O$$

the other by strong base

$$M—O—H + OH^- = MO^- + H_2O$$

because the formation of water is so highly favored:

$$H^+ + OH^- = H_2O \qquad K_{25°} = 10^{14}$$

Similarly, hydrolytic reactions of many metal ions can be written

$$M^{n+} + H_2O = (MOH)^{(n-1)+} + H^+$$

However, in view of the fact that such ions are coordinated by water molecules, a more realistic equation is

$$M(H_2O)_x{}^{n+} = [M(H_2O)_{x-1}(OH)]^{(n-1)+} + H^+$$

Thus we may consider that the more covalent the M—O bond tends to be, the more acidic are the hydrogen atoms in the aquated ion, but at present there are no extensive correlations of the acidities of aquo ions with properties of the metal (see also page 163).

The hydroxide ion has the ability to form bridges between metal ions. Thus there are various compounds of the transition and other metals containing OH bridges, for example, $[(NH_3)_3Co(OH)_3Co(NH_3)_3]Cl_3$. This bridging is accomplished in the same way as is done by Cl or F, that is, as in 13-I.

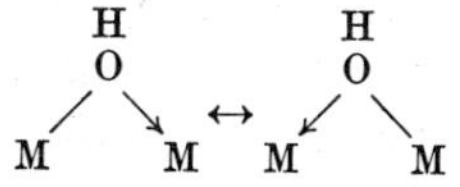

(13-Ia)   (13-Ib)

The formation of hydroxo bridges occurs at an early stage in the precipitation of hydrous metal oxides. In the case of Fe^{3+}, precipitation of $Fe_2O_3 \cdot xH_2O$—commonly, but not rigorously correctly, written $Fe(OH)_3$—proceeds through the stages:

$$[Fe(H_2O)_6]^{3+} \xrightarrow{-H^+} [Fe(H_2O)_5OH]^{2+} \longrightarrow [(H_2O)_4Fe(OH)_2Fe(H_2O)_4]^{4+} \xrightarrow{-xH^+}$$

pH < 0   0 < pH < 2   ~2 < pH < ~3

$$\text{colloidal } Fe_2O_3 \cdot xH_2O \xrightarrow{-yH^+} Fe_2O_3 \cdot zH_2O \text{ ppt.}$$

~3 < pH < ~5   pH ~5

12*

Analogous to the OH^- ion are the alkoxide ions, OR^-. These are even stronger bases as a rule, being immediately hydrolyzed by water:

$$OR^- + H_2O = OH^- + ROH$$

A considerable number of metal alkoxides are known, many stoichiometrically analogous to the metal hydroxides, for example, $Ti(OH)_4$ and $Ti(OR)_4$. These compounds are quite reactive, and as R becomes large they become essentially organic in their physical properties; such alkoxides are usually polymeric, with coordination numbers greater than those indicated by the simple stoichiometry, owing to the existence of OR bridge groups.

13-2. Covalent Compounds; Stereochemistry of Oxygen

Two-coordinate Compounds. The normal coordination number of oxygen is two, and in most of its compounds it forms two single bonds, as in water, ethers, alcohols, etc. In all such compounds there are two pairs of nonbonding electrons which play a role in the stereochemistry. There are several ways to account for the fact that the X—O—X bond angles are all more nearly equal to the tetrahedral angle than to the 90° expected if oxygen used two pure p orbitals for bonding. According to one view it is assumed that the oxygen orbitals are hybridized in a manner approximating to sp^3, tetrahedral. Thus, as in trivalent nitrogen compounds, the unshared electrons are not distributed symmetrically about the oxygen atom, but occupy directed hybrid orbitals. In R_3N compounds the R—N—R angles seem always to be less than 109°; it has been proposed that this is because repulsion between nonbonding electron pairs and bonding pairs is greater than repulsion between two pairs of bonding electrons, which, in turn, is attributed to the fact that the bonding pairs may be more densely concentrated in the bond directions. What degree of truth there may be in this view is not certain, but in some oxygen compounds the angles exceed 109°; consider OCl_2 ($\sim 113°$), $(CH_3)_2O$ (111°) and ozone (127°). It should be noted that there is no good reason to suppose that the central atom tends to form four equivalent sp^3 hybrid orbitals and that all deviations of bond angles from the exact tetrahedral angles must be due to other forces. If all four orbitals are not to be used in identical ways, there is no reason why they should inherently tend to be identical. Thus, the various bond angles in R_3N and R_2O compounds can simply be taken to imply slightly varying degrees of hybridization, all of which, however, are much closer to sp^3 than to p^2 or p^3 (i.e., the use of pure p orbitals by the central atom). However, other factors such as the possibility of slightly bent bonds (i.e., axes of electron distribution not corresponding exactly to internuclear lines), van der Waals repulsions and interelectronic repulsions doubtless also influence the bond angles, and the hybridization argument should not be taken too literally though hybridization seems likely to be the major factor.

Three-coordinate Compounds. Compounds in this class are mainly *oxonium ions*—that is, H_3O^+, R_2OH^+, ROH_2^+, R_3O^+—and donor–acceptor complexes with Lewis acids such as $F_3\overset{-}{B}$—$\overset{+}{O}(C_2H_5)_2$. The formation of oxonium ions is quite analogous to the formation of ammonium ions, NH_4^+, RNH_3^+, ...R_4N^+.

As would be expected on the assumption of approximately sp^3 hybridization of the oxygen orbitals, three-coordinate oxygen compounds should generally be pyramidal. An apparent exception is found in the compound 13-II, where the three bonds to oxygen are coplanar or nearly so.[1] The cause may be O → Si and/or O → Al $p\pi$–$d\pi$ bonding.

$$(CH_3)_3Si—O—Al(CH_3)_2$$
$$|\quad|$$
$$(CH_3)_2Al—O—Si(CH_3)_3$$
$$(13\text{-}II)$$

Various instances have been noted already in which R_2O compounds behave as donors. In hydrated cations water, which may be regarded as the prototype R_2O compound, behaves as a donor, for example, in $[Be(OH_2)_4]^{2+}$, although the bond strength in many such hydrates may be appreciably if not largely due to ion–dipole attraction. The mechanism of hydrolysis of many covalent halides such as $SiCl_4$ presumably involves initial formation of a donor bond from H_2O (or OH^-) to the central atom.

Four-coordinate Oxygen. Although the maximum coordination number for oxygen is four, it is seldom attained. Oxide ions are often four coordinate in ionic or partially ionic oxides. In the compounds $OM_4(OCOR)_6$, where M is Be or Zn, oxygen is four coordinate (see Fig. 9-3, page 252). Doubtless the O—M bonds here have considerable ionic character and, though four coordinate, the oxygen atom is not truly four covalent.

Multiple Bonding. Like nitrogen, oxygen has considerable ability to form double bonds. These may be of the $p\pi$–$p\pi$ type as in ketones, carboxylic acids, CO, CO_2, N_2O, NO, etc., and in the resonance structures making up the true electronic states of such species as NO_2^- and NO_3^-.

It is also possible for oxygen to form dative $d\pi$–$p\pi$ double bonds to second and third row elements similar in the nature of the overlaps involved to those discussed for $(H_3Si)_3N$. In disiloxane, $(SiH_3)_2O$, the Si—O—Si bond angle is very large; the exact value is not known, but it is definitely $\geqslant 150°$. This may be attributed to the tendency of the filled $p\pi$ orbitals

[1] P. J. Wheatley, *J. Chem. Soc.*, **1963**, 2562.

of oxygen to overlap with empty $d\pi$ orbitals on Si. In the limit this would lead to an Si—O—Si angle of 180°. In phosphine oxides, R_3PO, and sulfoxides, R_2SO, there is doubtless some $p\pi$–$d\pi$ bonding; that is, the actual state of the P—O or S—O bonds is described by a resonance between 13-IIIa and 13-IIIb, where one pair of electrons in 13-IIIb is in a bonding orbital

$$R_3\overset{+}{P}:\overset{-}{\underset{}{O}}: \leftrightarrow R_3P::\overset{}{O}$$

$$(13\text{-IIIa}) \qquad (13\text{-IIIb})$$

formed by $p\pi$–$d\pi$ overlap. With amine oxides this is, of course, not possible, and the NO bond is essentially just $\overset{+}{N}:\overset{..}{\underset{..}{O}}:^{-}$. Certain transition metal complexes also have oxygen bridges, M—O—M, which are linear, for example $[Cl_5Ru-O-RuCl_5]^{4-}$; the magnetic properties and structure can only be explained by $d\pi$–$p\pi$ bonding through the oxygen atom.

Oxo Acids and Oxo Anions. Oxygen occurs in an immense number of oxo acids and oxo anions of various types. The bonds are mainly covalent with varying degrees of partial ionic character and also varying degrees of multiple bond character. Common monomeric oxo anions are NO_3^-, SO_4^{2-}, CrO_4^{2-}, MnO_4^-, CO_3^{2-}, etc. There are polymeric anions such as $S_2O_7^{2-}$, $Cr_2O_7^{2-}$ and $P_2O_7^{4-}$, having oxygen bridges as well as more highly polymerized species, linear, cyclic and three dimensional as in silicates or molybdates. There are also a few dimeric anions—for example, $P_2O_6^-$ and $S_2O_4^{2-}$—in which there are no bridges.

Catenation. As with nitrogen, and even more so, catenation is limited. In peroxides and superoxides there are two consecutive oxygen atoms, in ozone, O_3F_2 and the O_3^- ion three, and in O_4F_2 there may be a chain of four. All species with O_3 and O_4 chains are very unstable. Sulfur and selenium have a much greater tendency to catenation, sulfur being probably second only to carbon in this respect.

THE ELEMENT

13-3. Occurrence, Properties and Allotropes

Oxygen occurs in nature in three isotopic species: ^{16}O (99.759%), ^{17}O (0.0374%) and ^{18}O (0.2039%). The rare isotopes, particularly ^{18}O, can be concentrated by fractional distillation of water, and concentrates containing up to 97 atom % ^{18}O or up to 4 atom % ^{17}O and other labeled compounds are commercially available. ^{18}O has been widely used as a tracer in studying reaction mechanisms of oxygen compounds. Although

[17]O has a nuclear spin, its low abundance means that even using enriched samples, a very sensitive nmr spectrometer is required. For both organic and inorganic compounds the resonances occur at lower fields for double-bonded oxygen, $=$O, than for single-bonded oxygen, —O—. The shifts can be correlated with the lowest energy ultraviolet or visible transitions, since interaction under the influence of a magnetic field of the ground state with excited states similar or identical to those involved in the observed electronic transitions makes an important contribution to the chemical shift.[2] An important use[3] of [17]O resonance studies has been to distinguish between H_2O in a complex, e.g., $[Co(NH_3)_5H_2O]^{3+}$, and solvent water; exchange reactions of water in complex ions have been similarly studied.

Elemental oxygen occurs in two allotropic forms; the common, stable O_2 and ozone, O_3. O_2 is paramagnetic in the gaseous, liquid and solid states and has the rather high dissociation energy of 117 kcal/mole. As has been discussed (page 63), the valence bond theory in its simplest form would predict the electronic structure $: \overset{\cdot\cdot}{O} = \overset{\cdot\cdot}{O} :$ which, while accounting for the strong bond, fails to account for the paramagnetism. Alternatively, but only as an after-the-fact rationalization, we might write $: \overset{\cdot\cdot}{O} — \overset{\cdot\cdot}{O} :$ to account for the presence of two unpaired electrons; but then we should scarcely expect as high a bond energy as is found, since the N—N, O—O and F—F single bond energies are, respectively, 32 (in N_2H_4), 33 (in H_2O_2) and 37 (in F_2) kcal/mole. However, simple molecular orbital theory straightforwardly predicts a bond order of 2 *and* the paramagnetism, (page 91). Like NO, which has one unpaired electron in an antibonding (π^*) MO, oxygen molecules associate only weakly, and true electron pairing to form a symmetrical O_4 species apparently does not occur even in the solid. Both liquid and solid O_2 are pale blue in color.

Ozone is usually prepared by the action of a silent electric discharge upon O_2; concentrations up to 10% O_3 can be obtained in this way. Ozone gas is perceptibly blue and is diamagnetic. Pure ozone can be obtained by fractional liquefaction of O_2–O_3 mixtures. There is a two-phase liquid system; one with 25% ozone is stable, but a deep purple phase with 70% ozone is explosive, as is the deep blue pure liquid (b $-112°$). The solid (m $-193°$) is black-violet. Small quantities of ozone are formed in electrolysis of dilute sulfuric acid, in some chemical reactions producing elemental oxygen, and by action of ultraviolet light on O_2. Ozone occurs in traces in the upper atmosphere, the maximum concentrations being at an altitude of ~ 25 km. It is very endothermic,

$$O_3 = \tfrac{3}{2}O_2 \qquad \Delta H = -34.0 \text{ kcal/mole}$$

[2] B. N. Figgis, R. G. Kidd and R. S. Nyholm, *Proc. Roy. Soc.*, **A269**, 469 (1962).
[3] J. H. Jackson, J. F. Lemons and H. Taube, *J. Chem. Phys.*, **32**, 553 (1960).

but decomposes only slowly at 250° in absence of catalysts and ultraviolet light.

The structure of O_3 is shown in Figure 13-1. Since the O—O bond distances are 1.49 A in HOOH (single bond) and 1.21 A in O_2 ($\sim$ double

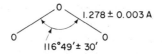

Fig. 13-1. The structure of ozone, O_3.

bond), it is apparent that the O—O bond in O_3 must have considerable double bond character. Four reasonable resonance structures (13-IV) may be written, with 13-IVa and 13-IVb predominating. In molecular

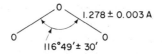

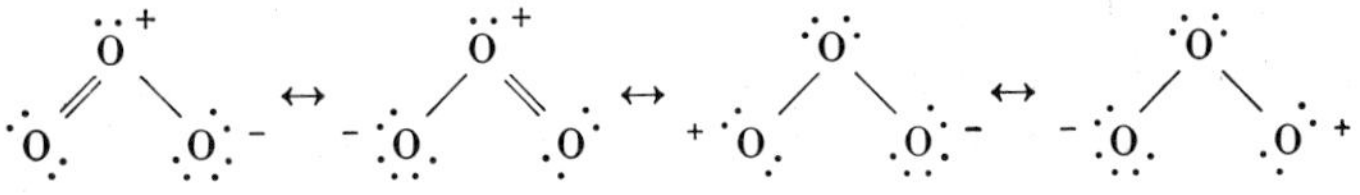

(13-IVa)   (13-IVb)   (13-IVc)   (13-IVd)

orbital theory the existence of strong, delocalized π bonding can be invoked.

The chemical reactivities of O_2 and O_3 differ vastly. Although O_2 will combine directly with practically all other elements, it will do so only at elevated temperatures in most cases, but ozone is a powerful oxidizing agent and reacts with many substances under conditions where O_2 will not. The reaction

$$O_3 + 2KI + H_2O = I_2 + 2KOH + O_2$$

is quantitative and can be used for the determination of ozone.

The following potentials indicate the oxidizing strengths of O_2 and O_3 in aqueous solution:

$$O_2 + 4H^+ + 4e = 2H_2O \qquad E^0 = +1.229 \text{ v}$$
$$O_2 + 2H_2O + 4e = 4OH^- \qquad E^0 = +0.401 \text{ v}$$
$$O_2 + 4H^+ (10^{-7} M) + 4e = 2H_2O \qquad E^0 = +0.815 \text{ v}$$
$$O_3 + 2H^+ + 2e = O_2 + H_2O \qquad E^0 = +2.07 \text{ v}$$
$$O_3 + H_2O + 2e = O_2 + 2OH^- \qquad E^0 = +1.24 \text{ v}$$
$$O_3 + 2H^+ (10^{-7} M) + 2e = O_2 + H_2O \qquad E^0 = +1.65 \text{ v}$$

The first step in the reduction of O_2 in aprotic solvents such as dimethylsulfoxide appears to be a one-electron step to give the superoxide anion:[4a]

$$O_2 + e = O_2^-$$

whereas in aqueous solution a two-electron step occurs to give HO_2^-

$$O_2 + 2e + 2H_2O = HO_2^- + OH^-$$

[4a] D. L. Maricle and W. G. Hodgson, *Chem. and Eng. News*, April 12, 1965, p. 53.

It has been possible to show the formation of O_2^- in pyridine solutions by spectroscopic methods and by esr.[4b]

In acid solution, O_3 is exceeded in oxidizing power only by fluorine, the perxenate ion, atomic oxygen, OH radicals and a few other such species. The rate of decomposition of ozone drops sharply in alkaline solutions, the half life being *ca* 2 minutes at $1N$ NaOH at 25°, 40 minutes at $5N$ and 83 hours at $20N$;[4c] the ozonide ion (see later) is also more stable in alkaline solution.

It can also be seen that neutral water when saturated with O_2 is a fairly good oxidizing agent. For example, although Cr^{2+} is just stable toward oxidation in pure water, in air-saturated water it is rapidly oxidized; Fe^{2+} is oxidized (only slowly in acid, but rapidly in base) to Fe^{3+} in presence of air, although in air-free water Fe^{2+} is quite stable,

$$Fe^{3+} + e = Fe^{2+} \qquad E^0 = +0.77 \text{ v}$$

The slowness of many oxygen oxidations in acid solution is attributable to the initial reduction to H_2O with HO_2^- as an intermediate if one-electron reducing agents are present

$$O_2 + 2H^+ + 2e = H_2O_2 \qquad E^0 = +0.682 \text{ v}$$
$$O_2 + H_2O + 2e = OH^- + HO_2^- \qquad E^0 = -0.076 \text{ v}$$

Oxygen is readily soluble in organic solvents, and merely pouring such liquids in air serves to saturate them with oxygen. This should be kept in mind when determining the reactivity of air-sensitive materials in solution in organic solvents.

Measurements of electronic spectra of alcohols, ethers, benzene and even saturated hydrocarbons show that there is interaction with the oxygen molecule of the charge-transfer type. However, there is no true complex formation since the heats of formation are negligible and the spectral changes are due to contact between the molecules at van der Waals distances.[5] The classic example is that of dimethylaniline which becomes yellow in air or oxygen but colorless again when the oxygen is removed by nitrogen. Such weak charge-transfer complexes make certain electronic transitions in molecules more intense; they are also a plausible first stage in photo oxidations.

A few transition metal complexes can act as reversible carriers of molecular oxygen; that is, they take up and release O_2 reversibly. Certain complexes, when bound to protein molecules as prosthetic groups, are

[4b] M. E. Peover, B. S. White and W. Slough, Chem. Comm., **1965**, 183, 184.

[4c] L. J. Heidt and V. R. Landi, *Chem. and Eng. News*, July 27, 1964, p. 38; also see ref. 24.

[5] D. F. Evans, *J. Chem. Soc.*, **1987** (1961); H. Tsubomwa and R. S. Mullikan, *J. Amer. Chem. Soc.*, **82**, 5966 (1960).

indispensable in life processes, notably respiration, and are found in living organisms. Hemoglobin and the hemocyanins are natural carriers; heme prosthetic groups contain an iron atom bound in a porphine derivative. There are several synthetic oxygen-carrying complexes known which provide model systems for the natural carriers. Examples of these are cobalt–histidine and cobalt–salicylaldehyde ethylenediimine complexes, which carry oxygen both in the solid state and in solution.

A quite simple compound $Ir^ICl(CO)(PPh_3)_2$ has been shown to take up oxygen reversibly in solution at atmospheric temperature and pressure and a crystalline non-ionic adduct can be isolated.[6] X-ray study[7] has shown that the oxygen molecule is bound as a peroxo group through two equivalent Ir—O bonds (i.e., side-on, as in 13-Va), the effective oxidation state of Ir being then $+3$ and its coordination number 6. The cobalt complexes appear also to have a peroxo group, but a bridging one between the metal atoms; although the precise nature of the bridge is not certain it appears to be of the type 13-Vb. The iridium complex gives H_2O_2 on acidification and is thus in principle similar in its behavior to other well-known peroxo complexes (see Chap. 29-C and -F).

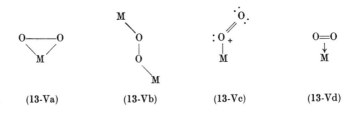

(13-Va)   (13-Vb)   (13-Vc)   (13-Vd)

The nature of the bonding of oxygen in the natural carriers is far from settled.[8] Proposals have included suggestions such as 13-Vc, which is in effect a type of coordinated superoxide group, and 13-Vd which involves donation of π-electron density as in ethylene complexes (Chap. 28). However, these are not entirely satisfactory in that it is difficult to accommodate the fact that hemoglobin, an Fe^{II} complex, HbFe, is diamagnetic and yet $HbFeO_2$ is also diamagnetic. It is also possible to regard oxyhemoglobin as having a peroxo group like 13-Va with the iron atom formally in the IV state. This could readily account for the oxidizing ability since H_2O_2, HO_2 or OH radicals could readily be formed from it (cf. below and also Chap. 29-E).

[6] L. Vaska, *Science*, **140**, 809 (1963).
[7] J. A. Ibers and S. J. La Placa, *Science*, **145**, 920 (1964).
[8] Cf. J. J. Weiss, *Nature*, **202**, 83; **203**, 182 (1964); L. Pauling, *Nature*, **203**, 182; R. O. Viale, *et al.*, *Nature*, **203**, 183.

OXYGEN COMPOUNDS

Most oxygen compounds are described in treating the chemistry of the other elements. Water and the hydroxonium ion have already been discussed (Chapter 6). A few important compounds and classes of compounds will be mentioned here.

13-4. The Dioxygenyl Cation

During studies on the chemistry of PtF_6, it was found that the deep red-brown vapor reacted with oxygen at room temperature to give an orange solid. The same product can be obtained by direct interaction of F_2 and O_2 on Pt sponge at 450°. The compound, which sublimes in vacuum at 100° but is hydrolyzed by water, has been shown to be a salt of the dioxygenyl ion, $O_2^+[Pt^VF_6]^-$. The salt is isomorphous with $KPtF_6$, which can be made from it by treatment with KF in IF_5, and with $KRuF_6$.[9] The realization that PtF_6 had an exceedingly high electron affinity sufficient to remove an electron from the oxygen molecule (1st ionization potential 12.10 ev) led Bartlett to the preparation of $XePtF_6$ (page 593).

A number of nitrosonium salts, e.g. $NO^+OsF_6^-$, are known and O_2^+ and NO^+ are similar in size, but the lower ionization potential of NO (9.23 ev) means that NO^+ complexes are more readily obtained. The $O—O^+$ distance from spectroscopic studies, 1.12 A, is shorter than the $O—O$ distance in O_2 (1.21 A) or O_2^- (1.28 A) as expected. The O_2^+ ion has a single unpaired electron and the magnetic moment of O_2PtF_6 is a combination of the separate moments for O_2^+ and $Pt^VF_6^-$. More recently[10] it has been shown that O_2F_2 (see below) will react with good F^- acceptors such as AsF_5, PF_5, SbF_5 to give other ionic dioxygenyl compounds, viz.,

$$O_2F_2 + MF_5 = O_2^+[MF_6]^- + \tfrac{1}{2}F_2$$

13-5. Oxygen Fluorides, OF_2, O_2F_2, O_3F_2 and O_4F_2

Since fluorine is more electronegative than oxygen, it is logical to call its binary compounds with fluorine oxygen fluorides rather than fluorine oxides, although the latter names are sometimes seen.

Oxygen difluoride, OF_2, is prepared either by passing fluorine rapidly through 2% sodium hydroxide solution or by electrolysis of aqueous HF–KF solutions. It is a pale yellow poisonous gas, b −145°. It is relatively unreactive. It can be mixed with H_2, CH_4 or CO without reaction, although sparking causes violent explosion. Mixtures of OF_2

[9] N. Bartlett and D. M. Lohman, *J. Chem. Soc.*, **1962**, 5253.
[10] A. R. Young II, T. Hirata and S. I. Morrow, *J. Amer. Chem. Soc.*, **86**, 20 (1964).

with Cl_2, Br_2 and I_2 explode at room temperature. It is fairly readily hydrolyzed by base:

$$OF_2 + 2OH^- = O_2 + 2F^- + H_2O$$

It reacts more slowly with water, but explodes with steam,

$$OF_2 + H_2O = O_2 + 2HF$$

and liberates other halogens from their acids or salts.

$$OF_2 + 4HX(aq) = 2X_2 + 2HF + H_2O$$

Metals and nonmetals are oxidized and/or fluorinated and in an electric discharge even Xe reacts to give a mixture of fluoride and oxofluoride. The other oxygen fluorides are obtained by high voltage electric discharges on appropriate mixtures of O_2 and F_2 at 10–20 mm pressure and temperatures 77–90°K. Like OF_2, they have been intensively studied as potential rocket fuels.

Dioxygen difluoride, O_2F_2, is a yellow orange solid (m 109.7°K) thermally decomposing into O_2 and F_2 in the gas at $-50°$ with a half-life of about 3 hr. It is an extremely potent fluorinating and oxidizing agent.[11] Many substances explode on exposure at low temperatures and even C_2F_4 is converted to COF_2, CF_4, CF_3OOCF_3, etc. With Cl_2 a purple, fairly stable intermediate $(O_2ClF_3)_n$ can be isolated. O_2F_2 has been used for oxidizing primary aliphatic amines to the corresponding nitroso compounds.[12]

Since O_3F_2 is a dark-red viscous liquid at 90°K it can be distinguished from O_2F_2; it can be distilled at 96–114°K at low pressures but is unstable at higher temperatures. O_4F_2 has not been extensively studied; it is a reddish-brown solid at 77°K. O_3F_2 is more reactive than either F_2 or F_2–O_2 mixtures.

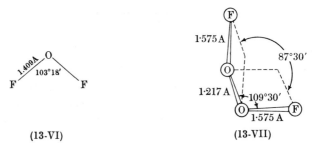

(13-VI)   (13-VII)

The structures of OF_2 and O_2F_2 only are known in detail (13-VI, VII) but O_3F_2 is paramagnetic and its esr spectrum indicates that it has axial

[11] A. G. Streng, *J. Amer. Chem. Soc.*, **85**, 1380 (1963).
[12] R. F. Merritt and J. K. Ruff, *J. Amer. Chem. Soc.*, **86**, 1392 (1964).

symmetry. The O—O bond in O_2F_2 is much shorter than that in H_2O_2 (1.48 A) and is about the same as that of O_2, while the O—F bonds are considerably longer than in OF_2. Thus the O—O bond seems to retain double bond character while the O—F bonds are weaker than regular OF single bonds. While an explanation involving a resonance hybrid of F—O—O—F with $F^-O{=}O^+$—F, etc., could be invoked, a rather neat explanation can be derived from the MO description (page 91) of the oxygen molecule.[13] This has unpaired electrons in the two π^* orbitals, one of which is of the form $(p_y^{(1)}-p_y^{(2)})$ and the other $(p_x^{(2)}-p_x^{(1)})$. This is shown in 13-VIII. With each of these a fluorine atom may interact

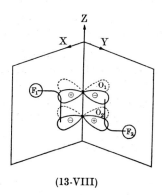

(13-VIII)

forming a 3-center (O—O—F) MO which is antibonding with respect to O—O but bonding with respect to O—F. Thus, the overall O—O bond order remains virtually unchanged, but the O—F bonds are relatively weak because they are part of a 3-center bonding system instead of being regular 2-center, 2-electron bonds.

13-6. Hydrogen Peroxide, H_2O_2

Hydrogen peroxide is obtained by electrolytic processes which involve the formation of peroxodisulfate ion and its subsequent hydrolysis. Sulfuric acid or ammonium sulfate–sulfuric acid solutions are electrolyzed at high current density (~ 1 amp./dm.^{2}) using electrode materials (usually Pt) with high overvoltages for O_2 evolution. Although the detailed mechanism of the process is not quite certain, stoichiometrically we have:

$$S_2O_8^{2-} + 2H^+ + 2e = 2HSO_4^- \qquad E^0 = 2.18 \text{ (acid)}$$
$$S_2O_8^{2-} + 2e = 2SO_4^{2-} \qquad E^0 = 2.06 \text{ (neutral)}$$

[13] R. H. Jackson, *J. Chem. Soc.*, **1962**, 4585.

An optimum residence time for the solution and low temperature ($-20°$) is used to minimize the hydrolytic reaction (eq. 13-1) in the cell and con-

$$H_2S_2O_8 + H_2O = \quad H_2SO_5 \quad + H_2SO_4 \qquad (13\text{-}1)$$

Peroxodi-   Peroxomonosulfuric   sulfuric acid;
acid   "Caro's" acid

sequent loss of product by decomposition reactions (eqs. 13-2a, b)

$$2H_2O_2 = 2H_2O + O_2 \qquad (13\text{-}2a)$$
$$H_2SO_5 + H_2O_2 = H_2SO_4 + H_2O + O_2 \qquad (13\text{-}2b)$$

The peroxodisulfuric acid solution is hydrolyzed separately

$$H_2S_2O_8 + H_2O = H_2SO_5 + H_2SO_4 \quad \text{(fast)}$$
$$H_2SO_5 + H_2O = H_2O_2 + H_2SO_4 \quad \text{(slow)}$$

and the H_2O_2 is rapidly removed by distillation at high temperature and low pressure. Dilute solutions of H_2O_2 so obtained are then concentrated by vacuum distillation to 28–35% by weight. Higher concentrations, 90–99%, are commercially achieved by further, multistage fractionation. Such concentrated materials are very susceptible to metal ion catalyzed decomposition and it is necessary to add inhibitors such as sodium pyrophosphate or stannate and to store them in pure aluminum ($> 99.6\%$) containers.

Hydrogen peroxide is also produced on a large scale by autoxidation of an anthraquinol, such as 2-ethylanthraquinol (13-IX), in a cyclic con-

(13-IX)

tinuous process. Hydrogen from the cracking of butane is used to reduce the quinone using Pd on an inert support in free suspension. H_2O_2 is extracted from the oxygenated organic solution by countercurrent columns and the aqueous product contains about 20% H_2O_2. The process needs only H_2, atmospheric oxygen and water as major raw materials; it is cheaper to operate than the electrolytic method.

Pure H_2O_2 is a pale blue, sirupy liquid, boiling at 152.1° and freezing at $-0.89°$. It resembles water in many of its physical properties. The pure liquid has a dielectric constant at 25° of 93 and a 65% solution in water has a dielectric constant of 120. Thus both the pure liquid and its aqueous solutions are potentially excellent ionizing solvents, but its utility in this respect is limited by its strongly oxidizing nature and its ready decomposition in the presence of even traces of many heavy metal ions according to the equation:

$$2H_2O_2 = 2H_2O + O_2 \qquad \Delta H = -23.6 \text{ kcal/mole} \qquad (13\text{-}3)$$

In dilute aqueous solution it is more acidic than water,

$$H_2O_2 = H^+ + HO_2^- \qquad K_{20°} = 1.5 \times 10^{-12}$$

The molecule H_2O_2 has a skew, chain structure (Fig. 13-2). There is only a low barrier to internal rotation about the O—O bond. In the liquid state H_2O_2 is even more highly associated via hydrogen bonding than is H_2O.

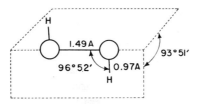

Fig. 13-2.   The structure of hydrogen peroxide.

Its oxidation–reduction chemistry in aqueous solution is summarized by the following potentials:

$$H_2O_2 + 2H^+ + 2e = 2H_2O \qquad E^0 = 1.77 \text{ v}$$
$$O_2 + 2H^+ + 2e = H_2O_2 \qquad E^0 = 0.68 \text{ v}$$
$$HO_2^- + H_2O + 2e = 3OH^- \qquad E^0 = 0.87 \text{ v}$$

from which it can be seen that hydrogen peroxide is a strong oxidizing agent in either acid or basic solution; only toward very strong oxidizing agents such as MnO_4^- will it behave as a reducing agent.

Dilute or 30% hydrogen peroxide solutions are widely used as oxidants. In acid solution oxidations with hydrogen peroxide are most often slow, whereas in basic solution they are usually fast. Decomposition of hydrogen peroxide according to reaction 13-3, which may be considered a self-oxidation, occurs most rapidly in basic solution; hence excess H_2O_2 may best be destroyed by heating in basic solution.

The oxidation of H_2O_2 in aqueous solution by Cl_2, MnO_4^-, Ce^{4+}, etc., and the catalytic decomposition caused by Fe^{3+}, I_2, MnO_2, etc., have been studied. In both cases, by using labeled H_2O_2, it has been shown that the oxygen produced is derived entirely from the peroxide and not from water. This suggests that oxidizing agents do not break the O—O bond, but simply remove electrons. In the case of oxidation by chlorine, a mechanism of the following kind is consistent with the lack of exchange of ^{18}O between H_2O_2 and H_2O:

$$Cl_2 + H_2{}^{18}O_2 \rightarrow H^+ + Cl^- + H^{18}O^{18}OCl$$
$$H^{18}O^{18}OCl \rightarrow H^+ + Cl^- + {}^{18}O_2$$

It is important to recognize, however, that very many reactions involving H_2O_2 (and also O_2) in solutions are free radical ones.[14] Metal ion catalyzed decomposition of H_2O_2 and other reactions can give rise to radicals of which HO_2 and OH are most important. HO_2 has been detected in ice irradiated at low temperature and also in aqueous solutions where H_2O_2 is being oxidized by Ce^{IV}.

A very "simple" reaction—that of Cl_2 with H_2O_2 in base solution:

$$Cl_2 + HO_2{}^- + OH^- = 2Cl^- + H_2O + O_2$$

has been found to give a red chemiluminescence in the oxygen bubbles due to production of O_2 in a vibrationally excited state;[15] this may provide a model for some natural bioluminescent processes. The methanol solution of $1M$ $NaClO$ and 30% H_2O_2 has been used to oxidize olefins; the products are similar to those given by dye-sensitized autoxidations.[16] Singlet oxygen, excited by electrodeless discharge, has also been used.[17]

Hydrogen peroxide has been estimated to be more than 10^6 times less *basic* than H_2O. However, it appears that on addition of concentrated H_2O_2 to tetrafluoroboric acid in tetrahydrothiophen-1,1-dioxide (sulfolane), the conjugate cation $H_3O_2{}^+$ can be obtained. The solutions are very powerful but unselective oxidants for benzene, cyclohexane and other organic materials.[18]

13-7. Peroxides, Superoxides and Ozonides

Ionic peroxides, which contain $O_2{}^{2-}$ ions, are known for the alkali metals, Ca, Sr and Ba. Sodium peroxide is made commercially by air oxidation of Na, first to Na_2O, then to Na_2O_2; it is a yellowish powder, very hygroscopic though thermally stable to $500°$, which contains also, according to esr studies, about 10% of the superoxide. Barium peroxide, which was originally used for making dilute solutions of hydrogen peroxide by treatment with dilute sulfuric acid, is made by action of air or O_2 on BaO; the reaction is slow below $500°$ and BaO_2 decomposes above $600°$.

[14] See, e.g., articles by N. Uri and by M-S. Tsao and W. K. Wilmarth in *Free Radicals in Inorganic Chemistry*, Advances in Chemistry Series No. 36, A.C.S., Washington, 1962.

[15] R. J. Brown and E. A. Ogryzlo, *Proc. Chem. Soc.*, **1964**, 117.

[16] C. S. Foote and S. Wexler, *J. Amer. Chem. Soc.*, **86**, 3879, 3880 (1964).

[17] E. J. Corey and W. C. Taylor, *J. Amer. Chem. Soc.*, **86**, 3881 (1964).

[18] R. W. Alder and M. C. Whiting, *J. Chem. Soc.*, **1964**, 4707.

The ionic peroxides with water or dilute acids give H_2O_2, and all are powerful oxidizing agents. They convert all organic materials to carbonate even at moderate temperatures. Na_2O_2 also vigorously oxidizes some metals, e.g., Fe violently gives FeO_4^{2-}, and it can be generally employed for oxidizing fusions. The alkali peroxides also react with CO_2.[19]

$$2CO_2(g) + 2M_2O_2 = 2M_2CO_3 + O_2$$

Peroxides can also serve as reducing agents for such strongly oxidizing substances as permanganate.

A number of other electropositive metals such as Mg, the lanthanides or uranyl ion also give peroxides which are intermediate in character between the ionic ones and the essentially covalent peroxides of metals such as Zn, Cd and Hg. The addition of H_2O_2 to solutions, e.g., of Zn^{2+} or UO_2^{2+} gives impure peroxides.

A characteristic feature of the ionic peroxides is the formation of well-crystallized hydrates and H_2O_2 adducts. Thus $Na_2O_2 \cdot 8H_2O$ can be obtained by adding ethanol to 30% H_2O_2 in concentrated NaOH at 15° or by rapid crystallization of Na_2O_2 from iced water. The alkaline earths all form the octahydrates, $M^{II}O_2 \cdot 8H_2O$. They are isostructural, containing discrete peroxide ions to which the water molecules are hydrogen bonded, giving chains of the type $\ldots O_2^{2-} \ldots (H_2O)_8 \ldots O_2^{2-} \ldots (H_2O)_8 \ldots$. Peroxide ion can function as a ligand, the best-known ones being the various peroxo compounds of chromium (see Sec. 29-C-8).

Superoxides. The action of oxygen at pressures near atmospheric on K, Rb and Cs gives yellow to orange crystalline solids of formula MO_2. NaO_2 can be obtained only by interaction of Na_2O_2 with O_2 at 300 atm and 500°. LiO_2 cannot be isolated and the only evidence for it is the similarity in the absorption spectra of the pale yellow solutions of Li, Na and K on rapid oxidation of the metals in liquid ammonia at $-78°$ by oxygen. Alkaline earth, Mg, Zn and Cd superoxides occur only in small concentrations as solid solutions in the peroxides. Tetramethyl-ammonium peroxide has been obtained as a yellow solid (m 97°) which is soluble in water, evolving O_2.[20] There is clearly a direct correlation between superoxide stability and electropositivity of the metal concerned.

The paramagnetism of the compounds corresponds to one unpaired electron per two oxygen atoms, consistent with the existence of O_2^- ions as first suggested for these oxides by Pauling. Crystal structure determinations show the existence of such discrete O_2^- ions. The compounds KO_2, RbO_2 and CsO_2 crystallize in the CaC_2 structure (Fig. 11–3a), which is a distorted NaCl structure. NaO_2 is cubic owing to a disorder in the

[19] M. M. Markowitz, D. A. Boryta and H. Stewart, *J. Inorg. Nucl. Chem.*, **26**, 2028 (1961).
[20] A. D. McElroy and J. S. Hashman, *Inorg. Chem.*, **3**, 1798 (1964).

orientation of the O_2^- ions. The superoxides are very powerful oxidizing agents. They react vigorously with water:

$$2O_2^- + H_2O = O_2 + HO_2^- + OH^-$$
$$2HO_2^- = 2OH^- + O_2 \text{(slow)}$$

The reaction with CO_2, which involves peroxocarbonate intermediates, is of some technical use for removal of CO_2 and regeneration of O_2 in closed systems. The over-all reaction is

$$4MO_2(s) + 2CO_2(g) = 2M_2CO_3(s) + 3O_2(g)$$

Ozonides. The interaction of O_3 with hydroxides of K, Rb and Cs has long been known to give materials neither peroxides nor superoxides. These are ozonides:

$$3KOH(s) + 2O_3(g) = 2KO_3(s) + KOH \cdot H_2O(s) + \tfrac{1}{2}O_2(g)$$

Recently the preparation of NH_4O_3 has also been reported.[22] KO_3 gives orange-red crystals; it decomposes to KO_2 and O_2 slowly.

The ozonide ion is paramagnetic with one unpaired electron and is apparently bent[23] ($\sim 100°$; O—O ~ 1.2 A) (cf. ClO_2). There is evidence that O_3^- occurs as a reaction intermediate in the decomposition of H_2O_2 in alkaline solution.[24]

Materials of composition approximating to M_2O_3 (M = alkali metal) are almost certainly mixtures of peroxide and superoxide and there is no evidence for the existence of an O_3^{2-} ion.

13-8. Other Peroxo Compounds

A large number of *organic peroxides* and *hydroperoxides* are known. Peroxo carboxylic acids, e.g., peracetic acid, $CH_3CO.OOH$, can be obtained by action of H_2O_2 on acid anhydrides. Peracetic acid is commercially made as 10–55% aqueous solutions containing some acetic acid by interaction of 50% H_2O_2, acetic acid and H_2SO_4 as catalyst at 45–60°; the dilute acid is distilled under reduced pressure; it is also made by air oxidation of acetaldehyde. The peroxo acids are useful oxidants and sources of free radicals, e.g., by treatment with Fe^{2+}(aq). Benzoyl peroxide and cumyl hydroperoxide are moderately stable and widely used as polymerization initiators and for other purposes where free radical initiation is required.

Organic peroxo compounds are also obtained by *autoxidation* of ethers,

[22] I. J. Solomon, *et al.*, *J. Amer. Chem. Soc.*, **84**, 34 (1962).
[23] L. V. Azaroff and I. Cowin, *Proc. Nat. Acad. (U.S.A.)*, **49**, 1 (1963).
[24] See, e.g., L. J. Heidt and V. R. Landi, *J. Chem. Phys.*, **41**, 176 (1964).

unsaturated hydrocarbons and other organic materials on exposure to air. The autoxidation is a free radical chain reaction which is initiated almost certainly by radicals generated by interaction of oxygen with traces of metals such as Cu, Co, Fe. The attack on specific reactive C—H bonds by a radical, X$\cdot$, gives first R$\cdot$ and then hydroperoxides which can further react:

$$RH + X\cdot = R\cdot + HX$$
$$R\cdot + O_2 = RO_2\cdot$$
$$RO_2\cdot + RH = ROOH + R\cdot$$

Peroxide formation can lead to explosions if oxidized solvents are distilled. Peroxides are best removed by washing with acidified $FeSO_4$ solution or, for ethers and hydrocarbons, by passage through a column of activated alumina. Peroxides are absent when $Fe^{2+} + SCN^-$ reagent gives no red color.

There are a great variety of inorganic peroxo compounds where —O— is replaced by —O—O— groups. Some of these are discussed elsewhere. Typical are peroxo anions such as peroxo sulfates 13-X and 13-XI. All peroxo acids yield H_2O_2 on hydrolysis. Peroxodisulfate, as the am-

(13-X)   (13-XI)
Peroxomonosulfate   Peroxodisulfate

monium salt, is commonly used as a strong oxidizing agent in acid solution, for example, to convert C to CO_2, Mn^{2+} to MnO_4^- or Ce^{3+} to Ce^{4+}. The latter two reactions are slow and normally incomplete in the absence of silver ion as a catalyst (see Sec. 30-I-2).

It is important to make the distinction between true peroxo compounds which contain —O—O— groups and compounds which contain hydrogen peroxide of crystallization such as $2Na_2CO_3 \cdot 3H_2O_2$ or $Na_4P_2O_7 \cdot nH_2O_2$. Esr studies of peroxoborates and blue peroxocarbonates have shown the presence of free radicals, but it is not yet certain what species are responsible.

References

Advances in Chemistry Series No. 21, *Ozone Chemistry and Technology*, American Chemistry Society, Washington, D.C., 1959.

Ardon, M., *Oxygen: Elementary Forms and Hydrogen Peroxide*, Benjamin, New York, 1965. Short reference text.

Bradley, D. C., *Progr. Inorg. Chem.*, **2**, 303 (1960). Metal alkoxides.

———, in *Metal Organic Compounds (Advances in Chemistry Series*, No. 23), American Chemical Society, Washington, D.C., 1959. Metal alkoxides.

Brewer, L., *Chem. Rev.*, **52**, 1 (1953). A comprehensive survey of thermodynamic properties of oxides.

—— and G. M. Rosenblatt, *Chem. Rev.*, **61**, 257 (1961). Dissociation energies of gaseous oxides, MO_2.

Carrington, A., and M. C. R. Symons, *Chem. Rev.*, **63**, 443 (1963). Structure and reactivity of oxo anions of transition metals.

Connor, J. A., and E. A. V. Ebsworth, *Adv. Inorg. Nucl. Chem.*, **6**, 279 (1964). Comprehensive review on peroxo compounds of transition metals.

Dole, M., *Chem. Rev.*, **51**, 263 (1952). Chemistry of isotopes of oxygen.

Edwards, J. O., ed., *Peroxide Reaction Mechanisms*, Interscience, New York, 1962.

Gimblett, F. G. R., *Inorganic Polymer Chemistry*, Butterworths, London, 1963. Contains good reviews of aggregation processes of hydroxo compounds and ions in aqueous solution, including discussion of experimental procedures.

Hawkins, E. G. E., *Quart. Rev.*, **4**, 25 (1950). Organic peracids and reactions of organic peroxides; *Organic Peroxides: their formation and reactions*, Spon, London, 1961.

Mackenzie, J. D., *Ad. Inorg. Chem. Radiochem.*, **4**, 293 (1962). Nature of oxides in melts.

Petrocelli, A. W., and D. L. Kraus, *J. Chem. Educ.*, **40**, 146 (1963). Inorganic superoxides.

——, and R. J. Chiarnenzelli, *J. Chem. Educ.*, **39**, 557 (1962). Ozonides.

Samuel, D., in *Oxygenases*, O. Hayaishi, ed., Academic Press, New York, 1962; an authoritative chapter on the methodology of the use of oxygen isotopes with extensive data and references.

——, and Steckel, F., *Bibliography of Stable Isotopes of Oxygen*, Pergamon Press, London, 1959.

Schumb, W. C., C. N. Satterfield and R. L. Wentworth, *Hydrogen Peroxide* (American Chemical Society Monograph, No. 128), Reinhold, New York, 1955. A comprehensive discussion of all phases of the chemistry of hydrogen peroxide and related compounds.

Selbin, J. H., *J. Chem. Educ.*, **41**, 86 (1964). Metal oxo cations.

Stewart, Ross, *Oxidation Mechanisms: Applications to Organic Chemistry*, Benjamin, New York, 1964. Short review of use of inorganic oxidants, e.g., CrO_3, MnO_4^-, $Pb(OCOCH_3)_4$, etc.

Streng, A. G., *Chem. Rev.*, **63**, 607 (1963). A comprehensive review of oxygen fluorides.

Swan, D., *Chem. Rev.*, **45**, 1 (1949). Organic peracids and reactions of organic peroxides.

Taube, H., *Ann. Rev. Nucl. Sci.*, **6**, 277 (1956). Oxygen isotopes in chemical studies.

——, *J. Gen. Physiology*, **49**, (1) Part 2, 29 (1965). This article, part of a symposium on the function of oxygen, is a detailed review of mechanisms of oxidation with molecular oxygen. Recommended reading.

Vannerberg, N-G., *Prog. Inorg. Chem.*, **4**, 125 (1962). Peroxides, superoxides and ozonides of the metals of Groups Ia, IIa and IIb.

Vogt, L. H., Jr., H. M. Faigenbaum and S. E. Wiberley, *Chem. Rev.*, **63**, 269 (1963). A review of synthetic oxygen carriers.

Wadsley, A. D., in *Non-Stoichiometric Compounds*, L. Mandelcorn, ed., Academic Press, New York, 1964. Clear, well-referenced text on binary and ternary oxides.

Ward, R., "Mixed Metal Oxides," *Progr. Inorg. Chem.* 1, 465 (1959). Comprehensive review of mixed metal oxides including their physical properties.

Yost, D. M., and H. Russell, *Systematic Inorganic Chemistry (of the 5th and 6th Group Elements)*, Prentice-Hall, New York, 1946. Excellent coverage of selected aspects of oxygen chemistry.

14

Fluorine

14-1. Introduction

Fluorine is a greenish diatomic gas, F_2. It is the most chemically reactive of all the elements, a fact which for a long time hindered its isolation. Fluorine combines directly at ordinary or elevated temperatures with all of the elements other than oxygen and the lighter noble gases, often with extreme vigor. It also attacks many other compounds, particularly organic compounds, breaking them down to fluorides; organic materials often inflame and burn in the gas.

The great reactivity of the element is in part attributable to the weakness of the F—F bond in the fluorine molecule, and reactions of atomic fluorine are strongly exothermic. Although the value of the *dissociation energy* long proved difficult to measure accurately, a value of 37.7 ± 0.2 kcal/mole now appears well established. This value is lower than those of the other halogens. The most satisfactory reason for this weakness is that it is due to repulsion between nonbonding electrons; in the other halogens, the longer bond distances and tighter binding of inner shell electrons tend to reduce this repulsion. A further reason has been suggested: the bonds in the other halogens are strengthened by some multiple bond character due to their ability, denied to fluorine, of being able to use valence shell d orbitals for such bonding.

Fluorine is the most electronegative of all the elements. Its ionization potential, 401 kcal/g-atom, combined with the dissociation energy, leads to the standard heat of formation of the gaseous F^+ ion of 420 kcal/g-atom (cf. Cl^+, 327; Br^+, 301; I^+, 268). Thus even solvated cationic species are unlikely, and no evidence whatever exists for a positive oxidation state of fluorine.

The *electron affinity* of fluorine is 83.5 ± 2 kcal/g-atom. This value is somewhat surprising, since one might have expected fluorine to have the highest electron affinity of all the halogens rather than one between those of chlorine (88) and bromine (82). This low value is, however, an inescapable consequence of the low dissociation energy of fluorine when the electron affinity is obtained from a Born–Haber cycle, and it has also been found by direct measurement.

The only stable isotope of fluorine is ^{19}F. This nucleus, with a spin of $\frac{1}{2}$, has a gyromagnetic ratio very near to that of protium, and thus ^{19}F nuclear resonance spectra are easily measured. Nmr studies have been widely used to establish structures and to study rate processes in fluorine compounds.

14-2. Types of Fluorides

The fluorine compounds of the elements are essentially of two main types, ionic and covalent, in all of which fluorine has a complete octet; examples are given in Table 14-1.

TABLE 14-1

Some Typical Fluorine Compounds

Compound	Nature	Properties
HF	Colorless liquid; b 19.4°	H-bonded polymer
CaF_2	Colorless crystals; m 1360°	Insoluble in water; fluorite structure
KHF_2	Colorless crystals; m 239°	Soluble in water, dissociated
SbF_3	White solid; m 292°	Hydrolyzes in H_2O; soluble in methanol
MoF_6	Colorless liquid; m 17.5°; b 35°	Hydrolyzed instantaneously
K_2OsF_6	Pale yellow crystals	Sparingly soluble in water
BrF_3	Yellow liquid	Explodes with water and vigorously fluorinates many compounds
SF_4	Colorless gas; m −121°	Hydrolyzes in H_2O; selectively fluorinates
SF_6	Colorless gas; m −56°	Stable to water and most reagents
CF_3I	Colorless gas; b −22.5°	Alcoholic KOH → CF_3H
CF_3COOH	Colorless liquid; b 72.4°	Strong acid; miscible with water
$(—CF_2—CF_2—)_n$	Translucent greasy solid	Very stable to all chemical reagents
$P(CF_3)_3$	Colorless liquid; b 17.5°	Donor molecule
$CF_3CCl_2CFClCF_3$	Colorless liquid; b 98°	Insoluble in water; stable to oxidants

Ionic Fluorides. These contain the F^- ion. The relatively small radius of F^-, 1.36 A, is almost identical with that of the oxide, O^{2-}, ion (1.40 A); consequently, many fluorides and oxides are ionic with similar formulas and crystal structure, for example, CaO and NaF. The compounds of the other halogens with the same formula usually form quite different lattices and may even give molecular lattices. Thus chlorides and other halides often resemble sulfides, just as the fluorides often resemble oxides. In several cases the fluorides are completely ionic, whereas the other halides are covalent; for example, CdF_2 and SrF_2 have the CaF_2 lattice (nearly all difluorides have the fluorite or rutile structures), but $CdCl_2$ and $MgCl_2$ have layer lattices with the metal atoms octahedrally surrounded by chlorine atoms. These differences also show up in the solubilities in water.

Covalent Fluorides. Covalent fluorides of many elements exist, and it is obvious that in view of the high electronegativity of fluorine such bonds have very considerable ionic character. It may be noted that fluorine shows the lowest affinity toward oxygen, which is not surprising in the light of their high electronegativities.

The high electronegativity of fluorine and its ability to withdraw electron density to itself are demonstrated by facts such as (a) CF_3COOH is a strong acid, (b) $(CF_3)_3N$ has no basic properties and (c) CF_3 derivatives are attacked much less readily by electrophilic reagents in anionic substitutions than are CH_3 compounds.

The coordination number of fluorine seldom exceeds 1. However, cases of fluorine atoms acting as bridges and being two coordinate are known. In BeF_2 glass, BeF_4 tetrahedra are joined together by shared fluorine atoms. The salt $K^+[(C_2H_5)_3Al—F—Al(C_2H_5)_3]^-$ has a linear and symmetrical Al—F—Al group with the Al—F distance equal to 1.82 A. The linearity of the Al—F—Al group may be due principally to the overlap of filled $2p$ orbitals on fluorine with empty $3d$ orbitals of the aluminum atoms; thus each Al—F bond has π as well as σ character. Fluorine bridges also are found in the tetrameric structures of certain transition metal pentafluorides (Fig. 30-B-2). While the pentachlorides of the same metals dimerize, forming $M\underset{Cl}{\overset{Cl}{\diagdown\diagup}}M$ bridges, the fluorides probably adopt the tetrameric structures which involve only single bridges, M—F—M, because the smaller size of F compared to Cl would introduce excessive M...M repulsion in an $M\underset{F}{\overset{F}{\diagdown\diagup}}M$ system. Fluorine bridging has also been invoked to explain the properties of SbF_5, which is a viscous, polymeric liquid. Below 15°, the ^{19}F nuclear resonance spectrum shows three peaks of relative intensities 2:2:1. This spectrum is consistent with either cyclic or linear polymers containing octahedral SbF_6 units linked through cis F atoms. Above 25°, exchange processes cause a collapse of the spectrum to a single line.

An important feature in the formation of fluorides is that in reactions with fluorine or with powerful fluorinating agents such as BrF_3, the elements usually give the highest known or maximum oxidation state; as noted previously, only oxides in comparable oxidation states are known. Thus silver gives AgF_2; the platinum metals give RuF_5, PtF_6 and OsF_6; and iodine gives IF_7.

Hydrogen Bonding. Along with N and O fluorine often engages in hydrogen bond formation. The hydride HF is consequently abnormal compared to the other halogen HX compounds, just as NH_3 and H_2O are abnormal. In all states[1,2] HF is polymeric; the structure has been noted previously (see page 213). HF gives complex ions such as HF_2^- and $H_2F_3^-$. Although the formula for the bifluoride ion is often written $[F—H—F]^-$ to indicate that it is linear and symmetrical, this may create the erroneous impression that hydrogen is forming two electron pair bonds. The electron structure of this ion can be expressed in terms of resonance theory as a hybrid (14-I); or it may be considered in terms of the concept

$$[\overset{-}{F}\cdots\overset{\delta^+}{H}—\overset{\delta^-}{F}]\leftrightarrow[\overset{\delta^-}{F}—\overset{\delta^+}{H}\cdots\overset{-}{F}]$$
$$\text{(14-Ia)}\qquad\text{(14-Ib)}$$

of three-center bonds (page 215).

The ability of fluorine to form hydrogen bonds is also shown by the hydration of certain fluorides, whereas the other halides are more commonly anhydrous. It must be noted, however, that the other halides do show some tendency to hydrogen bond formation, as evidenced by the behavior of $CHCl_3$ and the existence of salts with Cs^+, $[NR_4]^+$ and other large monovalent cations of stoichiometry $RHCl_2$.

Bond Distances and Bond Energies in Covalent Fluorides. Because of the low dissociation energy of fluorine, the heats of formation of fluorine compounds in their standard states are such that most fluorine compounds are strongly exothermic; this is the opposite of the situation with nitrogen compounds where the bond in N_2 is very strong. Further, because of the high electronegativity of fluorine, ionic–covalent resonance contributes substantially to the bond energies. In addition, small atoms such as fluorine can form stronger bonds owing to better overlap of their electron density, and π bonding is much more likely to occur for this reason. Multiple bond formation by fluorine is certainly one of the contributing factors to the shortness of many bonds in involving fluorine—for example, in BF_3 and SiF_4—when compared to those formed by the other halogens.

Organic Fluorine Derivatives. A vast number of organic compounds are now known in which hydrogen atoms are replaced by fluorine atoms.

[1] J. N. Maclean, F. J. C. Rossotti and H. S. Rossotti, *J. Inorg. Nucl. Chem.*, **24**, 1549 (1962).

[2] M. Atoji and W. N. Lipscomb, *Acta Cryst.*, **7**, 173 (1954).

Examples are $CF_3CCl_2CFClCF_3$, $CF_2{=}CF_2$, $CF_3C{\equiv}CCF_3$, $C_3F_7CH_2NH_2$ and $CF_3PO_3H_2$. Many of these compounds have chemical and physical properties strikingly different from the hydrogen analogs or from the analogous compounds of the other halogens where these exist.

THE ELEMENT

14-3. Occurrence, Isolation and Properties

Fluorine is widespread, occurring as insoluble fluorides of electropositive metals, notably *fluorspar*, CaF_2; *cryolite*, Na_3AlF_6; and *fluorapatite*, $3Ca_3(PO_4)_2Ca(F,Cl)_2$. It is more abundant (0.065%) than chlorine (0.055%) in the earth's crust.

The estimated standard potential of F^- ($E^0 = +2.85$ v) clearly indicates why early attempts to prepare the element by electrolytic methods in aqueous solution suitable for chlorine ($E^0 = +1.36$ v) failed. The element was first isolated in 1886 by Moissan, who pioneered the chemistry of fluorine and its compounds. The gas is obtained by electrolysis of fluorides in media with no other anions present. Anhydrous HF is nonconducting, but the addition of anhydrous KF gives conducting solutions. The most commonly used electrolytes are $KF \cdot 2$–$3HF$, which is molten at 70–100°, and KF–HF, which is molten at 250–270°. The electrolyte can be regenerated when the melting point begins to be too high by resaturation with HF from a storage tank. There have been many designs for fluorine cells; these are constructed of steel, copper or Monel metal, which become coated with an unreactive layer of fluoride, and steel or copper cathodes with ungraphitized carbon anodes are used. Although fluorine is often handled in metal apparatus, it can be handled in the laboratory in glass apparatus provided traces of HF, which attacks glass rapidly, are removed. This is achieved by passing the gas through sodium or potassium fluorides with which HF forms the bifluorides.

FLUORINE COMPOUNDS

14-4. Hydrogen Fluoride and its Salts

Hydrogen Fluoride. Hydrogen fluoride, HF, is made by the action of concentrated H_2SO_4 on CaF_2 and is the principal source of fluorine and its compounds. The liquid has a high dielectric constant (83.6 at 0°), and it is polymeric owing to hydrogen bonding. In the vapor phase HF is monomeric at high temperatures, but polymers, especially $(HF)_2$ and

$(HF)_6$, are formed at lower temperatures.[1]   Infinite zig-zag chains occur in the solid.[2]   After water, it is one of the most generally useful of solvents; indeed, in some respects it surpasses water as a solvent for both inorganic and organic compounds, the latter often forming highly conducting solutions (see below).   Very pure HF has a very low conductivity, 1.6×10^{-6} $\text{ohm}^{-1} \text{cm}^{-1}$ at $0°$.   The self-ionization equilibria in liquid HF are

$$2HF \rightleftharpoons H_2F^+ + F^- \qquad K \sim 10^{-10}$$
$$F^- + HF \rightleftharpoons HF_2^- \quad (H_2F_3^-, H_3F_4^-, \text{etc.})$$

so that fluoride ion is the conjugate base, and fluorides behave as bases in the HF solvent system.

In aqueous solution, the equilibria are

$$HF + H_2O \rightleftharpoons H_3O^+ + F^- \qquad K_1 = 7.2 \times 10^{-4}$$
$$F^- + HF \rightleftharpoons F_2H^- \qquad K_2 = 5.1$$

The weakness of HF as an acid in *dilute* aqueous solution is in great contrast to that of other hydrogen halides; this point is discussed elsewhere (page 222).   In $5-15M$ solutions ionization into H_3O^+, HF_2^- and more complex species ($H_2F_3^-$, $H_3F_4^-$, etc.) occurs, and HF becomes a strong acid.   The formation of these stable anions in liquid HF accounts for the extremely strong acidity of the pure substance.   Liquid HF is somewhat less acidic than 100% H_2SO_4, however, according to their Hammett acidity functions. Only a few substances, such as BF_3, AsF_5, SbF_5 and SnF_4, which are among the strongest fluoride ion acceptors, will function as "acids" in the liquid, thus increasing the H_2F^+ concentration

$$SbF_5 + 2HF = H_2F^+ + SbF_6^-$$

Such solutions can dissolve many metals.   Other strong acids such as nitric acid actually behave as bases in liquid HF,

$$HNO_3 + HF = H_2NO_3^+ + F^-$$

HNO_3 behaving as a proton acceptor.   Other reactions can be found to illustrate amphoteric behavior, solvolysis or complex formation in liquid HF.

The conductance of many solutions of organic substances in liquid HF is due primarily to protonation of the solute, e.g.,

$$C_2H_5OH + HF = C_2H_5OH_2^+ + F^-$$
$$C_6H_6 + HF = C_6H_7^+ + F^-$$

The aromatic hydrocarbons give colored solutions and their solubilities can be increased by adding fluoride acceptors such as SbF_5 and BF_3. The protonated species formed by some organic and organometallic molecules can be isolated as crystalline salts of BF_4^- or SbF_6^-.   In the gas phase also, stable hydrogen fluoride complexes are formed by a variety of compounds such as acetone or CH_3CN; hydrogen bonding is involved.[3]

Metal Fluorides; the Fluoride Ion. Many metals show their highest oxidation state in the fluorides which are often salt-like in their properties. Let us consider the Born–Haber cycle in equation 14-1.

$$M(s) \xrightarrow{\ S\ } M(g) \xrightarrow{\ I_4\ } M^{4+}(g) \searrow$$
$$MX_4(s) \qquad (14\text{-}1)$$
$$2X_2(g) \xrightarrow{\ 2D\ } 4X(g) \xrightarrow{\ 4A\ } 4X^-(g) \nearrow$$

The value of $(A - D/2)$, the energy change in forming 1 g-ion of X^- from $\frac{1}{2}$ g-mole of X_2, is ~ 60 kcal for all of the halogens, and S is small compared to I_4 in all cases. Although the structure of MX_4 and hence the lattice energy may not be known to allow us to say whether $4(A - D/2)$ plus the lattice energy will compensate for $(I_4 + S)$, we can say that the lattice energy and hence the potential for forming an ionic halide in a high oxidation state will be greatest for fluoride, since, generally, for a given cation size the greatest lattice energy will be available for the smallest anion, that is, F^-.

However, for very high oxidation states, which are formed notably with transition metals, for example, WF_6 or OsF_6, the energy available is quite insufficient to allow ionic crystals with, say, W^{6+} or Os^{6+} ions; consequently such fluorides are gases, volatile liquids or solids resembling closely the covalent fluorides of the nonmetals. The question as to whether a metal fluoride will be ionic or molecular cannot be reliably predicted, and the distinction between the types is not always sharp.

As noted previously, ionic oxides can also be obtained in high oxidation states, sometimes even higher than the fluorides, for example, RuF_5 and RuO_4. Fluorides in high oxidation states (unless the covalence maximum is attained) are often hydrolyzed by water, the important factors here being the greater stability of the ionic oxides and also the low dissociation of HF in aqueous solution. Thus, for example,

$$RuF_5 + H_2O \rightarrow RuO_2 + RuO_4 + HF$$

Many simple fluorides of metals in lower oxidation states are obtained by dissolving the oxides, carbonates, etc., in HF and drying the product, or by dry reaction. Higher fluorides, such as AgF_2 or CrF_4, usually require the use of elemental fluorine on the metal or a lower fluoride or other salt; bromine trifluoride has also been widely used as a fluorinating agent in place of fluorine.

---

[3] J. Arnold and D. J. Millen, *J. Chem. Soc.*, **1965**, 510.

The lanthanide elements and actinide elements in the $+3$ and $+4$ oxidation states give insoluble fluorides from aqueous solution. Fluorides of Li, Ca, Sr and Ba also are sparingly soluble, the lithium compound being precipitated by ammonium fluoride. Lead gives a sparingly soluble salt, PbClF, which can be used for gravimetric determination of F^-.

CaF_2 is used for prisms in infrared spectrometers since it gives better resolution than NaCl in the region 1500–4000 cm^{-1}. NH_4F differs from other ammonium halides in having a wurtzite rather than a rock salt or CsI structure; each nitrogen atom forms four tetrahedral N—H—F bonds of length 2.69 A. Although the N—H stretching frequency is lowered from 3300 to 2820 cm^{-1} here, the N—H bond length is the same as in NH_4Cl.

It is convenient to note here that the fluoride ion is basic and that the heavier alkali metal fluorides can act as catalysts in a variety of reactions both inorganic and organic.[4]

The nucleophilic nature is also shown by the catalytic rearrangement of fluoroolefins by CsF which involves initial addition to give a fluorocarbanion. A stabilized fluoro anion[5] is obtained by treating a perfluoroolefin complex $C_6F_8Fe(CO)_3$ with CsF to give $Cs[C_6F_9Fe(CO)_3]$.

Acid Fluorides. The alkali metal fluorides with HF give various acid fluorides; the structure of HF_2^- has been noted before. These salts are prepared by mixing the appropriate proportions of the constituents; examples are $KF \cdot 4HF$ (m 72°), $KF \cdot 3HF$ (m 65.8°) and $KF \cdot HF$ (m 239°); they contain polymeric hydrogen bonded ions[6], e.g., $H_2F_3^-$.

Fluoro Anions. Many metals and nonmetals form complex fluoro anions, if the simple fluoride is coordinately unsaturated; some fluorides, for instance BF_3 and PF_5, are strong F^- ion acceptors. Fusion of simple fluorides often gives the complex fluoro anions, as does the action of BrF_3 or F_2 on complex chlorides. A simple general method is the reaction of ammonium fluoride with metal bromides in acetone solution to give complexes such as NH_4MnF_3, NH_4BiF_4 and $(NH_4)_3InF_6$. Examples of other reactions leading to the formation of fluoro anions are:

$$3NaF + AlF_3 \xrightarrow{\text{fuse}} Na_3AlF_6$$
$$B(OH)_3 + 4HF(aq) \longrightarrow BF_4^- + H^+ + 3H_2O$$
$$SO_3 + HF(l) \longrightarrow HSO_3F$$
$$KBr + Ru \xrightarrow{\text{BrF}_3} KRuF_6$$

Many of the complex fluorides of metals are hydrolyzed by water; this is particularly true where higher oxidation states are involved. The factors

---

[4] L. Rand, J. V. Swisher and C. J. Cronin, *J. Org. Chem.*, **27**, 3505 (1962).

[5] G. W. Parshall and G. Wilkinson, *J. Chem. Soc.*, **1962**, 215.

[6] J. D. Forrester, M. E. Senko, A. Zalkin and D. H. Templeton, *Acta Cryst.*, **16**, 58 (1963).

governing the stability of fluoro anions are similar to those noted previously for simple fluorides.

The complex fluoro acids are all strong. In fact, it would be impossible for, say, HBF_4 to be otherwise without involving either pentavalent boron or divalent fluorine. In this case, study of the $HF–BF_3$ system shows that there is *no* 1:1 compound formed; that is, HBF_4 does not exist. If a solvent molecule is present to combine with the proton, compound formation can be observed as with $H_3O^+BF_4^-$. A similar situation exists with other fluoro anions, for example, PF_6^-.

14-5. Inorganic Molecular Fluorides

The molecular fluorides of both metals and nonmetals are usually gases or volatile liquids; analogs with the other halogens are often lacking, the reason being partly the size factor which with fluorine permits higher coordination numbers and partly the factors discussed above concerning the stability of higher oxidation states and covalent bond formation. Where the central atom has suitable vacant orbitals available, and especially if the polarity of the single bonds M—F would be such as to leave a considerable positive charge on M, as in, say, SF_6, multiple bonding can occur using filled p orbitals of fluorine for overlap with vacant orbitals of the central atom. The volatility of molecular fluorides is due to the absence of intermolecular bonding other than van der Waals forces, since the polarizability of fluorine is very low and no suitable outer orbitals exist for other types of attraction.

Where the fluoride gives the maximum covalence, as in CF_4 or SF_6, the compounds are exceedingly inert chemically. In other cases, rapid hydrolysis occurs in water or stable fluoro anions are formed; thus SeF_6 hydrolyzes on heating, and TeF_6 hydrolyzes at room temperature to $Te(OH)_6$, although SF_6 is inert to water.

The particular fluorides, where of interest, are discussed under the respective elements. Fluorine compounds of the other halogens are discussed under interhalogen compounds (page 584), but it is convenient to note here *perchloryl fluoride*. This compound, first made in 1952, is now produced in ton quantities as a powerful oxidizing agent. It is a stable gas, b $-46.7°$, inert and noncorrosive at room temperature except when wet. It has the highest dielectric constant of any known gas. The compound is prepared by the reaction

$$NaClO_4 + 2FSO_3H \xrightarrow{\text{warm}} FClO_3 + NaF + H_2S_2O_7$$

and in other ways. With aqueous ammonia, perchloryl fluoride reacts to give the ions $NClO_3{}^{2-}$ and $HNClO_3{}^{-}$ which can be precipitated as explosive Rb or Cs salts.

Chlorylfluoride, ClO_2F, also exists but it is extremely reactive and explosive.

14-6. Organic Fluorine Compounds

These compounds are prepared in a variety of ways, principally as follows:

1. *Replacement of other halogens using metal fluorides.* The driving force for a reaction

$$R\text{—}Cl + MF = R\text{—}F + MCl$$

depends in part on the free energy difference of MF and MCl, which is approximately equal to the difference in lattice energies. Since lattice energies are proportional to the reciprocal of the interionic distance, the increase in free energy when MCl is formed from MF is proportional to the difference of the reciprocals of the sums of the ionic radii in MF and MCl. Thus the larger the cation, M, the more favorable tends to be the free energy for the above reaction, and the fluorine-exchanging ability therefore increases with increasing metal ion radius in isomorphous compounds. For AgF the difference in lattice energies is small owing to contributions of nonionic bonding in AgCl, so that AgF is a very powerful fluorinating agent.

Other fluorinating agents, each having particular advantages under given conditions, are AgF_2, CoF_3, SbF_3 (+ $SbCl_5$ catalyst), HgF_2, KHF_2, ZnF_2, AsF_3, etc. Examples of some fluorinations are

$$PCl_3 + AsF_3 \xrightarrow{25°} PF_3 + AsCl_3$$
$$C_6H_5CCl_3 + SbF_3 \longrightarrow C_6H_5CF_3 + SbCl_3$$

Nonmetal fluorides are also often effective. Sulfur tetrafluoride is a particularly useful and selective fluorinating agent for organic oxygen compounds where, for example, $RR'C{=}O$ is converted to $RR'CF_2$.

An important commercial method for preparing organic fluorine compounds involves replacement of Cl with F by the action of liquid HF; $SbCl_5$ or other catalysts are required for these reactions to occur under mild conditions. For example:

$$SbCl_5 + 3HF = SbCl_2F_3 + 3HCl$$
$$SbCl_2F_3 + 2CCl_4 = SbCl_5 + CCl_3F + CCl_2F_2$$

2. *Hydrogen replacement using fluorides or fluorine.* Under controlled

conditions, usually in the vapor phase, fluorine (diluted with N_2) or cobaltic fluoride can be used, for example,

$$(CH_3)_3N \xrightarrow{\text{CoF3}} (CF_3)_3N + (CF_3)_2NF + CF_3NF_2 + NF_3$$

$$C_6H_6 + F_2 \xrightarrow[265°]{\text{copper catalyst}} C_6F_{12}$$

Direct fluorination appears to involve $F \cdot$ free radicals.

A special case of this type of substitution, which is widely used in the laboratory and commercially, is the electrolysis of compounds in liquid HF at a voltage below that required for the liberation of fluorine. Steel cells with nickel anodes and steel cathodes are used. Organic compounds, as noted before, often give conducting solutions in liquid HF and are fluorinated at the anode, usually into a perfluoro derivative. Examples of electrolytic fluorinations are

$$(C_2H_5)_2O \rightarrow (C_2F_5)_2O$$
$$C_8H_{18} \rightarrow C_8F_{18}$$
$$(CH_3)_2S \rightarrow CF_3SF_5 + (CF_3)_2SF_4$$
$$(C_4H_9)_3N \rightarrow (C_4F_9)_3N$$

Other methods sometimes used are the addition of HF to multiple bonds and thermal decomposition of aromatic diazonium fluoroborates, for example,

$$CCl_2{=}CCl_2 \xrightarrow[25°]{\text{PbO2 + HF}} CCl_2HCCl_2F$$

$$C_6H_5N_2Cl \xrightarrow{\text{NaBF4}} C_6H_5N_2BF_4 \xrightarrow{\text{heat}} C_6H_5F + N_2 + BF_3$$

The C—F bond energy is indeed very high (116 kcal/mole; C—H, 99 and C—Cl, 79 kcal/mole), but organic fluorides are not necessarily particularly thermodynamically stable; indeed, some of the stabilities of fluorine derivatives must be attributed to the impossibility of expansion of the octet of fluorine and the inability of, say, water to coordinate to fluorine or carbon as the first step in hydrolysis, whereas with chlorine this may be possible using outer d orbitals. Because of the small size of the F atom, H atoms can be replaced by F atoms with the least introduction of strain or distortion as compared to replacement by other halogen atoms. The F atoms also effectively shield the carbon atoms from attack. Finally, since C bonded to F can be considered to be effectively oxidized (whereas in C—H it is reduced), there is no tendency for oxidation by oxygen. Fluorocarbons are attacked only by hot metals, e.g., molten sodium. When pyrolyzed, fluorocarbons tend to split at C—C rather than C—F bonds.

The replacement of H by F leads to increased density, but not to the same extent as with other halogens. Completely fluorinated derivatives, C_nF_{2n+2}, have very low boiling points for their molecular weights and low intermolecular forces; the weakness of these forces is also shown by the very low coefficient of friction for polytetrafluoroethylene, $(CF_2—CF_2)_n$.

Commercially important organic fluorine compounds are chlorofluorocarbons, which are used as nontoxic, inert refrigerants, aerosol bomb propellants and heat transfer agents, and fluoroolefins, used as monomers for free-radical-initiated polymerizations to oils, greases, etc., and also as chemical intermediates. $CHClF_2$ is used for making tetrafluoroethylene:

$$2CHClF_2 \xrightarrow{500–1000°} CF_2{=}CF_2 + 2HCl$$

C_2F_4 is also made by quenching CF_2 radicals formed at temperatures above 1500° by the reaction of almost any source of fluorine with carbon. Tetrafluoroethylene, b $-76.6°$, can be polymerized thermally or in aqueous emulsion by use of oxygen, peroxides, etc., as free radical initiators. A convenient laboratory source of C_2F_4 is thermal cracking of polymer at 500–600°.

The fluorinated carboxylic acids are notable first for their strongly acid nature—for example, for CF_3COOH, $K_a = 5.9 \times 10^{-1}$, whereas CH_3COOH has $K_a = 1.8 \times 10^{-5}$. Second, many standard reactions of carboxylic acids can be made leaving the fluoroalkyl group intact, as in equation 14-2.

$$C_3F_7COOH \xrightarrow[C_2H_5OH]{H_2SO_4} C_3F_7COOC_2H_5 \xrightarrow{NH_3} C_3F_7CONH_2 \overset{\overset{P_2O_5}{\nearrow} C_3F_7CN}{\underset{LiAlH_4 \searrow C_3F_7CH_2NH_2}{}} \tag{14-2}$$

Trifluoroacetic anhydride obtained by action of P_2O_5 on the acid is widely used in organic chemistry as an acylating agent in presence of acid.

The $C_nF_{2n+1}COOH$ acids can be converted to *perfluoroalkyl halides* by, for example, the action of I_2 on the silver salt. These halides are relatively reactive, undergoing free radical reactions on heating or on irradiation, although, because of the very strong electron-attracting nature of the perfluoroalkyl groups, they fail to show many of the common nucleophilic reactions of alkyl halides. They do not, for example, readily form Grignard reagents. The activation energy for the reaction

$$CF_3I = CF_3· + I·$$

is only 1.7 kcal/mole. CF_3I is an important intermediate for preparation of trifluoromethyl derivatives. Thus the reaction of CF_3I and similar compounds with metals and nonmetals has led to an extensive range of CF_3 derivatives, for example,

$$CF_3I + P \xrightarrow{heat} (CF_3)_nPI_{3-n}$$

References

Banks, R. E., *Fluorocarbons and their Derivatives*, Oldbourne Press, London, 1965. Emphasizes properties and reactions of perfluoroalkyls of metalloids and non-metals.

——, and R. N. Haszeldine, *Adv. Inorg. Chem. Radiochem.*, **3**, 338 (1961). Polyfluoroalkyls of metalloids and nonmetals.

Clark, H. C., *Chem. Rev.*, **58**, 869 (1958). Physical and chemical properties of halogen fluorides and other covalent fluorides.

Hudlicky, M., *The Chemistry of Organic Fluorine Compounds*, Pergamon Press, 1961. A comprehensive text.

Hyman, H. H., and J. J. Katz, in *Non-Aqueous Solvents Systems*, Academic Press, New York, 1965. Liquid HF as solvent.

Mellor, J. W., *Comprehensive Treatise of Inorganic Chemistry*, Vol. II, Suppl. I, Part I, Longmans, Green, New York–London, 1956.

Pavpath, A. E., and A. L. Leffler, *Aromatic Fluorine Compounds*, Reinhold, New York, 1962. A comprehensive reference text.

Peacock, R. D., *Progr. Inorg. Chem.*, **2**, 193 (1960). Some fluorine compounds of the transition metals.

Rudge, A. J., *Manufacture and Use of Fluorine and its Compounds*, Oxford Univ. Press, 1962.

Sharpe, A. G., *Quart. Rev.*, **9**, 49 (1957). An excellent brief article on inorganic fluorine chemistry.

Simons, J. H., ed., *Fluorine Chemistry*, Vols. I–V, Academic Press, New York, 1954. Comprehensive reference books on special topics in fluorine chemistry. Vol. V contains a useful general survey of fluorine-containing compounds of the elements with 819 references and a survey of industrial aspects of F chemistry.

Stacey, M., J. C. Tatlow, and A. G. Sharpe, eds., *Advances in Fluorine Chemistry*, Butterworths. A series of annual review volumes covering all aspects of fluorine chemistry. Vol. I: halogen fluorides, transition metal fluorides, fluoroboric acids, electrochemical fluorinations, metallic fluorinations; Vol. II: thermochemistry, fluorine resources, mass spectrometry, direct fluorination of organic compounds, actinide fluorides, physiology; Vol. III: effects of C_nF_{2n+1} groups on $>C=O$ activity, perfluoroalkyl compounds, nitrogen fluorides, industrial fluorochemicals, halogen exchange preparations; Vol. IV: inorganic fluorine techniques, main group fluorides; Vol. V: nitrogen oxofluorides, phosphorus fluorides.

Treichel, P. M., and F. G. A. Stone, *Adv. Organomet. Chem.*, **1**, 143 (1964). Fluorocarbon derivatives of metals.

15

Stereochemistry and Bonding in
Compounds of Nontransition Elements

15-1. Introduction

We have now completed our discussion of those elements of the first short period which strictly obey the octet rule. Several of them also have a strong tendency to form multiple bonds. The stereochemistry of their compounds is governed by these two facts. In the chapters immediately following we shall discuss the chemistry of the remaining nontransition elements, that is, the congeners of the elements of the first short period. For many of these elements the presence of low-lying d orbitals means that the number of electron pairs in the valence shell may exceed four; that is, the octet rule no longer holds rigorously and is indeed very often violated. In addition, for these heavier atoms, participation in double bond formation by the use of $p\pi$ orbitals is much less important than for their congeners in the first short period, whereas they can use low-lying $d\pi$ orbitals to participate in varying degrees of multiple bonding. Thus the stereochemistry and bonding in compounds of the heavier elements is more varied and complex.

The problem to be considered in this chapter is that of finding relationships between the structures of molecules and the nature of the chemical bonds which they contain. This problem has two aspects. The one to which we shall devote most attention concerns the shapes of the molecules, that is, the angles between the bonds formed by a given atom. The second and shorter part of the discussion will deal with certain aspects of multiple bonding, that is with certain questions of bond lengths.

We shall implicitly assume that in two-center bonds the electron density is distributed symmetrically about the internuclear axis. In other words, we shall not explicitly consider the possibility of bent bonds. While this is unquestionably a good and useful approximation—doubtless a much better one than many others usually made in simple valence theory—it is well to remember that, except in special cases where symmetry considerations prohibit it, chemical bonds may well be, *at least a little*, bent.[1]

BOND ANGLES ABOUT ATOMS WITH OCTETS

To a certain extent this section will be a review and codification of principles mentioned already in discussions of the elements of the first short period. However, we shall also deal with heavier elements in compounds where they have octets. First we shall consider the cases where all valence shell electrons are present either as unshared pairs or in single bonds and then those cases where some of the valence shell electrons are in multiple bonds formed by the atom using its p orbitals.

15-2. Molecules with Only Single Bonds

TABLE 15-1

Bond Angles in Some AB_2, AB_3 and ACB_3 Molecules

(Atom A having an Octet)

Molecule	Angle, deg	Molecule	Angle, deg	Molecule[a]	Angle, deg
NH_3	107	NF_3	103	OCl_2	~111
PH_3	94	PF_3	104	ClO_2	~117
AsH_3	92	PCl_3	100	OF_2	102
SbH_3	91	PBr_3	~100	POF_3	103 (FPF)
OH_2	105	AsF_3	102	SO_2F_2	93 (FSF)
SH_2	92	$AsCl_3$	98	PSF_3	100 (FPF)
		$SbCl_3$	104	SCl_2	~102
		$SbBr_3$	~96		
		SbI_3	~98		

[a] A few of the molecules in the last column contain multiple bonds (e.g., PO, PS, SO) as well as single bonds. However, except for ClO_2, this is not believed to influence significantly the bond angles.

In Table 15-1 are listed some representative molecules of the types AB_2, AB_3, ACB_3 and a few others, in which the central atom A has an octet of electrons in its valence shell. It will be seen that the bond angles lie in the range 91–117° with all but two between 91 and ~107°. In NH_3 and H_2O the angles come closest to the tetrahedral angle of 109°28'. Several different explanations have been put forward for the observed variations in bond angles. However, these proposals should not be regarded as mutually exclusive alternatives, but rather as complementary to one another either

[1] W. H. Flygare, *Science*, **140**, 1179 (1963).

13*

in the sense of being different ways of stating essentially the same thing, or in emphasizing different but important contributions to the final, observed effect. One explanation involves the assumption that the central atoms, O and N, tend to assume sp^3 hybridization. However, because the bonding and nonbonding electron pairs are not equivalent, we might expect that the orbitals holding the unshared pairs and the orbitals used in bonding would not be exactly equivalent to one another. The deviations of the angles are toward values less than $109°28'$. It has been suggested that the bonding pairs are more concentrated along the internuclear axes so that the lone-pairs tend to occupy relatively more space. Thus the hybridization is such as to give bonding orbitals with a somewhat smaller angle between them in order that the best energetic compromise may be reached between maximizing bond strengths and minimizing interelectronic repulsions. Once again, we may repeat that it has been shown that the electrostatic forces of repulsion between the relatively positive hydrogen atoms in NH_3 and H_2O would be insufficient to account for an expansion from 90° if we had assumed that the central atoms preferred using pure p orbitals for bonding.

It is striking that, on going from NH_3 to PH_3, the angle drops sharply to $\sim 94°$ and then to $\sim 92°$ in AsH_3 and SbH_3. Similarly, the HSH angle is only $\sim 92°$. This could result from the ability of the heavier elements to form stronger bonds to hydrogen using nearly pure p orbitals. Similarly, in halides, especially fluorides, the angles are generally much below the tetrahedral value indicating increased p character in the bonding orbitals and decreased p character in the orbitals holding lone-pairs. There appears to be some evidence from microwave studies that the contribution of d character in H_2S and other non-first-row compounds is of the same order as the s character and this might tend to lower the angle in H_2S to about 90°.

It has been pointed out—and is apparent from the data in Table 15-1 —that smaller angles usually occur in those molecules in which the central atom is less electronegative than the atoms to which it is bound. This can be explained by considering that the configuration of lowest potential energy is determined not only by the dependence of overlap, and hence intrinsic bond strength, on the angles but also by the variation of repulsive energy between the various electron pairs (i.e., lone-pair–bonding pair, lone-pair–lone-pair and bonding pair–bonding pair repulsions, designated subsequently as LP—BP, LP—LP and BP—BP respectively). As the bonding electrons in AB_3, for example, are drawn further away from A, the BP—BP repulsion will lessen, permitting some closing up of the bond angles in order to decrease LP—BP repulsions. The large bond angle in ClO_2 has not been explained definitely. It seems probable, however, that there is appreciable Cl—O π bonding which causes extensive delocalization of the odd electron and also influences the bond angle.

15-3. Molecules with Multiple Bonds

In molecules in which there are *multiple bonds*, but with all atoms obeying the octet rule, it is possible to predict the *symmetry* of the molecules quite reliably either by valence bond theory or by molecular orbital theory; at the same time neither approach used in the simple forms to be described below can be counted on to give angles to within better than 10–15° or so.

From the VB point of view, we may consider that in any atom having an octet of electrons these will tend to be arranged so that a pair of electrons is centered around each apex of a tetrahedron. Now, in a molecule like ethane, we find that the structure is correctly predicted by treating the C—C single bond as corresponding to the sharing of an apex by two tetrahedra about the carbon atoms. This approach may be extended to the cases of double and triple bonds. A *double bond* is considered to result from the sharing of a common edge by two tetrahedra. Thus, for example, in the general case of an ABX=YCD type molecule the structure should be as shown in Figure 15-1, with the angles AXY, CYX, etc., equal to

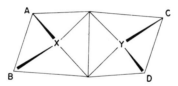

Fig. 15-1. The formation of a double bond by sharing a common edge of two tetrahedra.

about 125° and the angles AXB and CYD equal to about 109°. Note that this approach predicts qualitatively that the entire molecule should be planar and provides a kind of mechanical analogy for remembering that rotation about a double bond is strongly hindered. This most general formulation includes cases where A, B, C and D are all atoms, as in ethylenes, as well as cases in which one, two or three of them are only unshared pairs, as in $R_2C=N(OH)$, $Cl_2C=O$, $C_6H_5N=N(OH)$ or $ClN=O$.

From the point of view of MO theory, molecules with double bonds can be treated in the following way, taking again the general case ABX=YCD. Each of the atoms X and Y is assumed to possess a set of hybrid orbitals approximating to, and let us for simplicity at the outset say exactly, sp^2, made up of the atomic orbitals, s, p_x and p_y. One of these on each atom, X and Y, is used to form an X—Y σ bond. The remaining two are used to house electron pairs either in bonds to the atoms A, B, C and D or to house unshared pairs of electrons. Finally, the p_z orbitals on X and Y, each containing one electron, combine to form an X—Y π bond. Again, therefore, we would predict coplanarity of the ABX=YCD skeleton and, because of the π bond, a strong hindrance to internal rotation. If we keep to our original assumption that the hybridization of X and Y is exactly sp^2, then we must expect *all* bond angles to be 120°. But, considering X, for example, this assumption is over-restrictive since there is no reason why the orbitals used by X to bind the three different groups, A, B and Y, should be exactly equivalent. If they are not, then deviations of the bond angles from 120° may be expected.

In order to test the utility of these two approaches, both of which lead to identical predictions regarding symmetry and substantially the same predictions as to the order of magnitude of the bond angles, we may refer to some data on representative molecules assembled in Table 15-2.

TABLE 15-2
Structures of Some Molecules of the Type ABX=YCD

Molecule	A	B	X	Y	C	D	Planar	Bond angle, deg			
								YXA	YXB	XYC	XYD
$H_2C=CH_2$	H	H	C	C	H	H	Yes	120	120	120	120
$Cl_2C=CCl_2$	Cl	Cl	C	C	Cl	Cl	Yes	123	123	123	123
$H_2N=NO_2$	H	H	N	N	O	O	Yes	Unknown		115	115
$(CH_3)_2C=N(OH)$	C	C	C	N	O	—	Yes	131	113	111	—
$[ON=NO]^{2-}$	O	—	N	N	—	O	Yes	All unknown			
ClNO	Cl	—	N	O	—	—	Yes	116	—	—	—
BrNO	Br	—	N	O	—	—	Yes	114	—	—	—
$Cl_2C=O$	Cl	Cl	C	O	—	—	Yes	124	124	—	—
$F_2C=O$	F	F	C	O	—	—	Yes	~124	~124	—	—
HFC=O	H	F	C	O	—	—	Yes	Unknown	122	—	—

There remains one other case of double bond formation by atoms with octets, namely, the general case A=X=B. From the VB approach we should predict linearity for such an arrangement, that is, an AXB angle of 180° as shown in Figure 15-2. Using the MO approach, we reach precisely

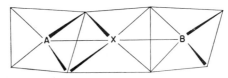

Fig. 15-2. Formation of two double bonds according to the valence bond view.

the same conclusion by the following analysis. The atom X uses two sp hybrid orbitals to form σ bonds to the atoms A and B. It then has two p orbitals, at right angles to one another in a plane perpendicular to the

AXB axis, which can combine with corresponding orbitals on A and B to form π bonds. This is illustrated in Figure 15-3. In each case one would also predict great hindrance to rotation of A relative to B. A few examples of molecules of this sort which substantiate the predictions are:

H$_2$C=C=O (ketene): $\angle$CCO = 180°; $\angle$HCH = 123°
O=C=O: Linear
N=N=O (in resonance with N≡N—O): Linear
O=C=C=C=O: Linear
H$_2$C=C=CH$_2$ (allene): $\angle$CCC = 180°; $\angle$HCH = 117°
H—N=C=O: $\angle$NCO = 180°; $\angle$HNC = 126°
H—N=C=S: $\angle$NCS = 180°; $\angle$HNC = 131°

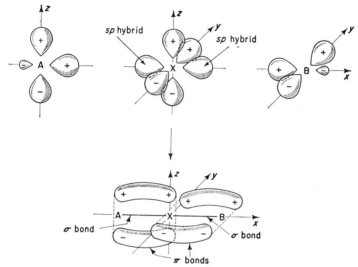

Fig. 15-3. Formation of two double bonds according to the molecular orbital view.

Now let us consider *triple bonds*, for which the general case would be A—X≡Y—B. In VB theory we consider the triple bond as the sharing between X and Y of a tetrahedron face. As can be seen in Figure 15-4,

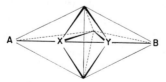

Fig. 15-4. Formation of a triple bond according to the valence bond view.

this leads to the prediction that the A—X≡Y—B chain should be completely linear. Taking an MO approach, we assume that atoms X and Y each use linear sp hybrid orbitals to form the σ bonds A—X—Y and X—Y—B. Then there remain, on both X and Y, pairs of p orbitals at right angles to one another and in planes perpendicular to the AXYB axis which overlap to form two π bonds (Fig. 15-5). Thus, again, both approaches have given the same prediction as to symmetry, and all available data indicate that this prediction is correct. Thus, for example,

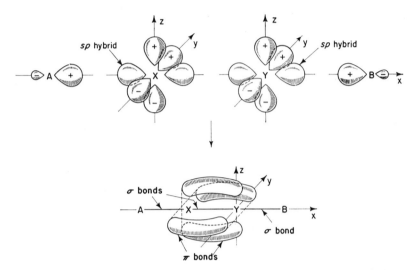

Fig. 15-5. Formation of a triple bond according to the molecular orbital view.

acetylene and all its derivatives, e.g., N≡C—C≡CH, Cl—C≡C—H, CH_3—C≡C—CH_3, etc., are linear, as are HC≡N, N≡C—C≡N and others.

A few additional remarks are pertinent lest too optimistic a view of the state of simple structural theory be given. The above ideas have their limitations and involve further complications in their application. The chief limitation is that except in the cases such as the AXB angle in A═X═B and the AXY and XYB angles in A—X≡Y—B, *exact* bond angles cannot be predicted. To take a concrete example, for a molecule of the type X_2C═CX_2 the XCX angles are never exactly 109° as predicted by VB theory or 120° as predicted by the MO treatment in the above simple forms and, moreover, they vary with the nature of the atoms X. Thus in H_2C═CH_2 the HCH angle is 119.9°, and in H_2C═CBr_2 the BrCBr angle is 113.5°. Such variability is actually to be expected, just as in the case of molecules without multiple bonds. In terms of the VB approach it simply means that the four electron pairs do not lie at the corners of a perfectly regular tetrahedron, and, since the environments at the various corners are not identical, we should not be surprised at the lack of precise regularity. Similarly, in terms of the MO treatment, the deviations from 120° bond angles simply mean that the carbon atoms do not use three equivalent sp^2 hybrid orbitals, but that those used to form the σ bonds to the atoms X differ somewhat from the one used to form the σ bond to carbon, and that the variation in the orbitals depends somewhat on the identity of the atoms X. It is quite reasonable to expect such variation.

In molecules where several resonance forms are important, there is some additional complexity. It sometimes happens that all important canonical forms predict *exactly* the same bond angles, and the interpretation remains unambiguous. Examples of this are 15-I and 15-II. The next most

$$:\overset{..}{\underset{..}{N}}{=}\overset{+}{N}{=}\overset{..}{O}: \leftrightarrow :N{\equiv}\overset{+}{N}{-}\overset{..}{\underset{..}{O}}:$$

(15-Ia)   (15-Ib)

$$:N{\equiv}C{-}C{\equiv}N: \leftrightarrow :\overset{..}{\underset{..}{N}}{=}C{=}C{=}\overset{+}{\underset{..}{N}}: \leftrightarrow :\overset{+}{\underset{..}{N}}{=}C{=}C{=}\overset{..}{\underset{..}{N}}:$$

(15-IIa)   (15-IIb)   (15-IIc)

complicated case is one in which two or more important canonical forms have similar but not identical symmetries. A typical example of this would be carbonyl chloride with molecular symmetry C_{2v} (15-III). All three resonance structures require planarity, and the molecule is indeed

(15-IIIa)   (15-IIIb)   (15-IIIc)

planar, but each would be most stable with a somewhat different set of bond angles. Only 15-IIIa has C_{2v} symmetry. The actual angles must be assumed to be the best compromise energetically. In the case of the nitrate ion we use the VB description shown in 15-IV. Now, no one of the energetically equivalent structures 15-IVa–c, *if* it existed, would have

(15-IVa)   (15-IVb)   (15-IVc)

the three-fold symmetry (D_{3h}) which the nitrate ion actually has, but, of course, we must remember that the canonical structures are hypothetical. They must be assumed to have the geometry of the actual molecule, even though the distribution of the electrons is less symmetrical.

In concluding this section, we may briefly consider the relation between the VB and MO treatments of multiple bonding which have been shown to be equally good in accounting for the symmetry of molecules with multiple bonds. Although both seem about equally useful, we might ask the question: Are both equally valid fundamentally? In other words, is there any basic theoretical reason for preferring Figure 15-6a over 15-6b as a description of a double bond, or Figure 15-6c over 15-6d as a description

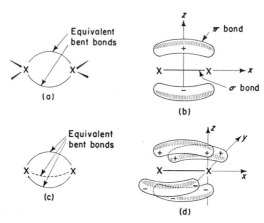

Fig. 15-6. Representations of multiple bonds.

of a triple bond, or can one choose whichever is handiest for a particular purpose?

The answer is that in quantitative calculations both formulations can be shown to be correct to a fairly high degree of approximation. In fact, the two bent bonds in Figure 15-6a are mathematically *equivalent* to the $(\sigma + \pi)$ combination in Figure 15-6b, and the three bent bonds in Figure 15-6c are mathematically *equivalent* to the $(\sigma + 2\pi)$ combination in Figure 15-6d. It happens, particularly in organic chemistry, that the $(\sigma + \pi)$ formulation of multiple bonding has certain conceptual advantages and is fashionable, but it is not fundamentally any more *correct* than the valence bond formulation. It is well to develop facility in using both concepts in considering possible structures for molecules.

BOND ANGLES ABOUT ATOMS WITH VALENCE SHELLS OF MORE THAN EIGHT ELECTRONS

The nontransition elements in groups IV, V, VI and VII of the second and higher periods form various compounds in which their valence shells are occupied by more than four electron pairs, counting both shared and unshared pairs. Furthermore the molecular structures encountered in such compounds are often surprising in the degree to which they deviate from the symmetrical structures which might have been expected, although there are many such compounds which do have symmetrical structures.

For the most part we shall deal with molecules of the general types AB_n or AB_nC_m, in which there is a central atom, A, from one of the higher non-transition periods, to which all other atoms in the molecule are bound. These other atoms may be of one or of several different chemical species. The theoretical problem is to provide a set of orbitals capable of holding all the electrons in the valence shell of atom A, both those involved in A—B and A—C bonds and those which are nonbonding, and to do this in such a way that the orbitals which hold bonding pairs are directed along the A—B and A—C axes.

There have been two main approaches to this problem. One is based on the idea that s–p–d hybrid orbitals are formed in sufficient number for all bonds to be two-center, two-electron ($2c$–$2e$) bonds. The other assumes that the central atom uses its p orbitals to form three-center, four-electron ($3c$–$4e$) bonds, while leaving the d orbitals out of consideration. The first of these, which is older, better known and probably more widely accepted, we shall call the *Full Hybridization Theory*, and the other, which has not been as broadly applied, we shall call the 3-*Center Bond Theory*. Each of these represents an extreme, that is, a drastic oversimplification, and therefore, neither can be expected to be entirely adequate. We shall see, indeed, that neither one is, but each has its merits and its realm of superiority in providing a *simple* way to correlate and rationalize many structural facts.

15-4. The Full Hybridization Theory

Mode of Application. The first stage beyond the octet is the decet, in molecules of general formula AB_5. In order for A to house five electron pairs, it must have five bonding orbitals. Its ns and three np orbitals provide the components of only four hybrid orbitals. In order to make five, an additional atomic orbital of the lowest possible energy must also be used. This is presumed to be one of the nd orbitals.* Thus, the bonding orbitals will be some kind of sp^3d hybrids. As noted on page 79, there are two sorts of sp^3d hybrids possessing some degree of symmetry: $sp^3d_{z^2}$, in which the five hybrids are directed to the apices of a trigonal bipyramid, and $sp^3d_{x^2-y^2}$ (or sp^3d_{xy}), in which they are directed to the corners of a

---

* It has been pointed out that the selection of a d orbital rather than some other higher-lying orbital is often arbitrary from a purely energetic point of view. Cf. W. Klemperer, *J. Amer. Chem. Soc.*, **83**, 3910 (1961).

square pyramid. It is impossible to predict with certainty which set will give the more stable compound in any given case, but experimental evidence indicates that it will generally be the $sp^3d_{z^2}$ set, since all known structures are of the trigonal bipyramid type, as in PCl_5 (gas), PF_5, $SbCl_5$ and SOF_4, with the recently discovered exception of $Sb(C_6H_5)_5$ in the solid state.

In compounds of type AB_6, where all valence shell electrons of atom A are bonding electrons, atom A must have six hybrid orbitals, and these may reasonably be expected to be of the octahedral sp^3d^2 type. Thus, such molecules should be octahedral, and all of them which are known do indeed have this structure. These include such molecules and ions as SF_6, SeF_6, TeF_6, PF_6^-, $SnCl_6^{2-}$, SiF_6^{2-}, etc., as well as $F_5S—SF_5$, in which each sulfur atom is octahedrally surrounded by five fluorine atoms and a sulfur atom.

Molecules or ions of type AB_7 with fourteen electrons in the valence shell orbitals of atom A are quite rare. They could only be of the following types: AB_7, where A is in group VII; AB_7^-, where A is in group VI; AB_7^{2-}, where A is in group V; or AB_7^{3-}, where A is in group IV. There are no examples known of the ions, and only one neutral molecule, namely, IF_7. The seven bonding orbitals used by iodine are then assumed to be some sort of sp^3d^3 hybrids, although it is not impossible that $4f$ orbitals might play some part in the hybridization. Even assuming that $4f$ orbitals may be neglected, there are various possible arrangements depending upon which three d orbitals are used. The most symmetrical possibility would be a pentagonal bipyramid (symmetry D_{5h}), and this is the structure of IF_7 in both the vapor and crystalline states, although in the crystal there is significant distortion.

We can now consider the class of molecules in which the valence shell of atom A in an AB_n molecule contains ten, twelve or fourteen electrons and also more than n electron pairs; in other words, cases in which there are unshared electron pairs on the central atom.

Let us first consider molecules of type AB_4 in which there is *one unshared pair* on atom A. There are a fair number of such molecules known, and most of those for which the structures have been established are listed in Table 15-3. The bond angles and distances are quoted with reference to Figure 15-7, which shows the type of structure characteristic of all such molecules so far as is known. Although such a relatively unsymmetrical structure seems a little surprising, it may be explained in the following way. We assume that the central atom uses a set of sp^3d trigonal bipyramid orbitals for holding the five electron pairs in its valence shell and that the unshared pair occupies one of the equatorial orbitals. Ideally, this would mean that the BAB angle should be 180° and the B'AB' angle should be

TABLE 15-3

Structures of AB_4 and AB_2C_2 Molecules with One Unshared Pair on Atom A

Molecule	Distance, A		Angle, deg	
	A—B	A—B′ (A—C)	BAB	B′AB′
SF_4	1.646 ± 0.003	1.545 ± 0.003	173.0 ± 0.5	101.5 ± 0.5
SeF_4	~1.76	~1.76	160–180	~120
$(C_6H_5)_2SeCl_2$	Se—Cl: 2.30 ± 0.05	Se—C: ?	180 ± 5	?
$(C_6H_5)_2SeBr_2$	Se—Br: 2.52 ± 0.05	Se—C: 1.91 ± 0.03	180 ± 3	110 ± 10
$TeCl_4$	~2.33	~2.33	~170	90–120
$(C_6H_5)_2TeBr_2$	Te—Br: 2.682	Te—C: 2.18	178	95 ± 1
$(CH_3)_2TeCl_2$	Te—Cl: 2.51 ± 0.04	Te—C: 2.09 ± 0.03	172.3 ± 0.3	98.2 ± 1.1
$[IO_2F_2]^-$	I—F: 2.0 ± 0.1	I—O: 1.93 ± 0.05	~180	100 ± 7

120°. As in previous cases, we can expect only that the actual angles will approximate to these values. The data in Table 15-3, most of which are not extremely accurate, indicate that the above view enables one to predict the correct symmetry and approximately the correct bond angles. The tendency of the B′—A—B′ angles to be much less than 120° may be explained by assuming that the LP—BP repulsions are greater than BP—BP repulsions.

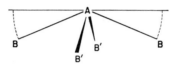

Fig. 15-7. The general structure of molecules of the types AB_4 or AB_2C_2 where atom A has an unshared pair of electrons (symmetry, C_{2v}).

We may extend the same analysis to account for the structures of AB_3 and AB_2 systems in which atom A has altogether five electron pairs in its valence shell.

There are three known examples of the AB_3 case (two unshared pairs), namely, ClF_3, BrF_3 and ICl_3, the structures of which are shown in Figure 15-8. The molecular parameters given for ClF_3 and BrF_3 are the extremely accurate ones determined by microwave studies of the gases. X-ray studies show only slight and insignificant variations in the crystalline materials. ICl_3 exists only as a solid and has the dimeric structure shown. The structures of ClF_3 and BrF_3 can be accounted for by assuming that the Cl and Br atoms use a set of sp^3d trigonal bipyramid orbitals to house three pairs of bonding electrons and two unshared pairs, the latter occupying equatorial orbitals. $(ICl_3)_2$ will be discussed presently.

The known AB_2 systems are XeF_2, KrF_2 and the various trihalide anions such as I_3^-, ICl_2^- and $ClBr^-$. All of these are linear and have the heaviest atom in the middle. By a natural extension of the preceding analysis, we may suppose that again the central atom has a set of sp^3d, trigonal bipyramid hybrid orbitals of which the axial ones are used in bond formation and the equatorial ones hold the unshared pairs.

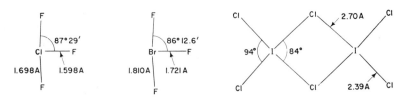

Fig. 15-8. The structures of ClF_3, BrF_3 and I_2Cl_6. The first two have C_{2v} symmetry while the dimer has D_{2h} symmetry.

In view of the presumed trigonal bipyramidal arrangement of the five electron pairs in the compounds we are discussing, their structures can be designated "ψ-trigonal bipyramidal." This is but one example of the general system of nomenclature in which a prefactorial ψ is used to indicate a certain arrangement of bonds which are considered to form part of the complete structure which would exist if the lone-pair or pairs were also used in bonding. It is a bad system of nomenclature in that it does not provide an entirely objective designation of purely experimental facts, but instead also implies an interpretation of the facts. However, it is a convenient way of designating certain structural types without any alternative of comparable simplicity and it is to be found frequently in the recent literature. Therefore, it will be used in this book *but without any implication that the theory of valence from which it derives is necessarily being espoused or recommended.*

In concluding the discussion of compounds with central atoms having ten-electron valence shells, it may be well to point out clearly that, although there is a consistent scheme to account for the structures, it is actually very empirical. In the first place, there is no substantial theoretical basis for preferring the trigonal bipyramid to the square pyramid type of sp^3d hybridization. It is only from the experimental data themselves that we know that the former is the generally correct choice. Second, we again are unable to explain with any certainty why it is always the *equatorial orbitals which hold the unshared pairs.* Actually we might have expected the opposite since the axial bonds in trigonal bipyramidal and ψ-trigonal bipyramidal molecules are always *longer* and thus, presumably, weaker than the equatorial ones. Third, it is not clearly demonstrable that the T-structure for the AB_3 compounds should involve less repulsion between electron pairs than the alternative structure in which the lone-pairs occupy the two axial orbitals. It is a question of whether the energy of six LP—BP plus three BP—BP (120°) repulsions should be less than the total energy of one LP—LP ($\geqslant 120°$), two LP—BP ($\leqslant 120°$), four LP—BP ($\geqslant 90°$) and two BP—BP ($\leqslant 90°$) repulsions. Obviously no purely qualitative order of the types of repulsion, namely LP—LP > LP—BP > BP—BP, though correct it may be, can answer such a question.

Let us now proceed to molecules AB_n in which the central atom A has six electron pairs in the valence shell with one or more being unshared. Those known to exist are of the types AB_5 with one unshared pair and AB_4 with two unshared pairs. Those of the types AB_5 and AB_4C with one unshared pair are ClF_5, BrF_5, IF_5 and $XeOF_4$. The structure of BrF_5 is that shown in Figure 15-9. The structures of the others have not been

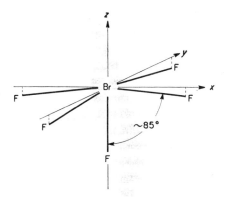

Fig. 15-9. The structure of BrF_5.

determined in detail but the infrared, Raman and nmr spectra strongly suggest that they also have C_{4v} symmetry, the O atom in $XeOF_4$ occupying the unique position on the 4-fold axis. This type of structure can be denoted "ψ-octahedral." These structures can easily be explained assuming that the central atom uses a set of sp^3d^2, octahedral hybrid orbitals with one containing an unshared pair. The bond angles of $\sim 85°$ may be assumed to result from the fact that LP—BP repulsions exceed BP—BP repulsions, as noted earlier. In addition to the four species already mentioned, there are several compounds of Sb^{III}, for example SbF_5^{2-}, in which the antimony atom is in a ψ-octahedral environment (see Chapter 20).

Of AB_4 species with twelve valence shell electrons on atom A, structural information is available for XeF_4, ICl_4^- and BrF_4^-, all of which are planar with equal A—B bond lengths and equal bond angles (symmetry D_{4h}). The planar structure may be explained by assuming sp^3d^2 hybridization of the central atom with the unshared pairs occupying *trans* positions in the octahedron. Assuming again that since nonbonding electron pairs form a more diffuse cloud than bonding pairs, it is reasonable that they would occupy *trans* rather than *cis* positions in order to minimize repulsion between electron pairs. The designation ψ-octahedral may thus be applied to this structure also.

Finally, we may return to $(ICl_3)_2$, the structure of which has already been given. This may be explained by assuming that each iodine atom has a twelve-electron valence shell (seven of its own, one from each terminal Cl and three from the pair of bridging chlorines) and that again the unshared pairs take *trans* positions in the octahedra.

Criticism. Despite the fact that the full hybridization theory correlates a great deal of structural data, as we have just seen, it is subject to a number of criticisms. We have already noted that a number of *ad hoc* assumptions have to be made and that the qualitative rule for the order of the different types of repulsion between electron pairs, while adequate in simple cases, is insufficient to give a unique specification of structure in more complicated ones.

There are other more positive and substantive criticisms to be made. First, the theory does not *always* work. It fails for some species of the type AB_6 where A has seven electron pairs. Species of this type include XeF_6, $IF_6{}^-$ and the numerous hexahalogeno complexes of Se^{IV}, Te^{IV} and Po^{IV}. The structures of all of these should be based on some form of polyhedron with seven vertices, one being occupied by the lone-pair. This might be a ψ- pentagonal bipyramid structure in view of the pentagonal bipyramidal structure of IF_7. While the structures of XeF_6 and $IF_6{}^-$ are still not established, in many cases the halogeno complexes of the group VI elements have been shown to have essentially regular octahedral structures. In some cases, the octahedral symmetry is rigorous in the crystallographic sense.[2]

The full hybridization theory does not provide any explanation for the different lengths of A—B bonds of different types in AB_n molecules, although these differences are not incompatible with the theory. More important, perhaps, is the fact that in some cases, particularly in the $ICl_4{}^-$ ion, the mean bond length,[3] 2.50A, is considerably longer than that expected for a normal single bond, ~ 2.32A, and actually found in the gaseous ICl molecule.

Another difficulty is that there are some more or less direct indications that the role of d orbitals is greatly exaggerated in the full hybridization theory. Thus, nuclear quadrupole resonance studies of the $ICl_2{}^-$ and

[2] D. Nakamura, K. Ito and M. Kubo, *J. Amer. Chem. Soc.*, **84**, 163 (1962). This paper gives nuclear quadrupole resonance results and reference to X-ray work.

[3] R. J. Elema, J. L. de Boer and A. Vos, *Acta Cryst.*, **16**, 243 (1963).

ICl_4^- ions have been interpreted as indicating that the I—Cl bonds are ionic to a degree which seems to preclude any significant d orbital participation.[4]

15-5. The Three-center Bond Theory

This approach is a limited MO treatment, predicated on two main ideas: (1) that the use of outer d orbitals of the central atom is so slight that they may be neglected altogether, and (2) that the persistent recurrence of bond angles close to 90° and 180° in AB_n molecules suggests that orbitals perpendicular to one another, namely p orbitals, are being used.

Two types of chemical bond are considered. First there is the ordinary two-center, two-electron $(2c-2e)$ bond, formed by the overlap of a p orbital of the central atom with a σ orbital of an outer atom. Second, and this is the novel and characteristic feature of this theory, there is the linear three-center, four-electron $(3c-4e)$ bond, formed from a p orbital of the central atom and the σ orbitals of two outer atoms. The formation of 3-center molecular orbitals has already been described (page 279) in connection with the bridge bonding in boron hydrides (where the bonding was of the $(3c-2e)$ type) and also, very briefly, in connection with the symmetrical hydrogen bond in FHF^- (page 215) where a $(3c-4e)$ bond was considered possible. The bonds of interest here are no different in principle, but we illustrate both the orbitals and the energy level diagram in Figure 15-10.

Several features of the $(3c-4e)$ bonding deserve emphasis. Of the four electrons populating the MO's, only two are bonding electrons. Hence the A—B bonds so formed should be weaker and longer than a normal $(2c-2e)$ A—B bond. Second, since the electrons in ψ_b are shared between the p_A orbital and the σ_B and $\sigma_{B'}$ orbitals while the electrons in the ψ_n orbital reside entirely on the B atoms, the A—B bonds are expected to be quite polar with the B atoms negative. Such a situation should be favored when B is more electronegative than A and in all of the compounds under discussion it is found that the central atom is the least electronegative in the molecule.

Mode of Application. Clearly, all of the linear species, XeF_2, and the various trihalide anions, are easily accommodated. In addition to nonbonding electrons on the B atoms and the electrons in the ψ_b and ψ_n orbitals, there are three pairs of electrons on A. These may be assigned to the s and the other two p orbitals of atom A.

The T-shaped molecules are considered to contain a $(3c-4e)$ bond in the nearly linear B—A—B group and a $(2c-2e)$ bond between A and the other

[4] C. D. Cornwell and R. S. Yamasaki, *J. Chem. Phys.*, **27**, 1060 (1957).

B atom with the remaining four electrons of atom A occupying the s orbital and the other p orbital of A. In the AB_4 molecules of the type in Table 15-3 the theory postulates one $(3c-4e)$ bond and two $(2c-2e)$ bonds with a lone-pair in the s orbital.

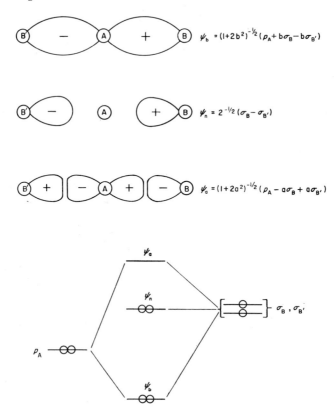

Fig. 15-10. The upper part shows how a set of three 3-center orbitals are formed from a p_σ orbital of the central atom, A, and σ orbitals on the two outer, B, atoms. The lower part shows approximately how the energies of the various atomic and molecular orbitals are related in a typical case and how the orbitals are populated.

For molecules in which there are six electron pairs the theory again works satisfactorily. The AB_4 species are postulated to have two $(3c-4e)$ bonds and unshared pairs in the remaining p orbital and the s orbital, while the AB_5 species have two $(3c-4e)$ bonds, one $(2c-2e)$ bond and a lone-pair in the s orbital.

Finally, the 3-center bond theory accounts nicely for the regular octahedral structure of some AB_6 species with seven electron pairs, since it postulates three $(3c-4e)$ bonds with the remaining electron pair residing in the s orbital. Since the latter is spherically symmetrical no distortion of the octahedron is expected to occur.

Criticism. The most serious criticism might be that the range of applicability of this approach is very limited. It does not seem reasonable that the compounds in which all electron pairs of the central atom are bonding pairs have drastically different electronic structures from those in which there are some unshared pairs. However, the bonding scheme postulated for SF_4 cannot be carried over directly to PF_5, for example. Nor does the pentagonal bipyramidal structure of IF_7 find a natural explanation within the framework of the 3-center bond theory.

It is also to be noted that while the 3-center bond theory does give a qualitatively correct explanation for the differences in bond lengths in the T-shaped AB_3 and the analogous AB_4 molecules, it is doubtful if the agreement is satisfactory in quantitative terms. Bond orders which are supposed to differ by a factor of 2 might be expected to have bond lengths differing by more than a mere 0.1A.

However, it should be stressed again that the 3-center bond approach is simply an artificially aborted MO theory, in which the basic set of orbitals on the central atom has been restricted to the p orbitals. A more general approach in which the s and d orbitals would also be included might well reduce to something very similar to the 3-center bond scheme in those cases where the latter is adequate and yet also embrace the cases where it is not. Furthermore, a general MO treatment should also embrace the main ideas of the full hybridization theory, except that *full* hybridization would not be uniformly required. Thus, in the cases where the full hybridization theory apparently fails, the more flexible MO approach might succeed because it would not necessarily always attach great importance to the use of d orbitals. Unfortunately this *ideal, general, flexible* MO theory is still to be reduced to practice and tested. At present, the only theories which have been reduced to practice are the more restricted, relatively inflexible ones we have just discussed.

MULTIPLE BONDING

15-6. $d\pi–p\pi$ Bonds

As noted earlier, the heavier nontransition atoms lack any significant tendency to use their valence shell p orbitals for π bonding. However, they do make considerable use of their valence shell d orbitals to form π bonds, particularly to oxygen, but also to nitrogen and fluorine. The experimental indications of multiple bonding are chiefly the high values of bond stretching force constants and the shortness of bonds compared to the lengths expected for single bonds. There are also cases in which bond angles at bridging atoms are indicative of the extent of π bonding. In this brief discussion, only the structural manifestations of $d\pi$–$p\pi$ bonding will be considered.

Tetrahedral Molecules. We must first consider what possibilities exist in principle, that is on the basis of compatibility of orbitals, for forming $d\pi$–$p\pi$ bonds. For a tetrahedral AB_4 molecule such as SiF_4 or PO_4^{3-}, each of the B atoms has two filled $p\pi$ orbitals perpendicular to the A—B bond axis and perpendicular to each other. The central atom, A, is assumed to use its s and p orbitals for σ bonding. A detailed examination of the suitability of the d orbitals of A for overlapping with the $p\pi$ orbitals on the B atoms shows that all of them are able to do so, but two, namely d_{z^2} and $d_{x^2-y^2}$, are particularly well suited for this.[5] Each of these two would be expected to have about $\sqrt{3}$ times as much overlap with the $p\pi$ orbitals of the four B atoms as one of the other three d orbitals. Figure 15–11

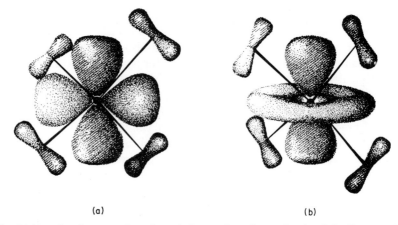

(a)   (b)

Fig. 15-11. Quasi-perspective view of the overlap of $p\pi$ orbitals of the B atoms in a tetrahedral AB_4 molecule with (a) the $d_{x^2-y^2}$ and (b) d_{z^2} orbitals of the A atom. (Adapted from ref. 5 by permission.)

shows in a rough schematic way the principal $d\pi$–$p\pi$ overlap possibilities.

Bond length data in the series of ions SiO_4^{4-}, PO_4^{3-}, SO_4^{2-}, ClO_4^- indicate that such $p\pi$–$d\pi$ bonding actually does occur. As shown in Table 15-4, the X—O bonds are all short relative to values reasonably expected for single bonds, and, moreover, the extent of shortening is closely parallel to the calculated magnitudes for $d\pi$–$p\pi$ overlaps.

Similarly, in SiF_4, even after due allowance is made for the effect of ionic–

[5] D. W. J. Cruickshank, *J. Chem. Soc.*, **1961**, 5486.

TABLE 15-4

Bond Lengths and $d\pi$–$p\pi$ Overlaps in $XO_4{}^{n-}$ Ions

Ion	Obs. X—O dist.,[a] in A	Est. X—O single[a] bond dist., in A	Shortening[a]	$p\pi$–$d\pi$ overlap[b]
$SiO_4{}^{4-}$	1.63	1.76	0.13	0.33
$PO_4{}^{3-}$	1.54	1.71	0.17	0.46
$SO_4{}^{2-}$	1.49	1.69	0.20	0.52
$ClO_4{}^{-}$	1.46	1.68	0.22	0.57

[a] From Ref. (5).
[b] From H. H. Jaffé, J. Phys. Chem., **58**, 185 (1954).

covalent resonance in strengthening and hence shortening the Si—F bonds, they appear to be around 0.13A shorter than the length expected for single bonds, and the implication, therefore, is that π bonding is present as well.

Other Molecules. In less symmetrical molecules the detailed analysis of π bonding is more difficult because the d orbitals of the central atom can interact with different types of outer atoms to different degrees. However, by utilizing the idea (page 112) that bond order and bond length are inversely related, it is possible to deduce approximate, relative degrees of π bonding in various compounds containing SiO, PO, SO and ClO groups, as well as, to a more limited extent, in other cases. For PO and SO bonds the data are most extensive. The various types of P—O bond vary in length from ~ 1.68 to ~ 1.40A, and it has been suggested[5] this last value, about the shortest observed distance for any SO, PO, SN or PN bond, corresponds to about a double bond, i.e., to a π bond order of about 1.

However, it is possible that this is an underestimate, since in SF_3N, where the S—N bond must be more nearly triple than double (see page 533) the length is 1.42A.

The configurations of molecules are often influenced by $d\pi$–$p\pi$ bonding, though the simultaneous influence of electrostatic forces in some cases should not be discounted. The well-known case of the flat Si_3N skeleton in $(SiH_3)_3N$ is discussed in detail on page 327. The bond angle at oxygen in various XOX bridge systems also indicates varying degrees of X—O π bonding. Thus, when this angle is relatively small ($\sim 120°$) there is only one pair of electrons on O which are properly oriented to form π bonds with the d orbitals of the X atoms, whereas, in the limit of an XOX angle of 180°, two π bonds, one for each XO group, could be formed. Thus, increasing XOX angles might at least roughly be taken to indicate increased XO π bonding. If this is correct, there should also be a correlation between increasing angle and decreasing bond length. The absence of a correlation would show that some factor(s) other than $d\pi$–$p\pi$ bonding was mainly responsible for determining the bond angles. To a certain extent such correlations have been found,[5] but the situation is still somewhat uncertain for lack of sufficient structural data of high accuracy.

15-7. The Use of Outer d Orbitals

In much of the preceding discussion the question of the availability of the nd orbitals of a central atom for use in bonding along with its ns and np orbitals has occupied a decisive position. However, attempts to settle this question directly have been inconclusive. It has been suggested that the outer d orbitals may be unable to make any effective contribution to bonding because their energies are too high and because they are too large and diffuse to overlap sufficiently with the valence orbitals of other smaller atoms. Certainly, if the d orbital wave functions are taken as those of the Slater type for the free atoms, corresponding to the experimentally observed energies, this is very likely so.

However, it has been shown[6] that, when the surrounding atoms (e.g., the F atoms in SF_6) are very electronegative, they drain enough charge from the central atom to cause a significant increase in the effective nuclear charge for the d orbitals and this results in a contraction of the radial d wave function. More recently, it has been reported[7] that from a Hartree–Fock calculation (see page 31) for one term (^7F) of the $3s3p^33d^2$ configuration of sulfur, the $3d$ wave function seems to be far more compact (mean radius, $\sim 1.9A$) than the Slater-type orbital (mean radius, $\sim 3.4A$). This would mean that d orbital participation might be more generally favorable than had been supposed, even without the orbital contraction effect of electronegative surrounding atoms.

Clearly, the solution to this problem of d orbital participation requires further work, especially the computation of Hartree–Fock orbitals for a range of atoms using data from more than one term of a configuration. It must also be expected that the compactness of the d orbitals will depend strongly on the atomic number and formal oxidation state of the atom, so that there is unlikely to be any easy, blanket generalization.

[6] D. P. Craig and E. A. Magnussen, *Discussions Faraday Soc.*, No. **26**, 116 (1958).

[7] D. W. J. Cruickshank, B. C. Webster and D. F. Mayers, *J. Chem. Phys.*, **40**, 3733 (1964).

References

Coulson, C. A., J. Chem. Soc., **1964**, 1442. Detailed treatment of bonding in xenon fluorides and related molecules.

Gillespie, R. J., J. Amer. Chem. Soc., **82**, 5978 (1960). Hydrides and halides of groups V and VI.

———, Can. J. Chem., **39**, 318 (1961). Bond lengths and angles in nontransition metal octahedral and trigonal bipyramidal compounds.

———, and R. S. Nyholm, Progr. Stereochem., **2**, 261 (1958). A general account of inorganic stereochemistry for nontransition and also transition elements.

———, Quart. Rev., **7**, 339 (1957). Another account of the inorganic stereochemistry for nontransition and transition elements.

Malm, J. G., H. Selig, J. Jortner and S. A. Rice, Chem. Rev., **65**, 199 (1965). In this review of xenon chemistry there is a lengthy and thoughtful discussion of bonding, which is relevant to all of the AB_n compounds.

Nyholm, R. S., Progr. Stereochem., **1**, 322 (1954). A general account of inorganic stereochemistry for nontransition and also transition elements.

Rundle, R. E., Records Chem. Progr., **23** (4), 195 (1962). A review of the three-center bond theory with a favorable bias.

Searcy, A. W., J. Chem. Phys., **31**, 1 (1959). A review of the stereochemical effects of unshared pairs of electrons.

Walsh, A. D., Progr. Stereochem., **1**, 1 (1954). Brief description of experimental methods and tables of data for small molecules.

Wiebenga, E. H., E. E. Havinga and K. H. Boswijk, Adv. Inorg. Chem. Radiochem., **3**, 133 (1961). Survey of structural data for interhalogen compounds with brief discussion of the bonding.

16

The Group I Elements: Na, K, Rb, Cs

GENERAL REMARKS

16-1. Introduction

The chemistry of the first member of the group I elements (the alkalies), lithium, has been described previously (Chapter 8); in many respects it is a prototype for the other members, although it has characteristic differences, which have already been discussed, because of its small atomic and ionic radii. The elements Na, K, Rb and Cs have the simplest of all elemental chemistries since the atoms have only a single s electron outside a noble gas core. The electronic configurations, ionization potentials and standard electrode reduction potentials are listed in Table 16-1. The low ionization

TABLE 16-1
Some Properties of Group I Metal Atoms

Element	Atomic number	Electronic configuration	Ionization potentials, ev		E^0, for $M^+(aq) + e = M(s)$, v
			1st	2nd	
Li	3	[He]2s	5.390	75.62	-3.02
Na	11	[Ne]3s	5.138	47.29	-2.71
K	19	[Ar]4s	4.339	31.81	-2.92
Rb	37	[Kr]5s	4.176	27.36	-2.99
Cs	55	[Xe]6s	3.893	23.4	-3.02
Fr	87	[Rn]7s	?	?	?

potentials for the outer electrons and the fact that the resulting M^+ ions have noble gas configurations and are thus spherical and of low polarizability result in the chemistry of these elements being essentially that of their $+1$ ions. No other oxidation states are known, nor are they to be expected considering the magnitudes of the second ionization potentials.

414

Although the chemistry of the elements is predominantly ionic, some degree of covalent bonding occurs in certain cases. The gaseous diatomic molecules—Na_2, Cs_2, etc.—are covalently bonded, and the bonds to oxygen, nitrogen and carbon in various chelate and organometallic compounds doubtless have some slight covalent character. The tendency to covalence is greatest with lithium and least with cesium, as would be expected from the charge/radius ratios.

The element *francium* is formed in the natural radioactive decay series and in appropriate artificial nuclear reactions. All of its isotopes are radioactive with short half-lives. Precipitation reactions and solubility and ion exchange studies have shown that the ion behaves as would be expected from its position in the group.

It is to be noted also that the isotope ^{40}K (β^-, K; 16.1×10^8 y; 0.0119% abundance) occurs in potassium in nature. Use is made of this in age determinations of potassium-containing minerals; the unusual abundance of ^{40}Ar in the earth's atmosphere is due to its formation by K-capture decay of ^{40}K. Rubidium is also naturally radioactive owing to ^{87}Rb (β^-, 6×10^{10} y; 27.2% abundance).

Of all the groups in the periodic table, the group I metals, including lithium, show most clearly and with least complication the effect of increasing size and mass on chemical and physical properties. Thus all of the following *decrease* through the series: (a) melting points and heats of sublimation of the metals; (b) lattice energies of all salts except those with the very smallest anions (because of irregular radius ratio effects); (c) the effective hydrated radii and the hydration energies (see Table 16-2); (d) the ease of thermal decomposition of nitrates and carbonates; (e) strength of the covalent bonds in the M_2 molecules; (f) heats of formation of fluorides, hydrides, oxides and carbides (because of higher lattice energies with the smaller cations). Other trends can readily be found.

The elements copper, silver and gold, the so-called coinage metals, are sometimes treated with the sodium group. The only justification for this procedure is that the atom of each of these elements has a single s electron outside of a closed shell. In this case, however, the closed shell is a d shell of the penultimate principal level. Although these elements do have +1 oxidation states, their over-all chemical resemblance to the sodium group is very slight. They are best considered as close relatives of the transition metals, which they resemble in much of their chemistry, such as formation of complexes, variable oxidation state, etc.

It is pertinent to note that there are other ions which have chemical behavior closely resembling the group I ions:

1. The most important of these are the ammonium ions, NH_4^+, RNH_3^+, $...R_4N^+$. NH_4^+ has an ionic radius (1.43 A) close to that of K^+ and

its salts generally resemble those of potassium quite closely in their solubilities and crystal structures.

2. In the $+1$ oxidation state, thallium, as Tl^+, behaves in certain respects as an alkali metal ion (although in others more like Ag^+). Its ionic radius (1.51 A) is comparable to that of Rb^+, although it is more polarizable. Thus thallous hydroxide is a water-soluble, strong base, which absorbs carbon dioxide from the air to form the carbonate. The sulfate and some other salts are isomorphous with the alkali metal salts.

3. A variety of other types of monopositive, essentially spherical cations often behave like alkali metal ions of comparable size. For example, the very stable di(π-cyclopentadienyl)cobalt(III) ion and its analogs with similar "sandwich" structures have precipitation reactions similar to those of Cs^+, and $[(\pi\text{-}C_5H_5)_2Co]OH$ is a strong base which absorbs carbon dioxide from the air and forms insoluble salts with large anions.

THE ELEMENTS

16-2. Preparation and Properties

The metals are obtained by electrolysis of fused salts or salt mixtures. Because there is only one valence electron per metal atom, the binding energies in the close-packed metal lattices are relatively weak and the metals are consequently very soft and have low melting points (Na, 97.5; K, 63.7; Rb, 38.5; Cs, 28.5°). Liquid alloys of the alkali metals are known, the most important being the Na–K alloys. The eutectic mixture in this system contains 77.2% K and melts at $-12.3°$. This alloy, which has a wide liquid range and high specific heat, has been considered as a coolant for nuclear reactors.

Studies of the spectra of group I metal vapors at about the boiling points of the metals show the presence of $\sim 1\%$ of diatomic molecules whose dissociation energies decrease with increasing atomic number (Li_2, 25.8; Na_2, 17.5; K_2, 11.9; Rb_2, 11.3; Cs_2, 10.4 kcal/mole at 0°K). These molecules provide the most unambiguous cases of covalent bonding of the alkalies.

All of the alkali metals are highly electropositive and react with most other elements directly. The reactivities toward air and water increase down the group; sodium effervesces with water, but the hydrogen evolved is not usually ignited; the heavier elements react explosively. In air sodium and potassium tarnish rapidly, and the other metals must be handled in an inert atmosphere as must Na–K alloys. Although Li, Na, K and Rb are silvery in appearance, Cs has a distinct golden-yellow cast.

The metals dissolve vigorously and exothermically in mercury, forming amalgams. Sodium amalgam (commonly symbolized by Na/Hg) is a liquid when dilute in sodium or a solid when rich in sodium; it is quite useful as a strong reducing agent.

Sodium metal may be dispersed by melting on various supporting solids such as sodium carbonate, Kieselguhr, etc., or by high speed stirring of a suspension of the metal in various hydrocarbon solvents held just above the melting point of the metal. Dispersions of the latter type are commercially available; they may be poured in air, and they react with water only with effervescence. They are often used synthetically where sodium shot or lumps would react too slowly. In addition, these dispersions can be converted by hydrogen to suspensions of sodium hydride, which are also commercially available as intermediates for preparation of other hydrides, for example, $NaBH_4$, for reductions, etc.

16-3. Solutions in Liquid Ammonia, Amines and Ethers

The group I metals, and to a lesser extent Ca, Sr, Ba and a few other electropositive metals, are soluble in liquid ammonia and in certain amines to give solutions which are blue when dilute. These solutions conduct electricity *electrolytically*, and measurements of transport numbers of the carriers suggest that the main current carrier is the *solvated electron*, by which is implied electrons which are free from their parent sodium atoms and occupy cavities in the liquid. At higher alkali metal concentrations the solutions are copper colored and have a metallic luster, and various physical data, such as their exceedingly high electrical conductivities, indicate that they are very similar to liquid metals.

In dilute solutions the metal is completely dissociated into metal ions and ammoniated electrons. Esr studies have shown the presence of "free" electrons, but the decrease of the paramagnetism with increasing concentration suggests that the ammoniated electrons can associate to form diamagnetic species containing electron pairs. Although there may be other equilibria, the data can be accommodated by equilibria such as

$$Na(s) \text{ (dispersed)} = Na \text{ (in solution)} = Na^+ + e$$
$$2e = e_2$$

Just how the electrons are associated with the ammonia molecules or the solvated metal ions is still a matter of discussion.[1] A suggestion has been made that in addition to solvated cations, *negative* ions stabilized by solvation may exist[2] in dilute solutions. These can be involved in an

---

[1] E. Arnold and A. Patterson, Jr., *J. Chem. Phys.*, **41**, 3089, 3098 (1964).
[2] S. Golden, C. Guttman and T. R. Tuttle, Jr., *J. Amer. Chem. Soc.*, **87**, 135 (1965).

14+A.I.C.

oxidation–reduction equilibrium involving the solvent S, with S^- then representing the solvated electron:

$$M^+ + 2S^- \rightleftharpoons M^- + 2S$$

In addition, ion pairing equilibria are involved:

$$M^+ + S^- \rightleftharpoons M^+ \cdot S^-; \qquad M^+ + M^- \rightleftharpoons M^+ \cdot M^-$$

With these and related assumptions, calculated and observed values of vapor pressure, conductance data and spectra agree quite well. Irrespective of what ions are present, the association of an electron or electrons with ammonia molecules can in any event account for the unusual densities of the solutions which are much lower than that of liquid ammonia.

Fairly stable solutions of K, Rb and Cs in various ethers have been obtained. Tetrahydrofuran, ethyleneglycol dimethyl ether and other methyl polyethers are among the best. The general properties of these solutions, insofar as they have been determined in view of the attack on the solvents, appear to be similar to those of the amine and liquid ammonia solutions; the alkali metal concentrations in saturated solutions are, however, only $\sim 10^{-4}$ g-atom/liter.

The ammonia and amine solutions of alkali metals are widely used preparatively in both organic and inorganic chemistry. Thus lithium in methylamine shows great selectivity in its reducing properties, but both this reagent and lithium in ethylenediamine are quite powerful and will reduce aromatic rings to cyclic monoolefins. Sodium in liquid ammonia is probably the most widely used system for preparative purposes. The solution is moderately stable, but the decomposition reaction

$$Na + NH_3(l) = NaNH_2 + \tfrac{1}{2}H_2$$

can occur photochemically and is catalyzed by transition metal salts. Sodium amide can be conveniently prepared by treatment of sodium with liquid ammonia in the presence of a trace of ferric chloride. Amines react similarly:

$$Li(s) + CH_3NH_2(l) \xrightarrow{50-60°} LiNHCH_3(s) + \tfrac{1}{2}H_2$$

The physical and chemical properties required of the solvent to make possible the formation of such solutions are not fully understood. The dielectric constant of the solvent is important in the same way as in the solution of an ionic solid, namely, to diminish the forces of attraction between the oppositely charged particles—in this case, M^+ ions and electrons. Furthermore, if the solvent molecules immediately surrounding these particles interact strongly with them, the energy of the system is further lowered. The detailed nature of the interaction of the electrons with the surrounding solvent molecules is still debatable, but it is fairly certain that the metal ions are solvated in the same way as they would be in a solution of a metal salt in the same solvent. It is therefore pertinent to discuss here the $[Na(NH_3)_4]^+$ ion which is formed on treatment of NaI with liquid ammonia. $[Na(NH_3)_4]I$ is a liquid of fair thermal stability. It freezes at 3° and at 25° has an equilibrium pressure of NH_3 of 420 mm; thus it must be kept in an atmosphere of ammonia with at least this pressure at 25°. The infrared and Raman spectra indicate the complex ion $[Na(NH_3)_4]^+$ to be tetrahedral with Na—N bonds about as strong as the Zn—N bonds in $[Zn(NH_3)_4]^{2+}$ or the Pb—C bonds in $Pb(CH_3)_4$. Bending and rocking frequencies, however, are quite low, suggesting that the Na—N bonding is mainly due to ion–dipole forces. Thus it may be assumed that Na^+ and other metal ions in the liquid ammonia, amine and ether solutions are strongly solvated in the same way. The well-known effectiveness of tetrahydrofuran and the dimethyl ethers of ethylene and diethylene glycols ("glyme" and "diglyme," respectively) as media for reactions involving sodium may be due in part to the slight solubility of the metal, but the solvation of ions by ether molecules undoubtedly provides the most important contribution. Indeed, in several instances crystalline etherates have been isolated, for example [Na diglyme$_2$]-[Ta(CO)$_6$] and [K diglyme$_3$][Mo(CO)$_5$I].

COMPOUNDS OF THE GROUP I ELEMENTS

The group I metals react directly with most nonmetals to give one or more binary compounds; they also form numerous alloys and compounds with other metals such as Pb and Sn. Many of these compounds are described under the appropriate element, although a few classes will be treated here.

16-4. Oxides

Sodium rapidly tarnishes in dry air, and the heavier metals are increasingly readily attacked to give oxides. On combustion at atmospheric pressure lithium gives only the oxide Li_2O; sodium gives the peroxide Na_2O_2; and potassium, rubidium and cesium give the superoxides, MO_2. Na_2O_2 will take up further oxygen at elevated pressures and temperatures to form NaO_2. The per- and superoxides of the heavier alkalies can also be prepared by passing stoichiometric amounts of oxygen into their liquid ammonia solutions, and ozonides, MO_3, are also known. The structures of the ions O_2^{2-}, O_2^- and O_3^- and of their alkali salts have already been

discussed (Chapter 13).   The increasing stability of the per- and superoxides as the size of the alkali ions increases is noteworthy and is a typical
example of the stabilization of larger anions by larger cations through lattice
energy effects.

Owing to the highly electropositive character of the alkali metals, the
various oxides (and also sulfides and similar compounds) are readily
hydrolyzed by water according to the following equations:

$$M_2O + H_2O = 2M^+ + 2OH^-$$
$$M_2O_2 + 2H_2O = 2M^+ + 2OH^- + H_2O_2$$
$$2MO_2 + 2H_2O = O_2 + 2M^+ + 2OH^- + H_2O_2$$

The oxide Cs_2O has the anti-$CdCl_2$ structure and is the only known oxide
with this type of lattice.   An abnormally long Cs—Cs distance and short
Cs—O distance imply considerable polarization of the Cs^+ ion.

The *hydroxides*, MOH, are white crystalline solids soluble in water and
in alcohols.   They can be sublimed unchanged at 350–400°, and the vapors
consist mainly of dimers, $(MOH)_2$.   KOH at ordinary temperatures is
monoclinic with each K surrounded by a distorted octahedron of O
atoms and the OH groups form a zig-zag hydrogen-bonded chain with
$O—H \cdots O = 3.35$ A.   The breaking of these bonds results in the formation
of the cubic high-temperature form.

16-5. Ionic Salts

Salts of the bases, MOH, with virtually all acids are known.   For the
most part they are colorless, crystalline, ionic solids.   Those which are
colored owe their color to the anions, except in special cases.   The colors
of metal ions are due to absorption of light of proper energy to excite
electrons to higher energy levels; for the alkali ions with their very stable
inert gas configurations, the energies required to excite electrons to the
lowest available empty orbitals could be supplied only by quanta far out
in the vacuum ultraviolet (the transition $5p^6 \rightarrow 5p^56s$ in Cs^+ occurs at
about 1000 A).   However, colored crystals of compounds such as NaCl
are sometimes encountered.   This is due to the presence of holes and
free electrons, called color centers, in the lattice, and such chromophoric
disturbances can be produced by irradiation of the crystals with X-rays
and nuclear radiations.   The color results from transitions of the electrons
between energy levels in the holes in which they are trapped.   These electrons behave in principle similarly to those in solvent cages in the liquid
ammonia solutions, but the energy levels are differently spaced and consequently the colors are different and variable.   Small excesses of
metal atoms produce similar effects, since these atoms form M^+ ions and
electrons which occupy holes where anions would be in a perfect crystal.

The structures and stabilities of the ionic salts are determined in part by the lattice energies and by radius ratio effects, which have been discussed in Chapter 2. Thus the large Cs^+ ion can accommodate eight near-neighbor Cl^- ions, and its structure is different from that of NaCl where the smaller cation Na^+ can accommodate only six near neighbors.

The salts are generally characterized by high melting points, by electrical conductivity of the melts, and by ready solubility in water. There are a few salts which are not appreciably water soluble, and thus there are a few important *precipitation reactions* of the group I ions. These are generally with large anions, and the larger the group I cation, the more numerous are its insoluble salts. Thus sodium has very few insoluble salts; the mixed sodium zinc and sodium magnesium uranyl acetates (e.g., $NaZn(UO_2)_3(CH_3COO)_9 \cdot 6H_2O$), which may precipitate almost quantitatively under carefully controlled conditions from dilute acetic acid solutions, are useful for analysis. The perchlorates and hexachloroplatinates of K, Rb and Cs are rather insoluble in water and virtually insoluble in 90% ethanol. These heavier ions may also be precipitated by cobaltinitrite ion, $[Co(NO_2)_6]^{3-}$, and various other large anions. $NaB(C_6H_5)_4$, which is moderately soluble in water, is a useful reagent for precipitating the tetraphenyl borates of K, Rb and Cs from neutral or faintly acid aqueous solutions, and quantitative gravimetric determinations of these ions may be made in this way.

Although alkali metal nitrates decompose on heating to nitrites, they can be distilled from their melts at 350–500° in vacuum (see page 351).

The group I salts are seldom hydrated when the anions are small, as in the halides, because the hydration energies of the ions are insufficient to compensate for the energy required to expand the lattices.

The large size of the Cs^+ and Rb^+ ions frequently allows them to form ionic salts with rather unstable anions, such as various polyhalide anions (page 589) and the superoxides already mentioned.

Apart from solvates, there are very few complexes of the alkali metal ions, although a number of chelate complexes which are soluble in organic compounds have been obtained using oxygenated ligands such as salicylaldehyde and benzoylacetone. As in the case of the solvates, the bonding is essentially electrostatic in these complexes. Even Rb^+ and Cs^+ form complexes with certain ligands, and these ions may be extracted from aqueous solutions by certain substituted hindered phenols[3] such as 4-*sec*-butyl-2(α-methylbenzyl)phenol. It is believed that the Cs^+ ion is solvated by hydrogen-bonded phenol dimers.

---

[3] W. J. Ross and J. C. White, *Anal. Chem.*, **36**, 1998 (1964); B. Z. Egan, R. A. Zingaro and B. M. Benjamin, *Inorg. Chem.*, **4**, 1055 (1965).

The M$^+$ *Ions in Solution.* The group I ions are hydrated in solution to rather indeterminate degrees. X-ray scattering studies have indicated that the primary hydration shell of K$^+$ contains four water molecules. Since Na$^+$ forms the very stable [Na(NH$_3$)$_4$]$^+$ ion in liquid ammonia, it is probable that it too has a primary hydration sphere of four water molecules. Nothing definite is known about the Rb$^+$ and Cs$^+$ ions. It is quite possible that they, especially Cs$^+$, might have six water molecules in the first hydration shell. However, electrostatic forces are still operative beyond the first hydration sphere, and additional water molecules will be bound in layers of decreasing definiteness and strength of attachment. Apparently, the larger the cation itself, the less it binds additional outer layers,

TABLE 16-2

Data on Hydration of Aqueous Group I Ions

	Li$^+$	Na$^+$	K$^+$	Rb$^+$	Cs$^+$
Crystal radii,[a] A	0.60	0.95	1.33	1.48	1.69
Hydrated radii (approx.), A	3.40	2.76	2.32	2.28	2.28
Approximate hydration numbers[b]	25.3	16.6	10.5	—	9.9
Hydration energies, kcal/mole	124.4	97.0	77.0	71.9	61.1
Ionic mobilities (at ∞ dil., 18°)	33.5	43.5	64.6	67.5	68

[a] For six coordination.
[b] From transference data.

so that, although the crystallographic radii increase down the group, the hydrated radii decrease as shown in Table 16-2. Also, the hydration energies (page 43) decrease. The decrease in the size of the hydrated ions is manifested in various ways. The mobility of the ions in electrolytic conduction increases, and also the strength of binding to ion exchange resins generally increases.

In a cation exchange resin, two cations compete for attachment at anionic sites in the resin, as in the following equilibrium:

$$A^+(aq) + [B^+R^-](s) = B^+(aq) + [A^+R^-](s)$$

where R represents the resin and A$^+$ and B$^+$ the cations. Such equilibria have been measured quite accurately, and the order of preference of the alkali cations is usually Li$^+$ < Na$^+$ < K$^+$ < Rb$^+$ < Cs$^+$, although irregular behavior does occur in some cases. This may be explained if we assume that the binding force is essentially electrostatic and that under ordinary conditions the ions within the water-logged resin are hydrated about as they are outside of it. Then the ion with the smallest hydrated radius (which is the one with the largest "naked" radius) will be able to approach most closely to the negative site of attachment and will hence be held most strongly according to the Coulomb law.

The reasons for the deviations from this simple pattern as well as selective passage of certain ions through cell walls are not properly understood, and factors other than mere size are doubtless important.

16-6. Organometallic Compounds

Only organo compounds of sodium, and to a much lesser extent potassium, are of importance, and both are less important than the lithium compounds. The derivatives are all essentially ionic and are not soluble to any appreciable extent in hydrocarbons; they are exceedingly reactive, being sensitive to air and hydrolyzed vigorously by water. Although alkyl and particularly aryl sodium derivatives can be prepared for *in situ* use as reaction intermediates, they are seldom isolated. More important are the compounds formed by acidic hydrocarbons such as cyclopentadiene, indene, acetylenes, etc. These are obtained by interaction with sodium in liquid ammonia or, more conveniently, sodium dispersed in tetrahydrofuran, glyme, diglyme or dimethylformamide.

$$3C_5H_6 + 2Na = 2C_5H_5^-Na^+ + C_5H_8$$
$$RC{\equiv}CH + Na = RC{\equiv}C^-Na^+ + \tfrac{1}{2}H_2$$

Many unsaturated and a few cyclic or cage-like saturated[4] hydrocarbons can form highly colored anions when treated with sodium or potassium in tetrahydrofuran at low temperatures; thus benzene gives the yellow benzenide ion, $C_6H_6^-$, which can be detected spectroscopically and by electron spin resonance, and cyclopropane gives $C_3H_6^-$. Anions of this type are obtained only when the negative charge can be delocalized. Other aromatic compounds such as ketones, triphenylphosphine oxide, triphenylarsine and azobenzene also form anions.

[4] K. W. Bowers, G. Nofi, Jr., and F. D. Greene, *J. Amer. Chem. Soc.*, **85**, 3707 (1963).

References

Advances in Chemistry Series No. 19, "Handling and Uses of Alkali Metals," American Chemical Society, Washington, D.C., 1957. Recovery, handling and manufacture of metals, hydrides and oxides of Li, Na and K.

De Boer, E., *Adv. Organometal. Chem.*, **2**, 115 (1965). Electronic structure of alkali metal adducts of aromatic hydrocarbons.

Fatt, I., and M. Tashima, *Alkali Metal Dispersions*, Van Nostrand, Princeton–London 1962. Extensive review with preparative details.

Jackson, C. B., ed., *Liquid Metals Handbook*, 3rd ed. (Sodium, NaK Supp .), Atomic Energy Commission and Bureau of Ships, Dept. of Navy, Washington, D.C., 1955.

Jolly, W., *Progr. Inorg. Chem.*, **1**, 235 (1959). The nature of the solutions of alkali metals in liquid ammonia.

Juza, R., *Angew. Chem. (Internat.)*, **3**, 471 (1964). Amides of alkali and alkaline earth metals; review.

Kaufmann, D. W., *Sodium Chloride* (American Chemical Society Monograph, No. 145), Reinhold, New York, 1960. An encyclopedic account of salt.

Le Poutre, G., and M. J. Sienko, eds., *Solutions Métal–Ammonaic*, Benjamin, New York, 1964. Authoritative review articles and discussion mostly in English.

Mellor's Comprehensive Treatise on Inorganic and Theoretical Chemistry, Vol. II, Supplement 2, Li, Na (1961); Supplement 3, K, Rb, Cs, Fr (1963). Longmans Green, London.

Perel'man, F. M., *Rubidium and Caesium*, Pergamon Press, London, 1965. Comprehensive reference book.

Schlosser, M., *Angew. Chem. (Internat.)*, **3**, 287, 362 (1964). Extensive review on organosodium and potassium compounds.

Stern, K. H., and E. S. Amis, *Chem. Rev.*, **59**, 1 (1959). Ionic size, a comprehensive review on radii in crystals and solutions.

Symons, M. C. R., *Quart. Rev.*, **13**, 99 (1959). The nature of the solutions of alkali metals in liquid ammonia.

———, and W. T. Doyle, *Quart. Rev.*, **14**, 62 (1960). Color centers in alkali halides.

17

The Group II Elements: Mg, Ca, Sr, Ba, Ra

GENERAL REMARKS

17-1. Introduction

As noted previously (Chapter 9), the first-row member of group II, beryllium, has unique chemical behavior; it also has a predominantly covalent chemistry in contrast to the other members now to be considered, which are predominantly ionic. Magnesium, the second-row element, does not stand in as close a relationship with the heavier members as might have been expected; it has considerable tendency to covalent bond formation, which is consistent with the following values of the charge to radius ratios: Be^{2+}, 6.5; Mg^{2+}, 3.3; Ca^{2+}, 1.8; Sr^{2+}, 1.2; Ba^{2+}, 1.0; Ra^{2+}, 0.7. Its chemistry is intermediate between that of beryllium and that of the closely allied series Ca–Ra. For instance, like beryllium, its hydroxide can be precipitated from aqueous solutions, whereas hydroxides of the other elements are all moderately soluble.

The metal atomic radii are smaller than those of the adjacent group I metals due to the increased nuclear charge; the number of bonding electrons in the metals is twice as great so that the metals have higher melting and boiling points and greater densities.

All the elements in this group are highly electropositive metals, however, as is shown by their high chemical reactivities, their ionization potentials, their standard electrode potentials and, for the heavier ones, the ionic nature of their compounds. Important numerical constants such as those mentioned are collected in Table 17-1. Although the energies required to vaporize and ionize these atoms to the M^{2+} ions are considerably greater than those required to produce the M^+ ions of the group I elements, the high lattice energies in the solid salts and the high hydration energies of the M^{2+}(aq) ions compensate for this (page 41) with the result that the

TABLE 17-1

Some Physical Parameters for the Group II Elements

Element	Electron configuration	Ionization potentials, ev		E^0 for $M^{2+}(aq) + 2e = M(s)$, v	Ionic radii, A
		1st	2nd		
Mg	[Ne]$3s^2$	7.64	15.03	−2.37	0.65
Ca	[Ar]$4s^2$	6.11	11.87	−2.87	0.94
Sr	[Kr]$5s^2$	5.69	10.98	−2.89	1.10
Ba	[Xe]$6s^2$	5.21	9.95	−2.90	1.29
Ra	[Rn]$7s^2$	5.28	10.10	−2.92	1.50

standard electrode potentials of the group II metals are rather similar to those of the group I metals. As with group I ions, various experimental data suggest that the radii of the hydrated ions are greatest for those with the smallest crystallographic radii.

All of the M^{2+} ions are smaller and considerably less polarizable than the isoelectronic M^+ ions. Thus deviations from complete ionicity in their salts due to polarization of the cations is even less important. However, for Mg^{2+} and, as noted, to an exceptional degree for Be^{2+}, polarization of anions by the cations does produce a degree of covalence for compounds of Mg and makes covalence characteristic for Be.

Calcium, strontium, barium and radium form a closely allied series in which the chemical and physical properties of the elements and their compounds vary systematically with increasing size in much the same manner as in group I, the ionic and electropositive nature being greatest for Ra. Again the larger ions can stabilize certain large anions: the peroxide and superoxide ions, polyhalide ions, etc. Some examples of systematic group trends in the series Ca–Ra are: (a) hydration tendencies of the crystalline salts increase; (b) solubilities of sulfates, nitrates, chlorides, etc. (fluorides are an exception) decrease; (c) solubilities of halides in ethanol decrease; (d) thermal stabilities of carbonates, nitrates and peroxides increase; (e) rates of reaction of the metals with hydrogen increase. Other similar trends can be found.

All isotopes of *radium* are radioactive, the longest-lived isotope being ^{226}Ra (α; ~ 1600 yr). This isotope is formed in the natural decay series of ^{238}U and was first isolated by the Curies. Once widely used in radiotherapy, it is now being supplanted by much cheaper radioisotopes made in nuclear reactors.

It may be noted that isotopically pure ^{87}Sr (99%) is found in some minerals, such as certain Canadian micas, where it is formed by β^- decay of ^{87}Rb.

The elements Zn, Cd and Hg, which have two electrons outside of filled penultimate d shells, are also classed in group II. Although the difference between the calcium and zinc subgroups is marked, Zn, and to a lesser extent Cd, show some resemblance to Mg in their chemistry. We shall discuss these elements separately, but it may be noted here that Zn, which has the lowest second ionization potential in the Zn, Cd, Hg group, still has a value (17.89 ev) similar to that of Be (18.21 ev) and its standard potential (-0.76 v) is considerably less negative than that of Mg.

There are a few ions in other parts of the periodic table with properties similar to those of Sr^{2+} or Ba^{2+}. Thus bivalent europium, Eu^{2+}, has a radius very similar to that of Ba^{2+}. Its hydroxide is a strong base, and its sulfate is insoluble in water, resembling the barium analogs. Because of this fortuitous chemical similarity, europium is frequently found in nature in group II minerals, and this is indeed a good example of the geochemical importance of such chemical similarity. Sm^{2+} and Yb^{2+} are also similar to Ba^{2+}, but they are much more readily oxidized than is Eu^{2+} and cannot persist in aqueous solution.

THE ELEMENTS

17-2. Occurrence, Isolation and Properties

The group II elements are widely distributed in minerals and in the sea. They occur in substantial deposits such as *dolomite*, $CaCO_3 \cdot MgCO_3$; *carnallite*, $MgCl_2 \cdot KCl \cdot 6H_2O$; *barytes*, $BaSO_4$; etc. Calcium is the third most abundant metal terrestrially. Radium occurs in low concentration in uranium ores as a product of radioactive decay.

Magnesium is produced in several ways. An important source is dolomite from which, after calcination, the calcium is removed by ion exchange using sea water, the equilibrium being favorable because of the lower solubility of $Mg(OH)_2$ relative to $Ca(OH)_2$:

$$Ca(OH)_2 \cdot Mg(OH)_2 + Mg^{2+} = 2Mg(OH)_2 + Ca^{2+}$$

The most important process for preparation of magnesium is the electrolysis of fused halide mixtures (e.g., $MgCl_2 + CaCl_2 + NaCl$) from which the least electropositive metal, Mg, is deposited. It may also be obtained by reduction of MgO or of calcined dolomite ($MgO \cdot CaO$). The latter is heated with ferrosilicon

$$CaO \cdot MgO + FeSi = Mg + \text{silicates of Ca and Fe}$$

and the magnesium distilled out. MgO can be heated with coke at 2000° and the metal deposited by rapid quenching of the high temperature equilibrium which lies well to the right:

$$MgO + C = Mg + CO$$

Calcium and the other metals are made only on a relatively small scale by electrolysis of fused salts or reduction of the halides with sodium.

Radium is isolated in the processing of uranium ores; after coprecipitation with barium sulfate, it can be obtained by fractional crystallization of a soluble salt.

Magnesium is a greyish white metal with a surface oxide film which protects it to some extent chemically—thus it is not attacked by water despite the favorable potential unless amalgamated. It is readily soluble in dilute acids and is attacked by most alkyl and aryl halides in ether solution to give Grignard reagents. Calcium and the other metals are soft and silvery, resembling sodium in their chemical reactivities although somewhat less reactive. These metals are also soluble, though less readily and to a lesser extent than sodium, in liquid ammonia, giving blue solutions of a similar nature[1] to those of the group I metals. These blue solutions are also susceptible to decomposition with the formation of the amides and have other chemical reactions similar to those of the group I metal solutions. They differ, however, in that moderately stable metal ammines such as $Ca(NH_3)_6$ can be isolated on removal of solvent at the boiling point.

COMPOUNDS OF THE GROUP II ELEMENTS

17-3. Binary Compounds

Oxides. The oxides, MO, are obtained most readily by calcination of the carbonates. They are white crystalline solids with ionic, NaCl-type lattices. Magnesium oxide is relatively inert, especially after ignition at high temperatures, but the other oxides react with water, evolving heat, to form the hydroxides. They also absorb carbon dioxide from the air. Magnesium hydroxide is insoluble in water ($\sim 1 \times 10^{-4}$ g/liter at 20°) and can be precipitated from Mg^{2+} solutions; it is a much weaker base than the Ca–Ra hydroxides, although it has no acidic properties and unlike $Be(OH)_2$ is insoluble in excess hydroxide. The Ca–Ra hydroxides are all soluble in water, increasingly so with increasing atomic number ($Ca(OH)_2$, ~ 2 g/liter; $Ba(OH)_2$, ~ 60 g/liter at $\sim 20°$) and all are strong bases.

As for the group I cations, there are no optical transitions in the electronic spectra of the M^{2+} ions and they are all colorless. Colors of salts are thus due only to colors of the anions or to lattice defects. For example, the oxides are often obtained with defects, and BaO crystals up to 1 cm × 2 mm have been grown in vacuum and are deep red due to $\sim 0.1\%$ excess of metal in the lattice.

[1] C. Hallada and W. L. Jolly, *Inorg. Chem.*, **2**, 1076 (1963).

Hydrides. The Ca–Ba group give ionic hydrides, MH_2 and MXH (Chapter 6), by direct reaction under fairly mild conditions. MgH_2 is also obtained by direct reaction using hydrogen under pressure, as a light grey powder stable in air; the product prepared by pyrolysis of magnesium alkyls is much more reactive, however. If the Ca–Ba hydrides are heated to $\sim 900°$ with their halides in an atmosphere of hydrogen, stable, mica-like solids, melting at 660–860°, of stoichiometry MXH are obtained. These are compounds, not mixed crystals, and have the PbClF structure. The MgClH from the reaction of RMgCl with diborane gives only a crystalline dietherate with tetrahydrofuran from which the ether cannot be removed.

Carbides. All of the metals in the Ca–Ba series or their oxides react directly with carbon in an electric furnace to give the carbides MC_2. These are ionic acetylides whose general properties (hydrolysis to $M(OH)_2$ and C_2H_2, structures, etc.) have already been discussed in Chapter 11. Magnesium at $\sim 500°$ gives MgC_2 but at 500–700° with excess carbon Mg_2C_3 is formed, which on hydrolysis gives $Mg(OH)_2$ and propyne and is presumably ionic, that is, $(Mg^{2+})_2(C_3^{4-})$.

Other Compounds. Direct reaction of the metals with other elements can lead to binary compounds such as borides, silicides, arsenides, sulfides, etc. Like the corresponding group I compounds, many of these are ionic and are rapidly hydrolyzed by water or dilute acids. At $\sim 300°$, magnesium reacts with nitrogen to give colorless, crystalline Mg_3N_2 (resembling Li and Be in this respect). The other metals also react, but their nitrides are much less stable.

17-4. Salts, Aqueous Solutions and Complexes of the M^{2+} Ions

Magnesium. In contrast to beryllium, the anhydrous halides and other salts are essentially ionic in nature due to the larger size of the Mg^{2+} ion. In water the hydrated ion (most likely $[Mg(H_2O)_6]^{2+}$) binds the water in the first coordination sphere much less strongly than does Be in $[Be(H_2O)_4]^{2+}$, and the aquo ion is not perceptibly acidic. The hydration energy, however, is still sufficiently high that magnesium salts usually crystallize from water as rather stable hydrates. $Mg(ClO_4)_2$ is an excellent drying agent. Most magnesium salts are water soluble; the fluoride, however, is only sparingly soluble.

Calcium, Strontium, Barium and Radium. Although calcium salts are usually hydrated and the anhydrous halides are deliquescent, the tendency to form hydrates as well as the solubilities in water decrease with increasing size. This is because the hydration energies decrease more rapidly than the lattice energies with increasing size. The fluorides vary inversely in solubility, Ca < Sr < Ba, because of the unusually small size of the F^- ion relative to the large M^{2+} ions. The lattice energies decrease unusually rapidly because the large cations make contact with one another without at the same time making contact with the F^- ions. The carbonates are all rather insoluble; sulfates of Sr, Ba and Ra are very insoluble, the solubility products of both carbonates and sulfates decreasing with increasing cation size. Calcium sulfate has a hemihydrate, $2CaSO_4 \cdot H_2O$ (plaster of Paris), which readily absorbs more water to form the very sparingly soluble $CaSO_4 \cdot 2H_2O$ (gypsum).

In aqueous solution the $M^{2+}(aq)$ ions are not at all hydrolyzed.

Rather weak *complexes* can be formed by the lighter group II elements. Thus although the magnesium halides do not have strong acceptor properties, these, the alkyls, and the Grignard species will form complexes with donor molecules, particularly oxygen compounds. Thus $MgBr_2$ and MgI_2 are soluble in alcohols, ketones and ethers; magnesium perchlorate is also quite soluble in such solvents.

Of the other ions only Ca^{2+} shows a tendency to similar behavior, calcium chloride being readily soluble in alcohols and carboxylic acids.

In aqueous solution, oxygen chelate compounds, among the most important being those of the ethylenediaminetetraacetate (EDTA) type, can give complexes in alkaline solution, such as

$$Ca^{2+}(aq) + EDTA^{4-} = [Ca(EDTA)]^{2-}$$

The complexing of calcium by EDTA and also by polyphosphates is of some importance not only for removal of calcium ions from water but in analysis, for example for the volumetric estimation of calcium using EDTA.

Only rather weak ammonia and amine complexes are known for Mg^{2+} and Ca^{2+}. Thus anhydrous $MgCl_2$ will absorb NH_3 to give an easily dissociated complex $[Mg(NH_3)_6]Cl_2$.

The only known chloro complex of magnesium $[Et_4N]_2MgCl_4$ was isolated by interaction of $MgCl_2$ and Et_4NCl in $SOCl_2$.[2]

17-5. Unipositive Magnesium

Although the ionization potentials of the group II elements might suggest the possibility of isolable stable compounds with unipositive ions, this is not the case. Calculations using Born–Haber cycles (page 41) clearly demonstrate that, because of the much greater lattice energies of MX_2 compounds, MX compounds would be quite unstable with respect to disproportionation

$$2MX = M + MX_2$$

[2] D. M. Adams, J. Chatt, J. M. Davidson and J. Gerratt, *J. Chem. Soc.*, **1963**, 2189.

Detailed studies of the M–MX$_2$ solid system for Ca, Sr and Ba halides confirm the absence of any M$^+$ ions.[3]

However, in the case of magnesium there is some evidence that Mg$^+$ ions may be formed under some conditions; they are only short-lived, however. The evidence comes mainly from studies on anodic dissolution of magnesium in aqueous salt solutions and in organic donor solvents such as pyridine containing sodium iodide. It is found, for example, that in aqueous solutions hydrogen is evolved near or at the anode, and more detailed studies have shown that Mg$^+$ ions must be present. It is possible to use electrically generated Mg$^+$ ions as reducing agents for a variety of organic compounds.

17-6. Organometallic Compounds

Where they are known, organometallic compounds of Ca, Sr and Ba are highly ionic and are of little importance. However, the magnesium derivatives are of very great importance since the Grignard reagents are undoubtedly the most widely used of all organometallic compounds. They are made by direct interaction of magnesium with an organic halide, RX, in a donor solvent, usually an ether. The reactions of Grignard reagents are in keeping with the formulation "RMgX."

There has been very considerable controversy concerning the structure of Grignard reagents in solutions and discordant results have often been obtained because of failure to eliminate impurities such as traces of water or oxygen which can aid or inhibit the attainment of equilibrium and the occurrence of exchange reactions.

X-ray diffraction studies[4] of two crystalline Grignard reagents, C$_6$H$_5$MgBr·2Et$_2$O (Fig. 17-1) and C$_2$H$_5$MgBr·2Et$_2$O show that there are discrete molecules with the organic radical, a bromine atom and two ether molecules bound tetrahedrally to a single magnesium atom.

The species and equilibria in solutions have still not been completely elucidated: these probably contain some or all of the species shown in the equilibria:

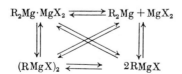

Complete statistical exchange of tracer *Mg in mixtures of Et$_2$Mg and

[3] Emons, H.-H., *Zeit. anorg. Chem.*, **323**, 114 (1963).
[4] G. D. Stucky and R. E. Rundle, *J. Amer. Chem. Soc.*, **85**, 1002 (1963); **86**, 4825 (1964).

*MgBr$_2$, of Ph$_2$Mg and *MgBr$_2$ and of EtMgBr and *MgBr$_2$ in ether,[5] gives evidence for an equilibrium of the type

$$R_2Mg + MgX_2 \rightleftharpoons 2RMgX \rightleftharpoons (RMgX)_2$$

The nature of the solvent has a profound effect and the degree of association, i, varies with the solvent and with X, but not with R. Thus

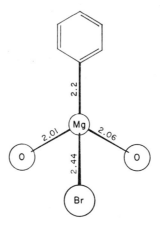

Fig. 17-1. The partial structure of C$_6$H$_5$MgBr·2(C$_2$H$_5$)$_2$O. The bond angles about Mg are all within < 10° of tetrahedral; distances in A.

in tetrahydrofuran at 0.1–0.3M, EtMgBr and EtMgCl are monomeric; in diethyl ether i can vary from ~1 to 1.4 for RMgBr and RMgI (R = Me, Et, Ph) and from 1.85 to 2.0 for RMgCl (R = Et, i-Pr). As changing R has no effect, even when R = mesityl, the lack of steric effects make forms such as R$_2$Mg·MgBr$_2$ seem less likely.

At concentrations of about 0.2M, magnesium halides are insoluble, or form two layers with ethers, ruling out the formulation MgX$_2$ + R$_2$Mg for the monomeric solutions.

Nuclear magnetic resonance and infrared spectra have shown little difference between the solutions of Grignard reagents and the corresponding dialkyls. The splitting, and growth on addition of excess MgBr$_2$, of a band at 550–350 cm^{-1} in RMgX attributed to the Mg—C stretch[6] supports the equilibrium

$$R_2Mg + MgX_2 \rightleftharpoons 2RMgX$$

in tetrahydrofuran solutions, but no difference was seen in diethyl ether solutions.

[5] R. E. Dessy, S. E. Green and R. M. Salinger, *Tetrahedron Letters*, **21**, 1369 (1964); J. D. Roberts, D. O. Cowan and J. Hsu, *J. Org. Chem.*, **29**, 3689 (1964).

[6] R. M. Salinger and H. S. Mosher, *J. Amer. Chem. Soc.*, **36**, 1782 (1964).

Present evidence hence suggests that RMgX is the main species in monomeric solutions but that R_2Mg and MgX_2 may predominate under some circumstances. The dimeric form may be either the halogen bridged species $(RMgX)_2$ or $R_2Mg \cdot MgX_2$ or both forms in equilibrium. In diethyl ether, it appears quite certain that the initial reaction of RX with Mg gives RMgX[7] and that this species is present in the solution.

The dialkyl and aryl magnesium derivatives can often be isolated in a pure state; their reactions are generally similar to those of Grignard reagents, and they are hydrolyzed by water and sensitive to air. X-ray crystallographic study[8] of $(C_2H_5)_2Mg$ shows that it has a polymeric chain structure very similar to that of $(CH_3)_2Be$, with bridging methylene groups and a tetrahedral coordination of the metal atom. The colorless, crystalline, ionic cyclopentadienide, $Mg(C_5H_5)_2$, has been shown to have the same "sandwich" configuration as ferrocene (Chapter 28); it can be readily made by the direct action of cyclopentadiene vapor on heated magnesium or by thermal decomposition of cyclopentadienylmagnesium halides.

References

Kharasch, M. S., and O. Reinmuth, *Grignard Reactions of Non-Metallic Substances*, Constable and Co., London, and Prentice-Hall, New York, 1954.

Pannell, E. V., *Magnesium: Its Production and Use*, Pitman, London, 1948.

Rausch, M. D., W. E. Ewen and J. Kleinberg, *Chem. Rev.*, **57**, 417 (1957). Use of Mg$^+$ as a reducing agent in organic chemistry.

Salinger, R. M., *Survey of Progr. Chem.*, **1**, 301 (1963). Review on structure of Grignards (as then known) and reaction mechanisms thereof.

Yoffe, S. T., and A. N. Nesmeyanov, *Handbook of Magnesium Organic Compounds*, Vols. I–III, Pergamon Press, London.

[7] E. C. Ashby, *J. Amer. Chem. Soc.*, **87**, 2509 (1965).
[8] E. Weiss, *J. Organomet. Chem.*, **4**, 101 (1965).

18

The Group III Elements: Al, Ga, In, Tl

GENERAL REMARKS

18-1. Electronic Structures and Valences

The electronic structures and some other important fundamental properties of the elements are listed in Table 18-1.

TABLE 18-1

Some Properties of the Group III Elements

Element	Electronic structure	Ionization potentials, ev				E^0, v[a]	Melting point °C
		1st	2nd	3rd	4th		
B	$[He]2s^22p$	8.30	25.15	37.92	259.30	Not measurable	~2200
Al	$[Ne]3s^23p$	5.98	18.82	28.44	119.96	-1.66	660
Ga	$[Ar]3d^{10}4s^24p$	6.00	20.43	30.6	63.8	-0.53	29.8
In	$[Kr]4d^{10}5s^25p$	5.79	18.79	27.9	57.8	-0.342	157
Tl	$[Xe]4f^{14}5d^{10}6s^26p$	6.11	20.32	29.7	50.5	$+0.72^{b}$	304

[a] For $M^{3+}(aq) + 3e = M(s)$.
[b] $Tl^+ + e = Tl(s)$, $E^0 = -0.3363$.

Aluminum and its congeners, Ga, In and Tl, are considerably larger than boron (atomic radii of Al and B being 1.26 and 0.88 A, respectively), and hence they are much more metallic and ionic in their character. Elemental aluminum itself is clearly metallic, but it is nevertheless still on the borderline (like beryllium) between ionic and covalent character in its compounds. So also are Ga, In and Tl. Although electronegativity values are not particularly useful in interpreting the chemistry of these rather metallic elements, the available values (Allred–Rochow) are: B, 2.01; Al, 1.47; Ga, 1.82; In, 1.49; Tl, 1.44. The irregularity of the sequence is discussed on page 458.

While the trivalent state is important for all four elements, the univalent state becomes progressively more stable as the group is descended and for thallium the Tl^I–Tl^{III} relationship is a dominant feature of the chemistry. This occurrence of an oxidation state two below the group valency is sometimes attributed to the so-called *inert pair* effect which first makes itself evident here, although it is adumbrated in the low reactivity of mercury in group II, and it is much more pronounced in groups IV and V. The term refers to the resistance of a pair of s electrons to be lost or to participate in covalent bond formation. Thus mercury is difficult to oxidize, allegedly because it contains only an inert pair ($6s^2$), Tl readily forms Tl^I rather than Tl^{III} because of the inert pair in its valence shell ($6s^2 6p$), etc. The concept of the inert pair does not actually tell us anything about the ultimate reasons for the stability of certain lower valence states, but it is useful as a label and is often encountered in the literature.   In fact, it has been pointed out[1a] that the true cause of the phenomenon is not intrinsic inertness, that is, unusually high ionization potential of the pair of s electrons, but rather the decreasing strengths of bonds as a group is descended.   Thus, for example, the sum of the 2nd and 3rd ionization potentials is lower for In (46.7 ev) than for Ga (51.0 ev), with Tl (50.0 ev) intermediate. There is, however, a steady decrease in the mean thermochemical bond energies, for example, among the trichlorides: Ga, 57.8; In, 49.2; Tl, 36.5 kcal/mole.   The relative stabilities of oxidation states differing in the presence or absence of the inert pair are further discussed on page 458.

In the trihalide, trialkyl and trihydride compounds there are some resemblances to the corresponding boron chemistry.   Thus MX_3 compounds behave as Lewis acids and can accept either neutral donor molecules or anions to give tetrahedral species; the acceptor ability generally decreases Al > Ga > In, with the position of Tl uncertain.   There are, however, notable distinctions from boron. These arise in part due to the reduced ability to form multiple bonds and to the ability of the heavier elements to have coordination numbers exceeding four.   Thus while boron gives $Me_2\overset{-}{B}{=}\overset{+}{N}Me_2$, Al, Ga and In give dimeric species, e.g., $[Me_2AlNMe_2]_2$, in which there is an NMe_2 bridging group and both the metal and nitrogen atoms are 4-coordinate.   Similarly, the boron halides are all monomeric, while those of Al, Ga and In are all dimeric.   The polymerization of trivalent Al, Ga, In and Tl compounds to achieve coordination saturation is general and 4-membered rings appear to be a common way despite the valency-angle strain implied.   Secondly, compounds such as $(Me_3N)_2AlH_3$ have trigonal bipyramidal structures which of course are impossible for

[1a] R. S. Drago, *J. Phys. Chem.*, **62**, 353 (1958).

boron adducts. Finally, in contrast to boron, there is a well-defined aqueous cationic chemistry; aquo ions, e.g., $[In(H_2O)_6]^{3+}$, salts of oxo anions and complexes, all with octahedral stereochemistry, exist; for Al^{3+} (aq) the coordination number six has been proved by ^{17}O nuclear resonance studies.[1b]

THE ELEMENTS

18-2. Occurrence, Isolation and Properties

Aluminum, the commonest metallic element in the earth's crust, occurs widely in nature in silicates such as micas and feldspars, as the hydroxo oxide (*bauxite*), and as *cryolite* (Na_3AlF_6). The other three elements are found only in trace quantities. Gallium and indium are found in aluminum and zinc ores, but the richest sources contain less than 1% of gallium and still less indium. Thallium is widely distributed; the element is usually recovered from flue dusts from the roasting of certain sulfide ores, mainly pyrites.

Aluminum is prepared on a vast scale from bauxite. This is purified by dissolution in sodium hydroxide and reprecipitation using carbon dioxide. It is then dissolved in molten cryolite at 800–1000° and the melt electrolyzed. Aluminum is a hard, strong, white metal. Although highly electropositive, it is nevertheless resistant to corrosion because a hard, tough film of oxide forms on the surface. Thick oxide films, some with the proper porosity when fresh to trap particles of pigment, are often electrolytically applied to aluminum. Aluminum is soluble in dilute mineral acids, but is passivated by concentrated nitric acid. If the protective effect of the oxide film is overcome, by scratching or by amalgamation, for example, rapid attack even by water can occur. The metal is attacked under ordinary conditions by hot alkali hydroxides, halogens and various nonmetals. Highly purified aluminum is quite resistant to acids and is best attacked by hydrochloric acid containing a little cupric chloride or in contact with platinum, some H_2O_2 also being added during the dissolution.

Gallium, indium and *thallium* are usually obtained by electrolysis of aqueous solutions of their salts; for Ga and In this possibility arises because of large overvoltages for hydrogen evolution on these metals. They are soft, white, comparatively reactive metals, dissolving readily in acids; however, thallium dissolves only slowly in sulfuric and hydrochloric acids since the Tl^I salts formed are only sparingly soluble. Gallium, like aluminum, is soluble in sodium hydroxide. The elements react rapidly at room temperature, or on warming, with the halogens and with nonmetals such as sulfur.

[1b] R. E. Connick and D. N. Fiat, *J. Chem. Phys.*, **39**, 1349 (1963).

The exceptionally low melting point of gallium has no simple explanation. Since its boiling point (2070°) is not abnormal, gallium has the longest liquid range of any known substance and finds use as a thermometer liquid.

CHEMISTRY OF THE TRIVALENT STATE

18-3. Aqueous Chemistry

Both $Al(OH)_3$ and $Ga(OH)_3$ are amphoteric. The following approximate constants have been reported:

$$Al(OH)_3(s) = Al^{3+} + 3OH^- \qquad K \approx 5 \times 10^{-33}$$
$$Al(OH)_3(s) = AlO_2^- + H^+ + H_2O \qquad K \approx 4 \times 10^{-13}$$
$$Ga(OH)_3(s) = Ga^{3+} + 3OH^- \qquad K \approx 5 \times 10^{-37}$$
$$Ga(OH)_3(s) = GaO_2^- + H^+ + H_2O \qquad K \approx 10^{-15}$$

Both aluminum and gallium metals dissolve in acid to give Al^{3+} and Ga^{3+} and in base to give "aluminate," and "gallate" ions. The latter are sometimes written as MO_2^- but such species have no real existence either in solutions or in solid "aluminates" and "gallates." The latter are generally ionic solids, whereas the structures of the species in solution undoubtedly involve higher coordination numbers but are otherwise uncertain. It is perhaps most reasonable to suppose that aluminate and gallate ions in aqueous solution are four- or six-coordinate species such as $[M(OH)_4]^-$ or $[M(OH)_4(H_2O)_2]^-$. The oxides and hydroxides of indium and thallium are not amphoteric, but purely basic.

In aqueous solution the octahedral $[M(H_2O)_6]^{3+}$ ions are quite acidic. There is some evidence to suggest that the Tl^{III} aquo ion has two *trans* water molecules which are more strongly bound than the others (cf. stability of $TlCl_2^+$ below). For the reaction

$$[M(H_2O)_6]^{3+} = [M(H_2O)_5(OH)]^{2+} + H^+$$

the following constants have been determined: $K_a(Al)$, 1.12×10^{-5}; $K_a(Ga)$, 2.5×10^{-3}; and $K_a(In)$, 2×10^{-4}; $K_a(Tl)$, $\sim 7 \times 10^{-2}$. Although little emphasis can be placed on the exact numbers, the orders of magnitude are important, for they show that aqueous solutions of the M^{III} salts are subject to extensive hydrolysis. Indeed, salts of weak acids—sulfides, carbonates, cyanides, acetates, etc.—cannot exist in contact with water.

Studies of the hydrolysis of perchlorate solutions of Al^{III} have found widely divergent interpretations, in part due to the slowness in reaching equilibria; chloride solutions are even more complex. The most recent studies[2] suggest that the above hydrolysis equation is too simple and that

[2] J. Aveston, *J. Chem. Soc.*, **1965**, 4438.

the main species present are the ions $[Al_2(OH)_2]^{4+}$ and $[Al_{13}(OH)_{32}]^{7+}$, both of which exist in crystalline basic salts.

Hydrated thallic oxide precipitates from solutions even at pH 1–2.5.

Salts of most strong *oxo acids* are well known and are obtained as hydrates from acidified aqueous solution. It is likely that all contain the hexaquo metal ions. A class of aluminum compounds which are of importance because they are structural prototypes and give their name to a large group of analogous compounds formed by other elements are the *alums*. They have the general formula $MAl(SO_4)_2 \cdot 12H_2O$ in which M is practically any common univalent, monatomic cation except for Li^+, which is too small to be accommodated without loss of stability of the structure. The crystals are made up of $[M(H_2O)_6]^+$, $[Al(H_2O)_6]^{3+}$ and two SO_4^{2-} ions. There are actually three structures, all cubic, consisting of the above ions, but differing slightly in details depending on the size of the univalent ion. Salts of the same type, $M^IM^{III}(SO_4)_2 \cdot 12H_2O$, and having the same structures are formed by many other trivalent metal ions, including those of Ti, V, Cr, Mn, Fe, Co, Ga, In, Rh and Ir, and all such compounds are referred to as alums. The term is used so generally that those alums containing aluminum are designated, in a seeming redundancy, as aluminum alums.

Not much is known about the formation of *complexes* by the trivalent ions in aqueous solution. Because of the ready hydrolysis of the aquo ions, there are, of course, no complexes formed with ammonia or amines. The gallates and aluminates may be regarded as hydroxo complexes. The most important halide complexes appear to be the fluoride complexes of aluminum which are remarkably stable. All six species from AlF^{2+} to AlF_6^{3-} are formed, and the equilibrium and kinetic behavior of the system have been carefully studied; the Ga^{3+}–F^- system is similar and hexafluorogallates are known. In ClO_4^- solution the aquo ion $[In(H_2O)_6]^{3+}$ occurs but in sulfate solutions species such as $InSO_4^+$ and $In(SO_4)_2^-$ are formed.[3] Thallium also forms complexes and for chloride solutions the formation reactions up to and including $TlCl_6^{3-}$ have been studied in detail.[4] The dichloro ion $TlCl_2^+$ appears to be particularly stable, pre-sumably because it is linear and analogous to the linear, very stable and isoelectronic $HgCl_2$. The thermodynamic quantities are also consistent with a change of coordination number on formation of the tetrahedral $TlCl_4^-$ ion, e.g.,

$$trans\text{-}[TlCl_3(H_2O)_3] + Cl^- = TlCl_4^- + 3H_2O$$

[3] R. E. Hester, R. A. Plane and G. E. Walrafen, *J. Chem. Phys.*, **38**, 249 (1963).

[4] T. G. Spiro, *Inorg. Chem.*, **4**, 731 (1965), and references therein.

It may be noted also that Tl chloro complexes have formation constants ca 10^7 times greater than similar ones for Cr^{3+} and Fe^{3+} due primarily to differences in enthalpy changes and so in the type of bonding.

18-4. Oxygen Compounds

Stoichiometrically there is only one oxide of aluminum, alumina, Al_2O_3. However, this simplicity is compensated by the occurrence of various polymorphs, hydrated species, etc., the formation of which depends on the conditions of preparation. There are two forms of anhydrous Al_2O_3, α-Al_2O_3 and γ-Al_2O_3.* Various other trivalent metals (Ga, Fe) form oxides which crystallize in these same two structures. In α-Al_2O_3 the oxide ions form a hexagonally close-packed array and the aluminum ions are distributed symmetrically among the octahedral interstices. The γ-Al_2O_3 structure is sometimes regarded as a "defect" spinel structure, that is as having the structure of spinel with a deficit of cations (see below).

α-Al_2O_3 is stable at high temperatures and also indefinitely metastable at low temperatures. It occurs in nature as the mineral corundum and may be prepared from γ-Al_2O_3 or any hydrous oxide by heating above $1000°$. γ-Al_2O_3 is obtained by dehydration of hydrous oxides at low temperatures ($\sim 450°$). α-Al_2O_3 is very hard and resistant to hydration and attack by acids, whereas γ-Al_2O_3 readily takes up water and dissolves in acids. The Al_2O_3 which forms on the surface of the metal has still another structure, namely, a defect rock salt structure; there is an arrangement of Al and O ions in the rock salt ordering with every third Al ion missing.

There are several important hydrated forms of alumina corresponding to the stoichiometries $AlO \cdot OH$ and $Al(OH)_3$. Addition of ammonia to a boiling solution of an aluminum salt produces a form of $AlO \cdot OH$ known as böhmite, which may be prepared in other ways also. A second form of $AlO \cdot OH$ occurs in nature as the mineral diaspore. The true hydroxide, $Al(OH)_3$, is obtained as a crystalline white precipitate when carbon dioxide is passed into alkaline "aluminate" solutions.

The gallium oxide system quite closely resembles the aluminum oxide system, affording a high temperature α- and a low temperature γ-Ga_2O_3, $GaO \cdot OH$ and $Ga(OH)_3$. The trioxide is formed by heating the nitrate, the sulfate or the hydrous oxides which are precipitated from Ga^{III} solutions by the action of ammonia. β-Ga_2O_3 contains both tetrahedrally and octahedrally coordinated gallium with Ga—O distances of 1.83 and 2.00 A,

---

* "β-Al_2O_3" is actually $Na_2O \cdot 6Al_2O_3$, see R. Scholder and M. Mansmann, *Z. anorg. Chem.*, **321**, 246 (1963).

respectively. Indium gives yellow In_2O_3, which is known in only one form, and a hydrated oxide, $In(OH)_3$. Thallium has only the brown-black Tl_2O_3, which begins to lose oxygen at about 100° to give Tl_2O. The action of NaOH on Tl^{III} salts gives what appears to be the oxide, whereas with Al, Ga and In the initial products are basic salts.

Aluminum, Ga and Tl form mixed oxides with other metals. There are, first, aluminum oxides containing only traces of other metal ions. These include ruby (Cr^{3+}) and blue sapphire (Fe^{2+}, Fe^{3+} and Ti^{4+}). Synthetic ruby, blue sapphire and white sapphire (gem quality corundum) are now produced synthetically in large quantities. Second are mixed oxides containing macroscopic proportions of other elements, such as the minerals *spinel*, $MgAl_2O_4$, and *crysoberyl*, $BeAl_2O$. The spinel structure has been described and its importance as a prototype for many other $M^{II}M_2^{III}O_4$ compounds noted (page 51).

18-5. Halides

All four halides of each element are known with one exception. The compound TlI_3, obtained by adding iodine to thallous iodide, is not thallium(III) iodide, but rather thallium(I) triiodide, $Tl^I(I_3)$. This situation may be compared with the nonexistence of iodides of other oxidizing cations such as Cu^{2+} and Fe^{3+}, except that here a lower valent compound fortuitously has the same stoichiometry as the higher valent one.

The other thallium(III) halides are genuine but unstable. The chloride loses chlorine at about 40° and above to give the monochloride, and the tribromide loses bromine at even lower temperatures to give first "$TlBr_2$" which is actually $Tl^I[Tl^{III}Br_4]$. The fluoride is stable to about 500°; but, compared to the fluorides of the other group III elements, this is rather poor stability. These facts provide a very good illustration of the way in which the stability of the lower valence state dominates thallium chemistry.

The halides of the remaining elements, Al, Ga and In, form fairly homologous groups. The fluorides are high-melting solids (respectively m 1290°, sub 950°, m 1170°), whereas the chlorides, bromides and iodides all have low melting points, e.g., for MCl_3, respectively, m 193° (at 1700 mm), 78°, 586°. Although it is reasonable to expect that the metal–fluorine bonds have a greater intrinsic tendency to be ionic than do other metal–halogen bonds, the high melting points of MF_3 are best explained in terms of coordination numbers and structures. The Al^{3+}, Ga^{3+} and In^{3+} cations are sufficiently large to prefer a coordination number of six toward the relatively small fluorine atom. In order to achieve this, they adopt structures which are infinitely extended arrays of metal and fluorine atoms. Whether these are best regarded as ionic lattices or as giant polymers in which the bonds are significantly ionic is a moot point. Whether strictly covalent (as in diamond) or highly ionic (as in NaCl), such an infinitely extended structure would lead to a high melting point.

In the crystalline state $AlCl_3$, $InCl_3$ and $TlCl_3$ have a somewhat distorted chromium(III) chloride type (Sec. 29-C-3) layer structure in which the metal atom is octahedrally coordinated. The bromides and iodides and Ga_2Cl_6[5] give lattices containing dimeric molecules (Fig. 18-1) and since there are no strong lattice forces the melting points are low. In the vapor, aluminum chloride is also dimeric so that there is a radical change of coordination number on vaporization, and these covalent structures persist in the vapor phase at temperatures not too far above the boiling points. At sufficiently high temperatures, however, dissociation into planar, triangular monomers, analogous to the boron halides, occurs. There is some evidence that for gallium iodide this dissociation is very extensive even at the boiling point. The group III halides dissolve readily in many nonpolar solvents such as benzene, in which they are dimeric. The enthalpies of dissociation, $Al_2X_6(g) = 2AlX_3(g)$, have been measured and are 11–15 kcal/mole. As Figure 18-1 shows, the configuration of halogen atoms about

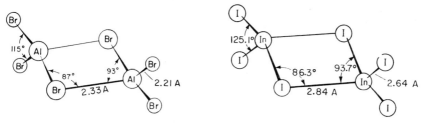

Fig. 18-1.   The structures Al_2Br_6 and In_2I_6.

each metal atom is roughly, though far from exactly, tetrahedral. The formation of such dimers is attributable to the tendency of the metal atoms to complete their octets. The dimers may be split by reaction with donor molecules giving complexes of the type R_3NAlCl_3. The halides dissolve in water giving acidic solutions from which hydrates may be obtained.

18-6. Other Binary Compounds

The group III elements form various compounds such as carbides, nitrides, phosphides and sulfides.

Aluminum *carbide*, Al_4C_3, is formed from the elements at temperatures

[5] S. C. Wallwork and I. J. Worral, *J. Chem. Soc.*, **1965**, 1816.

of 1000–2000°. It reacts instantly with water to produce methane, and X-ray studies have shown it to contain discrete carbon atoms (C—C = 3.16 A); for these reasons it is sometimes considered to be a "methanide," that is, a salt containing C^{4-}, but this is probably an oversimplification.

The *nitrides* AlN, GaN and InN are known. Only aluminum reacts directly with nitrogen. GaN forms on reaction of Ga or Ga_2O_3 at 600–1000° with NH_3 and InN by pyrolysis of $(NH_4)_3InF_6$. All have a wurtzite structure (Fig. 24-1). They are fairly hard and stable, as might be expected from their close structural relationship to diamond and the diamond-like BN.

Aluminum and especially Ga and In form 1:1 compounds with Group V elements, the so-called III–V compounds like GaAs. These compounds have semiconductor properties similar to those of elemental Si and Ge with which they are electronically and structurally similar. They can be obtained by direct interaction or in other ways. Thus GaP can be obtained as pale orange single crystals by the reaction of phosphorus and Ga_2O vapor at 900–1000°.

18-7. Complexes

Complexes containing both octahedrally and tetrahedrally coordinated metal ions are known, as well as a few in which the metal ion is five coordinate.

Aluminum forms octahedral complexes with some neutral ligands, giving such complex cations as $[Al(H_2O)_6]^{3+}$ and $\{Al[OS(CH_3)_2]_6\}^{3+}$, and with fluoride ion. There are many salts of the AlF_6^{3-} ion known, among which is cryolite whose structure (Fig. 18-2) is important since it is adopted by many other salts containing small cations and large octahedral anions and, in its *anti* form, by many salts of the same type as $[Co(NH_3)_6]I_3$. It is closely related to the structures adopted by many compounds of the types $M^+_2[AB_6]^{2-}$ and $[XY_6]^{2+}Z^-_2$. These latter two structures are essentially the fluorite and antifluorite structures (see Fig. 2-6, page 48), except that the anions (or cations) are octahedra whose axes are oriented parallel to the cube edges. The unit cell contains four formula units. Addition of four cations per unit cell, one at the center of the cube and one at the midpoint of each edge, gives the cryolite structure. Other complex fluorides of aluminum, such as Tl_2AlF_5 and NH_4AlF_4, also contain octahedrally coordinated aluminum. In the former the octahedra are joined at corners to form chains (Fig. 18-3a), and in the latter they share corners (but not edges on account of the high charge on Al^{3+}) to form sheets (Fig. 18-3b). Basic aluminum acetate has a structure similar to that of the basic acetates of chromium(III) and iron(III) and is probably $[Al_3O(OCOCH_3)_6].^+$

Presumably there is a central oxygen atom and three metal atoms in a plane with bidentate acetate groups bridging the metal atoms as in the Fe^{III} analog.

Aluminum and Ga give only the tetrahedral complex halide anions MX_4^- with larger halogens. Tetrachloroaluminates are hydrolyzed by water but

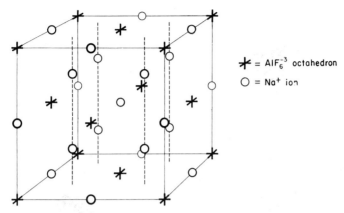

$\bigstar$ = AlF_6^{-3} octahedron

$\bigcirc$ = Na^+ ion

Fig. 18-2.   The cubic structure of cryolite, Na_3AlF_6.

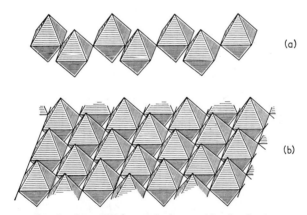

(a)

(b)

Fig. 18-3.   Diagrams showing how AlF_6^{3-} octahedra combine by sharing corners in the compounds (a) Tl_2AlF_5 and (b) NH_4AlF_4.

the $GaCl_4^-$ ion is not and gallium can be extracted from hydrochloric acid solutions by ethers, the organic phase containing $GaCl_4^-$ ions or ion-pairs with, say, Et_2OH^+. Salts of TlX_4^- for X = Cl, Br and I with a variety of large univalent cations are known.[6a] In TlI_4^-, the stability of I^- in contact with Tl^{III} is a result of the stability of the complex ion, since $Tl^{III}I_3$ itself is

[6a] F. A. Cotton, B. F. G. Johnson and R. M. Wing, *Inorg. Chem.*, **4**, 502 (1965).

unstable relative to $Tl^I(I_3)$. With PCl_5 in CH_2Cl_2,[6b] the trichlorides of Al, Ga and Tl give crystalline ionic compounds $[PCl_4^+][MCl_4^-]$.

The formation of $AlCl_4^-$ and $AlBr_4^-$ ions is essential to the functioning of Al_2Cl_6 and Al_2Br_6 as Friedel–Crafts catalysts, since in this way the necessary carbonium ions are simultaneously formed:

$$RCOCl + AlCl_3 \rightarrow RCO^+ + [AlCl_4]^- \text{ (ion pair)}$$
$$RCO^+ + C_6H_6 \rightarrow [RCOC_6H_6]^+ \rightarrow RCOC_6H_5 + H^+$$

Many other distorted tetrahedral complexes are the 1:1 adducts of the trihalides with amines, ethers, ketones, alcohols, phosphines, etc. Similar hydride and alkyl complexes are discussed below. Salts of the anions $[InCl_6]^{3-}$, $[InBr_6]^{3-}$, $[TlCl_6]^{3-}$, $[TlBr_6]^{3-}$ and $[TlCl_5 \cdot H_2O]^{2-}$ are known.[6c] Thallium alone forms the interesting binuclear ion $[Tl_2Cl_9]^{3-}$, which has the structure shown in Figure 18-4, in which two octahedra share a face.

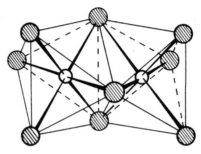

Fig. 18-4.   The structure of the binuclear complex anions $[Tl_2Cl_9]^{3-}$ and $[W_2Cl_9]^{3-}$.

The most important octahedral complexes of the group III elements are ones containing chelate rings. Typical are these of β-diketones, catechol (18-I), dicarboxylic acids (18-II) and 8-hydroxyquinoline (18-III). The

(18-I)   (18-II)   (18-III)

neutral complexes dissolve readily in organic solvents, but are insoluble in water. The acetylacetonates have low melting points ($< 200°$) and vaporize without decomposition. The anionic complexes are isolated as the salts

[6b] V. P. Petro and S. G. Shore, *J. Chem. Soc.*, **1964**, 336.
[6c] T. Spiro, *Inorg. Chem.*, **4**, 1290 (1965).

of large univalent cations.   The 8-hydroxyquinolinates are used for analytical purposes.   Tropone, T, gives an 8-coordinate anion of indium in $Na[InT_4]$.

The four elements form *alkoxides* which we can regard as complexes since they are all polymeric even in solution in inert solvents.   Only those of aluminum, particularly the isopropoxide, which is widely used in organic chemistry as a reducing agent for aldehydes and ketones, are of importance. They can be made by the reactions

$$Al + ROH \xrightarrow[\text{catalyst, warm}]{1\%HgCl_2} (RO)_3Al + \tfrac{3}{2}H_2$$

$$AlCl_3 + 3RONa \longrightarrow (RO)_3Al + 3NaCl$$

The alkoxides hydrolyze vigorously with water.   The *t*-butoxide is a cyclic dimer (18-IV) in solvents whereas the isopropoxide is tetrameric (18-V) at ordinary temperatures but trimeric at elevated temperatures. Terminal and bridging alkoxy groups can be distinguished by nmr spectra.[7]

(18-IV)   (18-V)

18-8. Hydrides and Complex Hydrides

Although there is some evidence for AlH_3 and Al_2H_6 in the gas phase at low pressures,[8] the only stable binary hydride is *alane*, $(AlH_3)_n$, which is obtained as a white powder by addition of Al_2Cl_6 to $LiAlH_4$ in ether; it is presumably a hydrogen-bridged polymer.   No corresponding gallane exists, but a viscous oil unstable above $-15°$, with an IR spectrum showing Ga—H bonds, has been obtained by the displacement reaction

$$Me_3NGaH_3(s) + BF_3(g) \xrightarrow{-15°} GaH_3(l) + Me_3NBF_3(g)$$

A similar reaction at room temperature gives some evidence for an unstable gaseous gallane.[9]   Gaseous Ga_2H_6, solid $(GaH_3)_n$ and $(C_2H_5)_2OGaH_3$ all

[7] V. J. Shriner, D. Whittaker and V. P. Fernandez, *J. Amer. Chem. Soc.*, **85**, 2318 (1963).
[8] P. Breisacher and B. Siegal, *J. Amer. Chem. Soc.*, **86**, 5053 (1964).
[9] N. N. Greenwood and M. G. H. Wallbridge, *J. Chem. Soc.*, **1963**, 3912.

have been reported some years ago but later work[10] leaves no doubt that these reports are erroneous.

There is, however, an extensive hydride chemistry of Al and Ga where the compounds can be regarded as arising from Lewis acid behavior of MH_3, even if the simple molecules are too unstable to be isolated, either by the formation of adducts with donor molecules such as NR_3, PR_3, SR_2 or with anions, viz.:

$$GaH_3 + NMe_3 = Me_3NGaH_3$$
$$AlH_3 + H^- = [AlH_4]^-$$

In such compounds there are close analogies to borane derivatives.

Hydride Anions. The alkali metal salts of AlH_4^- and GaH_4^- are similar to those of BH_4^-. The thermal and chemical stabilities vary according to the ability of the MH_3 group to act as an acceptor according to the above equation, the order being $B > Al > Ga$. Thus $LiGaH_4$ decomposes slowly even at 25° to LiH, Ga and H_2 and is a milder reducing agent than $LiAlH_4$. Similarly, although BH_4^- is stable in water, the Al and Ga salts are rapidly and often explosively hydrolyzed by water:

$$4H_2O + MH_4^- = 4H_2 + M(OH)_3 + OH^-$$

Lithium aluminum hydride is an important reducing agent in both organic and inorganic chemistry. It is a non-volatile, crystalline solid, white when pure but usually gray. It is stable below $\sim 120°$, and is soluble in diethylether and other ethers such as THF and various glymes. It accomplishes many otherwise tedious or difficult reductions, e.g., —COOH to —CH_2OH; some reactions are shown in Figure 18-5.

Both Al and Ga salts can be prepared by the reaction

$$4LiH + MCl_3 \xrightarrow{Et_2O} LiMH_4 + 3LiCl$$

However, for AlH_4^- the Li, Na and K salts are more conveniently obtained by direct interaction,[11] e.g.,

$$Na + Al + 2H_2 \xrightarrow[150°/2000 \text{ p.s.i./24h}]{THF} NaAlH_4$$

The salt is obtained by precipitation with toluene and can be efficiently converted to the lithium salt.

$$NaAlH_4 + LiCl \xrightarrow{Et_2O} NaCl(s) + LiAlH_4$$

If ethylene (or other olefin) is present and $AlEt_3$ is used as catalyst the direct interaction gives $Na[AlH_{4-n}Et_n]$; these compounds, the alkoxo

[10] D. F. Shriver, R. W. Parry, N. N. Greenwood, A. Storr and M. G. H. Wallbridge, *Inorg. Chem.*, **2**, 867 (1963).

[11] E. C. Ashby, G. J. Brendel and H. E. Robinson, *Inorg. Chem.*, **2**, 499 (1963).

hydrido and the orange dihydropyridino anions are useful for selected reductions; the latter reduces keto groups by H-transfer from dihydrido-pyridine. $Al(BH_4)_3$ has been discussed previously (page 203).

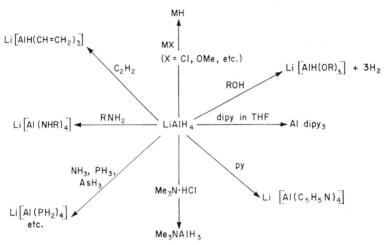

Fig. 18-5. Some reactions of lithium aluminum hydride.

Donor Adducts. These are again similar to borane adducts, the stability order being B > Al > Ga, and also to adducts of the halides and alkyls where the stability order is halides > alkyls > hydrides. The most studied adducts are the trialkylaminealanes.[12] Trimethylamine gives both 1:1 and 1:2 adducts but the latter is stable only in the presence of excess amine;

$$Me_3NAlCl_3 + 3LiH \xrightarrow{Et_2O} Me_3NAlH_3 + 3NaCl$$

$$Me_3N \cdot HCl + LiAlH_4 \xrightarrow[-60°]{Et_2O} Me_3NAlH_3 + LiCl + H_2$$

$$3LiAlH_4 + AlCl_3 + 4NMe_3 \longrightarrow 4Me_3NAlH_3 + 3LiCl$$

$$Me_3NAlH_3 + Me_3N \rightleftharpoons (Me_3N)_2AlH_3$$

The monoamine is a white, volatile, crystalline solid (m 75°), readily hydro-lyzed by water, which slowly decomposes to $(AlH_3)_n$. It is monomeric and tetrahedral. The bisamine is trigonal bipyramidal with axial N atoms and linear N—Al—N. Tetrahydrofuran also gives 1:1 and 1:2 adducts, but diethylether, presumably for steric reasons, gives only the 1:1 com-pound, though a mixed THF–Et$_2$O adduct exists.

[12] R. Ehrlich, et. al., Inorg. Chem., **2**, 650 (1963); G. W. Fraser, et. al., J. Chem. Soc., **1963**, 3742; F. M. Peters, et. al., Can. J. Chem., **41**, 1051 (1963); C. W. Heitsch, et. al., Inorg. Chem., **2**, 508 (1963).

A number of polymers with Al—N backbones have been made,[13] e.g., by the reaction of R_3NAlH_3 with ethylamine or acetonitrile. In one case, that of triethylenediamine, the aminealane can be obtained by direct interaction of the amine with Al at high pressures of hydrogen.[14]

There are similar monoamine gallanes[15] where the Ga—H stretch at ~ 1850 cm^{-1}, compared to ~ 1770 for the alane, suggests a stronger M—H bond and indeed the gallanes are less sensitive to hydrolysis. The $(Me_3N)_2GaH_3$ compound is unstable above $-60°$. The preparation of the gallanes illustrates a useful principle regarding the use of a weak donor as solvent;

$$Me_3NGaH_3 \ + \ BF_3 \xrightarrow[\text{weak}]{\text{Me}_2\text{S}} Me_2SGaH_3 \ + \ Me_3NBF_3$$
$$\text{strong–weak} \qquad \text{strong} \qquad \text{weak–weak} \qquad \text{strong–strong}$$

Because the weak–weak, strong–strong combination is favored over two weak–strong adducts, the net effect is to displace the strong donor, Me_3N, by the weaker one, Me_2S.

18-9. Organometallic Compounds

Those of aluminum are by far the most important and best known. They may be prepared by the classical reaction of aluminum with the appropriate organomercury compound:

$$2Al + 3R_2Hg \rightarrow 2R_3Al \text{ (or } [R_3Al]_2) + 3Hg$$

or reaction of Grignard reagents with $AlCl_3$,

$$RMgCl + AlCl_3 \rightarrow RAlCl_2, R_2AlCl, R_3Al$$

More direct methods suitable for large-scale use are now available. These procedures stemmed from studies which showed that aluminum hydride or $LiAlH_4$ reacts with olefins to give alkyls or alkyl anions—a reaction specific for B and Al hydrides:

$$AlH_3 + 3C_nH_{2n} = Al(C_nH_{2n+1})_3$$
$$LiAlH_4 + 4C_nH_{2n} = Li[Al(C_nH_{2n+1})_4]$$

Although $(AlH_3)_n$ cannot be made by direct interaction of Al and H_2, nevertheless in the presence of aluminum alkyl the following reaction to give the dialkyl hydride can occur:

$$Al + \tfrac{3}{2}H_2 + 2AlR_3 = 3AlR_2H$$

---

[13] R. Ehrlich, et. al., Inorg. Chem., 3, 628 (1964).

[14] E. C. Ashby, J. Amer. Chem. Soc., 86, 1882 (1964).

[15] D. F. Shriver, et. al., J. Amer. Chem. Soc., 84, 1322 (1962); N. N. Greenwood, et. al., Inorg. Chem., 2, 1036 (1963); D. F. Shriver and R. W. Parry, Inorg. Chem., 2, 1039 (1963); N. N. Greenwood and A. Storr, J. Chem. Soc., 1965, 3426.

This hydride will then react with olefins:

$$AlR_2H + C_nH_{2n} = AlR_2(C_nH_{2n+1})$$

Thus the direct interaction of Al, H_2 and olefin can be used to give either the dialkyl hydrides or the trialkyls.

Other technically important compounds are the "sesquichlorides" such as $MeAlCl_2$ or Et_2AlCl. These compounds can be made by direct interaction of Al or Mg–Al alloy with the alkyl chloride. This reaction fails for propyl and higher alkyls since the alkyl halides decompose in presence of the alkylaluminum halides to give HCl, alkanes, etc.

The lower aluminum alkyls are reactive liquids inflaming in air and explosively sensitive to water. All other derivatives are similarly sensitive to air and moisture though not all are spontaneously inflammable. The lower alkyls are dimerized (page 318) and the alkyl halides are also dimeric but with *halogen* bridges.[16]

At $-75°$ the proton nuclear resonance spectrum of $Al_2(CH_3)_6$ exhibits separate resonances for the terminal and bridging methyl groups, but on warming these begin to coalesce and at room temperature only one sharp peak is observed. This indicates that the bridging and terminal methyl groups can exchange places with a relatively low energy barrier. This may occur by partial or complete dissociation of the dimer.

The alkyls are Lewis acids, combining with donors such as amines, phosphines, ethers and thioethers to give tetrahedral, four-coordinate species. With tetramethyl hydrazine and $(CH_3)_2NCH_2N(CH_3)_2$, 5-co-ordinate species which appear to be of the kind shown in 18-VI are obtained,[17] although at room temperature exchange processes cause all methyl groups and all ethyl groups to appear equivalent in the proton nuclear resonance spectrum. With $(CH_3)_2NCH_2CH_2N(CH_3)_2$ a complex is formed which has an AlR_3 group bound to each nitrogen atom. Aluminum alkyls also combine with lithium alkyls:

$$(C_2H_5)_3Al + LiC_2H_5 \xrightarrow{\text{in benzene}} LiAl(C_2H_5)_4$$

X-ray study[18] has shown that $LiAl(C_2H_5)_4$ is built up of chains of alternating tetrahedral $Al(C_2H_5)_4{}^-$ and Li^+ in such a way that each lithium atom is tetrahedrally surrounded by four α-carbon atoms, close enough to indicate weak Li—C bonds.

---

[16] G. Allegra, G. Perego and A. Immirzi, *Makromol. Chem.*, **61**, 69 (1963).

[17] D. F. Clemens, W. S. Brey, Jr. and H. H. Sisler, *Inorg. Chem.*, **2**, 1251 (1963); N. R. Felter, B. Bartocha, F. E. Brinkman and D. E. Moore, *Can. J. Chem.*, **41**, 1359 (1963).

[18] R. L. Gerteis, R. E. Dickerson and T. L. Brown, *Inorg. Chem.*, **3**, 872 (1964).

15 + A.I.C.

When primary or secondary amines or phosphines are used, the 1:1 complexes can eliminate one or two hydrocarbon molecules to give bridged species[19] such as 18-VII or 18-VIII, the latter being comparable to the hydrocarbon cubane.

(18-VI)   (18-VII)   (18-VIII)

Other unusual reactions of the alkyls are with KF and HCN. The former, in toluene at 60°, reacts with $Al(C_2H_5)_3$ to give $K[(C_2H_5)_3AlFAl(C_2H_5)_3]$ in which the AlFAl group is linear.[20] This linearity has been attributed to the formation of Al—F sigma bonds by use of digonal sp_z hybrid orbitals of fluorine and Al—F π bonds by overlap of the filled p_x and p_y orbitals of fluorine with empty $d\pi$ orbitals of Al, in a manner similar to that of the bonding in some linear M—O—M groups found in transition metal complexes (Fig. 30-F-2). HCN reacts with the $(CH_3)_3M$ (M = Al, Ga, In and Tl) compounds to give air-sensitive, tetrameric compounds, $[(CH_3)_2MCN]_4$, which have linear MCNM groups.[21]

Triethylaluminum, the sesquichloride $(C_2H_5)_3Al_2Cl_3$ and alkyl hydrides are used together with transition metal halides or alkoxides or organometallic complexes as catalysts (e.g., Ziegler catalysts) for the polymerization of ethylene, propylene and a variety of other unsaturated compounds. These polymerizations are often stereospecific, giving crystalline, oriented polypropylenes, for example. The alkyls are also used as alkylating agents.

The trialkyls of Ga, In and Tl resemble those of aluminum but they have been less extensively investigated and are increasingly less stable. One signal point of difference is the lack of dimerization of the alkyls of B, Ga, In and Tl at ordinary temperatures, with the exception of the unusual polymerization of crystalline trimethylindium (see page 318). Thallium gives very stable ionic derivatives of the type R_2TlX (X = halogen, SO_4, CN, NO_3, etc.), which resemble mercury compounds R_2Hg, being unaffected by air and water. The ion $(CH_3)_2Tl^+$ in aqueous solution and in

[19] G. E. Coates and J. Graham, *J. Chem. Soc.*, **1963**, 233; T. R. R. McDonald and W. S. McDonald, *Proc.Chem. Soc.*, **1963**, 382; O. T. Beachley, G. E. Coates and G. Kohnstam, *J. Chem. Soc.*, **1965**, 3248.

[20] G. Natta, G. Allegra, G. Perego and A. Zambelli, *J. Amer. Chem. Soc.*, **83**, 5033 (1961).

[21] G. E. Coates and R. N. Mukherjee, *J. Chem. Soc.*, **1963**, 229.

crystals has been shown to be linear as would be expected since it is iso-electronic with $(CH_3)_2Hg$. In crystals however it is likely that the anions act as bridges similar to those found in dimethyl tin salts (see page 477) but this is not certain. Additional coordination can certainly occur and a complex $[Me_2Tlpy]ClO_4$ has been isolated.[22a] The Me_2Tlpy^+ ion appears to be T-shaped on the basis of spectroscopic measurements. Bispenta-fluorophenylthallium halides give what appear to be 5-coordinate adducts such as $(C_6F_5)_2TlCl(bipy)$.[22b]

LOWER VALENT COMPOUNDS

18-10. Lower Valences of Aluminum, Gallium and Indium

Since the elements have the outer electron configurations ns^2np, it is natural to consider whether monovalent ions might be capable of existence. It may be recalled that there is no evidence for B^I under chemically important conditions.

There is no evidence that compounds containing Al^I exist at ordinary temperatures. Anodic oxidation of aluminum at high current densities evidently produces lower valent aluminum ions, either Al^I or Al^{II}, or both, but they are ephemeral. There is no doubt that *gaseous* Al^I halide mole-cules exist at high temperatures, and their spectroscopic properties are well known. In the chloride system the equilibrium

$$AlCl_3(g) + 2Al(s) = 3AlCl(g)$$

has been thoroughly studied and its use in purifying aluminum proposed. The reaction proceeds to the right at high temperatures, but reverses readily at low temperatures. Similarly, it has been shown that gaseous Al_2O and AlO molecules exist above $1000°$, but no solid oxides containing lower valent aluminum have been shown definitely to exist under ordinary conditions. It is doubtful if the reported solid AlI is authentic, and no serious claim has ever been made for the existence of other monohalides.

A zerovalent complex, $Aldipy_3$, is formed by reduction of $AlCl_3$ with Li dipyridyl in THF; it is exceedingly air sensitive, green in color and paramagnetic ($\mu = 2.32$ BM),[23] (see, however, Sec. 27-8).

Gallium(I) compounds have been prepared in the gas phase at high temperatures by reactions such as

$$Ga_2O_3(s) + 4Ga(l) \xrightarrow{700°} 3Ga_2O(g)$$

$$Ga(l) + SiO_2(s) \rightleftharpoons Si \text{ (in Ga)} + 2Ga_2O(g)$$

$$GaCl_3(g) \xrightleftharpoons{1100°} GaCl(g) + Cl_2$$

[22a] I. R. Beattie and P. A. Cocking, *J. Chem. Soc.*, **1965**, 3860.

[22b] G. B. Deacon, J. H. S. Green and R. S. Nyholm, *J. Chem. Soc.*, **1965**, 3411.

[23] S. Herzog, K. Geisler and H. Präkel, *Angew. Chem. (Internat.)*, **2**, 47 (1963).

Although GaCl has not been isolated pure, Ga_2O and Ga_2S can be, although the latter solid is non-stoichiometric.

"Divalent" chalconides GaS, GaSe and GaTe can be made by direct interaction; they do not contain Ga^{2+}, however, which would lead to paramagnetism, but have Ga—Ga units in a layer lattice, each gallium atom being tetrahedrally surrounded by three S and one Ga. The best-known compounds are the "dihalides" GaX_2; these are known to have the salt-like structure $Ga^I[Ga^{III}X_4]$; the Ga^I ion can also be obtained in other salts such as $Ga[AlCl_4]$. Fused $GaCl_2$ is a typical conducting molten salt. These halides are prepared by the reaction

$$2Ga + 4GaX_3 = 3Ga[GaX_4]$$

Salts of the type $[GaL_4][GaCl_4]$ have been obtained with S, Se and As donors.

There is some evidence that unstable Ga^I species are important in the dissolution of gallium in acid. This postulation accounts for the stoichiometries observed and for the fact that gallium is one of the few reagents to reduce perchloric acid:

$$Ga + H^+ = Ga^+ + \tfrac{1}{2}H_2$$
$$4Ga^+ + 8H^+ + ClO_4^- = 4Ga^{3+} + Cl^- + 4H_2O$$

Some delayed reducing ability of gallium dissolved in HCl has been reported, and Raman spectra of solutions of Ga in HCl and HBr suggest that Ga^I complexes of uncertain composition are present.[24]

When $Ga[GaCl_4]$ or similar salts are treated with water, strongly reducing orange to black precipitates are formed, together with Ga and H_2. The precipitate analyzes[25] as $GaClOH \cdot \tfrac{1}{2}H_2O$ and can be vacuum dried at 100° to white GaClOH. It dissolves in excess sodium hydroxide[26] to give solutions initially orange, which slowly become colorless, losing hydrogen homogeneously with a half life of ca 5.2 h in $1M$ NaOH, in a reaction first order with respect to gallium:

$$Ga^I + 2H_2O + 2OH^- = Ga(OH)_4^- + H_2$$

The potential for Ga^I–Ga^{III} in basic solution has been estimated:

$$Ga(OH)_4^- + 2e = Ga^I + 4OH^- \qquad E_B^0 \leq -1.24 \text{ v}$$

In summary, there is no evidence for authentic Ga^{II} compounds. Those having stoichiometries superficially indicative of Ga^{II} either contain

---

[24] L. A. Woodward and M. J. Taylor, *J. Inorg. Nucl. Chem.*, **27**, 737 (1965).
[25] F. M. Brewer, *et al.*, *J. Inorg. Nucl. Chem.*, **25**, 322, 324 (1963).
[26] J. D. Corbett, *Inorg. Chem.*, **2**, 634 (1963).

Ga—Ga bonds and are properly regarded as compounds of Ga^{III}, or they contain Ga^{I} and Ga^{III} in 1:1 ratio.

Although it appears that lower valent indium compounds are more stable, as a class, than those of gallium, they are less well characterized. InF_2 appears to exist, but its structure is unknown. The monohalides, InCl, InBr and InI, exist. $InCl_2$ does not appear to exist as a distinct compound, but a phase, In_2Cl_3, for which the structure $In_3^I[In^{III}Cl_6]$ has been suggested, is stable. In_2O appears to be an authentic In^I compound, but its structure remains unknown. Cyclopentadienylindium, InC_5H_5, is discussed below in connection with its Tl analog.

No In^I species are known to be stable in aqueous solution.

18-11. Thallium(I)

With thallium, the unipositive state is quite stable. In aqueous solution it is distinctly more stable than Tl^{III}:

$$Tl^{3+} + 2e = Tl^{+} \qquad E^0 = +1.25 \text{ v } [E_f = +0.77, 1M \text{ HCl}; +1.26, 1M \text{ HClO}_4]$$

The thallous ion is not very sensitive to pH, although the thallic ion is extensively hydrolyzed to $TlOH^{2+}$ and the colloidal oxide even at pH 1–2.5; the redox potential is hence very dependent on pH as well as on presence of complexing anions. Thus, as indicated by the above potentials, the presence of Cl^- stabilizes Tl^{3+} more (by formation of complexes) than Tl^+ and the potential is thereby lowered.

The colorless thallous ion has a radius of 1.44 A, which can be compared with those of K^+, Rb^+ and Ag^+, (1.33, 1.48 and 1.26 A), since in its chemistry this ion resembles either the alkali or argentous ions; it is usually 6 or 8-coordinate in crystalline salts. The yellow hydroxide is thermally unstable, giving the black oxide, Tl_2O, at about 100°. The latter and the hydroxide are readily soluble in water to give strongly basic solutions which absorb carbon dioxide from the air; TlOH is a weaker base than KOH, however. Many thallous salts have solubilities somewhat lower than the corresponding alkali salts, but otherwise are similar to and quite often isomorphous with them. Examples of such salts are the cyanide, nitrate, carbonate, sulfate, phosphates, perchlorate and alums. Thallous solutions are exceedingly poisonous[27] and in trace amounts cause loss of hair.

Thallous sulfate, nitrate and acetate are moderately soluble in water, but—except for the very soluble TlF—the halides are sparingly soluble. The chromate and the black sulfide, Tl_2S, which can be precipitated by

[27] A. Christie, *The Pale Horse*, Collins, London, 1961.

hydrogen sulfide from weakly acid solutions, are also insoluble. Thallous chloride also resembles silver chloride in being photosensitive, darkening on exposure to light. Incorporation of Tl^I halides into alkali halides gives rise to new absorption and emission bands due to the formation of complexes of the type that exist also in solutions, notably mainly TlX_2^- and TlX_4^{3-};[28] such thallium activated alkali halide crystals are used as phosphors, e.g., for scintillation radiation detectors. Thallous chloride is insoluble in ammonia, unlike silver chloride.

With the exception of those with halide, oxygen and sulfur ligands, Tl^I gives rather few complexes.

The two isotopes, ^{203}Tl and ^{205}Tl (70.48%), both have nuclear spin, and nmr signals are readily detected for thallium solutions or for solids. In solution both Tl^I and Tl^{III} resonances are markedly dependent on concentration and on the nature of anions present; such data have shown that thallous perchlorate is highly dissociated, but salts of weaker acids and TlOH have been shown to form ion pairs in solution.

Electron exchange reactions in the Tl^I–Tl^{III} have been intensively studied and appear to be two-electron transfer processes; various Tl^{III} complexes participate under appropriate conditions (see page 184).

The only known Tl^I organo compound is the polymeric TlC_5H_5 precipitated by addition of aqueous TlOH to cyclopentadiene; a similar In compound exists. Structural studies have shown that these compounds consist of discrete molecules in the gas phase having 5-fold symmetry. The metal atoms lie over the centers of the rings and are apparently bound by forces mainly of covalent nature.[29]

Thallium dissolves in alcohols to give alkoxides:

$$4Tl + 4C_2H_5OH = (TlOC_2H_5)_4 + 2H_2$$

which are liquids with the exception of the methoxide which is crystalline. All are tetramers and the methoxide has a distorted cube structure (Fig. 18-6) with the Tl and O atoms at corners of regular tetrahedra of different size, so that oxygen is 4-coordinate.[30]

[28] See, e.g., R. E. Curtice and A. B. Scott, *Inorg. Chem.*, **3**, 1383 (1964).
[29] S. Shibata, L. S. Bartell and R. M. Gavin, Jr., *J. Chem. Phys.*, **41**, 717 (1964).
[30] L. F. Dahl, *et al.*, *J. Inorg. Nucl. Chem.*, **24**, 357 (1962).

References

Bradley, D. C., *Advances in Chemistry Series* No. **23**, American Chemical Society, and also *Progr. Inorg. Chem.*, **2**, 303 (1960). Reviews on alkoxides including those of Group III.

Greenwood, N. N., *Adv. Inorg. Chem. Radiochem.*, **5**, 91 (1963). A review on the general chemistry of Ga with 310 references.

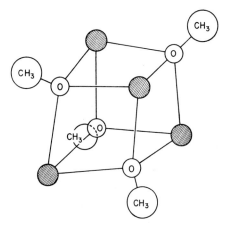

Fig. 18-6.   Structure of tetrameric thallium methoxide.

Köster, R., and P. Benger, *Adv. Inorg. Chem. Radiochem.*, Vol. 7 (1965).   Organo-aluminum compounds.

Lehmkuhl, H., *Angew. Chem. (Internat.)*, **3**, 107 (1962).   Review on organoaluminum complexes.

Olah, G. A., ed., *Friedel–Crafts and Related Reactions*, Vol. I, Wiley, New York, 1963.   Contains articles on Lewis acids, coordination compounds of B, Al and Ga halides.   Vols. II–IV contain detailed reviews mainly of organic interest.

Sinn, H., and F. Patat, *Angew. Chem. (Internat.)*, **3**, 93 (1964).   Review on mechanism of Ziegler-type catalyses involving Al alkyls.

Stone, F. G. A., *Chem. Revs.*, **88**, 101 (1957).   Stability relationships in analogous molecular addition compounds of group III elements (including boron).

Surtees, J. W., *Rev. Pure Appl. Chem.*, **13**, 91 (1963).   Aluminum aryls.

Thomas, C. A., *Anhydrous Aluminum Chloride in Organic Chemistry,* Reinhold, New York, 1941.

Willardson, R. K., and H. L. Goering, eds., *Compound Semiconductors, Vol. I.   Preparation of III–V Compounds*, Reinhold, New York, 1962.   The preparation and properties of Al, Ga and In phosphides, nitrides, arsenides, etc.   A comprehensive account.

Ziegler, K., in Sir A. R. Todd, ed., *Perspectives in Organic Chemistry*, Interscience, New York–London, 1956.   Use of organoaluminum compounds in syntheses.

———, *International Conference on Coordination Chemistry*, *Chem. Soc. (London), Spec. Publ. No. 13* (1959).   Use of organoaluminum compounds in syntheses.

———, in H. H. Zeiss, ed., *Organometallic Chemistry* (American Chemical Society Monograph No. 147), Reinhold, New York, 1960, p. 194.   Organoaluminum compounds.

19

The Group IV Elements : Si, Ge, Sn, Pb

GENERAL REMARKS

19-1. Group Trends and Stereochemistry

The general trend from electronegative to electropositive character with increasing atomic number which is found in several groups is strikingly evident in group IV. Carbon is strictly nonmetallic; silicon is chemically essentially nonmetallic; germanium is a metalloid; tin and especially lead are metallic. There is scarcely any more striking example of an enormous discontinuity in general properties between the first and second row elements followed by a relatively smooth change toward more metallic character thereafter than in this group. Little of the chemistry of silicon can be inferred from that of carbon. Some properties of the elements are given in Table 19-1.

TABLE 19-1

Some Properties of the Group IV Elements

Element	Electronic structure	Ionization potentials, ev				Electro-negativities[a]	Covalent radius,[b] A
		1st	2nd	3rd	4th		
C	$[He]2s^2 2p^2$	11.264	24.376	47.864	64.476	2.50	0.77
Si	$[Ne]3s^2 3p^2$	8.149	16.34	33.46	45.13	1.74	1.17
Ge	$[Ar]3d^{10}4s^2 4p^2$	7.88	15.93	34.23	45.7	2.02	1.22
Sn	$[Kr]4d^{10}5s^2 5p^2$	7.332	14.63	30.6	39.6	1.72	1.40[c]
Pb	$[Xe]4f^{14}5d^{10}6s^2 6p^2$	7.415	15.03	32.0	42.3	1.55	1.54[d]

[a] According to Allred and Rochow.
[b] Tetrahedral, i.e., sp^3 radii.
[c] Covalent radius of Sn^{II}, 1.63 (reference 8).
[d] Ionic radius of Pb^{2+}, 1.21.

456

The tendency to *catenation* appears at present to vary somewhat irregularly, but the apparent irregularity may be due as much to the incompleteness of the data as to any inherent irregularity. Silicon forms a series of hydrides, Si_nH_{2n+2}, and halides, Si_nX_{2n+2}, ($X = Cl, F$), which contain Si—Si bonds, while for germanium only the hydrides are known. For tin, catenated hydrides or halides are unknown, but an extensive series of $(R_2Sn)_n$ compounds, both cyclic and linear (in which cases, the mode of chain termination is not certain), are known. Lead is not known to form any catenated compounds; however in alloys such as Na_4Pb_4 and Na_4Pb_9 there appear to be distinct polyatomic lead anions and the Pb_9 ion has been suggested[1] to have a structure similar to Bi_9^{5+} in "bismuth monochloride" (page 497). On the whole, however, there is a decrease in the tendency to catenation in the order $C \ggg Si > Ge \approx Sn \ggg Pb$. This general, if not entirely smooth, decrease in the tendency to catenation may be ascribed partly to diminishing strength of the C—C, Si—Si, Ge—Ge, Sn—Sn and Pb—Pb bonds. The energies of these bonds are believed to be about as follows:

| C—C | 83 kcal/mole | Ge—Ge | 40 kcal/mole |
| Si—Si | 42 kcal/mole | Sn—Sn | 37 kcal/mole |

The strengths of single covalent bonds between group IV atoms and other atoms generally decrease in going down the group, as can be seen from Table 19-2; it will be noticed that in some cases there is an initial rise from

Table 19-2

Some Average Bond Energies

Group IV[a] element	Energy of bond, kcal/mole, with						
	H	C	F	Cl	Br	I	O
C	99	83	116	79	66	57	82
Si	70	69	129	86	69	51	88
Ge	74	71		85	68	50	
Sn	71	68		82	65	47	

[a] Data derived mainly from MX_4 type compounds which are unstable or nonexistent when M = Pb.

C to Si followed by a decrease. These energies do not, of course, reflect the ease of heterolytic breaking of bonds which is the usual way in chemical reactions; thus, for example, in spite of the high Si—Cl or Si—F bond energies, compounds containing these bonds are highly reactive. Since the charge separation in a bond is a critical factor, the bond ionicities must also

[1] D. Britton, *Inorg. Chem.*, **3**, 305 (1964).

15*

be considered in order to interpret the reactivities toward nucleophilic reagents. Thus SiCl bonds are much more reactive than SiC bonds because, though stronger, they are more polar, $Si^{\delta+}$—$Cl^{\delta-}$, rendering the silicon more susceptible to attack by a nucleophile such as OH^-.

It will be noted from Table 19-1 that the electronegativities for the sp^3-hybridized elements do not decrease monatonically as might have been expected following the trend usually observed in the groups. The order C > Ge > Si $\approx$ Sn > Pb has been obtained by a variety of different methods and appears to be significant. A similar anomalous order occurs in group III. This alternation has been attributed to the effects of the filling of the d, and later f, shells in the transition elements and in the lanthanides, which affects the screening of the valence electrons in the elements following them.

In group IV there is a certain amount of chemical behavior which supports the above order, although, owing to the numerous factors which affect chemical behavior, good correlations solely with electronegativity cannot be expected. However, it can be noted that Zn and hydrochloric acid reduce only germanium halides to the hydrides, which suggests a higher electronegativity for Ge than for Si or Sn. Also, 15% NaOH does not affect GeH_4 or SnH_4, while SiH_4 is rapidly hydrolyzed by water containing a trace of OH^-, which is consistent with, though not necessarily indicative of, the Ge—H or Sn—H bonds either being nonpolar or having the positive charge on hydrogen. Finally, we note that germanium halides are hydrolyzed in water only slowly and reversibly.

The Divalent State. The term lower valence indicates the use of fewer than four electrons in bonding. Thus, although the *oxidation state* of carbon in CO is usually formally taken to be 2, this is only a formalism and carbon uses more than two valence electrons in bonding. For carbon, true divalence is not found in stable compounds (see below) and the same is true for silicon. However the divalent state becomes increasingly stable and is dominant for Pb. All R_2Sn compounds (except where R = C_5H_5) are actually Sn^{IV} compounds since there are Sn—Sn bonds, although genuine Sn^{II} compounds do exist. Inspection of Table 19-1 clearly shows that this trend cannot be explained exclusively in terms of ionization potentials, since these are essentially the same for all of the group IV elements; the "inert pair" concept is not particularly instructive either, especially since the nonbonding electrons are known not be inert in a stereochemical sense, e.g., $SnCl_3^-$ is ψ-tetrahedral and functions as a donor.

The other factors which undoubtedly do govern the relative stabilities of the oxidation states are promotion energies and bond strengths for covalent compounds and lattice energies for ionic compounds. Taking first the former, it is rather easy to see why the divalent state becomes stable if we remember that the M—X bond energies generally decrease in the order Si—X, Ge—X, Sn—X, Pb—X(?). Referring to the promotion energy diagram for methane (page 68), we see that the factor which stabilizes CH_4 relative to $CH_2 + H_2$, despite the much higher promotional energy required in forming CH_4, is the great strength of the C—H bonds and the fact that two more of these are formed in CH_4 than in CH_2. Thus if we have a series of reactions $MX_2 + X_2 = MX_4$ in which the M—X bond energies are decreasing, it is obviously possible that this energy may eventually become too small to compensate for the $M^{II} \rightarrow M^{IV}$ promotion energy and the MX_2 compound becomes the more stable. For ionic compounds matters are not so simple, but since the sizes of the (real or hypothetical) ions, M^{2+} and M^{4+}, will increase down the group, it is possible that lattice energy differences will no longer favor the M^{4+} compound relative to the M^{2+} compound in view of the considerable energy expenditure required for the process

$$M^{2+} = M^{4+} + 2e$$

Of course there are few compounds of the types MX_2 or MX_4 which are entirely covalent or ionic (almost certainly no ionic MX_4 compounds) so that the above arguments are oversimplifications, but they indicate roughly the factors involved.

While it is true that C^{II} compounds cannot be isolated, nevertheless there is an extensive chemistry of organic reactions in which transient *carbene* intermediates such as $:CH_2$, $:CF_2$, etc., are known to take part. The stable divalent compounds of the other elements can be regarded as carbene-like in the sense that they are bent with a lone-pair, and undergo the general type of carbene reactions to give two new bonds to the element, i.e.,

$$\begin{array}{c} R \\ \diagdown \\ C: \rightarrow \\ \diagup \\ R \end{array} \quad \begin{array}{c} R \\ \diagdown \\ C \\ \diagup \\ R \end{array}$$

Some inorganic reactions of difluorocarbene, made by heating $(CF_3)_3PF_2$, have been described.[2]

$$(CF_3)_3PF_2 \rightleftharpoons (CF_3)_2PF_3 + CF_2$$
$$(CF_3)_2PF_3 \rightleftharpoons CF_3PF_4 + CF_2$$
$$CF_3PF_4 \rightleftharpoons PF_5 + CF_2$$

The CF_2 polymerizes to C_2F_4 and C_3F_6 or it can be trapped by I_2, HCl or O_2 to give respectively CF_2I_2, HCF_2Cl and COF_2.

While the stability of the divalent state for heavier elements can be accounted for in part by the factors discussed above, part of the reactivity of carbenes may be the greater accessibility of the sp^2-hybridized lone-pair in the smaller carbon atom.

[2] W. Mahler, *Inorg. Chem.*, **2**, 230 (1963).

Multiple Bonding. Silicon, germanium, tin and lead do not form $p\pi$ multiple bonds either to themselves or to other elements, whereas carbon has a profound tendency to do so. Thus there are numerous classes of carbon compounds such as olefins, ketones, imides, etc., which have no analogs among silicon and the heavier elements. Purely stoichiometric analogs such as CO_2, SiO_2, $(CH_3)_2CO$, $(CH_3)_2SiO$ exist, but they are totally different kinds of substances structurally. For example, dehydration of the silanol $R_2Si(OH)_2$ gives not a ketone analog but a disiloxane $R_2Si(OH)$—O—$Si(OH)R_2$ and silicones $(R_2SiO)_n$.

However, there is considerable evidence that in certain bonds to silicon, notably with O and N, there is some $d\pi$–$p\pi$ double bond character. This has been mentioned previously in the discussion of $N(SiH_3)_3$ (page 327). This type of multiple bond character is evidenced also, for example, by the rather large bond angles in siloxanes, the very much weaker basicity of $O(SiH_3)_2$ compared to $O(CH_3)_2$,[3] and by the much stronger acidity and hydrogen bonding of silanols such as $(CH_3)_3SiOH$ compared to $(CH_3)_3COH$; the latter can be ascribed to Si—O π bonding involving one of the two unshared pairs of the silanol oxygen and the $3d$ orbital of Si to give a situation somewhat similar electronically to the nitrogen atom in an imine $R_2C{=}N$—H. The fact that one unshared pair still remains on the oxygen is consistent with the fact that *base* character of the silanol is not much lowered in spite of its stronger acidity, compared to the alcohol. There is some direct evidence for bond shortening due to π bonding in, e.g., H_3SiNCS.[4] Recent studies[5] have shown that the phosphorus analog of trisilylamine, $P(SiH_3)_3$, also has a planar skeleton, suggesting that $p\pi$–$d\pi$ bond formation between Si and P occurs. Such π bonding has previously not been confirmed between two second row elements.

The tendency toward use of d orbitals for π bonding seems to decrease from Si to Ge, since in $O(GeH_3)_2$ and $S(GeH_3)_2$, the Ge—O—Ge and Ge—S—Ge groups appear to be highly bent[6] whereas in $O(SiH_3)_2$ the Si—O—Si angle is around 150°.[3] Also Ge—X bonds seem to be less shortened relative to the sum of covalent radii than are Si—X bonds;[7] the shortening is considered to be due, at least in part, to $p\pi$–$d\pi$ bonding. Further evidence of the lowering, or nonexistence, of $p\pi$–$d\pi$ bonding in the elements below Si comes from hydrogen bonding indications of base strengths of the amines $N(SiMe_3)_3$, $N(GeMe_3)_3$ and $N(SnMe_3)_3$. Whereas

[3] R. Varma, A. G. MacDiarmid and J. G. Miller, *Inorg. Chem.*, **3**, 1754 (1964).

[4] D. R. Jenkins, R. Kewley and T. M. Sugden, *Trans. Farad. Soc.*, **58**, 1284 (1962).

[5] G. Davidson, E. A. V. Ebsworth, G. M. Sheldrick and L. A. Woodward, *Chem. Comm.*, **1965**, 122.

[6] T. D. Goldfarb and S. Sujishi, *J. Amer. Chem. Soc.*, **86**, 1679 (1964).

[7] J. E. Griffiths and K. B. McAfee, *Proc. Chem. Soc.*, **1961**, 456.

the Si compound is virtually non-basic, the Ge compound is about as basic as an organic amine, while the Sn compound is *more* basic than any organic amine.[8] Electronic spectra of phenylsilanes also show the ability of SiH_3 groups to withdraw electrons from the benzene ring into vacant $3d$ orbitals.[9]

Although discussion is outside the scope of this book, it may be noted that studies of the mechanism of substitution at tetrahedral silicon atoms also provide some evidence for the involvement of d orbitals. Thus the energy to reach the transition states in substitution reactions involving a five-coordinate intermediate appears lower than would be expected without use of the silicon d orbitals.

Stereochemistry. Table 19-3 summarizes the stereochemical properties of Group IV compounds. For Si the only important valency is IV, in which the stereochemistry is nearly always tetrahedral though occasionally

TABLE 19-3

Valency and Stereochemistry of Group IV Elements

Valency	Coordination number	Geometry[a]	Examples
Si⁰	6	Octahedral	$Sidipy_3$
Ge^{II}, Sn^{II}, Pb^{II}	2	ψ-Trigonal (angular)	$SnCl_2(g)$, $Pb(C_5H_5)_2$, GeF_2
	3	ψ-Tetrahedral (pyramidal)	$SnCl_2 \cdot 2H_2O$, $SnCl_3{}^-$, $SnCl_2(s)$, GeF_2
	4	ψ-Tbp	Pb^{II} in Pb_3O_4
	5	ψ-Octahedral	SnO (blue-black form)
	6	Octahedral	PbS(NaCl type), $GeI_2(CaI_2$ type)
	7	Complex[b]	$[SC(NH_2)_2]_2PbCl$
Si^{IV}, Ge^{IV}, Sn^{IV}, Pb^{IV}	4	Tetrahedral	SiO_4 (silicates, SiO_2), SiS_2, $SiCl_4$, $PbMe_4$, GeH_4
	5	Tbp	$Me_3SnClpy$, $Me_3SnX(X = F^-, AsF_6{}^-, ClO_4{}^-)$
	5	?	$[SiPh_3dipy]^+$
	6	Octahedral	$SiF_6{}^{2-}$, $[Siacac_3]^+$, $SnCl_6{}^{2-}$, GeO_2, SnO_2 (rutile str.), $PbCl_6{}^{2-}$, cis-$SnCl_4(OPCl_3)_2$ SnF_4, $trans$-$GeCl_4py_2$, Pb^{IV} in Pb_3O_4
	8(?)	?	$Sn(NO_3)_4$, $[Snox_4]^{4-}$, $Pb(O_2CMe)_4$

[a] ψ indicates that a coordination position is occupied by lone-pair.
[b] See *Acta. Cryst.*, **12**, 727 (1959).

[8] E. W. Abel, private communication.
[9] L. Goodman, A. H. Konstam and L. H. Sommer, *J. Amer. Chem. Soc.*, **87**, 1012 (1965).

octahedral. For the other elements, Ge–Pb, the relative importance of octahedral structures increases. Penta-coordination is also found in some compounds such as the adducts of $(CH_3)_3SnX$ compounds with various Lewis bases and in the "siliconium ion" compounds formed[10a] by Ph_3SiX ($X = I$ or Br) with 2,2'-dipyridyl:

$$Ph_3SiX + dipy \xrightarrow{CH_2Cl_2} \left[\begin{array}{c} Ph \\ Ph \end{array} \!\! \begin{array}{c} N \\ Si-N \\ Ph \end{array} \right]^{+} + X^{-}$$

For tetrahedral Si and Ge and octahedral Si compounds, optical activity has been found. Thus $Si(Me)(Ph)(Et)(C_6H_4COOH)$ and $GeH(Me)(Ph)$-(α-naphthyl) have been resolved, as has $[Si(acac)_3]^{+}$.

For Ge^{II}, and especially Sn^{II}, it is known that the pair of electrons which is unused in bonding has important effects on the stereochemistry.[10b] Thus in the blue-black form of SnO, each Sn atom is surrounded by five oxygen atoms at approximately the vertices of an octahedron, the sixth vertex being presumably occupied by the lone-pair. This is called a ψ-octahedral arrangement. In $SnCl_2$, SnS, SnSe (orthorhombic form), $SnCl_2 \cdot 2H_2O$, $K_2SnCl_4 \cdot H_2O$ and $SnSO_4$, there are ψ-tetrahedral groupings, that is, atoms at 3 corners of a tetrahedron and a lone-pair of electrons at the fourth. Thus $SnCl_2 \cdot 2H_2O$ has a pyramidal $SnCl_2OH_2$ molecule, the second H_2O not being coordinated (it is readily lost at 80°), while $K_2SnCl_4 \cdot H_2O$ actually consists of ψ-tetrahedral $SnCl_3^{-}$ ions and Cl^{-} ions. The ψ-tetrahedral SnF_3^{-} ion is also known[11] as well as the $Sn_2F_5^{-}$ ion which consists of two SnF_3^{-} ions sharing a fluorine atom.[12] Other Sn^{II} compounds such as $SnCl_2$ or SnS are similarly 3-coordinate but with a bridge group between the metal atoms.

THE ELEMENTS

19-2. Occurrence, Isolation and Properties

Silicon is second only to oxygen in weight percentage of the earth's crust ($\sim 28\%$) and is found in an enormous diversity of silicate minerals. Germanium, tin and lead are relatively rare elements ($\sim 10^{-3}$ weight percent), but are well known because of their technical importance and the

[10a] J. Y. Corey and R. West, *J. Amer. Chem. Soc.*, **85**, 4034 (1963).
[10b] R. E. Rundle and D. H. Olson, *Inorg. Chem.*, **3**, 596 (1964).
[11] J. D. Donaldson and J. D. O'Donoghue, *J. Chem. Soc.*, **1964**, 271.
[12] R. R. McDonald, A. C. Larson and D. T. Cromer, *Acta Cryst.*, **17**, 1104 (1964).

relative ease with which they are obtained from natural sources in the cases of tin and lead.

Silicon is obtained in the ordinary commercial form by reduction of SiO_2 with carbon or CaC_2 in an electric furnace. Similarly, germanium is prepared by reduction of the dioxide with carbon or hydrogen. Silicon and germanium are used as semiconductors, especially in transistors. For this purpose exceedingly high purity is essential, and special methods are required to obtain usable materials. For silicon, methods vary in detail but the following general procedure is followed.

1. Ordinary, "chemically" pure Si is converted, by direct reaction, to a silicon halide or to $SiCl_3H$. This is then purified (of B, As, etc.) by fractional distillation in quartz vessels.

2. The SiX_4 is then reconverted to elemental silicon by reduction with hydrogen in a hot tube or on a hot wire, when X is Cl or Br,

$$SiX_4 + 2H_2 = Si + 4HX$$

or by direct thermal decomposition on a hot wire when X is I. Very pure Si can also be obtained by thermal decomposition of silane.

3. Pure silicon is then made "super-pure" (impurities $< 10^{-9}$ atom percent) by zone refining. In this process a rod of metal is heated near one end so that a cross-sectional wafer of molten silicon is produced. Since impurities are more soluble in the melt than they are in the solid they concentrate in the melt and the melted zone is then caused to move slowly along the rod by moving the heat source. This carries impurities to the end. The process may be repeated. The impure end is then removed.

Super-pure germanium is made in a similar way. Germanium chloride is fractionally distilled and then hydrolyzed to GeO_2, which is then reduced with hydrogen. The resulting metal is zone melted.

Tin and lead are obtained from their ores in various ways, commonly by reduction of their oxides with carbon. Further purification is usually effected by dissolving the metals in acid and depositing the pure metals electrolytically.

Silicon is ordinarily rather unreactive. It is attacked by halogens giving tetrahalides, and by alkalies giving solutions of silicates. It is not attacked by acids except hydrofluoric; presumably the stability of SiF_6^{2-} provides the driving force here. A highly reactive form of silicon has been prepared by the reaction:

$$3CaSi_2 + 2SbCl_3 = 6Si + 2Sb + 3CaCl_2$$

For example, it reacts with water to give SiO_2 and hydrogen. It has been suggested that this form is a graphite-like allotrope, but proof is as yet lacking, and its reactivity may be due to a state of extreme subdivision as in certain reactive forms of amorphous carbon.

Germanium is similar to but somewhat more reactive than silicon. It will dissolve in concentrated sulfuric and nitric acids. Tin and lead are more reactive. They dissolve in several acids, are rapidly attacked by halogens, and are slowly attacked by cold alkali, and rapidly by hot, to form stannates and plumbites. Lead often appears to be much more noble and unreactive than would be indicated by the potential

$$Pb^{2+} + 2e = Pb \qquad E^0 = -0.13 \text{ v}$$

This low reactivity can be attributed to high overvoltage for hydrogen and also in some cases to insoluble surface coatings. Thus lead is not dissolved by dilute sulfuric and concentrated hydrochloric acids.

19-3. Allotropic Forms

Silicon and germanium normally occur in only one structural form, which is the same as that of diamond. Recently, by use of very high pressures, denser forms have been produced. The dense form of Si (2.55 g/cm^3 as compared to 2.33 g/cm^3 for ordinary Si) has a cubic lattice containing distorted tetrahedra with bond distances of 2.30 and 2.39A (cf. 2.35A in ordinary Si). The dense form of germanium is tetragonal but has a similar structure. The graphite structure is peculiar to carbon, which is understandable since such a structure requires the formation of $p\pi$–$p\pi$ bonds and silicon and germanium are unable to engage in such bonding.

Tin has three crystalline modifications, with the following equilibrium transition temperatures

$$\alpha\text{-Sn} \underset{\text{``grey''}}{\overset{13.2°}{\rightleftharpoons}} \beta\text{-Sn} \underset{\text{``white''}}{\overset{161°}{\rightleftharpoons}} \gamma\text{-Sn} \overset{232°}{\rightleftharpoons} \text{Sn(l)}$$

α-Tin, or grey tin (density at $20° = 5.75$), has the diamond structure. This form is unstable above $13.2°$ and is transformed to β-tin or white tin (density at $20° = 7.31$) which has a metallic nature; γ-tin is also metallic. In the metallic forms there exist distorted close-packed arrangements of the metal atoms. The approach to ideal close packing accounts for the considerably greater density of the β-metal compared to the diamond form.

The most metallic of the group IV elements, lead, exists only in a ccp, metallic form. This is a reflection of both its preference for divalence rather than tetravalence and of the relatively low stability of the Pb—Pb bond.

COMPOUNDS OF THE GROUP IV ELEMENTS

19-4. Hydrides

While for carbon the stoichiometrically analogous alkanes, C_nH_{2n+2}, occur without known limit on n, the hydrides of Si and Ge form limited series, due to the weakness of the metal–metal bonds, up to Si_6H_{14} and Ge_9H_{20}. So far as is known all have structures based upon a tetrahedral disposition of bonds about the metal atoms.

The *silanes* can be made by the sulfuric or phosphoric acid hydrolysis of magnesium silicide, Mg_2Si, which is easily prepared by heating silicon and magnesium together in absence of air. The hydrolysis gives *ca* 25% yield of a mixture in the approximate proportions: 40% SiH_4, 30% Si_2H_6, 15% Si_3H_8, 10% Si_4H_{10}, 5% Si_5H_{12} and Si_6H_{14}, with perhaps traces of still higher members of the series. The individual silanes can be separated by fractional distillation or by gas–liquid chromatography; the latter method has allowed separation of the isomers.[13] Monosilane (b $-112°$) is conveniently prepared by the action of lithium aluminum hydride on silicon tetrachloride. It can also be obtained directly[14] from SiO_2 and silicates in high purity and yield (*ca* 80%) by hydrogenation at 400 atm, and 175° in a NaCl–AlCl$_3$ eutectic (m 120°) containing Al metal. An unstable volatile aluminum chlorohydride is thought to be an intermediate. $SiCl_4$ can be similarly directly hydrogenated.

$$Al + AlCl_3 \overset{H_2}{\rightleftharpoons} AlH_xCl_{3-x} \overset{SiO_2}{\longrightarrow} SiH_4$$

The important physical and chemical properties of the silanes are the following. All are colorless. The boiling points rise steadily with increasing molecular weight so that trisilane, Si_3H_8, is a liquid at room temperature. All are very reactive; they are spontaneously inflammable in air, e.g.,

$$Si_4H_{10} + \tfrac{13}{2}O_2 = 4SiO_2 + 5H_2O$$

They are stable toward neutral or acid water, but in the presence of base, even the traces provided by glass vessels, they are rapidly hydrolyzed in a manner typical of compounds containing hydridic hydrogen (the electronegativity of hydrogen is greater than that of silicon; cf. also the hydrolysis of the boranes):

$$Si_2H_6 + (4 + 2n)H_2O = 2SiO_2 \cdot nH_2O + 7H_2$$
$$\text{(Hydrous silica)}$$

The silanes are strong reducing agents. They react explosively with halogens at room temperature, but controlled replacement of H by Br or Cl may be effected in the presence of AlX_3 to give halosilanes such as

[13] See, e.g., S. D. Gokhale and W. L. Jolly, *Inorg. Chem.*, **3**, 946 (1964).
[14] H. L. Jackson, F. D. Marsh and E. L. Muetterties, *Inorg. Chem.*, **2**, 43 (1963).

SiH_3Cl. The ease of thermal decomposition of the silanes increases with increasing number of Si—Si links; thus the higher silanes decompose slowly although SiH_4 and Si_2H_6 are indefinitely stable at room temperature.

A great variety of alkyl and other substituted silanes are known, and silyl compounds containing the SiH_3 group have been much studied.

The reactivity of the Si—H bond toward water and oxygen is much the same in whatever compound it may occur. Si—H bonds have an ionic contribution Si^+H^-, in contrast to that of the C—H bond, C^-H^+, and react accordingly.

The *germanes* are similar to the silanes in their general properties. Monogermane (b $-90°$) is obtained almost quantitatively, plus small amounts of Ge_2H_6 and Ge_3H_8, by addition of alkali borohydride to GeO_2 in acid solution.[15] Alkylgermanes can be made from, e.g., CH_3GeBr_3 at 30–35°. Germanes up to Ge_9H_{20} are obtained from GeH_4 using high pressure electric discharges. They are less inflammable than silanes, but they are rapidly oxidized by oxygen to GeO_2 and H_2O, increasingly so with increasing molecular weight. They are also far more stable to hydrolysis than are the silanes, monogermane being stable even to $\sim 30\%$ alkali. Mixed Si–Ge hydrides are also known.[16]

For tin and lead only SnH_4, Sn_2H_6[16a] and PbH_4 are known. SnH_4 can be prepared by reduction of $SnCl_4$ with $LiAlH_4$ in ether at $-30°$. It is a gas which decomposes slowly at room temperature and very rapidly at $\sim 150°$. Stannane is stable toward 15% sodium hydroxide solution and dilute acids. It is attacked by some oxidizing agents such as $HgCl_2$. Plumbane is not very well characterized. It forms in minute quantities on acid hydrolysis of Mg–Pb alloys or in cathodic reduction of lead salts. Although the simple hydrides are unstable, comparatively stable alkylated hydrides R_nMH_{4-n} are known for tin and lead; they are prepared from the corresponding chlorides by treatment with $LiAlH_4$.

19-5. Halides

All of the possible group IV tetrahalides are known except for $PbBr_4$ and PbI_4. In addition, silicon forms a number of catenated halides; with bromine and iodine, Si_2X_6 is the highest, but with fluorine and chlorine many higher ones are known. Only one catenated halide of germanium, Ge_2Cl_6, is known, and with tin and lead none have been prepared. A number of mixed halides of silicon such as SiF_3I, $SiCl_2Br_2$, $SiFCl_2Br$ are

[15] J. E. Drake and W. L. Jolly, *J. Chem. Soc.*, **1962**, 2087; J. E. Griffiths, *Inorg. Chem.*, **2**, 375 (1963).

[16] P. L. Timms, C. C. Simpson and C. S. G. Phillips, *J. Chem. Soc.*, **1964**, 1467.

[16a] W. L. Jolly, *Angew. Chem.*, **72**, 268 (1960).

known, although the ultimate one, SiFClBrI, which would exist in enantiomorphs, has never been obtained.

The nonexistence of $PbBr_4$ and PbI_4 can be attributed to the inability of Br_2 and I_2 to oxidize Pb^{II} to Pb^{IV}, or, what is equivalent, to the reducing powers of Br^- and I^-. Even $PbCl_4$ must be kept at low temperatures to prevent decomposition into $PbCl_2$ and Cl_2.

The silicon halides, except SiF_4, are immediately and completely hydrolyzed by water to give "silicic acid." Germanium tetrachloride and $GeBr_4$ are also hydrolyzed, but in 6–9M acid there is an equilibrium involving species such as $[Ge(OH)_nCl_{6-n}]^{2-}$, and from concentrated acid solutions the tetrahalide can be distilled and separated. Stannic and plumbic chlorides are also not completely hydrolyzed except in dilute solution, and in excess acid complex ions such as $SnCl_6^{2-}$ and $SnCl_5^-$ are known.

Silicon and germanium tetrafluorides with water give hydrous oxides, but the main product, and in excess hydrofluoric acid the only product, is the fluoro anion, SiF_6^{2-} or GeF_6^{2-}. Tin(IV) fluoride is a white solid subliming at 705°; the tin is octahedrally coordinated by four bridging and two nonbridging fluorine atoms. PbF_4 is also salt-like.

The known chlorides of silicon[17a] are Si_nCl_{2n+2} where $n = 1$–6. The higher members which have highly branched structures are relatively newly discovered, arising by amine-catalyzed reactions of the types:

$$5Si_2Cl_6 \rightarrow Si_6Cl_{14} \cdot SiCl_4 + 3SiCl_4$$
$$3Si_3Cl_8 \rightarrow Si_5Cl_{12} + 2Si_2Cl_6$$
$$15Si_3Cl_8 \rightarrow 6Si_6Cl_{14} \cdot SiCl_4 + 3SiCl_4$$

The Si_6Cl_{14} is easily separated by distillation from the adduct $Si_6Cl_{14} \cdot SiCl_4$.

The reaction of SiF_4 and Si at 1150° produces gaseous SiF_2 which can be condensed to a plastic polymer, $(SiF_2)_n$; the latter on heating generates all perfluorosilanes from SiF_4 to $Si_{14}F_{30}$. All are spontaneously inflammable in air.[17b]

For silicon only, a number of *oxo halides* of the type $Cl_3SiO(SiCl_2O)_nSiCl_3$ are obtained by the action of a mixture of chlorine and oxygen on silicon at red heat; analogous oxobromides exist. Members of both series up to $n = 4$ have been characterized. The oxochlorides may also be obtained by controlled hydrolysis of $SiCl_4$ with moist ether. The oxochlorides but not the oxobromides can be esterified with ethanol to yield compounds of the general formula $(EtO)_3SiO—[Si(OEt)_2O]_n—Si(OEt)_3$. In addition to these linear oxo halides there are cyclic ones such as $(SiOX_2)_4$ in which there is an eight-membered ring of alternate Si and O atoms.

By careful hydrolysis of Si_2Cl_6 in ether, compounds believed to contain

[17a] G. Urry, et al., J. Inorg. Nucl. Chem., **26**, 409, 415, 421, 427, 435 (1964).
[17b] J. L. Margrave, et al., J. Amer. Chem. Soc., **87**, 2824 (1965).

alternate Si—Si and Si—O—Si links can be obtained; these are typified by Cl_3Si—$SiCl_2$—O—$SiCl_2$—$SiCl_3$.

19-6. Oxygen Compounds of Silicon

Silica. Silicon dioxide, also commonly called silica, occurs in several crystallographic forms. In all of them, with one exception noted later, the silicon is tetrahedrally surrounded by, and bound to, four oxygen atoms by single bonds doubtless having considerable ionic character. The crystal symmetries and equilibrium interconversion temperatures of the various polymorphs which are stable at 1 atm are shown in Figure 19-1.

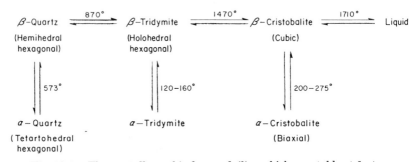

Fig. 19-1.   The crystallographic forms of silica which are stable at 1 atm.

In cristobalite the silicon atoms are placed as are the atoms in the diamond structure, with the oxygen atoms midway between each pair. In quartz and tridymite, there are helices so that these forms have optical isomers. Enantiomorphic crystals of quartz are easily recognized and mechanically separated. Interconversion of quartz, tridymite and cristobalite requires breaking and reforming of bonds; consequently, the activation energies of these transformations are high, and they occur only very slowly. Thus all three forms are found in nature, although, of course, only one, α-quartz, is thermodynamically stable at ordinary temperatures. The other forms are metastable. This phenomenon of metastability is often encountered; examples noted previously in this text include diamond relative to graphite, pure o- or p-hydrogen, etc. The interconversions of the α and β forms of each basic structural type occur without bond breaking and hence rapidly and at rather low temperatures.

Slow cooling of molten silica or heating any form of solid silica to the softening temperature gives an amorphous material which is glassy in appearance and is indeed a glass in the general sense, that is, a material with no long range order but rather a disordered array of polymeric chains, sheets or three-dimensional units.

In 1953 a new dense form of silica,[18] not previously found in nature was made by high pressure (35 katm), high temperature (250°) techniques. This material, *coesite*, is resistant to concentrated HF. Later (1960) coesite was found in Meteor Crater, Arizona, evidently formed by the action of temperature and pressure accompanying meteor impact. Still another form of silica, *stishovite*,[19a] has been made by use of superpressure ($\sim$120 katm at $\sim$1300°). This too was subsequently found in meteor craters. It is even more chemically inert than coesite, and is 60% denser than quartz. These facts are explained by its structure, which is of the rutile type (cf. GeO_2, SnO_2, PbO_2); thus the Si is 6-coordinate. Both coesite and stishovite revert to normal forms of SiO_2 when heated to 1200° and 400° respectively at 1 atm.

Silica in its normal forms is rather unreactive. It resists attack by chlorine, bromine, hydrogen and most acids and metals at ordinary and slightly elevated temperatures. It is attacked by fluorine, hydrofluoric acid and alkalies.

Silicates. When alkali metal carbonates are fused with silica ($\sim$1300°), CO_2 is driven off and a complex mixture of alkali silicates is obtained. When the mixtures are rich in alkali, the products are soluble in water, but with low alkali contents they become quite insoluble. Presumably the latter contain very large, polymeric anions. Sodium silicate solutions hydrolyze to give monomeric, tetrameric and other polymers, depending on the concentration.[19b]

Most of our understanding of silicate structures comes from studies of the many naturally occurring (and some synthetic) silicates of heavier metals. In such substances the basic unit of structure is the SiO_4 tetrahedron. These tetrahedra occur singly, or by sharing oxygen atoms, in small groups, in small cyclic groups, in infinite chains or in infinite sheets.

Simple Orthosilicates. A few silicates are known in which there are simple, discrete SiO_4^{4-}, orthosilicate, anions. In such compounds the associated cations are coordinated by the oxygen atoms, and various structures are found depending on the coordination number of the cation. In phenacite, Be_2SiO_4, and willemite, Zn_2SiO_4, the cations are surrounded by a tetrahedrally arranged set of four oxygen atoms. There are a number of compounds of the type M_2SiO_4, where M^{2+} is Mg^{2+}, Fe^{2+}, Mn^{2+} or some other cation with a preferred coordination number of six, in which the SiO_4^{4-} anions are so arranged as to provide interstices with six oxygen atoms at the apices of an octahedron in which the cations are found. In zircon, $ZrSiO_4$, the Zr^{4+} ion is eight-coordinate although not all Zr—O

[18] L. Coes, Jr., *Science*, **118**, 131 (1953).
[19a] S. M. Stishov and S. V. Popova, *Geokhimiya*, **10**, 837 (1961).
[19b] J. Aveston, *J. Chem. Soc.*, **1965**, 4444.

distances are equal. It may be noted that, although the M—O bonds are probably more ionic than the Si—O bonds, there is doubtless some covalent character to them, and these substances should not be regarded as literally ionic in the sense $[M^{2+}]_2[SiO_4^{4-}]$ but rather as somewhere between this extreme and the opposite extreme of infinite giant molecules. There are also other silicates containing discrete SiO_4 tetrahedra.

Other Discrete, Noncyclic Silicate Anions. The simplest of the condensed silicate anions—that is, those formed by combining two or more SiO_4 tetrahedra by sharing of oxygen atoms—is the pyrosilicate ion, $Si_2O_7^{6-}$. This ion occurs in thortveitite ($Sc_2Si_2O_7$), hemimorphite ($Zn_4(OH)_2Si_2O_7$) and in at least three other minerals. It is interesting that the Si—O—Si angle varies from 131 to 180° in these substances.[20]

Cyclic Silicate Anions. Only two such ions are known, namely, $Si_3O_9^{6-}$ and $Si_6O_{18}^{12-}$, the structures of which are shown schematically in Figure 19-2. It should be clear that the general formula for any such ion must be

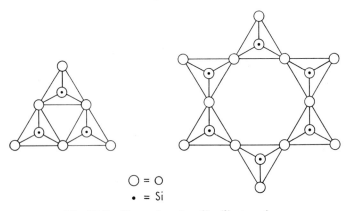

$$\bigcirc = O$$
$$\bullet = Si$$

Fig. 19-2.   Examples of cyclic silicate anions.

$Si_nO_{3n}^{2n-}$. The ion $Si_3O_9^{6-}$ occurs in benitoite, $BaTiSi_3O_9$, and probably in $Ca_2BaSi_3O_9$. The ion $Si_6O_{18}^{12-}$ occurs in beryl, $Be_3Al_2Si_6O_{18}$.

Infinite Chain Anions. These are of two main types, the *pyroxenes*, which contain single-strand chains of composition $(SiO_3^{2-})_n$ (Fig. 19-3), and the *amphiboles* which contain double-strand, crosslinked chains or bands of composition $(Si_4O_{11}^{6-})_n$. Note that the general formula of the anion in a pyroxene is the same as in a silicate with a cyclic anion. Silicates with this general stoichiometry are often, especially in older literature, called "metasilicates." There is actually no metasilicic acid nor any discrete metasilicate anions. With the exception of the few "metasilicates" with cyclic anions, such compounds contain infinite chain anions.

[20] D. W. J. Cruickshank, H. Lynton and G. A. Barclay, *Acta Cryst.*, **15**, 491 (1962).

Examples of pyroxenes are enstatite, $MgSiO_3$, diopside, $CaMg(SiO_3)_2$, and spodumene, $LiAl(SiO_3)_2$, an important lithium ore. In the latter there is one unipositive and one tripositive cation instead of two dipositive cations. Indeed the three compounds cited illustrate very well the important principle that, within rather wide limits, *the specific cations or*

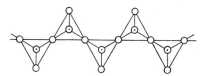

Fig. 19-3.   A linear chain silicate anion.

even their charges are unimportant so long as the total positive charge is sufficient to produce electroneutrality. This may be easily understood in terms of the structure of the pyroxenes in which the $(SiO_3)_n$ chains lie parallel and are held together by the cations which lie between them. Obviously the exact identity of the individual cations is of minor importance in such a structure.

A typical amphibole is tremolite, $Ca_2Mg_5(Si_4O_{11})_2(OH)_2$. Although this would not seem to be absolutely necessary, amphiboles apparently always contain some hydroxyl groups which are attached to the cations. Aside from this, however, they are structurally similar to the pyroxenes, in that the $(Si_4O_{11}^{6-})_n$ bands lie parallel and are held together by the metal ions lying between them. Like the pyroxenes and for the same reason, they are subject to some variability in the particular cations incorporated.

Because of the strength of the $(SiO_3)_n$ and $(Si_4O_{11})_n$ chains in the pyroxenes and amphiboles and the relative weakness and lack of strong directional properties in the essentially electrostatic forces between them via the metal ions, we might expect such substances to cleave most readily in directions parallel to the chains. This is in fact the case, dramatically so in the various asbestos minerals which are all amphiboles.

Infinite Sheet Anions. When SiO_4 tetrahedra are linked into infinite two-dimensional networks as shown in Figure 19-4, the empirical formula for the anion is $(Si_2O_5^{2-})_n$. Many silicates have such sheet structures with the sheets bound together by the cations which lie between them. Such substances might thus be expected to cleave readily into thin sheets, and this expectation is confirmed in the micas which are silicates of this type.

Framework Minerals. The next logical extension in the above progression from simple SiO_4^{4-} ions to larger and more complex structures would be to three-dimensional structures in which *every* oxygen is shared between two tetrahedra. The empirical formula for such a substance would be simply $(SiO_2)_n$; that is, we would have silica. However, if, in such a three-dimensional framework structure, some silicon atoms are replaced by aluminum atoms, the framework must be negatively charged and there must be other cations uniformly distributed through it. Aluminosilicates of this type are the feldspars, zeolites and ultramarines which (excepting

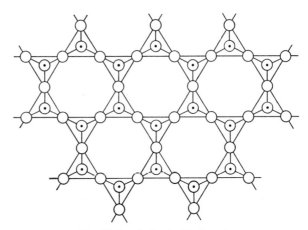

Fig. 19-4.   A sheet silicate anion.

the last) are among the most widespread, diverse and useful silicate minerals in nature. Moreover, many synthetic zeolites have been made in the laboratory and several are manufactured industrially for use as ion exchangers and "molecular sieves." The feldspars are the major constituents of igneous rocks and include such minerals as orthoclase, $KAlSi_3O_8$, which may be written $K[(AlO_2)(SiO_2)_3]$ to indicate that one-fourth of the oxygen tetrahedra are occupied by Al atoms, and anorthite, $CaAl_2Si_2O_8$ or $Ca[(AlO_2)_2(SiO_2)_2]$, in which half of the tetrahedra are AlO_4 and half SiO_4. The ultramarines are synthetically produced silicates which are strongly colored. In addition to cations sufficient to balance the negative charge of the $[(SiAl)O_2]$ framework these substances contain additional cations and anions such as Cl^-, SO_4^{2-} and S^{2-}. The framework of the ultramarines is rather open, permitting fairly ready exchange of both cations and anions. The exact reasons for their colors are not certain. Apparently certain of the cations and anions, perhaps S^{2-} especially, are responsible.

Undoubtedly the most important and interesting framework silicates are the zeolites. Their most important characteristic is the openness of the $[(Al,Si)O_2]_n$ framework (Figs. 19-5 and 19-6). It is this characteristic which makes possible their principal uses: (a) as ion exchangers and (b) as selective adsorbants or "molecular sieves." There are many natural zeolites, some of which have been synthesized, and also several dozen synthetic ones not known to occur in nature. The general composition is always of the type $M_{x/n}[(AlO_2)_x(SiO_2)_y] \cdot zH_2O$ where n is the charge of the metal cation, M^{n+}, which is usually Na^+, K^+ or Ca^{2+}, and the z is the number of moles of water of hydration, which is highly variable.

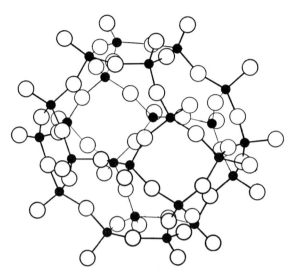

Fig. 19-5. The arrangement of AlO_4 and SiO_4 tetrahedra which gives the cubo-octahedral cavity in some zeolites and feldspathoids. ● represents Si or Al.

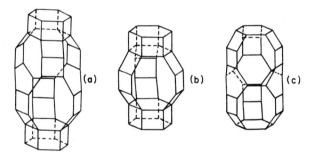

Fig. 19-6. Cavities of different dimensions in (a) chabazite, $(Ca,Na_2)OAl_2O_3 \cdot 4SiO_2 \cdot 6H_2O$; (b) gemelinite, $(Na_2,Ca)O \cdot Al_2O_3 \cdot 4SiO_2 \cdot 6H_2O$; (c) erionite, $(Ca,Mg,Na_2,K_2)O \cdot Al_2O_3 \cdot 6SiO_2 \cdot 6H_2O$.

The zeolites function as cation exchangers because when a zeolite containing a particular cation, say A^+, is placed in a solution containing another cation, say B^+, an equilibrium distribution of each cation between the zeolite and the aqueous phases will be set up. The equilibrium distribution is achieved rapidly since the porous structure makes possible rapid passage of ions in and out. Because in general one ion will have a slightly greater preference for the zeolite environment than the other, it will tend to concentrate there. The naturally occurring zeolites were the first ion exchangers discovered; they now have heavy competition for this purpose from the synthetic organic exchange resins which are made for both cation and anion exchange.

The use of zeolites as selective adsorbants is a recent and rather fascinating development. One of the synthetic ones which has been rather thoroughly investigated will serve as a good example for discussion. By slow crystallization under definite, well-controlled conditions of a sodium aluminosilicate gel of proper composition, the crystalline compound $Na_{12}[(AlO_2)_{12}(SiO_2)_{12}] \cdot 27H_2O$ may be obtained. In this hydrated form it can be used as a cation exchanger in basic solution. To obtain the "molecular sieve," the water of hydration is removed by heating in vacuum to 350°. The crystalline substance is of cubic symmetry. The AlO_4 and SiO_4 tetrahedra are linked together so as to form a ring of eight oxygen atoms on each face of the unit cube and an irregular ring of six oxygen atoms across each corner. In the center of the unit cell is a large cavity about 11.4 A in diameter which is connected to six identical cavities in adjacent unit cells by the eight-membered rings which have inner diameters of about 4.2 A. In addition, the large cavity is connected to eight smaller cavities, about 6.6 A in diameter, by the six-membered rings, which provide openings about 2.0 A in diameter. In the hydrated form all of the cavities contain water molecules. In the anhydrous state these same cavities may be occupied by other molecules brought into contact with the zeolite, providing such molecules are able to squeeze through the apertures connecting cavities. Molecules within the cavities then tend to be held there by attractive forces of electrostatic and van der Waals types. Thus the zeolite will be able to absorb and strongly retain molecules just small enough to enter the cavities. It will not absorb at all those too big to enter, and it will absorb weakly very small molecules or atoms which can enter but also leave easily. For example, the zeolite under discussion will absorb straight-chain hydrocarbons but not branched-chain or aromatic ones.

19-7. Oxygen Compounds of Germanium, Tin and Lead

Oxides and Hydroxides. The oxides GeO_2, SnO_2 and PbO_2 are all well-characterized compounds. GeO_2 differs from SiO_2 in that it exists in two forms; the stable high temperature form has a cristobalite lattice[21] and the other a rutile lattice; the radius ratio is close to that at which the

[21] G. S. Smith and P. B. Isaacs, *Acta Cryst.*, **17**, 842 (1964).

change from tetrahedral to octahedral coordination should occur theoretically. SnO_2 exists in three different modifications of which the rutile form (in the mineral cassiterite) is most common and important. It has long been known that the hydrous SnO_2 obtained by slow, low temperature hydrolysis of Sn^{IV} in solution (α-oxide) is readily soluble in acids or bases, whereas that obtained by high temperature hydrolysis or by the action of nitric acid on the metal (β-oxide) is quite inert. Actually, X-ray studies show that both have the rutile structure, with adsorbed water, and the differences in reactivity must be due to differences in particle sizes, nature of the surfaces of the particles, etc. PbO_2 occurs only with the rutile structure.

There is no evidence for any stoichiometric hydroxides $M(OH)_4$, and materials so considered in the older chemical literature are best written $MO_2 \cdot nH_2O$ where n may be about 2, but is not in general sharply defined.

The basicity of the MO_2 oxides increases as the group is descended. As we have seen, SiO_2 is purely acidic. GeO_2 is not as strongly so, but is not appreciably basic either, although in concentrated HCl solution the tetrachloride is formed. SnO_2 is definitely amphoteric. PbO_2 is not well characterized in this respect since it is rather inert.

Oxo Anions. Germanates, stannates and plumbates are all known, although these classes of compounds have not been studied nearly as extensively as have the silicates. Both metagermanates, $M_2^I GeO_3$, and orthogermanates, for example, $Mg_2 GeO_4$, have been obtained in crystalline form, and have been shown to have structures analogous to the corresponding meta- and orthosilicates. Thus $SrGeO_3$ contains a cyclic $Ge_3 O_9$ ion. In dilute aqueous solution[22] the major germanate ions appear to be $[GeO(OH)_3]^-$, $[GeO_2(OH)_2]^{2-}$ and $\{[Ge(OH)_4]_8(OH)_3\}^{3-}$. Crystalline alkali metal stannates and plumbates can be obtained as trihydrates, for instance, $K_2 SnO_3 \cdot 3H_2O$. Actually such materials are not simply hydrated "meta" stannates or plumbates, but contain the anions $Sn(OH)_6^{2-}$ and $Pb(OH)_6^{2-}$ in which Sn and Pb are surrounded octahedrally by six OH^- ions. No silicates containing $Si(OH)_6^{2-}$ ions have ever been reported, but a few germanates, $Fe[Ge(OH)_6]$, for example, are known. In the latter, the Fe and Ge atoms are arranged as in the rock salt lattice and each is surrounded by a distorted octahedron of oxygen atoms.

19-8. Organometallic Compounds

There is a very extensive chemistry of the group IV elements bound to carbon. The organosilicon derivatives are the most extensive and best

---

[22] K. H. Gayer and O. T. Zajicek, *J. Inorg. Nucl. Chem.*, **26**, 951 (1964); J. Haas, N. Konopik, F. Mark and A. Neckel, *Monatsh.*, **95**, 1141, 1166, 1173 (1964); N. Ingri and G. Schorsch, *Acta. Chem. Scand.*, **17**, 590, 597 (1963).

studied, but certain tin and lead compounds are of importance. Although the Si—C bond dissociation energy is quite high, silicon compounds are more reactive than the carbon compounds. This is true, first, because the Si—C bond is somewhat polar, Si^+C^-, so that nucleophilic attack on Si or electrophilic attack on C can occur, and second, as noted previously, because displacement reactions of silicon are facilitated by its ability to utilize $3d$ orbitals.

The tetraalkyl and aryl silicons are thermally very stable; thus $(C_6H_5)_4Si$ boils at about 530° without decomposition. The alkyl and aryl silicon halides are of special importance because of their hydrolytic reactions. They may be obtained by normal Grignard procedures from $SiCl_4$, or, in the case of the methyl derivatives, by the Rochow process in which methyl chloride is passed over a heated, copper-activated silicon

$$CH_3Cl + Si(Cu) \rightarrow (CH_3)_nSiCl_{4-n}$$

The halides are liquids which are readily hydrolyzed by water, usually in an inert solvent. In certain cases, the *silanol* intermediates R_3SiOH, $R_2Si(OH)_2$ and $RSi(OH)_3$ can be isolated, but the diols and triols usually condense under the hydrolysis conditions to *siloxanes* which have Si—O—Si bonds. The exact nature of the products depends on the hydrolysis conditions and linear, cyclic and complex crosslinked polymers of varying molecular weights can be obtained. Controlled hydrolysis of the alkyl halides in suitable ratios can give products of particular physical characteristics. The polymers may be liquids, rubbers or solids which have in general high thermal stability, high dielectric strength and resistance to oxidation and chemical attack.

Examples of simple siloxanes are $Ph_3SiOSiPh_3$ and the cyclic trimer or tetramer $(Et_2SiO)_{3(or\ 4)}$; the linear polymers contain —SiR_2—O—SiR_2—O— chains, whereas the crosslinked sheets have the basic unit

$$\begin{array}{c} R \\ | \\ -O-Si-O- \\ | \\ O \\ | \end{array}$$

The commercial "silicone" polymers usually have $R = CH_3$, but other alkyl or phenyl groups may be incorporated for special purposes.

Germanium, tin and lead form similar alkyl and aryl compounds. For a given type of compound in the series, the Pb compounds are the least stable thermally and chemically as would be expected from the increasing weakness and polarity of the M—C bonds. Germanium compounds are not particularly important, but aryl and alkyl tin compounds have acquired some technical importance.

An unusual feature of the organotin compounds is the ionization of some of the R_3SnX and R_2SnX_2 compounds in water. R_3SnX and R_3PbX form 1:1 adducts with various Lewis bases (cf. also the tetrahalides below). These apparently all contain 5-coordinate trigonal bipyramidal molecules,[23] a structure proved for $(CH_3)_3SnCl \cdot py$,[24] which has equatorial methyl groups. There has been considerable discussion concerning the species Me_3SnX as to whether they contain planar Me_3Sn^+ ions or not. While those in which X = Cl, Br or I contain simple tetrahedral molecules, it now seems likely that compounds with anions such as ClO_4^-, F^-, CO_3^{2-}, BF_4^-, NO_3^-, AsF_6^- give 5-coordination about the tin atom.[25] While the Me_3Sn may be close to planar in some cases, the anions are either bridging or chelate (19-I, II). The fluoride forms chains where the Sn—F—Sn bonds

(19-I)   (19-II)

are not equidistant or linear and the chains are linked by van der Waals forces. The perchlorate and nitrate react with ammonia to give salts of the ion $[Me_3Sn(NH_3)_2]^+$ which is presumably trigonal bipyramidal. For dimethyl tin compounds, $(CH_3)_2SnX_2$, in aqueous solutions, the aquo ion appears to be $[(CH_3)_2Sn]^{2+}$, which, like $(CH_3)_2Hg$, $(CH_3)_2Tl^+$, $(CH_3)_2Pb^{2+}$ and $(CH_3)_2Cd$ has a linear C—M—C group; there are presumably four water molecules weakly coordinated in the equatorial plane.[26] The linearity in these species appears to result from maximizing of s character in the bonding orbitals of the metal atoms. The ions $(CH_3)_2SnCl^+$ and $(CH_3)_2SnOH^+$ also exist, and, in alkaline solution $trans$-$[(CH_3)_2Sn(OH)_4]^{2-}$.

Catenated linear and cyclic organotin compounds are relatively numerous and stable. For example,[27] the reaction of Na in liquid ammonia with $Sn(CH_3)_2Cl_2$ gives "$[Sn(CH_3)_2]_n$," which consists mainly of linear molecules with chain lengths of 12–20 (and perhaps more), as well as at least one cyclic compound, $[Sn(CH_3)_2]_6$. There is no evidence for branching of chains. Similar results have been obtained with other alkyl and aryl groups,[28] e.g.,

[23] N. A. Matwiyoff and R. S. Drago, *Inorg. Chem.*, **3**, 337 (1964).

[24] R. Hulme, *J. Chem. Soc.*, **1963**, 1524.

[25] H. C. Clark, R. J. O'Brien, *Inorg. Chem.*, **2**, 740, 1020 (1963); H. C. Clark, R. J. O'Brien and J. Trotter, *J. Chem. Soc.*, **1964**, 2332.

[26] R. S. Tobias and C. E. Freidline, *Inorg. Chem.*, **4**, 215 (1965), and references therein.

[27] T. L. Brown and G. L. Morgan, *Inorg. Chem.*, **2**, 736 (1963).

[28] W. V. Farrar and H. A. Skinner, *J. Organo-Metallic Chem.*, **1**, 434 (1964).

the cyclic hexamer and nonamer of $(C_2H_5)_2Sn$, the cyclic pentamer and hexamer of $(C_6H_5)_2Sn$ and the cyclic tetramer of $(t\text{-}C_4H_9)_2Sn$ have been isolated, as well as linear species. It has been reported that in some cases the terminal groups of the linear species are SnR_2H. The structure of $[Ph_2Sn]_6$ is known;[29] it contains an Sn_6 ring in a chair configuration, with the Sn—Sn bonds about the same length as those in grey tin.

The most important organolead compounds are the tetraethyl and tetramethyl which are used as antiknock agents in gasoline; they are viscous toxic liquids. They can be made by the action of the alkyl chloride on sodium–lead alloy, or by electrolysis[30] of alkylmagnesium halide in a mixture of ethers in presence of a lead anode which is attacked by alkyl anions or radicals to give the lead alkyl.

19-9. Complexes

Aside from the octahedral chelate complex ions of Si and Ge formed by β-diketones and tropolone,[31] T, such as $SiT_3{}^+$ or $[Ge(acac)_3]^+$, most of the complexes of Group IV elements can be regarded as arising from Lewis acid behavior of the tetrahalides toward halide ions and donor ligands.

All four elements form complex halides such as $SiF_6{}^{2-}$, $GeCl_6{}^{2-}$, $SnBr_6{}^{2-}$ and $PbCl_6{}^{2-}$ in solutions and in crystalline salts. Silicon gives only the fluoro complex, whose high stability accounts for the incomplete hydrolysis of SiF_4 by water:

$$2SiF_4 + 2H_2O = SiO_2 + SiF_6{}^{2-} + 2H^+ + 2HF$$

Dissolution of SiO_2 or silicates in aqueous HF gives the $SiF_6{}^{2-}$ ion.

Germanium and tin fluoro and chloro complexes are stable in solutions and crystals but the lead analogs are readily hydrolyzed. In base solution, the Ge and Sn anions also hydrolyze. In the fluoride system for tin[32] several hydroxofluoro species as well as complexes with bases such as methanol have been characterized by ^{19}F nmr spectra, e.g.,

$$SnF_6{}^{2-} + H_2O \rightleftharpoons SnF_5OH^{2-} + HF$$
$$SnF_4 + SnF_6{}^{2-} + 2MeOH = 2SnF_5MeOH^-$$

The dissolution of SnS_2 in excess S^{2-} gives thiostannate, written $SnS_3{}^{2-}$, although its structure is unknown.

[29] D. H. Olson and R. E. Rundle, *Inorg. Chem.*, **2**, 1310 (1963).
[30] *Chem. and Eng. News*, Dec. 7, 1964, p. 52.
[31] E. L. Muetterties and C. M. Wright, *Inorg. Chem.*, **4**, 21 (1965).
[32] P. A. W. Dean and D. F. Evans, *Proc. Chem. Soc.*, **1964**, 407; R. O. Ragsdale and B. B. Stewart, *Inorg. Chem.*, **4**, 740 (1965).

Adducts. Donor ligands with N, O, P or S atoms give adducts with the tetrahalides. In some cases 1:1 complexes are obtained (e.g., $SiCl_4NMe_3$, GeF_4SMe_2) but it is not always certain whether these solids are salts, as in the case of $[H_3SiNMe_3]^+I^-$, have halide bridges, as in GeF_4 adducts, or whether they are 5-coordinate. A number of adducts of SnF_4 with pyridine and other ligands are probably 6-coordinate.[33a] Detailed spectroscopic studies of 1:1 adducts of SnX_4 with substituted anilines[33b] show that the acid strength decreases $SnCl_4 \gg SnBr_4 > SnI_4$. $SnCl_4$ is a good Friedel–Crafts catalyst.

The numerous 1:2 adducts, or adducts with bifunctional ligands such as 2,2′-dipyridyl or acetic anhydride, are evidently octahedral.[34] The stereochemistry depends on the nature of the ligand; less sterically hindered donors appear to give *cis* complexes, e.g., *cis*-$SnCl_4$ (acetone)$_2$, whereas more sterically hindered donors give *trans* species, e.g., *trans*-$SnCl_4[N(CH_3)_3]_2$.

A tetrapyridine adduct of SiI_4 has been found to be $[SiI_2py_4]^{2+}I_2^-$.

19-10. Other Compounds

Silicon–Nitrogen Compounds. The action of ammonia on $SiCl_4$ gives a white amide, $Si(NH_2)_4$, which on heating gives an imide and finally silicon nitride, Si_3N_4. The latter occurs in two forms differing only in the sequence in which the planes of like atoms are linked in a layer lattice. There is a very extensive chemistry of compounds with Si—N bonds, especially with organic groups bound to Si; some examples are $N(SiH_3)_3$, $N[Si(CH_3)_3]_3$, $[(CH_3)_3Si]_2NCH_2CH_2NH[Si(CH_3)_3]$. There is also a similar chemistry of Ge—N and Sn—N bonds.

Sulfides. A lead disulfide is not known, but for the other elements direct interaction of the elements gives MS_2. The silicon and germanium compounds are colorless crystals hydrolyzed by water. The structures of SiS_2 and GeS_2 are chains of tetrahedral MS_4 linked by the sulfur atoms (see page 532). SnS_2 has a CaI_2 lattice, each Sn atom having six sulfur neighbors.

Alkoxides, Esters and Oxo Salts. All four elements form alkoxides, for example, $Si(OC_2H_5)_4$, and esters, for example, $Pb(OCOCH_3)_4$. The latter, lead tetraacetate, which is obtained by the action of acetic acid on Pb_3O_4 or electrolytic oxidation of Pb^{II} in carboxylic acids, is used in organic chemistry as a strong, but selective, oxidizing agent.

[33a] C. J. Wilkins and H. M. Haendler, *J. Chem. Soc.*, **1965**, 3174.

[33b] D. P. N. Satchell and J. W. Wardell, *J. Chem. Soc.*, **1964**, 4134.

[34] I. R. Beattie and L. Rule, *J. Chem. Soc.*, **1964**, 3267; **1965**, 2995; J. E. Ferguson, W. R. Roper and C. J. Wilkins, *J. Chem. Soc.*, **1965**, 3716.

The tetravalent elements form few salts of oxo acids. Tin(IV) sulfate, $Sn(SO_4)_2 \cdot 2H_2O$, can be crystallized from the solutions obtained by oxidation of Sn^{II} sulfate. It is extensively hydrolyzed in water.

Tin(IV) nitrate is obtained[35] as a colorless volatile solid by interaction of N_2O_5 with $SnCl_4$. It reacts with organic materials, the attack probably being due to NO_3 radicals formed by dissociation to NO_3 and $Sn(NO_3)_2$. A hexanitrato complex $Cs_2[Sn(NO_3)_6]$ is also known but corresponding Ge^{IV} or Pb^{IV} complexes could not be obtained; it is made by treating the $SnCl_6^{2-}$ salt with N_2O_4. Whether the NO_3 groups are chelate as in $[Th(NO_3)_6]^{2-}$ is not certain.[35a]

19-11. Lower Valences

The reduction of $SiCl_4 \cdot dipy$ with Lidipy gives $Sidipy_3$[36] which is a black paramagnetic solid ($\mu_{eff} = 1.37$ BM). It may be formally regarded as an octahedral complex of Si^0 (see, however, Section 27-8).

Divalent silicon species have been identified only at high temperature and the compounds appear to be thermodynamically unstable under ordinary conditions. Thus SiO exists in the vapor above $Si + SiO_2$ at high temperatures and species such as $SiCl_2$ and SiS have been found also.

The divalent state becomes progressively more stable as is shown for example by the case of addition of chlorine to the dichlorides:

$$GeCl_2 + Cl_2 = GeCl_4 \quad \text{(uncontrollably rapid)}$$
$$SnCl_2 + Cl_2 = SnCl_4 \quad \text{(slow)}$$
$$PbCl_2 + Cl_2 = PbCl_4 \quad \text{(only under forcing conditions)}$$

Further, tin(II) aqueous solutions are mild reducing agents whereas lead(II) solutions are not:

$$Sn^{4+} + 2e = Sn^{2+} \qquad E^0 = 0.15 \text{ v}$$
$$PbO_2(s) + 4H^+ + 2e = Pb^{2+} + 2H_2O \qquad E^0 = 1.455 \text{ v}$$

It is doubtful whether Sn^{2+} ions exist in any appreciable concentration in aqueous solutions; in the acid solutions usually employed (see page 482) a more meaningful potential is

$$SnCl_6^{2-} + 2e = SnCl_3^- + 3Cl^- \qquad E^0 = ca\ 0.0 \text{ v} \ (1M\ HCl, 4M\ Cl^-)$$

Cationic tin(II) species do occur however; Pb^{2+} ions certainly exist in PbF_2 (fluorite structure) and in aqueous solution.

Divalent Germanium. The germanium(II) halides are quite well-established substances. The chloride may be prepared by passing $GeCl_4$

[35] C. C. Addison and W. B. Simpson, *J. Chem. Soc.*, **1965**, 598, **1966** A, 775.
[35a] K. W. Bagnall, D. Brown and J. G. H. du Preez, *J. Chem. Soc.*, **1965**, 5523.
[36] S. Herzog and F. Krebs, *Naturwiss*, **50**, 330 (1963).

vapors over heated germanium metal, the dichloride being isolated in the cold part of the apparatus. It rather readily disproportionates, however,

$$2GeCl_2 = Ge + GeCl_4$$

beginning about 75° and being completely decomposed at $\sim 450°$. It can be dissolved in concentrated HCl, and on addition of Cs^+ or Rb^+ ions the salts $CsGeCl_3$ and $RbGeCl_3$ are obtained. $GeBr_2$ and GeI_2 are also known. Both tend to disproportionate at elevated temperatures. GeI_2 has the CdI_2 structure. The fluoride is obtained as a white crystalline solid (m 111°) by the reaction of Ge and HF at 200° in a bomb.[37] Its structure appears to be related to that of SeO_2 (page 541), that is, ψ-tetrahedral with a lone-pair and three F atoms, the latter being shared to give chains. With F^- it forms a complex anion, GeF_3^-, which is hydrolytically stable but oxidized in HF solution by air to GeF_6^{2-}.

A yellow, amphoteric hydroxide, "$Ge(OH)_2$," chemically similar to "$Sn(OH)_2$," is precipitated from solutions containing Ge^{IV}, for example, by addition of base after reduction with zinc in 25% H_2SO_4 or by reduction with hypophosphorous acid. The wet precipitate is readily oxidized by air to GeO_2. However, the hydrous material can be completely dehydrated by heating to $\sim 650°$ in a nitrogen atmosphere, to yield black crystals. It is possible that these are only metastable since it has been reported that, at higher temperature, the phase diagram of the GeO_2–Ge system does not indicate the existence of a GeO phase. GeS is made by reducing GeS_2 with hydrogen or ammonia, or by the reaction

$$GeS_2 + Ge = 2GeS$$

whereby black crystals resembling in appearance those of iodine are obtained.

Divalent Tin. The tin halides are made by heating Sn with HX; only SnF_2 and $SnCl_2$ are important. They dissolve readily in donor solvents such as acetone, ethyl acetate or pyridine to give weak complexes which are probably pyramidal (ψ-tetrahedral) (cf. Section 19-1). The halides also accept halide ions,

$$SnF_2 + F^- \rightleftharpoons SnF_3^- \qquad pK \sim 10$$
$$SnCl_2 + Cl^- \rightleftharpoons SnCl_3^- \qquad pK \sim 2.$$

These SnX_3^- ions are the major anionic species in aqueous solutions but SnF^+, and possibly $Sn_2F_5^-$, also occur[11] and at high concentrations of Cl^- ion, possibly also other chloro complexes. Solutions of SnF_3^- absorb oxygen, presumably to give a weak complex,[37] but are not oxidized (cf. GeF_3^{2-}) although they slowly hydrolyze to SnO.

---

[37] E. L. Muetterties, *Inorg. Chem.*, **1**, 342 (1962).

The $SnCl_3^-$ ion functions as a donor π-bonding ligand [38] in platinum metal complexes (see Sec. 30-H-1).

The so-called stannous ion, written Sn^{2+}, is hardly simple; in chloride or halide solutions it is doubtful if the aquo ion ever occurs, and this is probably true of sulfate solutions. Tin(II) solutions are readily oxidized by air (especially in light) and always, unless stringent precautions are taken, contain some Sn^{IV}. Studies of perchlorate solutions prepared by the reaction

$$Cu(ClO_4)_2(aq) + Sn/Hg = Cu + Sn^{2+} + 2ClO_4^-$$

have shown that the major ion is $[Sn_3(OH)_4]^{2+}$.

$$3Sn^{2+} + 4H_2O \rightleftharpoons [Sn_3(OH)_4]^{2+} + 4H^+ \qquad \log K = -6.77$$

Other minor components of the solutions are $[Sn_2(OH)_2]^{2+}$ and $SnOH^+$.[39] The trimer probably has a cyclic structure.

From chloride solutions, a basic salt of stoichiometry $Sn_4(OH)_6Cl_2$[40] can be obtained at pH 1.14–4.5. Since the solutions contain both anionic and cationic tin, the salt is probably $[Sn_3(OH)_4]^{2+}[Sn(OH)_2Cl_2]^{2-}$. The trimeric cation has been shown to exist in crystalline nitrate and sulfate salts.

Addition of alkali base to Sn^{II} solutions or hydrolysis of the formate gives the hydrous oxide $5SnO \cdot 2H_2O$.[40,41] It can be dehydrated above $120°$ in nitrogen to give the stable blue-black SnO. A metastable red SnO can also be obtained. Excess base gives solutions of stannites which are quite strong reducing agents and perhaps contain the ion $[Sn(OH)_6]^{4-}$; alkaline stannite solutions deposit SnO on standing and at $70–100°$ also slowly form β-tin and Sn^{IV} by disproportionation. Some other tin(II) compounds are the very stable, crystalline and sparingly soluble phosphite, $SnHPO_3$,[42] which is easily made by adding H_2O to the melt of SnO and H_3PO_3, and also the formate.[41]

Divalent Lead. There are several crystalline salts but with the exception of $Pb(NO_3)_2$ and $Pb(OCOCH_3)_2 \cdot 2H_2O$ (which is incompletely ionized) most lead salts are sparingly soluble (PbF_2, $PbCl_2$) or insoluble ($PbSO_4$, $PbCrO_4$, etc.) in water. The halides, unlike the tin(II) halides, are always anhydrous and have complex crystal structures with distorted close-packed halogen lattices. In water, species such as PbX^+ are formed and, on

[38] J. F. Young, R. D. Gillard and G. Wilkinson, *J. Chem. Soc.*, **1964**, 5176.

[39] R. S. Tobias, *Acta. Chem. Scand.*, **12**, 198 (1958).

[40] J. D. Donaldson, W. Moser and W. B. Simpson, *J. Chem. Soc.*, **1963**, 1727.

[41] J. D. Donaldson and J. F. Knifton, *J. Chem. Soc.*, **1964**, 4801.

[42] J. D. Donaldson, W. Moser and W. B. Simpson, *J. Chem. Soc.*, **1964**, 323.

addition of excess halogen acid, $PbX_n^{(n-2)-}$; with the fluoride, only PbF^+ occurs,[43a] but with Cl^- several complex ions are formed.[43b]

The plumbous ion is partially hydrolyzed in water. In perchlorate solutions the principal equilibria appear to be

$$Pb^{2+} + H_2O = PbOH^+ + H^+ \qquad \log K \sim -7.9$$
$$4Pb^{2+} + 4H_2O = [Pb_4(OH)_4]^{4+} + 4H^+ \qquad \log K \sim -19.5$$

Other polymers besides the tetramer are known; the latter, formulated as $[Pb_4(OH)_4(ClO_4)_2]^{2+}$, where the charge is reduced by perchlorate complexing, with the Pb atoms at the corners of a tetrahedron, is consistent with solution X-ray data.[44]

With H_2S, Pb^{II} solutions give PbS, and all salts except PbS are soluble in excess OH^- to give plumbates. The "hydroxide" is a non-stoichiometric hydrous oxide. The yellow to brown PbO occurs in two crystalline modifications,[45] both of which are isostructural with the tin ones. However, lead alone forms an oxide containing the metal in both II and IV states. This is red lead, Pb_3O_4, which is not a mixture although in its ordinary chemistry it behaves as if it were. There are $Pb^{IV}O_6$ octahedra in chains sharing opposite edges linked by Pb^{II} atoms, each bound to three oxygens.[45]

Organometallic compounds of Sn^{II} and Pb^{II} are ill defined. The air-sensitive, thermally stable crystalline cyclopentadienyls, $(C_5H_5)_2M$, are believed to be covalently bound with the metal (sp^2-hybridized) to ring axes at an angle, with a lone-pair of electrons. The covalent nature and the symmetrical metal to ring bonding (see Chapter 28) is indicated by the symmetrical splitting of the cyclopentadienyl proton resonance lines by the tin isotopes ^{117}Sn and ^{119}Sn.

As noted earlier, dialkyls of tin, R_2Sn, are either evanescent or non-existent; stable substances with this stoichiometry are linear or cyclic polymers of Sn^{IV}.

[43a] E. Bottari and L. Ciavatta, *J. Inorg. Nucl. Chem.*, **27**, 133 (1965).

[43b] G. P. Haight, Jr., and J. R. Peterson, *Inorg. Chem.*, **4**, 1073 (1965).

[44] F. C. Hentz, Jr., and S. Y. Tyree, Jr., *Inorg. Chem.*, **3**, 844 (1964).

[45] For structures and bonding, see B. Dickens, *J. Inorg. Nucl. Chem.*, **27**, 1495 et seq. (1965).

References

Allred, A. L., and E. G. Rochow, *J. Inorg. Nucl. Chem.*, **5**, 264, (1958). New electro-negativity scale and application to C, Si, Ge, Sn and Pb in homologous compounds.

Amphlett, C. B., *Inorganic Ion Exchangers*, Elsevier, New York, 1964. Good review on zeolites, heteropoly acids and hydrous oxides as ion-exchangers.

Anderson, J. S., and M. Sterns, *J. Inorg. Nucl. Chem.*, **11**, 272 (1959). Non-stoichiometric lead oxides.

Barrer, R. M., *Endeavour*, **23**, 122 (1964) and in *Non-Stoichiometric Compounds*, L. Mandelcorn, ed., Academic Press, New York and London, 1964. Zeolites, inclusion compounds and physical chemistry thereof.

Beattie, I. R., *Quart. Rev.*, **17**, 382 (1963). Adducts of Group IV halides with donor molecules.

Belyayev, D. V., *Handbook of the Metallurgy of Tin.*, Macmillan, New York, 1963. Comprehensive treatise.

Breck, D. W., *J. Chem. Educ.*, **41**, 678 (1964). Molecular sieves.

Deer, W. A., R. A. Howie and J. Zussman, *Rock Forming Minerals*, Vols. 1–5, Longmans, London, 1962 et seq. Vol. V contains nonsilicates, e.g., oxides, phosphates.

Donaldson, J. D., *A Review of the Chemistry of Tin(II) Compounds*, Publication No. 348, Tin Research Institute, Greenford, Middlesex, England, 1964.

Eaborn, C., *Organosilicon Compounds*, Butterworths, London, 1960.

Ebsworth, E. A. V., *Volatile Silicon Compounds*, Pergamon Press 1962. Mainly hydrides and their derivatives, nmr data on Si–H and Si–F compounds.

Eitel, W., ed., *Silicate Science*, Vols. I–V, Academic Press, New York. Vol. I, 1965, contains thorough discussion of silicate structures; Vol. II, 1965, deals with glasses, enamels and slags; other volumes to deal with dry silicate systems, hydrothermal systems and ceramics.

Fessenden, R., and J. S. Fessenden, *Chem. Rev.*, **61**, 361 (1961). A review of the chemistry of silicon–nitrogen compounds.

Fordham, S., *Silicones*, Philosophical Library Inc., New York, 1960. Mostly technical matters.

Fritz, G., J. Grobe and D. Kummer, *Adv. Inorg. Chem. Radiochem.*, Vol. 7 (1965). Carbosilanes.

Haas, A., *Angew. Chem. (Internat.)*, **4**, 1014 (1965). Chemistry of silicon–sulfur compounds.

Hausner, H. H., ed., *Modern Materials*, Academic Press, New York. Vol. I, 1958, deals with Si and Ge, and Vol. IV, 1964, with carbon and graphite.

Hersh, C. K., *Molecular Sieves*, Chapman and Hall, London, 1961.

Ingram, R. K., S. D. Rosenberg and H. Gilman, *Chem. Rev.*, **60**, 459 (1960). Organotin compounds—an exhaustive review (924 references).

Johnson, O. H., *Chem. Rev.*, **51**, 319 (1951); **52**, 431 (1952). Organic and inorganic compounds of germanium.

Kuivila. H. G., *Adv. Organomet. Chem.*, **1**, 47 (1963). Reactions of organotin hydrides.

Leeper, R. W., L. Summers and H. Gilman, *Chem. Rev.*, **54**, 101 (1954). Chemistry of bivalent lead compounds.

Lindqvist, I., *Inorganic Adduct Molecules of Oxo Compounds*, Springer–Verlag 1963. Includes donor adducts of Group IV elements.

MacDiarmid, A. G., *Adv. Inorg. Nucl. Chem.*, **3**, 207 (1961). Silanes and their derivatives.

Nowotny, H., and A. Wittman, *16th International Congress of Pure and Applied Chemistry Experientia, Suppl.*, No. 7, 239 (1957). Syntheses and properties of inorganic germanium compounds.

Petrov, A. D., B. F. Mironov, V. A. Ponomarenko and E. A. Chernyshev, *Synthesis of Organosilicon Monomers*, Consultants Bureau, New York, 1964. Exhaustive collection of data and references on organosilicon compounds.

Quane, D., and R. S. Bottei, *Chem. Rev.*, **63**, 403 (1963). Organogermanium compounds.

Rochow, E. G., *An Introduction to the Chemistry of the Silicones*, 2nd ed., Wiley, New York, 1951.

Schick, H. L., *Chem. Rev.*, **60**, 331 (1960). High temperature vaporization properties of silica.

Sommer, L. H., *Stereochemistry, Mechanism and Silicon*, McGraw-Hill, New York, 1965. A comprehensive account of substitution mechanisms, etc.

Stone, F. G. A., *Hydrogen Compounds of the Group IV Elements*, Prentice Hall, 1962. Review with many references.

Stone, F. G. A., and D. Seyferth, *J. Inorg. Nucl. Chem.*, **1**, 112 (1955). Review of use of d orbitals in silicon chemistry.

Wannagat, U., *Adv. Inorg. Nucl. Chem.*, **6**, 225 (1964). Review on chemistry of Si–N compounds.

Zuckerman, J. J., *Adv. Inorg. Nucl. Chem.*, **6**, 383 (1964). Review on direct synthesis of organosilicon compounds.

20

The Group V Elements : P, As, Sb, Bi

GENERAL REMARKS

20-1. Group Trends

The electronic structures and some other properties of the elements are listed in Table 20-1. The valence shells have a structure formally similar

TABLE 20-1

Some Properties of P, As, Sb and Bi

	P	As	Sb	Bi
Electronic structure	[Ne]$3s^2 3p^3$	[Ar]$3d^{10} 4s^2 4p^3$	[Kr]$4d^{10} 5s^2 5p^3$	[Xe]$4f^{14} 5d^{10} 6s^2 6p^3$
Sum of 1st three				
ionization potentials, ev	60.4	58.0	52.3	52.0
Electronegativity[a]	2.06	2.20	1.82	1.67
Radii, A				
Ionic	2.12 (P^{3-})		0.92 (Sb^{3+})	1.08 (Bi^{3+})
Covalent[b]	1.10	1.21	1.41	1.52
Melting point °C	44.1 (α-form)	814 (36 atm)	603.5	271.3

[a] Allred–Rochow type.
[b] For trivalent state.

to that of nitrogen, but, beyond the stoichiometries of some of the simpler compounds—NH_3, PH_3, NCl_3, $BiCl_3$, for example—there is little resemblance between the characteristics of these elements and those of nitrogen.

The elements P, As, Sb and Bi show a considerable range in chemical behavior. There are fairly continuous variations in certain properties and characteristics, although in several instances there is no regular trend, for example, in the ability of the pentoxides to act as oxidizing agents. Phosphorus, like nitrogen, is essentially covalent in all of its chemistry, whereas arsenic, antimony and bismuth show increasing tendencies to cationic behavior. Although the electronic structure of the next noble gas could be achieved by electron gain, considerable energies are involved, e.g., ~ 350 kcal/mole to form P^{3-} from P, and thus significantly ionic compounds like Na_3P are few. The loss of valence electrons is similarly difficult to achieve because of the high ionization potentials. The $+5$ ions do not exist, but for trivalent antimony and bismuth cationic behavior does occur. BiF_3 seems predominantly ionic, and salts such as $Sb_2(SO_4)_3$ and $Bi(NO_3)_3 \cdot 5H_2O$, as well as salts of the oxo ions SbO^+ and BiO^+, exist.

Some of the more important trends are shown by the oxides, which change from acidic for phosphorus to basic for bismuth, and by the halides, which have increasingly ionic character, PCl_3 being instantly hydrolyzed by water to $HPO(OH)_2$, while the other trihalides give initially clear solutions which hydrolyze to As_2O_3, SbOCl and BiOCl, respectively. There is also an increase in the stability of the lower oxidation state with increasing atomic number; thus Bi_2O_5 is the most difficult to prepare and the least stable pentoxide.

20-2. Covalence and Stereochemistry

Although oxidation states or oxidation numbers can be and often are assigned to these elements in their compounds, they are of rather limited utility except in the formalities of balancing equations. The important valence features concern the number of covalent bonds formed and the stereochemistries. The general types of compounds and stereochemical possibilities are given in Table 20-2.

TABLE 20-2

Number of bonds to other atoms	Orbitals used in bonding	Geometry[a]	Examples
3	p^3 to sp^3	Pyramidal	PH_3, $AsCl_3$, Ph_3Sb
4	$sp^{3\,[b]}$	Tetrahedral	PH_4^+, $PO(OH)_3$, Cl_3PO
	sp^3d	ψ-Trigonal bipyramidal	KSb_2F_7
5	sp^3d	Trigonal bipyramidal	PF_5, AsF_5, $SbCl_5$, Ph_5P, Ph_5As
		Distorted tbp	$KSbC_4H_4O_7 \cdot \frac{1}{2}H_2O$
		Square pyramidal	Ph_5Sb
	sp^3d^2	ψ-Octahedral	K_2SbF_5, $[Sb_4F_{16}]^{4-}$, Sb_2S_3
6	sp^3d^2	Octahedral	PF_6^-, AsF_6^-, $[Sb(OH)_6]^{3-}$
			$(SbF_5)_n$, $[Bi_6O_6(OH)_3]^{3+}$

[a] The designation ψ- indicates central atom with bonds plus lone-pair(s).
[b] In some compounds, such as those with PO and PS bonds, d orbitals of P may be used in $d\pi$–$p\pi$ bonding.

The differences between N and P in their chemistries, which are due to the same factors responsible for the C–Si and O–S differences, can be summarized as follows:

Nitrogen	Phosphorus
(a) Very strong $p\pi$–$p\pi$ bonds	No known $p\pi$–$p\pi$ bonds
(b) No $p\pi$–$d\pi$ bonding	Weak to moderate but important $d\pi$–$p\pi$ bonding
(c) No valency expansion	Valency expansion

The point (a) leads to facts such as the existence of $P(OR)_3$ but not of $N(OR)_3$, nitrogen giving instead $O{=}N(OR)$, and the structural differences between nitrogen oxides and oxoacids and oxides such as P_4O_6 or P_4O_{10} and the polyphosphates. Point (b) is associated with rearrangements such as

$$\text{>P—OH} \rightleftharpoons \text{H—P}{=}\text{O}$$

and with the existence of phosphonitrilic compounds $(PNCl_2)_n$. Further, while PX_3, AsX_3 and SbX_3 (X = halogen, alkyl or aryl), like NR_3 compounds, behave as donors owing to the presence of lone-pairs, there is one major difference: the nitrogen atom can have no function other than simple donation because no other orbitals are accessible, but P, As and Sb have empty d orbitals of fairly low energy. Thus, when the atom to which the P, As or Sb donates has electrons in orbitals of the same symmetry as the empty d orbitals, back-donation resulting in over-all multiple bond character may result. This factor is especially important for the stability of complexes with transition elements where $d\pi$–$p\pi$ bonding contributes substantially to the bonding (see Chapter 27). The consequences of vacant d orbitals are also evident on comparing the amine oxides, R_3NO, on the one hand, with R_3PO or R_3AsO on the other. In the N-oxide the electronic structure can be represented by the single canonical structure $R_3\overset{+}{N}{-}\overset{-}{O}$, whereas for the others the bonds to oxygen have multiple character and are represented as resonance hybrids:

$$R_3\overset{+}{P}{-}\overset{-}{O} \leftrightarrow R_3P{=}O \overset{?}{\leftrightarrow} R_3\overset{-}{P}{\equiv}\overset{+}{O}$$

These views are substantiated by the shortness of the P—O bonds (~ 1.45 as compared to ~ 1.6 A for the sum of the single bond radii) and by the normal bond lengths and high polarities of N—O bonds. The amine oxides are also more chemically reactive, the P—O bonds being very stable indeed, as would be expected from their strength, ~ 127 kcal.

Point (c) is responsible for phenomena such as the Wittig reaction (page 507) and for the existence of compounds such as $(C_6H_5)_5P$, $P(OR)_5$,

$[P(OR)_6]^-$ and $[PR_4]^+[PR_6]^-$ in which the coordination number is 5 or 6. The extent to which hybridization employing $3d$ orbitals is involved is somewhat uncertain since the d levels are rather high for full utilization and the higher states may be stabilized in part by electrostatic forces; it is significant that the higher coordination numbers for P^V are most readily obtained with more electronegative groups such as halogens, OR^1 or phenyl.

It will be noted in Table 20-2 that the five-coordinate compounds have different stereochemistries depending upon the formal valence state of the element. This is in accord with the principles discussed in Chapter 15. In the pentavalent compounds the central atom has only the five bonding pairs in its valence orbitals and the usual trigonal bipyramidal arrangement is adopted. In the trivalent species (e.g., SbF_5^{2-}), there are six electron pairs; this anion is isoelectronic with BrF_5 and has the same ψ-octahedral structure (see page 405) where the five bonding and one nonbonding pairs of electrons are approximately at the apices of an octahedron and the larger charge cloud of the nonbonding pair makes the F—Sb—F angles somewhat less than 90°. Comparatively few crystal structures of Sb^{III} and Bi^{III} compounds are available but it appears that in a number of oxide systems, halides and some other compound lone-pairs are present and the concept of an "inert-pair" is again inadequate (cf. discussion, page 435).

Phosphorus shows a slight but real tendency to catenation, forming both cyclic and open chain compounds with up to five phosphorus atoms as well as P_2X_4 in which X may be H, Cl or I. Arsenic forms only a few R_2As—AsR_2 compounds.

THE ELEMENTS

20-3. Occurrence

Phosphorus occurs in various orthophosphate minerals, notably *fluorapatite*, $3Ca_3(PO_4)_2 \cdot Ca(F, Cl)_2$. Arsenic and antimony occur more widely, though in lower total abundance, and are often associated with sulfide minerals, particularly those of Cu, Pb and Ag. Bismuth ores are rather uncommon, the sulfide being the most important; bismuth also occurs in other sulfide minerals.

20-4. Elemental Phosphorus

The element is obtained by reduction of phosphate rock with coke and silica in an electric furnace. Phosphorus volatilizes as P_4 molecules (partly

---

[1] D. B. Denny and H. M. Relles, *J. Amer. Chem. Soc.*, **86**, 3879 (1964).

16*

dissociated above 800° into P_2) and is condensed under water as white phosphorus.

$$2Ca_3(PO_4)_2 + 6SiO_2 + 10C = P_4 + 6CaSiO_3 + 10CO$$

There are three main allotropic forms—white, red and black; each of these is polymorphic and there are in all about eleven known modifications, some amorphous, others of somewhat indefinite identity, and most of unknown structure. In the liquid and in solid white phosphorus, there are tetrahedral P_4 molecules; below 800°, where measurable dissociation to P_2 occurs, the element is also as P_4 molecules. The P—P distances are 2.21 A; the P—P—P angles, of course, are 60°. The low angle indicates considerable strain, and the strain energy has been estimated to be about 23 kcal/mole. This means that the total energy of the six P—P bonds in the molecule is that much smaller than would be the total energy of six P—P bonds of the same length formed by phosphorus atoms with normal bond angles. Thus the structure of the molecule is consistent with its high reactivity. It is most likely that pure $3p$ orbitals are involved even though the bonds are bent, since hybridization such as pd^2 which would give 60° angles would require a rather large promotion energy.

Red phosphorus is made by heating white P at 400° for several hours. Its nature remains to the present time uncertain. At least six modifications are thought to exist. Black P is obtained in crystalline form by heating white P either under very high pressure, or at 220–370° for 8 days in the presence of mercury as a catalyst and with a seed of black P. This form is the only one for which the structure has been established in detail. It consists of corrugated sheets, each P atom being bound to three neighbors (Fig. 20-1). The atoms in adjacent layers are more weakly bound than are

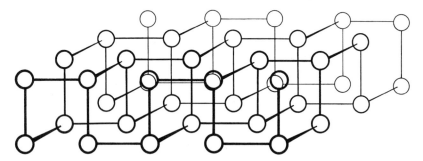

Fig. 20-1.   The arrangement of atoms in the corrugated planes found in crystalline black phosphorus.

the atoms within a layer and the crystals are therefore flaky, like graphite.

The main forms of phosphorus show considerable difference in chemical reactivity; the white is by far the most reactive form, and the black the least. White P is stored under water to protect it from the air, whereas the red and black are stable in air; indeed, black P can be ignited only with difficulty. White P inflames in air and is soluble in organic solvents such as CS_2 and benzene. Some reactions of both red and white P are shown in Figure 20-2.

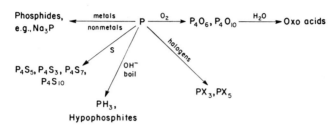

Fig. 20-2. Some typical and important reactions of red and white phosphorus.

20-5. Elemental Arsenic, Antimony and Bismuth

These elements are obtained by reduction of their oxides with hydrogen or carbon. For As and Sb unstable yellow allotropes, presumably containing tetrahedral As_4 and Sb_4 molecules, can be obtained by rapid condensation of vapors. They are easily transformed into the stable forms, and yellow Sb is stable only at very low temperatures. Bismuth does not occur in a yellow form. The normal forms of As, Sb and Bi are bright and metallic in appearance and have crystal structures similar to that of black P. The metals burn in air on heating to form the oxides, and they react directly and readily with halogens and some other nonmetals. They form alloys with various other metals. Dilute non-oxidizing acids are without effect on them. With nitric acid, As gives arsenic acid, Sb gives the trioxide and Bi dissolves to form the nitrate.

BINARY COMPOUNDS

20-6. Phosphides, Arsenides and Antimonides

Direct interaction of phosphorus with many metals and metalloids gives binary compounds of four major types. (1) Volatile, molecular compounds (mostly with S, Se and Te). (2) A few more or less ionic phosphides, e.g., Na_3P, Ca_3P_2, Sr_3P_2. These, as well as the phosphides of the alkaline earth, lanthanide and other electropositive metals, are generally rapidly hydrolyzed by water to PH_3. In phosphides such as K_2P_5 it is not certain whether discrete phosphide ions exist. (3) Covalently bound, complex polymers. (4) Metal-like compounds ranging from hard, essentially metallic solids to amorphous polymeric powders. Phosphides of transition metals, for example, Fe_2P, are commonly grey-black metallic substances, insoluble in water and conductors of electricity. They may also be ferromagnetic. The compositions and structures of these compounds are often very complex.[2]

Arsenic and antimony give similar compounds, but the tendency to form volatile molecular compounds is much less, decreasing in the order $P > As > Sb \gg Bi$.

20-7. Hydrides

All of the elements form gaseous hydrides of general formula MH_3 which can be obtained by treating phosphides or arsenides of electropositive metals with acids or by reduction of sulfuric acid solutions of arsenic, antimony or bismuth with an electropositive metal or electrolytically. The stability of these hydrides falls rapidly so that SbH_3 and BiH_3 are very unstable thermally, the latter having been obtained only in trace amounts. The average bond energies are in accord with this trend in stabilities: E_{N-H}, 93; E_{P-H}, 77; E_{As-H}, 59; and E_{Sb-H}, 61 kcal/mole.

Phosphine, PH_3, has been most thoroughly studied. The molecule is pyramidal with an HPH angle of 93.7°. Phosphine when pure is not spontaneously inflammable, but often inflames owing to traces of P_2H_4 or P_4 vapor. However, it is readily oxidized by air when ignited, and explosive mixtures may be formed. It is also exceedingly poisonous. These properties account for its commercial unavailability. Unlike NH_3, it is not associated in the liquid state and it is only sparingly soluble in water; pH measurements show that the solutions are neither basic nor acidic—the acid constant is $\sim 10^{-29}$ and the base constant $\sim 10^{-26}$. It does, however, react with some acids to give phosphonium salts; one, PH_4I, is discussed further below.

Arsine, AsH_3, is extremely poisonous. Its ready thermal decomposition to arsenic, which is deposited on hot surfaces as a mirror, is utilized in tests for arsenic, for example, the well-known Marsh test. *Stibine* is very similar to arsine but even less stable.

All these hydrides are strong reducing agents and react with solutions of many metal ions, such as Ag^I and Cu^{II}, to give the phosphides, arsenides or stibnides or a mixture of these with the metals. In basic solution

$$\tfrac{1}{4}P_4 + 3H_2O + 3e = PH_3 + 3OH^- \qquad E^0 = -0.89 \text{ v}$$

[2] S. Rundqvist, *Arkiv för Kemi*, **20**, 67 (1963).

Phosphorus alone forms a second hydride, P_2H_4, diphosphine. This is generally formed along with phosphine and can be condensed as a yellow liquid. It is spontaneously inflammable and decomposes on standing to form polymeric, amorphous yellow solids, insoluble in common solvents and of stoichiometry approximating, but varying around, P_2H. It differs from N_2H_4 in having no basic properties.

20-8. Halides

The binary halides are of two main types, MX_3 and MX_5. All of the trihalides excepting PF_3 are best obtained by direct halogenation, keeping the element in excess, whereas all of the pentahalides may be prepared by treating the element with excess of the halogens.

All four of the group V elements give all four trihalides. Besides the sixteen binary trihalides, a few of the many possible mixed trihalides are also known, namely, PF_2Cl, $PFCl_2$, PF_2Br, $PFBr_2$ and $SbBrI_2$. Others which apparently cannot be isolated have been identified in mixtures by spectroscopic techniques. Redistribution reactions such as

$$PCl_3 + PBr_3 = PCl_2Br + PClBr_2$$

seem to reach equilibrium in a few minutes, though when fluorine is involved the rates are slower. All of the trihalides, simple or mixed, are rapidly hydrolyzed by water and are rather volatile; the gaseous molecules have the expected pyramidal structures. Most have lattices which are entirely molecular, but the iodides AsI_3, SbI_3 and BiI_3 crystallize in layer lattices with no discrete molecules. BiF_3 has an ionic lattice.

All of the trichlorides and trifluorides except those of P will take on additional halide ions to form complex halo anions such as $[BiCl_6]^{3-}$, $[SbF_5]^{2-}$, $[SbCl_6]^{3-}$ and $[Sb_2F_7]^-$. The considerations of Chapter 15 would lead us to expect irregular polyhedra since there are unshared electron pairs in the metal valence shells, and in several cases this has been confirmed by X-ray studies. The $[SbF_5]^{2-}$ ion in K_2SbF_5 is ψ-octahedral, whereas the $[Sb_2F_7]^-$ ion is $CsSb_2F_7$ has the interesting structure shown in Figure 20-3a, which approximates to two trigonal bipyramids sharing an axial apex, with an equatorial position open on each. In no compound with stoichiometry $MSbF_4$ (M = K, Rb, Cs, NH_4, Tl) has an SbF_4^- ion been shown to exist. In $KSbF_4$ the polynuclear $Sb_4F_{16}^{4-}$ ion, built of ψ-octahedral SbF_5 units, is found (Fig. 20-3b).

Some complexes with nitrogen donors are known,[3] e.g., $Me_3N \cdot PCl_3$, $dipySbCl_3$, but their structures are uncertain; the dipyridyls ionize in nitrobenzene, presumably giving ions $[dipyMX_2]^+$.

[3] W. R. Roper and C. J. Wilkins, *Inorg. Chem.*, **3**, 1408 (1964).

*PF*₃. This is a colorless gas, best made by fluorination of PCl_3. One of its most interesting properties is its ability to form complexes with transition metals similar to those formed by carbon monoxide. Like CO, it is highly poisonous because of the formation of a hemoglobin complex.

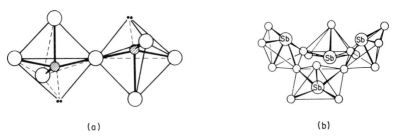

(a)   (b)

Fig. 20-3.   The structures of (a) $[Sb_2F_7]^-$ and (b) the anion in $KSbF_4$, viz., $[Sb_4F_{16}]^{4-}$.

Unlike the other trihalides, it is hydrolyzed only slowly by water, but it is attacked rapidly by alkalies.   Unlike AsF_3, it has not been observed to have any acceptor properties, nor to form complexes with F^-.

*PCl*₃. The most common of the phosphorus halides is a low-boiling liquid which is violently hydrolyzed by water to give phosphorous acid or, under special conditions, other acids of lower valent phosphorus. It also reacts readily with oxygen to give $OPCl_3$. The hydrolysis of PCl_3 may be contrasted with that of NCl_3 which gives HOCl and NH_3. Figure 20-4 illustrates some of the important reactions of PCl_3. Many of these reactions are typical of other MX_3 compounds and also, with obvious changes in formulas, of $OPCl_3$ and other oxohalides.

Arsenic, Antimony and Bismuth Trihalides. Arsenic trihalides are similar to those of phosphorus in both physical and chemical properties. However, they have appreciable electrical conductances and chemical evidence suggests that this is due to auto-ionization to, for example, SbF_2^+ and SbF_4^-. Thus, addition of KF or SbF_5 to liquid AsF_3 increases the conductance and the compounds $KAsF_4$ and $SbF_5 \cdot AsF_3$ $(AsF_2^+SbF_6^-)$ can be isolated. $SbCl_3$ (m 73.17°) has a high dielectric constant and is a strong Cl^- acceptor. Many chlorides dissolve in the melt to give conducting solutions:

$$MCl + SbCl_3 \rightleftharpoons M^+ + SbCl_4^-$$

Certain hydrocarbons also dissolve, e.g., perylene gives a free radical cation.[3a] SbF_3, a white, readily hydrolyzed solid, finds considerable use as a moderately active fluorinating agent. Both AsF_3 and SbF_3 can function as F^- acceptors, although the product is seldom the simple MF_4^- ion

[3a] J. R. Atkinson, T. P. Jones and E. C. Baughan, *J. Chem. Soc.*, **1964**, 5808.

(see above).   The AsF_3 and SbF_3 compounds have at best only slight Lewis basicity.   They form a great many compounds with donor molecules, but these appear to be mostly loose solvates. $SbCl_3$ differs from its P and As analogs in that it dissolves in a limited amount of water to give a clear

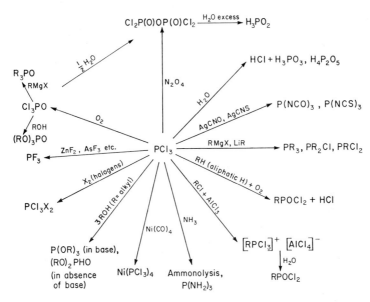

Fig. 20-4.   Some important reactions of PCl_3.   Many of these are typical for other MX_3 compounds as well as for MOX_3 compounds.

solution which, on dilution, gives insoluble oxochlorides such as $SbOCl$ and $Sb_4O_5Cl_2$.   There is, however, no evidence to suggest that any simple Sb^{3+} ions exist in the solutions. $BiCl_3$, a white, crystalline solid, is hydrolyzed by water to $BiOCl$, but may be obtained from aqueous solution containing concentrated HCl since this reaction is reversible; $BiOCl$ redissolves in concentrated HCl, and $BiCl_3$ is obtained on evaporating such solutions.

Addition of $(CH_3)_4NCl$ to Sb^{III} or Bi^{III} solutions in conc. HCl gives salts of the ions $Sb_2Cl_9{}^{3-}$ and $Bi_2Cl_9{}^{3-}$.   These ions do not exist in acid chloride solutions where there are only equilibria involving monomeric species,[4] the principal ones being $MCl_4{}^-$ and $MCl_6{}^{3-}$:

$$BiCl_4{}^- + 2Cl^- \rightleftharpoons BiCl_6{}^{3-}$$

Pentahalides.   Seven binary pentahalides are known, namely, the four fluorides, PCl_5, PBr_5 and $SbCl_5$. $AsCl_5$ has never been isolated and phase studies show that it does not exist in stable equilibrium.   There are a

[4] G. P. Haight, Jr., *et al.*, *Inorg. Chem.*, **3**, 195 (1964); **4**, 249 (1965).

number of mixed pentahalides, those which are well established being PCl_2F_3, PCl_4F, $PClF_4$, $SbCl_3F_2$, $SbCl_2F_3$ and $SbCl_4F$. In the gas phase these compounds show varying tendencies to dissociate into the trihalide and halogen. Thus PBr_5 is totally dissociated above about $35°$, PCl_5 is a few percent dissociated at $100°$ and one atm, while PCl_2F_3 is undissociated up to $150°$. For PF_5, PCl_5, PF_3Cl_2, AsF_5 and $SbCl_5$ there is evidence, albeit tenuous in two cases, that the molecules in the gas phase have trigonal bipyramidal structures. This structure has also been found in solid $SbCl_5$. PF_3Cl_2 and SbF_3Cl_2 both have trigonal bipyramidal structures with the F atoms in the equatorial positions.

Recent experiments[4a] suggest that PCl_5 is dimeric in CCl_4 solution, the structure being one with two octahedra sharing edges. In benzene or 1,2-dichloroethane it is monomeric, and apparently trigonal bipyramidal. Similar behavior has been observed for $NbCl_5$ (Sec. 30-B-2).

PF_5 is easily prepared by the interaction of PCl_5 with CaF_2 at $300–400°$. It is a very strong Lewis acid and forms complexes with amines, ethers and other bases as well as with F^- in which phosphorus becomes 6-coordinate. However, these organic complexes are less stable than those of BF_3 and are rapidly decomposed by water and alcohols. Like BF_3, PF_5 is a good catalyst, especially for ionic polymerization. AsF_5 and SbF_5, like PF_5, are powerful F^- acceptors, comparable to BF_3. They behave as acids in liquid HF because of this ability to combine with F^- to form the MF_6^- ions. Many salts of the hexafluorophosphate ion, PF_6^-, are known.

In the crystalline state both PCl_5 and PBr_5 have ionic structures: $[PCl_4]^+ [PCl_6]^-$ and $[PBr_4]^+Br^-$. The PX_4^+ cations are tetrahedral and the PCl_6^- anion octahedral as the principles of Chapter 15 would require. There is indirect evidence that the electrolytically conducting solution of PBr_5 in acetonitrile contains the PBr_6^- ion. By the action of AsF_3 on a solution of PCl_5 in $AsCl_3$ the compound $[PCl_4^+][PF_6^-]$ is readily formed. The PCl_4^+ ion appears to be a relatively stable entity and some of the addition compounds of PCl_5 with other halides are undoubtedly ionic in structure. For example, $PCl_5 \cdot BCl_3$ is probably $[PCl_4]^+[BCl_4]^-$, and $PCl_5 \cdot ICl$ is probably $[PCl_4]^+[ICl_2]^-$. These are many compounds known which are salts of $[AsCl_4]^+$ with large anions such as $[PCl_6]^-$, $[AlCl_4]^-$ and $[AuCl_4]^-$, although, as noted above, $AsCl_5$ does not exist. It is also known that the compounds obtained on addition of halogens to trialkyl and triaryl phosphines are ionic, $[R_3PX]^+X^-$, in the solid state.

The only arsenic pentahalide definitely known is the fluoride, which is similar to PF_5. The action of chlorine on AsF_3 at $0°$ gives a compound whose conductivity in excess AsF_3 suggests that it may be $[AsCl_4]^+[AsF_6]^-$.

Antimony pentafluoride is a viscous liquid which is associated even in

[4a] *Chem. and Eng. News.*, Sept. 27, 1965, p. 50.

the vapor state. These properties are due to molecular association via fluorine bridges. Nmr studies lead to the conclusion that each antimony atom is surrounded octahedrally by six fluorine atoms with two *cis* fluorines being shared with adjacent octahedra. The average length of the chains is probably 5–10 units. SbF_5 also has some unusual chemical behavior. For instance, it dissolves sulfur, selenium and tellurium, and from the solutions stable crystalline substances such as $(SbF_5)_2S$ may be isolated. SbF_5 is a very powerful F^- acceptor and a number of basic hydrocarbons, such as methylbenzene, and organometallic compounds, which can be protonated to give respectively free or coordinated carbonium ions, can be isolated as hexafluoroantimonates by reaction in liquid HF with SbF_5 (or $SbCl_5$).[4b]

Antimony pentachloride, a powerful chlorinating agent, is normally a fuming yellow liquid, but colorless when highly pure.

Bismuth pentafluoride, made by direct fluorination of liquid bismuth at 600° with fluorine at low pressure, is a white crystalline solid and an extremely powerful fluorinating agent.

Other Halides. Phosphorus and As form the so-called tetrahalides, P_2Cl_4, P_2I_4 and As_2I_4, which decompose on standing to the trihalide and nonvolatile yellow solids, and are readily decomposed by air and water. P_2I_4 has been shown to have an I_2P—PI_2 molecular structure with a *trans* rotomeric orientation in the solid[5] but probably staggered (like N_2H_4, page 338) in CS_2 solution.[6]

It has long been known that when metallic bismuth is dissolved in molten $BiCl_3$ a black solid of approximate composition BiCl can be obtained. This solid is now known[7] to be $Bi_{24}Cl_{28}$ and it has an elaborate constitution, consisting of four $BiCl_5{}^{2-}$, one $Bi_2Cl_8{}^{2-}$ and two $Bi_9{}^{5+}$ ions, the structures of which are depicted in Figure 20-5. The electronic structure of the $Bi_9{}^{5+}$ ion (a metal atom cluster, see page 497) has been successfully treated in terms of delocalized molecular orbitals.[8]

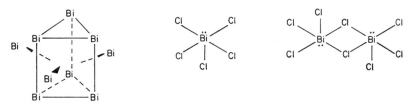

Fig. 20-5.   The structure of the species present in "BiCl," which is, in fact, $Bi_{24}Cl_{28}$.

[4b] See, e.g., G. A. Olah, *J. Amer. Chem. Soc.*, **87**, 1103 (1965).
[5] Y. C. Leung and J. Waser, *J. Chem. Phys.*, **60**, 539 (1965).
[6] M. Baudler and G. Fricke, *Z. anorg. Chem.*, **320**, 11 (1963).
[7] A. Hershaft and J. D. Corbett, *Inorg. Chem.*, **2**, 979 (1963).
[8] J. D. Corbett and R. E. Rundle, *Inorg. Chem.*, **3**, 1408 (1964).

20-9. Oxides

The following oxides of the group V elements are well characterized:

$$P_4O_6 \qquad As_4O_6 \qquad Sb_4O_6 \qquad Bi_2O_3$$
$$P_4O_{10} \qquad As_2O_5 \qquad Sb_2O_5$$

The reason for writing some with simplest empirical formulas and others as dimers will be explained shortly; the oxides should be compared with those of nitrogen (page 341).

The most thoroughly studied and best understood of the seven oxides is phosphorus pentoxide (named according to its empirical formula, P_2O_5, for historical reasons), the correct molecular formula of which is P_4O_{10}, as written above. It is usually the main product of burning phosphorus and, under proper conditions with excess oxygen, is the only product. It is a white, crystalline material which sublimes at 360° at 1 atm, and this constitutes an excellent method of purification since the products of incipient hydrolysis, which are the commonest impurities, are comparatively nonvolatile. Phosphorus pentoxide exists in three crystalline polymorphs, in an amorphous form, and also in a glassy form. A hexagonal crystal form, known as the H-form, is obtained on sublimation. It consists of P_4O_{10} molecules with the structure shown in Figure 20-6. In this

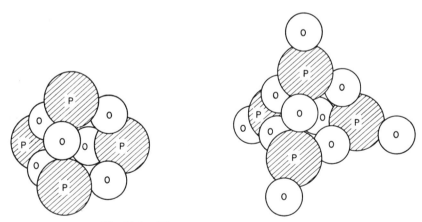

Fig. 20-6.   The structures of P_4O_6 and P_4O_{10}.

structure, the P atoms are at the corners of a tetrahedron with six oxygen atoms along the edges and the remaining four lying along extended three-fold axes of the tetrahedron. The twelve P—O distances between phosphorus atoms and shared oxygen atoms are 1.62 A, which is about the P—O single bond distance, but the other four apical P—O distances are only 1.39 A and indicate considerable $p\pi$–$d\pi$ double bonding.   The same molecular units persist in the gas phase.

On heating the H-form in a closed system for 24 hours at 450°, an orthorhombic form known as the O'-form is obtained.   By heating the H-form for only 2 hours at 400°, a metastable orthorhombic form known as the O-form is obtained.   In both of these, there are infinite sheets in which each phosphorus atom has essentially the same environment as in the P_4O_{10} molecules, namely, a tetrahedral set of bonds to three shared oxygen atoms and one unshared.   When the H-form is melted, a volatile liquid of low viscosity is initially obtained, but this eventually changes into a viscous, nonvolatile liquid which is the same as or similar to that obtained directly on melting the O- or the O'-form.   It thus appears that the molecular H-form melts to a molecular liquid which requires time to reorganize into a polymeric structure. The glassy solid is obtained on chilling the viscous liquid.

The most important chemical property of P_4O_{10} is its avidity for water. It is one of the most effective drying agents known at temperatures below 100°.   It reacts with water to form a mixture of phosphoric acids (see below) whose composition depends on the quantity of water and other conditions. It will even extract the elements of water from many other substances themselves considered good dehydrating agents; for example, it converts pure HNO_3 to N_2O_5 and H_2SO_4 to SO_3.   It also dehydrates many organic compounds, e.g., converting amides to nitriles.   With alcohols it gives esters of simple and polymeric phosphoric acids depending on reaction conditions.   The breakdown of P_4O_{10} with various reagents (alcohols, water, phenols, ethers, alkyl phosphates, etc.) is a very general one and is illustrative also of the general reaction schemes for the breakdown of P_4S_{10} and for the reaction of P_4 with alkali to give PH_3, hypophosphite, etc. Thus the first reaction of an alcohol with P_4O_{10} can be written as equation 20-1, followed by further reaction at the next most anhydride-like linkage until eventually products containing only one P atom are produced (eq. 20-2).

$$P_4O_{10} + 6ROH = 2(RO)_2PO \cdot OH + 2RO \cdot PO(OH)_2 \qquad (20\text{-}2)$$

The fusion of P_4O_{10} with basic oxides gives solid phosphates of various types, the nature depending on experimental conditions.

The other well-characterized oxide of phosphorus is the so-called trioxide, whose true molecular formula is P_4O_6. The structure of this molecule is very similar to that of P_4O_{10} except that the four nonbridging apical oxygens present in the latter are missing. P_4O_6 is a colorless, volatile compound (m 23.8°, b 175°) which forms in about 50% yield when white phosphorus is burned in a deficit of oxygen. It is difficult to separate from traces of unreacted phosphorus by distillation, but irradiation with ultraviolet light changes the white phosphorus into red, from which the P_4O_6 can be separated by dissolution in organic solvents.

On heating to temperatures above 210°, P_4O_6 decomposes into red P and another oxide, PO_2. It reacts vigorously with chlorine and bromine to give the oxohalides and with iodine in a sealed tube to give P_2I_4. It is stable to oxygen at room temperature. When it is shaken vigorously with an excess of *cold* water, it is hydrolyzed exclusively to phosphorous acid, H_3PO_3, of which it is the anhydride; P_4O_6 apparently cannot be obtained by dehydration of phosphorous acid. The reaction of phosphorus trioxide with *hot* water is very complicated, producing among other products PH_3, phosphoric acid and elemental P; it may be noted in partial explanation that phosphorous acid itself, and all trivalent phosphorus acids generally, are thermally unstable, for example,

$$4H_3PO_3 = 3H_3PO_4 + PH_3$$

The oxide PO_2 is not very well characterized. It can be sublimed at high temperatures to give transparent crystals which are deliquescent and very soluble in water. The species present in these aqueous solutions have not been satisfactorily identified.

Arsenic oxides are similar to those of P in most respects. Arsenic trioxide is formed on burning the metal in air. The gaseous molecules have the formula As_4O_6 and the same structure as P_4O_6. Three crystalline forms are known[9] plus a glass. The ordinary form contains the same tetrahedral As_4O_6 molecules as the gas, while in the other crystalline forms there are AsO_3 pyramids joined through the oxygen atoms to form layers. The As_4O_6 molecule can be thought of as consisting of four such AsO_3 units forming a closed group rather than an infinite sheet. The ordinary form is soluble in various organic solvents as As_4O_6 molecules and in water to give solutions of "arsenious acid." Arsenic pentoxide, whose true molecular formula and structure are unknown, cannot be obtained by direct reaction of arsenic with oxygen. It can be prepared by oxidation of As with nitric

[9] K. A. Becker, K. Plieth and I. N. Stranski, *Progr. Inorg. Chem.*, **4**, 1 (1962).

acid, followed by dehydration of the arsenic acid hydrates so obtained. It readily loses oxygen on heating to give the trioxide. It is very soluble in water, giving solutions of arsenic acid.

Antimony trioxide is also obtained by direct reaction of the metal with oxygen. In the vapor there are Sb_4O_6 molecules of the same tetrahedral structure as their P and As analogs. The solid form which is stable up to 570° has a molecular lattice of such molecules; above this temperature there is another solid form with a polymeric structure. The trioxide is insoluble in water and dilute nitric and sulfuric acids, but soluble in hydrochloric and certain organic acids. It dissolves in bases to give solutions of antimonates. Antimony pentoxide is prepared by the action of nitric acid on the metal. It loses oxygen on mild heating to give the trioxide.

On heating either oxide of Sb in air at about 900° there is formed a white insoluble powder of stoichiometry SbO_2. The structure has been found to consist of a network of fused $Sb^{III}O_6$ and Sb^VO_6 octahedra.

The only well-established oxide of bismuth is Bi_2O_3, a yellow powder soluble in acids to give bismuth salts but with no acidic character, being insoluble in alkalies. From solutions of bismuth salts, alkali or ammonium hydroxide precipitates a hydroxide, $Bi(OH)_3$, which is a definite compound. Like the oxide, this is completely basic in nature. It appears that a bismuth(V) oxide does exist, but that it is extremely unstable and has never been obtained in a completely pure state. It is obtained by the action of extremely powerful oxidizing agents on Bi_2O_3 and is a red-brown powder which rapidly loses oxygen at 100°.

The oxides of the group V elements clearly exemplify two important trends which are manifest to some extent in all groups of the periodic table: (1) the stability of the higher oxidation state decreases with increasing atomic number, and (2) in a given oxidation state, the metallic character of the elements, and therefore the basicity of the oxides, increase with increasing atomic number. Thus, P^{III} and As^{III} oxides are acidic, Sb^{III} oxide is amphoteric and Bi^{III} oxide is strictly basic.

20-10. Sulfides

Phosphorus and sulfur combine directly above 100° to give a number of sulfides, the most important being P_4S_3, P_4S_5, P_4S_7 and P_4S_{10}. It is possible to obtain any one of these compounds in high yield by heating stoichiometric quantities of red phosphorus and sulfur for a suitable length of time at the proper temperature. A melting point diagram for the P—S system has shown that these four are probably the only binary compounds which exist under equilibrium conditions, although there is some evidence for a phase between P_4S_5 and $P_4S_{6.9}$. P_4S_3 is used commercially in matches and is soluble in organic solvents such as carbon disulfide and benzene. The structures of all four compounds are known, and in terms of the structures the above formulas do not appear as irrational as they otherwise might. P_4S_{10} has the same structure as P_4O_{10}. The others (20-I, 20-II and 20-III) also have structures based on a tetrahedral group of phos-

(20-I)   (20-II)   (20-III)

phorus atoms with sulfur atoms bonded to individual P atoms or bridging along the edges of the tetrahedron; their symmetries are respectively C_{3v}, C_i and C_{2v}. Like P_4O_{10}, P_4S_{10} breaks down with alcohols, but with a different stoichiometry

$$P_4S_{10} + 8ROH = 4(RO)_2P(S)SH + 2H_2S$$

The difference is due to the fact that acids of the type $ROP(S)(SH)_2$ are more reactive than their oxygen analogs and react

$$ROP(S)(SH)_2 + ROH = (RO)_2P(S)SH + H_2S$$

These reactions of P_4S_{10} are important in that dialkyl and diaryl dithiophosphoric acids form the basis of many extreme pressure lubricants, of oil additives and of flotation agents. Phosphorus gives compounds with Se and Te; P_4Se_3 has been shown to have the same structure as P_4S_3.

Arsenic forms the sulfides As_4S_3, As_4S_4, As_2S_3 and As_2S_5 by direct interaction; the last two can also be precipitated from hydrochloric acid solutions of As^{III} and As^V by H_2S. As_2S_3 is insoluble in water and acids, but shows its acidic nature by dissolving in alkali sulfide solutions to give thio anions. As_2S_5 behaves similarly. As_4S_4 has a structure containing an As_4 tetrahedron (see page 533); As_2S_3 has the same structure as As_2O_3. The structure of at least one thioarsenite ion, AsS_3^{3-}, is known; it has the shape of a regular triangular pyramid.

Antimony forms the sulfides Sb_2S_3 and Sb_2S_5, both of which may be obtained either by direct combination or by precipitation with H_2S from Sb^{III} or Sb^V solutions. Like their As analogs, they are soluble in excess sulfide to give anionic thio complexes. Sb_2S_3, as well as Sb_2Se_3 and Bi_2S_3, has a ribbon-like polymeric structure in which each Sb atom and each S atom is bound to three atoms of the opposite kind, forming interlocking SbS_3 and SSb_3 pyramids (see page 532).

Bismuth gives dark brown Bi_2S_3 on precipitation of Bi^{III} solutions by H_2S; it is not acidic. A sulfide, BiS_2, is obtained[10] as grey needles by direct interaction at 1250° and 50 kbar; its structure is unknown but may be $Bi^{3+}(BiS_4)^{3-}$.

Selenides and tellurides of As, Sb and Bi can be made. Some of these, for example, bismuth telluride, have been studied intensively as semi-conductors.

OTHER COMPOUNDS

20-11. Oxo Halides

These compounds are of various stoichiometric types. Among the most important are the phosphoryl halides, X_3PO, in which X may be F, Cl or Br. The most important one is Cl_3PO, obtainable by the reactions:

$$2PCl_3 + O_2 = 2Cl_3PO$$
$$P_4O_{10} + 6PCl_5 = 10Cl_3PO$$

The reactions of Cl_3PO are much like those of PCl_3. The halogens can be replaced by alkyl or aryl groups using Grignard reagents, and by alkoxo groups using alcohols; hydrolysis by water yields phosphoric acid. Cl_3PO also has donor properties toward metal ions, and many complexes are known. The distillation of the Cl_3PO complexes of $ZrCl_4$ and $HfCl_4$ can be used to separate Zr and Hf, and the very strong $Cl_3PO-Al_2Cl_6$ complex has been utilized to remove Al_2Cl_6 from adducts with Friedel–Crafts reaction products.

The structure of all X_3PO molecules consists of a pyramidal PX_3 group with the oxygen atom occupying the fourth position to complete a distorted tetrahedron. Corresponding compounds, X_3PS and X_3PSe, exist.

More complex oxo halides containing P—O—P bonds are known; some of these have linear structures, while some form rings. The linear compound $Cl_2(O)P—O—P(O)Cl_2$ is obtained either by oxidation of PCl_3 with N_2O_4 or by partial hydrolysis of Cl_3PO; the fluorine analogs exist.

Antimony and bismuth form the important oxo halides SbOCl and BiOCl which are insoluble in water. They precipitate upon diluting solutions of Sb^{III} and Bi^{III} in concentrated HCl. They have quite different structures; both are complicated.

The only oxohalide of As, F_3AsO(b 26°), is made by fluorination of an equimolar mixture of $AsCl_3$ and As_2O_3.

[10] M. S. Silverman, *Inorg. Chem.*, **4**, 587 (1965).

20-12. Phosphonium Compounds

Although organic derivatives of the type $[MR_4]^+X^-$ are well known for M = P, As and Sb (see page 506), only phosphorus gives the hydrogen-containing prototype, PH_4^+, and this does not form any very stable compounds. The best-known phosphonium salt is the iodide, which forms as colorless crystals on mixing gaseous HI and PH_3. The chloride and bromide are even less stable; the dissociation pressure of PH_4Cl into PH_3 and HCl reaches 1 atm below 0°. The estimated basicity constant of PH_3 in water is about 10^{-26}, and phosphonium salts are completely hydrolyzed by water, releasing the rather insoluble gas PH_3:

$$PH_4I(s) + H_2O = H_3O^+ + I^- + PH_3(g)$$

Perhaps the most readily produced organic phosphonium compound is obtained by the interaction of phosphine with formaldehyde in hydrochloric acid solution:

$$PH_3 + 4CH_2O + HCl = [P(CH_2OH)_4]^+Cl^-$$

It is a white crystalline solid soluble in water and it is available commercially.

20-13. Phosphonitrilic Compounds

The reaction of PCl_5 with NH_4Cl or substituted ammonium chlorides either by fusion together or on refluxing in halogenated solvents gives a series of compounds of composition $(PNCl_2)_x$. From this mixture by fractional distillation, chromatography and other methods, the lower members can be obtained as moderately volatile, white, crystalline solids. By metathetical reactions of the chlorides and in other ways, other phosphonitrilic compounds, $(NPX_2)_n$, in which X is F, Br, SCN, NR_2, CH_3 or C_6H_5, may be prepared. Those with $n = 3$ or 4 have cyclic structures with alternating P and N atoms. The structure of the trimer is shown in Figure 20-7; the ring in the trimer is almost planar (i.e., of nearly D_{3h} symmetry), deviations probably being due to crystal forces. The structures of several tetramers have also been determined.[11] $(NPF_2)_4$ has a planar ring (D_{4h} symmetry), but all others, e.g., $(NPX_2)_4$ with X = Cl, $N(CH_3)_2$ and CH_3, have puckered rings with NPN angles of $\sim 120°$ and PNP angles of $\sim 132°$. The P—N distances, 1.56–1.61A, are shorter than a single P—N bond in the phosphoramidate zwitterion, $[NH_3PO_3]^-$. Geometrical isomers can occur in substituted derivatives; for example, by the reaction

$$PhPBr_2 + NH_4Br + Br_2 \xrightarrow{\text{CHBr}_2\text{CHBr}_2} (NPPhBr)_{3,4} + \text{oily polymers}$$

[11] G. J. Bullen, *J. Chem. Soc.*, **1962**, 3193.

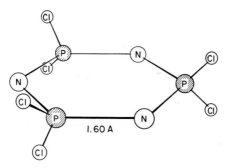

Fig. 20-7.   The structure of $P_3N_3Cl_6$.

The trimer has been shown to have *cis* (20-IV) and *trans* (20-V) isomers.[12]

(20-IV)   (20-V)

Higher members appear to be linear polymers; the polymer is end-stopped with the elements of PCl_5 at one end and PCl_4 at the other. These have rubber-like properties and give X-ray diffraction patterns typical of fibres; they are only temporarily and conditionally stable, however.

The formulas for the cyclic compounds are often written with double bonds (20-VI and 20-VII).   However, in view of the essential equality of

(20-VI)   (20-VII)

all PN bond lengths, such formulas should, if used at all, be regarded as only one of the two equivalent Kekulé-like canonical forms of a resonance hybrid.   Even then, such representations should be regarded circumspectly. While it is generally agreed that NP $p\pi$–$d\pi$ bonding plays a significant role in the electronic structures of the phosphonitrilic compounds (and also, to a much smaller degree, in the "thiazyls," i.e., compounds with $(SN)_n$ rings), the detailed nature of this bonding, particularly the extent of delocalization of π electrons all around the rings, is difficult to specify with certainty. At the very least there are "islands" of symmetrically distributed π electron density within NPN segments; there are also grounds for believing that delocalization is more extensive than that, however.[13] The problem is a complicated one owing to the large number of orbitals potentially involved and to the general lack of ring planarity which means that rigorous assignment of σ and π character to individual orbitals is impossible.

20-14. Organic Derivatives

For P and As there is a vast chemistry involving P—C and As—C bonds. At present, some 30 papers on organophosphorus chemistry are published each month and there is now an extensive knowledge of the mechanism of many reactions, such as phosphorylation, which are of biological importance.

With the exception of pentaphenyl compounds, the organo derivatives are compounds with only three or four bonds to the central atom. Organobismuth compounds are few and not very stable. The organo derivatives may be prepared in a great variety of ways, the simplest being by treatment of halides or oxo halides with Grignard reagents:

$$(O)MX_3 + 3RMgX = (O)MR_3 + 3MgX_2$$

Trimethylphosphine is spontaneously inflammable in air, but the higher trialkyls are oxidized more slowly. The R_3MO compounds, which may be obtained from the oxo halides as shown above or by oxidation of the corresponding R_3M compounds, are all very stable. The usual method of oxidation, by H_2O_2, with Ph_3P gives a H-bonded adduct, $(Ph_3PO)_2 \cdot H_2O_2$, which loses H_2O_2 only at $160°$.[14]

Trialkyl and triaryl phosphines, arsines and stibines are all good donors toward d-group transition metals and chelating di- and triphosphines and arsines have been especially widely used as π-acid ligands (Sec. 27-5). The oxides, R_3MO, also form many complexes, but they function simply as donors. Trialkyl and triaryl phosphines, arsines and stibines generally react with alkyl and aryl halides to form quaternary salts:

$$R_3M + R'X = [R_3R'M]^+X^-$$

[13] D. P. Craig and N. L. Paddock, *J. Chem. Soc.*, **1962**, 4118.
[14] D. B. Copley, F. Fairbrother, J. R. Miller and A. Thompson, *Proc. Chem. Soc.*, **1964**, 300.

The stibonium compounds form with the greatest difficulty and are the least common. These quaternary salts, excepting the hydroxides, which are obtained as sirupy masses, are white crystalline compounds. The tetraphenylphosphonium and -arsonium ions are useful for precipitating large anions such as ReO_4^-, ClO_4^- and complex anions of metals.

The basicities of phosphines and amines toward protons differ considerably, as shown in Table 20-3. Basicities of the amines are relatively constant, while those of the phosphines are extremely dependent on the degree of substitution. The total free energy of protonation in aqueous solution can be taken as the sum of three contributions: (1) Energy to rehybridize the P or N atom. (2) The energy of forming the P—H or N—H bond. (3) Solvation energy. Assuming that in the quaternary ions the hybridization is very close to sp^3, it is evident from Table 20-3 that the energy of rehybridization will be relatively small and approximately the same for all the amines, whereas it will be generally larger for the phosphines increasing from Me_3P to PH_3. Rough calculations suggest that the energies of protonation of PH_3 and NH_3 in the gas phase differ very little, but that the solvation energy of NH_4^+ exceeds that of PH_4^+ by about 20 kcal/mol. Since

$$\log K_P - \log K_N = \frac{\Delta F_N - \Delta F_P}{2.3RT}$$

at 300° K we have

$$pK_N - pK_P \approx \frac{20,000}{(2.3)(1.98)(300)} = 14.5$$

which shows that some 70% of the difference in the pK's is attributable to solvation energies in this case. The solvation energies of Me_3PH^+ and Me_3NH^+ should be very nearly the same, however.

TABLE 20-3

Effect of Substituents on the Basicities of Amines and Phosphines

Amine	pK^a	Bond angles	Phosphine	pK^a	Bond angles
NH_3	9.25	107°	PH_3	−12	93°
$MeNH_2$	10.64		$MePH_2$	∼0	
Me_2NH	10.72		Me_2PH	3.9	
Me_3N	9.74	108°	Me_3P	8.7	100°

a For the reaction: $MR_3H^+ = MR_3 + H^+$.

Triphenylphosphine, a white crystalline solid, is utilized widely in the Wittig reaction for olefin synthesis. This reaction involves the formation of alkylidene or arylidene triphenylphosphoranes from the action of butyllithium or other base on the quaternary halide, for example,

$$[(C_6H_5)_3PCH_3]^+ Br^- \xrightarrow{\text{n-butyllithium}} (C_6H_5)_3P{=}CH_2$$

This intermediate reacts very rapidly with aldehydes and ketones to give zwitterionic compounds (20-VIII) which eliminate triphenylphosphine oxide under mild conditions to give olefins (20-IX).

(20-VIII)   (20-IX)

The extensive series of dimethylarsenic compounds, often called "cacodyl" compounds, e.g., Me_2AsCl, cacodyl chloride, is worthy of mention. There are also diarsenic tetraalkyls such as dicacodyl, $Me_2AsAsMe_2$, and $Et_2AsAsEt_2$.

The tendency of phosphorus to catenation is shown in the relatively large number of stable polyphosphines which have been prepared in recent years. Most numerous are the cyclic ones, particularly those of the type $(RP)_4$ which can be obtained by the following fairly general reactions:[15]

$$2RPCl_2 + 2RPH_2 \rightarrow (RP)_4 + 4HCl$$
$$4RPCl_2 + 4Mg(\text{or } 8Li) \rightarrow (RP)_4 + 4MgCl_2 \text{ (or } 8LiCl)$$
$$4RH_2PO \xrightarrow{\Delta} (RP)_4 + 4H_2O$$
$$4(C_4H_9)_3P + 4PhPCl_2 = 4(C_4H_9)_3PCl_2 + (PhP)_4$$

The last reaction[16] can also be used to prepare diphosphines, e.g., from Ph_2PCl, and provides simple preparations from readily available materials. Other preparative reactions for cyclic polyphosphines are:

$$4CF_3PI_2 + 4Hg \rightarrow 4HgI_2 + (CF_3P)_4, \text{ also } (CF_3P)_5$$
$$5CH_3PF_2 \xrightarrow{\Delta} (CH_3P)_5 + 5F_2$$

In several cases the structures of cyclic compounds have been determined and the rings are puckered.

The known linear triphosphines all contain CF_3 and they are obtained by the reactions:[17]

$$2(CF_3)_2PI + CF_3PH_2 + 2(CH_3)_3N \rightarrow (CF_3)_2P{-}P(CF_3){-}P(CF_3)_2 + 2(CH_3)_3NHI$$
$$2(CF_3)_2PCl + CH_3PH_2 + 2(CH_3)_3N \rightarrow CH_3P[P(CF_3)_2]_2 + 2(CH_3)_3NHCl$$

[15] W. A. Henderson, Jr., M. Epstein and F. S. Seichter, *J. Amer. Chem. Soc.*, **85**, 2462 (1963).

[16] S. E. Frazier, R. P. Nielsen and H. H. Sisler, *Inorg. Chem.*, **3**, 292 (1964).

[17] A. B. Burg and J. F. Nixon, *J. Amer. Chem. Soc.*, **86**, 356 (1964); A. B. Burg and K. K. Joshi, *J. Amer. Chem. Soc.*, **86**, 353 (1964).

Finally, there are numerous examples of substituted 5-coordinate fluoro compounds such as $(C_2F_5)_2PF_3$, $PhPF_3N(C_2H_5)_2$, Ph_3BiF_2; the ^{19}F nmr spectra of these derivatives, which are trigonal bipyramidal, has thrown light on intramolecular ligand exchange processes which are common in such structures[18] (see page 132).

20-15. Aqueous Cationic Chemistry

Apart from the quaternary salts mentioned in the preceding section, there is no cationic chemistry of P and As. Although the reaction

$$As(OH)_3 = As^{3+} + 3OH^-$$

may occur to some slight extent, there is little direct evidence for the existence of significant concentrations of tripositive cations even in strong acid solutions.

Antimony has some definite cationic chemistry, but only in the trivalent state, the basic character of Sb_2O_5 being negligible. The "Sb^{3+}" ion has a great tendency to hydrolyze, and cationic compounds of Sb^{III} are mostly of the so-called "antimonyl" ion, SbO^+, although some of the "Sb^{3+}" ion, such as $Sb_2(SO_4)_3$, are known. Antimony salts readily form complexes with various acids in which the antimony forms the nucleus of an anion, for example, $[Sb(SO_4)_2]^-$, $[Sb(C_2O_4)_2]^-$ and $[Sb(OH)C_4H_3O_5]^-$. The last, as potassium antimony tartrate, is one of the best known of water-soluble antimony compounds. It is most unlikely that an SbO^+ ion exists under any circumstances. There is no such ion in $SbOCl$, and in the tartrate it is known that an $SbOH$ group exists. Three oxygen atoms of the tartrate ion (with a free $COOH$ group) and a lone-pair occupy the other four co-ordination positions.[19] It is best regarded as a derivative of the antimonite ion, $[Sb(OH)_4]^-$.

Only for bismuth can it be said that there is an extensive true cationic chemistry. Aqueous solutions contain well-defined hydrated cations. In neutral perchlorate solutions the main species is $[Bi_6O_6]^{6+}$ or its hydrated form, $[Bi_6(OH)_{12}]^{6+}$, and at higher pH $[Bi_6O_6(OH)_3]^{3+}$ is formed. From acid solution various hydrated crystalline salts such as $Bi(NO_3)_3 \cdot 5H_2O$, $Bi_2(SO_4)_3$ and double nitrates of the type $M_3^{II}[Bi(NO_3)_6]_2 \cdot 24H_2O$ can be obtained. Treatment of Bi_2O_3 with nitric acid gives bismuthyl salts such

[18] E. L. Muetterties, W. Mahler, K. J. Packer and R. Schmutzler, *Inorg. Chem.*, **3**, 1298 (1964); E. L. Muetterties and W. Mahler, *Inorg. Chem.*, **4**, 119 (1965).

[19] D. Grdenič and B. Kamenar, *Acta. Cryst.*, **18**, 197 (1965).

as $BiO(NO_3)$ and $Bi_2O_2(OH)(NO_3)$. Similar bismuthyl salts are pre-cipitated on dilution of strongly acid solutions of various bismuth com-pounds. Bismuthyl salts are generally insoluble in water. In solutions of Bi^{III} containing excess halide ions, BiX_4^- complexes are present.

THE OXO ANIONS

The oxo anions in both lower and higher states are a very important part of the chemistry of phosphorus and arsenic and comprise the only real aqueous chemistry of these elements. For the more metallic antimony and bismuth, oxo anion formation is less pronounced, and for bismuth only ill-defined "bismuthates" exist.

20-16. Oxo Acids and Anions of Phosphorus

All phosphorus oxo acids have POH groups where the hydrogen atom is ionizable; hydrogen atoms in P—H bonds are not ionized. There are a vast number of oxo acids or ions, some of them of great technical impor-tance; but with the exception of the simpler species, they have not been well understood structurally until quite recently.

We can attempt to deal only with some structural principles and some of the more important compounds. It is to be stressed that it is the *oxo anion* which is important, since in many cases the free acid cannot be isolated even though its salts are stable. Both lower, P^{III}, and higher, P^V, acids are known. A lower acid would normally be expected to have the P atom bound as in $P(OH)_3$, while a higher acid would be derived from $O{=}P(OH)_3$. Since the latter is the most stable configuration for phosphorus, this type of structure would be expected to predominate. In fact, attempts to make oxo acids based on three-covalent phosphorus fail since there is a tautomeric shift of hydrogen as noted on page 511. Thus, with the exception of the triesters, $P(OR)_3$ (20-XII), the free lower acid, mono- and disubstituted anions and esters (20-X, XI) *all* have a P—H bond with four bonds (sp^3) to

(20-X)	*and*	(20-XI)	*but*	(20-XII)
$H_2[HPO_3]$		Phosphite monoester		Phosphite triester

phosphorus. This hydrogen atom transfer in the lower oxo acids (eq. 20-3) is comparable to the keto-enol shift in carbonyl compounds (eq. 20-4),

$$\text{R}-\overset{\cdot\cdot}{\underset{\underset{\text{R}}{|}}{\text{P}}}-\text{OH} \rightarrow \text{R}-\overset{\cdot\cdot}{\underset{\underset{\text{R}}{|}}{\text{P}}}-\text{O}^- + \text{H}^+ \rightarrow \text{R}-\overset{\overset{\overset{\text{H}}{|}}{\text{P}^+}}{\underset{\underset{\text{R}}{|}}{}}-\text{O}^- \qquad (20\text{-}3)$$

$$\left[\text{R}-\overset{\overset{\text{H}}{|}}{\underset{\underset{\text{R}}{|}}{\text{P}^+}}-\text{O}^- \leftrightarrow \text{R}-\overset{\overset{\text{H}}{|}}{\underset{\underset{\text{R}}{|}}{\text{P}}}=\text{O} \right]$$

$$\text{R}-\overset{\overset{\text{H}}{|*}}{\underset{\underset{\text{H}}{|}}{\text{C}}}-\overset{\overset{\text{O}}{/\!/}}{\underset{\underset{\text{R}}{\backslash}}{\text{C}}} = \overset{\overset{\text{R}}{\backslash}}{\underset{\underset{\text{H}}{/}}{\text{C}^*}}=\overset{\overset{\text{OH}}{/}}{\underset{\underset{\text{R}}{\backslash}}{\text{C}}} \qquad (20\text{-}4)$$

except that in the carbon case there is a change of hybridization at C^* from sp^3 to sp^2, whereas in the phosphorus case little change occurs. Although the free acids based on three-covalent phosphorus can exist only as transitory species, kinetic evidence suggests that they are present in concentration of the order of 1 in 10^{12}. The keto-enol analogy can be illustrated by the reaction with sulfur. Dialkyl phosphites, $(RO)_2PHO$, do *not* add sulfur, whereas the solid derivatives, $(RO)_2PONa$, add sulfur very readily.

The fundamental structures of oxo anions containing one phosphorus atom are represented by 20-XIII, 20-XIV and 20-XV, where the structures have tetrahedral or distorted tetrahedral arrangements and the P—O bonds have appreciable multiple character.

$$\left[\text{H}-\overset{\overset{\text{H}}{|}}{\underset{\underset{\text{O}}{|}}{\text{P}}}-\text{O} \right]^- \qquad \left[\text{O}-\overset{\overset{\text{H}}{|}}{\underset{\underset{\text{O}}{|}}{\text{P}}}-\text{O} \right]^{2-} \qquad \left[\text{O}-\overset{\overset{\text{O}}{|}}{\underset{\underset{\text{O}}{|}}{\text{P}}}-\text{O} \right]^{3-}$$

| (20-XIII) | (20-XIV) | (20-XV) |
| Hypophosphite | Phosphite | Orthophosphate |

Lower Acids. *Hypophosphorous Acid*, $H[H_2PO_2]$. The salts are usually prepared by boiling white phosphorus with alkali or alkaline earth hydroxide. The main reactions appear to be:

$$P_4 + 4OH^- + 4H_2O = 4H_2PO_2^- + 2H_2$$
$$P_4 + 4OH^- + 2H_2O = 2HPO_3^{2-} + 2PH_3$$

The calcium salt is soluble in water, unlike that of phosphite or phosphate; the free acid can be made from it or obtained by oxidation of phosphine with iodine in water. Both the acid and its salts are powerful reducing agents, being oxidized to orthophosphate. The pure white crystalline solid is a monobasic acid, ($pK = 1.2$); other physical studies, such as nmr, confirm the presence of a PH_2 group. Either or both of the hydrogen atoms can be replaced, by indirect methods, with alkyl groups to give mono- or dialkyl *phosphonous* compounds.

Phosphorous Acid, $H_2[HPO_3]$. As noted above, this acid and its mono- and diesters have a P—H bond. The free acid is obtained by treating PCl_3 or P_4O_6 with water; when pure it is a deliquescent colorless solid (m 70.1°, $pK = 1.8$). The presence of the P—H bond has been demonstrated by a variety of structural studies as well as by the formation of only mono and di series of salts. It is oxidized to orthophosphate by halogen, sulfur dioxide and other agents, but the reactions are slow and complex. The mono-, di- and triesters can be obtained from reactions of alcohols with PCl_3 alone or in the presence of an organic base as hydrogen chloride acceptor. $RPO_3{}^{2-}$ ions are called *phosphonate* ions.

The *phosphite triesters*, $P(OR)_3$, are notable for forming donor complexes with transition metals and other acceptors. They are readily oxidized to the respective phosphates,

$$2(RO)_3P + O_2 = 2(RO)_3PO$$

They also undergo the Michaelis–Arbusov reaction with alkyl halides, forming dialkyl phosphonates:

$$P(OR)_3 + R'X = [(RO)_3PR'X] \rightarrow RO{-}\overset{\displaystyle O}{\overset{\displaystyle \|}{\underset{\displaystyle OR}{P}}}{-}R' + RX$$
$$\text{Phosphonium}$$
$$\text{intermediate}$$

The methyl ester easily undergoes spontaneous isomerization to the dimethyl ester of methylphosphonic acid:

$$P(OCH_3)_3 = CH_3PO(OCH_3)_2$$

Higher Acids. *Orthophosphoric Acid*, H_3PO_4, commonly called phosphoric acid, is one of the oldest known and most important phosphorus compounds. It is made in vast quantities, usually as 85% sirupy acid, by the direct reaction of ground phosphate rock with sulfuric acid and also by the direct burning of phosphorus and subsequent hydration of the oxide P_4O_{10}. The pure acid is a colorless crystalline solid (m 42.35°). It is very stable and has essentially no oxidizing properties below 350–400°. At elevated temperatures it is fairly reactive toward metals and is reduced;

it will also then attack quartz. Fresh molten H_3PO_4 has appreciable ionic conductivity[20] suggesting autoprotolysis

$$2H_3PO_4 \rightleftharpoons H_4PO_4^+ + H_2PO_4^-$$

Pyrophosphate is also produced

$$2H_3PO_4 = H_2O + H_4P_2O_7$$

but this conversion is temperature dependent and is slow at room temperature.

The acid is tribasic: at $25°$, $pK_1 = 2.15$, $pK_2 = 7.1$, $pK_3 \approx 12.4$. The pure acid and its crystalline hydrates have tetrahedral PO_4 groups connected by hydrogen bonds (Fig. 20-8). These persist in the concentrated

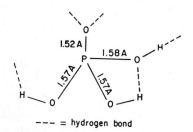

--- = hydrogen bond

Fig. 20-8.   Structure of anhydrous orthophosphoric acid.

solutions and are responsible for the sirupy nature. For solutions of concentration less than $\sim 50\%$, the phosphate anions are hydrogen-bonded to the liquid water rather than to other phosphate anions.

Phosphates of most metal ions and other cations are known. Some of these are of enormous commercial and practical importance, for example, ammonium phosphate fertilizers, alkali phosphate buffers, etc. Natural phosphate minerals are *all* orthophosphates, the major one being fluorapatite; hydroxoapatites, partly carbonated, make up the mineral part of teeth. The role of traces of F^- in strengthening dental enamel is presumably connected with these structural relationships, but a detailed explanation of the phenomenon is still lacking.

Orthophosphoric acid and phosphates form complexes with many transition metal ions. The precipitation of insoluble phosphates from fairly strong acid solution ($3–6N\ HNO_3$) is characteristic of $+4$ cations such as those of Ce, Th, Zr, U, Pu, etc.

Large numbers of phosphate *esters* are known. Some of these are important technically, particularly for solvent extraction of metal ions

[20] R. A. Munsen, *J. Phys. Chem.*, **68**, 3374 (1964).

from aqueous solutions. Other important phosphates are the sugar and glycerol phosphates. Phosphate esters are usually prepared by reactions such as

$$O{=}PCl_3 + 3ROH = O{=}P(OR)_3 + 3HCl$$
$$Ag_3PO_4 + 3CH_3COCl = (CH_3CO \cdot O)_3P{=}O + 3AgCl$$

Organic phosphates are of major importance in biological processes. The sugar phosphates are important in photosynthesis, and nucleic acids contain phosphate. Examples of such phosphates are glucose-6-phosphoric acid (20-XVI) and deoxyribonucleic acid (20-XVII, fragment of chain).

(20-XVI)   (20-XVII)

The rates of hydrolysis of phosphate esters and of triphosphate esters (see below) such as adenosine triphosphate, which is basically the hydrolysis of C—O—P bonds, and the associated energy changes are of fundamental importance in biological systems, since the driving forces for many reactions are provided by the hydrolytic free energy changes. Large numbers of enzymes are known which catalyze the scission and formation of C—O—P links.

Condensed Phosphates. Condensed phosphates are those containing more than one P atom and having P—O—P bonds. We may note that the *lower* acids can also give condensed species, although we shall deal here only with a few examples of phosphates.

There are three main building units in condensed phosphates: the end unit (20-XVIII), middle unit (20-XIX) and branching unit (20-XX).

(20-XVIII)   (20-XIX)   (20-XX)
$PO_{3.5}^{2-}$ PO_3^{-} $PO_{2.5}$

These units can be distinguished not only chemically—for example, the branching points are rapidly attacked by water—but also by the ^{31}P nmr spectra. These units can be incorporated into either (a) chain or *polyphosphates*, containing 2–10 P atoms, (b) cyclic or *metaphosphates*, containing 3–7 or more P atoms or (c) infinite *chain metaphosphates*. Not all possible combinations of the basic units are known. Some of the most important are:

Linear polyphosphates, which are salts of anions of general formula $[P_nO_{3n+1}]^{(n+2)-}$. Examples are $M^I_4P_2O_7$ (20-XXI), a pyrophosphate or dipolyphosphate, and $M^I_5P_3O_{10}$ (20-XXII), a tripolyphosphate.

(20-XXI)   (20-XXII)   (20-XXIII)

Cyclic polyphosphates, which are salts of anions of general formula $[P_nO_{3n}]^{n-}$. Examples are $M_3P_3O_9$, a trimetaphosphate (20-XXIII), and $M_4P_4O_{12}$, a tetrametaphosphate; the latter can have boat and chain forms.

Some metaphosphates have infinite chains rather than rings, for example, one of the several crystal forms of KPO_3.[21]

Condensed phosphates are usually prepared by dehydration of orthophosphates under various conditions of temperature (300–1200°) and also by appropriate hydration of dehydrated species, as, for example,

$$(n-2)NaH_2PO_4 + 2Na_2HPO_4 \xrightarrow{heat} Na_{n+2}P_nO_{3n+1} + (n-1)H_2O$$
$$\text{Polyphosphate}$$

$$nNaH_2PO_4 \xrightarrow{heat} (NaPO_3)_n + nH_2O$$
$$\text{Metaphosphate}$$

They can also be prepared by controlled addition of water or other reagents to P_4O_{10}, by treating chlorophosphates with silver phosphates, etc. The complex mixtures of anions that can be obtained are separated using ion exchange or chromatographic procedures as illustrated in Figure 20-9.

Condensed phosphates form soluble complexes with many metals, and chain phosphates are used industrially for this purpose, for example, as water softeners.

The most important *cyclic* phosphate is *tetrametaphosphate*, which can be prepared by heating copper nitrate with slightly more than an equimolar amount of phosphoric acid (75%) slowly to 400°. The sodium salt can be

[21] K. H. Jost, *Acta Cryst.*, **16**, 623 (1963).

obtained by treating a solution of the copper salt with Na_2S. Slow addition of P_4O_{10} to ice water gives $\sim75\%$ of the P as tetrametaphosphate.

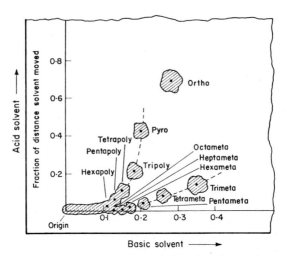

Fig. 20-9. Chromatographic separation of complex phosphate mixtures. Corner of a two-dimensional paper chromatogram showing the positions of the pentameta- through octametaphosphate rings in relation to the positions of the well-known ring and chain phosphates. The basic solvent traveled 23 cm in 24 hr, whereas the acid solvent traveled 11.5 cm in 5.5 hr.

Fluorophosphates. As with many other oxo anions, fluorine can replace OH in phosphate to give mono- and difluorophosphate salts and esters. The dialkyl monofluorophosphate esters have been found to inhibit cholinesterase in the body and to be exceedingly toxic. The *hexafluorophosphate* ion, $PF_6{}^-$, has been discussed (page 496).

20-17. Oxo Acids and Anions of Arsenic, Antimony and Bismuth

Arsenic. The nature of the lower acid is not firmly established, and it more likely is the hydrated oxide, $As_2O_3(aq)$; it is readily oxidized, even by air. However, in salts, the *arsenite* anion is known in the ortho as well as more complex forms. *Arsenic acid*, H_3AsO_4, is obtained by treating arsenic with concentrated nitric acid to give white crystals, $H_3AsO_4 \cdot \frac{1}{2}H_2O$. Unlike phosphoric acid, it is a moderately strong oxidizing agent in acid solution, the potentials being

$$H_3AsO_4 + 2H^+ + 2e = HAsO_2 + 2H_2O \qquad E^0 = 0.559 \text{ v}$$
$$H_3PO_4 + 2H^+ + 2e = H_3PO_3 + H_2O \qquad E^0 = -0.276 \text{ v}$$

Arsenic acid is tribasic but somewhat weaker than phosphoric acid, ($pK_1 = 2.3$). The arsenates generally resemble orthophosphates and are often isomorphous with them.

Condensed arsenic anions are much less stable than the condensed phosphates and, owing to rapid hydrolysis, do not exist in aqueous solution. Dehydration of KH_2AsO_4 gives three forms, stable at different temperatures, of metaarsenate; one form is known to contain an infinite chain polyanion, like that in one form of KPO_3.

There are also fluoroarsenates, such as the $M^I_2[As_2F_8O_2]$ compounds which contain arsenic atoms octahedrally coordinated by four fluoride ions and two bridging oxygen atoms.[22]

Antimony. No lower acid is known but only the hydrated oxide, $Sb_2O_3(aq)$; the antimonites are well-defined salts, however. The higher acid is known only in solution, but it gives crystalline antimonates of the type $K[Sb(OH)_6]$. There do not appear to be finite SbO_4^{3-} ions under any circumstances. Some "antimonates" obtained by heating oxides, for example, M^ISbO_3, $M^{III}SbO_4$ and $M_2^{II}Sb_2O_7$, contain SbO_6 octahedra and differ only in the manner of linking in the lattice. They are best regarded as mixed oxides.

Bismuth. When $Bi(OH)_3$ in strongly alkaline solution is treated with chlorine or other strong oxidizing agents, "bismuthates" are obtained, but never in a state of high purity. They can also be made, for example, by heating Na_2O_2 and Bi_2O_3 which gives $NaBi^VO_3$. Bismuthates are powerful oxidizing agents in acid solution.

[22] H. Dunken and W. Haase, *Z. Chem.*, **3**, 433 (1963).

References

Bent, H. A., *J. Inorg. Nuclear Chem.*, **19**, 43 (1961). Hybridization, bond angles and bond lengths in PX_3, X_3PO and X_3PS compounds.

Berlin, K. D., and G. B. Butler, *Chem. Rev.*, **60**, 243 (1960). Preparation and properties of phosphine oxides.

Booth, G., *Adv. Inorg. Chem. Radiochem.*, **6**, 1 (1964). Complexes of transition metals with phosphines, arsines and stibines.

Cadogan, J. G., *Quart. Rev.*, **16**, 208 (1962). Oxidation of PR_3 organo compounds.

Clark, V. M., *Proc. Chem. Soc.*, **1964**, 129; *Angew. Chem. (Internat.)*, **3**, 678 (1964). Phosphorylation in organic and biochemistry.

Crofts, P. C., *Quart. Rev.*, **12**, 34 (1958). Chemistry of compounds with P—C bonds.

Doak, G. O., and L. D. Freedman, *Chem. Rev.*, **61**, 31 (1961). Structure and properties of dialkyl phosphonates.

Frank, A. W., *Chem. Rev.*, **61**, 389 (1961). Phosphonous acids and their derivatives.

George, J. W., *Progr. Inorg. Chem.*, **2**, 33 (1960). Halides and oxohalides of the elements of groups Vb and VIb.

Gillespie, R. J., *J. Amer. Chem. Soc.*, **82**, 5978 (1960). Valence and bonding in hydrides and halides.

Grayson, M., and E. J. Griffith, (eds.), *Topics in Phosphorus Chemistry*, Vol. I, Interscience–Wiley, New York, 1964. Synthesis of organo P compounds, Michaelis–Arbusov and nucleophilic displacement reactions, lower oxo and condensed phosphates.

Hartley, S. B., *et al.*, *Quart. Rev.*, **17**, 204 (1963). Thermochemistry of phosphorus compounds.

Heath, D. F., *Organophosphorus Poisons*. Pergamon Press, London, 1961.

Holmes, R. R., *J. Chem. Educ.*, **40**, 125 (1963). Review on phosphorus halides.

Hudson, R. F., *Pure Appl. Chem.*, **9**, 371 (1964); *Adv. Inorg. Chem. Radiochem.*, **5**, 347 (1964). Bonding, structure and reactivity of organophosphorus compounds. The latter reference also contains discussion of $d\pi$–$p\pi$ bonding.

Hudson, R. F., and M. Green, *Angew. Chem. (Internat.)*, **2**, 11 (1963). Stereochemistry of displacement reactions at phosphorus atoms.

Huheey, J. E., *J. Chem. Educ.*, **40**, 153 (1963). Review on compounds with P—P bonds.

Jones, R. A. Y., and A. R. Katritsky, *Angew. Chem. (Internat.)*, **1**, 32 (1962). ^{31}P nuclear magnetic resonance spectra; data and references.

Kolditz, L., *Adv. Inorg. Chem. Radiochem.*, Vol. 7 (1965). Halides of P, As, Sb and Bi.

Kosolopoff, G. K., *Organophosphorus Compounds*, Wiley, New York, 1950.

Maier, L., *Progr. Inorg. Chem.*, **5**, 27 (1963). Chemistry of primary, secondary and tertiary phosphines.

Mann, F. G., *Progr. Stereochem.*, **2**, 196 (1958). Stereochemistry of N, P, As, Sb and Bi.

Märkl, G., *Angew. Chem. (Internat.)*, **4**, 1023 (1965). Heterocycles containing phosphorus.

Mooney, R. W., and M. A. Ais, *Chem. Rev.*, **61**, 433 (1961). Alkaline earth phosphates.

Paddock, N. L., *Roy. Inst. Chem. Lectures*, 1962, No. 2. Structure and reactions of phosphorus compounds; *Quart. Rev.*, **18**, 168 (1964). Phosphonitrilic derivatives.

———, and H. T. Searle, *Adv. Inorg. Chem. Radiochem.*, **1**, 348 (1959). Phosphonitrilic halides and their derivatives.

Payne, D. S., *Quart. Rev.*, **15**, 173 (1961). The halides of P, As, Sb and Bi.

———, in *Non-Aqueous Solvent Systems*, Academic Press, New York, 1965. Group V halides and oxohalides as solvents.

Schmulbach, C. D., *Progr. Inorg. Chem.*, **4**, 275 (1962). Phosphonitrilic compounds.

Schmutzler, R., *Angew. Chem. (Internat.)*, **4**, 496 (1965). Chemistry and nmr spectra of 5-coordinate fluorophosphoranes, R_nPF_{5-n}.

Thilo, E., *Angew. Chem. (Internat.)*, **4**, 1061 (1965). Structures of condensed phosphates.

Van Wazer, J. R., *Phosphorus and Its Compounds*, Vol. I, Interscience, New York–London, 1958. A comprehensive account of all phases of phosphorus chemistry. Vol. II, *Technology, Biological Functions, and Applications*, 1961.

——— and C. F. Callis, *Chem. Rev.*, **58**, 1011 (1958). Complexing of metals by phosphate.

Yost, D. M., and H. Russell, *Systematic Inorganic Chemistry (of the 5th and 6th Group Elements)*, Prentice-Hall, New York, 1946. An older but very useful account of some aspects of phosphorus chemistry.

21

The Group VI Elements: S, Se, Te, Po

GENERAL REMARKS

21-1. Electronic Structures, Valences and Stereochemistries

The outer electronic configurations of the elements and some other properties are given in Table 21-1.

TABLE 21-1

Some Properties of the Group VI Elements

Element	Electronic structure	Melting point °C	Boiling point °C	Radius X^{2-}	Covalent radius $-X-$	Electro-negativity
S	$[Ne]3s^23p^4$	119^a	444.6	1.90	1.04	2.44
Se	$[Ar]3d^{10}4s^24p^4$	217	684.8	2.02	1.17	2.48
Te	$[Kr]4d^{10}5s^25p^4$	450	1390	2.22	1.37	2.01
Po	$[Xe]4f^{14}5d^{10}6s^26p^4$	254	962	2.30		1.76

^{a} For monoclinic S (see text).

With electronic structures approaching the configurations of the next inert gas atoms, the elements show purely nonmetallic chemistry except for polonium and to a very slight extent tellurium. Their compounds are practically all covalent ones and, as with other nonmetallic elements, the concept of oxidation state has only formal significance. Some of the compounds formed by these elements can be considered to show their tendency to complete the inert gas configuration, of which they lack two electrons. Thus they form the *chalconide* ions, S^{2-}, Se^{2-} and Te^{2-}, although the existence of these ions as such in chalconides of metals other than the most electropositive ones is quite unlikely. The elements also form compounds in which there are two electron pair bonds, for example,

519

$(CH_3)_2S$, H_2S, SCl_2, etc., and ionic species in which there is one bond and one negative charge, for example, RS^-, or three bonds and one positive charge, for example, R_3S^+, can be formed.

In addition to such divalent species, the elements form compounds in oxidation states IV and VI with 4, 5 or 6 bonds; tellurium may give an 8-coordinate ion, TeF_8^{2-}. Some examples of compounds of Group VI elements and their stereochemistries are listed in Table 21-2.

TABLE 21-2

Compounds of Group VI Elements and their Stereochemistries

Valency	Number of bonds	Geometry	Examples
II	2	Angular	Me_2S, H_2Te
	3	Pyramidal	Me_3S^+
	4	Square planar	$Te[SC(NH_2)_2]_2Cl_2$
IV	2	Angular	SO_2
	3	Pyramidal	SF_3^+, OSF_2, SO_3^{2-}
		Trigonal planar	$(SeO_2)_n$
	4	ψ-Trigonal bipyramidal	SF_4, RSF_3, Me_2TeCl_2
		Tetrahedral	Me_3SO^+
	5	ψ-Octahedral	$SeOCl_2py_2$, SF_5^-, TeF_5^-
	6	Octahedral	$SeBr_6^{2-}$, PoI_6^{2-}
VI	3	Trigonal planar	$SO_3(g)$
	4	Tetrahedral	SeO_4^{2-}, $SO_3(s)$, SeO_2Cl_2
	5	Trigonal bipyramidal	SOF_4
	6	Octahedral	RSF_5, SeF_6, $Te(OH)_6$
	8(?)	?	TeF_8^{-2} (?)

21-2. Group Trends

There are great differences between the chemistry of oxygen and that of the other group VI elements and then more gradual variations through the sequence S, Se, Te, Po. Differences from oxygen are attributable, among other things, to the following:

1. The lower electronegativities of the S–Po elements lessens the ionic character of those of their compounds which are formally analogous to those of oxygen, alters the relative stabilities of various kinds of bonds and drastically lessens the importance of hydrogen bonding.

2. The maximum coordination number is not limited to four, nor is the valence limited to two, as in the case of oxygen, since d orbitals are available for use in bonding. Thus sulfur forms several hexacoordinate compounds, for example, SF_6, and for tellurium six is actually the characteristic coordination number.

3. Sulfur (but not Se or Te) has a particular tendency to catenation so that it forms several classes of compounds having no oxygen, selenium or tellurium analogs, for example, polysulfide ions, S_n^{2-}; sulfanes, XS_nX (where X may be H, halogen, —CN or —NR$_2$); and the polysulfonic acids, $HO_3SS_nSO_3H$ and their salts. Although selenium and tellurium have by no means the same tendency to catenation as sulfur, they do form rings (Se only) and long chains in their elemental forms. These chains are of course not branched because the valence of the element is only two.

In the S–Po group gradual changes of properties are evident with increasing size, decreasing electronegativity, etc. Among these are:

1. Decreasing thermal stability of the H_2X compounds. Thus H_2Te is quite endothermic.

2. Increasing metallic character of the elements.

3. Increasing tendency to form anionic complexes such as $SeBr_6^{2-}$, $TeBr_6^{2-}$, PoI_6^{2-}.

4. Decreasing stability of compounds in high formal positive oxidation states.

5. Emergence of cationic properties for Po and, very marginally, for Te. Thus TeO_2 and PoO_2 appear to have ionic lattices and they react with hydrohalic acids to give Te^{IV} and Po^{IV} halides and PoO_2 forms a hydroxide $Po(OH)_4$. There are also some ill-defined "salts" of Te and Po, such as $Po(SO_4)_2$, $TeO_2 \cdot SO_3$, etc.

Use of d Orbitals. In addition to the ability of the S–Po elements to bring d orbitals into hybridization with s and p orbitals so as to form more than four σ bonds to other atoms, sulfur particularly and also selenium appear to make frequent use of $d\pi$ orbitals to form multiple bonds. Thus, for example, in the sulfate ion, where the s and p orbitals are used in σ bonding, the shortness of the S—O bonds suggests that there must be considerable multiple bond character. The only likely explanation for this is that empty $d\pi$ orbitals of sulfur accept electrons from filled $p\pi$ orbitals of oxygen (see page 409). Similar $d\pi$–$p\pi$ bonding occurs in some phosphorus compounds, but it seems to be more prominent with sulfur and many instances will be cited later in this chapter.

THE ELEMENTS

21-3. Occurrence

Sulfur occurs widely in nature as the element, as H_2S and SO_2, in innumerable sulfide ores of metals and in the form of various sulfates such as *gypsum* and *anhydrite* ($CaSO_4$), magnesium sulfate, etc. Selenium and

17*

tellurium are much less abundant than sulfur and frequently occur as selenide and telluride impurities in metal sulfide ores. They are often recovered from flue dusts of combustion chambers for sulfur ores, particularly those of Ag and Au, and from lead chambers in sulfuric acid manufacture.

Polonium occurs in uranium and thorium minerals as a product of radioactive decay series. It was first isolated from pitchblende which contains less than 0.1 mg of Po per ton. The most accessible isotope used for chemical studies is ^{210}Po which decays by α-emission with a half-life of 138.4 days. It is now obtained in milligram to gram quantities by irradiation of bismuth in nuclear reactors:

$$^{209}Bi(n, \gamma)\ ^{210}Bi \rightarrow\ ^{210}Po + \beta^-$$

Polonium is separated from bismuth by sublimation or in a variety of chemical ways. Several other isotopes are known. The study of polonium chemistry is rendered quite difficult by the intense α radiation which causes damage to solutions and solids, evolves much heat, and makes necessary special handling techniques for protection of the chemist.

21-4. The Structures of Elemental Sulfur[1]

In each of the three phases, solid, liquid and gas, the structural relationships of sulfur are complex. We shall deal here only with the more important and definite facts.

Two crystalline modifications of sulfur are most common. One is the rhombic form which is the only stable form at room temperature and the other is the monoclinic form which becomes the stable form at 95.5° (368.46°K). The enthalpy of this transition is small (0.096 kcal/g-atom) and the process is slow. It is therefore possible by rapid heating to take rhombic sulfur up to its melting point, 112.8°. Monoclinic sulfur has a true melting point of 119°, but is often observed to melt a few degrees lower due to breakdown of the S_8 molecules. Both rhombic and monoclinic sulfur contain S_8 cyclic molecules in the crown configuration.[2a] The structure of the rhombic form is shown in Figure 21-1. Both forms show a high solubility in organic solvents, particularly carbon disulfide. Molecular weight measurement on such solutions show that the S_8 rings persist in the solutions at ordinary temperatures. If sulfur solutions in iodoform are

---

[1] For reviews see (a) M. Schmidt, in *Inorganic Polymers*, F. G. A. Stone and W. A. Graham, eds., Academic Press, New York, 1962; (b) F. G. R. Gimblett, *Inorganic Polymer Chemistry*, Butterworths, London, 1963; (c) B. Meyer, *Chem. Rev.*, **64**, 429 (1964)—the best and most comprehensive review of allotropes of S with 322 references.
[2a] D. E. Sands, *J. Amer. Chem. Soc.*, **87**, 1395 (1965).

crystallized, however, needles of a charge-transfer compound $CHI_3 \cdot 3S_8$ are obtained in which every iodine atom is bound to sulfur in the S_8 ring; isomorphous compounds with PI_3, AsI_3 and SbI_3 are known.[2b]

A third crystalline modification of sulfur, called $S\rho$ or Engel's sulfur, can be obtained by pouring an $Na_2S_2O_3$ solution into concentrated hydrochloric

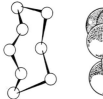
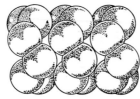

S - S = 2.059 A
$\angle$S - S - S = 107° 54'
Dihedral angle = 98.9°

Fig. 21-1.   The structure of rhombic sulfur, in which layers of cyclic S_8 molecules are stacked together.

acid at 0° and extracting with toluene, from which it crystallizes in a short time.   The hexagonal crystals are not very stable, reverting to a mixture of plastic and rhombic sulfur over several hours.   The crystals contain S_6 rings, which are puckered with a chair configuration.   The S—S bond distance is 2.06 ± 0.02 A, identical within experimental error with that found in the S_8 ring in rhombic sulfur.   The conversion to plastic and rhombic sulfur must proceed by opening and partial fragmentation of these S_6 rings to form chains and S_8 rings.

Plastic or amorphous sulfur is obtained by quenching liquid sulfur heated to 160° or more, for example, by pouring it into water.   This material can be drawn into fibers of considerable tensile strength, and X-ray studies have shown that the fibers contain helical chains of sulfur atoms with about ten sulfur atoms per three cycles of the helix.[3]   Amorphous sulfur can be made in other ways, but in all cases it is insoluble in organic solvents and slowly reverts to the crystalline form.

Liquid sulfur has been intensively studied.   At its melting point and a little above, it is yellow, transparent and mobile.   Above 159°, however, it rapidly turns brown, becoming increasingly viscous as the temperature is further raised until at about 200° the viscosity again begins to fall with increasing temperature.   At its boiling point of 444.60° it is again a rather mobile liquid.   These viscosity changes as well as the temperature variation of the specific heat are shown in Figure 21-2.   These facts are explained as follows.   The S_8 rings which originate in the crystalline solid become unstable as the temperature is raised.   It has been postulated that

[2b] T. Bjorvatten, *Acta Chem. Scand.*, **16**, 747 (1962).
[3] J. A. Prins and F. Tunstra, *Physica*, **29**, 328, 884 (1963).

six- and four-membered rings may form in equilibrium with the eight-membered rings, but this is not certain. Of prime importance, however, is the formation of open chains by homolytic fission of S—S bonds in the S_8 rings. Such chains are free radicals, actually diradicals, and they in turn

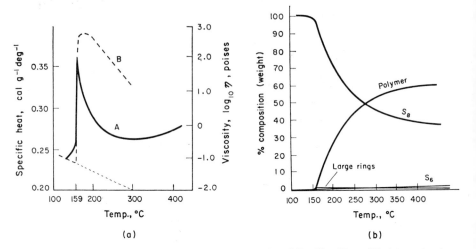

Fig. 21-2. (a) Specific heat (A) and viscosity (B) of liquid sulfur. (b) Approximate composition of liquid sulfur showing abundances of the various species. (Reprinted with permission from G. Gee, *Sci. Progr.*, **1955**, 193.)

will attack other rings and chains so that at any temperature an equilibrium between rings and chains of many lengths will eventually be set up. Esr studies have shown the presence of the radical ends of these chains in molten sulfur. Their concentration is about 6×10^{-3} mole/liter at 300°. It is presumed that the chains reach their greatest average length, 5–8 $\times$ 10^5 atoms, at about 200° where the viscosity is highest. The quantitative behavior of the system is sensitive to certain impurities, such as iodine, which can stabilize chain ends, for example, by formation of S—I bonds. In the formation of polymers, practically every S—S bond of an S_8 ring broken is replaced by an S—S bond in a linear polymer and the over-all heat of the polymerization is thus expected to be close to zero. An enthalpy of 3.2 kcal/mole of S_8 converted to polymer has been found at the critical polymerization temperature (159°). Figure 21-2 also shows the approximate composition of liquid sulfur from its melting to its boiling point.

Sulfur vapor is also known to contain various species in a temperature-dependent equilibrium. Those believed to be of greatest importance are S_8, S_6, S_4 and S_2, but except for the first and the last this is not absolutely certain nor are the structures of the intermediate ones known.

Assuming, however, that these are the only species present, the vapor density data require that at 450° and 500 mm pressure, for example, the amounts of these species are: S_8, 54%; S_6, 37%; S_4, 5%; S_2, 4%. As the temperature is raised and/or the pressure lowered, the proportion of S_2 rises rapidly, and at very high temperatures dissociation of S_2 into atoms becomes important. Between 25° and the boiling point the vapor contains significant fractions of all S_n species with $2 \leqslant n < 10$, and there are reasons to suppose that the S_3–S_{10} species are cyclic rather than linear.[4] If sulfur vapor at a temperature and pressure such that it contains contains largely S_2 is rapidly quenched in liquid nitrogen a highly colored, paramagnetic solid is obtained which is unstable above $-80°$. This substance is made up of S_2 molecules, which like O_2 molecules are paramagnetic with two unpaired electrons.[5]

21-5. The Structures of Elemental Selenium, Tellurium and Polonium

Selenium also exists in a variety of forms,[1a] but these have been less thoroughly studied than those of sulfur, to which they apparently bear some analogies though there are some distinct differences. There are two crystalline modifications, one rhombic and one monoclinic, both of which almost certainly contain Se_8 rings since they dissolve rather freely in carbon disulfide to give solutions in which the solute molecules have the molecular weight of Se_8. Both of these forms are obtained upon evaporation of the dark-red carbon disulfide solutions below about 72°. Both are thermodynamically unstable toward a gray crystalline modification which may be obtained by (*a*) heating the rhombic or monoclinic forms, (*b*) evaporating carbon disulfide solutions above about 75°, or (*c*) by slow cooling of molten selenium. This gray form, which has no sulfur analog, contains infinite chains of selenium atoms spiraling around axes parallel to one of the crystal axes. Although there are fairly strong single bonds between adjacent atoms in each chain, there is evidently weak interaction of a metallic nature between the neighboring atoms of different chains, and gray selenium is metallic in appearance and to some extent in some of its properties. It is not comparable with most true metals in its electrical conductivity in the dark, but it is markedly photoconductive.

Only one allotropic form of *tellurium* is definitely known, and this is silvery white, semimetallic and isomorphous with the gray form of selenium. Like the latter it is virtually insoluble in all liquids except those with which it reacts. Gray selenium and tellurium form a continuous range

[4] J. Berkowitz and J. B. Marquart, *J. Chem. Phys.*, **39**, 275 (1963).

[5] F. O. Rice and H. E. Radford, *J. Chem. Phys.*, **33**, 774 (1960); B. Meyer, *J. Chem. Phys.*, **37**, 1577 (1962).

of solid solutions which appear to contain chains in which Se and Te atoms alternate more or less randomly.

In selenium and tellurium vapors the concentration of paramagnetic Se_2 and Te_2 molecules and Se and Te atoms is evidently much higher under comparable conditions of temperature and pressure than that for sulfur, indicating decreased tendency toward catenation.

The trend toward greater metallic character in the group VI elements is complete at polonium. Whereas sulfur is a true insulator (specific resistivity in $\mu\Omega$-cm $= 2 \times 10^{23}$), selenium (sp. res., 2×10^{11}) and tellurium (sp. res. 2×10^5) are intermediate in their electrical conductivities and the temperature coefficient of resistivity in all three cases is negative, which is usually considered characteristic of nonmetals. Polonium in each of its two allotropes has a resistivity typical of true metals ($\sim 43\mu\Omega$-cm) and a positive temperature coefficient. The low temperature allotrope, which is stable up to about 100°, has a cubic structure, and the high temperature form is rhombohedral. In both forms, the coordination number is six.

21-6. Reactions of the Elements

Sulfur, selenium and tellurium are moderately reactive substances. They burn in air, on heating, to give dioxides, SO_2, SeO_2 and TeO_2. They combine directly with the halogens and with numerous metals and nonmetals. Sulfur, selenium and tellurium are not attacked by nonoxidizing acids, but polonium will dissolve in sulfuric acid, hydrofluoric acid, hydrochloric acid and concentrated nitric acid, which is in accord with the metallic character of Po. S, Se and Te are attacked on heating with concentrated sulfuric acid or nitric acid. Sulfur dissolves in fuming sulfuric acid giving yellow to blue solutions which contain as yet unidentified paramagnetic species. It is also soluble, with reaction, in amines such as piperidine to give colored solutions containing N,N'-polythiobisamines in which there are free radicals (about 1 per 10^4 S atoms),

$$2RR'NH + S_n = (RR'N)_2S_{n-1} + H_2S$$

Many sulfur reactions are catalyzed by amines and such S—S bond-breaking reactions to give free radicals may be involved. Sulfur and selenium and, to a limited extent, tellurium dissolve in aqueous solutions of their anions, S^{2-}, Se^{2-} and Te^{2-}, to form polyanions, S_n^{2-}, Se_n^{2-} and Te_n^{2-}.

Sulfur and selenium react with many organic molecules. For example, saturated hydrocarbons are dehydrogenated. The reaction of sulfur with olefins is of enormous technical importance, for it results in the vulcanization (formation of sulfur bridges between chains) of natural and syn-

thetic rubbers. Some important reactions of sulfur, which are also on the
whole typical of selenium and tellurium, are shown in Figure 21-3.

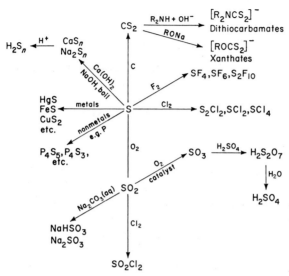

Fig. 21-3.   Some reactions of sulfur.

It is obvious that all reactions of S_8 require that the initial attack opens
the ring to give sulfur chains or sulfur chain compounds. Many reactions
can be rationalized by considering nucleophilic attack on S—S bonds.
Thus even a comparatively simple inorganic reaction—that of S_8 with
Na_2SO_3 to give $Na_2S_2O_3$—is complex and cannot possibly proceed by what
would be a 9th order reaction (!)

$$S_8 + 8Na_2SO_3 = 8Na_2S_2O_3$$

For compounds with S—S bonds, the activation energy for S_N2 attack
can be correlated with bond distances—the shorter the bond, the higher
the activation energy, which is consistent with poor acceptor property
of an S antibonding orbital for the incoming nucleophile in reactions such
as

$$N{\equiv}C^- + \quad \underset{X}{\overset{Y}{S-S}} \quad = \quad NCS \underset{X}{\overset{}{}} + {}^-SY$$

$$^{2-}O_3S + \quad \underset{X}{\overset{Y}{S-S}} \quad = \quad {}^-O_3S-S \underset{X}{\overset{}{}} + {}^-SY$$

Another "simple" reaction, that of $(C_6H_5)_3P$ with sulfur to give $(C_6H_5)_3PS$, has also been shown to be one involving nucleophilic attack:

$$Ph_3P + S_8 = Ph_3P^+\!\!-\!\!S\!\!-\!\!S\!\!-\!\!S\!\!-\!\!S\!\!-\!\!S\!\!-\!\!S\!\!-\!\!S\!\!-\!\!S^-$$

S_N2, rate determining, followed by

$$Ph_3P + Ph_3P^+\!\!-\!\!SSSSSSSS^- \rightarrow Ph_3PS + Ph_3P^+\!\!-\!\!SSSSSSS^-, \text{ etc.}$$

Further discussion of sulfur reactions is beyond the scope of this text.[1a,6]

BINARY COMPOUNDS

21-7. Hydrides

The simple hydrides, MH_2, are all gases with revolting odors and are extremely poisonous. Those of S, Se and Te are most readily obtained by the action of acids on metal chalconides. H_2Po has been prepared only in trace quantities by dissolving magnesium foil plated with Po in $0.2N$ HCl. The thermal stability and bond strengths decrease from H_2S to H_2Po. Although pure H_2Se is thermally stable to 280°,[7] H_2Te and H_2Po appear to be thermodynamically unstable with respect to their constituent elements. All behave as very weak acids in aqueous solution and the dissociation constants increase with increasing atomic number. The general reactivity of the simple hydrides also increases in the same direction. Only hydrogen sulfide is of general importance. It dissolves in water to give a solution about $0.1M$ under 1 atm pressure. Its dissociation equilibria in water are:

$$H_2S + H_2O = H_3O^+ + HS^- \qquad K = 1 \times 10^{-7}$$
$$HS^- + H_2O = H_3O^+ + S^{2-} \qquad K = \sim\!10^{-14}$$

Only for sulfur are higher hydrides, called *sulfanes*, known. The lower members, H_2S_2 through H_2S_6, have been isolated in a pure state, whereas higher members are so far known only in mixtures. All of the sulfanes are yellow liquids whose viscosities increase with chain length. They may be prepared in large quantities by reactions such as:

$$Na_2S_n(aq) + 2HCl(aq) \rightarrow 2NaCl(aq) + H_2S_n(l) \ (n = 4\text{–}6)$$
$$S_nCl_2(l) + 2H_2S(l) \rightarrow 2HCl(g) + H_2S_{n+2}(l)$$
$$S_nCl_2(l) + 2H_2S_2(l) \rightarrow 2HCl(g) + H_2S_{n+4}(l)$$

The oils from the first reaction can be cracked and fractionated to give

---

[6] *See* (a) W. A. Pryor, *Mechanism of Sulfur Reactions*, McGraw-Hill, New York, 1962; (b) R. E. Davis, "Nucleophilic Displacement Reactions at S—S Bonds" in *Survey of Progress of Chemistry*, Vol. II, A. F. Scott, ed., Academic Press, New York, 1964.

[7] K. E. Hayes and N. R. M. Haase, *J. Chem. Educ.*, **40**, 149 (1963).

H_2S_2 through H_2S_5 in a pure state, whereas the higher sulfanes are obtained from the other reactions. Although the sulfanes are all thermodynamically unstable with respect to the reaction

$$H_2S_n(l) = H_2S(g) + (n - 1)S(s)$$

these reactions are sufficiently slow that the compounds can be preserved for considerable periods of time. The sulfanes are, however, quite reactive.

21-8. Metal Chalconides

Most metallic elements react directly with S, Se, Te and, so far as is known, Po. Often they react very readily, mercury, for example, reacting with sulfur at room temperature. Binary compounds of great variety and complexity of structure can be obtained. The nature of the products usually also depends on the ratios of reactants, temperature of reaction and other conditions. Many elements form several compounds and sometimes long series of compounds with a given chalconide. We will give here only the briefest account of some of the most important types and we shall also, for the most part, deal only with the sulfides. These are best known and the selenides and tellurides are very often quite similar.

Ionic Sulfides. Only the more electropositive elements—alkalies and alkaline earths—form sulfides which appear to be mainly ionic. They are the only sulfides which dissolve in water and they crystallize in simple ionic lattices, for example, an antifluorite lattice for the alkali sulfides (and most other chalconides) and a rock salt lattice for the alkaline earth sulfides (and most other chalconides). In aqueous solutions the sulfide ions are extensively hydrolyzed:

$$S^{2-} + H_2O = SH^- + OH^-   K = {\sim}1$$

Aqueous solutions of polysulfides can be obtained by boiling solutions of the sulfides with sulfur. From such solutions, and also in some other ways, crystalline polysulfides may be obtained. Three polysulfides in which the existence and structure of the poly anion has been demonstrated are Cs_2S_6, BaS_3 and BaS_4 (Fig. 21-4).

Other Metallic Sulfides. Most metal sulfides cannot be well described by assuming them to be mainly ionic. They frequently have peculiar stoichiometries, are often nonstoichiometric phases rather than compounds in a classical sense, are often polymorphic and many of them are alloy-like or semimetallic in behavior. Metal sulfides tend to be much more covalent than metal oxides, with the result that quite often there is only limited and occasionally no stoichiometric analogy between the oxides and the sulfides of a given metal; very often, indeed possibly most of the time when there is a sulfide and an oxide of identical empirical formula, they will have different structures. To illustrate these generalizations, the following examples may be considered.

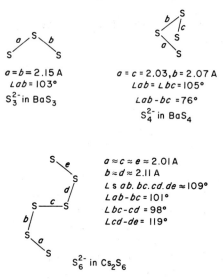

$a = b = 2.15$ A
$\angle ab = 103°$
S_3^{2-} in BaS$_3$

$a = c = 2.03, b = 2.07$ A
$\angle ab = \angle bc = 105°$
$\angle ab\text{-}bc = 76°$
S_4^{2-} in BaS$_4$

$a \approx c \approx e \approx 2.01$ A
$b \approx d \approx 2.11$ A
$\angle s\ ab.\ bc.\ cd.\ de \approx 109°$
$\angle ab\text{-}bc = 101°$
$\angle bc\text{-}cd = 98°$
$\angle cd\text{-}de = 119°$

S_6^{2-} in Cs$_2$S$_6$

Fig. 21-4.   Structures of representative polysulfide anions.

Several transition metal sulfides, for example, FeS, CoS and NiS, adopt a structure called the *nickel arsenide structure*, illustrated in Figure 21-5. In this structure each metal atom is surrounded octahedrally by six sulfur

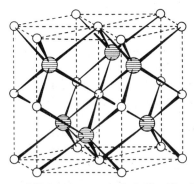

Fig. 21-5.   The structure of NiAs (As atoms shaded).   The Ni atom in the center of the diagram is surrounded octahedrally by six As atoms and has also two near Ni neighbors which are coplanar with four of the As atoms. (Reprinted with permission from A. F. Wells, *Structural Inorganic Chemistry*, Clarendon Press, Oxford, 1945, p. 387.)

atoms, but also approached fairly closely by two other metal atoms. These metal–metal distances are 2.60–2.68 A in FeS, CoS and NiS, and at such distances there must be a considerable amount of metal–metal bonding, thus accounting for their alloy-like or semimetallic character. Note that such a structure is not in the least likely for a predominantly ionic salt, requiring as it would the close approach of dipositive ions.

Another class of metal sulfides of considerable importance are the disulfides, represented by FeS_2, CoS_2 and a number of others. All of these contain discrete S_2 units with an S—S distance almost exactly equal to that to be expected for an S—S single bond. These assume one of two closely related structures. First there is the *pyrite structure* named after the polymorph of FeS_2 which exhibits it. This structure may be visualized as a distorted NaCl structure. The Fe atoms occupy Na positions and the S_2 groups are placed with their centers at the Cl positions but turned in such a way that they are not parallel to any of the cube axes. The *marcasite structure* is very similar but somewhat less regular.

FeS is a good example of a well-characterized nonstoichiometric sulfide. It has long been known that a sample with an Fe/S ratio precisely unity is rarely encountered, and in the older literature such formulas as Fe_6S_7 and $Fe_{11}S_{12}$ have been assigned to it. The iron–sulfur system assumes the nickel arsenide structure over the composition range 50–55.5 atom % sulfur, and, when the S/Fe ratio exceeds unity, some of the iron positions in the lattice are vacant in a random way. Thus the very attempt to assign stoichiometric formulas such as Fe_6S_7 is meaningless. We are dealing not with *one* compound, in the classical sense, but with a *phase* which may be perfect, that is, FeS, or may be deficient in iron. That particular specimen which happens to have the composition Fe_6S_7 is better described as $Fe_{0.858}S$.

An even more extreme example of nonstoichiometry is provided by the Co–Te (and the analogous Ni–Te) system. Here, a phase with the nickel arsenide structure is stable over the entire composition range CoTe to $CoTe_2$. It is possible to pass continuously from the former to the latter by

TABLE 21-3

Nonstoichiometry in a Metal–Sulfur System: Cr–S

Phase (ideal composition)	Structure	Range of stability
CrS	Monoclinic	$CrS_{0.95}$–CrS
Cr_7S_8	Partly disord., trigonal	$Cr_{0.88}S$–$Cr_{0.87}S$
Cr_5S_6	Trigonal	$\sim Cr_{0.85}S$
Cr_3S_4	Monoclinic	$Cr_{0.79}S$–$Cr_{0.76}S$
Cr_2S_3	Trigonal	$\sim Cr_{0.69}S$
Cr_2S_3	Rhombohedral	$\sim Cr_{0.67}S$

progressive loss of Co atoms from alternate planes (see Fig. 21-5) until, at $CoTe_2$, every other plane of Co atoms present in CoTe has completely vanished.

An example of a system in which many different phases occur (and each has a small range of existence so that each may be encountered in non-stoichiometric form) is the Cr–S system. The six phases occurring in the composition range $CrS_{0.95}$ to $CrS_{1.5}$ are shown in Table 21-3.

21-9. Other Binary Sulfides

Most nonmetallic or metalloid elements form sulfides. A number of these have been or will be discussed under the respective elements, but a few will be mentioned here. Silicon disulfide (21-I) consists of infinite chains of SiS_4 tetrahedra sharing edges, similar to the structure of $BeCl_2$.

(21-I) (21-II)

Sb_2S_3 and Bi_2S_3 are isomorphous (21-II), forming infinite bands which are then held together in parallel strips in the crystal by weak, secondary bonds.

Sulfur–Nitrogen Compounds. There is a fairly extensive chemistry of such compounds[8] and only a few of them can be specifically mentioned here. Among the most interesting and best characterized are S_4N_4 and some of its derivatives. *Tetrasulfur tetranitride* is obtained by reaction of sulfur with NH_3 in CCl_4 solution or, better, by passing S_2Cl_2 over heated pellets of NH_4Cl.[9] It forms orange-yellow crystals which are stable to air, but detonated by shock. Many other S–N compounds (e.g., S_4N_3Cl, $S_4N_4Cl_4$ and $S_4N_4H_4$) can be obtained from it. The structure of S_4N_4 is a cage with a square set of N atoms and a bisphenoid of S atoms (Fig. 21-6a), which is in interesting contrast to the structure of As_4S_4 (realgar) shown in Figure 21-6b. The S$\cdots$S distance, 2.59 A, is longer than the normal S—S single-bond distance, ~ 2.08 A, but short enough to indicate a significant interaction; even the S to S (linked by N) distance, 2.71 A, is indicative of direct S$\cdots$S interaction. The electronic structure is evidently a highly delocalized one which can be described best by molecular orbitals which include weak S—S bonding.[10a]

[8] O. Glemser, *Angew. Chem. (Internat.)*, **2**, 530 (1963).

[9] W. L. Jolly and H. Becke-Goehring, *Inorg. Chem.*, **1**, 76 (1962); see also N. Logan and W. L. Jolly, *Inorg. Chem.*, **4**, 1508 (1965).

[10a] P. S. Braterman, *J. Chem. Soc.*, **1965**, 2297.

Three derivatives of S_4N_4 have known structures. $S_4N_4H_4$, obtained by treating S_4N_4 with ethanolic $SnCl_2$, has the cyclic structure shown in

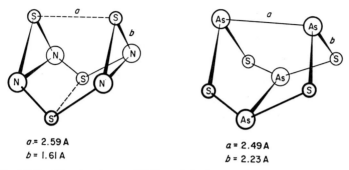

$a = 2.59 A$
$b = 1.61 A$

$a = 2.49 A$
$b = 2.23 A$

Fig. 21-6.   The structures of N_4S_4 and As_4S_4. Both have D_{2d} symmetry

Figure 21-7.   The S atoms form a square with all N atoms on the same side forming another square, and with the H atoms attached to N (C_{4v}). Moreover, all the S—N bond lengths are equal at 1.67 A, corresponding to approximately single S—N bonds. $S_4N_4F_4$ also has a cyclic structure,

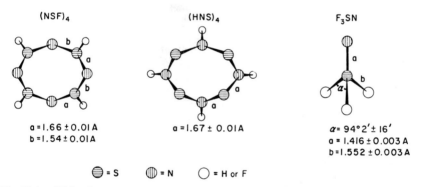

$(NSF)_4$ $(HNS)_4$ F_3SN

$a = 1.66 \pm 0.01 A$
$b = 1.54 \pm 0.01 A$

$a = 1.67 \pm 0.01 A$

$a = 94°2' \pm 16'$
$a = 1.416 \pm 0.003 A$
$b = 1.552 \pm 0.003 A$

⊜ = S   ⦀ = N   ○ = H or F

Fig. 21-7.   Molecular structures of some sulfur–nitrogen compounds derived from S_4N_4.

Figure 21-7, but it differs considerably from $S_4N_4H_4$ in having a bisphenoidal arrangement of N atoms about a square array of S atoms, the F atoms attached to S and alternating unequal S—N distances—four at 1.54 A and four at 1.66 A (S_4). This implies that there is $d\pi$–$p\pi$ character in four of them but an absence of delocalization. $(NSF)_4$ is isoelectronic with $(NPF_2)_4$ in which delocalization, at least to the extent that there are 3-center N⋯P⋯N π systems, is thought to occur.[10b]   The ion $S_4N_3{}^+$, obtained by

[10b] D. P. Craig and N. L. Paddock, *J. Chem. Soc.*, **1962**, 4118.

the action of HCl on S_4N_4, has in its nitrate obtained, by aqueous metathesis, a nearly *planar* cyclic structure with six N—S and one S—S bond.[10c]

Esr studies[11] of ions such as $S_4N_4^-$ which are obtained by treating S_4N_4 with potassium in dimethoxyethane suggest the possibility of delocalizing electron density over the whole S–N system. S_4N_4 also dissolves in concentrated H_2SO_4 undergoing cleavage to give radicals such as $S_2N_2^+$ and SN_2^+.

Finally, the compound NSF_3 obtained by the action of AgF_2 on S_4N_4 deserves mention; microwave study[12] shows the C_{3v} structure given in Figure 21-7. It may be considered as a derivative of SF_6 with three S—F bonds replaced by a triple bond, $S\equiv N$.

21-10. Halides

The halides of the group VI elements are listed in Table 21-4, along with their principal properties; only certain ones are discussed here.

TABLE 21-4

The Group VI Binary Halides[a]

Fluorides	Chlorides	Bromides	Iodides
	Sulfur		
$S_2F_2{}^b$ m -165, b -10.6	S_2Cl_2,[d] m -80, b 138	S_2Br_2,[d] m -46, d 90	
$[SF_2]^c$	SCl_2, m -78, d 59		
SF_4, m -121, b -40	SCl_4, d -31		
SF_6, sub -65, m -51			
S_2F_{10}, m -53, b 29			
	Selenium		
	Se_2Cl_2	Se_2Br_2, d in vapor	
	$SeCl_2$, d in vapor	$SeBr_2$, d in vapor	
SeF_4, m -10, b 106	$SeCl_4$, sub 191	$SeBr_4$, exists only as solid	
SeF_6, sub -47, m -35			
	Tellurium		
	$TeCl_2$, m 208, b 327	$TeBr_2$, m 210, b 339	
TeF_4, m 130	$TeCl_4$, m 225, b 390	$TeBr_4$, m 380, b 414 (d in vapor)	TeI_4, m 259,[e] d 100
TeF_6, sub -39, m -38			
Te_2F_{10}, m -34, b 53			

[a] All temperatures given in °C.

[b] Isomeric mixture of FSSF, m $-133°$, and F_2SS, b $-10.6°$.

[c] Existence not certain.

[d] Also the dichlorosulfanes, S_nCl_2, $2 < n < 100(?)$, and dibromosulfanes, S_nBr_2, $n > 2$.

[e] Melting point obtained in a sealed tube to prevent decomposition: $TeI_4 = Te + 2I_2$.

[10c] A. W. Cordes, R. F. Kruh and E. K. Gordon, *Inorg. Chem.*, **4**, 681 (1965).

[11] D. Chapman and A. G. Massey, *Trans. Farad. Soc.*, **58**, 1284 (1962).

[12] W. H. Kirchkoff and E. B. Wilson, Jr., *J. Amer. Chem. Soc.*, **84**, 334 (1962).

Sulfur Fluorides.[13]   Some reactions of S–F compounds are shown in Figure 21-8. The direct fluorination of sulfur yields principally SF_6 and only traces of SF_4 and S_2F_{10}. Reaction of AgF with sulfur in vacuum produces S_2F_2. There are two isomers, the more stable, volatile and abundant being $F_2S{=}S$, the other $F{-}S{-}S{-}F$.[14] *Sulfur tetrafluoride,*[15] SF_4, can be made in various other ways, of which the best is by reaction of SCl_2 with NaF in acetonitrile at 70–80°. SF_4 is an extremely reactive substance, instantly hydrolyzed by water to SO_2 and HF, but its fluorinating action is quite selective. It will convert $C{=}O$ and $P{=}O$ groups smoothly to CF_2 and PF_2 and COOH and P(O)OH groups to CF_3 and PF_3 groups without attack on most other functional or reactive groups which may be present. It is also quite useful for converting metal oxides to fluorides which are (usually) in the same oxidation state.

Aryl-substituted fluorides can be readily obtained by the reaction

$$(C_6H_5)_2S_2 + 6AgF_2 = 2C_6H_5SF_3 + 6AgF$$

which is carried out in trichloro- or trifluoromethane. The aryl sulfur trifluorides are more convenient laboratory fluorinating agents than SF_4 in that they do not require pressure above atmospheric. The structure of SF_4 and of substituted derivatives, RSF_3, is that of a trigonal bipyramid with an equatorial position occupied by the lone-pair. As expected, some donor compounds of SF_4 exist, including, perhaps, an SF_5^- ion.[16]

Sulfur hexafluoride is normally very resistant to attack and extreme conditions are often required. Thus SF_6 resists molten KOH, steam at 500° and oxygen even in an electric discharge. It will, however, react with molten sodium at 250°, with H_2 when sparked and with some red hot metals. Because of its chemical inertness, high dielectric strength and molecular weight, it is used as a gaseous insulator in high voltage generators and other electrical equipment.

SF_6 and its substituted derivatives (see below) have, or may be presumed to have, octahedrally bonded sulfur. In SF_6 the S—F bonds are about 0.2 A shorter than expected for S—F single bonds. The low reactivity, particularly toward hydrolysis, which contrasts with the very high reactivity of SF_4, is presumably due to a combination of factors including high S—F bond strength and the facts that sulfur is both coordinately saturated and sterically hindered, augmented in the case of SF_6 by the lack of polarity

[13] H. L. Roberts, *Quart. Rev.*, **15**, 30 (1961). An extensive review of S–F compounds.

[14] R. L. Kuczkowski, *J. Amer. Chem. Soc.*, **86**, 3617 (1964); F. Seel and R. Budentz, *Chem. Ber.*, **98**, 251 (1965); R. D. Brown, F. R. Burden and G. P. Pez, *Chem. Comm.*, **1965**, 276.

[15] W. C. Smith, *Angew. Chem. (Internat.)*, **1**, 467 (1962). Review of SF_4 chemistry.

[16] R. Tunder and B. Siegel, *J. Inorg. Nucl. Chem.*, **25**, 1097 (1963).

of the molecule. The low reactivity is due to kinetic factors and not to thermodynamic stability, since the reaction of SF_6 with H_2O to give SO_3 and HF would be decidedly favorable ($\Delta F = -110$ kcal/mole), and the average bond energy in SF_4, 78 kcal/mole, is slightly higher than that of SF_6. The possibility of electrophilic attack on SF_6 has been confirmed by its reactions with certain Lewis acids. Thus Al_2Cl_6 at 180–200° gives AlF_3, Cl_2 and sulfur chlorides, while the thermodynamically allowed reaction

$$SF_6 + 2SO_3 = 3SO_2F_2$$

proceeds[17,18] slowly at 250°. SF_6 also reacts rapidly and quantitatively with sodium in a solution of diphenyl-ethyleneglycoldimethylether at room temperature:

$$8Na + SF_6 = Na_2S + 6NaF$$

Electron transfer from a diphenyl radical ion to an SF_6 molecule to give an unstable SF_6^- ion is probably involved.[17b,18] The alleged reduction of SF_6 by gaseous HI has been shown[18] to be incorrect.

Disulfur decafluoride is best obtained by the photochemical reaction

$$2SF_5Cl + H_2 \underset{}{\overset{h\nu}{\rightleftharpoons}} S_2F_{10} + 2HCl$$

It is extremely poisonous (the reason for which is not clear) being similar in its physiological action to phosgene. It is not dissolved or hydrolyzed by water or alkalies and is not very reactive. Its structure is such that each sulfur atom is surrounded octahedrally by five fluorine atoms and the other sulfur atom. The S—S bond is unusually long, 2.21 A, as compared to about 2.08 A expected for a single bond, whereas the S—F bonds are, as in SF_6, about 0.2 A shorter than anticipated for an S—F single bond. At room temperature it shows scarcely any chemical reactivity, though it will oxidize the iodide in an acetone solution of KI. At elevated temperatures, however, it is a powerful oxidizing agent generally causing destructive oxidation and fluorination, presumably due to initial breakdown to free radicals,

$$S_2F_{10} \rightarrow 2SF_5\cdot$$
$$SF_5\cdot \rightarrow SF_4 + F\cdot$$

Substituted Sulfur Fluorides. There is an extensive chemistry of substituted sulfur fluorides of the types RSF_3 and RSF_5, examples of the former having been mentioned above. The SF_5 derivatives bear considerable resemblance to CF_3 derivatives with the principal difference

[17] (a) J. R. Case and F. Nyman, *Nature*, **193**, 473 (1963); (b) G. C. Demitras and A. G. MacDiarmid, *Inorg. Chem.*, **3**, 1198 (1964).

[18] J. R. Case and H. L. Roberts, *Inorg. Chem.*, **5**, 333 (1966).

that in reactions with organic or organometallic compounds the SF_5 group is fairly readily reduced whereas the CF_3 group is not. The mixed halide SF_5Cl is an important intermediate (Fig. 21-8). Although it can be

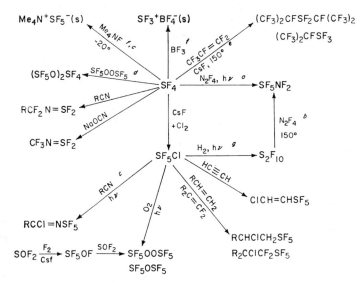

Fig. 21-8. Some reactions of sulfur–fluorine compounds.

[a] A. L. Logothetis, G. N. Sausen and R. J. Shozda, *Inorg. Chem.*, **2**, 173 (1963).
[b] E. C. Stump, C. D. Padgett and W. S. Brey, *Inorg. Chem.*, **2**, 648 (1963).
[c] C. W. Tullock, D. D. Coffman and E. L. Muetterties, *J. Amer. Chem. Soc.*, **86**, 357 (1964).
[d] C. I. Merrill and G. H. Cady, *J. Amer. Chem. Soc.*, **85**, 909 (1963).
[e] R. M. Rosenberg and E. L. Muetterties, *Inorg. Chem.*, **1**, 756 (1962).
[f] R. Tunder and B. Siegel, *J. Inorg. Nucl. Chem.*, **25**, 1097 (1963).
[g] H. L. Roberts, *J. Chem. Soc.*, **1962**, 3183.

made by interaction of S_2F_{10} with Cl_2 at 200–250° or by the reaction of SF_4 with ClF (made *in situ* by the reaction of ClF_3 with Cl_2) at *ca* 350°, it is best made by the interaction

$$SF_4 + Cl_2 + CsF \xrightarrow{100° \, 1 \, h., \, 175° \, 2 \, h.} SF_5Cl + CsCl$$

KF or other fluorides can be used but give lower yields.[19] A probable intermediate in this reaction is the salt $CsSF_5$ which dissociates significantly above 150°

$$CsF + SF_4 \underset{150°}{\overset{100°}{\rightleftharpoons}} CsSF_5$$

Pentafluorosulfur chloride is a colorless gas, b −19.1°, m −64°, which is

[19] C. W. Tullock, D. D. Coffman and E. L. Muetterties, *J. Amer. Chem. Soc.*, **86**, 357 (1964).

more reactive than SF_6, being rapidly hydrolyzed by alkalies, though it is inert to acids. Its hydrolysis and its powerful oxidizing action towards many organic substances is consistent with the charge distribution $F_5S^{\delta-}\!-\!Cl^{\delta+}$. Its radical reactions with olefins and fluoroolefins resemble those of CF_3I. The very reactive yellow pentafluorosulfur hypofluorite is one of the few known hypofluorites; it is obtained by the catalytic reaction

$$SOF_2 + F_2 \xrightarrow{\text{CsF. }25°} SF_5OF$$

SOF_4, which is obtained in absence of CsF, is also converted to SF_5OF by CsF.[20]

Selenium and Tellurium Fluorides. SeF_4 and TeF_4 are, like SF_4, highly reactive fluorinating agents, but their chemistry is not known in detail as yet. SeF_4 and sodium or tetraalkylammonium fluorides interact to give salts of the SeF_5^- ion. Selenium and tellurium hexafluorides are considerably more reactive than SF_6. In fact TeF_6 is fully hydrolyzed on contact with water for 24 hours. It is also interesting that TeF_6 has weak Lewis acidity, combining at 250° with CsF to give a solid whose composition approximates to Cs_2TeF_8, and with trialkyl amines to form adducts of the formula $(R_3N)_2TeF_6$. Ditellurium decafluoride is somewhat more reactive than its sulfur analog. There is as yet no report of the preparation of Se_2F_{10}, but it is presumably capable of existence.

Sulfur Chlorides. The chlorination of molten sulfur gives S_2Cl_2, an orange liquid, b 137°, of revolting smell. Using excess chlorine and traces of $FeCl_3$, $SnCl_4$, I_2, etc., as catalyst at room temperature, an equilibrium mixture containing *ca* 85% of SCl_2 is obtained. The dichloride readily dissociates within a few hours

$$2SCl_2 \rightleftharpoons S_2Cl_2 + Cl_2$$

but it can be obtained pure as a dark-red liquid, b 59°, by fractional distillation in presence of some PCl_5, small amounts of which will stabilize SCl_2 for some weeks.[21]

Sulfur chlorides are used as a solvent for sulfur (giving dichlorosulfanes up to about $S_{100}Cl_2$), in the vulcanization of rubber, as chlorinating agents and intermediates.[22] Specific higher chlorosulfanes can be obtained by reactions such as

$$2SCl_2 + H_2S_4 \xrightarrow{-80°} S_6Cl_2 + 2HCl$$

[20] J. K. Ruff and M. Lustig, *Inorg. Chem.*, **3**, 1422 (1964).
[21] R. J. Rosser and F. R. Whitt, *J. Applied Chem.*, **10**, 229 (1960).
[22] *See* L. A. Wiles and Z. S. Ariyan, *Chem. and Ind.*, **1962**, 2102, for reactions of S_2Cl_2 with organic compounds.

The sulfur chlorides are readily hydrolyzed by water. In the vapor S_2Cl_2 has a Cl—S—S—Cl structure with S—S = 2.05, S—Cl = 1.99 A and $\angle$ SSCl = 103° and twisted out of plane in the same way as H_2O_2 and FSSF.

On treatment of sulfur chlorides with Cl_2 at $-80°$, SCl_4 is obtained as yellow crystals. It dissociates above $-31°$; it may be $SCl_3{}^+Cl^-$.

Selenium and Tellurium Halides. These compounds are generally more stable than those of sulfur. They also differ in showing Lewis acidity, which is particularly manifested in their forming complex halides such as $K[SeF_5]$, $H_2[SeBr_6]$, $K_2[SeCl_6]$, $Cs_2[TeI_6]$ on heating the halide with hydrogen or alkali halides. The hexahaloselenates(IV) can also be obtained by dissolving H_2SeO_3 in concentrated HCl containing, e.g., KCl, and saturating the solution with HCl gas.

The $SeCl_6{}^{2-}$ and $TeCl_6{}^{2-}$ ions are both, rather surprisingly in view of the presence of a potential lone-pair, precisely octahedral. While this could be explained, e.g., for Te by hybridization $5p^35d^26s$, with the lone-pair in the $5s$ orbital, quadrupole resonance studies[23] have led to a suggestion that only p orbitals are used in bonding. On the other hand $SeCl_4$, $TeCl_4$ and Me_2TeCl_2 have the ψ-trigonal bipyramidal structure with an axial lone-pair, while the $TeCl_5{}^-$ in its $[OCN_2H_5]^+$ salt apparently has a random arrangement of square pyramidal $TeCl_5{}^-$ ions, and $TeBr_6{}^{2-}$ and $TeI_6{}^{2-}$ are possibly non-octahedral from quadrupole resonance studies.[24] The pyridine adduct $SeCl_4py_2$ is not analogous to $SeCl_6{}^{2-}$ but in acetonitrile acts like a salt of the ion $[SeCl_3py_2]^+$; this ion presumably has a ψ-octahedral structure like the isoelectronic $SeOCl_2py_2$.[25] The situation for these IV-valent species is still in the process of clarification.

Tellurium forms a number of complex halides in the II as well as IV states, some of the best-known being those with thiourea (tu) or substituted thioureas as ligands.[26] The red Te^{IV} compounds are made by treating TeO_2 in strong hydrochloric acid solution with, e.g., tetramethylthiourea (Me_4tu).

$$TeO_2 + 4HCl + 2Me_4tu = trans\text{-}Te^{IV}(Me_4tu)_2Cl_4 + 2H_2O$$

The ligand can further act as a reducing agent in methanolic 4N hydrochloric acid.

$$Te(Me_4tu)_2Cl_4 \xrightarrow{\text{heat}} Te^{II}(Me_4tu)Cl_2 + (Me_4tu)_2{}^{2+} + 2Cl^-$$

$$Te^{II}(Me_4tu)Cl_2 + Me_4tu \underset{\text{heat}}{\xrightarrow{\text{MeOH}}} Te^{II}(Me_4tu)_2Cl_2$$
$$\text{red} \qquad\qquad\qquad\qquad\qquad\qquad \text{yellow}$$

[23] D. Nakamura, K. Ito and M. Kubo, *Inorg. Chem.*, **2**, 61 (1963).

[24] E. E. Aynsley and A. C. Hazell, *Chem. and Ind.*, **1963**, 611.

[25] A. W. Cordes and T. V. Hughes, *Inorg. Chem.*, **3**, 1640 (1964).

[26] O. Foss, *et al.*, *Acta Chem. Scand.*, **15**, 1939 *et seq.*, 1615 *et seq.* (1961); **16**, 779 (1962); **17**, 1806 (1963).

The characteristic stereochemistry for Te^{II} is square planar but for $Te(Me_4tu)Cl_2$ there appear to be only three normal bonds, the fourth (to the chlorine of an adjacent molecule) being very long so that the complex is virtually 3-coordinate. The "trans" effect on halogens opposite is also shown in $C_6H_5Te(tu)Cl$ which is again virtually 3-coordinate. These effects are probably best attributed to use of a single p orbital for bonding at 180° so that if one ligand is more strongly bound then the other must be less so. This type of p bonding is related to similar situations in polyiodides and xenon compounds (cf. page 407).

For the 4-coordinate complexes cis–trans isomerism is possible but the halides such as $Te(tu)_2X_2$ are all cis, though the methane thiosulfonate is trans.

In some cases, cationic species can be obtained, e.g., with ethylenethiourea.

$$TeO_2 + entu \text{ (excess)} \xrightarrow{\text{HCl solution}} Te(entu)_4{}^{2+}$$

Polonium Halides. Polonium halides are similar to those of tellurium, being volatile above 150° and soluble in organic solvents. They are readily hydrolyzed and form complexes, for example, $Na_2[PoX_6]$, isomorphous with those of tellurium. There is tracer evidence for the existence of a volatile polonium fluoride. The metal is also soluble in hydrofluoric acid, and complex fluorides presumably exist.

21-11. Oxides

The following oxides of the group VI elements are the principal ones:

S_2O
SO_2 SeO_2 TeO_2 $PoO_2[PoO(OH)_2]$
SO_3 SeO_3 TeO_3

The lower oxide of sulfur is produced when a glow discharge is passed through SO_2 and in other ways, and was long thought to be SO. However, gases of this composition are equimolar mixtures of S_2O and SO_2. The extremely reactive biradical, SO, can be detected as an intermediate in the reactions, however, and $(SO)_2$ has also been detected by mass spectrometry. S_2O is believed to have the structure SSO. It is unstable at ordinary temperatures decomposing to SO_2 and polymeric oxides; it is orange-red when condensed from the gas phase at $-196°$.

The *dioxides* are obtained by burning the elements in air, though small amounts of SO_3 also form in the burning of sulfur. Sulfur dioxide is also produced when many sulfides are heated in air. Selenium and tellurium dioxides are also obtained by treating the metals with hot nitric acid to form H_2SeO_3 and $2TeO_2 \cdot HNO_3$, respectively, and then heating these to drive off water or nitric acid.

The dioxides differ considerably in structures. SO_2 is a gas (b $-10°$), SeO_2 is a white volatile solid (normal sublimation temperature 315°) and TeO_2 is a nonvolatile white solid. Gaseous SO_2 and SeO_2 are bent symmetrical molecules; in both cases the short S—O and Se—O bond distances imply that there is considerable multiple bonding. There is presumably $p\pi$–$p\pi$ bonding as indicated in the resonance structures 21-IIIa and 21-IIIb

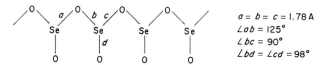

(21-IIIa)   (21-IIIb)

as well as $p\pi$–$d\pi$ bonding due to the overlap of filled $p\pi$ orbitals of oxygen with vacant $d\pi$ orbitals of sulfur. SO_2 solidifies to form a molecular lattice as far as is known, but SeO_2 forms infinite chains (Fig. 21-9). As the

$a = b = c = 1.78 A$
$\angle ab = 125°$
$\angle bc = 90°$
$\angle bd = \angle cd = 98°$

Fig. 21-9.   Section of infinite chain of SeO_2.

values of the angles imply, these chains are not planar. TeO_2 crystallizes in two apparently ionic crystalline forms, but their structures are uncertain in detail. PoO_2 also seems to exist in two ionic crystalline forms.

SO_2 has many uses, the chief one being in sulfuric acid production. It is also often used as a reducing agent, though it is not a powerful one except in basic solution where sulfite ion is formed (see below). A fair amount of work has been done using liquid SO_2 as a nonaqueous solvent. Although it is not a good ionizing solvent (dielectric constant ≈ 12), it dissolves many organic as well as inorganic substances; it can be used as a convenient non-protonic solvent in nmr studies. Self-ionization has been postulated:

$$2SO_2 = SO^{2+} + SO_3{}^{2-}$$

There is no direct evidence for this, and tracer experiments[27] indicate that this self-ionization, if it occurs at all, is unlikely to play an important role in the solvent properties of SO_2. In some cases, oxide ion transfer to more acidic solutes (e.g., SO_3) or from less acidic ones (to give $SO_3{}^{2-}$) best explains observed isotopic exchange data.

[27] T. H. Norris, J. Phys. Chem., **63**, 383 (1959).

Liquid SO_2 is a useful solvent and reactant for preparation of certain metal oxohalides, e.g.,

$$MoCl_5 + SO_2(l) = MoOCl_3(s) + SOCl_2$$

SO_2 has lone-pairs and can act as a Lewis base—indeed the first step in reactions such as the last mentioned is probably solvation. A few donor metal complexes of SO_2 are known[28] while certain amines give 1:1 charge-transfer complexes. In the latter, e.g., with p-toluidine which gives light yellow crystals, electrons from nitrogen are presumably transferred to antibonding acceptor orbitals localized on sulfur.[29] The crystals formed with quinol and other H-bonding compounds are clathrates, cf. $SO_2 \sim 7H_2O$ (page 545).

Of the *trioxides*, only sulfur trioxide is of importance. It is obtained by reaction of sulfur dioxide with molecular oxygen, a reaction which is thermodynamically very favorable but extremely slow in the absence of catalysts. Platinum sponge, V_2O_5 and NO serve as catalysts under various conditions. SO_3 reacts vigorously with water to form sulfuric acid. Commercially, for practical reasons, SO_3 is absorbed in concentrated sulfuric acid, to give oleum (see below), which is then diluted. SO_3 is also used as such for preparing sulfonated oils and alkylaryl sulfonate detergents. It is also a powerful oxidizing agent.

The free molecule, in the gas phase, has a planar, triangular structure which may be considered to be a resonance hybrid involving $p\pi$–$p\pi$ S—O bonding, as in 21-IV, with additional π bonding via overlap of filled oxygen

(21-IVa)   (21-IVb)   (21-IVc)

$p\pi$ orbitals with empty sulfur $d\pi$ orbitals, in order to account for the very short S—O distance of 1.43 A.

In view of this affinity of S in SO_3 for electrons, it is not surprising that SO_3 functions as a fairly strong Lewis acid toward those bases which it does not preferentially oxidize. Thus the trioxide gives crystalline complexes with pyridine, trimethylamine or dioxan, which can be used, like SO_3 itself, as sulfating agents for organic compounds.[30]

[28] E. H. Braye and W. Hübel, *Angew. Chem. (Internat.)*, **2**, 217 (1963); cf. also I. Lindqvist, *Inorganic Adduct Molecules of Oxo Compounds*, Springer-Verlag, 1963.

[29] W. E. Byrd, *Inorg. Chem.*, **1**, 762 (1962).

[30] E. E. Gilbert, *Chem. Rev.*, **62**, 549 (1962). Reactions of SO_3 and its adducts with organic compounds.

The structure of solid SO_3 is complex. At least three well-defined phases are known. There is first γ-SO_3, formed by condensation of vapors at $-80°$ or below. This ice-like solid (m 16.8°) contains cyclic trimers with structure 21-V.

(21-V)   (21-VI)

A more stable, asbestos-like phase, β-SO_3, has infinite helical chains of linked SO_4 tetrahedra (21-VI), and the most stable form, α-SO_3, which also has an asbestos-like appearance, presumably has similar chains cross-linked into layers.

Liquid γ-SO_3 (b 44.8°), which is a monomer–trimer mixture, can be stabilized by the addition of boric acid. In the pure state it is readily polymerized by traces of water.

Tellurium trioxide, which can be obtained by dehydration of telluric acid, $Te(OH)_6$, reacts but slowly with water to regenerate the acid though it dissolves in strong base to give tellurate ions. Selenium trioxide is difficult to obtain in a pure state.[31a] It tends to react explosively with all potential solvents because of its strong oxidizing nature. However, vacuum sublimed material dissolves in diethyl ether, dioxane, SO_2 and acetic anhydride and unstable adducts such as $SeO_3 \cdot OEt_2$, $SeO_3 \cdot C_4H_8O_2$ and $SeO_3 \cdot py$ (by action of pyridine on etherates) can be isolated. SeO_3 is hygroscopic, reacting readily with water to form selenic acid; it gives $(SeO_3)_4$ ring molecules in crystals.[31b]

OXO ACIDS

21-12. General Remarks

S, Se and Te form oxo acids. Those of sulfur are by far the most important and the most numerous. Some of the acids are not actually known as such, but like phosphorus oxo acids occur only in the form of their anions and salts. In Table 21-5 the various oxo acids of sulfur are grouped according to structural type. This classification is to some extent arbitrary, but it corresponds with the order in which we shall discuss these acids in the following sections. None of the oxo acids of sulfur in which there are

[31a] M. Schmidt, P. Bornmann and I. Wilhelm, *Angew. Chem. (Internat.)*, **2**, 691 (1963).
[31b] F. C. Mijlhoff, *Acta. Cryst.*, **18**, 795 (1965).

TABLE 21-5
Principal Oxo Acids of Sulfur

Formula	Structure[b]	Name
	Acids Containing One Sulfur Atom	
H_2SO_3[a]	$SO_3{}^{2-}$ (in sulfites)	Sulfurous
H_2SO_4	$\begin{matrix} & O \\ & \| \\ O- & S & -OH \\ & \| \\ & OH \end{matrix}$	Sulfuric
	Acids Containing Two Sulfur Atoms	
$H_2S_2O_3$	$\begin{matrix} & OH \\ & \| \\ HO- & S & -S \\ & \| \\ & O \end{matrix}$	Thiosulfuric
$H_2S_2O_4$[a]	$\begin{matrix} & O & O \\ & \| & \| \\ HO- & S & -S & -OH \end{matrix}$	Dithionous
$H_2S_2O_5$[a]	$\begin{matrix} & O & O \\ & \| & \| \\ HO- & S & -S & -OH \\ & \| \\ & O \end{matrix}$	Pyrosulfurous
$H_2S_2O_6$	$\begin{matrix} & O & O \\ & \| & \| \\ HO- & S & -S & -OH \\ & \| & \| \\ & O & O \end{matrix}$	Dithionic
$H_2S_2O_7$	$\begin{matrix} & O & & O \\ & \| & & \| \\ HO- & S & -O- & S & -OH \\ & \| & & \| \\ & O & & O \end{matrix}$	Pyrosulfuric
	Acids Containing Three or More Sulfur Atoms	
$H_2S_nO_6$	$\begin{matrix} & O & & O \\ & \| & & \| \\ HO- & S & -S_n- & S & -OH \\ & \| & & \| \\ & O & & O \end{matrix}$	Polythionic
	Peroxo Acids	
H_2SO_5	$\begin{matrix} & O \\ & \| \\ HOO- & S & -OH \\ & \| \\ & O \end{matrix}$	Peroxomonosulfuric
$H_2S_2O_8$	$\begin{matrix} & O & & O \\ & \| & & \| \\ HO- & S & -O-O- & S & -OH \\ & \| & & \| \\ & O & & O \end{matrix}$	Peroxodisulfuric

[a] Free acid unknown.

[b] In most cases the structure given is inferred from the structure of anions in salts of the acid.

S—S bonds have any known Se or Te analogs. With regard to a point of nomenclature, as is usual, salts of acids ending in -ous have names ending in -ite, while those of acids ending in -ic have names ending in -ate.

21-13. Sulfurous Acid

SO_2 is quite soluble in water; such solutions, which possess acidic properties, have long been referred to as solutions of sulfurous acid, H_2SO_3. Modern physical methods of study have shown, however, that H_2SO_3 is either not present or present only in infinitesimal quantities in such solutions. The so-called hydrate, $H_2SO_3 \cdot \sim 6H_2O$, which is equivalent to $SO_2 \cdot \sim 7H_2O$, contains no H_2SO_3 but is a clathrate of the same type as other gas hydrates (page 223). The equilibria in aqueous solutions of SO_2 are best represented as

$$SO_2 + xH_2O = SO_2 \cdot xH_2O \text{ (hydrated } SO_2)$$
$$[SO_2 \cdot xH_2O = H_2SO_3 \quad K \lll 1]$$
$$SO_2 \cdot xH_2O = HSO_3^-(aq) + H_3O^+ + (x - 2)H_2O$$

and the first acid dissociation constant for "sulfurous acid" is properly defined as follows:

$$K_1 = \frac{[HSO_3^-][H^+]}{[\text{Total dissolved } SO_2] - [HSO_3^-] - [SO_3^{2-}]} = 1.3 \times 10^{-2}$$

Although sulfurous acid itself evidently does not exist, two series of salts, the bisulfites, containing HSO_3^-, and the sulfites, containing SO_3^{2-}, are well known. The SO_3^{2-} ion in crystals is pyramidal. In bisulfite solutions there appear to be four species.[32] At low concentrations there are the tautomers 21-VIIa,b, which interact by hydrogen bonding at higher

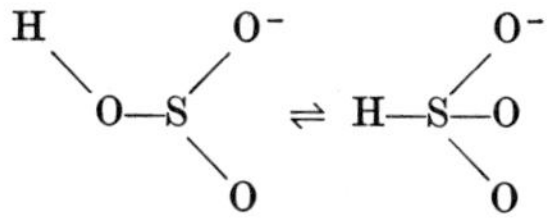

(21-VIIa)   (21-VIIb)

concentrations, $10^{-2}M$, to give 21-VIIc which in turn is in equilibrium with the pyrosulfite ion, 21-VIId.

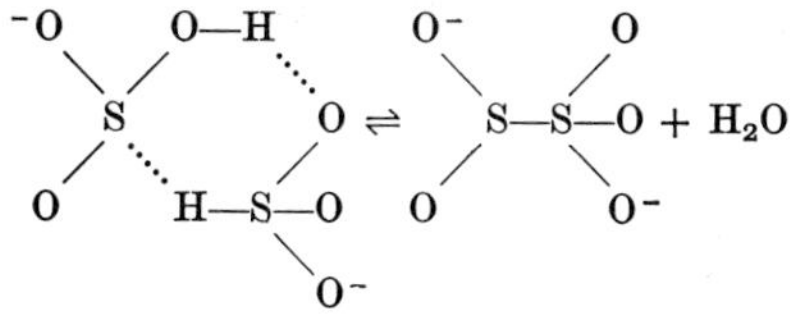

(21-VIIc)   (21-VIId)

---

[32] R. M. Golding, *J. Chem. Soc.*, **1960**, 3711.

18+A.I.C.

Only the alkali sulfites and bisulfites are commonly encountered; these are water soluble. On heating solid bisulfites or on passing SO_2 into their aqueous solutions, one obtains pyrosulfites:

$$2MHSO_3 \xrightleftharpoons{\text{heat}} M_2S_2O_5 + H_2O$$
$$HSO_3^-(aq) + SO_2 = HS_2O_5^-(aq)$$

Whereas pyroacids, for example, pyrosulfuric, $H_2S_2O_7$, to be discussed below, usually have oxygen bridges, pyrosulfite ion has an S—S bond and hence an unsymmetrical structure, O_2S—SO_3. Some important reactions of sulfites are shown in Figure 21-10.

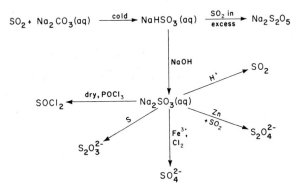

Fig. 21-10.   Some reactions of sulfites.

Solutions of SO_2 and of sulfites possess reducing properties and are often used as reducing agents.

$$SO_4^{2-} + 4H^+ + (x-2)H_2O + 2e = SO_2 \cdot xH_2O \qquad E^0 = 0.17 \text{ v}$$
$$SO_4^{2-} + H_2O + 2e = SO_3^{2-} + 2\,OH^- \qquad E^0 = -0.93 \text{ v}$$

The strong reducing action of basic solutions of sulfites may be attributable to the tautomeric species with an S—H bond which is known to exist in aqueous solution (21-VIIb). Tautomeric forms of diesters of sulfurous acids, dialkylsulfites, $OS(OR)_2$, and alkylsulphonic esters, $RSO_2(OR)$, occur.

21-14.   Selenous and Tellurous Acids

SeO_2 dissolves readily in water to give solutions which do contain selenous acid with the $OSe(OH)_2$ structure; Raman spectra show that it is negligibly dissociated in aqueous solution[33] while in half and fully neutralized solutions the ions $HSeO_3^-$ and SeO_3^{2-} are formed, salts of which can be isolated. Above $\sim 4M$, pyroselenate ions are formed:

$$2HSeO_3^- = Se_2O_5^{2-} + H_2O$$

The solid acid, though efflorescent, can be isolated and X-ray studies have shown the presence of layers of pyramidal SeO_3 groups connected by hydrogen bonds. The acid and its salts are moderately strong oxidizing agents

$$H_2SeO_3 + 4H^+ + 4e = Se + 3H_2O \qquad E^0 = 0.74 \text{ v}$$

and will oxidize SO_2, HI, H_2S, etc.

TeO_2 is virtually insoluble in water, giving very dilute solutions ($\sim 10^{-5}M$) called solutions of tellurous acid, though there is no information as to the species actually present, and no hydrated form of TeO_2 has been isolated. The dioxide does, however, dissolve in strong bases to give solutions of tellurites, bitellurites and various polytellurites which may be isolated as solids.

21-15. Sulfuric Acid

This is probably the most widely used and most important sulfur compound. It is prepared on an enormous scale by the lead chamber and contact processes. In the former, SO_2 oxidation is catalyzed by oxides of nitrogen (by intermediate formation of nitrosyl sulfuric acid, $HOSO_2ONO$); in the latter, heterogeneous catalysts such as platinum are used for the oxidation. Pure sulfuric acid, H_2SO_4, is a colorless liquid freezing at 10.37°. The phase diagram of the H_2SO_4–H_2O system is rather complicated. A number of eutectic hydrates such as $H_2SO_4 \cdot H_2O$ (m 8.5°) and $H_2SO_4 \cdot 2H_2O$ (m $-38°$) occur. The presence of H_3O^+ ions in some of these has been demonstrated.

Sulfuric acid is a strong dibasic acid. In dilute aqueous solution the first dissociation is essentially complete, and the second dissociation constant has a value of $\sim 10^{-2}$. Sulfates and acid sulfates of virtually all electropositive elements are known. Most are soluble in water except for the sulfates of the Ca–Ra group and a few other divalent cations.

When acid sulfate salts are heated, water is first liberated, resulting in the formation of *pyrosulfate* ions:

$$2MHSO_4 \xrightleftharpoons{150-200°} M_2S_2O_7 + H_2O$$

Further heating drives off SO_3 to leave the sulfate. The pyrosulfate ion

[33] G. E. Walrafen, *J. Chem. Phys.*, **36**, 90 (1962); **37**, 1468 (1962).

is hydrolyzed by water with first order kinetics at constant pH and a half-life of *ca* 1.7 min. at $25°$[34]

$$O_3SOSO_3^{2-} + H_2O \rightarrow 2H^+ + 2SO_4^{2-}$$

X-ray study of pyrosulfate salts has shown the structure to be $O_3S-O-SO_3$, with approximately tetrahedral bond angles about each sulfur atom and an $S-O-S$ angle of $\sim 123°$. The sulfate and bisulfate ions themselves are, of course, tetrahedral.

Sulfuric acid is not a very strong oxidizing agent, although the concentrated (98%) acid has some oxidizing properties. Concentrated sulfuric acid usually reacts with organic matter vigorously. Most commonly it reacts so as to remove the elements of water; thus it chars most carbohydrates. When diluted it sometimes sulfates organic substances and often serves mainly as a reaction medium.

Pure sulfuric acid contains a number of species in equilibrium,

$$2H_2SO_4 = H_2O + H_2S_2O_7$$
$$H_2SO_4 + H_2O = H_3O^+ + HSO_4^-$$
$$H_2SO_4 + H_2S_2O_7 = H_3SO_4^+ + HS_2O_7^-$$
$$2H_2SO_4 = H_3SO_4^+ + HSO_4^-$$

The latter, autoprotolytic reaction is of little importance; thus, at $25°$ the concentrations of $H_3SO_4^+$ and HSO_4^- are respectively only 0.013 and 0.018 molal. The solutions of SO_3 in H_2SO_4 are known as *oleum* or fuming sulfuric acid; with equimolar ratios the major constituent is pyrosulfuric acid. However, at higher concentrations of SO_3, Raman spectra indicate the formation of $H_2S_3O_{10}$ and $H_2S_4O_{13}$.[35] Some salts of higher acids, e.g., $(NO_2^+)_2S_3O_{10}$, are known. Pyrosulfuric acid behaves as a weak acid in H_2SO_4:

$$K = \frac{[H_3SO_4^+][HS_2O_7^-]}{[H_2S_2O_7][H_2SO_4]} = 0.0014$$

so that a $1M$ solution of $H_2S_2O_7$ is only *ca* 12% ionized. The main reactions in pure $H_2S_2O_7$ are:

$$2H_2S_2O_7 = H_2S_3O_{10} + H_2SO_4$$
$$H_2S_2O_7 = H_2SO_4 + SO_3$$

A great many substances dissolve in pure sulfuric acid, often undergoing protonation, and the species present and the equilibria have been studied in many cases. It can be a useful ionizing solvent in some instances, but the interpretation of cryoscopic data is often complicated.

[34] H. K. Hofmeister and J. R. van Wazer, *Inorg. Chem.*, **1**, 811 (1962).
[35] R. J. Gillespie and E. A. Robinson, *Can. J. Chem.*, **40**, 645, 658 (1962).

21-16. Selenic and Telluric Acids

The strong oxidation of selenites or fusion of selenium with potassium nitrate gives selenic acid (or its salts). The free acid forms colorless crystals, m 57°. It is very similar to sulfuric acid in its formation of hydrates, acid strength and in the properties of its salts, most of which are iso-morphous with the corresponding sulfates and bisulfates.

Raman spectra indicate that the aqueous selenic acid system closely resembles aqueous H_2SO_4 in the types of species, i.e., H_2SeO_4, $HSeO_4^-$ and SeO_4^{2-}, rather than the aqueous telluric acid system.[36] It differs mainly in being less stable. It evolves oxygen on heating above about 200° and is a strong, though usually not kinetically fast, oxidizing agent:

$$SeO_4^{2-} + 4H^+ + 2e = H_2SeO_3 + H_2O \qquad E^0 = 1.15 \text{ v}$$

Pyroselenates exist and appear to contain the ion $[O_3SeOSeO_3]^{2-}$ in crystals, but in solution the species appears to be $[SeO_3(OH)]^-$.

Telluric acid is quite different from sulfuric and selenic acids. Its formula is $Te(OH)_6$, and X-ray studies have shown that octahedral mole-cules of this composition exist in the crystals. There is little evidence for the existence of $HTeO_4^-$ or TeO_4^{2-} ions under any conditions.

The acid or its salts may be prepared by oxidation of tellurium or TeO_2 by H_2O_2, Na_2O_2, CrO_3 or other powerful oxidizing agents. It is a moder-ately strong, but, like selenic acid, kinetically slow, oxidizing agent ($E^0 = 1.02$ v). It is a very weak dibasic acid with $K_1 \approx 10^{-7}$, and two series of salts are known, $MTeO(OH)_5$, e.g., $K[TeO(OH)_5] \cdot H_2O$,[37] and $M_2TeO_2(OH)_4$.

21-17. Peroxo Acids

Two peroxo acids derived from sulfuric acid are well known. These are peroxomonosulfuric acid, H_2SO_5, and peroxodisulfuric acid, $H_2S_2O_8$. No peroxo acids containing selenium or tellurium are known.

Peroxodisulfuric acid can be obtained from its salts with alkali metal and ammonium ions. The latter can be crystallized from solutions of the sulfates after electrolysis at low temperatures and high current densities. The peroxodisulfate ion is one of the most powerful and useful oxidizing agents. It can oxidize Mn^{II} to permanganate and Cr^{III} to chromate:

$$S_2O_8^{2-} + 2e = 2SO_4^{2-} \qquad E^0 = 2.01 \text{ v}$$

Direct oxidation by peroxodisulfate generally proceeds slowly, but becomes rapid in the presence of catalysts, Ag^I ion being a common one. The

[36] G. E. Walrafen, *J. Chem. Phys.*, **39**, 1479 (1963).
[37] S. Raman, *Inorg. Chem.*, **3**, 634 (1964).

catalytic activity of Ag^I results from its being oxidized to the Ag^{III} ion which then oxidizes the reducing agent, becoming again Ag^I. Peroxodisulfate ion is known from X-ray studies of its salts to have the structure O_3S—O—O—SO_3, with approximately tetrahedral angles about each sulfur atom.

Peroxomonosulfuric acid, often called Caro's acid, is obtained by hydrolysis of peroxodisulfuric acid,

$$\underset{\underset{O}{\|}}{O=S}\underset{OH}{|}-O-O-\underset{\underset{O}{\|}}{S}\underset{OH}{|}=O + H_2O = \underset{\underset{O}{\|}}{O=S}\underset{OH}{|}-OH + \underset{\underset{O}{\|}}{O=S}\underset{OH}{|}-OOH$$

and also by the action of concentrated hydrogen peroxide on sulfuric acid or chlorosulfuric acid

$$H_2O_2 + H_2SO_4 = HOOSO_2OH + H_2O$$
$$H_2O_2 + HClSO_3 = HOOSO_2OH + HCl$$

The salts such as $KHSO_5$ can be obtained only impure, admixed with K_2SO_4 and $KHSO_4$; aqueous solutions decompose to give mainly O_2 and SO_4^{2-} with small amounts of H_2O_2 and $S_2O_8^{2-}$.

21-18. Thiosulfuric Acid

Thiosulfates are readily obtained by boiling sulfur with solutions of sulfites and in the decomposition of dithionites. The free acid is quite unstable at ordinary temperatures, but it has been isolated as an etherate at $-78°$ from the reaction:

$$SO_3 + H_2S = H_2S_2O_3$$

or, free of solvent, by the reaction

$$HO_3SCl + H_2S = H_2S_2O_3 + HCl$$

The alkali thiosulfates are manufactured for use mainly in photography where they are used to dissolve unreacted silver bromide from emulsion. They do this by formation of complexes with silver ion, $[Ag(S_2O_3)]^-$ and $[Ag(S_2O_3)_2]^{3-}$; the thiosulfate ion also forms complexes with other metal ions.

The thiosulfate ion has the structure[38] S—SO_3 with an S—S distance of 1.99 ± 0.03 A and S—O distances of 1.48 ± 0.06 A. These distances suggest some S—S π bonding and considerable S—O π bonding similar to that in SO_4^{2-} for which the S—O distance is 1.44 A.

[38] M. Nardelli and G. Fava, *Acta Cryst.*, **15**, 477 (1962).

The interaction of SO_3 with H_2S above can be extended to give series of sulfanemonosulfonic acids[1a] HS_xSO_3H:

$$HSSH + SO_3 = HSSSO_3H$$

They are stable only in ether solution at low temperatures and their salts are thermally unstable and reactive to water.

21-19. Dithionous (Hypo- or Hydrosulfurous) Acid

The reduction of sulfites in aqueous solutions containing excess sulfur dioxide, usually with zinc dust, gives the dithionite ion, $S_2O_4^{2-}$. Solutions of this ion are not very stable and decompose by disproportionation

$$2S_2O_4^{2-} + H_2O = S_2O_3^{2-} + 2HSO_3^-$$

as well as being oxidized by air. Decomposition is rapid in acid solution, producing then also elemental sulfur.

The zinc and sodium salts are powerful and usually rapid reducing agents in alkaline solution.

$$2SO_3^{2-} + 2H_2O + 2e = 4OH^- + S_2O_4^{2-} \qquad E^0 = -1.12 \text{ v}$$

In the presence of β-anthraquinone sulfonate (21-VIII) as a catalyst (Fieser's

(21-VIII)

solution), aqueous sodium dithionite efficiently removes oxygen from gases.

The structure of the dithionite ion (Fig. 21-11) has several remarkable features. The oxygen atoms, which must bear considerable negative charge, are closely juxtaposed by the eclipsed configuration and by the small value of the angle α, which would be 35° for sp^3 tetrahedral hybridization at the sulfur atom. Secondly, the S—S distance is much longer than S—S bonds in disulfides, polysulfides, etc., which are in the range ca 2.0–2.15 A. The long bond is believed to be due to weakening by repulsion of lone-pairs on sulfur resulting from dp hybridized bonding.[39] The weak bonding is consistent with the strong reducing properties and with the rapid exchange between $S_2O_4^{2-}$ and labeled $*SO_2$. Oxygen-free dithionite

[39] J. D. Dunitz, Acta Cryst., 9, 579 (1956).

solutions also show a strong esr line interpreted as due to the radical ion SO_2^-, which is also found in acidified formaldehyde sulfoxylate solutions,[40] and in solution there is a reversible dissociation:

$$S_2O_4^{2-} \rightleftharpoons 2SO_2^-$$

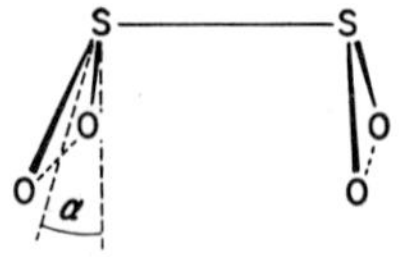

$$\alpha = 15°$$
$$S-O = 1.15 A$$
$$S-S = 2.39 A$$

Fig. 21-11. The structure of the dithionite ion, $S_2O_4^{2-}$, in $Na_2S_2O_4$.

21-20. Dithionic Acid

Although $H_2S_2O_6$ might at first sight appear to be the simplest homolog of the polythionates ($S_nO_6^{2-}$) to be discussed in the next section, dithionic acid and its salts do not behave like the polythionates. Furthermore, from a structural point of view, dithionic acid should not be considered as a member of the polythionate series, since dithionates contain no sulfur atom bound only to other sulfur atoms as do $H_2S_3O_6$ and all higher homologs, $H_2S_nO_6$. The dithionate ion has the structure O_3S-SO_3 with approximately tetrahedral bond angles about each sulfur, and the shortness of the S—O bonds (1.43 A, cf. 1.44 A in SO_4^{2-}) again suggests considerable double bond character.

Dithionate is usually obtained by oxidation of sulfite or SO_2 solutions with manganese(IV) oxide:

$$MnO_2 + 2SO_3^{2-} + 4H^+ = Mn^{2+} + S_2O_6^{2-} + 2H_2O$$

Other oxo acids of sulfur which form as by-products are precipitated with barium hydroxide, and $BaS_2O_6 \cdot 2H_2O$ is then crystallized. Treatment of aqueous solutions of this with sulfuric acid gives solutions of the free acid which may be used to prepare other salts by neutralization of the appropriate bases. Dithionic acid is a moderately stable strong acid which decomposes slowly in concentrated solutions and when warmed. The ion itself is quite stable; solutions of its salts may be boiled without decomposition. Although it contains sulfur in an intermediate oxidation state, it resists most oxidizing and reducing agents, presumably for kinetic reasons.

[40] R. G. Rinker, T. P. Gordon and W. H. Corcoran, *Inorg. Chem.*, **3**, 1467 (1964); P. W. Atkins, A. Horsfield and M. C. R. Symons, *J. Chem. Soc.*, **1964**, 5220.

21-21. Polythionates[41]

These anions have the general formula $[O_3SS_nSO_3]^{2-}$. The free acids are not stable, decomposing rapidly into sulfur, sulfur dioxide and sometimes sulfate. Also, no acid salts are known. The well-established polythionate anions are those with $n = 1$–4. They are named according to the total number of sulfur atoms and are thus called: $S_3O_6^{2-}$, trithionate; $S_4O_6^{2-}$, tetrathionate; $S_5O_6^{2-}$, pentathionate; $S_6O_6^{2-}$, hexathionate. It has been conclusively established in all four of these anions that there are sulfur chains, thus disposing of proposals commonly found in older literature and texts that there might be $S \rightarrow S$ linkages. The conformations of the chains in these anions are very similar to those of segments of the S_8 ring, whereas the configurations about the end sulfur atoms, —S—SO$_3$, are approximately tetrahedral. They can be regarded as derivatives of sulfanes, hence the name sulfanedisulfonic acids; e.g., tetrathionates can be called disulfanedisulfonates.

Polythionates can be prepared in various ways. Mixtures are obtained by reduction of thiosulfate solutions with sulfur dioxide in presence of arsenic(III) oxide and also by the reaction of hydrogen sulfide with an aqueous solution of sulfur dioxide which produces a solution called Wackenroder's liquid. Although individual polythionates can be separated from these mixtures, many are better obtained by selective preparations. For example, trithionate can be made by the action of hydrogen peroxide on cold saturated sodium thiosulfate solution:

$$2S_2O_3^{2-} + 4H_2O_2 = S_3O_6^{2-} + SO_4^{2-} + 4H_2O$$

Tetrathionates are obtained by treatment of thiosulfates with iodine in a reaction which is widely used in the volumetric determination of iodine:

$$2S_2O_3^{2-} + I_2 = 2I^- + S_4O_6^{2-}$$

OXOHALIDES AND HALOOXO ACIDS

21-22. Oxohalides

Only sulfur and selenium are known to form well-defined oxohalides. These are of the three main types: (a) the thionyl and selenyl halides, SOX_2 and $SeOX_2$; (b) the sulfuryl halides, SO_2X_2, and their one selenium analog, SeO_2F_2; and (c) a number of more complex sulfur oxochlorides and oxofluorides.

---

[41] See ref. 1a and M. Schmidt, *J. Inorg. Nucl. Chem.*, **26**, 1165 *et seq.* (1964).

18*

The following thionyl and selenyl halides are known:

$$SOF_2 \quad SOCl_2 \quad SOBr_2 \quad SOFCl$$
$$SeOF_2 \quad SeOCl_2 \quad SeOBr_2$$

With the exception of thionyl fluoride, all of these compounds react rapidly, and sometimes violently, with water, being completely hydrolyzed:

$$SOCl_2 + H_2O = SO_2 + 2HCl$$

Thionyl fluoride reacts only slowly with water.

These halides may be prepared in many ways. $SOCl_2$ is usually prepared by the following reaction:

$$PCl_5 + SO_2 = SOCl_2 + POCl_3$$

SOF_2 is obtained from $SOCl_2$ by reaction with SbF_3 in presence of $SbCl_5$ (Swarts reagent):

$$3SOCl_2 + 2SbF_3 = 3SOF_2 + 2SbCl_3$$

On a large scale, $SOCl_2$ is treated with anhydrous hydrogen fluoride. $SOBr_2$ is also prepared from $SOCl_2$ by treatment of the latter with HBr at $0°$. SOClF is usually a by-product in the preparation of SOF_2. Selenyl chloride may be obtained by reaction of SeO_2 with $SeCl_4$ in carbon tetrachloride, and the fluoride is obtained therefrom by halogen exchange with AgF or HgF_2. $SeOBr_2$ may be obtained by treating a mixture of Se and SeO_2 with bromine or by reaction of SeO_2 with $SeBr_2$.

The thionyl and selenyl halides are stable in vacuum at ordinary temperatures and below, but on strong heating they decompose, usually to a mixture of products including the dioxide, free halogen and lower halides. The structures are pyramidal, Figure 21-12a, the S and Se atoms using sets of,

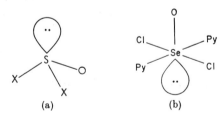

Fig. 21-12. The structures of (a) thionyl halides, X_2SO and (b) $SeOCl_2 py_2$

roughly, sp^3 hybrid orbitals, one of which holds the unshared pair. The S—O bonds in the thionyl halides are evidently resonance hybrids of the canonical structures 21-IX. In 21-IXb and 21-IXc the multiple

$$\overset{+}{S}-\overset{-}{O} \leftrightarrow S{=}O \leftrightarrow \overset{-}{S}{\equiv}\overset{+}{O}$$

$$(21\text{-IXa}) \quad (21\text{-IXb}) \quad (21\text{-IXc})$$

bonding results from overlap of filled $p\pi$ orbitals of oxygen with empty $d\pi$ orbitals of sulfur. The net bond order appears to be about 2, as indicated by the bond distances which are ~ 1.45 A as compared to ~ 1.7 A expected for an S—O single bond. The bond order also increases in the order $OSBr_2 < OSCl_2 < OSF_2$, the more electronegative halogen causing the greater amount of oxygen-to-sulfur dative π bonding.

Thionyl chloride finds use in preparing anhydrous metal halides from oxides, hydroxides and hydrated chlorides.

The thionyl and selenyl halides can function as weak Lewis bases, using lone-pairs on oxygen and also, more surprisingly, as weak Lewis acids, using vacant d orbitals. The structure of the compound $SeOCl_2 \cdot 2py$ is shown in Figure 21-12b.

Oxohalides of the type SO_2X_2 are called *sulfuryl halides*. Those known are SO_2F_2, SO_2Cl_2, SO_2FCl and SO_2FBr, of which sulfuryl chloride and fluoride are most important. The chloride is formed by direct reaction of SO_2 with chlorine in the presence of a catalyst and the fluoride by fluorination of SO_2Cl_2 or by thermal decomposition of barium fluorosulfate:

$$Ba(SO_3F)_2 \underset{}{\overset{500°}{\rightleftharpoons}} SO_2F_2 + BaSO_4$$

Sulfuryl fluoride is a chemically inert gas, unaffected by water even at 150°, but slowly hydrolyzed by strong aqueous alkali. Sulfuryl chloride is much less stable than the fluoride, decomposing thermally below 300° and reacting fairly rapidly with water. It fumes strongly in moist air. It can be used as a chlorinating agent.

SeO_2F_2 has been prepared by warming a mixture of barium selenate and fluorosulfonic acid. It is a rather reactive gas, readily hydrolyzed by water.

The sulfuryl halides are known to have distorted tetrahedral structures with S—O bonds similar to those in the thionyl halides.

Some of the more complex oxochlorides and oxofluorides of sulfur are those shown in Table 21-6 along with their structures, where known. These structures were determined, in large part, from ^{19}F nmr studies.

Peroxodisulfuryl fluoride, b 67°, can be obtained[42] by fluorination of SO_3:

$$SO_3 + F_2 \xrightarrow[165°]{Cu/AgF} S_2O_6F_2$$

It is a powerful oxidizing agent which, on localized heating at 120°, dissociates to give an intense brown color, probably of $SO_3F\cdot$ radicals. It reacts with certain metal chlorides to give fluorosulfates, e.g., $SnCl(SO_3F)_3$, and with chlorine at 125° to give $ClOSO_2F$.[43]

[42] F. B. Dudley, *J. Chem. Soc.*, **1963**, 3407

[43] M. Lustig and G. H. Cady, *Inorg. Chem.*, **1**, 714 (1962); W. P. Gilbreath and G. H. Cady, *Inorg. Chem.*, **2**, 496 (1963).

TABLE 21-6

Some Complex Oxohalides of Sulfur

Compound	Structure	Compound	Structure
$S_2O_5F_2$	$$\begin{array}{ccc} O & & O \\ \| & & \| \\ F-S-O-S-F \\ \| & & \| \\ O & & O \end{array}$$	SOF_6	$$\begin{array}{c} F \quad F \\ \| \diagup \\ F-S-OF \\ \diagup \| \\ F \quad F \end{array}$$
$S_2O_5Cl_2$	Presumably analogous to that of $S_2O_5F_2$	$S_2O_6F_2$	$$\begin{array}{ccc} O & & O \\ \| & & \| \\ F-S-O-O-S-F \\ \| & & \| \\ O & & O \end{array}$$
SOF_4	$$\begin{array}{c} F \quad F \\ \| \diagup \\ O-S \\ \| \diagdown \\ F \quad F \end{array}$$	$\left.\begin{array}{l} S_3O_8F_2 \\ S_3O_8Cl_2 \end{array}\right\}$	Structures not known, but probably
SO_3F_2	$$\begin{array}{c} O \\ \| \\ F-S-OF \\ \| \\ O \end{array}$$		$$\begin{array}{ccccc} O & & O & & O \\ \| & & \| & & \| \\ X-S-O-S-O-S-X \\ \| & & \| & & \| \\ O & & O & & O \end{array}$$

21-23. Halooxo Acids

Fluorosulfurous acid exists only as salts which are formed by the action of SO_2 on alkali fluorides, e.g.,

$$KF + SO_2 \rightleftharpoons KSO_2F$$

The salts have a measurable dissociation pressure at normal temperatures but are useful and convenient mild fluorinating agents, e.g.,

$$(PNCl_2)_3 + 6KSO_2F = (PNF_2)_3 + 6KCl + 6SO_2$$
$$C_6H_5COCl + KSO_2F = C_6H_5COF + KCl + SO_2$$

The sulfuryl halides may be considered, formally, as derivatives of sulfuric acid in which both OH groups have been replaced by halogen atoms. If only one OH group be replaced, the acids, FSO_3H, $ClSO_3H$ and $BrSO_3H$ are obtained. Fluorosulfuric acid is prepared by treating fuming sulfuric acid with KHF_2 or CaF_2 at $\sim 250°$ and industrially by the interaction of SO_3 and anhydrous HF

$$SO_3 + HF = HSO_3F$$

Its alkali and other metal salts are most conveniently made by the action of SO_3 on the metal fluorides at elevated temperatures, e.g.,

$$CaF_2 + 2SO_3 \xrightarrow{200°} Ca(SO_3F)_2$$

Fluorosulfuric acid is a colorless liquid, b 169°, and is a convenient laboratory fluorinating agent. It forms many stable salts which are similar in their solubilities to perchlorates and fluoroborates, and mixed crystals can often be formed. The acid is very strong and only slowly hydrolyzed by water. Chlorosulfuric acid is a colorless fuming liquid, explosively hydrolyzed by water, which forms no salts and finds its chief use as a sulfonating agent in organic chemistry. It is prepared by treating SO_3 with dry HCl. Bromosulfuric acid, prepared from HBr and SO_3 in liquid SO_2 at $-35°$, decomposes at its melting point ($8°$) into Br_2, SO_2 and H_2SO_4.

References

Abrahams, S. C., *Quart. Rev.*, **10**, 407 (1956). An excellent review of the stereochemistry of S, Se, Te, Po and O.

Bagnall, K. W., *The Chemistry of the Rare Radioelements*, Butterworths, London, 1957. Includes an exhaustive account of polonium chemistry.

Banks, R. E., and R. N. Haszeldine, *Adv. Inorg. Chem. Radiochem.*, **3**, 408 (1961). Polyfluoroalkyl derivatives of S and Se.

Becke-Goehring, M., *Adv. Inorg. Chem. Radiochem.*, **2**, 159 (1960). Sulfur nitride chemistry.

———, *Quart. Rev.*, **10**, 437 (1956). Sulfur nitride chemistry.

Cady, G. H., *Adv. Inorg. Chem. Radiochem.*, **2**, 105 (1960). Fluorine-containing sulfur compounds.

Cilento, G., *Chem. Rev.*, **60**, 147 (1960). Comprehensive survey of effects of utilization of d orbitals in organic sulfur chemistry.

Cruickshank, D. W. J., *J. Chem. Soc.*, **1961**, 5486. A detailed discussion of $d\pi–p\pi$ bonding in SO bonds.

Foss, O., *Adv. Inorg. Chem. Radiochem.*, **2**, 237 (1960). A comprehensive account of compounds with S—S bonds.

George, J. W., *Prog. Inorg. Chem.*, **2**, 33 (1960). Halides and oxohalides of the elements of groups Vb and VIb.

Gillespie, R. J., *J. Amer. Chem. Soc.*, **82**, 5978 (1960). Valence and bonding in hydrides and halides.

———, and E. A. Robinson, *Adv. Inorg. Chem. Radiochem.*, **1**, 386 (1959). Sulfuric acid as a solvent.

———, and E. A. Robinson, in *Non-aqueous Solvent Systems*, Academic Press, New York, 1965. Sulfuric acids as solvents.

Gosselck, J., *Angew. Chem. (Internat.)*, **2**, 660 (1963). Review of organoselenium compounds.

Milligan, B., and J. M. Swan, *Rev. Pure Appl. Chem.*, **12**, 73 (1962). Salts of S-aryl and alkyl thiosulfuric esters (Bunte salts).

Parker, A. J., and N. Kharasch, *Chem. Rev.*, **59**, 583 (1959). Scission of S—S bonds.

Price, C. C., and S. Oae, *Sulfur Bonding*, Ronald Press, New York, 1962. Chemical properties and bonding in sulfides, sulfoxides, sulfones, etc.

Reid, E. E., *Organic Chemistry of Bivalent Sulfur*, Chemical Publishing Co., New York, 1963. Vol. V covers CS_2, thiourea, etc.

Schenk, P. W., and R. Steudel, *Angew. Chem. (Internat.)*, **4**, 402 (1965). A review on lower oxides and polyoxides of S.

Sulphur Manual, Texas Gulf Sulphur Co., New York, 1959.

Symposium on the Inorganic Chemistry of Sulfur, Chem. Soc. (*London*), Spec. Publ., No. 12 (1958).

Taller, W. N., ed., *Sulphur Data Book*, McGraw-Hill, New York, 1954.

Thorn, G. D., and R. A. Ludwig, *The Dithiocarbamates and Related Compounds*, Elsevier, Amsterdam, 1962.

van der Heijde, H. B., in *Organic Sulfur Compounds*, N. Kharasch, ed., Pergamon Press, London, 1961. Inorganic sulfur acids.

Waddington, T. C., in *Non-aqueous Solvent Systems*, Academic Press, New York, 1965. Liquid sulfur dioxide.

Wadsley, A. D., in *Non-Stoichiometric Compounds*, L. Mandelcorn, ed., Academic Press, New York, 1964. A thorough discussion of metal chalconides.

Yost, D. M., and H. Russell, *Systematic Inorganic Chemistry (of the 5th and 6th Group Elements)*, Prentice-Hall, New York, 1946. Selected aspects of chemistry of S, Se and Te.

22

The Group VII Elements: Cl, Br, I, At

GENERAL REMARKS

22-1. Electronic Structures and Valences

The electronic structures and some other properties of the group VII elements (halogens) are given in Table 22-1. Since the structures of the

TABLE 22-1

Some Properties of the Halogens

Element	Electronic structure	Electron affinity, kcal/mole	Electro-negativity[a]	Boiling point °C	Melting point °C	Crystal radius, X$^-$	Covalent radius, X
F	$1s^2 2s^2 2p^5$	79.6	4.10	-188	-223	1.31	0.64
Cl	$[Ne]3s^2 3p^5$	83.3	2.83	-34.6	-103	1.81	0.99
Br	$[Ar]3d^{10}4s^2 4p^5$	77.5	2.74	58.76	-7.2	1.96	1.14
I	$[Kr]4d^{10}5s^2 5p^5$	70.6	2.21	184.35	113.5	2.219	1.33
At	$[Xe]4f^{14}5d^{10}6s^2 6p^5$	—	1.96	—	—	—	—

[a] By Allred–Rochow method; see Table 4-3.

atoms are only one electron short of the noble gas configuration, the elements form the uninegative ion X$^-$ or a single covalent bond —X. The chemistries of the elements are essentially completely nonmetallic and, in the main, the properties of the elements and their compounds change steadily with decreasing electronegativity. There is a much greater change between fluorine and chlorine than between the other pairs of elements, some of the factors involved here having been discussed under fluorine (page 379). Although there is no extensive chemistry of positive ions, there is reasonable evidence for cationic species of chlorine, bromine, iodine and—where studies have been possible—astatine.

Although fluorine normally forms only one bond, certain bridged fluorides, where the fluorine atom has a coordination number of two, are known, for example, $(SbF_5)_n$, $(BeF_2)_n$ and $K^+[(C_2H_5)_3Al—F—Al(C_2H_5)_3]^-$. For the other elements, higher covalencies (with formal oxidation states up to $+7$) are known, but only in oxygen compounds (e.g., ClO_4^-) or in interhalogen compounds (e.g., BrF_5). Expansion of the octet through utilization of d orbitals can, in principle, allow some multiple bond character in bonds to Cl, Br and I.

22-2. Pseudohalogens

A pseudohalogen or halogenoid is a molecule consisting of more than two electronegative atoms which, in the free state, resembles the halogens; these pseudohalogens give rise to anions which resemble the halide ions in their behavior. The most important are $(CN)_2$, cyanogen; $(SCN)_2$, thiocyanogen; $(SeCN)_2$, selenocyanogen; and $(SCSN_3)_2$, azidocarbondisulfide. In addition there are the azide, N_3^-, and cyanate OCN^-, ions which have no pseudohalogen parent.

The physical and chemical properties of the halogens and halide ions which should characterize substances to be classified as pseudohalogens or pseudohalide ions are:

1. The halogenoid should be a volatile substance consisting of a symmetrical combination of two radicals, X—X.

2. The halogenoids should combine with various metals to give salts containing X^- anions.

3. The salts of silver, mercury(I) and lead(II) should be insoluble in water.

4. There should exist acids HX.

5. The pseudohalogen radicals should form compounds among themselves, X—X', and with the halogens, for example, Cl—X.

6. The halogenoid ions should form complexes with metals as do the halide ions, e.g., $HgCl_4^{2-}$, $CoCl_4^{2-}$, etc.

7. The halogenoid should form covalent compounds analogous to covalent halides.

8. The X^- ion should be oxidized to X_2 by suitable oxidizing agents.

Some aspects of pseudohalogen chemistry have been discussed previously for carbon compounds (page 310) and azide (page 339) and the metal complexes will be often mentioned in Chapters 29 and 30. Although the literature contains allusions to the $TeCN^-$ ion, recent work[1] indicates that no such ion is actually known.

[1] N. N. Greenwood, R. Little and M. J. Sprague, *J. Chem. Soc.*, **1964**, 1292.

THE ELEMENTS

None of the halogens occur in the elemental state in nature because of their high reactivity. All exist as diatomic molecules, which, being homonuclear, are without permanent electrical polarity. The forces between these molecules in the condensed phases are only weak van der Waals forces. Hence the trend in melting and boiling points of the halogens parallels that in the noble gases since in both cases the same two factors are decisive, namely, increasing weight and increasing magnitude of the van der Waals forces as size and polarizability of the atoms or molecules increase. The increase in color of the elements and of their covalent compounds with increasing size is due in general to a progressive shift of charge-transfer bands to longer wavelengths in the absorption spectrum.

22-3. Chlorine

Chlorine is a pale green gas at ordinary temperatures. It occurs in nature mainly as sodium chloride both in sea water and in various inland salt lakes and as solid deposits originating presumably from the prehistoric evaporation of salt lakes. Chlorine is prepared industrially, almost entirely by electrolysis of brine:

$$Na^+ + Cl^- + H_2O = Na^+ + OH^- + \tfrac{1}{2}Cl_2 + \tfrac{1}{2}H_2$$

Chlorine and hydrogen can also be recovered by electrolysis of warm 22% hydrochloric acid which is obtained as a by-product in chlorination processes.

It is seldom necessary to prepare chlorine in the laboratory, but the oxidation of Cl^- in acid solution by a strong oxidizing agent such as MnO_2 is a satisfactory method:

$$2Cl^- + 4H^+ + MnO_2 = Mn^{2+} + 2H_2O + Cl_2$$

Chlorine is moderately soluble in water with which it reacts (see page 568).

On passing chlorine into dilute solutions of $CaCl_2$ at 0°, feathery crystals of "chlorine hydrate" are formed having the composition $Cl_2 \cdot 7.3H_2O$. This substance is a water clathrate of the gas hydrate type (see page 225) having all medium holes and $\sim 20\%$ of the small holes in the structure filled with chlorine molecules.

Naturally occurring chlorine consists of 75.4 atom % ^{35}Cl and 24.6 atom % ^{37}Cl. Samples enriched in one or the other of these stable isotopes are obtainable, and the enriched isotope can be used as a tracer. ^{36}Cl is an artificial radioactive isotope (β, 2×10^6 years) which is also useful as a tracer. Both naturally occurring nuclei have spin, and nuclear resonance studies are, in principle, possible, although few have been reported to date. Both nuclides have electrical quadrupole moments. Studies of the coupling of these nuclear quadrupole moments to asymmetric electrical fields in the electron distribution about the atoms have provided interesting information about the character of bonds to chlorine.

22-4. Bromine

Bromine occurs in nature principally as bromide salts of the alkali and alkaline earths in much smaller amounts than, but along with, chlorine. Industrially, bromine is obtained from brines and sea water by chlorination at a pH of ~ 3.5 and is swept out in a current of air. Laboratory methods for its preparation all involve oxidation of the bromide ion, and MnO_2 can be used in a reaction analogous to that for chlorine.

Bromine is a dense, mobile, dark-red liquid at room temperature. It is moderately soluble in water (33.6 g/liter at 25°) and miscible with nonpolar solvents such as CS_2 and CCl_4. Like Cl_2 it gives a crystalline hydrate which is, however, structurally different from that of chlorine.

Naturally occurring bromine consists of 50.57 atom % ^{79}Br and 49.43 atom % ^{81}Br. Both nuclei have nuclear spin and nuclear quadrupole moments, but, except for some studies of quadrupole coupling constants, these have not as yet been much studied for chemical purposes.

22-5. Iodine

Iodine is found in nature as iodide in brines and also in the form of sodium and calcium iodates. Also, various forms of marine life concentrate iodine in their systems. Production of iodine involves either oxidizing I^- or reducing iodates to I^- followed by oxidation to the elemental state. Exact methods vary considerably depending on the raw materials. A commonly used oxidation reaction, and one suited to laboratory use when necessary, is, again, oxidation of I^- in acid solution with MnO_2.

Iodine is a black solid with a slight metallic luster. At atmospheric pressure it sublimes without melting. The vapor is violet. Its solubility in water is slight (0.33 g/liter at 25°). It is readily soluble in nonpolar solvents such as CS_2 and CCl_4 to give violet solutions; iodine solutions are brown in solvents such as unsaturated hydrocarbons, liquid SO_2, alcohols, and ketones and pinkish brown in benzene (see below).

Iodine forms the well-known blue complex with starch where the iodine atoms are aligned in channels in the polysaccharide amylose.

Naturally occurring iodine is monoisotopic, consisting entirely of ^{127}I. This nuclide has spin and a quadrupole moment, and investigations of quadrupole coupling constants have been made for chemical purposes.

22-6. Astatine, At, Element 85

Several isotopes of element 85 have been identified as very short-lived branch products in the natural decay series of uranium and thorium. The element was first obtained in quantities sufficient to afford definite proof of its existence and a knowledge of some of its properties in 1940 by the cyclotron reaction: ^{209}Bi$(\alpha, 2n)^{211}$At. This isotope has a half-life of 7.5 hours and decays about 60% by electron capture and about 40% by α emission. The element was named astatine from the Greek meaning unstable. About 20 isotopes are now known, the longest lived being ^{210}At with a half-life of only 8.3 hours.

Because of the short half-lives of even the most stable isotopes, macroscopic quantities cannot be accumulated. Our knowledge of its chemistry is therefore based entirely on tracer studies, which show however that it behaves about as one might expect by extrapolation from the other halogens. The element is rather volatile. It is somewhat soluble in water from which it may, like iodine, be extracted into benzene or carbon tetrachloride. It cannot, like iodine, be extracted from basic solutions.

The At$^-$ ion is produced by reduction with SO_2 or zinc but not ferrous ion (which gives some indication of the oxidation potential of At$^-$). This ion is carried down in AgI or TlI precipitates. Positive oxidation states are known. Bromine and, to some extent, ferric ions oxidize it to what appears to be AtO$^-$ or HAtO. HClO or hot $S_2O_8^{2-}$ oxidize it to an anion carried by IO_3^- and therefore probably AtO$_3^-$. Astatine is also carried when $[Ipy_2]^+$ salts are isolated, indicating that $[Atpy_2]^+$ can exist. In $0.1M$ acid, the astatine potentials appear to be

$$\text{AtO}_3^- \xrightarrow{\quad 1.5 \quad} \text{HOAt(?)} \xrightarrow{\quad 1.0 \quad} \text{At} \xrightarrow{\quad 0.3 \quad} \text{At}^-$$

22-7. Charge-transfer Compounds of Halogens

As noted above, iodine gives solutions in organic solvents whose color depends on the nature of the solvent. It has been shown that in donor solvents, solvation and 1:1 complex formation, $I_2 \cdots S$, can occur; such interactions are said to be of the "charge-transfer" type and the complexes are called charge-transfer complexes. This name derives from the nature of the interaction, in which the bonding energy is attributable to a partial transfer of charge. The ground state of the system can be described as a resonance hybrid of 22-I and 22-II, with 22-I predominating. An electronic transition to an excited state, which is also a resonance hybrid of 22-I and 22-II with 22-II predominating, is characteristic of these complexes. It usually occurs near or in the visible region and is the cause of their typically intense colors. This transition is called a charge-transfer transition.

$$X_2 \qquad S \leftrightarrow \bar{X}_2 \cdots \overset{+}{S}$$
$$\text{(22-I)} \qquad \text{(22-II)}$$

Although iodine has been most extensively studied, chlorine and bromine also show similar behavior. For a given group of donors, the frequency of the intense charge-transfer absorption band in the ultraviolet is dependent upon the ionization potential of the donor solvent molecule and electronic charge can be transferred either from a π-electron system as in benzene or from lone-pairs as in ethers or amines.[2,3] Charge-transfer spectra and complexes are of importance elsewhere in chemistry (see, e.g., Sec. 26-14).

For halogens, and interhalogens such as ICl, charge-transfer compounds can in fact be isolated in the crystalline state,[4] though low temperatures are often required. Thus dioxan with Br_2 gives a compound with a chain structure (22-III) where the Br—Br distance (2.31 A) is only slightly larger than in Br_2 itself (2.28 A). For benzene (22-IV) the halogen molecules lie along the axis perpendicular to the center of the ring. Other

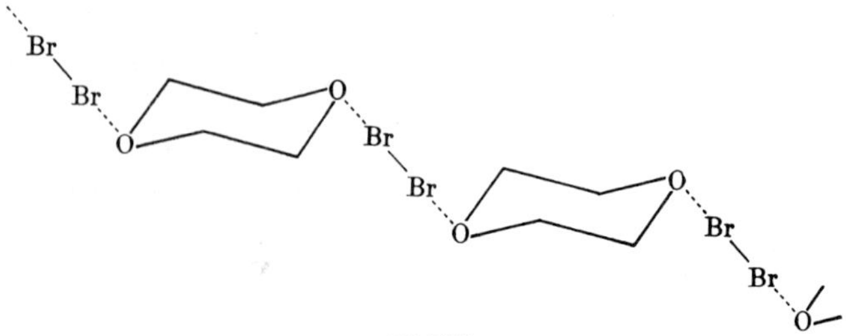

(22-III)

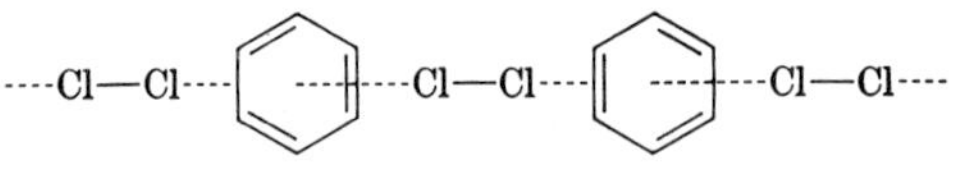

(22-IV)

[2] L. J. Andrews and R. M. Keefer, *Adv. Inorg. Chem. Radiochem.*, **3**, 91 (1961). An extensive review of halogen complexes.

[3] R. S. Mulliken and W. B. Person, *Ann. Rev. Phys. Chem.*, **13**, 107 (1962); J. N. Murrell, *Quart. Rev.*, **15**, 191 (1961); S. F. Mason, *Quart Rev.*, **15**, 353 (1961). Reviews on charge-transfer. For an example of spectroscopic studies (I_2-anthracene) see J. Peters and W. B. Person, *J. Amer. Chem. Soc.*, **86**, 10 (1964).

[4] O. Hassel and Chr. Rømming, *Quart. Rev.*, **16**, 1 (1962). Excellent short review on crystalline complexes.

crystals such as $(CH_3)_3NI_2$, $(CH_3)_2COI_2$ all have one halogen linked to the donor atom and the second atom pointing away as in $N \cdots X—X$. In many of the compounds, especially with O and N donors, there is considerable similarity to hydrogen bonding interactions.

In certain cases, charge-transfer complexes may be intermediates in reactions—thus I_2 first reacts with KCNS in water to give a yellow solution following which there is a slow reaction in neutral or basic solution.[5]

$$I_2 + SCN^- \xrightarrow{\text{rapid}} I_2NCS^- \xrightarrow{\text{slow}} ICN + SO_4^{2-}$$

OXIDES, OXO ACIDS AND THEIR SALTS

22-8. Oxides

The known oxides of chlorine, bromine and iodine are listed in Table 22-2. Oxides of fluorine have already been discussed; while these were

TABLE 22-2

Oxides of Chlorine, Bromine and Iodine

Chlorine	Boiling point, °C	Melting point, °C	Bromine[a]	Melting point, °C	Iodine[a]
Cl_2O	$\sim 4^b$	-116	Br_2O	-18	I_2O_4
ClO_2	$\sim 10^b$	-5.9	Br_3O_8 or BrO_3		I_4O_9
Cl_2O_6		3.5	BrO_2		I_2O_5
Cl_2O_7	82^b	-91.5	$Br_2O_7(?)$		I_2O_7

[a] Decompose on heating.
[b] Explodes.

called oxygen fluorides because of the greater electronegativity of fluorine, those of the remaining halogens are conventionally and properly called *halogen oxides* since oxygen is the more electronegative element, although not by a very great margin relative to chlorine. All of the oxides may be formally considered as anhydrides or mixed anhydrides of the appropriate oxo acids, but this aspect of their chemistry is of little practical consequence. For the most part they are neither common nor especially important.

Chlorine Oxides. All of them are highly reactive and unstable, tending to explode under various conditions. Probably the best characterized is chlorine monoxide, Cl_2O. It is a yellowish-red gas at room temperature. It explodes rather easily on heating or sparking to Cl_2 and O_2. Chlorine

[5] C. Lewis and D. A. Skoog, *J. Amer. Chem. Soc.*, **84**, 1101 (1962).

monoxide dissolves in water forming an orange-yellow solution which contains some HOCl, of which it is formally the anhydride; hypochlorite is formed in alkali. The molecule is angular and symmetrical with O—Cl = 1.71 A and a ClOCl angle of 111°. It is prepared by treating freshly prepared mercuric oxide with chlorine gas or with a solution of chlorine in carbon tetrachloride:

$$2Cl_2 + 2HgO = HgCl_2 \cdot HgO + Cl_2O$$

Chlorine dioxide is also highly reactive and liable to explode very violently. Apparently mixtures with air containing less than 50 mm or so partial pressure of ClO_2 are safe. Actually, ClO_2 is useful as a very active oxidizing agent in certain commercial processes and is made on a fairly large scale. However, because of its explosive nature it is never shipped but produced where and as required. The best preparation is the action of dilute H_2SO_4 on $KClO_3$ in presence of oxalic acid as reducing agent since the CO_2 liberated also serves as a diluent for the ClO_2. Commercially, the gas is made by the exothermic reaction of sodium chlorate in 4–4.5M sulfuric acid containing 0.05–0.25M chloride ion with sulfur dioxide.

$$2NaClO_3 + SO_2 + H_2SO_4 = 2ClO_2 + 2NaHSO_4$$

ClO_2 is a yellowish gas at room temperature. It has a symmetrical bent structure with Cl—O = 1.49 A and an OClO angle of 117°. It is to be noted that ClO_2 is an odd molecule. However, it apparently has no marked tendency to dimerize perhaps because the electron is less localized on the central atom than in other odd molecules. It is soluble in water, solutions containing up to 8 g/liter being stable in the dark. In light, solutions decompose slowly to HCl and $HClO_3$. In alkaline solution a mixture of chlorite and chlorate ions is formed fairly rapidly, whereas, in acid, reduction to $HClO_2$ occurs first, followed by decomposition to HCl + $HClO_3$.

Chlorine hexoxide, Cl_2O_6, forms on ultraviolet irradiation of chlorine dioxide or by the action of ozone on chlorine dioxide. It is a red oily liquid; molecular weight determinations in carbon tetrachloride solution indicate the dimeric formula, but it has been inferred from magnetic measurements that the pure substance and its aqueous solutions are slightly dissociated to ClO_3. It is unstable, decomposing even at its melting point into ClO_2 and O_2, and it reacts explosively with organic matter such as stopcock grease and other reducing agents. Chlorine hexoxide reacts with water or alkalies to give a mixture of chlorate and perchlorate ions. The structure of the molecule is unknown.

Chlorine heptoxide is the most stable of the chlorine oxides, but it, too, detonates when heated or subjected to shock. It is obtained as a colorless oily liquid by dehydration of perchloric acid with P_2O_5 at $-10°$ followed by vacuum distillation, with precautions against explosions. It reacts with water and alkalies to regenerate perchlorate ion. The infrared spectrum of the vapor is consistent with a structure $O_3ClOClO_3$.[6]

Bromine Oxides. The bromine oxides have been characterized only rather recently and are still not well studied. They are all of very low thermal stability. Br_2O, a dark-brown liquid, decomposes at an appreciable rate above $-50°$. Br_3O_8 (also claimed to be BrO_3) is a white solid unstable above $-80°$ except in an atmosphere of ozone. BrO_2 is a yellow solid unstable above about $-40°$; under certain conditions it decomposes in vacuum, evolving Br_2O, to a white solid which may be Br_2O_7.

Iodine Oxides. Of these, iodine pentoxide is the most important. When iodic acid is heated to about $240°$, white crystalline I_2O_5 is obtained.

$$2HIO_3 = I_2O_5 + H_2O \qquad (22\text{-}1)$$

It is stable up to about $300°$ where it melts with decomposition to iodine and oxygen. It is the anhydride of iodic acid and reacts immediately with water in the reverse sense of equation 22-1. It reacts as an oxidizing agent with various substances such as H_2S, HCl and CO. One of its important uses is as a reagent for the determination of CO, the iodine which is produced quantitatively according to equation 22-2 being then determined by standard iodometric procedures:

$$5CO + I_2O_5 = I_2 + 5CO_2 \qquad (22\text{-}2)$$

The infrared spectrum indicates the structure O_2IOIO_2.

The other oxides of iodine, I_2O_4, I_4O_9 and I_2O_7 are of less certain nature. They decompose on heating to $\sim 100°$ to I_2O_5 and iodine or to iodine and oxygen. The yellow solid I_2O_4, which is obtained by partial hydrolysis of $(IO)_2SO_4$ (discussed later), appears to have a network built up of polymeric I—O chains which are cross-linked by IO_3 groups.[7] I_4O_9, which can be made by treating I_2 with ozonided oxygen, can be regarded as $I(IO_3)_3$ similarly cross-linked. I_2O_7 has been obtained as an orange polymeric solid by the action of 65% oleum on HIO_4, despite the fact that in 100% H_2SO_4, HIO_4 decomposes to O_2, O_3 and $H_2IO_3^+$.[8]

22-9. Oxo Acids

The known oxo acids of the halogens are listed in Table 22-3. In general, the chemistry of these acids and their salts is very complicated. Solutions

[6] R. Savoie and P. A. Giguère, *Can. J. Chem.*, **40**, 990 (1962).
[7] W. E. Dasent and T. C. Waddington, *J. Inorg. Nucl. Chem.*, **25**, 132 (1963).
[8] H. C. Mishra and M. C. R. Symons, *J. Chem. Soc.*, **1962**, 1194.

TABLE 22-3

Oxo Acids of the Halogens

Fluorine	Chlorine	Bromine	Iodine
None	$HClO^a$	$HBrO^a$	HIO^a
	$HClO_2^a$	$HBrO_2(?)^a$	—
	$HClO_3^a$	$HBrO_3^a$	HIO_3
	$HClO_4$	—	HIO_4, H_5IO_6, $H_4I_2O_9$

[a] Not obtainable in pure state.

of all of the acids and of several of the anions can be obtained by reaction of the free halogens with water or aqueous bases. We shall discuss these reactions first.

Reaction of Halogens with H_2O and OH^-. A considerable degree of order can be found in this area if full and proper use is made of thermodynamic data in the form of oxidation potentials and equilibrium constants and if the relative rates of competing reactions are also considered. The basic thermodynamic data are given in Table 22-4. From these all necessary potentials and equilibrium constants can be derived.

TABLE 22-4

Standard Potentials (in Volts) for Reactions of the Halogens

Reaction	Cl	Br	I
(1) $H^+ + HOX + e = \frac{1}{2}X_2(g,l,s) + H_2O$	1.63	1.59	1.45
(2) $3H^+ + HXO_2 + 3e = \frac{1}{2}X_2(g,l,s) + 2H_2O$	1.64	—	—
(3) $6H^+ + XO_3^- + 5e = \frac{1}{2}X_2(g,l,s) + 3H_2O$	1.47	1.52	1.20
(4) $8H^+ + XO_4^- + 7e = \frac{1}{2}X_2(g,l,s) + 4H_2O$	1.42	—	1.34
(5) $\frac{1}{2}X_2(g,l,s) + e = X^-$	1.36	1.07	0.54[a]
(6) $XO^- + H_2O + 2e = X^- + 2OH^-$	0.89	0.76	0.49
(7) $XO_2^- + 2H_2O + 4e = X^- + 4OH^-$	0.78	—	—
(8) $XO_3^- + 3H_2O + 6e = X^- + 6OH^-$	0.63	0.61	0.26
(9) $XO_4^- + 4H_2O + 8e = X^- + 8OH^-$	0.56	—	0.39

[a] Indicates that I^- can be oxidized by oxygen in aqueous solution.

The halogens are all to some extent soluble in water. However, in all such solutions there are species other than solvated halogen molecules, since a disproportionation reaction occurs *rapidly*. Two equilibria serve to define the nature of the solution:

$$X_2(g,l,s) = X_2(aq) \qquad K_1$$
$$X_2(aq) = H^+ + X^- + HOX \qquad K_2$$

The values of K_1 for the various halogens are: Cl_2, 0.062; Br_2, 0.21; I_2, 0.0013. The values of K_2 can be computed from the potentials in Table

22-4 to be 4.2×10^{-4} for Cl_2, 7.2×10^{-9} for Br_2 and 2.0×10^{-13} for I_2. We can also estimate from

$$\tfrac{1}{2}X_2 + e = X^-$$

and

$$O_2 + 4H^+ + 4e = 2H_2O \qquad E^0 = 1.23$$

that the potentials for the reactions

$$2H^+ + 2X^- + \tfrac{1}{2}O_2 = X_2 + H_2O$$

are -1.62 for fluorine, -0.13 for chlorine, 0.16 for bromine and 0.69 for iodine.

Thus for saturated solutions of the halogens in water at 25° we have the final results shown in Table 22-5. There is an appreciable concentration

TABLE 22-5

Equilibrium Concentrations in Aqueous Solutions of the Halogens, 25°, mole/l

	Cl_2	Br_2	I_2
Total solubility	0.091	0.21	0.0013
Concentration $X_2(aq)$, mole/liter	0.061	0.21	0.0013
$[H^+] = [X^-] = [HOX]$	0.030	1.15×10^{-3}	6.4×10^{-6}

of hypochlorous acid in a saturated aqueous solution of chlorine, a smaller concentration of HOBr in a saturated solution of Br_2, but only a negligible concentration of HOI in a saturated solution of iodine.

Note that the hypohalous acids are all weak. Their dissociation constants are: HOCl, 3.4×10^{-8}; HOBr, 2×10^{-9}, HOI, 1×10^{-11}. As can be readily seen, reaction of halogens with water does not constitute a suitable method for preparing aqueous solutions of the hypohalous acids owing to the unfavorable equilibria. A useful method is the following general reaction, which is carried out by passing the halogen into a well-agitated suspension of mercuric oxide:

$$2X_2 + 2HgO + H_2O = HgO \cdot HgX_2 + 2HOX$$

All of the hypohalous acids are rather unstable, HOI being the most unstable, and none can be obtained in the pure state. They are all good oxidizing agents, especially in acid solution (see Table 22-4).

The hypohalite ions can all be produced in principle by dissolving the halogens in base according to the general reaction

$$X_2 + 2OH^- = X^- + XO^- + H_2O$$

For these reactions the equilibrium constants are all quite favorable—7.5×10^{15} for Cl_2, 2×10^8 for Br_2 and 30 for I_2—and the reactions are rapid.

However, the situation is complicated by the tendency of the hypohalite ions to disproportionate further in basic solution to produce the halate ions:

$$3XO^- = 2X^- + XO_3^-$$

For this reaction, the equilibrium constant is in each case very favorable, that is, 10^{27} for ClO^-, 10^{15} for BrO^- and 10^{20} for IO^-. Thus the actual products obtained on dissolving the halogens in base depend on the rates at which the hypohalite ions initially produced undergo disproportionation, and these rates vary from one to the other and with temperature.

The disproportionation of ClO^- is slow at and below room temperature. Thus when chlorine reacts with base "in the cold," reasonably pure solutions of Cl^- and ClO^- are obtained. In hot solutions, $\sim 75°$, the rate of disproportionation is fairly rapid and, by using proper conditions, good yields of ClO_3^- can be secured.

The disproportionation of BrO^- is moderately fast even at room temperature. Consequently solutions of BrO^- can only be made and/or kept at around $0°$. At temperatures above room temperature—say, 50–$80°$—quantitative yields of BrO_3^- are obtained according to equation 22-3.

$$3Br_2 + 6OH^- = 5Br^- + BrO_3^- + 3H_2O \qquad (22\text{-}3)$$

The rate of disproportionation of IO^- is very fast at all temperatures, so that it is unknown in solution. Reaction of iodine with base gives IO_3^- quantitatively according to an equation analogous to 22-3.

It remains now to consider the equilibria and kinetic relations of the other oxo anions not yet mentioned to those we have discussed. Halite ions and halous acids do not arise in the hydrolysis of the halogens. First, the only halous acid known definitely is $HClO_2$. HIO_2 apparently does not exist and $HBrO_2$ is doubtful. $HClO_2$ does not form by disproportionation of $HClO$ if for no other reason than that the equilibrium constant is quite unfavorable:

$$2HClO = Cl^- + H^+ + HClO_2 \qquad K \sim 10^{-5}$$

The reaction

$$2ClO^- = Cl^- + ClO_2^- \qquad K \sim 10^7$$

is favorable, but disproportionation of ClO^- to ClO_3^- and Cl^- (see above) is so much greater that it is not observed.

Finally, we must consider the possibility of production of perhalate ions by disproportionation of the halate ions. Since the acids HXO_3 and HXO_4 are all strong, these equilibria are independent of pH. The reaction

$$4ClO_3^- = Cl^- + 3ClO_4^-$$

has an equilibrium constant of 10^{29}, but takes place only very slowly in solution even near 100°; hence perchlorates are not readily produced. Since perbromic acid and perbromates apparently do not exist, bromate is quite stable. The equilibrium constant for disproportionation of iodate is 10^{-53} so that, irrespective of the question of rate, no disproportionation of IO_3^- occurs.

In addition to the reactions already noted, the following additional facts are of importance.

The only definitely known halous acid is chlorous acid. We have seen that it does not arise in the disproportionation of HClO. It may be obtained in aqueous solution by treating a suspension of barium chlorite with sulfuric acid and filtering off the precipitate of barium sulfate. It is a relatively weak acid ($K_a \approx 10^{-2}$) and cannot be isolated in the free state. Chlorites themselves are obtained by reaction of ClO_2 with solutions of bases,

$$2ClO_2 + 2OH^- = ClO_2^- + ClO_3^- + H_2O$$

Chlorites are used as bleaching agents. Alkaline solutions are fairly stable, whereas in acid solutions the weak acid is formed and this decomposes rather rapidly, probably according to the equation

$$4HClO_2 = 2ClO_2 + ClO_3^- + Cl^- + 2H^+ + H_2O$$

Of the halic acids only iodic acid is known in the free state. This is a stable white solid obtained by oxidizing iodine with concentrated nitric acid, hydrogen peroxide, ozone and various other strong oxidizing agents. It can be dehydrated to its anhydride, I_2O_5, as already noted. Although salts such as KHI_2O_6 exist in the solid state, due to favorable lattice energies and low solubility, there is no evidence for polymerization of iodic acid in aqueous solutions up to $0.1M$, though polymerization in very concentrated solution is not yet excluded.[9] Chloric and bromic acids are best obtained in solution by treating the barium halates with sulfuric acid. All the halic acids are strong and are powerful oxidizing agents. The halate ions, XO_3^-, are all pyramidal as is to be expected from the presence of an octet, with one unshared pair, in the halogen valence shell.

Iodates of certain $+4$ metal ions—notably those of Ce, Zr, Hf and Th— are insoluble in, and can be precipitated from, $6N$ nitric acid to provide a useful means of separation.

Of the peracids, perbromic and perbromate ion are unknown. Perchloric and periodic acids are rather different from one another. Both are of considerable importance.

Perchloric Acid and Perchlorates. Although disproportionation of ClO_3^- to ClO_4^- and Cl^- is thermodynamically very favorable, the reaction

[9] J. F. Harvey, J. P. Redfern and J. E. Salmon, *J. Inorg. Nucl. Chem.*, **26**, 1326 (1964).

occurs only very slowly in solution and does not constitute a useful preparative procedure. Perchlorates are most commonly prepared by electrolytic oxidation of chlorates. Also, if solid potassium chlorate is carefully heated, it disproportionates in the following way

$$4KClO_3 = 3KClO_4 + KCl$$

Perchlorates of practically all electropositive metals are known. Except for a few with large cations of low charge, such as $CsClO_4$, $RbClO_4$ and $KClO_4$, they are readily soluble in water. Solid perchlorates containing the tetrahedral perchlorate ion are often isomorphous with permanganates, sulfates, fluoroborates and other salts of tetrahedral anions. A particularly important property of the perchlorate ion is its very slight tendency to serve as a ligand in complexes. Thus perchlorates are widely used in studies of complex ion formation, the assumption being made that no appreciable correction for the concentration of perchlorate complexes need be considered. While this may be true for aqueous solutions, and very likely it is, there have been indications recently that when no other donors are present to compete, perchlorate ion exercises a donor capacity. The $(CH_3)_3SnClO_4$ and $[Co(MeSC_2H_4SMe)_2(ClO_4)_2]$ structures[10] provide perhaps the most certain instances of this.

Perchloric acid can be obtained by vacuum distillation of aqueous solutions and is a colorless liquid freezing at $-112°$. Commercial, concentrated perchloric acid is 72% by weight. It is a very strong acid in aqueous solution. As the potential in Table 22-4 shows, perchlorates and perchloric acid are strong oxidizing agents. Nonetheless, both the acid and its salts tend to be unreactive at room temperature; however, when hot and concentrated, solutions of the acid or its salts react vigorously and even violently. Perchloric acid can react explosively with organic matter, and organometallic perchlorates especially may be dangerously explosive.

There is no evidence for the existence of the perbromate ion. The reason for this can hardly be a steric one and is best ascribed to the poor overlap of $4d$ orbitals of bromine with oxygen $2p$ orbitals to give a π-bonding contribution. For second-row elements, the σ bonding decreases from SiO_4^{4-} across the periodic table to ClO_4^-, but the π bonding increases at the same time since there is an increasing nuclear field which acts to shrink the $3d$ orbitals. The third-row anions GeO_4^{4-}, AsO_4^{3-}, SeO_4^{2-} are increasingly less stable which accords with poorer π bonding and culminates in complete instability of BrO_4^-.[11]

Periodic Acid and Periodates. Periodic acid exists in solution as tetrahedral IO_4^- and in several hydrated forms such as $IO_4(OH_2)^-$ and

---

[10] H. C. Clark and R. J. O'Brien, *Inorg. Chem.*, **2**, 740 (1963); F. A. Cotton and D. L. Weaver, *J. Amer. Chem. Soc.*, **87**, 4189 (1965).

[11] For discussion see D. S. Urch, *J. Inorg. Nucl. Chem.*, **25**, 771 (1963).

$IO_4(OH_2)_2^-$ or, respectively, $H_2IO_5^-$ and $H_4IO_6^-$. In strongly acid solutions it exists as *paraperiodic acid*, H_5IO_6. This is a fairly weak acid.

$$H_5IO_6 = H^+ + H_4IO_6^- \qquad K_a = 5.1 \times 10^{-4}$$

The $H_4IO_6^-$ ion is in equilibrium with $H_3IO_6^{2-}$

$$H_4IO_6^- = H^+ + H_3IO_6^{2-} \qquad K = 2 \times 10^{-7}$$

and also with the *metaperiodate* ion, IO_4^-,

$$IO_4^- + 2H_2O = H_4IO_6^- \qquad K = 0.025 \qquad (22\text{-}4)$$

In concentrated aqueous acids, e.g., $10M$ $HClO_4$, further protonation occurs to give $I(OH)_6^-$,[8] while in strong base dimerization of periodate to $[O_4IOIO_4]^{4-}$ occurs.[12a]

The various periodate equilibria are apparently established rapidly and are pH dependent. The reaction 22-4 has a specific (pseudo first order) rate constant of 1.9×10^2, which may be compared to the corresponding rate constants for the hydration of SO_2 and CO_2, of 3.4×10^6 and 4×10^{-2}, respectively. The mechanism is still uncertain, but 1-step and 2-step paths (Fig. 22-1) are consistent with the kinetic data, although for other reasons the 2-step path is considered more likely.[12b]

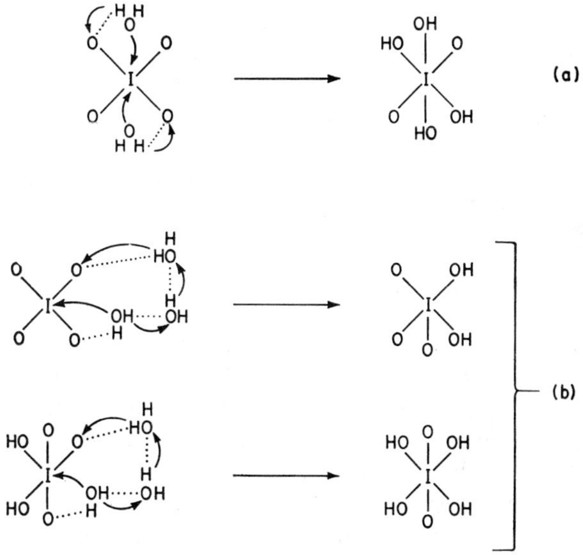

Fig. 22-1. Schematic representation of (a) the single-step and (b) the two-step mechanism for aquation of IO_4^- to $IO_2(OH)_4^-$. Dotted lines represent hydrogen bonds.

[12a] G. J. Buist and J. D. Lewis, *Chem. Comm.*, **1965**, 66.
[12b] K. Kustin and E. C. Liberman, *J. Phys. Chem.*, **68**, 3869 (1964).

The chief characteristic of periodic acids and periodates is that they are powerful oxidizing agents which usually react smoothly and rapidly. They are thus quite useful for analytical purposes, for example, to oxidize manganous ion to permanganate. Ozone (derived from O atoms) may be liberated in the reactions, but not hydrogen peroxide.

Salts of periodic acid are of several types. The commonest are the acid paraperiodates such as $NaH_4IO_6 \cdot H_2O$, $Na_2H_3IO_6$ and $Na_3H_2IO_6$. Metaperiodates with tetrahedral IO_4^- ions are also known in the solid state. Other salts, such as $K_4I_2O_9 \cdot H_2O$, contain the ion $[O_3(OH)IO_2IO_3(OH)]^{4-}$ with octahedral IO_6 groups sharing one edge.[13] The IO_6 group in periodates has generally been shown to be octahedral; the free acid can be dehydrated to $H_4I_2O_9$ at 80° and to HIO_4 at 100°. The complexity of the periodates is similar to that found for the oxo acids of antimony and tellurium, and periodates resemble tellurates in many respects.

HALIDES AND HALIDE COMPLEXES

With the exception of He, Ne and Ar, all the elements in the periodic table form halides, often in several oxidation states, and halides generally are among the most important and common compounds. The ionic and covalent radii of the halogens are shown in Table 22-1.

There are almost as many ways of classifying halides as there are types of halides—and this is many. There are not only binary halides which can range from simple molecules with molecular lattices to complicated polymers and ionic arrays but also oxohalides, hydroxo halides and other complex halides of varied structural types.

22-10. Binary Ionic Halides

Metal halides are substances of predominantly ionic character,[14] although partial covalence is important in some. Actually of course there is a uniform gradation from halides which are for all practical purposes purely ionic, through those of intermediate character, to those which are essentially covalent. As a rough guide we can consider those halides in which the lattice consists of discrete ions rather than definite molecular units to be basically ionic, although there may still be considerable covalence in the metal–halogen interaction.

[13] H. Siebert and H. Wedemeyer, *Angew. Chem. (Internat.)*, **4**, 523 (1965); A. Ferrari, A. Braibanti and A. Tiripicchio, *Acta. Cryst.*, **19**, 629 (1965).
[14] For discussion of ionic character see R. G. Pearson and H. B. Gray, *Inorg. Chem.*, **2**, 358 (1963).

The halides of the alkali metals, except perhaps lithium, of the alkaline earths, with the definite exception of beryllium, and of most of the lanthanides and a few halides of the actinides can be considered as mainly ionic materials. As the charge/radius ratio of the metal ions increases, however, covalence increases. Consider for instance the sequence KCl, $CaCl_2$, $ScCl_3$, $TiCl_4$. KCl is completely ionic, whereas $TiCl_4$ is essentially covalent. Similarly, for a metal with variable oxidation state, the lower halides will tend to be ionic, whereas the higher ones will tend to be covalent. As examples we can cite $PbCl_2$ and $PbCl_4$, and again UF_4, which is an ionic solid, while UF_6 is a gaseous covalent compound.

The size and polarizability of the halide ion is also important in determining the character of the halide. Thus we have the rather classic case of the aluminum halides, where AlF_3 is basically ionic, $AlCl_3$ has a layer lattice, while $AlBr_3$ and AlI_3 exist as covalent dimers.

Most ionic halides dissolve in water to give hydrated metal ions and halide ions, although some, such as the chlorides, bromides and iodides of Ag^I, Cu^I, Hg^I and Pb^{II}, are quite insoluble. The reverse however is not necessarily so, since the hydrogen halides are covalent, but, excepting HF, are essentially completely dissociated in aqueous solution. Solubility through a series of mainly ionic halides of a given element, MF_n, MCl_n, MBr_n, MI_n, may vary in either order. In cases where all four halides are essentially ionic, the solubility order will be iodide > bromide > chloride > fluoride, since the governing factor will be the lattice energies which increase as the ionic radii decrease. This order is found among the alkali, alkaline earth and lanthanide halides. In the last two cases, the fluorides are quite insoluble. On the other hand, if covalence is fairly important, it can invert the trend making the fluoride most and the iodide least soluble, as in the familiar cases of silver and mercurous halides.

It should be clear that no broad simple generalizations are possible, and the properties of metal halides are determined by the interplay of a number of factors.

22-11. Covalent Halides

Just as we considered halides which in the crystalline state consisted of separate metal and halide ions to be essentially ionic with perhaps some covalent character, so we can roughly define a covalent halide as one in which there are discrete molecules which persist even in the crystalline state. A solid consisting of separate molecules held together by van der Waals forces and perhaps dipole–dipole and dipole–induced dipole forces will have a low lattice energy; therefore covalent halides are generally quite volatile compared to ionic halides.

Most of the electronegative elements and the metals in very high oxidation states form covalent halides. Among the most important covalent halides are the hydrogen halides. The main properties of these substances should already be familiar and will be reviewed only briefly and in part here; also, HF has already been discussed at some length (page 383). HCl, HBr and HI are all gases at room temperature, readily soluble in water with essentially complete dissociation to H^+ and X^- ions. Actually the acid strengths increase in the order HCl < HBr < HI. The reasons for this, as well as the weakness of HF, have been considered already (page 222). The H—X bond energies and the thermal stabilities decrease markedly in the order HF > HCl > HBr > HI, that is with increasing atomic number of the halogen. This same trend is found, in varying degrees, among the halides of all elements giving a set of covalent halides, such as those of carbon and boron already noted, and those of P, As, Sb, Si, Ge, Sn, S, Se, Te, etc.

All three acids give the hydrogen bonded anions HX_2^- although salts of HBr_2^- and HI_2^- are rather unstable. They can be prepared by direct interaction of HX with salts such as $(CH_3)_4NX$; their thermochemical properties have been studied.[15] There is evidence[16] that $[ClHCl]^-$ has a symmetrical structure analogous to that of $[FHF]^-$.

A fairly general property of covalent halides is their easy hydrolysis to produce the hydrohalic acid and an acid of the other element. Typical examples are:

$$BCl_3 + 3H_2O = B(OH)_3 + 3H^+ + 3Cl^-$$
$$PBr_3 + 3H_2O = HPO(OH)_2 + 3H^+ + 3Br^-$$
$$SiCl_4 + 4H_2O = Si(OH)_4 + 4H^+ + 4Cl^-$$

However, the detailed properties of a given covalent halide depend intimately on the particular element concerned, and further discussion of covalent halides will be found in chapters dealing with the other elements.

The formation of *halogen bridges* between two other atoms—usually, but not exclusively, metallic—is a common occurrence. Although such bridges are often written as involving donation from lone-pair electrons on the halogen atom, as in 22-V and 22-VI, the bond distances in the bridge are

(22-V)   (22-VI)

[15] D. H. McDaniell and R. E. Vallee, *Inorg. Chem.*, **3**, 996 (1963).

[16] S. S. Chang and E. F. Westrum, Jr., *J. Chem. Phys.*, **36**, 2571 (1962); see also K. M. Harmon, *et al.*, *J. Amer. Chem. Soc.*, **87**, 1700 (1965).

usually the same and the bonds are equivalent. Both simple molecular or ionic species, for example Al_2Br_6, $Tl_2Cl_9^{3-}$ and $Mo_6Cl_8^{4+}$, and highly polymeric bridged halides are known; a few compounds having single bridges are known. The formation of labile intermediates in which single halogen bridges are present has been demonstrated in a variety of systems.

22-12. Preparation of Anhydrous Halides

Although preparations of individual halogen compounds are mentioned throughout the text, anhydrous halides are of such great importance in chemistry that a few of the more important general methods of preparation can be noted.

1. *Direct interaction.* This method is perhaps the most important preparative method for all halides, and the halogens or their acids where appropriate are employed. Elevated temperatures are usually required with transition metals although rapid reaction can often occur with Cl_2 or Br_2 when tetrahydrofuran or other ethers are used as the reaction medium, the halide being obtained as a solvate; where different oxidation states are possible, chlorine, at elevated temperatures, usually gives a higher state than bromine or iodine. Nonmetals, such as phosphorus, usually react readily without heating.

2. *Halogen exchange.* Many halogen compounds will undergo rapid halogen exchange with either the elements or their acids. An excess of reagent is usually required since the reactions are normally equilibrium ones.

3. *Halogenation by halogen compounds.* This is an important method, particularly for metal halides, notably chlorides. The reactions involve treatment of anhydrous compounds, principally oxides, with halogen compounds such as CCl_4, hexachlorobutadiene, hexachloropropene at elevated temperatures:

$$UO_3 + CCl_2{=}CCl{-}CCl{=}CCl_2 \xrightarrow{\text{reflux}} UCl_4$$
$$Pr_2O_3 + 6NH_4Cl(s) \xrightarrow{300°} 2PrCl_3 + 3H_2O + 6NH_3$$
$$Sc_2O_3 + CCl_4 \xrightarrow{600°} ScCl_3$$

4. *Dehydration of hydrated halides.* Hydrated halides are usually obtained easily from aqueous solutions. They can sometimes be dehydrated by heating in vacuum, but often this leads to oxohalides or impure products. Various reagents can be used to effect dehydration. For example $SOCl_2$ is often useful for chlorides. Another fairly general reagent is 2,2-dimethoxypropane.

$$[Cr(H_2O)_6]Cl_3 + SOCl_2 \overset{\text{reflux}}{=} CrCl_3 + 12HCl + 6SO_2$$
$$MX_n \cdot mH_2O + mCH_3C(OCH_3)_2CH_3 = MX_n + m(CH_3)_2CO + 2mCH_3OH$$

In many cases the acetone adduct and/or methanol becomes coordinated to the metal but gentle heating or pumping usually gives the solvate-free halide.

22-13. Halide Complexes

All of the halide ions including fluorine have the ability to function as ligands and form, with various metal ions or covalent halides, complexes such as $FeCl_4^-$, SiF_6^{2-}, HgI_4^{2-}, etc., as well as mixed complexes along with other ligands, for example, $[Co(NH_3)_4Cl_2]^+$. We merely make some general remarks and cite some typical characteristics of such complexes, reserving detailed discussions for other places in connection with the chemistries of the complexed elements.

One of the important general questions which arise concerns the relative affinities of the several halide ions for a given metal ion. There is no simple answer to this however. For crystalline materials it is obvious that lattice energies play an important role[17] and there are cases, such as BF_4^-, BCl_4^-, BBr_4^-, in which the latter two are known only in the form of crystalline salts with large cations, where lattice energies are governing. In considering the stability of the complex ions in solution it is important to recognize that (a) the stability of a complex involves not only the absolute stability of the $M—X \leftrightarrow M^+ \cdots \cdot X^-$ bond, but also its stability relative to the stability of ion–solvent bonds, and (b) in general an entire series of complexes will exist, $M^{n+}(aq)$, $MX^{(n-1)+}(aq)$, $MX_2^{(n-2)+}(aq)$, ..., $MX_x^{(n-x)+}(aq)$, where x is the maximum coordination number of the metal ion. Of course, these two points are of importance in all types of complexes in solution.

It has been found from a survey of all of the available data on the stability of halide complexes that generally the stability decreases in the series $F > Cl > Br > I$, but with some metal ions the order is the opposite,[18a] namely, $F < Cl < Br < I$. No rigorous theoretical explanation for either sequence or for the existence of the two classes of acceptors relative to the halide ions has been given. It is likely that charge/radius ratio, polarizability, and the ability to use empty outer d orbitals for back bonding are significant factors, but their relative importance remains a subject for investigation. From the few available results it appears that for complexes where the replacement stability order is $Cl < Br < I$, the actual order of $M—X$ bond strengths is $Cl > Br > I$ so that ionic size and polarizability appear to be the critical factors.[18b]

[17] Cf. A. B. Blake and F. A. Cotton, *Inorg. Chem.*, **3**, 907 (1963), for lattice energies of some compounds containing chloro complexes.

[18a] S. Ahrland, J. Chatt and N. R. Davies, *Quart. Rev.*, **12**, 256 (1958).

[18b] A. J. Poë and M. S. Vaidya, *J. Chem. Soc.*, **1961**, 1023.

The literature contains many references to the effect of steric factors in accounting for such facts as the existence of $FeCl_4^-$(aq) as the highest ferric complex with Cl^- whereas FeF_6^{3-} is rather stable, and similar cases such as $CoCl_4^{2-}$ SCl_4, $SiCl_4$ as the highest chloro species compared to the fluoro species CoF_6^{3-}, SF_6, SiF_6^{2-}. In many such cases thorough steric analysis, considering the probable bond lengths and van der Waals radii of the halide ions, shows that this steric factor alone cannot account for the differences in maximum coordination number. This point is also one requiring further study.

Finally, it may be mentioned that in effecting the separation of metal ions for analytical or radiochemical purposes, halide complex formation equilibria may be taken advantage of in conjunction with anion exchange resins. In fact, the objective of metal ion separation has stimulated much research on metal–halide complex equilibria. To take an extreme example, Co^{2+} and Ni^{2+}, which are not easily separated by classical methods, can be efficiently separated by passing a strong hydrochloric acid solution through an anion exchange column. Co^{2+} forms the anionic complexes $CoCl_3^-$ and $CoCl_4^{2-}$ rather readily, whereas it does not seem that any anionic chloro complexes of nickel form in aqueous solution even at the highest attainable activities of Cl^-; however, tetrachloronickelates can be obtained in fused salt systems or in nonaqueous media. More commonly, effective separation depends on properly exploiting the *difference* in complexation between two cations *both* of which have some tendency to form anionic halide complexes.

POSITIVE OXIDATION STATES OF THE HALOGENS

22-14. General Evidence of Electropositive Character

In groups IV, V and VI we have seen that metallic and electropositive character increases markedly in going down the groups. The result of this trend in these groups is actually to make the heaviest members decidedly metallic (Pb, Bi and Po) and the next heaviest members either decidedly metallic (Sn) or at least partially so (Sb, Te) even though the first members of these groups are quite distinctly nonmetals (C, N, O). We shall now consider the trend toward increasingly metallic character with increasing atomic number in the halogens. For two reasons we might expect to find less evidence of distinctly metallic character in the heavier members of this group than in the preceding ones. First, we have practically no conclusive knowledge about At which should be the most metallic. Second, because of the trend to less metallic character *across* each *period* of the table, we expect iodine to be less metallic than tellurium (just as Te is less so than Sb which is less so than Sn). In fact, elemental iodine is not metallic at all. The only evidence we have of a *tendency*, which is never actually realized, toward metallic character in the series F, Cl, Br, I is the increasing stability of positive oxidation states. It is this evidence which will now be considered.

For fluorine there are no known compounds in which the fluorine atom appears to be appreciably positive. In ClF evidence from chlorine nuclear quadrupole coupling shows that the bonding is best represented in terms of the resonance:

$$Cl-F \leftrightarrow Cl^+F^-$$

In the oxygen fluorides there is no direct physical evidence, but it is likely that the fluorine is at least neutral and probably somewhat negative with respect to oxygen. It is also to be recalled that no oxofluoric acids or anions exist.

With Cl, Br and I there is evidence for electropositive behavior. We may, for convenience, divide this evidence into two classes. The first class, which is for the most part only loosely defined, concerns polarities of bonds. In ClF, as we have already noted, the nuclear quadrupole spectrum of Cl indicates with certainty that the canonical structure Cl^+F^- makes a substantial contribution to the electronic state of the molecule. Nuclear quadrupole spectroscopy has also given evidence of the importance of I^+CN^- in ICN, and I^+Cl^- in ICl. In general, we expect that when a halogen atom forms a bond with another atom which is more electronegative than itself, the bond will be polar, the halogen having a partial positive charge. However, we can scarcely say that the halogen atom is in a positive oxidation *state*, although we may assign positive oxidation *numbers* (e.g., $+7$ to Cl in ClO_4^-) in an essentially arbitrary way for convenience in balancing oxidation–reduction equations.

22-15. Positive Halogen Ions and Compounds

(a) *Iodine cations:* There is no evidence for the existence of Cl^+ or Br^+ cations but there is good evidence for I^+, I_3^+ and I_5^+ as well as I_2Cl^+, I_2Br^+ and ICl_2^+ ions under special conditions.[19a,b] Since such ions are powerful electrophiles, they can exist only in media with low nucleophilic properties and have been characterized so far only in H_2SO_4 or IF_5 as solvents; in more strongly donor solvents (see below) either attack takes place or strongly solvated species such as py_2I^+ are formed.

[19a] Review: J. Arotsky and M. C. R. Symons, *Quart. Rev.*, **16**, 283 (1962).

[19b] See also J. Arotsky, H. C. Mishra and M. C. R. Symons, *J. Chem. Soc.*, **1962**, 2582; R. A. Garrett, R. J. Gillespie and J. B. Senior, *Inorg. Chem.*, **4**, 563 (1965).

Iodine dissolves in 100% sulfuric acid to give a pink solution with an absorption spectrum similar to that for I_2 vapor; the addition of Ag_2SO_4 to the solution increases the solubility of I_2 from 10^{-3} to $0.5M$ due to formation of the AgI_2^+ ion. However when I_2 is dissolved in 30% oleum, a brown, $0.5M$ solution can be obtained which contains I_3^+ or, with excess iodine, I_5^+. The I_3^+ ion is probably bent with an angle near $90°$, similar to ICl_2^+ in the crystals of $[ICl_2]^+[SbCl_6]^-$. The addition of KIO_3 as oxidizing agent to the brown solution, or of HIO_3 to I_2 in 100% H_2SO_4, gives a deep blue solution:

$$HIO_3 + 2I_3^+ + 8H_2SO_4 = 7I^+ + 3H_3O^+ + 8HSO_4^-$$

Similar, blue solutions in 60% oleum acting as an oxidant are given directly by I_2 and by ICl.

$$I_2 + H_2S_2O_7 + 2SO_3 = 2I^+ + HS_2O_7^- + HSO_4^- + SO_2$$
$$ICl + H_2S_2O_7 + SO_3 = I^+ + HS_2O_7^- + HSO_2Cl$$

In high concentrations in 100% H_2SO_4, I^+ appears to disproportionate:

$$4I^+ + H_2O + 2HSO_4^- = IO^+ + I_3^+ + 2H_2SO_4$$

The solutions of $IOSO_2F$ and I_3OSO_2F (which are obtained by inter-action of I_2 and $S_2O_6F_2$) in HSO_3F give colors and spectra characteristic of I^+ and I_3^+, respectively.[20a] Using IF_5 as a solvent,[20b] iodine gives brown solutions whose spectra are similar to those of pyridine–iodine solutions, but on addition of a trace of water, dark-blue solutions comparable to the ones in sulfuric acid are obtained:

$$6IF_5 + 2I_2 = 5I^+ + 5IF_6^-$$

The blue cation migrates to the cathode on electrolysis in IF_5 (in H_2SO_4 + SO_3, the $H_2S_2O_7^-$ ion carries all the current by a proton switch mechanism), is paramagnetic, $\mu_{eff} = 1.5–1.9$ BM, and has three absorption bands in its spectrum. The low moment for two unpaired electrons can be accounted for by strong spin-orbit coupling (see Sec. 25-5) and the spectra by splitting of the $3p$ orbitals into a lower singlet and an upper doubly degenerate pair due to an asymmetric solvent field (cf. ligand field theory, Chap. 26).

Ions similar to I_3^+ can be obtained with suitable anions for ICl_2^+, BrF_2^+ and Br_3^+; since molten iodine is electrically conducting, we may write

$$3I_2 \rightleftharpoons I_3^+ + I_3^-$$

(b) *Unipositive halogen compounds:* As noted above I^+ is a powerful nucleophile and likely to be strongly solvated. Compounds containing

[20a] F. Aubke and G. H. Cady, *Inorg. Chem.*, **4**, 269 (1965).
[20b] E. E. Aynsley, N. N. Greenwood and D. H. W. Wharmby, *J. Chem. Soc.*, **1963**, 5369.

py_2I^+ have long been known. They are generally prepared by treatment of a silver salt with the stoichiometric amount of iodine and an excess of pyridine in chloroform according to the typical equation

$$AgNO_3 + I_2 + 2py = Ipy_2NO_3 + AgI$$

The silver iodide is immediately precipitated and the complex can then be precipitated from the filtered supernatant liquid by addition of ether or petroleum. The compound $IpyNO_3$ can also be prepared. It appears that I^+ has a strong tendency to be two coordinate, so that Ipy_2NO_3 should be formulated $[pyIpy]^+NO_3^-$ and $IpyNO_3$ as $[pyIONO_2]$. The former gives a much more highly conducting solution in acetone than does the latter. When the anion is perchlorate, only Ipy_2ClO_4 can be obtained, in agreement with the requirement of bicoordination for the I^+ since ClO_4^- is well known to have only slight capacity to function as a ligand. The addition of I_2 to $AgClO_4$ in ether at $-85°$ gives AgI and a solution containing a weak complex $AgClO_4 \cdot IClO_4$; addition of pyridine to the solution gives $py_2I^+ClO_4^-$. If $AgClO_4$ is added to excess iodine in ether at $-85°$, a different reaction occurs and a solution of yellow $I(ClO_4)_3$ is formed:[21]

$$I_2 + 2AgClO_4 = AgI + AgClO_4 \cdot IClO_4$$
$$AgClO_4 \cdot IClO_4 + IClO_4 = AgI + I(ClO_4)_3$$

With carboxylate anions, the compounds are generally of the type $[pyIOCOR]$, and give only very weakly conducting solutions in acetone. Evidence that the iodine in these compounds is unipositive is of several kinds. All compounds release iodine when they are dissolved in a sodium hydroxide solution containing iodide and the solution acidified:

$$[L_nI]^+ + I^- = I_2 + nL$$

This reaction is quantitative. Electrolysis of $[pyIpy]^+NO_3^-$ in anhydrous chloroform yields iodine at the *cathode* only. Bases other than pyridine may be used, in particular various methyl-substituted pyridines.

In the compound "py_2I_2," obtained by direct interaction of pyridine with iodine, X-ray studies show the presence of the essentially planar cation $[pyIpy]^+$ along with I_3^- and I_2 molecules.

Similar but, as expected, less stable complexes of unipositive bromine, for example, $[pyBrpy]^+NO_3^-(ClO_4^-)$, have been prepared by methods similar to those used in preparing the iodine compounds. The chlorine compound $[pyClpy]^+NO_3^-$ has also been reported.

(c) *Compounds of iodine(III):* Although there is no evidence for I^{3+} (or I^{2+}) ions as such, there are several compounds which appear to contain I^{III}. It may be said immediately that no comparable compounds of bromine

[21] N. W. Alcock and T. C. Waddington, *J. Chem. Soc.*, **1962**, 2510.

or chlorine are known, so that the existence of these iodine compounds shows that iodine has the greatest tendency to electropositive behavior. Fuming nitric acid in the presence of acetic anhydride oxidizes iodine producing the compound $I(OCOCH_3)_3$. Analogous compounds have been obtained with chloro-, dichloro- and trichloroacetic acids. $I(OCOCH_3)_3$ reacts with methylsulfuric acid to give $(CH_3SO_3)_3I$. On oxidation of iodine with concentrated nitric acid in the presence of acetic anhydride and phosphoric acid, the compound IPO_4 is obtained. Unfortunately no direct structural information is available for these compounds, but electrolytic studies seem to leave no choice but to believe that I^{3+} ions, stabilized by coordination, are present. When a saturated solution of $I(OCOCH_3)_3$ in acetic anhydride is electrolyzed, the quantity of silver iodide formed at a silvered platinum gauze *cathode* is in good agreement with Faraday's law calculations assuming the presence of I^{3+}:

$$I^{3+} + Ag + 3e \rightarrow AgI$$

These compounds are quite sensitive to moisture and are not stable much above room temperature. They are hydrolyzed with disproportionation of the I^{III} as illustrated with IPO_4

$$5IPO_4 + 9H_2O = I_2 + 3HIO_3 + 5H_3PO_4$$

It may also be noted that covalent I^{III} is known in the compounds triphenyl iodine, $(C_6H_5)_3I$, and a large number of diaryl iodonium salts, such as $(C_6H_5)_2I^+X^-$, where X may be one of a number of common anions.[22] Aryl compounds such as $C_6H_5ICl_2$ are also well known and can be prepared by direct interaction; they can be regarded as trigonal bipyramidal with axial chlorine atoms and equatorial phenyl group and lone-pairs. The compounds can be used for chlorination of olefins.[23]

(d) *Oxo compounds:* The so-called iodosyl sulfate, $(IO)_2SO_4$, which is a yellow solid obtained by the action of H_2SO_4 on I_2O_5 and I_2, has been shown not to contain IO^+ ions as such, but to have polymeric I—O—I chains cross-linked by the anion. Similarly HIO_3 in H_2SO_4 gives monomeric IO_2HSO_4[24] in dilute solution but at high concentrations polymerization occurs and a white solid $I_2O_5 \cdot SO_3$ can be obtained which probably has a structure of the type 22-VII. However, in 65% oleum $(IO)_2SO_4$

(22-VII)

[22] See, e.g., F. M. Beringer and R. A. Falk, *J. Chem. Soc.*, **1964**, 4442.
[23] See, e.g., J. L. Cotter, L. J. Andrews and R. M. Keefer, *J. Amer. Chem. Soc.*, **84**, 793 (1962).
[24] R. J. Gillespie and J. B. Senior, *Inorg. Chem.*, **3**, 441, 972 (1964).

which is nonionic in 100% H_2SO_4 gives a paramagnetic ion and a salt $IO^+HS_2O_7^-$.[19b]

$$(IO)_2SO_4 + H_2SO_4 \rightleftharpoons 2IOHSO_4$$
$$IOHSO_4 + H_2S_2O_7 \rightleftharpoons IO^+ + HS_2O_7^- + H_2SO_4$$

This ion can be related to the I^+ and I_3^+ ions since there are the following equilibria

$$4I^+ + 3HS_2O_7^- + 2H_2SO_4 \underset{\text{slow}}{\overset{\text{rapid}}{\rightleftharpoons}} IO^+HS_2O_7^- + I_3^+ + 3H_2S_2O_7 \text{ (in 5–50\% oleum)}$$
$$3I_3^+ + 3HS_2O_7^- + 2H_2SO_4 \rightleftharpoons IO^+HS_2O_7^- + 4I_2 + 3H_2S_2O_7 \text{ (in 100\% } H_2SO_4)$$

An iodyl fluorosulfate has been made but its structure is uncertain.[25]

INTERHALOGEN COMPOUNDS

22-16. General Survey

The halogens form various compounds which are binary and ternary combinations of the halogens among themselves. With the exception of BrCl, ICl, ICl_3 and IBr, the compounds are all halogen fluorides (Table 22-6) such as ClF, BrF_3, IF_5 and IF_7. Ternary compounds occur only as polyhalide ions, and the principal types of binary and ternary polyhalide salts are listed in Table 22-7 (page 589).

It will be noted that all of the interhalogen compounds are of the type XX'_n where n is an odd number and X' is always the lighter halogen when n is greater than 1. Because n is always odd it follows that all interhalogen compounds are diamagnetic having all valence electrons present either as shared (bonding) or unshared pairs. The general scarcity and instability of odd molecules makes this seem reasonable, and it is to be expected that any further interhalogens, if discovered, will also contain an even number of atoms. No ternary interhalogen compounds are known, although attempts have been made to prepare them. This is probably because any ternary molecules formed can readily redistribute to form a mixture of the (presumably) more stable binary compounds and/or elemental halogens. Another general observation which may be made is that stability of the compounds with higher n increases as X becomes larger and X' smaller.

The structures of the interhalogen compounds are all known with varying degrees of accuracy. For the diatomic compounds there is no question. For the XX'_3 species, ClF_3 and BrF_3 are T-shaped, whereas ICl_3 is T-shaped but dimerized. IF_5 contains a square pyramidal IF_4 grouping with

[25] F. Aubke, G. M. Cady and C. H. L. Kennard, *Inorg. Chem.*, **3**, 1799 (1964).

the fifth fluorine along the four-fold axis on the *same* side as the other four. The structures of BrF_5 and ClF_5 have not been firmly established, but appear to be analogous to that of IF_5. IF_7 has been shown to be a pentagonal bipyramid, perhaps somewhat distorted in the solid state. These structures and the reasons for them in terms of the electronic configuration of the molecules have already been discussed in Chapter 15.

In their physical properties, the diatomic interhalogens XX′ are usually intermediate between the constituent halogens X_2 and X'_2. They are of course polar, whereas the halogen molecules are not. ClF is colorless, BrF, BrCl, ICl and IBr are red or red-brown.

Chemically, the interhalogens are all quite reactive. They behave as oxidizing agents, and they attack most other elements producing mixtures of the halides. They are all more or less readily hydrolyzed (some such as BrF_3 being dangerously explosive in this respect), in some cases according to the equation

$$XX' + H_2O = H^+ + X'^- + HOX$$

The diatomic compounds often add to ethylenic double bonds and may react with the heavier alkali and alkaline earth metals to give polyhalide salts.

The diatomic compounds are ClF, BrF, BrCl, IBr and ICl. IF is unknown except in minute amounts observed spectroscopically. It is apparently too unstable with respect to disproportionation to IF_5 and I_2 to permit its isolation. The other isolable diatomic compounds have varying degrees of stability with respect to disproportionation and fall in the following stability order where the numbers in parentheses represent the disproportionation constants for the gaseous compounds and the elements in their standard states at 25°: ClF (2.9×10^{-11}) > ICl (1.8×10^{-3}) > IBr (4.9×10^{-2}) > BrCl (0.34). BrF is omitted since it is extremely unstable and its characteristic disproportionation is to Br_2 and BrF_3. This is due not to any particular weakness of the BrF bond (50 kcal/mole) but to the even greater stabilities of the products of disproportionation.

ClF may be prepared by direct reaction of the elements in a copper vessel at 250°. It is best prepared free of ClF_3, however, by mixing Cl_2 and ClF_3 in equimolar quantities. BrF also results on direct reaction of Br_2 and F_2, but has never been obtained in high purity because of its ready disproportionation. Iodine monochloride is obtained as brownish-red tablets (β form) by treating liquid chlorine with solid iodine in stoichiometric amount, and cooling to solidify the liquid product. It readily transforms to the α form, ruby-red needles. BrCl has never been isolated in a pure state, but there is much evidence for its existence in equilibrium with Br_2 and Cl_2 under various conditions. IBr as a solid results from

19*

direct combination of the elements. It is endothermic and extensively dissociated in the vapor.

ICl_3 is also formed (like ICl) by treatment of liquid chlorine with the stoichiometric quantity of iodine, or with a deficiency of iodine followed by evaporation of the excess chlorine. It forms as a fluffy orange powder, unstable much above room temperature.

The remaining molecular interhalogen compounds are all halogen fluorides.

22-17. The Halogen Fluorides

The halogen fluorides and some of their important physical properties are listed in Table 22-6.

TABLE 22-6
Some Physical Properties of Halogen Fluorides

	Melting point, °C	Boiling point, °C	Specific conductivity[a] at 25°C, ohm^{-1} cm^{-1}	Dielectric constant of liquid at 25°C	Trouton's constant
ClF	−154	−101	—	—	28.0
ClF_3	−76	12	3.9×10^{-9}	4.304	23.1
ClF_5	> −196	—	—	—	—
BrF	−33	20	—	—	20.5
BrF_3	9	126	8.0×10^{-3}	—	25.7
BrF_5	−60	41	9.1×10^{-8}	7.76	23.2
IF_3[b]	—	—	—	—	—
IF_5	10	101	5.4×10^{-6}	36.14	26.3
IF_7	6.3–6.5	277 (subl.)	—	—	—

[a] The literature values may be quite inaccurate in view of the possibility of hydrolysis by traces of water.

[b] Alleged to be a yellow powder obtained by fluorination of I_2 in freon at −78° and to decompose to I_2 and IF_5 above −35°.

The preparations of ClF and BrF have already been mentioned. ClF_3 may be prepared by direct combination of the elements and is also available commercially. ClF_5 is prepared by reaction of ClF_3 with F_2 (mole ratio 1:14) at 250 atm and 350°; it has not yet been obtained entirely free of ClF_3. It appears to be a white solid at −196°. The infrared spectrum indicates a square pyramidal structure.[26] BrF_3 is also conveniently obtainable in the laboratory by direct combination of the elements at 200° or higher or by action of ClF_3 on Br_2 at 10°. IF_5 is prepared by reaction of

[26] D. F. Smith, *Science*, **141**, 1039 (1963).

iodine in excess with fluorine at ordinary and slightly elevated temperatures, whereas IF_7 is obtained if the reaction occurs at temperatures of 250–270° using excess fluorine.

IF_7 is best prepared pure by fluorination of PdI_2 since I_2 is difficult to dry and the product made from I_2 is usually contaminated with IOF_5. The latter, *oxoiodine pentafluoride*, is formed by action of IF_7 on SiO_2 at 100° (cf. $XeF_6 + SiO_2 \rightarrow XeOF_4$) and is a colorless liquid, m $\sim$ −10°; the only other octahedral oxo fluorides are of Os and Re (see Chaps. 30-D and -F).

There are two principal features of the chemistry of halogen fluorides. The first is their activity as fluorinating agents. Although in most cases only qualitative data on the rates and products of the reactions are available, all are moderately to vigorously reactive, the approximate order of reactivity being $ClF_3 > BrF_5 > IF_7 > ClF > BrF_3 > IF_5 > BrF$.

The second feature, and one which has been studied rather actively in the past few years, is the functioning of several halogen fluorides as solvent systems. Inspection of the data in Table 22-6 will indicate their potentialities in this respect. First let us consider the Trouton constants.* With the exception of IF_7, for which this datum is unavailable, and BrF, the Trouton constants indicate varying but appreciable degrees of association of the liquids. This is believed to occur through fluorine bridging, which in BrF_3, for example, may be indicated as in formula 22-VIII, which is comparable to the dimeric structure of ICl_3.

(22-VIII)

In addition to association, reasonably common to all, it will be seen that in BrF_3 and IF_5 the conductivity indicates appreciable self-ionization; moreover, the dielectric constant of IF_5 is extremely high, which would enable it to function as a good ionizing solvent. Unfortunately BrF_3 is so reactive that no reliable measurement of its dielectric constant has been reported, although it is probably high. Thus it might be expected that

---

* The Trouton constant is the heat of vaporization in cal/mole at the normal boiling point divided by the normal boiling point in °K. It is thus the entropy of vaporization at the boiling point and gives a measure of association in the liquid as compared to the gas phase. For "normal" liquids, for example, those not appreciably associated in either phase, it averages 17–21. Higher values indicate association in the liquid phase. Thus the Trouton constant of methane is 17.5, whereas those of NH_3 and H_2O are 23.3 and 28.3, respectively.

these two liquids would be useful reaction media and would give rise to systems of acids and bases. These expectations have been confirmed especially for BrF_3 which has been extensively studied and will now be discussed in some detail.

The reported conductivity of BrF_3 suggests appreciable self-ionization, and this might be expected to be

$$2BrF_3 = BrF_2^+ + BrF_4^-$$

In this system the acid is then BrF_2^+ and the base BrF_4^- (compare H_3O^+, OH^- and NH_4^+, NH_2^- in the H_2O and NH_3 systems). In order to provide chemical confirmation that this is in fact the correct dissociation reaction, three kinds of evidence have been adduced.

1. Compounds which can be considered as acids and bases have been isolated and shown to give highly conducting solutions when dissolved in BrF_3. Typical are $BrF_2^+SbF_6^-$ and $BrF_2^+AuF_4^-$. It is possible that these compounds are not entirely ionic as solids, there being some fluorine bridging, but they do ionize when dissolved in BrF_3. Among the bases isolated are $KBrF_4$ (shown by X-ray studies definitely to contain discrete planar BrF_4^- ions), $AgBrF_4$ and $Ba(BrF_4)_2$.

2. Neutralization reactions have been carried out producing salts. For example:

$$AgBrF_4 + BrF_2SbF_6 = AgSbF_6 + 2BrF_3$$
$$\text{Base} \qquad \text{Acid} \qquad \text{Salt} \qquad \text{Solvent}$$

3. It has also been shown that acids may be titrated with bases and vice versa, and that when these titrations are followed conductimetrically they show sharp end points (minimum in conductivity) at a 1:1 mole ratio of reactants.

The reaction of $BrF_3(g)$ with $ClF_3(g)$ yields a colorless solid, $BrClF_6$, which is shown by conductance data to be ionic, presumably[27] $ClF_2^+BrF_4^-$. Similarly,[28] by dissolving AsF_5 and SbF_5 in ClF_3, the ionic compounds $ClF_2^+AsF_6^-$ and $ClF_2^+SbF_6^-$ may be obtained.

Although chemical evidence for the dissociation of IF_5 according to

$$2IF_5 = IF_4^+ + IF_6^-$$

is much less complete than for BrF_3, it is likely that this ionization reaction is the correct one and that it is of importance. Thus the acid IF_4^+ SbF_6^- and the base $K^+IF_6^-$ have been isolated and on mixing their solutions in IF_5 and removing excess solvent, the salt $KSbF_6$ is isolated.

[27] H. Selig and J. Shamir, *Inorg. Chem.*, **3**, 294 (1964).
[28] F. Séel and O. Detmer, *Z. anorg. Chem.*, **70**, 163 (1958).

22-18. Polyhalide Anions

Table 22-7 indicates the general types of such ions. A few, such as I_3^-,

TABLE 22-7

Principal Types of Binary and Ternary Polyhalide Salts
(M represents a large univalent cation, e.g., Cs^+, $(CH_3)_4N^+$, etc.)

Type X_n^-	Type XX'_n		Type $XX'X''_n$
MBr_3	$MClF_2^a$	$MClF_4$	$MIBrF$
MI_3	$MIBr_2$	$MBrF_4$	$MIFCl_3$
MI_5	$MICl_2$	$MBrF_6$	$MIClBr$
MI_7	$MBrCl_2$	MIF_4	
MI_9	$MClBr_2$	MIF_6	
	$MICl_4$		

[a] as NO^+ salt only (see ref. 30).

are stable in solution, but most of them, especially the larger ones, exist only in crystalline salts with large cations. The salts are simply made by crystallizing the halide salt in presence of excess of the halogen. For triiodide only, spectral studies have shown that in CCl_4 at 25° there is the equilibrium:

$$I^- + I_2 = I_3^- \qquad K = 7.1 \times 10^{-2}$$

The action of IF_5 on alkali iodides and fluorine on alkali chlorides gives white powders such as KIF_4 and $CsClF_4$, while K, Rb and Cs fluorides react with ClF_3 or BrF_5 to give salts of ClF_4^- and BrF_6^-; the latter are powerful oxidants which explode with organic solvents.[29] So far as is known, all those with three atoms are linear with the heaviest atom in the middle. In the case of $ClBr_2^-$, however, it is not known whether the structure is Br—Cl—Br or Br—Br—Cl. The structure of the rather unstable and powerfully oxidizing NO^+ salt of ClF_2^-[30] is not certain but it is probably again linear. The ICl_4^- ion is square planar. The structure of IF_6^- is unknown. As noted in Chapter 15, knowledge of this structure (and that of the isoelectronic XeF_6 also) would be valuable in appraising and refining theoretical ideas on bonding in such compounds. The I_5^-, I_7^- and I_9^- ions are rather loose aggregates. In the tetramethyl-ammonium salt, I_5^- has been shown to have the structure depicted in Figure 22-2. The short I—I distance is greater than in the I_2 molecule,

[29] E. D. Whitney, et al., J. Amer. Chem. Soc., 83, 2583 (1964).
[30] K. O. Christie and J. P. Guertin, Inorg. Chem., 4, 905 (1965).

that is, 2.67 A, but the long I—I distance indicates very weak bonding, and the ion can be considered to consist of two I_2 molecules fairly weakly coordinated to I^-.

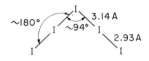

Fig. 22-2. Structure of the pentaiodide ion, I_5^-, as it occurs in $[(CH_3)_4N]I_5$.

References

Anders, E., *Ann. Rev. Nuclear Sci.*, **9**, 203 (1959). A good review of the nuclear and chemical properties of the element astatine.

Das, T. P., and E. L. Hahn, *Nuclear Quadrupole Resonance Spectroscopy*, Academic Press, New York, 1958. Detailed discussion of theory and experimental results for many halogen compounds.

Dehnicke, K., *Angew. Chem. (Internat.)*, **4**, 22 (1965). Synthetic methods for oxohalides.

Hyde, E. K., *J. Chem. Educ.*, **36**, 15 (1959). Review on astatine.

Jolles, Z. E., ed., *Bromine and its Compounds*, Benn, London, 1966. Reference book.

Mellor, J. W., *Comprehensive Treatise on Inorganic Chemistry*, Suppl. II, Pt. I, Longmans, Green, New York–London, 1956. Contains all the group VII elements.

Novikov, S. S., V. V. Sevost'yanova and A. A. Fainzil'berg, *Russ. Chem. Rev.*, **1962**, 671. Positive halogen organic compounds.

Schmeisser, M., and K. Brändle, *Adv. Inorg. Chem. Radiochem.*, **5**, 41 (1963). Oxides and oxofluorides of halogens. A comprehensive review.

Schumaker, J. C., ed., *Perchlorates* (A. C. S. Monograph, No. 146), Reinhold, New York, 1960. An extensive review of perchloric acid and perchlorates.

Sconce, J. S., ed., *Chlorine: its manufacture, properties, and uses* (A. C. S. Monograph, No. 154), Reinhold, New York, 1962.

Sharpe, A. G., *Quart. Rev.*, **4**, 115 (1950). Interhalogen compounds and polyhalides.

Wiebenga, E. H., E. E. Havinga and K. H. Boswijk, *Adv. Inorg. Chem. Radiochem.*, **3**, 133 (1961). A survey of structures, properties and bonding in interhalogen compounds.

Zinov'ev, A. A., *Russ. Chem. Rev.*, **1963**, 268. Perchloric acid and Cl_2O_7.

23

The Noble Gases

THE ELEMENTS

23-1. Group Trends

The atoms of the noble gases—sometimes called rare gases or inert gases—all have valence shells which are closed octets (except He, where there is a duet). These closed shells are quite stable, as shown by the high ionization potentials, especially of the lighter members of the group (Table 23-1). The elements are all low-boiling gases whose physical properties vary fairly systematically with atomic number. The boiling point of helium is the lowest of any known substance. The boiling points increase monotonically with increasing atomic number, which is a consequence of the monotonic increase in the heats of vaporization.

The heats of vaporization are measures of the work which must be done to overcome interatomic attractive forces. Since there are no ordinary electron pair interactions between noble gas atoms, these weak forces must be of the van der Waals or London type; such forces are proportional to the polarizability and inversely proportional to the ionization potentials of the atoms. They increase therefore as the size and diffuseness of the electron clouds increase.

The ability of the noble gases to enter into chemical combination with other atoms is very limited, only Kr, Xe and Rn having so far been induced to do so. This ability would be expected to increase with decreasing ionization potential and decreasing energy of promotion to states with unpaired electrons. The data in Table 23-1 for ionization potentials and for the lowest energy promotion process show that chemical activity should increase down the group. According to present knowledge, the threshold of actual chemical activity is reached only at Kr. The chemical activity of Xe is markedly greater. That of Rn is presumably still greater but it is difficult to assess in detail because the radioactivity of Rn places serious limitations on experimental study.

TABLE 23-1

Some Properties of the Noble Gases

Outer shell configuration	Atomic number	1st IP, ev	Normal b, °K	ΔH_{vap}, kcal/mole	% by volume in the atmosphere	Promotion energy ev, $ns^2np^6 \rightarrow ns^2np^5(n+1)s$
He $1s^2$	2	24.58	4.18	0.022	5.24×10^{-4}	—
Ne $2s^22p^6$	10	21.56	27.13	0.44	1.82×10^{-3}	16.6
Ar $3s^23p^6$	18	15.76	87.29	1.50	0.934	11.5
Kr $4s^24p^6$	36	14.00	120.26	2.31	1.14×10^{-3}	9.9
Xe $5s^25p^6$	54	12.13	166.06	3.27	8.7×10^{-6}	8.3
Rn $6s^26p^6$	86	10.75	208.16	4.3		6.8

23-2. Occurrence, Isolation and Applications

The noble gases occur as minor constituents of the atmosphere (Table 23-1). Helium is also found as a component (up to $\sim 7\%$) in certain natural hydrocarbon gases in the United States. This helium undoubtedly originated from decay of radioactive elements in rocks, and certain radioactive minerals contain occluded helium which can be released on heating. All isotopes of radon are radioactive and are occasionally given specific names (e.g., actinon, thoron) derived from their source in the radioactive decay series. The isotope with the longest half-life (^{222}Rn, 3.825 days; α) is formed in the decay of radium and is normally obtained by pumping off the gas from radium chloride solutions. Ne, Ar, Kr and Xe are commercially obtainable as products of fractionation of liquid air.

The main uses of the gases are in welding (argon provides an inert atmosphere), in gas-filled electric light bulbs, radio tubes and Geiger counters (argon) and in discharge tubes (neon); radon has been used therapeutically as an α particle source in the treatment of cancer.

Some of the noble gases arise as products of radioactive decay in minerals, and the amount present can be used to determine the age of the specimen. For example, in the course of the decay of ^{238}U, eight α particles are produced. These easily acquire electrons to form He atoms by oxidizing other elements present. If the rock is sufficiently impermeable, the total He remains trapped therein. If the amounts of trapped helium and remaining ^{238}U are measured, the age of the specimen can be calculated, for one-eighth of the atoms of He represent the number of ^{238}U atoms which have decayed. (A correction must be applied for thorium, which also decays by α emission and generally occurs in small amounts with uranium.) Argon arises in potassium-containing minerals by electron capture of ^{40}K. A complication arises here since ^{40}K also decays by β^- emission to ^{40}Ca, and the accuracy of the age determination in this case depends on the accuracy of our knowledge of the branching ratio of ^{40}K, which at present is only moderate.

The trapping of Ar, Kr and Xe in clathrate compounds has been discussed in Chapter 6.

23-3. Special Properties of Helium

Naturally occurring helium is essentially all ^{4}He, although ^{3}He occurs to the extent of $\sim 10^{-7}$ atom %. ^{3}He can be made in greater quantities by nuclear reactions and by β^- decay of tritium.

Liquid ^{3}He appears to be a normal liquid, but ^{4}He exhibits astonishing properties not possessed by any other known substance. The liquid formed at 4.18°K is called He I and has normal liquid properties. On further cooling at 1 atm a second form, called He II, appears, the equilibrium temperature being 2.178°K. This transition temperature is called the λ point and varies slightly with pressure. The transition from He I to He II is accompanied by discontinuous changes of some physical properties. He II has a viscosity at least as low as the most sensitive methods of measurement can detect and is an extraordinary conductor of heat. It forms exceedingly thin films, only a few hundred atoms thick, which flow apparently without friction. If the levels in two concentric vessels are unequal, it will flow from one to the other, even going uphill where necessary. Some workers have referred to He II as a fourth state of matter. No fully satisfactory theoretical explanation of these properties has yet been devised.

THE CHEMISTRY OF THE NOBLE GASES

The discovery that the noble gases can engage in genuine chemical reactions is quite recent; this chemistry is largely that of xenon, with the little which is known for krypton and radon being homologous to it.

Following his observation that O_2 reacts with PtF_6 to give the compound $[O_2^+][PtF_6^-]$ (page 369), N. Bartlett in 1962 recognized that since the ionization potential of xenon is almost identical with that of the oxygen molecule, an analogous reaction should occur with xenon. He then confirmed this prediction by obtaining a red crystalline solid, originally believed to be $XePtF_6$, by direct interaction of Xe with PtF_6. This discovery of Bartlett's led to extremely rapid and extensive developments in xenon chemistry.

Subsequent work has shown that the stoichiometry of the hexafluoroplatinate(V) is complex and that compounds of the type $Xe(PtF_6)_x$ are formed where $1 \leqslant x \leqslant 2$ and the true nature is not entirely clear. Studies with other hexafluorides indicate that those which are thermodynamically unstable (PtF_6, RuF_6, RhF_6, PuF_6) react with xenon at room temperature whereas the stable hexafluorides (e.g., UF_6, NpF_6, IrF_6) do not react under ordinary conditions.

23-4. The Chemistry of Xenon

Xenon reacts directly with only one element, fluorine, but compounds in oxidation states from II to VIII are now known, some of which are exceedingly stable and can be obtained in large quantities. The more important compounds and some of their properties are given in Table 23-2.

TABLE 23-2
Principal Xenon Compounds [a]

Oxidation state	Compound	Form	Melting point °C	Structure	Remarks
II	XeF_2	Colorless crystals	140	Linear	Hydrolyzed to Xe + O_2; v. soluble in HF(l)
	$XeF_2 \cdot 2SbF_5$	Yellow solid	63		
IV	XeF_4	Colorless crystals	114	Planar	Stable, $\Delta H_f^{298°} = -68$ kcal/mole
	$XeOF_2$	Colorless crystals	90		Barely stable
VI	XeF_6	Colorless crystals	47.7	Distorted octahedral	Stable, $\Delta H_f^{298°} = -96$ kcal/mole
	$CsXeF_7$	Colorless solid			Decomp. $> 50°$
	Cs_2XeF_8	Yellow solid			Stable to 400°
	$XeOF_4$	Colorless liquid	-28	Square pyramid	Stable
	XeO_3	Colorless crystals		Trigonal pyramidal	Explosive, $\Delta H_f^{298°} = +96$ kcal/mole. Hygroscopic; stable in solution
VIII	XeO_4	Colorless gas		Tetrahedral	Explosive
	XeO_6^{4-}	Colorless salts		Octahedral	Anions $HXeO_6^{3-}$, $H_2XeO_6^{2-}$, $H_3XeO_6^-$ also exist

[a] Other species have been observed in mass spectra, e.g., XeO_2F_2, or in emission spectra, e.g., XeO, while XeF, XeF_5, XeF_8, $XeOF_3$, etc., have not been fully established or are unstable.

Fluorides. The fluorides XeF_2, XeF_4 and XeF_6 are well established. The equilibrium constants for the reactions

$$Xe + F_2 = XeF_2$$
$$XeF_2 + F_2 = XeF_4$$
$$XeF_4 + F_2 = XeF_6$$

are now known over the temperature range 300–775° so that, in principle, the binary fluorides should be obtainable in reasonable purity by deliberate choice of reaction conditions. In practice, however, the following optimum preparative methods were developed without recourse to the equilibrium constants.

In order to prepare XeF_2 by direct interaction, it must be removed from the reaction zone before it can react further to form XeF_4. Typically, mixtures of Xe and F_2 have been circulated through a loop containing a section of nickel tubing heated to 400° and a U-tube maintained at $-50°$ where the XeF_2 is condensed. Conversion is complete in about 8 hours. It can be made almost quantitative by interaction[1] of Xe and excess O_2F_2 at $-118°$.

XeF_4 is by far the easiest Xe compound to prepare. Essentially quantitative conversion of Xe to XeF_4 occurs when a 1:5 mixture of Xe and F_2 is heated in a nickel can at 400° and about 6 atm pressure for a few hours.

XeF_6 requires more severe conditions. In general, greater than 95% conversion to XeF_6 is obtained with a F_2/Xe ratio of about 20 and a pressure of 50 atm; rapid reaction occurs at 200–250°. At 700° and about 200 atm essentially quantitative conversion to XeF_6 occurs.

XeF_2 and XeF_4 both have vapor pressures of several millimeters at 300°, sublime easily, and are therefore conveniently handled in a conventional vacuum line. Both are stable provided they are dry and pure; they can be stored in nickel vessels or in scrupulously dried glass vessels.

XeF_6 is a colorless solid at 43°; it becomes yellow at this temperature and melts to a yellow liquid at 47.7°. The vapor is also yellow. It is stable at room temperature and can be stored indefinitely in nickel containers. However, it reacts rapidly with quartz giving $XeOF_4$:

$$2XeF_6 + SiO_2 = 2XeOF_4 + SiF_4$$

Structural evidence that XeF_6 is not octahedral and may be considered to have a lone-pair is supported by the formation of adducts with Lewis acids (see below) as well as by the conductance of solutions in liquid HF; the nature of these species is not yet established. However, XeF_6 also appears to act as an acceptor for F^- since it reacts with alkali metal

[1] S. I. Morrow and A. R. Young II, *Inorg. Chem.*, **3**, 759 (1964).

fluorides (other than LiF)[2] to give heptafluoroxenates(VI) or, for NaF and KF, apparently octafluoroxenates(VI):

$$XeF_6 + RbF = RbXeF_7$$

The Rb and Cs salts are well characterized; above 20° and 50° respectively they decompose:

$$2MXeF_7 = XeF_6 + M_2XeF_8$$

This formation from XeF_6 of XeF_7^- and XeF_8^{2-} salts resembles the behavior of UF_6. The Rb and Cs octafluoroxenates are the most stable compounds yet made and decompose only above 400°; they hydrolyze in the atmosphere to give xenon-containing oxidizing products. The sodium fluoride adduct of XeF_6 decomposes below 100° and can be used to purify XeF_6.

Adducts such as $XeF_6 \cdot 2SbF_5$ (m 108°) or $XeF_6 \cdot BF_3$ are formed[3] but their nature is not fully known. However, an addition compound $XeF_2 \cdot XeF_4$ has discrete molecules of the components in the crystal. The short intermolecular distances are presumably due to electrostatic interactions.[4]

The only well-characterized oxofluoride of xenon, $XeOF_4$, is best prepared by partial hydrolysis of XeF_6,

$$XeF_6 + H_2O = XeOF_4 + 2HF$$

but, as noted earlier, it also arises by reaction of XeF_6 with silica. It is somewhat more volatile than XeF_6 and appears to be stable at room temperature. It can be stored indefinitely in nickel containers, but seems to react slowly with quartz and polyethylene. It reacts with water to give, as the final product, XeO_3. XeO_2F_2 may be an intermediate, but this is uncertain.

The molecular structures of XeF_2, XeF_4 and $XeOF_4$ are similar to those of their respective isoelectronic analogs. These structures, and the associated questions of bonding and valence, have been treated in Chapter 15.

No chlorides are known but there is evidence from Mössbauer spectra for the existence of tracer quantities of $XeCl_4$ in the lattice of a salt of ICl_4^- when radioactive ^{129}I undergoes β^--decay to give an excited state of ^{129}Xe whose γ-ray can be studied.[5]

[2] R. D. Peacock, H. Selig and I. Sheft, *Proc. Chem. Soc.*, **1964**, 285; I. Sheft, T. M. Spittler and F. H. Martin, *Science*, **145**, 701 (1964).
[3] G. L. Gard and G. H. Cady, *Inorg. Chem.*, **3**, 1745 (1964).
[4] J. H. Burns, R. D. Ellison and H. A. Levy, *Acta Cryst.*, **18**, 11 (1965).
[5] G. J. Perlow and M. R. Perlow, *J. Chem. Phys.*, **41**, 1157 (1964).

Aqueous chemistry; oxygen compounds. The aqueous chemistry of the xenon fluorides has been partly elucidated. Although XeF_2 is rapidly hydrolyzed by aqueous base

$$XeF_2 + 2OH^- = Xe + \tfrac{1}{2}O_2 + 2F^- + H_2O$$

it dissolves (25 g/liter at 0°) in acidic media giving solutions which are colorless, have a pungent odor and are powerful oxidants. Hydrolysis proceeds slowly (half-time of 7 hr at 0° in dilute HF).

Both XeF_4 and XeF_6 are hydrolyzed by water to give Xe^{VI}, evidently in the form of undissociated XeO_3.

$$3XeF_4 + 6H_2O = XeO_3 + 2Xe + \tfrac{3}{2}O_2 + 12HF$$
$$XeF_6 + 3H_2O = XeO_3 + 6HF.$$

Aqueous solutions, colorless, odorless and stable, as concentrated as $11M$ in Xe^{VI}, have been obtained. They are non-conducting. On evaporation, solid XeO_3 is obtained; this is a powerful explosive. The presence of XeO_3 molecules in solution is suggested by the lack of conductance and by the Raman spectrum. In strong base, however, the predominant Xe^{VI} species seems to be $HXeO_4^-$ or a hydrated form thereof:

$$HXeO_4^- = XeO_3 + OH^- \qquad K \approx 7 \times 10^{-4}$$

The $HXeO_4^-$ species slowly disproportionates to produce Xe^{VIII} and Xe:

$$2HXeO_4^- + 2OH^- = XeO_6^{4-} + Xe + O_2 + 2H_2O$$

Aqueous Xe^{VIII} arises not only in the above disproportionation, but by passing ozone through a dilute solution of Xe^{VI} in base. These *perxenate* solutions are powerful and rapid oxidizing agents. It appears that their nature is described by the following equilibria:

$$HXeO_6^{3-} + H^+ = H_2XeO_6^{2-} \qquad K \approx 10^{10.5}$$
$$H_2XeO_6^{2-} + H^+ = H_3XeO_6^- \qquad K \approx 10^6$$

$H_3XeO_6^-$ then decomposes liberating oxygen:

$$H_3XeO_6^- = HXeO_4^- + \tfrac{1}{2}O_2 + H_2O$$

This oxidation of water by perxenate has been recently[6] shown to proceed almost entirely through the formation of OH radicals according to the scheme

$$Xe^{VIII} + H_2O \rightleftharpoons Xe^{VII} + OH^\bullet$$
$$Xe^{VII} + H_2O \rightleftharpoons Xe^{VI} + OH^\bullet$$
$$2OH^\bullet \rightarrow H_2O_2$$
$$Xe^{VIII} + H_2O_2 \rightarrow Xe^{VI} + O_2$$

[6] E. H. Appelman and M. Anbar, *Inorg. Chem.*, **4**, 1066 (1965).

Stable, insoluble perxenate salts can be precipitated from Xe^{VIII} solutions, e.g., $Na_4XeO_6 \cdot 8H_2O$, $Na_4XeO_6 \cdot 6H_2O$, $Ba_2XeO_6 \cdot 1.5H_2O$. X-ray crystallographic studies[7] of the first two have shown that XeO_6 octahedra are present.

The redox behavior of Xe and its oxo species is summarized in the following diagrams of standard potentials.

Acid solution:

$$H_4XeO_6 \xrightarrow{\ +3.0\ } XeO_3 \xrightarrow{\ +1.8\ } Xe$$
$$\underset{-1.6}{\big\lfloor} \quad XeF_2 \quad \underset{+2.2}{\big\rfloor}$$

Alkaline solution:

$$HXeO_6{}^{3-} \xrightarrow{\ +0.9\ } HXeO_4{}^- \xrightarrow{\ +0.7\ } XeO(?) \xrightarrow{\ +1.3\ } Xe$$
$$\big\lfloor \underset{+0.9}{\hspace{4cm}} \big\rfloor$$

XeO_4 is an unstable substance formed by reaction of sodium perxenate with concentrated sulfuric acid. Solid specimens have exploded at temperatures as low as $-40°$. The infrared spectrum suggests that the molecule may be tetrahedral.

23-5. Chemistry of Other Noble Gases

Helium, neon and argon have so far not been brought into chemical combination, even with fluorine, and it seems unlikely that they are capable of reaction. Krypton, however, reacts with fluorine upon irradiation of a mixture of the gases at low pressure or by passing an electric discharge through the mixture.[8] An earlier report that KrF_4 is formed is apparently incorrect, the only product being KrF_2. This is a white crystalline solid which sublimes well below $0°$ and can be handled in dry pyrex or poly(chlorofluoroethylene) containers. It is a highly reactive fluorinating agent and decomposes spontaneously at room temperature. Upon hydrolysis at -30 to $-60°$ it yields "kryptic acid," about which virtually nothing is yet known. It also gives $KrF_2 \cdot 2SbF_5$, which is more stable and less volatile than KrF_2.

[7] J. A. Ibers, W. C. Hamilton and D. R. MacKenzie, *Inorg. Chem.*, **3**, 1412 (1964); A. Zalkin, J. D. Forrester and D. H. Templeton, *Inorg. Chem.*, **3**, 1417 (1964); A. Zalkin, J. D. Forrester, D. H. Templeton, S. M. Williamson and C. W. Koch, *J. Amer. Chem. Soc.*, **86**, 3569 (1964).

[8] F. Schreiner, J. G. Malm and J. C. Hindman, *J. Amer. Chem. Soc.*, **87**, 25 (1965).

The existence of a radon fluoride has been established by tracer experiments [9] but its composition has not been determined. The energy generated by radioactive decay of radon makes assessment of its inherent stability and reactivity quite difficult.

References

Chernick, C. L., *Record of Chem. Prog.*, **24**, 139 (1963). Noble gas chemistry, especially good on historical background.

Cook, G. A., ed., *Argon, Helium, and the Rare Gases*, 2 vols., John Wiley (Interscience), New York, 1961. A comprehensive source book, exclusive of chemical behavior.

Coulson, C. A., *J. Chem. Soc.*, **1964**, 1442. An exceedingly detailed and thorough treatment of bonding in xenon fluorides and related molecules.

Dugdale, J. S., *Trans. Roy. Soc. Canada*, **2**, 267 (1964). Review on solid helium.

Hollaway, J. H., *Prog. Inorg. Chem.*, **6**, 241 (1964). A general summary of noble gas chemistry.

Hyman, H. H., ed., *Noble Gas Compounds*, University of Chicago Press, 1963. A collection of papers from a symposium.

Keesom, W. H., *Helium*, Elsevier, New York, 1942.

Malm, J. G., H. Selig, J. Jortner and S. A. Rice, *Chem. Rev.*, **65**, 199 (1965). A thorough and authoritative review of Xe chemistry and of the theoretical approaches to the electronic structures of Xe compounds.

Moody, G. J., and Thomas, J. D. R., *Noble Gases and Their Compounds*, Pergamon Press, London, 1964. A well-written short introduction.

[9] P. R. Fields, L. Stein and M. H. Zirin, *J. Amer. Chem. Soc.*, **84**, 4164 (1962).

24

Zinc, Cadmium and Mercury

GENERAL REMARKS

24-1. Electronic Structures

These three elements follow copper, silver and gold and have two s electrons outside filled d shells. Their configurations, ionization potentials and some other properties are given in Table 24-1. Whereas in the elements

TABLE 24-1

Some Properties of the Group IIb Elements

	Zinc	Cadmium	Mercury
Outer electronic configuration	$3d^{10}4s^2$	$4d^{10}5s^2$	$5d^{10}6s^2$
Ionization potentials, ev			
1st	9.39	8.99	10.43
2nd	17.89	16.84	18.65
3rd	40.0	38.0	34.3
Melting point, °C	419	321	-38.87
Boiling point, °C	907	767	357
Heat of vaporization, kcal/mole	31.2	26.8	14.7
E_0 for $M^{2+} + 2e = M$, v	-0.762	-0.402	0.854
Radii of divalent ions, A	0.69	0.92	0.93

Cu, Ag and Au the filled d shells lose one or two d electrons to give ions or complexes in the II and III oxidation states, this is no longer possible for the group II elements and there is no evidence for oxidation states higher than II. This follows from the fact that the third ionization potentials are extremely high for Zn, Cd and Hg, and energies of solvation or lattice formation cannot suffice to render the III oxidation states chemically stable.

The primary divergence from the group valence lies in the rather special case of mercurous mercury, where the unique ion Hg_2^{2+} is formed. There have been some unconfirmed[1] reports of univalent zinc, and Cd^I, as Cd_2^{2+}, has been obtained in melts; there is no evidence for Zn^I or Cd^I in aqueous solution, however. There are, in fact, no paramagnetic ions with an electron in an s orbital for any of the elements of the first, second or third long periods, and where such ions might have been expected, there is either disproportionation as in $Ga^{II} \rightarrow Ga^I + Ga^{III}$ (page 451) or formation of a metal–metal bond as in Ga_2S_2, Cd_2^{2+} and Hg_2^{2+}.

Thus since these elements do not exhibit multiple valence to any important degree and form no compounds in which the d shell is other than full, they are regarded as nontransition elements, whereas by the same criteria Cu, Ag and Au are considered as transition elements. Zinc, cadmium and mercury differ in other ways from the transition metals. Thus, although they are metals, they are softer and lower melting, and Zn and Cd are considerably more electropositive, than their near neighbors in the transition groups. However, there is some resemblance to the transition elements in their ability to form complexes, particularly with ammonia, amines, halide ions and cyanide.

In complexes of these elements, even with CN^-, it must be borne in mind that the possibility of any $d\pi$ bonding between the metal and the ligand is very much lowered compared to the d-transition elements, owing to the electronic structure, and no carbonyls, nitrosyls, olefin complexes, etc., of the type given by transition metals are known. There are also no ligand field stabilization effects.

24-2. Trends in the Group

Although the chemistry of cadmium is essentially homologous to that of zinc, mercury is more different than similar to Zn and Cd both in the properties of the element and in its compounds.

As would be expected, $Cd(OH)_2$ is more basic than $Zn(OH)_2$, which is amphoteric, whereas $Hg(OH)_2$ is an extremely weak base. Zinc and cadmium form halides which are essentially ionic, crystallizing in layer lattices, but the mercuric halides are covalent; thus discrete $HgCl_2$ molecules may be discerned in the crystal lattice and mercuric halides are almost undissociated in aqueous solution.

Although Zn and Cd are electropositive metals, mercury has unusually high ionization potentials, a high positive standard electrode potential and is generally rather inert chemically. These properties of mercury may be

---

[1] W. L. James and G. E. Stoner, *J. Amer. Chem. Soc.*, **85**, 1354 (1963).

regarded as a manifestation of the "inert pair" effect which has been noted also in the chemical properties of Tl, Pb and Bi and to a lesser extent in In and Sn.

The Zn^{2+} and Cd^{2+} ions are rather similar in many respects to Mg^{2+} and have numerous isomorphous salts. While all of the ions Zn^{2+}, Cd^{2+} and Hg^{2+} have a pronounced tendency to form complexes, the Hg^{2+} complexes are usually orders of magnitude more stable than those of Zn^{2+} and Cd^{2+} as can be seen from Table 24-2. All three elements form a variety of covalently bound compounds, and the polarizing ability of the M^{2+} ions appears to be larger than might have been expected by comparing their radii with those of the Mg–Ra group, a fact that can be associated with the greater ease of distortion of the filled d shell compared to the noble-gas-like ions of the latter elements.

In line with its superior tendency to form covalent bonds, mercury forms a large number of organometallic compounds, generally R_2Hg and $RHgX$,

TABLE 24-2

Equilibrium Constants for Some Typical Complexes of
Zn, Cd and Hg
$(M^{2+} + 4X = [MX_4]; K = [MX_4]/[M^{2+}][X]^4)$

	K		
X	Zn^{2+}	Cd^{2+}	Hg^{2+}
Cl^-	1	10^3	10^{16}
Br^-	10^{-1}	10^4	10^{22}
I^-	10^{-2}	10^6	10^{30}
NH_3	10^9	10^7	10^{19}
CN^-	10^{16}	10^{18}	10^{41}

which are stable to air and water. The corresponding zinc and cadmium compounds are unstable to air and water and more generally reactive. The unusual stability of the mercury compounds is not indicative of high bond strengths—on the contrary, these are not high, usually in the range 13–52 kcal/mole—but must be attributed to the very low affinity of mercury for oxygen.

THE ELEMENTS

24-3. Occurrence and Isolation

The elements are of relatively low abundance in nature but have long been well known because they occur in localized deposits and are rather easily won from their ores. Zinc occurs in a number of minerals—*zinc blende*, ZnS; *smithsonite* or *calamine*, $ZnCO_3$; *willemite*, Zn_2SiO_4; *zincite*, ZnO; and several others. Cadmium is most commonly found associated with zinc in such ores, but in small amounts. The commercially important zinc ores are mainly the carbonate and the sulfide. On roasting either in air, the oxide is obtained. This may then be reduced, commonly with coke, and the metal distilled. Any cadmium present can be separated by fractional distillation since the boiling points differ appreciably. Alternatively, the ZnO may be dissolved in acid and the metal electrodeposited. This is possible because the high overvoltage of hydrogen on zinc (a phenomenon not well understood) allows zinc to deposit in the presence of H^+ despite the fact that *equilibrium* electrode potentials would require hydrogen to be reduced preferentially to zinc. Cadmium may be obtained by treating the solution, prior to electrolysis, with zinc dust which reduces the Cd^{2+}:

$$Zn + Cd^{2+} = Zn^{2+} + Cd \qquad E^0 = 0.36 \text{ v}$$

The only important ore of mercury is *cinnabar*, HgS. Roasting converts HgS to the oxide, which at about 500° decomposes and mercury distills out.

24-4. Physical and Chemical Properties

The main properties of the elements are listed in Table 24-1. Zinc and cadmium are white, lustrous, but tarnishable metals. Like Be and Mg, with which they are isostructural, their structures deviate from perfect hexagonal close packing by elongation along the six-fold axis. Mercury is a shiny liquid at ordinary temperatures. All are remarkably volatile for heavy metals, mercury, of course, uniquely so. Mercury gives a monatomic vapor and has an appreciable vapor pressure (1.3×10^{-3} mm) at 20°. It is also surprisingly soluble in both polar and nonpolar liquids; for example, a saturated solution in air-free water[2] at 25° has 6×10^{-8} g/g. Because of its high volatility and toxicity, mercury should always be kept in stoppered containers and handled in well-ventilated areas.

As may be seen from the standard potentials, Zn and Cd are fairly electropositive whereas mercury is "noble." Both Zn and Cd react readily with nonoxidizing acids releasing hydrogen and giving the divalent ions, whereas Hg is inert to nonoxidizing acids. Zinc also dissolves in strong bases because of its ability to form zincate ions, commonly written ZnO_2^{2-}, but certainly better represented as $[Zn(OH)_3(H_2O)]^-$, $[Zn(OH)_3(H_2O)_3]^-$ or $[Zn(OH)_4]^{2-}$. Although the structure of the species in solution is not definitely known, solid zincates such as $NaZn(OH)_3$ and $Na_2Zn(OH)_4$ can be obtained from concentrated solutions. Using the simpler formula, the reaction can be written

$$Zn + 2OH^- = ZnO_2^{2-} + H_2$$

[2] S. S. Choi and D. G. Tuck, *J. Chem. Soc.*, **1962**, 4080.

Cadmium does not react with base since cadmiate ions are of negligible stability.

Zinc and cadmium react readily with oxygen on heating to give the oxides. Although mercury and oxygen are unstable with respect to HgO at room temperature, their rate of combination is exceedingly slow; the reaction proceeds at a useful rate at 300–350°, but, around 400° and above, the stability relation reverses and HgO decomposes rapidly into the elements

$$HgO(s) = Hg(s) + \tfrac{1}{2}O_2 \qquad \Delta H_{diss} = 38.2 \text{ kcal/mole}$$

This ability of mercury to absorb oxygen from air and regenerate it again in pure form was of considerable importance in the earliest studies of oxygen by Lavoisier and Priestley.

All three elements react directly with halogens and with sulfur and other nonmetals such as phosphorus, selenium, etc.

Zinc and cadmium form very many alloys, some, such as brass, being of technical importance. Mercury combines with many other metals, sometimes with difficulty but sometimes, as with sodium or potassium, very vigorously; these alloys are called *amalgams*. Some amalgams have definite compositions; that is, they are compounds, such as Hg_2Na. Some of the transition metals do not form amalgams, and iron is commonly used for containers of mercury. Sodium amalgams and amalgamated zinc are commonly used as reducing agents for aqueous solutions.

Zinc has been shown to be more volatile in presence of $ZnCl_2$ (and also ZnO) at 285–350°, suggesting the formation of species such as $(ZnCl)_2$ which disproportionate at room temperature.[3]

ZINC AND CADMIUM COMPOUNDS

24-5. Oxides and Hydroxides

The oxides, ZnO and CdO, are formed on burning the metals in air or by pyrolysis of the carbonates or nitrates; oxide smokes can be obtained by combustion of the alkyls, cadmium oxide smokes being exceedingly toxic. Zinc oxide is normally white but turns yellow on heating; cadmium oxide varies in color from greenish yellow through brown to nearly black, depending on its thermal history. These colors are the result of various kinds of lattice defects. Both oxides sublime without decomposition at very high temperatures.

The hydroxides are precipitated from solutions of salts by addition of bases. The solubility products of $Zn(OH)_2$ and $Cd(OH)_2$ are about 10^{-11}

---

[3] D. H. Kerridge, *J. Chem. Soc.*, **1963**, 1178.

and 10^{-14}, respectively, but $Zn(OH)_2$ is more soluble than would be expected from this constant owing to the equilibrium

$$Zn(OH)_2(s) = Zn(OH)_2(aq) \qquad K = 10^{-6}$$

Further, $Zn(OH)_2$ readily dissolves in excess alkali bases to give zincate ions, probably $[Zn(OH)_4]^{2-}$. $Cd(OH)_2$ is insoluble in bases. Both hydroxides readily dissolve in excess of strong ammonia to form the ammine complexes, for example, $[Zn(NH_3)_4]^{2+}$.

24-6. Sulfides, Selenides, Tellurides

These are all crystalline substances, insoluble in water. Three structures are represented among the eight compounds as shown in Table 24-3. The

TABLE 24-3

Structures[a] of Zn and Cd Oxides and Chalconides[b]

Metal	O	S	Se	Te
Zn	W, Z	Z, W	Z	Z, W
Cd	NaCl	W, Z	W, Z	Z

[a] W = wurtzite structure; Z = zinc blende structure; NaCl = rock salt structure.

[b] Where two polymorphs occur, the one stable at lower temperatures is listed first.

rock salt and zinc blende structures have been described earlier (pages 36 and 46). In the former, the cation is octahedrally surrounded by six anions, whereas in the latter the cation is tetrahedrally surrounded by anions. The *wurtzite structure* (from the mineral wurtzite, which is the stable high temperature modification of ZnS) also gives the cations tetrahedral coordination and is shown in Figure 24-1. It will be seen from

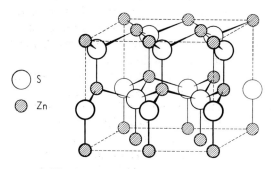

Fig. 24-1. The wurtzite structure.

Table 24-3 that, with the exception of CdO, zinc and cadmium prefer tetrahedral coordination in their chalconides.

24-7. Halides and Halide Complexes

All four halides of both zinc and cadmium are known. Some of their relevant properties are given in Table 24-4.

TABLE 24-4

Some Properties of the Zinc and Cadmium Halides

	Solubility in water, mole/liter	Melting point, °C	Boiling point, °C	Structure
ZnF_2	1.57 (20°)	872	1502	Rutile
$ZnCl_2$	31.8 (25°)	275	756	Three forms; see text
$ZnBr_2$	20.9 (25°)	394	697	c.c.p. anions with Zn in tetra-
ZnI_2	13 (25°)	446	(Sublimes)	hedral interstices
CdF_2	0.29 (25°)	1110	1747	Fluorite
$CdCl_2$	7.7 (20°)	868	980	
$CdBr_2$	4.2 (20°)	568	1136	Close-packed anions with Cd in octahedral interstices
CdI_2	2.3 (20°)	387	(Sublimes)	

Both ZnF_2 and CdF_2 show distinct evidence of being considerably more ionic than the other halides of the same element. Thus they have higher melting points and boiling points, and they are considerably less soluble in water. The latter fact is attributable not only to the high lattice energies of the fluorides but also to the fact that the formation of halo complexes in solution, which enhances the solubility of the other halides, does not occur for the fluorides.

The structures of the chlorides, bromides and iodides may be viewed as close-packed arrays of halide ions, but there is a characteristic difference in that zinc ions occupy tetrahedral interstices whereas cadmium ions occupy octahedral ones. Actually, there are at least three polymorphs of $ZnCl_2$ known, two of which are similar and in which the presence of zinc ions in tetrahedral holes has been demonstrated.

Complex anions are formed by both metals, but the equilibrium constants vary rather widely as the data in Table 24-5 show. The exact values are not important since ionic strength effects are rather large, but certain qualititative features can be discerned. The formation of fluoro complexes is quite restricted, and none have been isolated as solids. There is evidence for the attainment of all four stages of complexation by both zinc and cadmium for Cl^-, Br^- and I^-, with the cadmium complexes being

TABLE 24-5

Some Formation Constants of Zinc and Cadmium Halide Complexes (At 25°)

Halogen	Log K_1	Log K_2	Log K_3	Log K_4	Medium
Zn F	0.75	Not obs.	Not obs.	Not obs.	0.5–1.0M NaClO$_4$
Cl	−1.0 to +1.0	−1.0 to +1.0	−1.0 to +1.0	−1.0 to +1.0	Variable
Br	−0.60	−0.37	−0.73	0.44	Ionic str. = 4.5
I	−2.93	1.25	−0.07	−0.59	Ionic str. = 4.5
Cd F	0.46	0.07	Not obs.	Not obs.	1.0M NaClO$_4$
Cl	1.77	1.45	−0.25	−0.05	2.1M KNO$_3$
Br	1.97	1.25	0.24	0.15	1M KNO$_3$
I	2.96	1.33	1.07	1.00	1.6M KNO$_3$

moderately stable while those of zinc are of rather low stability. The ZnX_4^{2-} complexes can be isolated as salts of large cations. Zn^{2+} tends to form stronger bonds to F and O whereas Cd^{2+} is more strongly bound to Cl, S and P ligands. Raman spectra[4] show that, depending on the concentration, the species present in aqueous solutions of $ZnCl_2$ are $[Zn(H_2O)_6]^{2+}$, $ZnCl^+(aq)$, $ZnCl_2(aq)$ and $[ZnCl_4(H_2O)_2]^{2-}$, but no indication was found of $[ZnCl_3]^-$ or $[ZnCl_4]^{2-}$.

It has long been known that aqueous solutions of cadmium halides appear, superficially, to be incompletely dissociated, that is, to be weak electrolytes. Although there are significant amounts of the undissociated halides, CdX_2, present in moderately concentrated solutions, there are other species also present as shown in Table 24-6. Thus the solutions are

TABLE 24-6

Approximate Concentrations of Dissociated and Undissociated Species in 0.5M CdBr$_2$ Solution at 25°

	Concentration, M		Concentration, M
Cd^{2+}	0.013	Br$^-$	0.200
CdBr$^+$	0.259	CdBr$_2$	0.164
CdBr$_3^-$	0.043	CdBr$_4^{2-}$	0.021

best regarded as systems containing all possible species in equilibrium rather than simply as solutions of a weak electrolyte; of course, the ratios of the species vary with conditions of concentration and pH.

The zinc halides are dissociated to a greater extent than the cadmium halides but are also more hydrolyzed in water (see below). The major hydrolysis product of $CdCl_2$ appears to be $Cd(OH)Cl$.

[4] D. E. Irish, B. McCarroll and T. F. Young, *J. Chem. Phys.*, **39**, 3436 (1963).

Zinc chloride is so soluble in water that mole ratios $H_2O–ZnCl_2$ can easily be less than $2:1$.[5] Both zinc and cadmium halides are quite soluble in alcohol, acetone and similar donor solvents, and in some cases adducts can be obtained.

24-8. Other Salts

Salts of oxo acids such as the nitrate, sulfate, sulfite, perchlorate and acetate are soluble in water. The Zn^{2+} and Cd^{2+} ions are rather similar to Mg^{2+}, and many of their salts are isomorphous with magnesium salts, for example, $Zn(Mg)SO_4 \cdot 7H_2O$ and $M^I_2SO_4 \cdot Zn(Cd, Mg, Hg)SO_4 \cdot 6H_2O$. The aquo ions are quite strong acids and aqueous solutions of salts are hydrolyzed.[6] In perchlorate solution the only species for Zn, Cd (and Hg) below $0.1M$ are the MOH^+ ions, e.g.,

$$Zn^{2+}(aq) + H_2O \rightleftharpoons ZnOH^+(aq) + H^+$$

For more concentrated cadmium solutions, the principal species is Cd_2OH^{3+}

$$2Cd^{2+}(aq) + H_2O \rightleftharpoons Cd_2OH^{3+}(aq) + H^+$$

Zinc forms a basic acetate isomorphous with the oxoacetate of beryllium, $Zn_4O(OCOCH_3)_6$, on distillation of the normal acetate in vacuum. It is a crystalline solid rapidly hydrolyzed by water, unlike the beryllium compound, the difference being due to the possibility of coordination numbers exceeding four for zinc.

Simple cyanides, $M(CN)_2$, and complex cyanides, such as $[M(CN)_4]^{2-}$, are also well characterized; carbonates and hydroxo carbonates are also known.

24-9. Organometallic Compounds

The organozinc compounds are historically important since they were the first organometallic compounds to be prepared; their discovery by Frankland in 1849 played a decisive part in the development of modern ideas of chemical bonding. The zinc and cadmium compounds are also of interest since their mild reactivities toward certain organic functional groups give them unique synthetic potentialities.

---

[5] R. F. Kruh and C. L. Standley, *Inorg. Chem.*, **1**, 941 (1962).

[6] D. Dyrssen and P. Lumme, *Acta Chem. Scand.*, **16**, 1785 (1962); G. Biedermann and L. Ciavatta, *Acta. Chem. Scand.*, **16**, 2221 (1962); D. D. Perrin, *J. Chem. Soc.*, **1962**, 4500.

Organozinc compounds of the types "RZnX" and R_2Zn are known, whereas only R_2Cd compounds have been isolated. The constitution of RZnX has presented a problem similar to that for Grignard reagents (page 431); thus, in addition to RZnX, there may be $(RZnX)_2$ and $(R_2Zn + ZnX_2)$ present. For ethylzinc iodide, at least, spectroscopic and other evidence[6a] indicate that the main species in ether or tetrahydrofuran solution is C_2H_5ZnI; this species is solvated and probably tetrahedral.

For mercury, both R_2Hg and RHgX are well defined.

The zinc alkyls can be obtained by thermal decomposition of RZnI, which is prepared by the reaction of alkyl iodides with a zinc–copper couple

$$C_2H_5I + Zn(Cu) = C_2H_5ZnI \xrightarrow{\text{heat}} \tfrac{1}{2}(C_2H_5)_2Zn + \tfrac{1}{2}ZnI_2$$

The alkyls may also be prepared and the diaryls most conveniently obtained by the reaction of zinc metal with an organomercury compound

$$R_2Hg + Zn = R_2Zn + Hg$$

or by reaction of zinc chloride with organolithium or Grignard reagents.

The only satisfactory preparation of R_2Cd compounds is by treatment of the anhydrous cadmium halide with RLi or RMgX. The reaction of cadmium metal with a dialkyl or diaryl mercury gives an equilibrium mixture which is difficult to separate

$$Cd + R_2Hg = R_2Cd + Hg$$

The R_2Zn and R_2Cd compounds are nonpolar liquids or low-melting solids soluble in most organic liquids. The lower alkyl zinc compounds are spontaneously inflammable, and all react vigorously with oxygen and with water. The cadmium compounds are less sensitive to oxygen but are less stable thermally.

Both zinc and cadmium compounds react readily with compounds containing active hydrogen, such as alcohols,

$$R_2M + R'OH = RMOR' + RH$$

and are generally similar to RLi or RMgX, although their lower reactivity allows selective alkylations not possible with the more standard reagents. An important example is the use of the cadmium compounds in the synthesis of ketones from acyl chlorides:

$$2RCOCl + R'_2Cd = 2RCOR' + CdCl_2$$

Diphenylzinc and diphenylcadmium react with excess phenyllithium to form complexes such as $Li[Zn(C_6H_5)_3]$.

[6a] D. F. Evans and I. Wharf, *J. Organomet. Chem.*, **5**, 108 (1966).

24-10. Complex Compounds: Stereochemistry

It must be noted first of all that there are no ligand field stabilization effects in the Zn^{2+} and Cd^{2+} ions because of their completed d shells. Thus the stereochemistry of their compounds is determined solely by considerations of size, electrostatic forces and covalent bonding forces. The effect of size is to make Cd^{2+} more likely than Zn^{2+} to assume a coordination number of six. For example, ZnO crystallizes in lattices where the Zn^{2+} ion is in tetrahedral holes surrounded by four oxide ions, whereas CdO has the rock salt structure. Similarly $ZnCl_2$ crystallizes in at least three polymorphs, two or more of which have tetrahedrally coordinated zinc atoms; $CdCl_2$, on the other hand, has only one form, involving octahedral coordination.

In their complexes, zinc and cadmium often have coordination numbers of six, but four is more common; some examples are given in Table 24-7.

TABLE 24-7

Stereochemistry of Zinc and Cadmium

Coordination number	Bonding	Geometry	Examples
2	sp	Linear	$Zn(CH_3)_2$, $Cd(C_6H_5)_2$
4	sp^3	Tetrahedral	$[Zn(CN)_4]^{2-}$, $[CdBr_4]^{2-}$, $ZnCl_2(s)$, $[Cd(NH_3)_4]^{2+}$, $Zn(NH_3)_2Cl_2$
5	sp^3d	Distorted trigonal bipyramidal or square pyramidal	Terpyridyl $ZnCl_2$, $Zn(acac)_2 \cdot H_2O$
6	sp^3d^2	Octahedral	$[Zn(NH_3)_6]^{2+}$ (in crystals only)

A few cases of square four-coordinate zinc are known, for example, bis(glycinyl)zinc.

Zinc complexes of dithiocarbamates and of other sulfur compounds are important accelerators in the vulcanization of rubber by sulfur. The dithiocarbamates form 5-coordinate 1:1 complexes with amines; a similar cadmium complex is probably the only example of a 5-coordinate Cd^{II} complex.[7] Zinc β-diketonates also form 5-coordinate 1:1 adducts with nitrogen bases.[8] Zinc is also an essential constituent of several enzymes, e.g., carboxypeptidase.

[7] E. Coates, B. Rigg, B. Saville and D. Skelton, *J. Chem. Soc.*, **1965**, 5613.
[8] D. P. Graddon and D. G. Weedon, *Austral. J. Chem.*, **17**, 607 (1964).

24-11. Univalent Cadmium

When cadmium is dissolved in molten cadmium halides, very dark red-black melts are obtained. The high color may be due to the existence of both Cd^I and Cd^{II} joined by halide bridges, since mixed valence states in complexes are known to give intense colorations in many other cases. If aluminum chloride is added to the $Cd-CdCl_2$ melt, for example, only a green-yellow melt is obtained and phase studies here and for the bromide have shown the presence of Cd^I. Yellow solids such as $CdAlCl_4$ can be isolated, and their spectra show the presence of the tetrahaloaluminate. Since they are diamagnetic, the solids can be formulated $(Cd_2)^{2+}(AlCl_4^-)_2$. When they are added to donor solvents or to water, cadmium metal is at once formed, together with Cd^{2+}, so that it is not surprising that there is no evidence for Cd^I in aqueous solution. The stabilization by the tetrahaloaluminate ions is presumably due to the lowering of the difference between the lattice energies of the two oxidation states and a lowering of the tendency to disproportionate. A similar case of this type of stabilization has been noted for Ga^I, as in $Ga^+AlCl_4^-$.

Raman spectra of the melts have definitely established the presence of a Cd_2^{2+} ion comparable to Hg_2^{2+}.[9] However, the force constant for the Cd—Cd bond is only 1.11 mdynes/A which can be compared to 0.98 for K_2 and 1.72 for Na_2 and I_2 molecules. Although the Hg_2^{2+} bond distance is very sensitive to environment (see below) and direct comparison in the melt situation is difficult, a value for Hg_2^{2+} of 2.5 mdynes/A is reasonable. The relative stabilities of the ions are further discussed below.

MERCURY COMPOUNDS

24-12. The Mercurous Ion and Mercurous–Mercuric Equilibria

As noted in Section 24-2, the chemistry of mercury differs from that of zinc and cadmium not only because of inherent peculiarities of the element and of mercuric compounds but also because of the existence of the mercurous ion, ^+Hg—Hg^+, which is readily obtained by reduction of mercuric salts and is also easily oxidized to them.

There have been many lines of evidence showing the binuclear nature of Hg_2^{2+}. A few of these may be noted:

1. Mercurous compounds are diamagnetic both as solids and in solution, whereas Hg^+ would have an unpaired electron.

[9] J. D. Corbett, *Inorg. Chem.*, **1**, 700 (1962).

2. X-ray determination of the structures of several mercurous salts shows the existence of individual Hg_2^{2+} ions. The Hg—Hg distances are far from constant (Table 24-8) and there appears to be a bond length decrease and a bond strength increase with decreasing tendency to covalent bonding.

TABLE 24-8

Mercury–Mercury Bond Lengths
in Mercurous Compounds

Salt	Hg—Hg, A
Hg_2F_2	2.43
Hg_2Cl_2	2.53
Hg_2Br_2	2.58
Hg_2I_2	2.69
$Hg_2(NO_3)_2 \cdot 2H_2O$	2.54

3. The Raman spectrum of an aqueous solution of mercurous nitrate contains a strong line which can only be attributed to an Hg—Hg stretching vibration.

4. There are various kinds of equilibria for which constant equilibrium quotients can be obtained only by considering the mercurous ion to be Hg_2^{2+}. For example, suppose we add an excess of mercury to a solution initially X molar in mercuric nitrate. An equilibrium between Hg, Hg^{2+} and mercurous ion will be reached (see below); depending on the assumed nature of mercurous ion the following equilibrium quotients can be written:

$$Hg(l) + Hg^{2+} = Hg_2^{2+} \qquad K = [Hg_2^{2+}]/[Hg^{2+}] = f/(1-f)$$
$$Hg(l) + Hg^{2+} = 2Hg^{+} \qquad K' = [Hg^{+}]^2/[Hg^{2+}] = (2fX)^2/(1-f)X = 4f^2X/(1-f)$$

where f represents the fraction of the initial Hg^{2+} found by analysis or otherwise to have disappeared when equilibrium is reached. It is found that when values of K and K' are calculated from experimental data at different values of X, the former are substantially constant while the latter are not.

5. The electrical conductances of solutions of mercurous salts resemble closely in magnitude and variation with concentration the conductances of uni-divalent rather than uni-univalent electrolytes.

The greater strength of the Hg—Hg bond in Hg_2^{2+} compared to Cd—Cd in Cd_2^{2+} is reflected also by comparison of the bond energies HgH^{+} > CdH^{+} in the spectroscopic ions, and qualitatively the stability of Hg_2^{2+} is probably related to the large electron affinity of Hg^{+}. The electron affinity of M^{+} (equal to the first ionization potential of the metal) is 1.4 ev greater for Hg^{+} than for Cd^{+}. This results from the fact that the $4f$ shell in Hg shields the $6s$ electrons relatively poorly. The high ionization potential of Hg also accounts for the so-called "inert pair" phenomenon, namely, the exceptionally noble character of mercury and its low energy of vaporization.

Hg^I–Hg^{II} *Equilibria.*   An understanding of the thermodynamics of these equilibria is essential to an understanding of the chemistry of the mercurous state.   The important thermodynamic values are the potentials:

$$Hg_2^{2+} + 2e = 2Hg(l) \qquad E^0 = 0.789 \text{ v} \qquad (24\text{-}1)$$
$$2Hg^{2+} + 2e = Hg_2^{2+} \qquad E^0 = 0.920 \text{ v} \qquad (24\text{-}2)$$
$$Hg^{2+} + 2e = Hg(l) \qquad E^0 = 0.854 \text{ v} \qquad (24\text{-}3)$$

For the disproportionation equilibrium

$$Hg_2^{2+} = Hg(l) + Hg^{2+} \qquad E^0 = -0.131 \text{ v} \qquad (24\text{-}4)$$

we then have

$$K = [Hg^{2+}]/[Hg_2^{2+}] = 6.0 \times 10^{-3}$$

The implication of the standard potentials is clearly that only oxidizing agents with potentials in the range -0.79 to -0.85 v can oxidize mercury to Hg^I but not to Hg^{II}.   Since no common oxidizing agents meet this requirement, it is found that when mercury is treated with an excess of oxidizing agent it is entirely converted to Hg^{II}.   However, when mercury is in at least 50% excess only Hg^I is obtained since, according to equation 24-4, Hg(l) readily reduces Hg^{2+} to Hg_2^{2+}.

The equilibrium constant for reaction 24-4 shows that, although Hg_2^{2+} is stable with respect to disproportionation, it is only so by a small margin. Thus any reagents which reduce the activity (by precipitation or complexation) of Hg^{2+} to a significantly greater extent than they lower the activity of Hg_2^{2+} will cause disproportionation of Hg_2^{2+}.   There are many such reagents, so that the number of stable Hg^I compounds is rather restricted.

Thus on adding OH^- to a solution of Hg_2^{2+}, a dark precipitate consisting of Hg and HgO is formed; evidently mercurous hydroxide, if it could be isolated, would be a stronger base than HgO.   Similarly, addition of sulfide ions to a solution of Hg_2^{2+} gives a mixture of Hg and the extremely insoluble HgS.   Mercurous cyanide does not exist because $Hg(CN)_2$ is so slightly dissociated though soluble.   The reactions in these cited cases are:

$$Hg_2^{2+} + 2OH^- = Hg(l) + HgO(s) + H_2O$$
$$Hg_2^{2+} + S^- = Hg(l) + HgS$$
$$Hg_2^{2+} + 2CN^- = Hg(l) + Hg(CN)_2(aq)$$

24-13. Mercurous Compounds

As indicated above, no hydroxide, oxide or sulfide can be obtained by addition of the appropriate anion to aqueous Hg_2^{2+}, nor have these compounds been otherwise made.

Among the best known of the few mercurous compounds are the *halides*. The fluoride is unstable toward water, being hydrolyzed to hydrofluoric acid and unisolable mercurous hydroxide which disproportionates as above. The other halides are highly insoluble, which thus precludes the possibilities of hydrolysis or disproportionation to give Hg^{II} halide complexes. Mercurous *nitrate* is known only as the dihydrate $Hg_2(NO_3)_2 \cdot 2H_2O$, which X-ray studies have shown to contain the ion $[H_2O-Hg-Hg-OH_2]^{2+}$; a *perchlorate*, $Hg_2(ClO_4)_2 \cdot 4H_2O$, is also known. Both are very soluble in water, and the halides and other relatively insoluble salts of Hg_2^{2+} may conveniently be prepared by adding the appropriate anions to their solutions. Other known mercurous salts are the sparingly soluble sulfate, chlorate, bromate, iodate and acetate.

Mercurous ion forms few *complexes*; this may in part be due to a low tendency for Hg_2^{2+} to form coordinate bonds, but is probably due mainly to the fact that mercuric ion will form even more stable complexes with most ligands, for example, CN^-, I^-, amines and alkyl sulfides, so that the Hg_2^{2+} disproportionates. Only in the case of aniline is there definite evidence for an amine complex of Hg^I, viz., $[Hg_2C_6H_5NH_2]^{2+}$, which is sufficiently stable to be detected in appreciable concentration.[10] However complexes can readily be obtained in solution with ligands which form essentially ionic metal–ligand bonds and hence no strong complexes with mercury(II). Such ligands are oxalate, succinate, pyrophosphate and tripolyphosphate.[11] Pyrophosphate gives the species $[Hg_2(P_2O_7)_2]^{6-}$ (pH range 6.5–9) and $[Hg_2(P_2O_7)OH]^{3-}$ for which stability constants have been measured.

24-14. Mercuric Oxide and Sulfide

Red mercuric oxide is formed on gentle pyrolysis of mercurous or mercuric nitrate, by direct interaction of mercury and oxygen at 300–350°, or as red crystals by heating an alkaline solution of K_2HgI_4. Addition of OH^- to aqueous Hg^{2+} gives a yellow precipitate of HgO; the yellow form differs from the red only in particle size. The usual form of the oxide has a structure with zigzag chains —Hg—O—Hg— with Hg—O = 2.03 A, $\angle HgOHg = 109°$ and $\angle OHgO = 179°$; there is only weak bonding between the chains, the shortest Hg—O distance here being 2.82 A.

No hydroxide has been obtained, but the oxide is soluble (10^{-3} to 10^{-4} mole/liter) in water, the exact solubility depending on particle size, to give a solution of what is commonly assumed to be the hydroxide, although

[10] T. H. Wirth and N. Davidson, *J. Amer. Chem. Soc.*, **86**, 4314, 4318, 4322, 4325 (1964).
[11] T. Yamane and N. Davidson, *J. Amer. Chem. Soc.*, **81**, 4438 (1959).

there is no proof for such a species. This "hydroxide" is an extremely weak base,

$$K = [Hg^{2+}][OH^-]^2/[Hg(OH)_2] = 1.8 \times 10^{-22}$$

and is somewhat amphoteric, though more basic than acidic. The equilibria involved in red HgO dissolved in $HClO_4$ have been interpreted in terms of the species Hg^{2+}, $HgOH^+$ and $Hg(OH)_2$. There is no evidence for any hydroxo complexes even in $2M$ NaOH, however.

Mercuric *sulfide*, HgS, is precipitated from aqueous solutions as a black, highly insoluble compound. The solubility product is 10^{-54}, but the sulfide is somewhat more soluble than this figure would imply because of some hydrolysis of Hg^{2+} and S^{2-} ions. The black sulfide is unstable with respect to a red form identical with the mineral cinnabar and changes into it on heating or digesting with alkali polysulfides or mercurous chloride. The red form has a distorted sodium chloride lattice with Hg—S chains similar to HgO. Another form, occurring as the mineral metacinnabarite, has a zinc blende structure, as have the selenide and telluride.

24-15. Mercuric Halides

The *fluoride* is essentially ionic and crystallizes in the fluorite structure; it is almost completely decomposed, even by cold water, as would be expected for an ionic compound which is the salt of a weak acid and an extremely weak base. Not only does mercury(II) show no tendency to form covalent Hg—F bonds, but no fluoro complexes are known.

In sharp contrast to the fluoride, the other halides show marked covalent character, and indeed for $HgCl_2$ the covalent character is extreme. Mercuric *chloride* crystallizes in an essentially molecular lattice, the two short Hg—Cl distances being about the same length as the Hg—Cl bonds in gaseous $HgCl_2$ while the next shortest distances are much longer (see Table 24-9). The *bromide* and *iodide* both crystallize in layer lattices; in

TABLE 24-9

Hg—X Distances in Mercuric Halides (in A)

Compound	Solid			Vapor
	Two at	Two at	Two at	
HgF_2		Eight at 2.40		—
$HgCl_2$	2.25	3.34	3.63	2.28 ± 0.04
$HgBr_2$	2.48	3.23	3.23	2.40 ± 0.04
HgI_2		Four at 2.78		2.57 ± 0.04

$HgBr_2$ each mercury atom is surrounded by six bromine atoms, but two are so much closer than the other four that one can consider that perturbed molecules are present. The lattice of HgI_2 is not in any sense molecular; regular HgI_4 tetrahedra are found with an Hg—I distance appreciably in excess of the Hg—I distance in the free molecules. In the vapor all three halides are distinctly molecular as they are also in solutions. Relative to ionic HgF_2, the other halides have very low melting and boiling points (Table 24-10). They also show marked solubility in many organic solvents.

TABLE 24-10

Some Properties of Mercuric Halides

Halide	Melting point, °C	Boiling point, °C	Solubility, moles/100 moles at 25°			
			In H_2O	In C_2H_5OH	In $C_2H_5OCOCH_3$	In C_6H_6
HgF_2	645	650	Hydrolyzes	Insol.	Insol.	Insol.
$HgCl_2$	280	303	0.48	8.14	9.42	0.152
$HgBr_2$	238	318	0.031	3.83	—	—
HgI_2	257	351	0.00023	0.396	0.566	0.067

In aqueous solution they exist almost exclusively ($\sim 99\%$) as HgX_2 molecules.

24-16. Other Mercuric Salts

Among the mercuric salts which are quite ionic and hence highly dissociated in aqueous solution are the nitrate, sulfate and perchlorate. Because of the great weakness of mercuric hydroxide, aqueous solutions of these salts tend to hydrolyze extensively and must be acidified to be stable.

There are also salts which, like the halides and chalconides, are partly or wholly undissociated or insoluble in water and hence stable toward it. Among these are the cyanide, oxalate, phosphate and thiocyanate as well as carboxylates which partly dissociate. The *cyanide* has been found to have a rather unexpected structure where almost linear $Hg(CN)_2$ molecules are linked together in endless zig-zag chains through a long Hg—N (2.70 A) bond (see Fig. 24-2).

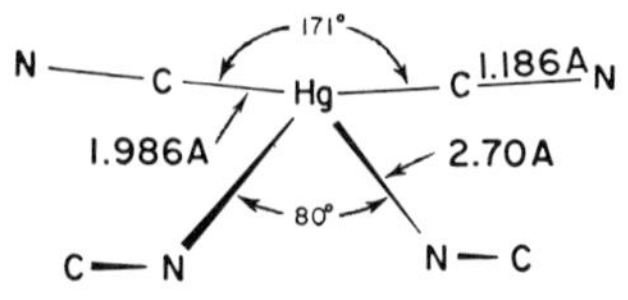

Fig. 24-2. Details of the coordination of the Hg^{2+} ion in mercury(II) cyanide.

Mercury(II) forms numerous compounds in which there are bonds to other metal atoms, including transition metal atoms (see page 752), which are best formulated as Hg^{II} compounds. Thus the action of $HgCl_2$ on carbonylate anions or hydrides gives "mercury salts" such as $[\pi-C_5H_5Mo(CO)_3]_2Hg$ and $HgFe(CO)_4$. Other types of complex are known: thus it has long been known that ruthenium(III) chloride solutions when boiled with Hg_2Cl_2 give green solutions containing ruthenium–mercury complexes. The interaction of complex hydrides of Rh, Os and Ir with $HgCl_2$ or Hg_2Cl_2 gives again a metal–metal bond,[12] e.g.,

$$(Ph_2MeAs)_3 \, RhHCl_2 + HgCl_2 = (Ph_2MeAs)_3 \, Rh(HgCl)Cl_2 + HCl$$

Mercuric ions are also known to catalyze a number of reactions of complex compounds, e.g., the aquation of $[M(NH_3)_5X]^{2+}$, M = CO or Cr, but the mechanism is not entirely clear although chloride bridged transition states are probably involved (see page 167).[13]

24-17. Novel Compounds of Mercury(II) with Nitrogen

It has been known since the days of alchemy that when Hg_2Cl_2 is treated with aqueous ammonia a black residue is formed, and this reaction is still used in qualitative analysis to identify Hg_2Cl_2. Only relatively recently has the nature of the reaction been clarified. These residues contain nitrogen compounds of Hg^{II} plus metallic mercury, and the Hg^{II} compounds can be obtained directly from Hg^{II} salts.

There are three known products of the reaction of $HgCl_2$ with ammonia, the proportion of any one of them depending on the conditions. The possible products are $Hg(NH_3)_2Cl_2$, $HgNH_2Cl$ and $Hg_2NCl \cdot H_2O$ and they are formed according to the following equations:

$$HgCl_2 + 2NH_3 = Hg(NH_3)_2Cl_2(s)$$
$$HgCl_2 + 2NH_3 = HgNH_2Cl(s) + NH_4^+ + Cl^-$$
$$2HgCl_2 + 4NH_3 + H_2O = Hg_2NCl \cdot H_2O + 3NH_4^+ + 3Cl^-$$

The equilibria represented here seem to be liable so that the product obtained can be controlled by varying the concentrations of NH_3 and NH_4^+. In concentrated NH_4Cl solution, the diammine $Hg(NH_3)_2Cl_2$ is precipitated, whereas, with dilute ammonia and no excess NH_4^+, the amide $HgNH_2Cl$ is formed. The compound $Hg_2NCl \cdot H_2O$ is probably not produced in a pure state by the above reaction, but it can be obtained by

[12] R. S. Nyholm and K. Vrieze, *J. Chem. Soc.*, **1965**, 5331, 5337.
[13] J. H. Espenson and J. P. Birk, *Inorg. Chem.*, **4**, 527 (1965), and references therein.

20*

treating the compound $Hg_2NOH \cdot 2H_2O$ (Millon's base) with hydrochloric acid. Millon's base itself is made by the action of aqueous ammonia on yellow mercuric oxide.

The diammine has been shown to consist of discrete tetrahedral molecules. The amide has infinite chains $-Hg-NH_2-Hg-NH_2-$, where the $N-Hg-N$ segments are linear while the bonds about nitrogen are tetrahedral; the chloride ions lie between the chains. The analogous bromide has the same structure.

Millon's base has a three dimensional framework of composition Hg_2N with the OH^- ions and water molecules occupying rather spacious cavities and channels. Many salts of Millon's base are known, for example, $Hg_2NX \cdot nH_2O$ ($X = NO_3^-$, ClO_4^-, Cl^-, Br^-, I^-; $n = 0-2$). In these the framework appears to remain essentially unaltered, and thus it is an ion exchanger similar to a zeolite.

Returning to the dark residues given by mercurous chloride, one or both of $HgNH_2Cl$ and $Hg_2NCl \cdot H_2O$ are present together with free metal. The insolubility of these compounds causes the disproportionation of the Hg_2^{2+}, for example,

$$Hg_2Cl_2(s) + 2NH_3 = Hg(l) + HgNH_2Cl(s) + NH_4^+ + Cl^-$$

There is no evidence for any intermediate ammonobasic or ammine compounds of mercury(I).

24-18. Organomercury Compounds

A vast number of organomercury compounds, some of which have useful physiological properties, are known. They are of the types $RHgX$, and R_2Hg, and are obtained from mercuric chloride and Grignard reagents in the appropriate mole ratios.

In the case of arylmercury compounds, many other reactions may be used. Notable among these is the fairly general "mercuration" reaction of aromatic hydrocarbons by mercuric acetate shown in equation 24-5. The

$$X\langle\bigcirc\rangle + Hg(OCOCH_3)_2 = o\text{- or } p\text{-}(\bigcirc)Hg(OCOCH_3) + CH_3COOH \qquad (24\text{-}5)$$
$$X$$

variation in rates of reactivities with varying X suggests that attack upon the aromatic ring is by a positive species, but the mechanism is not well understood.[14]

---

[14] Cf. discussion: A. J. Kresge and J. F. Brennan, *Proc. Chem. Soc.*, **1963**, 215 and references therein.

The *RHgX compounds* are crystalline solids whose properties depend on the nature of X.   When X is an atom or group which can form covalent bonds to mercury, for example, Cl, Br, I, CN, SCN, OH, the compound is a covalent nonpolar substance more soluble in organic liquids than in water.   When X is SO_4^{2-} or NO_3^-, the substance is salt-like and presumably quite ionic, for instance, $[RHg]^+NO_3^-$.   Acetates behave as weak electrolytes.

Exchange reactions such as

$$MeHgBr + *HgBr_2 \rightleftharpoons Me*HgBr + HgBr_2$$

have been extensively studied using tracer mercury.   It was shown that the electrophilic substitution reactions, S_E2, proceed with full retention of configuration when an optically active group, s-butyl, is present.[15]   The reaction, which is also catalyzed by anions, is believed to proceed through cyclic transition state such as 24-I.   Reactions such as

$$R_2Hg + HgX_2 = 2RHgX$$

have equilibrium constants of 10^5–10^{11} and proceed at rates which are slow and solvent-dependent.   Nmr studies[16] have also shown that, in solutions of RHgI compounds, there is relatively fast exchange of R groups and, again, a mechanism involving a cyclic intermediate or transition state (24-II) has been postulated.

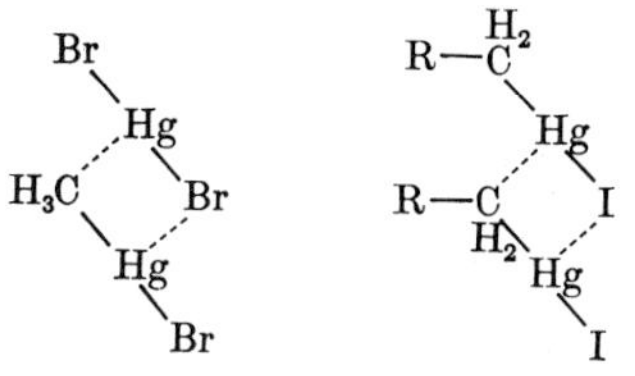

(24-I)   (24-II)

The *dialkyls* and *diaryls* are nonpolar, volatile, toxic liquids or low-melting solids.   All are thermally rather unstable and light sensitive, but can be kept for months without great loss.   Their principal use, and a valuable one, is in the preparation of other organometallic compounds by direct interchange, for example,

$$\frac{n}{2} R_2Hg + M = R_nM + \frac{n}{2} Hg$$

This reaction proceeds essentially to completion with alkali metals, alkaline

[15] C. K. Ingold, *et al.*, *J. Chem. Soc.*, **1964**, 3900, and references therein.
[16] M. D. Rausch and J. R. van Wazer, *Inorg. Chem.*, **3**, 761 (1964).

earths, Zn, Al, Ga, Sn, Pb, Sb, Bi, Se and Te, but with In, Tl and Cd reversible equilibria are established.

The R_2Hg compounds have very low reactivity toward oxygen, water, active hydrogen and organic functional groups in general. They are quite useful for partial alkylations of reactive halides, for instance,

$$(C_2H_5)_2Hg + AsCl_3 = C_2H_5HgCl + C_2H_5AsCl_2$$

There are also numerous compounds formed by the addition of mercuric salts to *olefins*. While it has been considered that some of these have olefin–metal μ bonds (see page 775), there is no good evidence for such bonding. Present evidence favors the view that addition of HgX_2 occurs across the double bond, followed in many cases by hydrolysis in aqueous solution, for example,

$$CH_2{=}CH_2 + Hg(NO_3)_2 + OH^- = HO{-}CH_2{-}CH_2{-}Hg^+NO_3^- + NO_3^-$$

The catalytic action of mercuric salts in sulfuric acid solutions in converting acetylene to acetaldehyde probably proceeds through such intermediates.

Methanolic solutions of Hg^{II} acetate readily absorb carbon monoxide at atmospheric pressure and the resulting compound can be converted by halide salts to compounds of the type $XHgCOOCH_3$. It has been shown that carbon monoxide is, in effect, inserted between the Hg and O of a solvolyzed mercuric ion, though the mechanism is not established in detail:

$$Hg(OCOCH_3)_2 + CH_3OH \rightleftharpoons CH_3COOHgOCH_3 + CH_3COOH$$
$$CH_3COOHg{-}OCH_3 + CO \rightleftharpoons CH_3COOHg(CO)OCH_3$$

The CO can be regenerated from the compounds by heating or by action of concentrated hydrochloric acid.[17]

No organomercury(I) compounds have been prepared.

24-19. Mercuric Complexes

A number of these have been mentioned above. The Hg^{2+} ion has indeed a strong tendency to complex formation, and the characteristic coordination numbers and stereochemical arrangements are two-coordinate, linear, and four-coordinate, tetrahedral. Octahedral coordination is less common; other complexes which may be five-coordinate are also known. There appears to be considerable covalent character in the mercury–ligand bonds, especially in the two-coordinate complexes. The most stable

---

[17] J. Halpern and S. F. Kettle, *Chem. and Ind.*, **1961**, 668; T. C. Mak and J. Trotter, *J. Chem. Soc.*, **1962**, 3423.

complexes are those with halogen, carbon, nitrogen, phosphorus and sulfur as ligand atoms.

For the halogens, there are the species $[HgX]^+$, HgX_2, $[HgX_3]^-$ and $[HgX_4]^{2-}$. Mercuric cyanide is soluble in excess cyanide to give the tetrahedral $[Hg(CN)_4]^{2-}$ ion; the thiocyanate $[Hg(SCN)_4]^{2-}$ is similar.

There are a number[18] of complexes of oxo anions, e.g., $[Hg(SO_3)_2]^{2-}$, $[Hgox_2]^{2-}$ and $[Hg(NO_3)_4]^{2-}$. The yellow crystals long considered to be "potassium mercurinitrite," obtained by adding KNO_2 to $Hg(NO_3)_2$ solutions, have been shown to be $K_3[Hg(NO_2)_4]\cdot NO_3$, with a tetrahedral $[Hg(NO_2)_4]^{2-}$ ion.

Dialkyl sulfides give complexes of the type $R_2S\cdot HgX_2$ (X = Cl, Br, I), which are dimeric (24-III), and also monomeric $(R_2S)_2HgX_2$ complexes.

(24-III)   (24-IV)

Phosphines and arsines form complexes with the halides similarly and also give more highly bridged structures such as 24-IV. Although there is a tendency to form ammonobasic compounds, a variety of amines form complexes[10] with Hg^{II} and the affinity of Hg^{II} for nitrogen ligands in aqueous solution exceeds that of transition metals. In addition to the ammonia and amine complexes of the type $Hg(NH_3)_2X_2$, tetrammines such as $[Hg(NH_3)_4](NO_3)_2$ can be prepared in saturated aqueous ammonium nitrate. The ion $[Hgen_3]^{3+}$ has octahedral Hg^{II}, as have complexes of the type $[HgL_6](ClO_4)_2$ obtained when suitable oxygen donors are added to Hg^{II} perchlorate in ethanol. Although less sterically hindered donors such as pyridine N-oxide react,[19] more bulky oxides such as Ph_3PO do not. Tetrahedral complexes are of course given by such ligands, e.g., $HgCl_2$-$2Ph_3AsO$.[20]

Mercuric β-diketonates have been shown not to have the usual chelate rings but to be enolates of the type $Hg(OCR\!=\!CHCOR)_2$.[21] It also appears that mercuric perchlorate and nitrate react with aqueous acetone to give complex species which have the acetone bound to mercury as the enolate anion.[22]

[18] J. I. Bullock and D. G. Tuck, *J. Chem. Soc.*, **1965**, 1877 and references therein.

[19] R. L. Carlin, J. Rottman, M. Dankleff and J. O. Edwards, *Inorg. Chem.*, 1, 182 (1962).

[20] C.-I. Brandon, *Acta Chem. Scand.*, 17, 1363 (1963).

[21] D. C. Nonhebel, *J. Chem. Soc.*, **1963**, 738.

[22] R. R. Miano and R. A. Plane, *Inorg. Chem.*, 3, 987 (1964).

References

Deacon, G. B., *Rev. Pure Appl. Chem. (Australia)*, **13**, 189 (1963).   Review of halogeno-mercurate(II) complexes.

Grdenič, D., *Quart. Rev.*, **19**, 303 (1965).   A detailed review of the structural chemistry of mercury compounds.

Grosse, A. V., *J. Inorg. Nucl. Chem.*, **27**, 773 (1965).   An authoritative account of the physical properties of elemental mercury.

Lipscomb, W. N., *Anal. Chem.*, **25**, 737 (1953).   Structures of mercury–nitrogen compounds.

PART THREE

Chemistry of the Transition Elements

25

Introductory Survey of Transition Elements

The purpose of this chapter is to provide brief general discussions of a few topics which pertain to the transition elements as a class, rather than to any particular one or group within the class. Of course some of these topics, such as magnetism or optical rotation, have indeed still greater generality, but they are discussed here because of their special pertinence among the transition elements.

ELECTRONIC STRUCTURES

25-1. Definition and General Characteristics of Transition Elements

The transition elements may be strictly defined as those which, *as elements*, have partly filled d or f shells. Here we shall adopt a slightly broader definition and include also elements which have partly filled d or f shells in any of their commonly occurring oxidation states. This means that we treat the coinage metals, Cu, Ag and Au, as transition metals, since Cu^{II} has a $3d^9$ configuration, Ag^{II} a $4d^9$ configuration and Au^{III} a $5d^8$ configuration. From a purely chemical point of view it is also appropriate to consider these elements as transition elements since their chemical behavior is, on the whole, quite similar to that of other transition elements.

With the above broad definition in mind, one finds that there are at present some 55 transition elements, counting the heaviest elements out through the one of atomic number 103. Clearly, the majority of all known elements are transition elements. All of these transition elements have certain general properties in common:

1. They are all metals.

2. They are practically all hard, strong, high-melting, high-boiling metals which conduct heat and electricity well. In short, they are "typical" metals of the sort we meet in ordinary circumstances.

3. They form alloys with one another and with other metallic elements.

4. Many of them are sufficiently electropositive to dissolve in mineral acids, although a few are "noble"—that is, they have such low electrode potentials that they are unaffected by simple acids.

5. With very few exceptions, they exhibit variable valence, and their ions and compounds are colored in one if not all oxidation states.

6. Because of partially filled shells they form at least some paramagnetic compounds.

This large number of transition elements is subdivided into three main groups: (a) the main transition elements or d-block elements, (b) the lanthanide elements and (c) the actinide elements.

The main transition group or d block includes those elements which have partially filled d shells only. Thus, the element scandium, with the outer electron configuration $4s^23d$, is the lightest member. The eight succeeding elements, Ti, V, Cr, Mn, Fe, Co, Ni and Cu, all have partly filled $3d$ shells either in the ground state of the free atom (all except Cu) or in one or more of their chemically important ions (all except Sc). This group of elements is called the *first transition series*. At zinc the configuration is $3d^{10}4s^2$, and this element forms no compounds in which the $3d$ shell is ionized, nor does this ionization occur in any of the next nine elements. It is not until we come to yttrium, with ground state outer electron configuration $5s^24d$, that we meet the next transition element. The following eight elements, Zr, Nb, Mo, Tc, Rh, Pd and Ag, all have partially filled $4d$ shells either in the free element (all but Ag) or in one or more of the chemically important ions (all but Y). This group of nine elements constitutes the *second transition series*.

Again there follows a sequence of elements in which there are never d-shell vacancies under chemically significant conditions until we reach the element lanthanum, with an outer electron configuration in the ground state of $6s^25d$. Now, if the pattern we have observed twice before were to be repeated, there would follow eight elements with enlarged but not complete sets of $5d$ electrons. This does not happen, however. The $4f$ shell now becomes slightly more stable than the $5d$ shell, and, through the next fourteen elements, electrons enter the $4f$ shell until at lutetium it becomes filled. Lutetium thus has the outer electron configuration $4f^{14}5d6s^2$. Since both La and Lu have partially filled d shells and no other partially filled shells, it might be argued that both of these should be considered as d-block elements. However, for chemical reasons, it would be unwise to classify them in this way, since all of the fifteen elements La ($Z = 57$) through Lu ($Z = 71$) have very similar chemical and physical properties, those of lanthanum being in a sense prototypal; hence, these elements are called the *lanthanides*, and their chemistry will be considered separately in Chapter 31. Since the properties of Y are extremely similar to, and those of Sc mainly like, those of the lanthanide elements proper, and quite different from those of the regular d-block elements, we will treat them also in Chapter 31.

For practical purposes, then, the *third transition series* begins with hafnium, having the ground state outer electron configuration $6s^2 5d^2$, and embraces the elements Ta, W, Re, Os, Ir, Pt and Au, all of which have partly filled $5d$ shells in one or more chemically important oxidation states as well as (excepting Au) in the neutral atom.

Continuing on from mercury, which follows gold, we come via the noble gas radon and the radioelements Fr and Ra to actinium, with the outer electron configuration $7s^2 6d$. Here we might expect, by analogy to what happened at lanthanum, that in the following elements electrons would enter the $5f$ orbitals, producing a lanthanide-like series of fifteen elements. What actually occurs is, unfortunately, not so simple. Although, immediately following lanthanum, the $4f$ orbitals become decisively more favorable than the $5d$ orbitals for the electrons entering in the succeeding elements, there is apparently not so great a difference between the $5f$ and $6d$ orbitals until later. Thus, for the elements immediately following Ac, and their ions, there may be electrons in the $5f$ or $6d$ orbitals or both. Since it does appear that later on, after four or five more electrons have been added to the Ac configuration, the $5f$ orbitals do become definitely the more stable, and since the elements from about americium on do show moderately homologous chemical behavior, it has become accepted practice to call the fifteen elements beginning with Ac (not all of which are known as yet) the *actinide elements*.

There is an important distinction, based upon electronic structures, between the three classes of transition elements. For the d-block elements the partially filled shells are d shells, $3d$, $4d$ or $5d$. These d orbitals project well out to the periphery of the atoms and ions so that the electrons occupying them are strongly influenced by the surroundings of the ion and, in turn, are able to influence the environments very significantly. Thus, many of the properties of an ion with a partly filled d shell are quite sensitive to the number and arrangement of the d electrons present. In marked contrast to this, the $4f$ orbitals in the lanthanide elements are rather deeply buried in the atoms and ions. The electrons which occupy them are largely screened from the surroundings by the overlying shells ($5s$, $5p$) of electrons, and therefore reciprocal interactions between the $4f$ electrons and the surroundings of the atom or the ion are of relatively little chemical significance. This is why the chemistry of all the lanthanides is so homologous, whereas there are seemingly erratic and irregular variations in chemical properties as one passes through a series of d-block elements. The behavior of the actinide elements lies between the two types described above because the $5f$ orbitals are not so well shielded as are the $4f$ orbitals, although not so exposed as are the d orbitals in the d-block elements.

25-2. Position in the Periodic Table

We now consider the question of why the various transition series occur where they do in the periodic table. Figure 25-1 shows in a qualitative way the variations, especially the relative variations, in the energies of the atomic orbitals as a function of atomic number in neutral atoms. The first observation one might make about this diagram is that it is rather complicated. This observation is not without value, since it is well to realize that in a multielectron atom, one with say twenty or more electrons, the energies of all of the levels are more or less dependent on the populations of all of the other levels, as already explained (page 30) in the discussion of self-consistent field methods of computing radial wave functions.

Turning now to the details of the diagram, we see that in hydrogen all of the subshells of each principal shell are equi-energic. As we proceed to more complex atoms, these various subshells, s, p, d, f, g, etc., split apart and at the same time drop to lower energies. This descent in energy occurs because the degree to which an electron in a particular orbital is shielded from the nuclear charge by all of the other electrons in the atom is insufficient to prevent a steady increase in the *effective nuclear charge* felt by that electron with increasing atomic number. In other words, each electron is imperfectly shielded from the nuclear charge by the other electrons. According to the equation for the energy of an electron in an atom,

$$ E = - \frac{2\pi^2 \mu e^4 (Z^*)^2}{n^2 \mathbf{h}^2} \tag{25-1} $$

where Z^* is the effective nuclear charge, the energy of the electron falls as Z^* increases.

The reason why the diagram is so complicated, however, is that all subshells do not drop in parallel fashion, but rather in varying and somewhat irregular ways. This is because the several subshells of the same principal shell are shielded to different degrees by the core of electrons beneath. This point has been mentioned briefly before (Section 1-8), but will be considered in more detail here.

From Figure 25-1 we see that the $1s$, $2s$, $2p$, $3s$ and $3p$ levels occur in that sequence in all known atoms. Thus through those atoms (H—Ar) in which this sequence of orbitals is being filled, they are filled in that order. While the filling of this set of orbitals is taking place, the energies of the

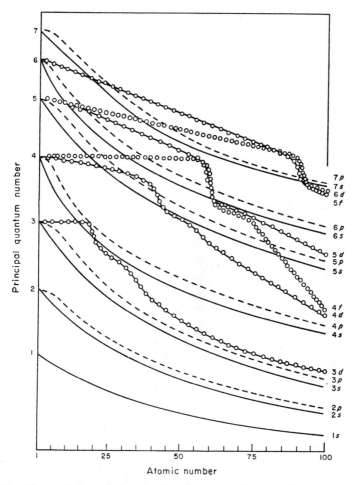

Fig. 25-1. The variation of the energies of atomic orbitals with increasing atomic number in neutral atoms (energies not strictly to scale).

higher and as yet unfilled orbitals are being variously affected by the screening power of these first eighteen electrons. In particular, the $3d$ levels, which penetrate the argon core rather little, have scarcely dropped in energy when we reach argon, whereas the $4s$ and $4p$ levels, especially the former, which penetrate the argon core quite a bit, have dropped rather steeply. Thus, when two more electrons are added to the argon configuration to give the potassium and calcium atoms, they enter the $4s$ orbital, which has fallen below the $3d$ orbitals. As these two electrons are added, the nuclear charge is also increased by two units. Since the $3d$ orbitals penetrate the electron density in the $4s$ orbitals very considerably, the net result is that the effective nuclear charge for the $3d$ orbitals increases rather abruptly, and they now drop well below the $4p$ orbitals to about the level of the $4s$ orbital. The next electron therefore enters the $3d$ shell, and scandium has the configuration $[\mathrm{Ar}]4s^2 3d$. This $3d$ electron screens the $4p$ levels more effectively than it screens the remaining $3d$ orbitals so the latter remain the lowest available orbitals and the next electron is also added to the $3d$ shell to give Ti with the configuration $[\mathrm{Ar}]4s^2 3d^2$. This process continues in a similar way until the entire $3d$ shell is filled. Thus at Zn we have the configuration $[\mathrm{Ar}]4s^2 3d^{10}$, and the $4p$ orbitals, now the lowest available ones, become filled in the six succeeding elements.

This same sequence of events is repeated again in the elements following krypton, which has the electron configuration $[\mathrm{Ar}]3d^{10}4s^2 4p^6$. Because of the way in which the shielding varies, the $4d$ levels, which in a one-electron atom would be next in order of stability, are higher in energy than the $5s$ and $5p$ orbitals, so that the next two electrons added go into the $5s$ orbitals, giving the alkali and alkaline earth elements Rb and Sr. But the shielding of the $4d$ orbitals by these $5s$ electrons is very poor so that the $4d$ orbitals feel strongly the increase of two units of nuclear charge and take a sharp drop, becoming appreciably more stable than the $5p$ orbitals, and the next electron added becomes a $4d$ electron. Thus the next element, Y, is the first member of the second transition series. This series is completed at Ag, configuration $[\mathrm{Kr}]4d^{10}5s^2$, and then six $5p$ electrons are added to make Xe, the next noble gas.

At Xe ($Z = 54$) the next available orbitals are the $6s$ and $6p$ orbitals. The $4f$ orbitals are so slightly penetrating with respect to the Xe core that they have scarcely gained any stability, while the more penetrating $6s$ and $6p$ levels have dropped a good deal. Hence the next two electrons added are $6s$ electrons, giving again an alkali and an alkaline earth element, Cs and Ba, respectively. However, the $6s$ shell scarcely shields the $4f$ orbitals, so the latter abruptly feel an increase in effective nuclear charge and thus suffer a steep drop in energy. At the same time, however, the $5d$ levels also drop abruptly, just as $(n - 1)d$ levels have done previously as electrons are added to the ns level, and the final situation is one in which, at Ba, the $6s$, $5d$ and $4f$ levels are all of about the same energy. The next entering electron, in the element lanthanum, enters a $5d$ orbital, but the following element, cerium, has the configuration $6s^2 4f^2$. Through the next twelve elements electrons continue to enter the $4f$ orbitals, and it is likely that even at cerium they are intrinsically more stable than the $5d$'s. Certainly they are so by the time we reach ytterbium, with the configuration $6s^2 4f^{14}$. Now, with the $6s$ and $4f$ shells full, the next lowest levels are unequivocally the $5d$'s, and from lutetium, with the configuration $6s^2 4f^{14} 5d$, through mercury, with the configuration $[Xe]6s^2 4f^{25}5d^{10}$, the ten $5d$ electrons are added. Chemically, lanthanum and lutetium, each of which has a single $5d$ electron, are very similar to one another, and all of the elements in between, with configurations $[Xe]4f^n 6s^2$, have chemical properties intermediate between those of lanthanum and lutetium. Consequently these fifteen elements are all considered as members of one class, the lanthanides. Hafnium, $[Xe]4f^{14}5d^2 6s^2$, through gold are the eight elements which we regard as the members of the third transition series.

Following mercury there are six elements in which electrons enter the $6p$ orbitals until the next noble gas, radon, is reached. Its configuration is $[Xe]4f^{14}5d^{10}6s^2 6p^6$. The $5f$ orbitals have dropped so much more slowly, because of their relatively nonpenetrating character, than have the $7s$ and $7p$ orbitals that the next two electrons beyond the radon core are added to the $7s$ level, and again an alkali and an alkaline earth element are formed, namely, Fr, $[Rn]7s$, and Ra, $[Rn]7s^2$. But, again in analogy to the situation one row up in the periodic table, both the $5f$ and $6d$ orbitals penetrate the $7s$ orbitals very considerably; they are thus abruptly stabilized relative to the $7p$ orbitals, and the next electrons added enter them. It appears that as we proceed through actinium and the following elements, the energies of the $6d$ and $5f$ orbitals remain for a while so similar that the exact configuration is determined by interelectronic forces of the sort discussed in Section 25-3. In the case of protactinium it is not certain whether the ground state is $[Rn]7s^2 6d^3$, $[Rn]7s^2 6d^2 5f$, $[Rn]7s^2 6d5f^2$ or $[Rn]7s^2 5f^3$. These four configurations doubtless differ very little in energy, and for chemical purposes the question of which is actually the lowest is not of great importance. The next element, uranium, appears definitely to have the configuration $[Rn]7s^2 5f^3 6d$, and the elements thereafter are all believed to have the configurations $[Rn]7s^2 5f^n 6d$. The important point is that, around actinium, the $6d$ and $5f$ levels are of practically the same energy, with the $5f$'s probably becoming slowly more stable later on.

25-3. Electron Configurations of the Atoms and Ions

In this section we shall look more closely at the factors determining the electron configurations of transition metal atoms and ions. The discussion in the preceding section is not entirely adequate or accurate because it takes account only of the shielding of a given electron from the nuclear charge by other electrons in the atom. One electron may help to determine the orbital occupied by another electron not only in this indirect way but also because of direct interactions between the electrons. It is these direct interactions which cause the differences in energy between different states derived from the same configuration, as explained in more detail in Section 1-8. In cases where the energies of two orbitals differ by an amount which is comparable to or less than the energies arising from electron–electron interactions, it is not possible to predict electron configurations solely by consideration of the order of orbital energies, and the problem requires a more searching analysis.[1]

One of the most important examples of this sort of situation is the special stability of configurations in which subshells are either filled or exactly half filled. It can be shown by general arguments that such configurations give rise to S states, that is states with $L = 0$, which are exceptionally stable because of a large amount of so-called exchange energy.

This is exemplified in the first transition series by the "anomalous" configurations of the atoms of chromium and copper,

	Sc	Ti	V	Cr	Mn	Fe	Co	Ni	Cu	Zn
$4s$	2	2	2	1	2	2	2	2	1	2
$3d$	1	2	3	5	5	6	7	8	10	10

and in the lanthanides by the configuration of gadolinium:

	Sm	Eu	Gd	Tb
$6s$	2	2	2	2
$5d$	0	0	1	0
$4f$	6	7	7	9

In the first two cases an electron is "borrowed out of turn," so to speak, from an orbital of similar energy in order to achieve the exchange-energy-stabilized half-filled or filled shell, whereas in the case of gadolinium an electron is turned away into another shell of similar energy in order to preserve intact a half-filled arrangement.

In the second transition series the irregularities become more complex, as shown in the following order:

	Y	Zr	Nb	Mo	Tc	Ru	Rh	Pd	Ag	Cd
$5s$	2	2	1	1	1	1	1	0	1	2
$4d$	1	2	4	5	6	7	8	10	10	10

No simple analysis is possible here; both nuclear–electron and electron–electron forces play their roles in determining these configurations. Although a preference for the filled $4d$ shell is evident at the end of the series and the elements Nb and Mo show a preference for the half-filled

---

[1] R. M. Hochstrasser, *J. Chem. Educ.*, **42**, 154 (1965).

shell, the configuration of Tc shows that this preference is not controlling throughout this series.

It is also well to point out that the interelectronic forces and variations in total nuclear charge play a large part in determining the configurations of ions. We cannot say that because $4s$ orbitals became occupied before $3d$ orbitals, they are always more stable. If this were so, then we would expect the elements of the first transition series to ionize by loss of $3d$ electrons, whereas, in fact, they ionize by loss of $4s$ electrons first. Thus it is the net effect of all of the forces—nuclear–electronic attraction, shielding of one electron by others, interelectronic repulsions and the exchange forces—which determines the stability of an electron configuration; and, unfortunately, there are many cases in which the interplay of these forces and their sensitivity to changes in nuclear charge and the number of electrons present cannot be simply described.

MAGNETIC PROPERTIES OF CHEMICAL SUBSTANCES

25-4. The Importance of Magnetism in Transition Element Chemistry

Many—indeed, most—compounds of the transition elements are paramagnetic, and much of our understanding of transition metal chemistry has been derived from magnetic data. Consequently, it is necessary to explain the salient facts and principles of magnetism, from a chemical viewpoint, before proceeding to detailed discussion of chemistry.

All of the magnetic properties of substances in bulk are ultimately determined by the electrical properties of the subatomic particles, electrons and nucleons. Because the magnetic effects due to nucleons and nuclei are some 10^{-3} times those due to electrons, they ordinarily have no detectable effect on magnetic phenomena of direct chemical significance. This is not to say that chemical phenomena do not have significant effects upon nuclear magnetism; it is just such effects that make nuclear magnetic resonance spectroscopy an extremely useful tool for the chemist. Thus we shall concentrate our attention entirely on the properties of the electron and on the magnetic properties of matter which result therefrom. We shall see that there are direct and often sensitive relationships between the magnetic properties of matter in bulk and the number and distribution of unpaired electrons in its various constituent atoms or ions.

There are several kinds of magnetism, qualitatively speaking; the salient features of each are summarized in Table 25-1. In the following sections we shall consider first *paramagnetism*. A substance which is paramagnetic is attracted into a magnetic field with a force proportional to the field

TABLE 25-1

Main Types of Magnetic Behavior

Type	Sign of χ_M	Magnitude[a] of χ_M in cgs units	Dependence of χ_M on H	Origin
Diamagnetism	—	1–500×10^{-6}	Independent	Electron charge
Paramagnetism	+	0–10^{-2}	Independent	Spin and orbital motion of electrons on individual atoms
Ferromagnetism	+	10^{-2}–10^{6}	Dependent	Cooperative interaction between magnetic moments of individual atoms
Antiferromagnetism	+	0–10^{-2}	May be dependent	

[a] Assuming molecular or ionic weights in the range of about 50–1000. χ_M is the susceptibility per mole of substance, as explained on page 639.

strength times the field gradient. Paramagnetism is generally caused by the presence in the substance of ions, atoms or molecules which have unpaired electrons. Each of these has a definite paramagnetic moment which exists in the absence of any external magnetic field. A *diamagnetic* substance is repelled by a magnetic field. All matter has this property to some extent. Diamagnetic behavior is due to small magnetic moments which are induced by the magnetic field but do not exist in the absence of the field. Moments so induced are in opposition to the inducing field, thus causing repulsion. Finally, there are the more complex forms of magnetic behavior known as ferromagnetism and antiferromagnetism, and still others which will not be discussed here.

25-5. Origin of Paramagnetic Moments

Electrons determine the magnetic properties of matter in two ways. First, each electron is, in effect, a magnet in itself. From a pre-wave mechanical viewpoint, the electron may be regarded as a small sphere of negative charge spinning on its axis. Then, from completely classical considerations, the spinning of charge produces a magnetic moment. Second, an electron which is traveling in a closed path around a nucleus, again according to the pre-wave mechanical picture of an atom, will also produce a magnetic moment, just as does an electric current traveling in a loop of wire. The magnetic properties of any individual atom or ion will result from some combination of these two properties, that is, the inherent *spin moment* of the electron and the *orbital moment* resulting from the motion of the electron around the nucleus. These physical images should not, of course, be taken too literally, for they have no place in wave mechanics, nor do they provide a basis for quantitatively correct predictions. They are qualitatively useful conceptual aids, however.

The magnetic moments of atoms, ions and molecules are usually expressed in units called *Bohr magnetons,* abbreviated BM. The Bohr magneton is defined in terms of fundamental constants as

$$1 \text{ BM} = \frac{e\mathbf{h}}{4\pi mc} \tag{25-2}$$

where e is the electronic charge, $\mathbf{h}$ is Planck's constant, m is the electron mass and c is the speed of light. This is *not,* however, the moment of a single electron. Because of certain features of quantum theory, the relationship is a little more complicated.

The magnetic moment, μ_s, of a single electron is given, according to wave mechanics, by the equation

$$\mu_s \text{ (in BM)} = g\sqrt{s(s+1)} \tag{25-3}$$

in which s is simply the absolute value of the spin quantum number and g is the gyromagnetic ratio, more familiarly known as the "g factor." The quantity $\sqrt{s(s+1)}$ is the value of the angular momentum of the electron, and thus g is the ratio of the magnetic moment to the angular momentum, as its name is intended to suggest. For the free electron, g has the value 2.00023, which may be taken as 2.00 for most purposes. From equation 25-3 we can calculate the spin magnetic moment of one electron as:

$$\mu_s = 2\sqrt{\tfrac{1}{2}(\tfrac{1}{2}+1)} = \sqrt{3} = 1.73 \text{ BM}$$

Thus any atom, ion or molecule having one unpaired electron (e.g., H, Cu^{2+}, ClO_2) should have a magnetic moment of 1.73 BM from the electron spin alone. This may be augmented or diminished by an orbital contribution as will be seen later.

There are transition metal ions having one, two, three ... up to seven unpaired electrons. As indicated in Section 1-8, the spin quantum number for the ion as a whole, S, is the sum of the spin quantum numbers, $s = \tfrac{1}{2}$, for the individual electrons. For example, in the manganese(II) ion with five unpaired electrons, $S = 5(\tfrac{1}{2}) = \tfrac{5}{2}$ and in the gadolinium(III) ion with seven unpaired electrons, $S = 7(\tfrac{1}{2}) = \tfrac{7}{2}$. Thus we can use equation 25-3, substituting S for s, to calculate the magnetic moment due to the electron spins alone, the so-called "spin-only" moment, for any atom or ion provided we know the total spin quantum number, S. The results are summarized in Table 25-2 for all possible real cases.

In the two examples chosen above, namely, Mn^{II} and Gd^{III}, the observed values of their magnetic moments agree very well with the spin-only values

TABLE 25-2

"Spin-Only" Magnetic Moments for Various Numbers
of Unpaired Electrons

No. of unpaired electrons	S	μ_S, BM
1	$\frac{1}{2}$	1.73
2	1	2.83
3	$\frac{3}{2}$	3.87
4	2	4.90
5	$\frac{5}{2}$	5.92
6	3	6.93
7	$\frac{7}{2}$	7.94

in Table 25-2. Generally, however, experimental values differ from the spin-only ones, usually being somewhat greater. This is because the orbital motion of the electrons also makes a contribution to the moment. The theory by which the exact magnitudes of these orbital contributions may be calculated is by no means simple and we shall give here only a superficial and pragmatic account of the subject. More detailed discussion of a few specific cases will be found in several places later in the text (for example, pages 872, 883 and 911).

For Mn^{II}, Fe^{III}, Gd^{III} and other ions whose ground states are S states, there is no orbital angular momentum even in the free ion. Hence there cannot be any orbital contribution to the magnetic moment, and the spin-only formula applies exactly.* In general, however, the transition metal ions in their ground states, D or F being most common, do possess orbital angular momentum. Wave mechanics shows that for such ions, if the orbital motion makes its full contribution to the magnetic moments, they will be given by:

$$\mu_{S+L} = \sqrt{4S(S+1) + L(L+1)} \tag{25-4}$$

in which L represents the orbital angular momentum quantum number for the ion.

In Table 25-3 are listed magnetic moments actually observed for the common ions of the first transition series together with the calculated values of μ_S and μ_{S+L}. It will be seen that observed values of μ frequently exceed μ_S, but seldom are as high as μ_{S+L}. This is because the electric fields of other atoms, ions and molecules surrounding the metal ion in its compounds restrict the orbital motion of the electrons so that the orbital

* Because of certain high order effects and also, in part, because of covalence in metal-ligand bonds, slight departures (i.e., a few tenths of a BM) from the spin-only moments are sometimes observed

TABLE 25-3

Theoretical and Experimental Magnetic Moments for Various Transition Metal Ions
(In Bohr magnetons)

Ion	Ground state quantum numbers		Spectroscopic symbol	μ_S	μ_{S+L}	Observed moments
	S	L				
V^{4+}	$\frac{1}{2}$	2	^2D	1.73	3.00	1.7–1.8
Cu^{2+}	$\frac{1}{2}$	2	^2D	1.73	3.00	1.7–2.2
V^{3+}	1	3	^3F	2.83	4.47	2.6–2.8
Ni^{2+}	1	3	^3F	2.83	4.47	2.8–4.0
Cr^{3+}	$\frac{3}{2}$	3	^4F	3.87	5.20	∼3.8
Co^{2+}	$\frac{3}{2}$	3	^4F	3.87	5.20	4.1–5.2
Fe^{2+}	2	2	^5D	4.90	5.48	5.1–5.5
Co^{3+}	2	2	^5D	4.90	5.48	∼5.4
Mn^{2+}	$\frac{5}{2}$	0	^6S	5.92	5.92	∼5.9
Fe^{3+}	$\frac{5}{2}$	0	^6S	5.92	5.92	∼5.9

angular momentum and hence the orbital moments are wholly or partially "*quenched.*" In some cases, e.g., d^3 and d^8 ions in octahedral environments and d^7 ions in tetrahedral ones, the quenching of orbital angular momentum in the ground state is expected to be complete according to the simplest arguments, and yet such systems deviate from spin-only behavior. However, when the effect of spin-orbit coupling is considered, it is found that orbital angular momentum is mixed into the ground state from the first excited state of the system. This phenomenon is discussed quantitatively for the d^7 ion Co^{II} on page 869. In the case of a d^3 ion in an octahedral environment, the orbital contribution is introduced in *opposition* to the spin contribution and moments slightly below the spin-only value are therefore observed, as for Cr^{III}.

Finally, it is noteworthy that in many systems which contain unpaired electrons, as well as in a few, e.g., CrO_4^{2-}, which do not, weak paramagnetism which is *independent* of temperature can arise by a coupling of the ground state of the system with excited states of high energy under the influence of the magnetic field. This *temperature independent paramagnetism*, TIP, thus resembles diamagnetism in that it is not due to any magnetic dipole existing in the molecule but is induced when the substance is placed in the magnetic field. It also resembles diamagnetism in its temperature independence and in its order of magnitude, viz., 0–500 × 10^{-6} cgs units per mole (cf. Table 25-1). It is often ignored in interpreting the paramagnetic behavior of ions with unpaired electrons, but in work which pretends to accuracy it should not be. Certainly, when measured susceptibilities are corrected for diamagnetism (see next section) it is illogical not to correct them also for TIP if this is known to occur in the system concerned.

25-6. Diamagnetism

Diamagnetism is a property of all forms of matter. All substances contain at least some if not all electrons in closed shells. In closed shells the electron spin moments and orbital moments of individual electrons balance one another out so that there is no net magnetic moment. However, when an atom or molecule is placed in a magnetic field, a small magnetic moment directly proportional to the strength of the field is induced. The electron spins have nothing to do with this induced moment; they remain tightly coupled together in antiparallel pairs. However, the planes of the orbitals are tipped slightly so that a small net orbital moment is set up in opposition to the applied field. It is because of this opposition that diamagnetic substances are repelled from magnetic fields.

Even an atom with a permanent magnetic moment will have diamagnetic behavior working in opposition to the paramagnetism when placed in a magnetic field, provided only that the atom has one or more closed shells of electrons. Thus, the net paramagnetism measured is slightly less than the true paramagnetism because some of the latter is "canceled out" by the diamagnetism.

Since diamagnetism is usually several orders of magnitude weaker than paramagnetism, substances with unpaired electrons almost always have a net paramagnetism. Of course, a very dilute solution of a paramagnetic ion in a diamagnetic solvent such as water may be diamagnetic because of the large ratio of diamagnetic to paramagnetic species in it. Another important feature of diamagnetism is that its magnitude does not vary with temperature. This is because the moment induced depends only on the sizes and shapes of the orbitals in the closed shells and these are not temperature dependent.

25-7. Magnetic Susceptibility

Chemically useful information is obtained by proper interpretation of measured values of magnetic moments. However, magnetic moments are not measured directly. Instead, one measures the magnetic susceptibility of a material from which it is possible to calculate the magnetic moment of the paramagnetic ion or atom therein.

Magnetic susceptibility is defined in the following way. If a substance is placed in a magnetic field of magnitude H, the flux B, within the substance, is given by

$$B = H + 4\pi I \tag{25-5}$$

I is called the intensity of magnetization. The ratio B/H, called the magnetic permeability of the material, is given by

$$B/H = 1 + 4\pi(I/H) = 1 + 4\pi\kappa \qquad (25\text{-}6)$$

κ is called the magnetic susceptibility per unit volume, or simply the volume susceptibility. The physical significance of equation 25-6 is easily seen. The permeability, B/H, is just the ratio of the density of lines of force within the substance to the density of such lines in the same region in the absence of the specimen. Thus, the volume susceptibility of a vacuum is by definition zero, since in a vacuum it must be that $B/H = 1$. The susceptibility of a diamagnetic substance is negative because lines of force from induced dipoles cancel out some lines of force due to the applied field. For paramagnetic substances the flux is greater within the substance than it would be in a vacuum, and thus paramagnetic substances have positive susceptibilities.

There are numerous methods for measuring magnetic susceptibilities, all of which depend on measuring the force exerted upon a body when it is placed in an inhomogeneous magnetic field. The more paramagnetic the body is, the more strongly will it be drawn toward the more intense part of the field.

25-8. Magnetic Moments from Magnetic Susceptibilities

It is generally more convenient to discuss magnetic susceptibility on a weight basis than on a volume basis and thus the following relations are used:

$$\kappa/d = \chi \qquad (25\text{-}7a)$$

$$M\chi = \chi_M \qquad (25\text{-}7b)$$

In these equations d is the density in g cm^{-3} and M is the molecular weight. χ is called the gram susceptibility and χ_M is called the molar susceptibility. When a value of χ_M is obtained from the measured volume susceptibility, κ, it can be corrected for the diamagnetic contribution and for the TIP to give a "corrected" molar susceptibility, χ_M^{corr}, which is the most useful quantity in drawing conclusions about electronic structure.

In his classic studies, Pierre Curie showed that paramagnetic susceptibilities depend inversely on temperature and often follow or closely approximate the behavior required by the simple equation

$$\chi_M^{corr} = C/T \qquad (25\text{-}8)$$

Here T represents the absolute temperature, and C is a constant which is characteristic of the substance and known as its Curie constant. Equation 25-8 expresses what is known as *Curie's law**.

Now, on theoretical grounds, just such an equation is to be expected. The magnetic field in which the sample is placed tends to align the moments of the paramagnetic atoms or ions; at the same time, thermal agitation tends to randomize the orientations of these individual moments. The situation is entirely analogous to that encountered in the electric polarization of matter containing electric dipoles, with which the student is probably already familiar from a standard physical chemistry course. Applying a straightforward statistical treatment, one obtains the following equation showing how the molar susceptibility of a substance containing independent atoms, ions or molecules, each of magnetic moment μ (in BM), will vary with temperature:

$$\chi_M{}^{corr} = \frac{N\mu^2/3k}{T} \tag{25-9}$$

where N is Avogadro's number, and k is the Boltzmann constant. Obviously, by comparison of equations 25-8 and 25-9,

$$C = N\mu^2/3k \tag{25-10}$$

and at any given temperature

$$\mu = \sqrt{3k/N} \cdot \sqrt{\chi_M{}^{corr} T} \tag{25-11}$$

which, on evaluating $\sqrt{3k/N}$ numerically, becomes

$$\mu = 2.84\sqrt{\chi_M{}^{corr} T} \tag{25-12}$$

Thus, to recapitulate, one first makes a direct measurement of the volume susceptibility of a substance from which χ_M is calculated, and, in accurate work, corrected for diamagnetism and TIP. From this corrected molar susceptibility and the temperature of the measurement, equation 25-12 enables one to calculate the magnetic moment of the ion, atom or molecule responsible for the paramagnetism.

From equation 25-8 we should expect that if we measure χ_M for a substance at several temperatures and plot the reciprocals of the $\chi_M{}^{corr}$ values against T, we shall obtain a straight line of slope C which intersects the origin. Although there are many substances which, within the limits of experimental error, do show this behavior, there are also many others for which the line does not go through the origin, but instead looks some-

---

* Actually Curie's law was originally based on χ, that is the effects of diamagnetism and TIP were neglected. However, its significance and utility are enhanced when these are taken into account.

what like one of those shown in Figure 25-2, cutting the T axis at a temperature below 0°K as in (a) or above 0°K as in (b). Obviously, such a line can be represented by a slight modification of the Curie equation,

$$\chi_M{}^{corr} = \frac{C}{T - \theta} \qquad (25\text{-}13)$$

Here θ is the temperature at which the line cuts the T axis. This equation expresses what is known as the *Curie–Weiss law*, and θ is known as the

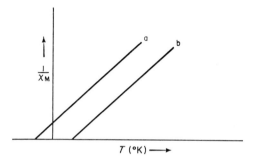

Fig. 25-2. Some deviations from the Curie law which may be fitted to the Curie–Weiss law.

Weiss constant. Actually, just such an equation can be derived if one assumes, not that the dipoles in the various ions, atoms or molecules of a solid are completely independent—as was assumed in deriving equation 25-9—but that instead the orientation of each one is influenced by the orientations of its neighbors as well as by the field to which it is subjected. Thus the Weiss constant can be thought of as taking account of the interionic or intermolecular interactions, thereby enabling us to eliminate this extraneous effect by computing the magnetic moment from the equation

$$\mu = 2.84\sqrt{\chi_M{}^{corr}(T - \theta)} \qquad (25\text{-}14)$$

instead of from equation 25-12. Unfortunately, there are also cases in which magnetic behavior appears to follow the Curie–Weiss equation without the Weiss constant having this simple interpretation. In such cases, it is often quite wrong to use equation 25-14. In cases where the Curie law does not accurately fit the data, and where the applicability of the Curie–Weiss law is in doubt (even though it *may* fit the data), the best practice is to compute a magnetic moment at a given temperature using the Curie law, e.g., 25-12, and call this an *effective magnetic moment*, μ_{eff}, at the specified temperature. In this way no possibly unjustified implications are attached to empirically sound facts.

21 + A.I.C.

25-9. Ferromagnetism and Antiferromagnetism

In addition to the simple paramagnetism we have discussed, where the Curie or Curie–Weiss law is followed and the susceptibility shows no dependence on field strength, there are other forms of paramagnetism in which the dependence on both temperature and field strength is complicated. Two of the most important of these are ferromagnetism and antiferromagnetism. No attempt will be made to explain either of these in detail, either phenomenologically or theoretically, but it is important for the student to recognize their salient features. Figure 25-3 compares the

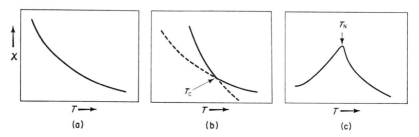

Fig. 25-3. Diagrams indicating the qualitative temperature dependence of magnetic susceptibility for (a) simple paramagnetism, (b) ferromagnetism and (c) antiferromagnetism.

qualitative temperature dependence of the susceptibility for (a) simple paramagnetism, (b) ferromagnetism and (c) antiferromagnetism. Of course (a) is just a rough graph of Curie's law. In (b) it should be noted that there is a discontinuity at some temperature, T_C, called the Curie temperature. Above the Curie temperature the substance follows the Curie or the Curie–Weiss law; that is, it is a simple paramagnetic. Below the Curie temperature, however, it varies in a different way with temperature and is also field-strength dependent. For antiferromagnetism there is again a characteristic temperature, T_N, called the Néel temperature. Above T_N the substance has the behavior of a simple paramagnetic, but below the Néel temperature the susceptibility *drops* with decreasing temperature.

These peculiarities in the behavior of ferromagnetic and antiferromagnetic substances below their Curie or Néel points are due to interionic interactions which have magnitudes comparable to the thermal energies at the Curie or Néel temperature and thus become progressively greater than thermal energies as the temperature is further lowered. In the case of antiferromagnetism, the moments of the ions in the lattice tend to align themselves so as to cancel one another out. Above the Néel temperature thermal agitation prevents very effective alignment, and the interactions are manifested only in the form of a Weiss constant which is of the same general magnitude as the Néel temperature itself. However, below the Néel temperature this antiparallel aligning becomes effective and the susceptibility is diminished. In ferromagnetic substances the moments of the separate ions tend to align themselves parallel and thus to reinforce one another. Above the Curie temperature, thermal energies are more or less able to randomize the orientations; below T_C, however, the tendency to alignment becomes controlling, and the susceptibility increases much more rapidly with decreasing temperature than it would if the ion moments behaved independently of one another.

Presumably, even in those substances we ordinarily regard as simple paramagnetics there are some interionic interactions, however weak, and therefore there must be some temperature, however low, below which they will show ferromagnetic or antiferromagnetic behavior, depending on the sign of the interaction. The question of why such interactions are so large in some substances that they have Curie or Néel temperature near and even above room temperature is still something of an unsolved problem. Suffice it to say here that in many cases it is certain that the magnetic interactions cannot be direct dipole–dipole interactions but instead the dipoles are coupled through the electrons of intervening atoms in oxides, sulfides, halides and similar compounds.

In general, ferro- and antiferromagnetic interactions are decreased when the magnetic species are separated from one another physically. Thus, when the magnetic behavior of a solid shows the effects of interionic coupling, solutions of the same substance will be free of such interactions. This includes solid solutions; for example, when K_2OsCl_6, which has μ_{eff} per Os atom at 300°K of 1.44 BM, is contained at a level of ≤ 10 mole percent in diamagnetic and isomorphous K_2PtCl_6, its μ_{eff} value at the same temperature rises to 1.94 BM due to the elimination of antiferromagnetic coupling between the Os^{IV} ions through intervening chlorine atoms.

There are special cases, of considerable interest, in which antiferromagnetic coupling occurs between a few, say 2 or 3, paramagnetic ions which are held together in a polynuclear complex. Of course such interactions correspond to incipient bond formation and when they become strong enough they lead to a situation in which the state with paired electron spins, the bonded state, is so stable that the substance is entirely diamagnetic at normal temperatures. However, in some cases, as illustrated by the dimeric carboxylates of Cu^{II} (see page 654), the energy of interaction between the unpaired electrons is small relative to thermal energy at room temperature and the compound remains paramagnetic.

However, μ_{eff} is less than that for isolated ions, and it decreases markedly with decreasing temperature. For example, μ_{eff} for Cu^{II} is normally about 1.8–1.9 BM at 300°K, but in $Cu_2(CH_3COO)_4 \cdot 2H_2O$, it is ~1.4 BM and drops to lower values at lower temperatures. Presumably at 0°K, or close to it, where thermal energy becomes unavailable, the moment would become zero.

25-10. Electron Spin Resonance, esr

This relatively newly observed phenomenon opens new dimensions in the inference of chemically important features of molecular electronic structure by magnetic measurements. Because its proper understanding requires an extensive knowledge of wave mechanics, beyond the scope of this text, we shall present here only a brief and heuristic account, intended to draw attention to the kinds of useful results which may be obtained.

Electron spin resonance may be observed when molecules or ions containing one or more unpaired electrons are placed in a magnetic field. In a molecule containing a single unpaired electron in an S state ($l = 0$), the effect of the magnetic field is to lift the spin degeneracy, that is, to make the energy of the electron different for its two M_S values, $+\frac{1}{2}$ and $-\frac{1}{2}$. This effect is easily understood by thinking of the electron classically as a small magnet in the field of a larger one. When its field is lined up with that of the larger one (Fig. 25-4a), there is an increase in potential energy,

(a)   (b)

Fig. 25-4. Diagram indicating (a) unfavorable and (b) favorable alignments of a small magnet (e.g., an electron) in the field of a larger one.

whereas the opposite alignment (Fig. 25-4b) decreases the potential energy. A quantitative treatment shows that the energy difference between these two electron spin alignments is equal to $g\beta H$, where g is the same gyromagnetic ratio discussed earlier, β is the Bohr magneton and H is the strength of the magnetic field. The lower state is slightly more populated than the upper one at thermal equilibrium. Thus, when radiation of frequency ν such that $\mathbf{h}\nu = g\beta H$ is applied to the system, there is a net absorption because absorptive transitions upward are more numerous than radiative transitions downward. By sweeping the frequency of an oscillator (in the microwave region) through the appropriate frequency range, ν is observed as the frequency of maximum absorption. From this the g value may be calculated. In this simple case, it would be 2.00, but in other cases, more complex behavior is observed. It is the added complexities from which detailed information on electronic structure can often be obtained. The three main types of more complex behavior and their significance will now be mentioned briefly.

1. It will often happen that the observed g value will differ from 2.00. This deviation can be attributed to orbital contributions to the magnetism, and, from the very precise data afforded by esr measurements, these orbital contributions can be evaluated quite precisely. With such information, fairly detailed knowledge of orbital populations, degrees of hybridization, etc., may often be obtained.

In some substances there are two (or more) identical ions in different chemical environments or differently oriented with respect to the crystallographic axes. In a bulk susceptibility measurement, only the average magnetic properties of both ions could be determined, but even slight differences between them will result in their resonance frequencies being detectably different in an esr measurement.

2. Magnetic anisotropy can often be observed by making measurements on small, oriented, single crystals. The anisotropy means that the g value and hence the resonance frequency vary according to the orientation of the crystal with respect to the direction of the external magnetic field, H. The g value in any particular arbitrary direction can be expressed as the tensor resultant of three tensor components, g_x, g_y, g_z, in mutually perpendicular directions. There are many cases in which two of these tensor components are equal, and the two separate g values are called $g_\parallel$ and $g_\perp$; $g_\parallel$ is the value in the unique direction, while $g_\perp$ is the value in any direction in the plane perpendicular to this direction. From the properties of tensors, it follows that the g value averaged over all directions, g_{av}, is given by

$$g_{av}{}^2 = \tfrac{1}{3}(g_x{}^2 + g_y{}^2 + g_z{}^2) = \tfrac{1}{3}(g_\parallel{}^2 + 2g_\perp{}^2) \qquad (25\text{-}15)$$

Thus, although a bulk susceptibility measurement made in the usual way on a powdered sample could provide only a value of g_{av}, and give no hint about the individual g_x, g_y, g_z, or $g_\parallel$ and $g_\perp$ values, a relatively simple esr measurement using a small single crystal can provide detailed knowledge of anisotropy. Anisotropy measurements can be and have been made by making bulk susceptibility measurements on quite large single crystals, but the experimental problems are formidable and the results of relatively low accuracy. Anisotropy data can usually be interpreted to give quite detailed information on metal–ligand bonding in complexes.

3. It often happens that the small magnetic fields of atomic nuclei cause splittings (fine structure) of esr lines. From the magnitudes of such

splittings, semiquantitative information as to "electron densities" of the unpaired electrons in particular orbitals of particular atoms can be obtained.

In conclusion, one other great advantage and one disadvantage of esr measurements relative to bulk susceptibility measurements should be recorded. Esr is extremely sensitive, responding, under optimum conditions (of line width, instrumental sensitivity, and signal-to-noise ratio), to $\sim 10^{-12}$ paramagnetic species per liter, whereas bulk susceptibility measurements can be accurate, as a rule, only when the net paramagnetism is greatly in excess of the diamagnetism in the sample and when the available quantity is relatively large (≥ 100 mg). Thus, esr can be used to study minute samples or larger samples containing the paramagnetic species, either ions or free radicals, at very low concentrations. A frequent disadvantage of the esr method is that very low temperatures, for example, liquid nitrogen or even liquid helium temperatures, are often required in order to reduce spin-lattice relaxation effects sufficiently to make lines observable. In many instances, especially with paramagnetic ions having even numbers of electrons, there has been only slight success at observing resonance under any experimental conditions. Also, the apparatus for esr measurements is expensive and complex, and the interpretation of the spectra often requires considerable skill. Bulk susceptibility measurements do have the advantage that they can always be made and used to obtain some idea of the magnetic moment of the paramagnetic ion if it is present in sufficient concentration. Esr measurements have by no means supplanted bulk susceptibility measurements except for special cases and special purposes. The bulk susceptibility measurement still remains one of the chemist's most valuable and frequently used tools in his efforts to understand the electronic structures of transition metal compounds.

OPTICAL ACTIVITY

The most important optically active inorganic compounds, or at least those most intensively studied in recent years, are complexes of transition metals containing two or three chelate rings. The existence of such optical isomers has already been noted (see page 146). The special importance of transition metal complexes in the study of optical activity is due to two things. First, there are several transition metal ions, especially Co^{III}, Cr^{III}, Rh^{III}, Ir^{III} and Pt^{IV}, which give such kinetically inert complexes that resolution of optical isomers is possible and the rates of racemization are slow enough that spectroscopic studies may be conveniently carried out. Secondly, detailed studies of optical activity require as a starting point a reasonably clear understanding of the energy levels and electronic spectra of the compounds to be studied, and the studies are greatly facilitated if the compounds have easily observable absorption bands in the visible, both of which requirements are uniquely met by transition metal compounds.

25-11. Basic Principles and Definitions

Optical activity in a molecule can be expected when and only when the molecule is so structured that it cannot be superposed on its mirror image. Such a molecule is said to be *disymmetric*, and disymmetry will occur whenever a molecule has neither an improper axis, S_n, nor a center of symmetry, i, nor a plane of symmetry, σ (see page 116). Since an S_2 axis is the same as a center of inversion, and σ can also be considered as S_1, the condition for disymmetry can be succinctly stated as the absence of any improper axis, S_n, with $n \geq 1$. The six-coordinate chelate complexes of the types M(bidentate ligand)$_3$ and *cis*-M(bidentate ligand)$_2$X$_2$, which have symmetries D_3 and C_2 respectively, clearly fulfill this condition, and are the commonest cases in which the "center of disymmetry" is the metal ion itself.

The simplest way in which optical activity may be observed is doubtless already familiar. It consists in the observation that the plane of polarization of plane polarized monochromatic light is rotated upon passing through a solution containing one or the other—or an excess of one or the other—of two enantiomorphic molecules.

In order to appreciate more fully this phenomenon and some others closely related to it, the nature of plane polarized light must be considered in more detail. When observed along the direction of propagation, a beam of plane polarized light appears to have its electric vector, which oscillates as a sine wave with the frequency of the light, confined to one plane. There is also an oscillating magnetic vector confined to a perpendicular plane, but we shall not be specifically interested in this.

It is exceptionally useful to think of a beam of plane polarized light as the resultant of two coterminous beams of right- and left-circularly polarized light which have equal amplitudes and are in phase. A circularly polarized beam is one in which the electric vector rotates uniformly about the direction of propagation by 2π during each cycle. Figure 25-5 shows how two such beams, circularly polarized in opposite senses, give a plane-polarized resultant. The most important property of the two circularly polarized components to be noted here is that they are enantiomorphous to one another, that is one is the nonsuperposable mirror image of the other.

Now, just as there are molecules AB consisting of two separately disymmetric halves, say A(+), A(−), and B(+), B(−), which are different substances, for example the diastereoisomers A(+)B(+) and A(−)B(+), having numerically different physical properties, so the physical interactions of the two circularly polarized beams with a given enantiomorph of a disymmetric molecule will be quantitatively different. The two important differences are (1) the refractive indices for left- and right-circularly polarized light, n_l and n_r, respectively, will be different, and (2) the molar absorbances, ϵ_l and ϵ_r, will be different.

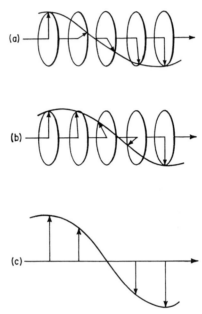

Fig. 25-5. (a) Right-circularly polarized light. (b) Left-circularly polarized light. (c) The plane-polarized resultant of (a) and (b). The horizontal arrow gives the direction of propagation and the arrows perpendicular to this direction denote the instantaneous spatial direction of the electric vector. (Reproduced by permission from S. F. Mason, *Chemistry in Britain*, **1965**, 245.)

If only the refractive index difference existed, the rotation of the plane of polarization would be explained as shown in Figure 25-6, since the retarding of one circularly polarized component relative to the other can be seen to have this net effect.

Actually, the simultaneous existence of a difference between ϵ_l and ϵ_r means that the rotated "plane" is no longer strictly a plane. This can be seen in Figure 25-7; since one rotating electric vector is not exactly equal in length to the other after the two components have traversed the optically active medium, their resultant describes an ellipse, whose principal axis defines the "plane" of the rotated beam and whose minor axis is equal to the absolute difference $|\epsilon_l - \epsilon_r|$. This difference is usually very small so that it is a very good approximation to speak of rotating "the plane." However, it can be measured and constitutes the *circular dichroism*.

It is most important that both the optical rotation and the circular dichroism are dependent on wavelength, especially in the region of an

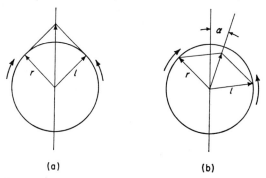

(a)   (b)

Fig. 25-6.   (a) An instantaneous view along the direction of propagation of the two vectors r and l of the circularly polarized beams and their resultant which lies in a vertical plane.   (b) If $n_l > n_r$, beam l is retarded relative to beam r thus causing the plane of the resultant to be tilted by the angle α.

electronic absorption band of the atom or ion lying at the "center of disymmetry." Moreover at a given wavelength the values of $n_l - n_r$ and

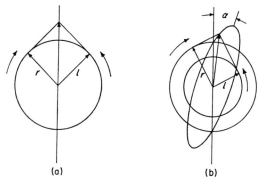

(a)   (b)

Fig. 25-7.   (a) Same as 25-6(a).   (b) If $n_l > n_r$ and also $\epsilon_l > \epsilon_r$, the vectors r and l will be affected, qualitatively, as shown, and they will then give rise to a resultant which traces out the indicated ellipse. Note that the quantity $\epsilon_l - \epsilon_r$ here is vastly exaggerated compared to real cases in order to make the diagram clear.

$\epsilon_l - \epsilon_r$ for one enantiomorph are equal and opposite to those for the other enantiomorph. The variations of $n_l - n_r$ and $\epsilon_l - \epsilon_r$ with a wavelength for a pair of enantiomorphs in the region of an absorption band with a maximum at λ_0 are illustrated schematically in Figure 25-8.   The

21*

variation of the angle of rotation with wavelength is called *optical rotatory dispersion*, ORD. This, together with the circular dichroism, CD, and the attendant introduction of ellipticity into the rotated beam, are, all together, called the *Cotton effect*, in honor of the French physicist, Aimé

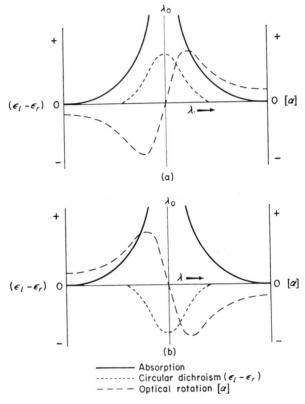

Fig. 25-8. The Cotton effect, as manifested in circular dichroism, $\epsilon_l - \epsilon_r$, and optical rotatory dispersion, $[\alpha]$, as would be given by a disymmetric compound with an absorption band centered at λ_0, assuming that there are no other absorption bands close by. (a) A positive Cotton effect. (b) A negative Cotton effect.

Cotton, who made pioneering studies of the wavelength dependent aspects of these phenomena in 1895.

25-12. Applications

Cotton effects are studied today by inorganic chemists for two principal purposes. First, they can be used to correlate the configurations of related disymmetric molecules and thus to follow the steric course of certain reactions.   Second, data on the magnitudes of the ORD and CD effects are useful in determining or confirming the assignments of electronic absorption bands and in refining our knowledge of the electronic structures of complexes.   This second phase of the subject is still in a state of active investigation and no generally accepted comprehensive theory has yet been developed; hence we shall not deal with it further in this book.

The use of ORD and CD data in correlating configurations of related molecules is increasing, but this phase too remains a subject for current research.   At present, rigorous correlations of the Cotton effect with absolute configurations are being sought, but this problem is not definitively solved.   For closely related molecules purely empirical correlations can be made readily, as illustrated in Figure 25-9, which shows the CD curves for $(+)[\text{Coen}_3]^{3+}$ and $(+)[\text{Co}(l\text{-pn})_3]^{3+}$, where the $(+)$ signs indicate that these are the enantiomers which have positive values of $[\alpha]$ at the sodium D line, and l-pn is shown in 5-XXXVb (page 148).   Clearly these two complex ions must have the same absolute configuration.   That of the $(+)[\text{Coen}_3]^{3+}$ ion has been determined by means of anomalous X-ray dispersion and is indicated schematically in Figure 25-9.

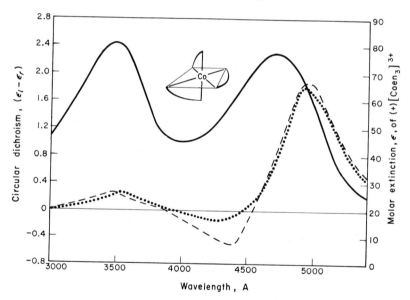

Fig. 25-9.   (a) The visible absorption spectrum of $(+)[\text{Coen}_3]^{3+}$, ———.   (b) The circular dichroism of $(+)[\text{Coen}_3]^{3+}$, ·······   (c) The circular dichroism of $(+)[\text{Co}(l\text{-pn})_3]^{3+}$, - - - - -.   The molar absorbence scale is to the right, the CD scale to the left.   The absorption spectrum of $(+)[\text{Co}(l\text{-pn})_3]^{3+}$ is practically identical to that of $(+)[\text{Coen}_3]^{3+}$. The small sketch shows the absolute configuration of $(+)[\text{Coen}_3]^{3+}$ as determined by anomalous scattering of X-rays.

METAL–METAL BONDS

25-13. General Remarks

It has become increasingly apparent in recent years that the transition elements of the d block form a number of interesting compounds containing two or more metal atoms in which there are bonds between the metal atoms themselves. Not very long ago such bonds were considered to be uncommon, but it now appears that there is at least one example for every d-block transition element and that for some elements, especially the heavier ones in their lower oxidation states, the tendency to form bonds to themselves (homophilicity) is a governing fact in their chemistry. Homophilicity is particularly pronounced in Nb, Ta, Mo, W and Re.

To begin a survey of metal–metal bonds it is necessary to consider carefully how such bonds are to be defined, for there are, in various compounds, all degrees of metal–metal interaction ranging from a mere weak coupling of electron spins (as in $Cu_2(O_2CCH_3)_4(H_2O)_2$) to the formation of strong multiple bonds (as in the $Re_2X_8^{2-}$ species).

The surest indication of the existence of a metal–metal bond is provided by the molecular structure, when this is fully known. In cases such as $Mn_2(CO)_{10}$ or $Re_2Cl_8^{2-}$, where the metal atoms are adjacent to each other and there are no bridging groups, the existence of metal–metal bonds is self-evident. More generally, short distances between metal atoms are indicative of the existence of a bond, even if bridging groups are present, but the distance criterion must be used cautiously, since great variations are possible. For example, in $[\pi\text{-}C_5H_5Mo(CO)_3]_2$ there is necessarily an Mo—Mo bond because the dimer has adjacent Mo atoms and no bridging groups; the Mo—Mo distance is 3.22 A. In MoO_2, on the other hand, where Mo—Mo bonding is also postulated, the Mo atoms lie in chains, bridged by pairs of oxygen atoms, with the alternating Mo—Mo distances of 2.50 and 3.10 A. The shorter ones are considered to correspond to bonds and the latter ones not, and yet the latter is shorter than the bond distance in $[\pi\text{-}C_5H_5Mo(CO)_3]_2$.

Undoubtedly, the length of a bond of given multiplicity between a given pair of metal atoms is a sensitive function of oxidation states, nature of additional ligands and other aspects of the molecular structure, and the use of interatomic distances to infer the existence and strength of metal–metal bonds requires caution.

Another kind of evidence frequently adduced to show the existence of metal–metal bonds is the lowering (even to zero) of magnetic moments compared to the values expected for isolated metal ions of the kinds present. The lowering is assumed to be due to pairing of spins in metal–

metal interactions. Because magnetic susceptibilities are relatively easy to measure, this indirect criterion has often been used, but in fact the greatest care is required if erroneous conclusions are to be avoided, as the following observations will show.

(1) Where ions with an even number of electrons are concerned, pairing of spins may often be due to distortions or irregularities in the environment about the isolated ion, which split apart orbitals which would otherwise be degenerate. This possibility is particularly relevant for the heavier transition elements, where intraionic spin pairing is easiest.

(2) Interionic spin pairing may occur by means of electron interactions through intervening anions. Good examples of this in binuclear complexes are provided by $[(EtOCS_2)_2MoO]_2O$ and $[(RuCl_5)_2O]^{4-}$, both of which contain linear M—O—M groups, as described in detail at appropriate places in Chapter 30. A more elaborate case is that of RuO_2. This compound has the rutile structure (page 48). Each Ru^{IV} ion is in the center of a practically regular octahedron of oxide ions, while each of the oxide ions is shared between three Ru^{IV} ions. Thus there are no localized two-center interactions between the ruthenium ions, nor do the rather long Ru—Ru distances seem consistent with there being any strong direct metal–metal interactions. Nonetheless, this compound, which contains octahedrally coordinated d^4 ions, is essentially diamagnetic. The most likely explanation here is the formation of extended molecular orbitals—in effect, energy bands—by extended overlap of metal and oxygen orbitals.[2] On the other hand, MoO_2 has a distorted rutile structure in which the $Mo^{IV}(d^2)$ ions are drawn together in pairs, as noted already. This compound is also essentially diamagnetic, but here at least part, if not all, of the pairing of electron spins is attributable to metal–metal bonding. The point to be emphasized here is that, from the magnetic data alone, the difference between the two cases could not have been appreciated and the magnetic properties might have been used as a basis for postulating direct metal–metal interactions in both compounds whereas in only one of them does it necessarily occur.

(3) The high values of the spin-orbit coupling constants in the heavier transition elements can often lead to very low magnetic susceptibilities in the absence of metal–metal bonds. This matter is discussed further on page 911.

The general category of compounds with metal–metal bonds may be subdivided for purposes of discussion along various lines. One general line of division is between those with bonds between like atoms and those with bonds between unlike atoms. Another is between compounds

---

[2] J. B. Goodenough, *Bull. soc. chim.* (*France*), **4**, 1200 (1965).

containing only two-center interactions, i.e., M_2 groups, and those in which three or more metal atoms each interact with all or several of the others. Compounds of the latter type, called *metal atom cluster compounds*, will be considered in Section 25-15. Virtually all of the clusters now recognized consist of identical metal atoms so that practically all discussion of bonds between dissimilar metal atoms can be covered in a discussion of the two-center interactions. However, there is no known reason why metal atom clusters consisting of dissimilar atoms should not be capable of existence.

Several authors[3,4,5] have discussed the factors which influence the formation of metal–metal bonds, particularly those between like atoms, in an effort to find correlations of predictive value in the discovery and preparation of new compounds containing metal–metal bonds. Correlations with sublimation energy of the metal, orbital sizes, repulsion effects between filled orbitals and ionic charges have been considered, but no straightforward guidelines have yet been proved valid. It seems likely that more experimental data are required, especially a clearer indication of the limits of stability in terms of position of the metal atoms in the periodic table, their oxidation states and the nature of the ligands also bonded to each metal atom.

25-14. Compounds with Two-center Metal–Metal Bonds

Bonds between Identical Atoms. These occur in a great variety of compounds and the number which have been recognized is quite large. Some examples from different classes of compounds are the following.

(1) *Metal carbonyl and organometallic compounds.* Metal–metal bonds occur both with and without bridging groups, as in $Fe_2(CO)_9$ and $Mn_2(CO)_{10}$ respectively. Nearly all polynuclear metal carbonyls and their derivatives contain metal–metal bonds. Structural details will be found in Chapter 27.

(2) *Carboxylate salts.* The carboxylates of Cu^{II} have already been mentioned; here the strength of the metal–metal interaction is only of the order of 1 kcal/mole and cannot truly be called a bond.[5a] However, the same kind of structure is found in the acetates of Mo^{II}, Rh^{II}, Re^{III} and in a variety of carboxylates of Cr^{II}. In these cases, the existence of relatively short metal–metal distances and the pairing of a large number of electrons lead us to believe that genuine chemical bonds exist between the metal atoms. The M—M distances, in Angstroms, in the acetates of Cu^{II}, Cr^{II},

[3] H. Schafer and H. G. Schnering, *Angew. Chem.*, **76**, 833 (1964).

[4] J. C. Sheldon, *Aust. J. Chem.*, **17**, 1191 (1964).

[5] J. Lewis and R. S. Nyholm, *Sci. Progr.*, **52**, 557 (1964).

[5a] See, however, D. J. Royer, *Inorg. Chem.*, **4**, 1830 (1964).

Rh^{II} and Mo^{II}, followed by Pauling's estimates of single bond distances for the metals, are respectively: 2.64(2.34), 2.46(2.36), 2.45(2.50) and 2.11(2.60). For the Cu^{II} compound the weakness of the interaction is consistent with the fact that the metal–metal distance is long in comparison to the single bond distance for the metal. For the Cr^{II} and Rh^{II} compounds, in which four and three electrons per metal atom become paired, the distances are indicative of pronounced metal–metal interaction, but it is questionable whether quadruple and triple bonds exist in these cases. Presumably some of the spin-pairing interactions are relatively weak. However, in the case of Mo^{II} acetate, the extremely short Mo—Mo distance suggests that a multiple bond exists. It is even possible that here the bond is quadruple, as in the isoelectronic and structurally similar [Re$_2$X$_8$]$^{2-}$ species to be mentioned next.

(3) *The* [Re$_2$X$_8$]$^{2-}$ *ions and derivatives.* In these, two square ReX$_4$ groups are joined through the rhenium atoms, without any bridging groups. The structure is remarkable in having an Re—Re distance of only 2.24 A and in having the angle of internal rotation such that the two ReX$_4$ groups are in an eclipsed rather than a staggered orientation. The structure of the [Re$_2$Br$_8$]$^{2-}$ ion is shown in Figure 30-D-5. It has been shown[6] that these two structural features and the diamagnetism of the compound can be best explained in terms of a quadruple bond between the rhenium atoms. This bond is made up of a σ bond, two π bonds and a δ bond. A δ bond is one which has two nodal planes that intersect along the internuclear axis, and in this case it is formed by the d_{xy} orbitals of the rhenium atoms (taking the Re—Re line as the z axis).

(4) *Crystalline halides and chalcogenides.* The majority of these compounds contain the metal atoms in octahedra formed by the halide or chalcogenide ions. In many instances the latter form infinite arrays in which they are close packed or with a distorted form of close packing, although the octahedra are sometimes joined only into small groups or into bands. The existence of metal–metal bonds causes the metal atoms to move off the centers of the octahedra and to approach one another across the faces or edges of the octahedra. Examples of bonds formed across faces and edges respectively are provided by [W$_2$Cl$_9$]$^{3-}$ and NbI$_4$; both structures are illustrated in Chapter 30.

(5) *Miscellaneous.* In various compounds such as Ni(DMGH)$_2$ and platinum(II) complexes of the type[Pt(NH$_3$)$_4$][PtBr$_4$], there is spectroscopic evidence for metal–metal interactions. However, the strength is probably not great. Although we have chosen to classify mercury as a nontransition element, it is close enough in some respects to the transition metals to

[6] F. A. Cotton, *Inorg. Chem.*, **4**, 337 (1965).

justify a reference here to the Hg_2^{2+} ion which occurs in mercurous compounds. Finally, the existence of Mo—Mo interactions in many compounds and complexes of Mo^{IV} (e.g., MoO_2) and Mo^V (e.g., the $[Mo_2O_4(C_2O_4)_2(H_2O)_2]^{2-}$ ion) may be noted.

Bonds between Dissimilar Metal Atoms. The total number of such bonds presently known does not exceed a few dozen, but this is only because, until recently, little work had been carried out with the object of preparing them. There can be no doubt that a great number and variety are capable of existence. Some of those presently known are the following:

Those in mixed carbonyls:

$(OC)_5Mn—Re(CO)_5$, $(\pi-C_5H_5)(OC)_2Fe—Mo(CO)_3(\pi-C_5H_5)$

Those containing gold, silver and copper:

$Ph_3PAu—Mn(CO)_5$, $Ph_3PAu—Co(CO)_4$, $(triarsAg)_2Fe(CO)_4$,
$(triarsCu)_2Fe(CO)_4$

The tin to transition metal bonds:

$R_3Sn—Mn(CO)_5$, $Pt(SnCl_3)_5^{3-}$

The mercury to transition metal bonds:

$(ClHg)_2Fe(CO)_4$, $ClHgCo(CO)_4$.

25-15. Metal Atom Clusters

These are groups of three or more metal atoms in which each is bound to all—or most—of the others. Although a few have been known for many years, most have been discovered or recognized rather recently, and the field is under active investigation at present. Clusters are found in various types of compounds, but the two principal classes in which they occur are metal carbonyls and lower halides.

Among carbonyls there are trinuclear clusters, e.g., Os_3 in $Os_3(CO)_{12}$, tetranuclear ones, e.g., Co_4 in $Co_4(CO)_{12}$, and hexanuclear ones, e.g., Rh_6 in $Rh_6(CO)_{16}$. The structure of some of these compounds will be illustrated and discussed in Chapter 27. There are several polynuclear carbonylate anions such as $Fe_3(CO)_{11}^{2-}$ and $Ni_4(CO)_9^{2-}$, which probably contain clusters, but proof is as yet lacking except in the case of $[HFe_3(CO)_{11}]^-$. The compound $(\pi-C_5H_5)_3Ni_3(CO)_2$ also contains a trinuclear cluster. The metal–metal bonding in these clusters has not been investigated in detail as yet, although there are indications that a molecular orbital picture allowing for delocalization may be most suitable.

Among lower halides only triangular M_3 and octahedral M_6 groups have been found, but there are several variants of each differing in the arrangement of the halide ions which are also bound to the metal atoms. The four most common arrangements are shown in Figure 25-10. Details pertaining to particular compounds containing these clusters will be given at appropriate places in Chapter 30.

The electronic structures of these clusters have been treated by both valence bond and molecular orbital methods but the latter seem in general to be the more useful.[7] A few compounds representative of the structural types shown in Figure 25-10 may serve to illustrate the considerations involved.

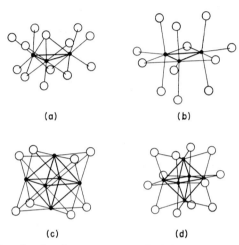

(a)   (b)

(c)   (d)

Fig. 25-10. Sketches showing four structures which have been found in metal atom cluster compounds. Small filled circles represent metal atoms and open circles represent nonmetal (e.g., oxygen or halogen) atoms. (a) The unit found in $Zn_2Mo_3O_8$ and Nb_3Cl_8. (b) The unit occurring in many Re^{III} halide derivatives. (c) The unit found in $[Mo_6X_8]^{4+}$ compounds. (d) The unit found in various lower halides of Nb and Ta.

The type of trinuclear cluster shown in Figure 25-10a was first observed in the oxide $Zn_2Mo_3O_8$ and then later in Nb_3Cl_8. A simple LCAO–MO treatment leads to the result[8] that the types and relative energies of the bonding molecular orbitals are as follows: $A_1^{(1)} \ll E < A_1^{(2)}$. The A_1 orbitals are singly degenerate, while the E orbital is doubly degenerate. In the $Mo_3O_8^{4-}$ case there are six electrons giving the closed shell configuration $(A_1^{(1)})^2(E)^4$, in agreement with the absence of unpaired electrons. For Nb_3Cl_8 there are seven electrons, and thus the $A_1^{(2)}$ orbital should be singly occupied. The advantage of an MO treatment, in which all orbitals of the cluster are delocalized, over a VB treatment in which localized two-center overlaps are used, is well illustrated by this compound. Since the structure of Nb_3Cl_8 is such that all three Nb atoms are equivalent, each must be assigned the same, fractional oxidation number, 8/3; such a situation is cumbersome to formulate in terms of classical two-center bonds.

[7] F. A. Cotton and T. E. Haas, *Inorg. Chem.*, **3**, 10 (1964).
[8] F. A. Cotton, *Inorg. Chem.*, **3**, 1217 (1964).

The other type of trinuclear cluster, Figure 25-10b, is characteristic of compounds derived from rhenium(III) halides, where there are twelve electrons to be accommodated in orbitals of the cluster. An MO treatment indicates that there are just six MO's which are of a bonding nature; these are exactly filled by the twelve electrons, which is in accord with the diamagnetism of the compounds containing this type of cluster. In an approximate way, it can be said that the bond order of the Re—Re bonds is two, since there are six electron pairs occupying bonding MO's and three pairs of adjacent metal atoms. It has been proposed that rhenium(IV) chloride may also contain Re_3 clusters, with the same type of structure,[9] on the basis of magnetic data and certain chemical facts. The withdrawal of three electrons from $Re_3Cl_{12}{}^{3-}$ to give Re_3Cl_{12} ($\equiv Re^{IV}Cl_4$) should leave one unpaired electron distributed over the Re_3 cluster and the experimental data are consistent with this.

The M_6X_8 type of cluster, Figure 25-10c, occurs in the so-called dihalides of molybdenum and tungsten and their derivatives. The group $Mo_6Cl_8{}^{4+}$ persists through many chemical reactions. Each Mo atom is in the formal oxidation state II, meaning that there are altogether $6 \times 4 = 24$ electrons to occupy orbitals of the Mo_6 cluster. An MO treatment indicates the existence of just twelve bonding orbitals, but the postulation of twelve two-center, two-electron bonds equally well explains the diamagnetism of the cluster.

The second type of octahedral cluster, M_6X_{12}, in which a bridging halide ion occurs over each edge of the octahedron, is the most commonly occurring of the four types shown in Figure 25-10 according to the structural data available at the present time. It occurs mainly in several lower halides of Nb and Ta, including those of the types $MX_{2.33}$ and $MX_{2.5}$ as well as in the hydrated compounds $M_6X_{14}\cdot7H_2O$. The latter contain diamagnetic $M_6X_{12}{}^{2+}$ groups, in which the metal atoms are in the fractional average oxidation state 7/3. There are 16 electrons to occupy orbitals of the M_6 cluster and, according to a simple MO treatment, there are just eight bonding MO's. The $MX_{2.33}$ compounds are simply the anhydrous analogs. The $MX_{2.5}$ compounds have the metal atoms in the mean oxidation state 2.5, of course, which means that there are only 15 electrons to occupy orbitals of the M_6 cluster, and accordingly, the magnetism of these compounds corresponds to one unpaired electron per six metal atoms.

An interesting relationship between the electronic structures of the M_6X_8 and M_6X_{12} type clusters has recently been suggested, in which it is assumed that the latter contain a three-center molecular orbital on each octahedral face, with each of these occupied by an electron pair.[10]

[9] R. Colton and R. L. Martin, *Nature*, **205**, 239 (1965).
[10] S. F. A. Kettle, *Theoret. Chim. Acta*, **3**, 211 (1965).

References

Adv. Chem. Series, No. 49, A.C.S., Washington, D.C., 1965.   Mechanism of inorganic reactions, mainly transition metal chemistry.

Carrington, A., and H. C. Longuet-Higgins, *Quart. Rev.*, **14**, 427 (1960).   Electron spin resonance in crystalline transition metal compounds.

Figgis, B. N., and J. Lewis, *Prog. Inorg. Chem.*, **6**, 37 (1964).   The most recent extended discussion of both theory and experimental results concerning magnetochemistry of the transition elements.

——, *Technique of Inorganic Chemistry*, H. B. Jonassen and A. Weissberger, eds., Volume IV, Interscience–Wiley, New York, 1965.   Detailed introduction to experimental techniques of magnetochemistry.

Gillard, R. D., *Prog. Inorg. Chem.*, Volume 7, 1966.   Optical activity of complexes.

Ingram, D. J. E., *Spectroscopy at Radio and Microwave Frequencies*, Butterworths, London, 1955.   An excellent introductory text dealing in part with electron spin resonance.

Lewis, J., *Pure and Applied Chem.*, **10**, 11 (1965).   Metal–metal interaction in transition metal complexes.

Nyholm, R. S., and M. L. Tobe, *Adv. Inorg. Chem. Radiochem.*, **5**, 1 (1963).   General discussion on stability of oxidation states in transition metal compounds.

Rado, G. T., and H. Suhl, eds., *Magnetism: A Treatise on Modern Theory and Materials*, Academic Press, New York.   Several volumes dealing mostly with the physics of magnetically ordered materials.

Sargeson, A. M., in *Chelating Agents and Metal Chelates*, F. P. Dwyer and D. P. Mellor, eds., Academic Press, London, 1964.   General article on optical phenomena, methods of resolution, rotatory dispersion, etc.

Velluz, L., M. Legrand and M. Grosjean, *Optical Circular Dichroism*, Academic Press, New York, 1965.   Principles, measurements and applications (mostly to organic chemistry).

Woldbye, F., *Rec. Chem. Prog.*, **24**, 197 (1964).   Optical activity of complexes.

——, *Technique of Inorganic Chemistry*, H. B. Jonassen and A. Weissberger, eds., Vol. IV, Interscience–Wiley, New York, 1965.   A thorough and scholarly discussion of experimental methods, empirical correlations and other practical aspects of the optical activity of complexes.

26

The Electronic Structures of Transition Metal Complexes: Ligand Field Theory

---

INTRODUCTION

26-1. Genealogy of the Several Theories

We noted in Section 5-2 that the studies of Werner and his contemporaries followed by the ideas of Lewis and Sidgwick on electron pair bonding led to the idea that ligands are groups which can in some way donate electron pairs to metal ions or other acceptors, thus forming the so-called coordinate link. This approach to bonding in complexes was extended by Pauling and developed into the *valence bond theory* of metal–ligand bonding. This theory enjoyed great and virtually exclusive popularity among chemists through the 1930's and 1940's, but during the 1950's it was supplemented by the *ligand field theory*. This was developed betweeen 1930 and 1940 by physicists, mainly J. H. Van Vleck and his students, and rediscovered in the early 1950's by several theoretical chemists. The ligand field theory as we have it today evolved out of a purely electrostatic theory called the *crystal field theory* which was first expounded in 1929 by H. Bethe.

The crystal field theory, CFT, as we shall see, treats the interaction between the metal ion and the ligands as a purely electrostatic problem in which the ligand atoms are represented as *point* charges (or as point dipoles). At the opposite extreme, so to speak, the metal–ligand interaction can be described in terms of *molecular orbitals* formed by overlap of ligand and metal orbitals. Although these two methods certainly use different physical representations of the problem and are, at least superficially, very different in their algebraic form, there is a close fundamental relationship between them, as Van Vleck pointed out long ago, because both make explicit and rigorous use of the symmetry properties of the complex. More recently, this relationship has been explored further and CFT has been described as an "operator-equivalent" formalism.[1] After the CFT and MO methods have been described in detail we shall return to this question and indicate more specifically the relationship between these two theories and also their relationships to the valence bond description of the electronic structure.

The basic difficulty with the CFT treatment is that it takes no account of the partly covalent nature of the metal–ligand bonds, and therefore whatever effects and phenomena stem directly from covalence are entirely inexplicable in simple CFT. On the other hand, CFT provides a very simple and easy way to treat numerically many aspects of the electronic structures of complexes. MO theory, in contrast, does not provide numerical results in such an easy way. Therefore, a kind of modified CFT has been devised in which certain parameters are empirically adjusted to allow for the effects of covalence without explicitly introducing covalence into the CFT formalism. This modified CFT is often called ligand field theory, LFT. However, LFT is sometimes also used as a general name for the whole gradation of theories from the electrostatic CFT to the MO formulation. We shall use LFT in the latter sense in this chapter, and we introduce the name *adjusted crystal field theory*, ACFT, to specify the form of CFT in which some parameters are empirically altered to allow for covalence without explicitly introducing it.

Ligand field theory, in the sense of the term indicated above, can be defined as the theory of (1) the origin and (2) the consequences of the splitting of inner orbitals of ions by their chemical environments. The inner orbitals of usual interest in this connection are partly filled ones, i.e., d or f orbitals. However, we shall restrict this discussion to d orbitals. To a considerable degree, it is possible to consider the two parts of LFT separately, which has the important consequence that many phenomena which are due to the existence of d orbital splitting can be understood pragmatically even if an exact explanation of why the splitting exists is not available. Of course a truly rigorous discussion of all the consequences of d orbital splittings cannot be divorced from a discussion of the forces responsible for the splittings.

We shall begin by outlining the CFT formalism. It is extremely important for the reader to bear in mind while reading Section 26-2, however, that this is a sheer formalism, devoid of physical meaning because *ligand atoms are not points*. On the contrary, they are bodies with about the same size and structure as the metal atom itself. However, the CFT formalism is actually the historical origin of ligand field theory, it does provide

[1] J. S. Griffith, *J. Chem. Phys.*, **41**, 516 (1964).

useful results and it is absolutely necessary to be conversant with it in order to read the literature.

THE ELECTROSTATIC CRYSTAL FIELD THEORY, CFT

26-2. The Splitting of d Orbitals by Electrostatic Fields

Let us consider a metal ion, M^{m+}, lying at the center of an octahedral set of point charges, as shown in Figure 26-1. Let us suppose that this

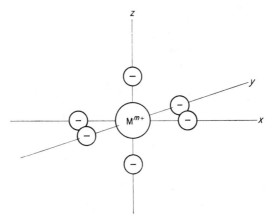

Fig. 26-1. Sketch showing six negative charges arranged octahedrally around a central M^{m+} ion with a set of Cartesian axes for reference.

metal ion has a single d electron outside of closed shells; such an ion might be Ti^{III}, V^{IV}, etc. In the free ion, this d electron would have had equal probability of being in any one of the five d orbitals, since all are equivalent. Now, however, the d orbitals are not all equivalent. Some are concentrated in regions of space closer to the negative ions than are others, and the electron will obviously prefer to occupy the orbital(s) in which it can get as far as possible from the negative charges. Recalling the shapes of the d orbitals (Fig. 1-8) and comparing them with Figure 26-1, we see that both the d_{z^2} and $d_{x^2-y^2}$ orbitals have lobes which are heavily concentrated in the vicinity of the charges, whereas the d_{xy}, d_{yz} and d_{zx} orbitals have lobes which project between the charges. This is illustrated in Figure 26-2. It can also be seen that each of the three orbitals in the latter group, namely, d_{xy}, d_{yz}, d_{zx}, is equally favorable for the electron; these three orbitals have entirely equivalent environments in the octahedral complex. The two relatively unfavorable orbitals, d_{z^2} and $d_{x^2-y^2}$, are also equivalent;

this is not obvious from inspection of Figure 26-2, but Figure 26-3 shows why it is so. As indicated, the d_{z^2} orbital can be resolved into a linear combination of two orbitals, $d_{z^2-x^2}$ and $d_{z^2-y^2}$, each of which is obviously equivalent to the $d_{x^2-y^2}$ orbital. It is to be stressed, however, that these

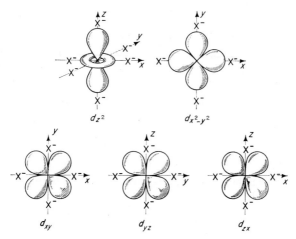

Fig. 26-2. Sketches showing the distribution of electron density in the five d orbitals with respect to a set of six octahedrally arranged negative charges (cf. Fig. 26-1).

two orbitals do not have separate existences, and the resolution of the d_{z^2} orbital in this way is only a device to persuade the reader *pictorially* that d_{z^2} is equivalent to $d_{x^2-y^2}$ in relation to the octahedral distribution of charges.

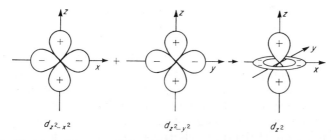

Fig. 26-3. Sketches of $d_{z^2-x^2}$ and $d_{z^2-y^2}$ orbitals which are usually combined to make the d_{z^2} orbital.

Thus, in the octahedral environment of six negative charges, the metal ion now has two kinds of d orbitals: three of one kind, equivalent to one another and conventionally labeled t_{2g} (sometimes $d\epsilon$ or γ_5), and two of another kind, equivalent to each other, conventionally labeled e_g (sometimes $d\gamma$ or γ_3); furthermore, the e_g orbitals are of higher energy than the

t_{2g} orbitals. These results may be expressed in an energy level diagram as shown in Figure 26-4a.

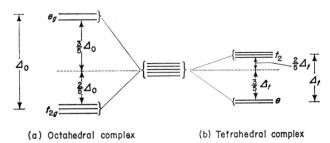

(a) Octahedral complex   (b) Tetrahedral complex

Fig. 26-4.   Energy level diagrams showing the splitting of a set of d orbitals by octahedral and tetrahedral electrostatic crystal fields.

In Figure 26-4a it will be seen that we have designated the energy difference between the e_g and the t_{2g} orbitals as Δ_o, where the subscript o stands for octahedral. The additional feature of Figure 26-4a—the indication that the e_g levels lie $\frac{3}{5}\Delta_o$ above and the t_{2g} levels lie $\frac{2}{5}\Delta_o$ below the energy of the unsplit d orbitals—will now be explained. Let us suppose that a cation containing ten d electrons, two in each of the d orbitals, is first placed at the center of a hollow sphere whose radius is equal to the M—X internuclear distance, and that charge of total quantity $6e$ is spread uniformly over the sphere. In this spherically symmetric environment the d orbitals are still five-fold degenerate.* The entire energy of the system, that is, the metal ion and the charged sphere, has a definite value. Now suppose the total charge on the sphere is caused to collect into six discrete point charges, each of magnitude e, and each lying at an apex of an octahedron but still on the surface of the sphere. Merely redistributing the negative charge over the surface of the sphere in this manner cannot alter the total energy of the system when the metal ion consists entirely of spherically symmetrical electron shells, and yet we have already seen that as a result of this redistribution electrons in e_g orbitals now have higher energies than those in t_{2g} orbitals. It must therefore be that the total increase in energy of the four e_g electrons equals the total decrease in energy of the six t_{2g} electrons. This then implies that the rise in the energy of the e_g orbitals is $\frac{6}{4}$ times the drop in energy of the t_{2g} orbitals, which is equivalent to the $\frac{3}{5}:\frac{2}{5}$ ratio shown.

This pattern of splitting, in which the algebraic sum of all energy shifts of all orbitals is zero, is said to "preserve the center of gravity" of the set of levels. This center of gravity rule is quite general for any splitting

* The energy of all orbitals is, of course, greatly but *not equally* raised when the charged sphere encloses the ion.

pattern when the forces are purely electrostatic and where the set of levels being split is well removed in energy from all other sets with which they might be able to interact.

By an analogous line of reasoning it can be shown that the electrostatic field of four charges surrounding an ion at the apices of a tetrahedron causes the d shell to split up as shown in Figure 26-4b. In this case the d_{xy}, d_{yz} and d_{zx} orbitals are less stable than the d_{z^2} and $d_{x^2-y^2}$ orbitals. This may be appreciated qualitatively if the spatial properties of the d orbitals are considered with regard to the tetrahedral array of four negative charges as depicted in Figure 26-5. If the cation, the anions and the

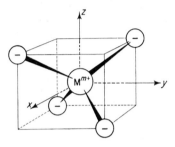

Fig. 26-5. Sketch showing the tetrahedral arrangement of four negative charges around a cation, M^{m+}, with respect to coordinate axes which may be used in identifying the d orbitals.

cation–anion distance are the same in both the octahedral and tetrahedral cases, it can be shown that

$$\Delta_t = \tfrac{4}{9}\Delta_o$$

In other words, other things being about equal, the crystal field splitting in a tetrahedral complex will be about half the magnitude of that in an octahedral complex.

The above results have been derived on the assumption that ionic ligands, such as F^-, Cl^- or CN^-, may be represented by point negative charges. Ligands which are neutral, however, are dipolar (e.g., 26-I and 26-II), and

$H^{\delta+}$ $H^{\delta+}$

$\delta-:N\!-\!H^{\delta+}$ $\delta-:\overset{..}{\underset{..}{O}}$

$H^{\delta+}$ $H^{\delta+}$

(26-I)   (26-II)

they approach the metal ion with their negative poles. Actually, in the field of the positive metal ion such ligands are further polarized. Thus, in a complex such as a hexammine, the metal ion is surrounded by six dipoles with their negative ends closest; this array has the same general effects upon the d orbitals as an array of six anions, so that all of the above results are valid for complexes containing neutral, dipolar ligands.

We next consider the pattern of splitting of the d orbitals in tetragonally distorted octahedral complexes and in planar complexes. We begin with an octahedral complex, MX_6, from which we slowly withdraw two *trans* ligands. Let these be the two on the z axis. As soon as the distance from M^{m+} to these two ligands becomes greater than the distance to the other four, new energy differences among the d orbitals arise. First of all, the degeneracy of the e_g orbitals is lifted, the z^2 orbital becoming more stable than the $(x^2 - y^2)$ orbital. This happens because the ligands on the z axis exert a much more direct repulsive effect on a d_{z^2} electron than upon a $d_{x^2-y^2}$ electron. At the same time the three-fold degeneracy of the t_{2g} orbitals is also lifted. As the ligands on the z axis move away, the yz and zx orbitals remain equivalent to one another, but they become more stable than the xy orbital because their spatial distribution makes them more sensitive to the charges along the z axis than is the xy orbital. Thus for a small tetragonal distortion of the type considered, we may draw the energy level diagram shown in Figure 26-6. It should be obvious that for the

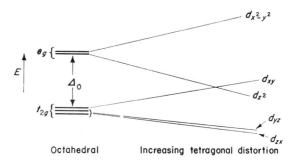

Fig. 26-6. Energy level diagram showing the further splitting of the d orbitals as an octahedral array of ligands becomes progressively distorted by the withdrawal of two *trans* ligands, specifically those lying on the z axis.

opposite type of tetragonal distortion, that is, one in which two *trans* ligands lie closer to the metal ion than do the other four, the relative energies of the split components will be inverted.

As Figure 26-6 shows, it is in general *possible* for the tetragonal distortion to become so large that the z^2 orbital eventually drops below the xy orbital. Whether this will *actually happen* for any particular case, even when the two *trans* ligands are completely removed so that we have the limiting case of a square, four-coordinated complex, depends upon quantitative properties of the metal ion and the ligand concerned. Semiquantitative calculations with parameters appropriate for square complexes of Co^{II}, Ni^{II} and

Cu^{II} lead to the energy level diagram shown in Figure 26-7, in which the z^2 orbital has dropped so far below the xy orbital that it is nearly as stable as the (yz, zx) pair. As Figure 26-6 indicates, the d_{z^2} level might even drop

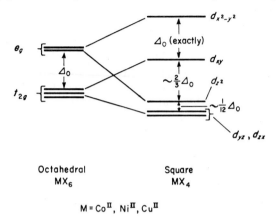

Fig. 26-7.   Approximate energy level diagram for corresponding octahedral and square complexes of some metal ions in the first transition series.

below the (d_{xz}, d_{yz}) levels and in fact experimental results suggest that in some cases (e.g., $PtCl_4{}^{2-}$) it does.

SOME CONSEQUENCES AND APPLICATIONS OF ORBITAL SPLITTING

We have now shown how the d orbitals are split by octahedral, tetrahedral and square arrays of ligands according to the CFT formalism. Regardless of what may be said concerning the artificiality of the model, it is a fact that, qualitatively, these splittings are correctly predicted. We shall now examine some important consequences of the splittings, intending to return later to a discussion of more realistic explanations of the origin of the splittings.

26-3. Magnetic Properties from Crystal Field Theory

In a study of the magnetic properties of a transition metal complex, our first concern will be to know how many unpaired electrons are present. We shall now see how this property may be understood in terms of the orbital splittings described in the preceding section. We have already noted in several places* that it is a general rule that if a group of n or less

* See, for example, pages 21 and 30.

electrons occupy a set of n degenerate orbitals, they will spread themselves out among the orbitals and give n unpaired spins. This is Hund's first rule, or the rule of maximum multiplicity. It means that pairing of electrons is an unfavorable process; energy must be expended in order to make it occur. If two electrons are not only to have their spins paired but also to be placed in the same orbital, there is a further unfavorable energy contribution because of the increased electrostatic repulsion between electrons which are compelled to occupy the same regions of space. Let us suppose now that in some hypothetical molecule we have two orbitals separated by an energy ΔE and that two electrons are to occupy these orbitals. Referring to Figure 26-8, we see that when we place one electron

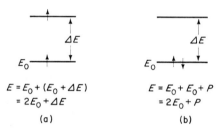

Fig. 26-8. A hypothetical two-orbital system in which two possible distributions of two electrons and the resulting total energies are as shown.

in each orbital, their spins will remain uncoupled and their combined energy will be $(2E_0 + \Delta E)$. If we place both of them in the lower orbital, their spins will have to be coupled to satisfy the exclusion principle, and the total energy will be $(2E_0 + P)$, where P stands for the energy required to cause pairing of two electrons in the same orbital. Thus, whether this system will have distribution (a) or (b) for its ground state depends on whether ΔE is greater or less than P. If $\Delta E < P$, the triplet state (a) will be the more stable; if $\Delta E > P$, the singlet state (b) will be the more stable.

Octahedral Complexes. We shall first apply an argument of the type outlined above to octahedral complexes, using the d-orbital splitting diagram previously deduced from CFT. As indicated in Figure 26-9, we may place one, two and three electrons in the d orbitals without any possible uncertainty about how they will occupy the orbitals. They will naturally enter the more stable t_{2g} orbitals with their spins all parallel, and this will be true irrespective of the strength of the crystal field as measured by the magnitude of Δ. Further, for ions with eight, nine and ten d electrons, there is only one possible way in which the orbitals may be occupied to give the lowest energy (see Fig. 26-9). For the remaining configurations, d^4, d^5, d^6 and d^7, two possibilities exist, and the question of which one represents the ground state can only be answered by comparing the values of Δ_0 and P, an average pairing energy. The two configurations for each case, together with simple expressions for their energies, are set out in Figure 26-10. The configurations with the maximum possible number of

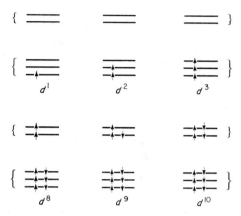

Fig. 26-9. Sketches showing the unique ground state occupancy schemes for d orbitals in octahedral complexes with d configurations d^1, d^2, d^3, d^8, d^9, d^{10}.

unpaired electrons are called the *high-spin* configurations, and those with the minimum number of unpaired spins are called the *low-spin* or *spin-paired* configurations. These configurations can be written out in a notation

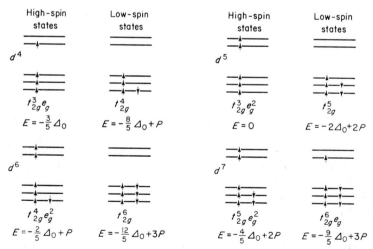

Fig. 26-10. Diagrams showing the possible high-spin and low-spin ground states for d^4, d^5, d^6 and d^7 ions in octahedral crystal fields including the notation for writing out the configurations and expressions for their energies, derived as explained in the text.

similar to that used for electron configurations of free atoms, whereby we list each occupied orbital or set of orbitals, using a right superscript to show the number of electrons present. For example, the ground state for a d^3 ion in an octahedral field is t_{2g}^3; the two possible states for a d^5 ion in an octahedral field are t_{2g}^5 and $t_{2g}^3 e_g^2$. This notation is further illustrated in Figure 26-10. The energies are referred to the energy of the unsplit configuration (the energy of the ion in a spherical shell of the same total charge) and are simply the sums of $-\frac{2}{5}\Delta_0$ for each t_{2g} electron, $+\frac{3}{5}\Delta_0$ for each e_g electron and P for every pair of electrons occupying the same orbital.

For each of the four cases where high- and low-spin states are possible, we may obtain from the equations for the energies which are given in Figure 26-10 the following expression for the relation between Δ_0 and P at which the high- and low-spin states have equal energies:

$$\Delta_0 = P$$

The relationship is the same in all cases, and means that the spin state of any ion in an octahedral electrostatic field depends simply upon whether the magnitude of the field as measured by the splitting energy, Δ_0, is greater or less than the mean pairing energy, P, for the particular ion. For a particular ion, of the d^4, d^5, d^6 or d^7 type, the stronger the crystal field, the more likely it is that the electrons will crowd as much as possible into the more stable t_{2g} orbitals, whereas in the weaker crystal fields, where $P > \Delta_0$, the electrons will remain spread out over the entire set of d orbitals as they do in the free ion. For ions of the other types, d^1, d^2, d^3, d^8, d^9 and d^{10}, the number of unpaired electrons is fixed at the same number as in the free ion irrespective of how strong the crystal field may become.

Approximate theoretical estimates of the mean pairing energies for the relevant ions of the first transition series have been made from spectroscopic data. In Table 26-1 these energies, along with Δ_0 values for some complexes (derived by methods to be described in the next section), are listed. It will be seen that the theory developed above affords correct predictions in all cases. It will further be noted that the mean pairing energies vary irregularly from one metal ion to another as do the values of Δ_0 for a given set of ligands. Thus, as Table 26-1 shows, the d^5 systems should be exceptionally stable in their high-spin states, whereas the d^6 systems should be exceptionally stable in their low-spin states. These expectations are in excellent agreement with the experimental facts.

Finer details of magnetic properties such as orbital contributions, unusual temperature dependencies of magnetic moments and magnetic anisotropies can also be calculated using CFT, or better ACFT, and the results are generally good approximations. They are not perfect because the basic

TABLE 26-1

Crystal Field Splittings, Δ_0, and Mean Electron Pairing Energies, P,
for Several Transition Metal Ions

(Energies in cm^{-1})

Config-uration	Ion	P^a	Ligands	Δ	Spin state	
					Predicted	Observed
d^4	Cr^{2+}	23,500	$6H_2O$	13,900	High	High
	Mn^{3+}	28,000	$6H_2O$	21,000	High	High
d^5	Mn^{2+}	25,500	$6H_2O$	7,800	High	High
	Fe^{3+}	30,000	$6H_2O$	13,700	High	High
d^6	Fe^{2+}	17,600	$6H_2O$	10,400	High	High
			$6CN^-$	33,000	Low	Low
	Co^{3+}	21,000	$6F^-$	13,000	High	High
			$6NH_3$	23,000	Low	Low
d^7	Co^{2+}	22,500	$6H_2O$	9,300	High	High

^{a} It will be shown later that due to the so-called nephelauxetic effect these energies should probably be $\sim 20\%$ lower in the complexes than the free-ion values given. It can be seen, however, that even if they are decreased by this amount the correct spin states are still predicted.

premise in the theory—namely, that the interaction between the metal ion and its surroundings is a purely electrostatic perturbation by nearest neighbors—is not perfect.

Tetrahedral Complexes. Metal ions in tetrahedral electrostatic fields may be treated by the same procedure outlined above for the octahedral cases. For tetrahedral fields it is found that for the d^1, d^2, d^7, d^8 and d^9 cases only high-spin states are possible, whereas for d^3, d^4, d^5 and d^6 configurations both high-spin and low-spin states are in principle possible. Once again the existence of low-spin states requires that $\Delta_t > P$. Since Δ_t values are only about half as great as Δ_0 values, it is to be expected that low-spin tetrahedral complexes of first transition series ions with d^3, d^4, d^5 and d^6 configurations would be scarce or even unknown. None have so far been shown to exist, and at present there seems to be little chance that any will be found.

Square and Tetragonally-distorted Octahedral Complexes. These two cases must be considered together because, as noted earlier, they merge into one another.

We must also consider the effect of distortions of the coordination polyhedron upon the magnetic properties. Even when the strictly octahedral environment does not permit the existence of a low-spin state, as in the d^8 case, distortions of the octahedron will cause further splitting of degenerate orbitals which may become great enough to overcome pairing energies and cause electron pairing. Let us consider as an example the d^8 system in an octahedral environment which is then subjected to a tetragonal distortion. We have already seen (Figure 26-6) how a decrease in the electrostatic field along the z axis may arise, either by moving the two z-axis ligands out to a greater distance than are their otherwise identical neighbors in the xy plane, or by having two different ligands on the z axis which make an intrinsically smaller contribution to the electrostatic potential than do the four in the xy plane. Irrespective of its origin, the result of a tetragonal distortion of an initially octahedral field is to split apart the $(x^2 - y^2)$ and z^2 orbitals. We have also seen that if the tetragonal distortion, that is, the disparity between the contributions to the electrostatic potential of the two z axis ligands and the other four, becomes sufficiently great, the z^2 orbital may fall below the xy orbital. In either case, the two least stable d orbitals are now no longer degenerate but are separated by some energy, Q. Now the question of whether the tetragonally distorted d^8 complex will have high or low spin depends on whether the pairing energy, P, is greater or less than the energy Q. Figure 26-11a shows the

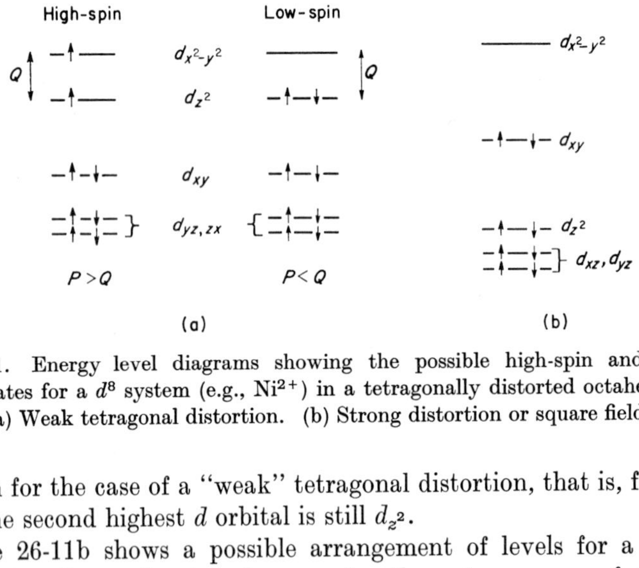

Fig. 26-11. Energy level diagrams showing the possible high-spin and low-spin ground states for a d^8 system (e.g., Ni^{2+}) in a tetragonally distorted octahedral field. (a) Weak tetragonal distortion. (b) Strong distortion or square field.

situation for the case of a "weak" tetragonal distortion, that is, for one in which the second highest d orbital is still d_{z^2}.

Figure 26-11b shows a possible arrangement of levels for a strongly tetragonally distorted octahedron, or for the extreme case of a square, four-coordinate complex (compare with Fig. 26-7), and the low-spin form of occupancy of these levels for a d^8 ion. In this case, due to the large separation between the highest and second highest orbitals the high-spin configuration is impossible of attainment with the pairing energies of the real d^8 ions, e.g., Ni^{II}, Pd^{II}, Pt^{II}, Rh^{I}, Ir^{I} and Au^{III}, which normally occur, and all square complexes of these species are diamagnetic (unless the ligands have unpaired electrons, as has been postulated in some cases, cf. page 759).   Similarly, for a d^7 ion in a square complex, as exemplified by certain Co^{II} complexes, only the low-spin state with one unpaired electron should occur, and this is in accord with observation.

The simple theory just outlined enables us to predict, or at least to understand, the number of unpaired electrons possessed by the transition metal ions in various environments.   As we shall see later, the valence bond theory can also do this, although there are certain d^n configurations for which its predictions are misleading.   The great advantage of crystal field theory (and of ligand field theory) is that the prediction of actual magnetic moments is also possible.   Such quantitative numerical calculations require the use of relatively sophisticated quantum mechanics (introduction of spin-orbit coupling as a first order perturbation being the least complex of the required operations) and they will not therefore be discussed in general terms in this book.   However, a few examples, such as the d^7 configuration in a tetrahedral field (page 871) and some others, are mentioned elsewhere.

26-4. Absorption Spectra

d^1 and d^9 Systems.   Let us first consider the simplest possible case, an ion with a d^1 configuration, lying at the center of an octahedral field, for example, the Ti^{III} ion in $[Ti(H_2O)_6]^{3+}$.   The d electron will occupy a t_{2g} orbital.   Upon irradiation with light of frequency ν, equal to $\Delta_0/\mathbf{h}$, where $\mathbf{h}$ is Planck's constant and Δ_0 is the energy difference between the t_{2g} and the e_g orbitals, it should be possible for such an ion to capture a quantum of radiation and convert that energy into energy of excitation of the electron from the t_{2g} to the e_g orbitals.   The absorption band which results from this process is found in the visible spectrum of the hexaquotitanium(III) ion, shown in Figure 26-12, and is responsible for its violet color.   Three features of this absorption band are of importance here: its position, its intensity and its breadth.

In discussing the positions of absorption bands in relation to the splittings of the d orbitals, it is convenient and common practice to use the same unit, the reciprocal centimeter or wave number, abbreviated cm^{-1}, for both the unit of frequency in the spectra and the unit of energy for the orbitals.   With this convention, we see that the spectrum of Figure 26-12 tells us that Δ_0 in $[Ti(H_2O)_6]^{3+}$ is 20,000 cm^{-1}.   Since there are 350 cm^{-1} per kilocalorie, this means that the splitting energy is ~ 57 kcal/mole, which is quite comparable with the usual values of chemical bond energies.   In general, we shall see that the crystal field theory enables us to calculate the energy separations between various states of the d electrons from the

22 + A.I.C.

frequencies of the absorption bands in the visible spectra. In the present case the relationship is the simplest possible one, namely, the observed frequency is identical with the d orbital splitting.

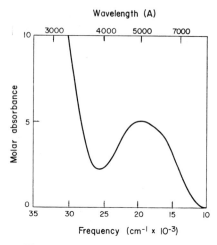

Fig. 26-12.   The visible absorption spectrum of $[\text{Ti}(\text{H}_2\text{O})_6]^{3+}$.

Turning now to the intensity of this absorption band in the $[\text{Ti}(\text{H}_2\text{O})_6]^{3+}$ ion, we note that it is extremely weak by comparison with absorption bands found in many other systems. The reason for this is that the electron is jumping from one orbital which is centrosymmetric to another which is also centrosymmetric, and that all transitions of this type are nominally "forbidden" by the rules of quantum mechanics. One-electron transitions which are "allowed" have intensities which give molar absorbance values at the absorption peaks of $\sim 10^4$. If the postulate of the crystal field theory, that in both the ground and excited states the electrons of the metal ion occupy completely pure d orbitals which have no other interaction than a purely coulombic one with the environment of the ion, were precisely correct, the intensity of this band would be precisely zero. It gains a little intensity because the postulate is not perfectly valid in ways which will be discussed in Section 26-8. Suffice it to say here that low intensities, indicative of essentially "forbidden" character, are observed in the d–d transitions of all of the metal ions of the first transition series.

Finally, we note that the observed absorption is not an infinitely thin line lying at precisely the frequency equivalent to Δ_0. The breadth of the absorption is caused by the fact that the electronic excitation is accompanied by a host of vibrational excitations, spread over a range of several thousand wave numbers. This, too, is a general phenomenon found in the spectra of all d^n systems in crystal fields, although there are certain cases, for example, Mn^{II} and Cr^{III} spectra, in which relatively narrow lines are found. Further discussion of line breadths will be found in Section 29-D-6.

It is also possible to interpret the d–d spectrum of a d^9 ion as simply as we have done with the spectrum of a d^1 ion. This is another application of the *hole formalism* (see page 28) according to which a d^{10-n} configuration will have the same behavior in a crystal field, except for certain changes in the signs of energy terms, as a d^n configuration. The former has as many holes in its d shell as the latter has electrons. According to the hole formalism, which is perfectly rigorous within the limits of the electrostatic crystal field theory, n holes in the d shell may be treated like n positrons. Now all of the d level splittings which we have deduced for the static fields will be quantitatively the same for one positron, *except* that the patterns will be inverted because a positron will be most electrostatically stable in just those regions where an electron is least electrostatically stable, and vice versa. We can thus look upon a Cu^{II} ion in an octahedral environment as a one-positron ion in an octahedral field and deduce that in the ground state the positron will occupy an e_g orbital from which it may be excited by radiation providing energy Δ_0 to a t_{2g} orbital.

Experimentally it is found, however, that the absorption band of the Cu^{II} ion in aqueous solution is not a simple, symmetrically shaped band but instead appears to consist of several nearly superposed bands. The observant reader may have noticed that the absorption band of the $[Ti(H_2O)_6]^{3+}$ ion is not quite a simple, symmetrical band either. In each case these complications are traceable to distortions of the octahedral environment which are required by the Jahn–Teller theorem. We shall discuss this theorem a little later (page 683).

d^2–d^8 Ions; Energy Level Diagrams. In order to interpret the spectra of complexes in which the metal ions have more than one but less than nine d electrons, we must introduce the device of the energy level diagram based upon the Russell–Saunders states of the relevant d^n configuration in the free (uncomplexed) ion. It can be shown that just as the set of five d orbitals is split apart by the electrostatic field of surrounding ligands to give two or more sets of lower degeneracy, so also are the various Russell–Saunders states of a d^n configuration. The number and types of the components into which an octahedral or tetrahedral field will split a state of given L is the same regardless of the d^n configuration from which it arises, and these facts are summarized in Table 26-2. The designations of the states of the ion in the crystal field are the *Mulliken* symbols; their origin is in group theory, but they may be regarded simply as labels.

Although the states into which a given free ion state is split are the same in number and type in both octahedral and tetrahedral fields, the pattern

TABLE 26-2

Splitting of Russell–Saunders States in Octahedral
and Tetrahedral Electrostatic Fields

State of free ion	States in the crystal field
S	A_1
P	T_1
D	$E + T_2$
F	$A_2 + T_1 + T_2$
G	$A_1 + E + T_1 + T_2$
H	$E + 2T_1 + T_2$

of energies is inverted in one case relative to the other. This is quite analogous to the results in the d^1 case as we have already seen (Fig. 26-4).

A discussion of the way in which the energies of the crystal field states are calculated would be beyond the scope of this book. For the inorganic chemist it is not essential to know how the energy level diagrams are obtained in order to use them; it is, of course, necessary to know how to interpret them properly. At this point we shall examine several of them in some detail in order to explain their interpretation. Others will be introduced subsequently in discussing the chemistry of particular transition elements. For the convenience of the reader, a complete set of diagrams are presented in Appendix B. The diagrams used in the body of the text will generally represent the relative energies only qualitatively, whereas those in the appendix (the Tanabe and Sugano diagrams) are semi-quantitative.

We shall look first at the energy level diagram for a d^2 system in an octahedral field, as shown in Figure 26-13. The ordinate is in energy units, usually cm^{-1}, and the abscissa is in units of crystal field splitting energy as measured by Δ_0, the splitting of the one-electron orbitals. At the extreme left are the Russell–Saunders states of the free ion. It may be seen that each of these splits up in the crystal field into the components specified in Table 26-2. Three features of this energy level diagram which are particularly to be noted because they will be found in all such diagrams are:

1. States with identical designations never cross.

2. The crystal field states have the same spin multiplicity as the free ion states from which they originate.

3. States which are the only ones of their type have energies which depend linearly on the crystal field strength, whereas, when there are two or more states of identical designation, their lines will in general show curvature. This is because such states interact with one another as well as with the crystal field.

It is interesting to note in this diagram that a triplet state lies lowest at all field strengths shown, and, since its slope is as steep as the slope of any other state, it will continue to be the lowest state no matter how intense the crystal field may become.   This is in complete agreement with our previous conclusion, based on the simple splitting diagram for the d

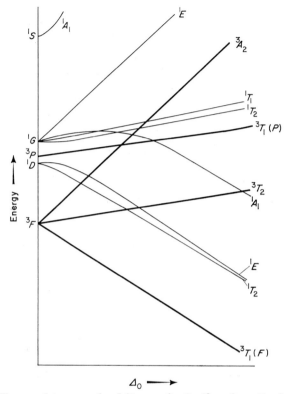

Fig. 26-13.   The complete energy level diagram for the d^2 configuration in an octahedral crystal field.   The heavier lines are those for the triplet states.

orbitals, which showed that the two d electrons would have their spins parallel in an octahedral field irrespective of how strong the field might be.

   In order to use this energy level diagram to predict or interpret the spectra of octahedral complexes of d^2 ions, for example, the spectrum of the $[V(H_2O)_6]^{3+}$ ion, we first note that there is a quantum mechanical selection rule which forbids transition between states of different spin multiplicity.   This means that in the present case only three transitions, those from the $^3T_1$ ground state to the three triplet excited states, $^3T_2$, $^3A_2$ and $^3T_1(P)$, will occur.   Actually, spin-forbidden transitions, that is, those between levels of different spin multiplicity, do occur very weakly because of weak spin-orbit interactions, but they are several orders of magnitude weaker than the spin-allowed ones and are ordinarily not observed.

Experimental study of the $[V(H_2O)_6]^{3+}$ ion reveals just three absorption bands with energies of about 17,000, 25,000 and 38,000 cm^{-1}. Using an energy level diagram like that in Figure 26-13, in which the separations of the free ion states are adjusted to match exactly those appropriate for V^{III}, one finds that, at a Δ_0 of 21,500 cm^{-1}, the three transitions are expected at 17,300, 25,500 and 38,600 cm^{-1}, in excellent agreement with observation. For high-spin complexes of the first transition series metals in their normal oxidation states, quantitative agreement of this sort, or nearly as good, is not always attained unless the adjusted CFT (ACFT) treatment, in which the actual energies of the free ion states are somewhat altered as will be explained in Section 26-11, is used.

We shall look next at the energy level diagram for a d^8 ion in an octahedral field (Fig. 26-14), restricting our attention to the triplet states

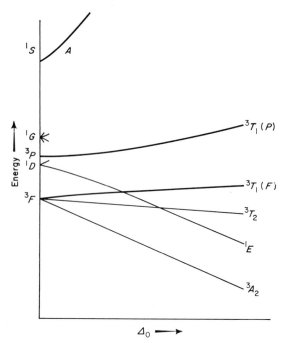

Fig. 26-14.   Partial energy level diagram for a d^8 ion in an octahedral field, showing the triplet states and only the lowest singlet state.

except for the lowest energy singlet state which comes from the ^1D state of the free ion. This has been included to show that for this system the ground state will always be a spin triplet no matter how strong the crystal field, a result in agreement with the conclusion previously drawn from consideration of the distribution of eight electrons among a set of five d orbitals.

On comparing the arrangements of the three components derived from the ^3F ground state for the d^2 and the d^8 cases, we note that one pattern is the inverse of the other. This is a manifestation of the hole formalism for the d^2–d^{10-2} configurations which is fundamentally quite analogous to the d^1–d^{10-1} example we previously examined.

Similar energy level diagrams may be drawn for d^n systems in tetrahedral crystal fields. There is an interesting relationship between these and the ones for certain systems in octahedral fields. We have already seen that the splitting pattern for the d orbitals in a tetrahedral field is just the inverse of that for the d orbitals in an octahedral field. A similar inverse relationship exists between the energy level diagrams of d^n systems in tetrahedral and octahedral fields. The components into which each Russell–Saunders state is split are reversed in their energy order in the tetrahedral compared to the octahedral cases. Furthermore, as in the one-electron case, a purely electrostatic interaction between metal ion and ligands will produce only $\frac{4}{9}$ the splittings in the tetrahedral case as in the octahedral case, all other factors such as metal–ligand distance being kept constant.

Finally, there are rather extensive qualitative similarities between the energy level diagrams of groups of the d^n systems because of the combined effects of reversals in the splitting patterns by changing from an octahedral to a tetrahedral field and by changing from a d^n to a d^{10-n} configuration. When we go from d^n in an octahedral field to d^n in a tetrahedral field, all splittings of the Russell–Saunders states are inverted. But the same inversions occur on changing from the d^n configuration in an octahedral (tetrahedral) field to the d^{10-n} configuration in an octahedral (tetrahedral) field. These relations, combined with the fact that, for the free ions, the Russell–Saunders states of the pairs of d^n and d^{10-n} systems are identical in number, type and relative (though certainly not absolute) energies, mean that various pairs of configuration–environment combinations have qualitatively identical energy level diagrams in crystal fields, and that these differ from others only in the reversal of the splittings of the individual free ion states. These relations are set out in Table 26-3.

It will be evident from the foregoing description and illustrations of energy level diagrams that they may be used to determine from observed spectral bands the magnitudes of Δ_0 and Δ_t in complexes. It may be noted in the diagrams for the d^2 and d^8 systems that there are three spin-allowed absorption bands whose positions are all determined by the one*

---

* This is only approximately true because the separation between the ^3F and ^3P states is not the same in the complexed ion as it is in the free ion, and this separation therefore becomes a second parameter, in addition to Δ, to be determined from experiment. We shall return to this point on page 697.

TABLE 26-3

Relations between Energy Level Diagrams for Various d^n Configurations
in Octahedral and Tetrahedral Crystal Fields

Octahedral d^1 and tetrahedral d^9	Reverse[a] of	Octahedral d^9 and tetrahedral d^1
Octahedral d^2 and tetrahedral d^8	Reverse of	Octahedral d^8 and tetrahedral d^2
Octahedral d^3 and tetrahedral d^7	Reverse of	Octahedral d^7 and tetrahedral d^3
Octahedral d^4 and tetrahedral d^6	Reverse of	Octahedral d^6 and tetrahedral d^4
Octahedral d^5	Identical with	Tetrahedral d^5

[a] "Reverse" means that the order of levels coming from each free ion state is reversed; it does *not* mean that the diagram as a whole is reversed.

parameter, Δ_0 or Δ_t. Thus in these cases the internal consistency of the theory may be checked.

Certain generalizations may be made about the dependence of the magnitudes of Δ values on the valence and atomic number of the metal ion, the symmetry of the coordination shell and the nature of the ligands. For octahedral complexes containing high-spin metal ions, it may be inferred from the accumulated data for a large number of systems that:

1. Δ_0 values for complexes of the first transition series are 7500–12,500 cm^{-1} for divalent ions and 14,000–25,000 cm^{-1} for trivalent ions.

2. Δ_0 values for corresponding complexes of metal ions in the same group and with the same valence increase by 30–50% on going from the first transition series to the second and by about this amount again from the second to the third. This is well illustrated by the Δ_0 values[2] for the complexes $[Co(NH_3)_6]^{3+}$, $[Rh(NH_3)_6]^{3+}$ and $[Ir(NH_3)_6]^{3+}$, which are, respectively, 23,000, 34,000 and 41,000 cm^{-1}.

3. Δ_t values are about 40–50% of Δ_0 values for complexes differing as little as possible except in the geometry of the coordination shell, in agreement with theoretical expectation.

4. The dependence of Δ values on the identity of the ligands follows a regular order known as the spectrochemical series which will now be explained.

26-5. The Spectrochemical Series

It has been found by experimental study of the spectra of a large number of complexes containing various metal ions and various ligands, that ligands may be arranged in a series according to their capacity to cause d-orbital splittings. This series, for the more common ligands, is: $I^- < Br^- < Cl^-$ $< F^- < OH^- < C_2O_4{}^{2-} \sim H_2O < —NCS^- < py \sim NH_3 < en < dipy <$

[2] H. H. Schmidtke, *J. Mol. Spect.*, **11**, 483 (1963).

o-phen $<$ NO_2^- $<$ CN^-. The idea of this series is that the d-orbital splittings and hence the relative frequencies of visible absorption bands for two complexes containing the same metal ion but different ligands can be predicted from the above series whatever the particular metal ion may be. Naturally, one cannot expect such a simple and useful rule to be universally applicable. The following qualifications must be remembered in applying it.

1. The series is based upon data for metal ions in common oxidation states. Because the nature of the metal–ligand interaction in an unusually high or unusually low oxidation state of the metal may be in certain respects qualitatively different from that for the metal in a normal oxidation state, striking violations of the order shown may occur for complexes in unusual oxidation states.

2. Even for metal ions in their normal oxidation states inversions of the order of adjacent or nearly adjacent members of the series are sometimes found.

26-6. Structural Effects of Crystal Field Splittings

We have so far considered how the electrostatic effects of ligands cause the d electrons to prefer certain regions of space (i.e., certain orbitals) to others. We shall now look briefly at some ways in which the nonspherical distribution of the d electrons, caused by the environment, reacts back upon the environment.

Ionic Radii. We consider first the effect of d-orbital splittings on the variation of ionic radii with atomic number in a series of ions of the same charge. We shall use as an example the octahedral radii of the divalent ions of the first transition series. Figure 26-15 shows a plot of the experimental values. The points for Cr^{2+} and Cu^{2+} are indicated with open circles because the Jahn–Teller effect, to be discussed shortly, makes it impossible to obtain these ions in truly octahedral environments, thus rendering the assessment of their "octahedral" radii somewhat uncertain. A smooth curve has also been drawn through the points for Ca^{2+}, Mn^{2+} and Zn^{2+} ions which have the electron configurations $t_{2g}^0 e_g^0$, $t_{2g}^3 e_g^2$ and $t_{2g}^6 e_g^4$, respectively. In these three cases the distribution of d electron density around the metal ion is spherical because all d orbitals are either unoccupied or equally occupied. Because the shielding of one d electron by another from the nuclear charge is imperfect, there is a steady contraction in the ionic radii. It is seen that the radii of the other ions are all below the values expected from the curve passing through Ca^{2+}, Mn^{2+} and Zn^{2+}. This is because the d electrons in these ions are not distributed uniformly (i.e., spherically) about the nuclei as we shall now explain.

22*

The Ti^{2+} ion has the configuration t_{2g}^2. This means that the negative charge of two d electrons is concentrated in those regions of space away from the metal–ligand bond axes. Thus, compared to the effect that they would have if distributed spherically around the metal nucleus, these two elec-

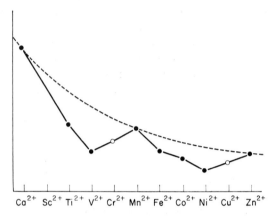

$$Ca^{2+} \quad Sc^{2+} \quad Ti^{2+} \quad V^{2+} \quad Cr^{2+} \quad Mn^{2+} \quad Fe^{2+} \quad Co^{2+} \quad Ni^{2+} \quad Cu^{2+} \quad Zn^{2+}$$

Fig. 26-15.   The relative ionic radii of divalent ions of the first transition series. The dashed line is a theoretical curve explained in the text.

trons provide abnormally little shielding between the positive metal ion and the negative ligands; therefore the ligand atoms are drawn in closer than they would be if the d electrons were spherically distributed. Thus, in effect, the radius of the metal ion is smaller than that for the hypothetical, isoelectronic spherical ion. In V^{2+} this same effect is found in even greater degree because there are now three t_{2g} electrons providing much less shielding between metal ion and ligands than would three spherically distributed d electrons. For Cr^{2+} and Mn^{2+}, however, we have the configurations $t_{2g}^3 e_g$ and $t_{2g}^3 e_g^2$, in which the electrons added to the t_{2g}^3 configuration of V^{2+} go into orbitals which concentrate them mainly between the metal ion and the ligands. These e_g electrons thus provide a great deal more screening than would be provided by spherically distributed electrons, and indeed the effect is so great that the radii actually increase. The same sequence of events is repeated in the second half of the series. The first three electrons added to the spherical $t_{2g}^3 e_g^2$ configuration of Mn^{2+} go into the t_{2g} orbitals where the screening power is abnormally low, and the radii therefore decrease abnormally rapidly. On going from Ni^{2+}, with the configuration $t_{2g}^6 e_g^2$, to Cu^{2+} and Zn^{2+}, electrons are added to the e_g orbitals where their screening power is abnormally high, and the radii again cease to decrease and actually show small increases. Similar effects may be expected with trivalent ions, with ions of other transition series and in tetrahedral environments as well, although in these other circumstances fewer experimental data are available to verify the predictions which may be made by reasoning similar to that used above.

Jahn–Teller Effects. In 1937 Jahn and Teller proved a rather remarkable theorem which states that any nonlinear molecular system in a degenerate electronic state will be unstable and will undergo some kind of distortion which will lower its symmetry and split the degenerate state. Although it may sound somewhat abstract, this simple theorem has great practical importance in understanding the structural chemistry of certain transition metal ions. In order to illustrate this, we shall begin with the Cu^{2+} ion. Suppose this ion finds itself in the center of an octahedron of ligands. As shown on page 675, this ion may be thought of as possessing one hole in the e_g orbitals and the electronic state of the ion is hence a degenerate, E_g, state. According to the Jahn–Teller theorem then, the octahedron cannot remain perfect at equilibrium but must become distorted in some way.

The dynamic reason for the distortion is actually rather easy to appreciate in terms of simple physical reasoning. Let us suppose that, of the two e_g orbitals, it is the $(x^2 - y^2)$ orbital which is doubly occupied while the z^2 orbital is only singly occupied. This must mean that the four negative charges or the negative ends of dipoles in the xy plane will be more screened from the electrostatic attraction of the Cu^{2+} ion than will the two charges on the z axis. Naturally, then, the latter two ligands will be drawn in somewhat more closely than the other four. If, conversely, the z^2 orbital is doubly occupied and the $(x^2 - y^2)$ orbital only singly occupied, the four ligands in the xy plane will be drawn more closely to the cation than will the other two on the z axis. It is also possible that the unpaired electron could be in an orbital which is some linear combination of $(x^2 - y^2)$ and z^2, in which case the resulting distortion would be some related combination of the simple ones considered above. These simple considerations call attention to several important facts relating to the operation of the Jahn–Teller theorem.

1. The theorem only predicts that for degenerate states a distortion must occur. It does not give any indication of what the geometrical nature of the distortion will be nor how great it will be.

2. In order to make a prediction of the nature and magnitude of the distortion, detailed calculations must be made of the energy of the entire complex as a function of all possible types and degrees of distortion. The configuration having the lowest over-all energy may then be predicted to be the equilibrium one. Such *a priori* calculations, however, are extremely laborious and few have been attempted.

3. It may be noted that there is one general restriction on the nature of

the distortions, namely, that if the undistorted configuration has a center of symmetry, so also must the distorted equilibrium configuration.

In order to give a little more insight into the energy problem noted under paragraph 2 above, let us consider what happens to the d-orbital energies when there occurs a small distortion of the type in which the octahedron becomes stretched along its z axis. The effects are shown in Figure 26-16.

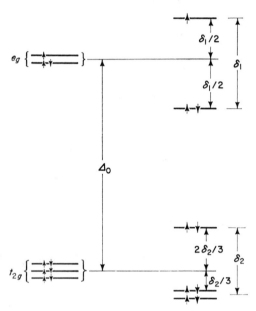

Fig. 26-16. Schematic diagram of the splittings caused by an elongation of an octahedron along one axis. The various splittings are not to the same scale, δ_1 and δ_2 being much smaller relative to Δ_0 than indicated.

In this diagram the various splittings are not drawn to scale in the interest of clarity. Both of the splittings due to the distortion are much smaller than Δ_0 and, as noted below, δ_2 is much smaller than δ_1. It should also be noted that each of the splittings obeys a center of gravity rule. The two e_g orbitals separate so that one goes up as much as the other goes down; the t_{2g} orbitals separate so that the doubly degenerate pair goes down only half as far as the single orbital goes up. It can be seen that, for the d^9 case, there is no net energy change for the t_{2g} electrons, since four are stabilized by $\delta_2/3$ while two are destabilized by $2\delta_2/3$. For the e_g electrons, however, a net stabilization occurs, since the energy of one electron is raised by $\delta_1/2$, but two electrons have their energies lowered by this same amount; the net lowering of the electronic energy is thus $\delta_1/2$. It is this stabilization which provides the driving force for the distortion.

It is easy to see from Figure 26-16 that, for both the configurations $t_{2g}{}^6 e_g$ and $t_{2g}{}^6 e_g{}^3$, distortion of the octahedron will cause stabilization; thus we predict, as could also be done directly from the Jahn–Teller theorem, that distortions are to be expected in the octahedral complexes of ions with these configurations, but not for ions having $t_{2g}{}^6$, $t_{2g}{}^6 e_g{}^2$ or $t_{2g}{}^6 e_g{}^4$ configurations. In addition it should also be obvious from the foregoing considerations that a high-spin d^4 ion, having the configuration $t_{2g}{}^3 e_g$, will also be subject to distortion. Some real ions having these configurations which are subject to distortion are:

$t_{2g}{}^3 e_g$:   high-spin Cr^{II} and Mn^{III}
$t_{2g}{}^6 e_g$:   low-spin Co^{II} and Ni^{III}
$t_{2g}{}^6 e_g{}^3$: Cu^{II}

For low-spin Co^{II} no satisfactory structural data are available, but in the other four cases there are ample data to show that distortions do occur and that they take the form of elongation of the octahedron along one axis. Indeed, in a number of Cu^{II} compounds the distortions of the octahedra around the cupric ion are so extreme that the coordination is best regarded as virtually square and, of course, Cu^{II} forms many square complexes. Specific illustrations of distortions in the compounds of these several ions will be mentioned when the chemistry of the elements is described in Chapter 29.

It may also be noted that the Jahn–Teller theorem applies to excited states as well as to ground states, although in such cases the effect is a complicated dynamic one because the short lifetime of an electronically excited state does not permit the attainment of a stable equilibrium configuration of the complex. To illustrate the effect on excited states, we may consider the $[Ti(H_2O)_6]^{3+}$, $[Fe(H_2O)_6]^{2+}$ and $[CoF_6]^{3-}$ ions. The first of these has an excited state configuration e_g. The presence of the single e_g electron causes the excited state to be split, and it is this which accounts for the broad, flat contour of the absorption band of $[Ti(H_2O)_6]^{3+}$ as seen in Figure 26-12. In both $[Fe(H_2O)_6]^{2+}$ and $[CoF_6]^{3-}$, the ground state has the configuration $t_{2g}{}^4 e_g{}^2$, and the excited state with the same number of unpaired electrons has the configuration $t_{2g}{}^3 e_g{}^3$. Thus, the excited states of these ions are subject to Jahn–Teller splitting into two components, and this shows up very markedly in their absorption spectra, as Figure 26-17 shows for $[CoF_6]^{3-}$.

Jahn–Teller distortions can also be caused by the presence of 1, 2, 4 or 5 electrons in the t_{2g} orbitals of an octahedrally coordinated ion. This can easily be seen by referring to the lower part of Figure 26-16. If one t_{2g} electron is present, distortion by elongation on one axis will cause stabilization by $\delta_2/3$. Distortion by flattening along one axis would produce a splitting of the t_{2g} orbitals which is just the reverse of that shown in Figure

26-16 for elongation, and thus would cause stabilization by twice as much, namely, $2\delta_2/3$. The same predictions can obviously be made for the t_{2g}^{4} case. For a t_{2g}^{2} configuration (assuming, with good reason since δ_2 will be much less than the electron pairing energy, that pairing of electrons

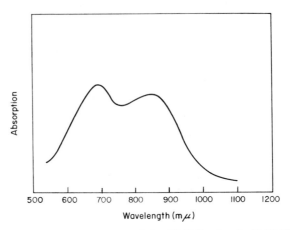

Wavelength (mμ)

Fig. 26-17. The absorption spectrum of the $[CoF_6]^{3-}$ ion in $K_2Na[CoF_6]$ showing the splitting due to a Jahn–Teller distortion of the excited state with the configuration $t_{2g}^{3}e_{g}^{3}$.

will not occur) the elongation distortion would be favored, since it will provide a total stabilization of

$$2 \times \delta_2/3 = 2\delta_2/3$$

whereas the flattening would give a net stabilization energy of only

$$2\delta_2/3 - \delta_2/3 = \delta_2/3$$

For the t_{2g}^{5} case, flattening is again predicted to cause the greater stabilization.

There is, however, little experimental confirmation of these predictions of Jahn–Teller effects for partially filled t_{2g} shells. This is mainly due to the fact that the effects are expected, theoretically, to be much smaller than those for partially filled e_g orbitals. In terms of Figure 26-16, theory shows that for a given amount of distortion δ_2 is much smaller than δ_1. Thus the stabilization energies, which are the driving forces for the distortions, are evidently not great enough to cause well-defined, clearly observable distortions in cases of partially occupied t_{2g} orbitals. From the CFT point of view the relation $\delta_2 \ll \delta_1$ is easily understood. Since the e_g orbitals are directed right at the ligands, the presence of an electron in one e_g orbital but not in the other will cause a much larger disparity in the metal–ligand distances than will nonuniform occupancy of t_{2g} orbitals, which concentrate their electrons between the metal–ligand bonds where their effects on metal–ligand distances is much less (cf. the discussion of ionic radii at the beginning of this section).

In terms of MO theory, as given later, the reason for $\delta_2 \ll \delta_1$ is also very simple. The e_g orbitals are antibonding with respect to the metal–ligand σ bonds, and thus a change in the population of these orbitals should strongly affect the metal–ligand bond strength. On the other hand, t_{2g} orbitals are nonbonding in respect to metal–ligand σ interaction, though they may have antibonding or bonding character in respect to metal–ligand π bonding. However, since σ bonding is usually far more important than π bonding, changes in the t_{2g} population have much less influence on the metal–ligand bond strengths.

26-7. Thermodynamic Effects of Crystal Field Splittings

We have seen in Section 26-2 that the d orbitals of an ion in an octahedral field are split so that three of them become more stable (by $2\Delta_0/5$) and two of them less stable (by $3\Delta_0/5$) than they would be in the absence of the splitting. Thus, for example, a d^2 ion will have each of its two d electrons stabilized by $2\Delta_0/5$, giving a total stabilization of $4\Delta_0/5$. Recalling from Section 26-4 that Δ_0 values run about 10,000 and 20,000 cm^{-1} for di- and trivalent ions of the first transition series, we can see that these "extra" stabilization energies—extra in the sense that they would not exist if the d shells of the metal ions were symmetrical as are the other electron shells of the ions—will amount to ~ 25 and ~ 50 kcal/mole, respectively, for di- and trivalent d^2 ions. These *ligand field stabilization energies*, LFSE's, are of course of the same order of magnitude as the energies of most chemical changes, and they will therefore play an important role in the thermodynamic properties of transition metal compounds.

Let us first of all consider high-spin octahedral complexes. Every t_{2g} electron represents a stability increase (i.e., energy lowering) of $2\Delta_0/5$, whereas every e_g electron represents a stability decrease of $3\Delta_0/5$. Thus, for any configuration $t_{2g}{}^p e_g{}^q$, the net stabilization will be given by $(2p/5 - 3q/5)\Delta_0$. The results* obtained for all of the ions, that is, d^0 to d^{10}, using this formula are collected in Table 26-4. Since the magnitude of Δ_0 for any particular complex can be obtained from the spectrum, it is possible

---

* The same results are obtained, a little less easily, from a molecular orbital treatment, and thus the concept of LFSE's is valid regardless of the model, CFT or otherwise, used to derive the d orbital splittings (cf. F. A. Cotton, *J. Chem. Educ.*, **41**, 466 (1964) for details).

TABLE 26-4

Ligand Field Stabilization Energies, LFSE's, for Octahedrally and
Tetrahedrally Coordinated High-spin Ions

Number of d electrons	Stabilization energies		Difference, Oct. − Tetra.[b]
	Oct.	Tetra.	
1, 6	$2\Delta_0/5$	$3\Delta_t/5$	$\Delta_0/10$
2, 7[a]	$4\Delta_0/5$	$6\Delta_t/5$	$2\Delta_0/10$
3, 8	$6\Delta_0/5$	$4\Delta_t/5$	$8\Delta_0/10$
4, 9	$3\Delta_0/5$	$2\Delta_t/5$	$4\Delta_0/10$
0, 5, 10	0	0	0

[a] For the d^2 and d^7 ions, the figure obtained in this way and given
above is not exactly correct because of the effect of configuration
interaction.

[b] Assuming $\Delta_0 = 2\Delta_t$.

to determine the magnitudes of these crystal field stabilization energies
independently of thermodynamic measurements and thus to see what part
they play in the thermodynamics of the transition metal compounds.

Hydration, Ligation and Lattice Energies. As a first example, let us
consider the heats of hydration of the divalent ions of the first transition
series. These are the energies of the processes:

$$M^{2+}(gas) + \infty H_2O = [M(H_2O)_6]^{2+}(aq)$$

and they can be estimated using thermodynamic cycles. The energies
calculated are shown by the filled circles in Figure 26-18. It will be seen

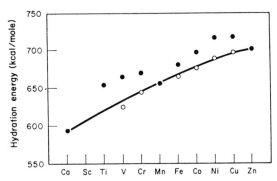

Fig. 26-18. Hydration energies of some divalent ions. Solid circles are the experimentally derived hydration energies. Open circles are energies corrected for LFSE.

that a smooth curve, which is nearly a straight line, passes through the
points for the three ions, Ca^{2+} (d^0), Mn^{2+} (d^5) and Zn^{2+} (d^{10}), which have
no LFSE while the points for all other ions lie above this line. On sub-

tracting the LFSE from each of the actual hydration energies, the values shown by open circles are obtained, and these fall on the smooth curve. It may be noted that, alternatively, LFSE's could have been estimated from Figure 26-18 and used to calculate Δ_0 values. Either way, the agreement between the spectrally and thermodynamically assessed Δ_0 values provides evidence for the fundamental correctness of the idea of d-orbital splitting.

Two more examples of these thermodynamic consequences of crystal field splittings are shown in Figures 26-19 and 26-20. In Figure 26-19 the

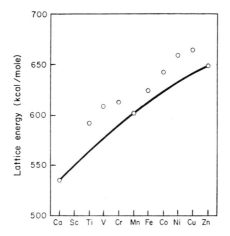

Fig. 26-19.   The lattice energies of the dichlorides of the elements from Ca to Zn.

lattice energies of the dichlorides of the metals from calcium to zinc are plotted versus atomic number. Once again they define a curve with two

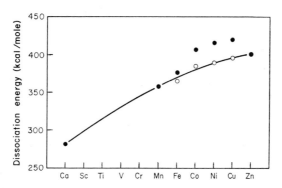

Fig. 26-20.   Dissociation energies of the hexammines of some divalent metal ions; ● represents the total energies; ○ represents the total energies minus the ligand field stabilization energies estimated from spectroscopically derived Δ_0 values.

maxima and a minimum at Mn^{2+}. As before, the energies for all the ions having LFSE's lie above the curve passing through the energies of the three ions which do not have any ligand field stabilization energy. Similar plots are obtained for the lattice energies of other halides and of the chalconides of di- and trivalent metals. In Figure 26-20 are plotted the gas phase dissociation energies, estimated by means of thermodynamic cycles, for the hexammine ions of some divalent metals. These energies are for the process:

$$[M(NH_3)_6]^{2+}(g) = M^{2+}(g) + 6NH_3(g)$$

and thus are equal to six times the mean M—NH_3 bond energy. The hydration energies discussed above do not have quite this simple interpretation because they include the energy of further hydration of the hexaquo ions in addition to the energy of the process:

$$M^{2+}(g) + 6H_2O(g) = [M(H_2O)_6]^{2+}(g)$$

decreased by the heat of vaporization of six moles of water. Although the data for the dissociation of the hexammines are limited, they show the same trend as do the hydration and lattice energies and, as shown by the open circles of Figure 26-20, the deviations from the smooth curve are equal within experimental error to the spectroscopically estimated LFSE's.

It will be noted in all three of the Figures, 26-18 to 26-20, that the smooth curves from Ca^{2+} through Mn^{2+} to Zn^{2+}, on which the corrected energies do, or presumably would, fall, rise with increasing atomic number. This is to be expected, since the smooth curve on which the radii of (real or hypothetical) spherical ions lie, as shown in Figure 26-15, falls from Ca^{2+} to Zn^{2+}. A steady decrease in ionic radius naturally leads to a steady increase in the electrostatic interaction energy between the cation and the ligand anions or dipoles. A feature of particular importance, which is most directly evident in Figure 26-20, is that the LFSE's, critical as they may be in explaining the *differences* in energies between various ions in the series, make up only a small fraction, 5–10%, of the *total* energies of combination of the metal ions with the ligands. In other words, the LFSE's, though crucially important in many ways, are not by any means major sources of the binding energies in complexes.

Formation Constants of Complexes. It is a fairly general observation that the equilibrium constants for the formation of analogous complexes of the divalent metal ions of Mn through Zn with ligands which contain nitrogen as the donor atom fall in the following order of the metal ions: $Mn^{2+} < Fe^{2+} < Co^{2+} < Ni^{2+} < Cu^{2+} > Zn^{2+}$. There are occasional exceptions to this order, sometimes called the Irving–Williams order, which may be attributed to the occurrence of spin-pairing in strong crystal fields. Spin-pairing, naturally, affects the relative energies in a different way. The great generality of the above order of stability constants receives quite a natural explanation in terms of LFSE's. It must first be noted that the magnitudes of stability constants are proportional to the antilogarithms of standard free energy changes so that the above order is also that of the $-\Delta F^0$ values for the formation reactions. Now the standard free energies of formation are related to the enthalpies by the relation:

$$-\Delta F^0 = -\Delta H^0 + T\Delta S^0$$

and since there are good reasons to believe that entropies of complex formation are substantially constant in the above series of ions, we come finally to the conclusion that the above order of formation constants is also the order of $-\Delta H^0$ values for the formation reactions. Indeed, in a few cases direct measurements of the ΔH^0 values have shown this to be true.

Let us now remember that the formation of the complex involves the displacement of water molecules by ligands. If the metal ion concerned is subject to crystal field stabilization, as is, for example, Fe^{2+}, this stabilization will be greater in the complex than that in the aquo ion, since the nitrogen-containing ligand will be further along in the spectrochemical series than in H_2O (see page 680). For Mn^{2+}, however, there is no LFSE in the hexaquo ion or in the complex so that complexation cannot cause any increased stabilization. Thus the Fe^{2+} ion has more to gain by combining with the ligands than does Mn^{2+}, and it accordingly shows a greater affinity for them. Similarly, of two ions, both of which experience crystal field stabilization, the one which experiences the greater amount from both the ligand and from H_2O will also experience the larger increase on replacement of H_2O by the ligand. Thus the order of the ions in the stability series follows their order in regard to crystal field stabilization energies with only the exception of the position of Cu^{2+} relative to Ni^{2+}. There are several possible reasons for this discrepancy, but further work is needed to provide a completely unambiguous explanation.

Octahedral vs Tetrahedral Coordination. Finally, in this section we shall consider a phenomenon which is structural in nature but which depends quite directly on LFSE's, namely, variation in the relative stability of octahedral and tetrahedral complexes for various metal ions. It should be clearly understood that the ΔH^0 of transformation of a tetrahedral complex of a given metal ion to an octahedral complex of the same ion, as represented, for instance, by the equation

$$[MCl_4]^{2-} + 6H_2O = [M(H_2O)_6]^{2+} + 4Cl^- \tag{26-1}$$

is a quantity to which the difference in LFSE's of the octahedral and tetrahedral species makes only a small contribution. The metal–ligand bond energies, polarization energies of the ligands, hydration energies and other contributions all play larger roles, and the calculation of ΔH^0 for a particular metal, M, is a difficult and, as yet, insuperable problem. However, if a reaction of this type occurs (actually or hypothetically as a step in a thermodynamic cycle) for a series of metal ions increasing regularly in atomic number, say the ions Mn^{2+}, Fe^{2+}, ..., Cu^{2+}, Zn^{2+}, it is reasonable to suppose that the various factors contributing to ΔH^0 will all change uniformly *except* the differences in the LFSE's. The latter therefore might be expected to play a decisive role, despite being inherently small parts of the entire ΔH^0 in each individual case, in determining an irregular variation in the equilibrium constants for such reactions from one metal ion to another. There are two cases in which experimental data corroborate this expectation.

For reaction 26-1 mentioned above, carried out hypothetically in the vapor phase, the enthalpies have been estimated from thermodynamic data for the metals, M, in the series Mn^{2+}, Fe^{2+}, ..., Cu^{2+}, Zn^{2+}. At the same time, from the spectra of the $[M(H_2O)_6]^{2+}$ and $[MCl_4]^{2-}$ ions the values of Δ_0 and Δ_t have been evaluated and the differences between the two LFSE's calculated. Figure 26-21 shows a comparison between these two sets of quantities. It is evident that the qualitative relationship is

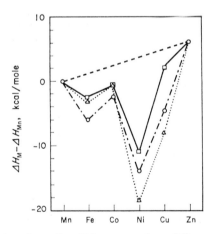

Fig. 26-21.   Enthalpies of reaction 26-1 expressed as differences between ΔH for a particular metal and ΔH for the Mn^{2+} compounds.   □ and ○ are "experimental" values derived in different ways from thermodynamic data while △ are values calculated from LFSE differences.   In each case the ΔH values are plotted relative to the interpolated value between Mn^{2+} and Zn^{2+} as indicated by the straight line between the points for these two ions. (From A. B. Blake and F. A. Cotton, *Inorg. Chem.*, **3**, 9 (1964).)

very close even though some quantitative discrepancies exist. The latter may well be due to inaccuracies in the ΔH values since these are obtained as net algebraic sums of the independently measured enthalpies of several processes. The qualitatively close agreement between the variation in the enthalpies and the LFSE difference justifies the conclusion that it is the variations in LFSE's which account for gross qualitative stability relations such as the fact that tetrahedral complexes of Co^{II} are relatively stable while those of Ni^{II} are not.

A second illustration of the importance of LFSE's in determining stereochemistry is provided by the *site preference* problem in the mixed metal oxides which have the spinel (or inverse spinel) structures. These structures have been described on page 51, but the reason for the occurrence of inverse spinels was not given. In every case where inversion occurs, an explanation in terms of LFSE's can be given. For example, $NiAl_2O_4$ is inverted, that is Ni^{2+} ions occupy octahedral interstices and half the aluminum ions occupy tetrahedral ones. It could *not* be predicted that this would necessarily occur simply because the LFSE of Ni^{2+} is much greater in octahedral than in tetrahedral environments, because there are other energy differences which oppose exchanging the sites of Ni^{2+} ions and Al^{3+} ions. However, it can be said that Ni^{2+} is the ion most likely to participate in such an inversion and that if inversion is to occur at all, it must occur with $NiAl_2O_4$. For $FeAl_2O_4$, in contrast, LFSE differences would again dictate a qualitative preference by Fe^{2+} for the octahedral site, but inversion does not occur. However, as Table 26-4 shows, the magnitude of the preference energy may be around an order of magnitude smaller than for Ni^{2+}.

Another example of the role of LFSE's in determining site preferences is provided by the series of oxides Fe_3O_4, Mn_3O_4 and Co_3O_4, of which only the first is inverted. All energy changes connected with inversion should be quite similar in the three compounds except the differences in LFSE's, and these are just such as to favor inversion in Fe_3O_4 but not in the others. Thus, transfer of the d^5 Fe^{3+} ion involves no change in LFSE, but transfer of the high-spin d^6 Fe^{2+} ion from a tetrahedral to an octahedral hole produces a net gain in LFSE. For Mn_3O_4, transfer of the d^5 Mn^{2+} ions makes no change in LFSE, but transfer of the d^4 Mn^{3+} ion from an octahedral to a tetrahedral hole would decrease the LFSE, so that the process of inverting Mn_3O_4 is disfavored. For Co_3O_4 the transfer of the Co^{2+} ions to octahedral holes would be only slightly favored by the LFSE's, whereas the transfer of a low-spin d^6 Co^{3+} ion from an octahedral hole to a tetrahedral one where it would presumably become high-spin would cause an enormous net decrease in LFSE, so that here, even more than in the case of Mn_3O_4, we do not expect inversion.

26-8. Some Other Applications of Orbital Splittings

There are some other important applications of the splitting of orbitals (and free ion states) which limitations of space or their inherent complexity do not permit us to describe in any detail, but several should at least be mentioned.

Reaction Mechanisms of Complexes. As explained in Chapter 5, there is an enormous variation in the rates of ligand exchange reactions of complexes. For nontransition metals, there is a reasonably satisfactory correlation of rates with cation size and charge, but the rates for transition metal complexes vary widely (over some 6 powers of 10) in a manner unrelated to these factors. While a quantitatively satisfactory explanation for the variation in rates, which has not yet been given, would have to include a number of factors, crude calculations have shown that the irregularly varying contribution of LFSE's to the activation energies must be a major factor, perhaps even the dominant one. For example, Fe^{3+} $(t_{2g}^3 e_g^2)$ complexes react rapidly while those of Cr^{3+} (t_{2g}^3) and Co^{3+} (t_{2g}^6) react slowly. For Fe^{3+} changes in the shape or number of ligands in the coordination sphere will not make any change in the LFSE since there is none for a high-spin d^5 ion in any circumstances, whereas octahedrally coordinated Cr^{3+} and Co^{3+} ions have very high LFSE's and rough calculations show that all of the plausible transition states for reactions of these ions will involve an appreciable fractional decrease in these large LFSE's. The same holds for Ni^{2+} in comparison to the other divalent ions of the first transition series, and in fact, Ni^{2+} complexes do react appreciably slower than those of the other +2 ions.

Optical Activity. The phenomenological aspects of optical activity have been sketched earlier (page 646). Attempts to account quantitatively for the varying magnitudes of the rotation and circular dichroism in different absorption bands of a given complex naturally begin with the same analysis of the orbital or state splittings utilized to interpret the absorption spectra. However, optical activity can only be treated using far more sophisticated atomic physics than is assumed as a prerequisite to the study of this book, and accordingly we can say little in detail about it. In addition, the problem has not been solved quantitatively as yet. It has, however, been shown that only those electronic transitions which are allowed by magnetic dipole selection rules should have large rotational strengths. The energy level diagrams discussed earlier in this section provide sufficient information to determine which transitions are qualitatively expected to exhibit large rotations, but further explanation cannot be given here.

EVIDENCE FOR COVALENCE AND THE ADJUSTED
CRYSTAL FIELD THEORY (ACFT)

26-9. Experimental Evidence for Metal–Ligand Orbital Overlap

Electron Spin Resonance Spectra. One source of such evidence, probably the most direct one we possess, is electron spin resonance data. The nature of electron spin resonance has been briefly described earlier (page 644). In many cases it has been found that instead of the single absorption band expected for a group of d electrons localized on a particular metal atom, there is observed a complex pattern of sub-bands, as shown in Figure 26-22 for the now classic case of the $[IrCl_6]^{2-}$ ion. The pattern

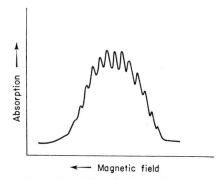

Fig. 26-22.   The esr spectrum of the $[IrCl_6]^{2-}$ ion, obtained with the applied magnetic field aligned along one of the Cl—Ir—Cl axes of the complex ion in a single crystal of $Na_2PtCl_6 \cdot 6H_2O$ containing about 0.5% Ir^{IV} substitutionally replacing Pt^{IV}.

of sub-bands, called the hyperfine structure, has been satisfactorily explained by assuming that certain of the iridium orbitals and certain orbitals of the surrounding chloride ions overlap to such an extent that the single unpaired electron is not localized entirely on the metal ion but instead is about 5% localized on each Cl^- ion. The hyperfine structure is caused by the nuclear magnetic moments of the chloride ions, and the hyperfine splittings are proportional to the fractional extent to which the unpaired electron occupies the orbitals of these chloride ions. The electron is thus only 70% an "iridium(IV) $4d$ electron," instead of the 100% that is assumed in the purely electrostatic crystal field theory. Another similar example is that of the $[Mo(CN)_8]^{3-}$ ion. The esr spectrum of this ion when it is enriched in ^{13}C, which has a nuclear spin (^{12}C does not), exhibits marked hyperfine structure showing that the unpaired electron is significantly delocalized on to the carbon atoms of the CN^- ions. There are numerous other examples.

Nuclear Magnetic Resonance Spectra. Closely related to esr experiments of the sort just mentioned are nuclear magnetic resonance experiments in which the nuclear resonances of atoms in ligands are found to be affected by unpaired electrons in a manner which can only be explained by assuming that electron spin density is transferred from metal orbitals into orbitals of ligand atoms. Thus, for example, the resonance frequency of the ring protons, H_α, in tris(acetylacetonato)vanadium(III) (Fig. 26-23) is con-

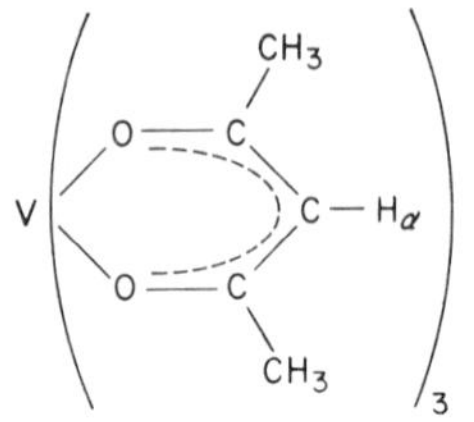

Fig. 26-23. Tris(acetylacetonato)vanadium(III) indicating the ring hydrogen, H_α, whose nuclear resonance frequency is strongly affected by the unpaired electrons on the V^{III} ion.

siderably shifted from its position in a comparable diamagnetic compound, say its Al^{III} analog. In order to account for the magnitude of the shift, it is necessary to assume that the spin density of unpaired electrons, *formally* restricted to t_{2g} metal orbitals in the crystal field treatment, actually moves out into the π electron system of the ligand to a significant extent and eventually into the $1s$ orbitals of the hydrogen atoms. Perhaps the most extensive and detailed studies of this phenomenon are those which have been made on the Ni^{II} complexes of aminotroponeimines (see page 890). Even in $MF_6{}^{2-}$ octahedra, where we should certainly expect the metal–ligand bonding to be as electrostatic as anywhere, fluorine nuclear resonance spectra have shown that delocalization of the spin density of metal ion d electrons takes place to the extent of 2–5%.

Intensities of "d–d" Transitions. Another indication that metal ion and ligand orbitals overlap with the result that the d orbitals of the metal ions are not pure metal ion d orbitals is given by the intensities of the optical absorption bands due to "d–d" transitions. If the crystal field approximation were perfect, the only mechanisms by which these absorptions could gain intensity would be by interactions of the d orbital wave functions with vibrational wave functions of the complex ion and by mixing of d orbitals with other *metal ion* orbitals in those complexes (e.g., tetrahedral ones) where there is no center of symmetry. There are, however, cases in which it is fairly certain that these two processes are insufficient to account for the intensities observed, and it must be assumed then that the additional process of overlap and mixing of the metal d orbitals with various ligand atom orbitals, which is a powerful mechanism for enhancing the intensities, occurs to a significant degree.

The Nephelauxetic Effect. It was noted on page 679, that if the energy level diagrams for transition metal ions with two to eight d electrons are calculated, assuming that the separations between the various Russell–Saunders states are exactly the same in the complexed ion as they are in the free, gaseous ion (which leaves Δ as the only variable parameter), the fitting of experimental data is not exact. In some cases the discrepancies are quite marked. It is invariably found that the fit can be improved by assuming that the separations between the Russell–Saunders states are smaller in the complexed ion than in the free ion. Now the separations between these states are attributable to the repulsions between the d electrons in the d^n configuration, so that the decrease in the energy separations between the states suggests that the d electron cloud has expanded in the complex, thus increasing the mean distance between d electrons and decreasing the interelectronic repulsions. It is now generally believed that this expansion of the d electron cloud occurs at least partly because the metal ion d orbitals overlap with ligand atom orbitals thus providing paths by which d electrons can, and do, escape to some extent from the metal ion. This effect of ligands in expanding the d electron clouds has been named the *nephelauxetic* (from the Greek, meaning "cloud expanding") effect, and it has been found that the common ligands can be arranged in order of their ability to cause cloud expansion. This order, which is more or less independent of the metal ion, similarly to the spectrochemical series, is in part: $F^- < H_2O < NH_3 <$ oxalate $\sim$ ethylenediamine $< -NCS^-$ $< Cl^- \sim CN^- < Br^- < I^-$.

Antiferromagnetic Coupling. Still another evidence of some overlap between metal ion d orbitals and ligand orbitals in compounds which are usually described as "ionic" comes from detailed consideration of antiferromagnetism as it is observed in, for example, the oxides MnO, FeO, CoO and NiO. As we have already noted (page 642), an antiferromagnetic substance is one which follows a Curie or Curie–Weiss law at high temperatures but below a certain temperature (the Néel temperature) shows decreasing rather than increasing magnetic susceptibility as the temperature is lowered further. It has been conclusively shown by neutron diffraction studies that this effect is not due to pairing of electron spins within individual ions but is due rather to a tendency of half of the ions to have their magnetic moments lined up in the opposite direction to those of the other half of the ions. Such antiparallel aligning, in which nearest neighbor metal ions separated by an oxide ion collinear with them have opposed moments, cannot be explained merely by the direct effect, over the intervening distance, of one magnetic dipole on another; their separation is too great to permit an effect of the observed magnitude. Instead, the oxide ions are assumed to participate in the following way. Let us consider an M^{2+}—O^{2-}—M^{2+} set in which each metal ion possesses an unpaired electron. The oxide ion also has pairs of electrons occupying π orbitals. If there is overlap between that d orbital of one metal ion which contains its un-paired electron and a π orbital of the oxide ion, an electron from the oxide ion will move so as to occupy partially the d orbital. In so doing, however, it must have its spin opposed to that of the d electron because of the exclusion principle. The other π electron then has its spin aligned parallel to that of the d electron on the first metal ion. If it moves to some extent into the d orbital of the second metal ion which already contains that metal ion's unpaired d electron, the spin of that d electron will have to be aligned opposite to that of the entering π electron and, hence, opposite to that of the d electron on the first metal ion. The net result is that by this intervention of the oxide ion, which can only occur because there is some finite though not necessarily large degree of overlap between metal d and oxygen π orbitals, we obtain from a system in which the two metal ion d electrons were free to orient their spins independently one in which they are coupled together with their spins antiparallel. If this latter state has slightly lower energy at low temperatures than does the former, then as the temperature is lowered the entire metal oxide lattice will tend to drop into it, and antiferromagnetism will be exhibited. This, in somewhat simplified form, is the currently accepted explanation of anti-ferromagnetic behavior in most "ionic" salts, oxides and chalconides, and its key assumption is that these substances are not in fact completely ionic but instead involve some significant degree of overlap between metal ion d orbitals and anion orbitals.

26-10. The Theoretical Failure of an Ionic Model

It is obvious, as noted already, that the CFT model cannot have any *physical* value, because it does not attempt to represent the ligands as they really are, even in purely electrostatic particulars. However, the question naturally arises as to what result would be obtained if we were to represent the ligands in a realistic manner, that is, as finite spheres of negative charge with a positive charge located at the center of the sphere, but still use only coulombic forces between these realistic ligand atoms and the d electrons of the metal ion. This question has been investigated quanti-tatively,[3] with results which will now be summarized in a simplified,

[3] W. H. Kleiner, *J. Chem. Phys.*, **20**, 1784 (1952); A. J. Freeman and R. E. Watson, *Phys. Rev.*, **120**, 1254 (1960). The latter paper should be read by all serious students of ligand field theory.

qualitative form.   Figure 26–24 shows schematically the spacial relation-ship of metal ion d orbitals and the charge clouds and nuclei of ligand atoms in a complex.

An electron occupying an orbital which has lobes such as A and A′ in Figure 26-24 directed at the ligand atoms will feel the positive charge of the

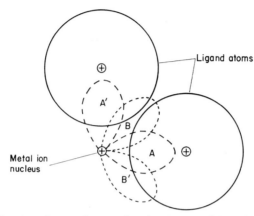

Fig. 26-24.   A drawing of part of a complex showing two lobes, A, A′ of an e_g type metal orbital, two lobes, B, B′ of a t_{2g} type metal orbital and two ligand atoms.   The spheres enclosing most of the electron clouds of the ligand atoms are also shown.

nucleus (or the net positive charge of the compact core, in a heavier atom) rather strongly, thus off-setting appreciably the repulsive effect it feels from the diffuse electron cloud into which it penetrates.   On the other hand, an electron occupying an orbital which has lobes, such as B and B′ in Figure 26-24, directed between ligand atoms feels the repulsive effect of the elec-tron cloud nearly as much as the electron in A, but feels the counter-vailing effect of the nucleus less.   Thus, instead of concluding that the elec-tron must be much more stable in orbital B than in A, as we do in the point charge model, we conclude that the stability difference will be either only slightly in favor of B, or possibly, even *slightly in favor of orbital A*.   Actual calculations, using realistic (i.e., Hartree–Fock) orbitals for metal and ligand atoms, have shown this to be true quantitatively.

26-11. The Adjusted Crystal Field Theory, ACFT (also called Ligand Field Theory)

We have now recognized that the central assumption of crystal field theory, namely, that the metal ion and the surrounding ligand atoms inter-act with one another in a purely electrostatic way and do not mix their orbitals or share electrons, is never strictly true.   The question then is whether we may still use the crystal field theory, perhaps with certain modifications and adjustments, as a *formalism* to make predictions and calculations even though we do not take its assumptions literally. The answer to this question is in the affirmative provided the degree of orbital overlap is not too great, and experience has now shown that, for most complexes of metals in their normal oxidation states, the amount of overlap is small enough to be manageable in such a way. The crystal field theory so modified to take account of the existence of moderate amounts of orbital overlap we shall call the adjusted crystal field theory, although the term ligand field theory has often been used to designate this particular form of CFT. When the amount of orbital overlap is excessive—and this is likely to happen for complexes which contain the metals in unusual oxidation states—we must have recourse to the molecular orbital theory which is outlined in the next section.

The most straightforward modifications of simple crystal field theory which make allowance for orbital overlap involve using all parameters of interelectronic interactions as variables rather than taking them equal to the values found for the free ions. Of these parameters, three are of decisive importance, namely, the spin-orbit coupling constant, λ, and the interelectronic repulsion parameters, which may be the Slater integrals, F_n, or certain usually more convenient linear combinations of these called the Racah parameters, B and C.

The spin-orbit coupling constant plays a considerable role in deter-mining the detailed magnetic properties of many ions in their complexes, for example, the deviations of some actual magnetic moments from spin-only values and inherent temperature dependence of some moments. All studies to date show that in ordinary complexes the values of λ are 70–85% of those for the free ions. It is possible to get excellent agreement between crystal field theory predictions and experimental observations simply by using these smaller λ values.

The Racah parameters are measures of the energy separations of the various Russell–Saunders states of an atom. The energy differences be-tween states of the same spin multiplicity are, in general, multiples of B only, whereas the differences between states of different multiplicity are expressed as sums of multiples of both B and C. To illustrate their use, let us take the d^8 (2 positron) system as it occurs in some tetrahedral nickel(II) complexes. As a 2-positron system in a tetrahedral field, it has, qualitatively, the same energy level diagram as a 2-electron system in an octahedral field which we have already shown in Figure 26-13. Now an exact calcu-lation of the energy of the transition, ν_3, from the $^3T_1(F)$ ground state to the $^3T_1(P)$ state gives the result:

$$\nu_3 = (E_P - E_F) + \tfrac{6}{5}\Delta_t$$

In the $[NiX_4]^{2-}$ complexes (X = Cl^-, Br^-, I^-), this transition is observed at $\sim 14,000$ cm^{-1}. It is completely impossible to account for this result if we assume that the energy difference $(E_P - E_F)$ has the same value in these complexes as it has in the free ion, for in the free ion it is about 16,000 cm^{-1}, which is greater than ν_3. The only way out of this paradox is to assume that $(E_P - E_F)$ shrinks to $\sim 70\%$ of the free ion value. Now theory expresses $(E_P - E_F)$ as $15B$, so that this is equivalent to saying that B', the value of this Racah parameter for the Ni^{2+} ion in the complexes, is $\sim 70\%$ of B, the value in the free ion. Similarly, it is found that the observed energies of several transitions from the $^3T_1(F)$ ground state to excited singlet states require that their separations from the ground state be reduced to about 70% of the free ion values. This implies that the Racah parameter C is also diminished and by about the same amount as B. Indeed it is a general rule that

$$B'/B \approx C'/C \approx 0.7$$

Moreover, for a series of analogous complexes with different ligands, the B'/B ratios will be in the order required by the nephelauxetic series.

Thus in order to calculate an energy level diagram and/or details of magnetic behavior in ligand field theory, one proceeds in the same manner as in crystal field theory except that, instead of assuming the free ion values for λ, B and C, one either assumes somewhat smaller ones or leaves them as parameters to be evaluated from the experimental observations. In this way all the computational and conceptual advantages of the simple electrostatic theory are preserved while allowance is made—in an indirect and admittedly artificial way—for the consequences of finite orbital overlap. One also bears in mind that there are other consequences, for example, electron delocalization, of the overlap.

THE MOLECULAR ORBITAL THEORY

26-12. Qualitative Introduction

The molecular orbital theory starts with the premise that overlap of orbitals will occur, to some degree, whenever symmetry permits. It thus includes the electrostatic situation (no overlap) as one extreme, maximal overlapping of orbitals as the other extreme, and all intermediate degrees of overlap in its scope. The first task in working out the MO treatment for a particular type of complex is to find out which orbital overlaps are and are not possible because of the inherent symmetry requirements of the problem. This can be done quite elegantly and systematically using some principles of group theory, but such an approach is outside the scope of this discussion. Instead we shall simply present the results that are obtained for octahedral complexes, illustrating them pictorially. It may be noted that, ultimately, for the experimental inorganic chemist, this pictorial representation is much more important than mathematical details, for it provides a basis for visualizing the bonding and thinking concretely about it.

The molecular orbitals we shall use here will be of the LCAO type (see page 82). Our method for constructing them, which we shall apply specifically to octahedral complexes, will take the following steps.

1. We note that there are nine valence shell orbitals of the metal ion to be considered. Six of these—d_{z^2}, $d_{x^2-y^2}$, s, p_x, p_y and p_z—have lobes lying along the metal–ligand bond directions (i.e., are suitable for σ bonding), whereas three, namely, d_{xy}, d_{yz}, d_{zx}, are so oriented as to be suitable only for π bonding. Figures 1-8 and 26-2 should be consulted to verify these statements.

2. We shall assume initially that each of the six ligands possesses one σ orbital. These individual σ orbitals must then be combined into six

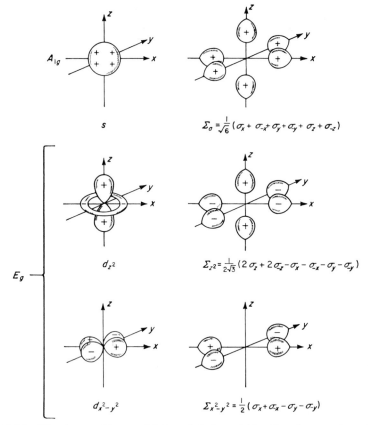

Fig. 26-25.   The six metal ion σ orbitals and their matching ligand symmetry orbitals.

"symmetry" orbitals, each constructed so as to overlap effectively with a particular one of the six metal ion orbitals which are suitable for σ bonding. Each of the metal orbitals must then be combined with its matching symmetry orbital of the ligand system to give a bonding and an antibonding molecular orbital.

3. If the ligands also possess π orbitals, these too must be combined into "symmetry" orbitals constructed so as to overlap effectively with the metal ion π orbitals, and the bonding and antibonding MO's then formed by overlap.

Complexes with No π Bonding. The six σ symmetry orbitals are indicated in Figure 26-25, in which they are illustrated pictorially, expressed algebraically as normalized linear combinations of the individual ligand σ orbitals, and juxtaposed with the metal ion orbitals with which they are matched by symmetry. On the left side of Figure 26-25 are the symmetry symbols, A_{1g}, E_g and T_{1u}, for these orbitals. These symbols are of group theoretical origin, and they stand for the symmetry class to which belong the metal orbital, the matching symmetry orbital of the ligand system,

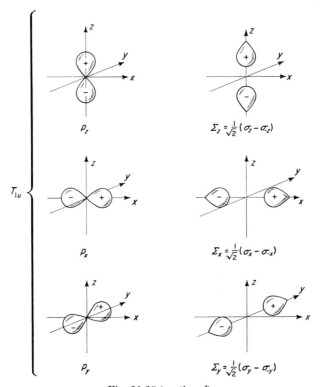

Fig. 26-25 (*continued*)

and the molecular orbitals which will result from the overlap of these two. They are very commonly used simply as convenient labels, but they also carry information. The symbol A_{1g} always represents a single orbital which has the full symmetry of the molecular system. The symbol E_g represents a pair of orbitals which are equivalent except for their orientations in space, whereas T_{1u} represents a set of three orbitals which are equivalent except for their orientations in space. The subscripts g and u are used to indicate whether the orbital(s) is centrosymmetric (g from the German *gerade* meaning even) or anticentrosymmetric (u from the German *ungerade* meaning uneven).

The final step now to obtain the molecular orbitals themselves is to allow each metal orbital to overlap with its matching symmetry orbital of the ligand system. As before (pages 82ff.), two combinations are to be considered: one in which the matched orbitals unite with maximum positive overlap, thus giving a bonding MO, and the other in which they unite with maximum negative overlap to give the corresponding antibonding MO. Let us illustrate this process for the pair p_z and Σ_z. The results are shown pictorially in Figure 26-26. From the energy point of view, these results may be expressed in the usual type of MO energy level diagram (see page

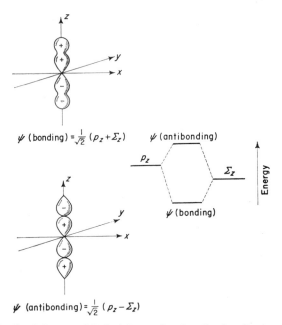

Fig. 26-26. To the left are orbital pictures showing the bonding and antibonding molecular orbitals which are the z components of the T_{1u} sets. To the right is an energy level diagram showing how the energies of the various orbitals are related.

85), and this is done at the right side of Figure 26-26.   It will be noted there that the p_z and Σ_z orbitals are not assumed to have the same energies, for in general they do not.   To a first approximation, the energies of the bonding and antibonding MO's lie equal distances below and above, respectively, the mean of the energies of the combining orbitals.

In just the same way, the other metal ion orbitals combine with the matching symmetry orbitals of the ligand system to form bonding and anti-bonding MO's.   The MO's of the same symmetry class—which are equivalent except for their spacial orientations—have the same energies, but orbitals of different symmetry classes do not in general have the same energies, since they are not equivalent.   The energy level diagram which results when all of the σ interactions are considered is shown in Figure 26-27.   Here we name the orbitals only by their symmetry designations, using the asterisk to signify that a molecular orbital is antibonding.   It should be noted in Figure 26-27 that the three metal ion d orbitals which

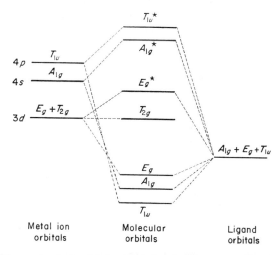

Fig. 26-27.   The molecular orbital energy level diagram, qualitative, for an octahedral complex between a metal ion of the first transition series and six ligands which do not possess π orbitals.

are suitable for forming π bonds but not σ bonds are given their appropriate symmetry label, T_{2g}, and shown as remaining unchanged in energy, since we are considering ligands which have no π orbitals with which they might interact.

There are certain implications of this energy level diagram deserving of special attention.   In general, in molecular orbital diagrams of this type, it may be assumed that, if a molecular orbital is much nearer in energy to one

23 + A.I.C.

of the atomic orbitals used to construct it than to the other one, it has much more the character of the first one than of the second. On this basis then, Figure 26-27 implies that the six bonding σ MO's, three T_{1u}'s, the A_{1g} and the two E_g's, have more the character of ligand orbitals than they do of metal orbitals. It can then be said that electrons occupying these orbitals will be mainly "ligand electrons" rather than "metal electrons," though they will partake of metal ion character to some significant extent. Conversely, electrons occupying any of the antibonding MO's are to be considered as predominantly metal electrons. Any electrons in the T_{2g} orbitals will be *purely* metal electrons when there are no ligand π orbitals as in the case being considered.

Let us now look at the center of the MO diagram, where we see the T_{2g} orbitals and, somewhat higher in energy, the $E_g{}^*$ orbitals. The latter, as noted, are predominantly of metal ion d-orbital character though with some ligand orbital character mixed in. Is this not the same situation, qualitatively speaking, as we obtained from the electrostatic arguments of crystal field theory? Indeed it is, and, moreover, it is the same result we get from the adjusted crystal field theory, where we allow for the occurrence of orbital overlap which destroys to some extent the "purity" of the metal ion d orbitals. We shall explore this relationship further in Section 26-16.

Complexes with π Bonding. If the ligands have π orbitals, filled or unfilled, it is necessary to consider their interactions with the T_{2g} d orbitals, that is, the d_{xy}, d_{yz} and d_{zx} orbitals. The simplest case is the one where each ligand has a pair of π orbitals mutually perpendicular, making $6 \times 2 = 12$ altogether. From group theory it is found that these may be combined into four triply degenerate sets belonging to the symmetry classes T_{1g}, T_{2g}, T_{1u} and T_{2u}. Those in the classes T_{1g} and T_{2u} will remain rigorously nonbonding. (We use the terms bonding, nonbonding and antibonding with reference to the metal–ligand interactions regardless of the character of the orbitals in respect to bonding between atoms within polyatomic ligands.) This is for the simple reason that the metal ion does not possess any orbitals of these symmetries with which they might interact. The T_{1u} set can interact with the metal ion p orbitals, which are themselves a set with T_{1u} symmetry, and in a quantitative discussion it would be necessary to make allowance for this. However, in a qualitative treatment we may assume that since the p orbitals are already required for the σ bonding, we need not consider π bonding by means of T_{1u} orbitals, which are thus nonbonding in character. This then leaves us with only the T_{2g} set of symmetry orbitals to overlap with the metal ion T_{2g} d orbitals.

The ligand π orbitals may be simple $p\pi$ orbitals, as in the Cl^- ion, simple $d\pi$ orbitals as in phosphines or arsines, or molecular orbitals of a polyatomic ligand as in CO, CN^- or pyridine. When they are simple $p\pi$ or $d\pi$ orbitals, it is quite easy to visualize how they combine to form the proper symmetry orbitals for overlapping with the metal ion orbitals. This is illustrated for $p\pi$ orbitals in Figure 26-28.

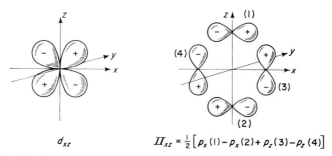

$$d_{xz} \qquad\qquad \Pi_{xz} = \tfrac{1}{2}\left[p_x(1) - p_x(2) + p_z(3) - p_z(4)\right]$$

Fig. 26-28. At the right is the symmetry orbital made up of ligand p orbitals which has the proper symmetry to give optimum interaction with the metal ion d_{zx} orbital shown at the left. There are quite analogous symmetry orbitals, π_{xy} and π_{yz}, which are similarly related to the metal ion d_{xy} and d_{yz} orbitals.

The effects of π bonding via molecular orbitals of the T_{2g} type upon the energy levels must now be considered. These effects will vary depending on the energy of the ligand π orbitals relative to the energy of the metal T_{2g} orbitals and on whether the ligand π orbitals are filled or empty. Let us consider first the case where there are empty π orbitals of higher energy than the metal T_{2g} orbitals. This situation is found in complexes where the ligands are phosphines or arsines, for example. As shown in Figure 26-29a,

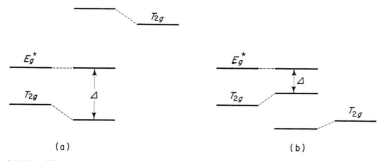

Fig. 26-29. Energy level diagrams showing how π interactions can affect the value of Δ. (a) Ligands have π orbitals of higher energy than the metal T_{2g} orbitals; (b) ligands have π orbitals of lower energy than the metal T_{2g} orbitals.

the net result of the π interaction is to stabilize the metal T_{2g} orbitals (which, of course, also acquire some ligand orbital character in the process) relative to the metal $E_g{}^*$ orbitals. In effect, the π interaction causes the Δ value for the complex to be greater than it would be if there were only σ interactions.

708 THE TRANSITION ELEMENTS

A second important case is the one in which the ligands possess only filled π orbitals of lower energy than the metal T_{2g} orbitals. As shown in Figure 26-29b, the interaction here destabilizes the T_{2g} orbitals relative to the E_g^* orbitals and thus diminishes the value of Δ. This is probably the situation in complexes of metal ions in their normal oxidation states, especially the lower ones, with the ligand atoms oxygen and fluorine.

There are also important cases in which the ligands have both empty and filled π orbitals. In some, such as the Cl^-, Br^- and I^- ions, these two types are not directly interrelated, the former being outer d orbitals and the latter valence shell p orbitals. In others, such as CO, CN^- and pyridine, the empty and filled π orbitals are the antibonding and bonding $p\pi$ orbitals. In such cases the net effect is the result of competition between the interaction of the two types of ligand π orbitals with the metal T_{2g} orbitals, and simple predictions are not easily made. Figure 26-30 shows a diagram for

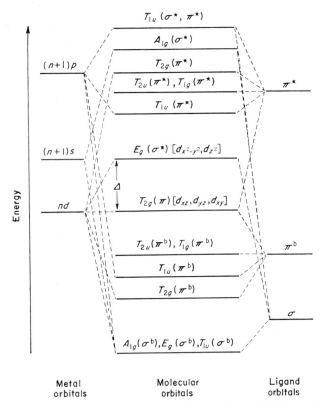

Fig. 26-30. A qualitative molecular orbital diagram for an $M(CO)_6$ or $[M(CN)_6]^{n-}$ compound. (Adapted from H. B. Gray and N. A. Beach, *J. Amer. Chem. Soc.*, **85**, 2922 (1963).)

octahedral metal cyano complexes and carbonyls which is based on some rough calculations of overlaps and comparisons with absorption spectra. While it has only a qualitative value, and even in this sense may not be entirely correct, most workers would probably consider it to be essentially correct for the group VI hexacarbonyls and cyano complexes of Fe^{II}, Ru^{II} and Os^{II}. However, the order of some of the MO's may well be changed by large changes in the metal orbital energies, as, for example, on going from a normal oxidation state of the metal to an unusually low or high one.

26-13. Quantitative Calculations.

In recent years considerable effort has been devoted to devising and testing schemes by which quantitative molecular orbital energy level diagrams might be obtained without excessive computation. Virtually all of this work has used the LCAO approximation together with the assumption that the energies of the MO's can be estimated from the magnitudes of the overlaps as explained earlier (page 85). The general approach was first described by Wolfsberg and Helmholz some years ago (1952) and is sometimes called the Wolfsberg–Helmholz method, but, in recognition of the importance of the postulated relationship between overlap integrals and energy integrals, which was first put forward by Mulliken, it might better be called the Mulliken–Wolfsberg–Helmholz (MWH) method.

There are, however, a number of possible variations of the MWH method, depending on how the values of certain initial parameters (orbital energies, radial wave functions, the proportionality factor relating overlaps to energies) are chosen, on the number of orbitals and overlaps included in the calculation, and on the manner in which initial parameters are permitted to vary during the calculation so as to lead to a final result which is "self-consistent," that is, so that the parameter values used in the final cycle of calculation are consistent with the electron distribution which is calculated in that cycle. The main steps in the MWH method, with some comments on the alternative procedures for handling the details, will now be sketched.[4-9]

[4] C. J. Ballhausen and H. B. Gray, *Molecular Orbital Theory*, Benjamin, New York, 1964, Chapter 8 and references therein. Note, however, that this presents a rather serene view of the problem and references 5–7 should also be consulted.

[5] R. F. Fenske and C. C. Sweeney, *Inorg. Chem.*, **3**, 1105 (1964).

[6] R. F. Fenske, *Inorg. Chem.*, **4**, 33 (1965).

[7] F. A. Cotton and T. E. Haas, *Inorg. Chem.*, **3**, 1004 (1964).

[8] W. E. Hatfield, H. D. Bedon and S. M. Horner, *Inorg. Chem.*, **4**, 1181 (1965).

[9] L. L. Lohr and W. N. Lipscomb, *Inorg. Chem.*, **2**, 911 (1963).

1. The ligand orbitals are combined into symmetry-correct combinations. The general nature of these combinations has been indicated already in Section 26-12. Although the form of the combinations of a given set of ligand orbitals is rigorously fixed by symmetry requirements, there have been some differences in the choice of ligand orbitals to be used. For instance, in some calculations the ligand s and p orbitals have been considered separately, whereas in other cases hybrids have been formed according to a reasonable but nonetheless questionable procedure, and only the $s–p$ hybrid which points toward the metal atom has been used to make a symmetry correct set of σ-type ligand orbital combinations. It has been shown that, other features of the calculation being kept invariant, good results are obtained with the double set of σ orbitals but not with the hybrid set in some cases, whereas, in others, the reverse is true. It is results like this which clearly indicate that the method is as yet far from a perfected and reliable instrument.

2. The overlaps are calculated. First, the overlaps between metal orbitals and individual ligand orbitals are calculated using, preferably, the best available wave functions, namely the Hartree or Hartree–Fock types, although for the heavier metal atoms these are not yet available. Then, using the expressions for the symmetry-correct combinations of ligand orbitals, the so-called group overlaps are calculated. These group overlaps are those between a ligand orbital combination as a whole and the metal orbital (or orbitals) with which it gives nonzero overlap. In some calculations the overlap of the ligand orbitals with one another is also considered.

3. The energies of the metal orbitals and the ligand orbital combinations are estimated. This is a complex and nonrigorous procedure, subject to numerous variations in the hands of different workers. For both metal and ligand orbitals, the energies vary with the state of ionization of the atoms and it is necessary to determine the required relationship, so that as the charge distribution varies through successive cycles of calculation (see step 6), the energies may be appropriately reassigned. The rate of variation of energy of an orbital with state of ionization is, however, difficult to estimate accurately, because *in a molecule* it does not vary as it would in the free atom. Instead, it varies less, but a quantitative relationship can be only roughly estimated.

4. The values of the integrals of the type

$$\int \psi_i \mathscr{H} \Sigma_i \, d\tau$$

where ψ_i and Σ_i represent, respectively, a metal orbital and a combination of ligand orbitals with the same symmetry, are evaluated by assuming that they are proportional to the corresponding overlap integrals times the mean energy of the overlapping orbitals and times a proportionality constant. The constant has usually been taken as 2.00, but the possibilities that it should be varied with orbital type (i.e., σ or π) and perhaps from one metal to another have been suggested in certain cases.

5. An initial charge distribution is chosen, the orbital energies and the interaction energies are calculated and the secular equation is solved to give the energies and the compositions (i.e., metal and ligand orbital coefficients) of the molecular orbitals. The choice of initial charge distribution is such that the metal ion carries only a small charge, say, ca $+0.5$, since experience shows that the final cycle of calculation (see next step) will lead to only a small net charge on the metal, whatever its *formal* oxidation state.

6. With the results of the preceding step, electrons are assigned to the MO's and, using a method of "population analysis" due to Mulliken, the net charge on each atom is assessed. If these differ from the charge distribution initially assumed, steps 5 and 6 are repeated using the new charge distribution (or a compromise between this and the original one). Once again, if a discrepancy between the assumed and calculated charge distribution is found, another cycle of steps 5 and 6 is carried out. This practice is repeated until only a negligible difference is obtained.

Aside from the difficulty that many arbitrary choices are necessary in executing an MWH calculation, and that there is as yet no general agreement on the optimum set of choices, the MWH method may well suffer from other more profound difficulties. Among these, are (1) the likelihood that it overestimates the degree of covalence, particularly in the π bonding, and (2) the fact that some overlaps which it usually ignores, on the grounds that physically they should not be important, actually have very considerable magnitudes. Finally, even when a calculation has been completed direct application of the results is hampered by the fact that electron–electron interactions must still be considered.

However, despite the foregoing difficulties and uncertainties, the MWH method has enough attractive features for it to certainly continue to be studied, used and, hopefully, gradually improved. It should be clearly recognized, however, that at present it would be a grave error to use it blindly or overconfidently. The watch-word, on the contrary, should be circumspection.

26-14. Some Further Remarks

Nonoctahedral Complexes. The molecular orbital treatment can be applied to other classes of complexes—planar, tetrahedral, linear, etc.—but the simplicity of the energy level diagrams is rapidly lost as we proceed to the less symmetric situations. The same loss of simplicity also occurs in ligand field theory.

Even for tetrahedral complexes, the analysis becomes more complicated because there is no center of symmetry to keep various kinds of orbitals symmetrically distinct from one another. For instance, the three p orbitals and the three d orbitals, d_{xy}, d_{yz} and d_{zx}, are in the same symmetry class in a tetrahedral complex and thus they mix with one another. Obviously, this makes it harder to produce simple predictions from simple considerations.

Suffice it to say that it would be beyond the scope of our objectives in this book to treat any other types of complex in any detail. In Table 26-5, however, are summarized some useful facts about the bonding capabilities of various metal orbitals in several types of complex.

TABLE 26-5

Bonding Capabilities of Metal Atom Orbitals in Some Relatively Symmetrical Complexes

Stereochemistry	σ orbitals	π orbitals	Notes
Linear, LML	s, p_z	p_x, p_y d_{xz}, d_{yz}	z axis is molecular axis
Tetrahedral, ML$_4$	s, p_x, p_y, p_z s, d_{xy}, d_{xz}, d_{yz}	d_{z^2}, $d_{x^2-y^2}$; d_{xy}, d_{xz}, d_{yz} d_{z^2}, $d_{x^2-y^2}$; p_x, p_y, p_z	Axes as in Figure 26-5
Square, ML$_4$	$d_{x^2-y^2}$, s, p_x, p_y $d_{x^2-y^2}$, d_{z^2}, p_x, p_y	p_z, d_{xz}, d_{yz}	z axis is perpendicular to plane
Trigonal bipyramid, ML$_5$	s, p_x, p_y, p_z, d_{z^2}	p_x, p_y, p_z; $d_{x^2-y^2}$, d_{xy}; d_{xz}, d_{yz}	z axis is the three-fold axis

Square Complexes of d^8 Ions. It is notable that d^8 ions have a pronounced tendency to form square complexes, even though there are no Jahn–Teller forces operating in an octahedral d^8 complex. This means that even though small tetragonal distortions of the octahedron are not favored, the complete removal of two *trans* ligands to leave a square four-coordinated complex (or at least a very *great* lengthening of two *trans* bonds) is often favored, depending on the properties of the ligands. Also, the tendency to form square complexes is far greater for Pd^{II} and Pt^{II} than for Ni^{II}. For the two heavier metals no *regular* octahedral complexes are known at all; moreover, the tetrahalo complexes of Pd^{II} and Pt^{II} are square while those of nickel are tetrahedral.

In order to explain why a complex with only four metal–ligand bonds is more stable than one with six, we must look for factors peculiar to the square complex but not to an octahedral one which contribute to its stability. The most likely ones are the following:

(1) *Increased σ bond strength in the square complex.* In both octahedral and square complexes, the $d_{x^2-y^2}$ orbital, or, more exactly, the MO which has the largest amount of $d_{x^2-y^2}$ character, is strongly antibonding with respect to the four ligands in the xy plane. In the square complexes, this orbital is empty; thus there is an increase in σ bond strength which contributes to the stability of the four-coordinate compound, although this contribution must be somewhat diminished by the pairing energy in going from a $d_{z^2}{}^1 d_{x^2-y^2}{}^1$ to a $d_{z^2}{}^2 d_{x^2-y^2}{}^0$ configuration. In addition, the d_{z^2} orbital, which is not needed for binding ligands along the z axis can now be hybridized with the s orbital to provide a greater contribution to the in-plane σ bonding, while the pair of nonbonding electrons occupies the hybrid orbital which is concentrated *mainly above and below* the molecular plane.

(2) *Increased π bond strength in the square complex.* By means of the d_{xz}, d_{yz} and p_z orbitals, a higher degree of metal–ligand out-of-plane π bonding can be established in square complexes than in the octahedral ones. Presumably this factor is particularly important for the heavier elements due to the ability of their more extended orbitals to overlap better with ligand π orbitals.

In the case of Ni^{II}, it has been found in several cases that the metal–ligand bonds in square complexes are 0.15–0.20 A shorter than those in comparable octahedral complexes, in agreement with point (1) above. As for metal–ligand π bonding in square complexes of Pd^{II} and Pt^{II}, the experimental evidence (Section 30-H-1) indicates that it is quite extensive.

Charge Transfer Spectra. When the absorption of radiation causes an electronic transition between two molecular orbitals such that one is more heavily concentrated on one atom while the other is more heavily concentrated on a different atom, we speak of this as a charge transfer transition and the plot of absorption versus wavelength of light as a charge transfer band or spectrum. The actual degree of charge transfer can, of course, vary from the almost negligible to the almost complete, and transitions so classified are found in many classes of compound. We wish here only to note very briefly that for metal complexes there are often charge transfer bands occurring in the ultraviolet region. They are generally far more intense than the d–d bands considered previously, and often even the low energy wing of a strong charge transfer band in the ultraviolet will extend far enough into the visible region to obscure d–d transitions. General types which are known to occur in the near ultraviolet part of the spectrum (from about 1800 to 4000 A) are:

1. Those in which electrons from σ bonding orbitals are excited to empty T_{2g} or $E_g{}^*$ orbitals. Since the former are predominantly ligand orbitals and the latter mainly metal orbitals, these transitions transfer charge from ligand to metal.

23*

2. Those in which electrons from filled π orbitals localized mainly on the ligands are excited to the $E_g{}^*$, $A_{1g}{}^*$ or $T_{1u}{}^*$ orbitals. Again transfer of charge is from ligand to metal.

3. Those in which electrons from bonding σ orbitals are excited to vacant π orbitals localized predominantly on the ligands. In these the charge transfer is modest and from metal to ligand.

Charge transfer bands cannot of course be interpreted using CFT, or even ACFT. The MO approach is required, but because of the difficulties in making quantitative calculations, most of the attempts to assign or interpret charge transfer bands have been of a qualitative or empirical nature. For halo complexes rather extensive correlations have been made leading to a set of so-called optical electronegativities of the metals in their several oxidation states.

26-15. The Valence Bond Method

This approach, which was widely used by chemists until the advent of ligand field theory, originated shortly after the formulation of wave mechanics, largely through the efforts of L. Pauling. It may be considered as a direct attempt to invest the Lewis–Langmuir–Sidgwick ideas of the coordinate bond with quantum mechanical validity. Today it is still useful for some qualitative explanations of stereochemistry, magnetic properties, etc., and since so much of the literature on coordination chemistry from about 1935 until the late 1950's uses its concepts and terminology, it is necessary that a brief summary be given and that its relationship to the more useful theories already described be indicated.

In its application to an octahedral complex it takes the following form. Each of the ligands is considered as the donor of an electron pair to the metal ion. In order to accept these six electron pairs, the metal ion must have available a set of six equivalent σ orbitals with their lobes directed toward the apices of an octahedron. As we have already seen (page 79), such a set of orbitals may be constructed out of s, p and d atomic orbitals in only one way, namely, by hybridizing the following group of orbitals: s, p_x, p_y, p_z, $d_{x^2-y^2}$, d_{z^2}.

For a complex such as $[Cr(NH_3)_6]^{3+}$, the following sort of diagram is then drawn:

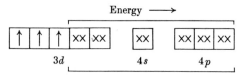

This is intended to convey the following information:

1. It shows, in an entirely qualitative manner, that the order of the energies of the valence shell orbitals is $4p > 4s > 3d$.

2. It indicates that a set of d^2sp^3 hybrid orbitals has been formed and that these are occupied by electron pairs (xx) donated by the six NH_3 ligands.

3. It shows that three of the d orbitals remain to be occupied by the three $3d$ electrons and that this occurs in accordance with Hund's first rule (maximum number of unpaired spins). It thus predicts that there will be paramagnetism due to three unpaired electrons—which is, of course, correct.

Suppose that we now apply this treatment to $[Co(NH_3)_6]^{3+}$. Since the Co^{3+} ion has six $3d$ electrons, which, following Hund's rule, occupy the orbitals in the following way:

it is evident that the required d^2sp^3 hybrid orbitals cannot be constructed until the necessary two d orbitals are cleared. What is to become of the two electrons removed from them? One possibility is that they be promoted to the next lowest orbitals above the $4p$ orbitals, these being either the $4d$ or $5s$ orbitals, probably the latter. The other alternative is to put them into two of the other $3d$ orbitals; the energy opposing this is twice the average pairing energy for this configuration. Enough was known years ago of the approximate values of the energies required to dispose of the two electrons in each of these two ways to indicate quite surely that the latter way would be the more likely. Accordingly, the following diagram of the electron distribution is obtained:

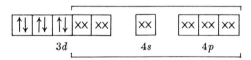

Thus the prediction is made that the $[Co(NH_3)_6]^{3+}$ ion should have no unpaired electrons, and this is correct.

It is evident, however, that it will also be predicted that *all* octahedral complexes of Co^{III} must be diamagnetic. Although virtually every known cobalt(III) complex is diamagnetic, there is at least one indubitable exception, namely, the $[CoF_6]^{3-}$ ion. In this, the Co^{III} has four unpaired electrons just as it does in the free state. In order to account for this, it was proposed that here the metal–ligand bonds are ionic, not covalent as in other cases, and that the d orbitals need not, therefore, be disturbed.

Although this ionic bond postulate might be considered acceptable in the case of $[CoF_6]^{3-}$, there are other cases where its credibility becomes strained. The octahedral complexes of Ni^{II}, which has eight d electrons, provide a good illustration here. With only one possible exception, all of these are paramagnetic (two unpaired electrons) as is the free Ni^{II} ion:

3d   4s   4p

Now, aside from the energetically unacceptable assumption that two $3d$ electrons are promoted to the $4d$ orbitals, the only apparent explanation for the paramagnetism is to assume that all of the octahedral complexes of nickel(II), for example, $[Ni(H_2O)_6]^{2+}$, $[Ni(NH_3)_6]^{2+}$, $[Ni(o\text{-phen})_3]^{2+}$, $[Ni(en)_3]^{2+}$, are ionic. This hardly seems believable, and in the early 1950's another alternative was proposed, namely, that the d^2sp^3 set was made up, using $4d$ (so-called "outer" d) orbitals, thus leaving the $3d$ electrons unaffected. It then became fashionable to speak of high-spin complexes as "outer orbital complexes" rather than "ionic complexes" and low-spin complexes as "inner orbital complexes" rather than "covalent complexes."

Let us now compare this theory with the molecular orbital theory. It is evident that the VB method considers only those orbitals which are identified in MO theory as the bonding σ MO's and the metal d orbitals of the T_{2g} set; it ignores the existence of all of the antibonding orbitals. Therefore, whenever there are more electrons present than can be accommodated in the bonding σ MO's and the T_{2g} d orbitals, it becomes necessary either to introduce the *ad hoc* assumption of ionic bonding or the unsupported postulate of "outer orbital" hybridization.

In addition to its *ad hoc* and artificial prescriptions as to the nature of the bonds, there are various other grounds for regarding the VB treatment of transition metal complexes as generally less useful than CFT or MO theory. The major ones are:

1. Because, in its usual form, it pays no attention to the existence of excited states, let alone their energies, it offers no explanation at all for the spectra of complexes.

2. It offers no possibility of predicting or explaining magnetic behavior beyond the level of specifying numbers of unpaired electrons.

COMPARISON OF THEORIES

26-16. Comparison of the CFT and MO Methods

To make the comparison of the crystal field and molecular orbital treatments more concrete, let us consider, for example, the particular case of the ferrous ion, Fe^{2+}, which is a d^6 system, in the hexammine ion, $[Fe(NH_3)_6]^{2+}$.

The MO treatment tells us that the $3d_{z^2}$, $3d_{x^2-y^2}$, $4s$, $4p_x$, $4p_y$ and $4p_z$ orbitals of the ferrous ion combine with the appropriate symmetry orbitals made up from the σ orbitals of the six ammonia molecules. The six electron pairs which occupied the σ orbitals of the individual ammonia molecules before they entered into the $[Fe(NH_3)_6]^{2+}$ ion now occupy the six bonding σ MO'S. But, as noted, these will be mainly ligand orbitals in character. The six d electrons of the ferrous ion now find that the lowest unoccupied molecular orbitals are, in order of increasing energy, T_{2g}, $E_g{}^*$, $A_{1g}{}^*$, $T_{1u}{}^*$. As indicated in Figure 26-27, the last two types are of very high energy relative to the T_{2g} and $E_g{}^*$ orbitals and, so far as we know, are never occupied in the ground states of real complexes. The six d electrons must therefore arrange themselves in the T_{2g} and $E_g{}^*$ orbitals. Thus we finally arrive at the same problem as the one treated in connection with crystal field and ligand field theory, namely, how will the d electrons be distributed among the d orbitals (or nearly pure d orbitals) of the metal ion when it is surrounded by six ligands at the apices of an octahedron?

In summary, we may say that CFT (and ACFT) focuses attention entirely on the metal ion d orbitals, saying nothing at all as to the behavior of the other metal orbitals and the ligand orbitals. It will be clear that so long as we deal with complexes where the metal–ligand interactions are not so extensive as seriously to mix metal and ligand orbitals, this procedure will not be unreasonable. Moreover, we need not be too concerned that the splitting of the d orbitals is attributed exclusively to electrostatic inter-actions in the crystal field theory, whereas the molecular orbital theory shows that the origin of the splitting is more complex. After all, we do not attempt to calculate Δ from first principles in using the crystal field theory: we only consider how its magnitude will influence the properties of the system.

References

Ballhausen, C. J., *Introduction to Ligand Field Theory*, McGraw-Hill, New York, 1962. The best book for the inorganic chemist who wants to learn the quantitative aspects of LFT. Also contains an excellent review of experimental data.

Dunitz, J. D., and L. E. Orgel, *Adv. Inorg. Chem. Radiochem.*, **2**, 1 (1960). Effects of electronic structures on molecular structures.

Dunn, T. M., in J. Lewis and R. G. Wilkins, eds., *Modern Coordination Chemistry*, Interscience, New York–London, 1960, p. 229. Survey of LFT.

Figgis, B. N., *Introduction to Ligand Fields*, Wiley, London, 1966.

George, P., and D. S. McClure, *Progr. Inorg. Chem.*, **1**, 38 (1959). Effects of crystal field splittings on thermodynamic properties of compounds.

Gray, H. B., *J. Chem. Educ.*, **41**, 2 (1964). Qualitative outline of the MO approach.

Griffith, J. S., *The Theory of Transition Metal Ions*, Cambridge University Press, 1961. A comprehensive mathematical treatise.

Jørgensen, C. K., *Absorption Spectra and Chemical Bonding in Complexes*, Pergamon, London, 1961.

———, *Progr. Inorg. Chem.*, **4**, 23 (1962). Authoritative article on nephelauxetic effects.

McClure, D. S., *Solid State Phys.*, **9**, 399 (1959).

Moffitt, W., and C. J. Ballhausen, *Ann. Rev. Phys. Chem.*, **7**, 107 (1956). Review of CFT.

Nyholm, R. S., *Proc. Chem. Soc.*, **1961**, 273. Electron configurations of transition metal elements.

Orgel, L. E., *An Introduction to Transition Metal Chemistry, Ligand Field Theory*, John Wiley, New York, 1960. A comprehensive, non-mathematical introduction to LFT.

———, *Quart. Rev.*, **9**, 422 (1954). Charge transfer spectra and some related phenomena.

27

Complexes of π-Acceptor (π-Acid) Ligands

A characteristic feature of the d-group transition metals is their ability to form complexes with a variety of neutral molecules such as carbon monoxide, isocyanides, substituted phosphines, arsines, stibines or sulfides, nitric oxide, various molecules with delocalized π orbitals, such as pyridine, 2,2-dipyridyl, 1,10-phenanthrolene and with certain ligands containing 1,2-dithioketone or 1,2-dithiolene groups, such as the dithiomaleonitrile anion. Certain platinum metals can also form complexes where the trichlorostannite ion, $SnCl_3^-$, is a ligand. Very diverse types of complex exist, ranging from binary molecular compounds such as $Cr(CO)_6$ or $Ni(PF_3)_4$ through mixed species such as $Co(CO)_3NO$ and $(C_6H_5)_3PFe(CO)_4$, to complex ions like $[Fe(CN)_5CO]^{3-}$, $[Mo(CO)_5I]^-$, $[Mn(CNR)_6]^+$, $[V\,phen_3]^+$ and $\{Ni[S_2C_2(CN)_2]_2\}^{2-}$.

In many of these complexes, the metal atoms are in low-positive, zero or low-negative oxidation states. It is a characteristic of the ligands now under discussion that they can stabilize low oxidation states; this property is associated with the fact that the donor atoms of these ligands possess vacant orbitals in addition to lone-pairs. These vacant orbitals accept electron density from filled metal orbitals to form a type of π bonding which supplements the σ bonding arising from lone-pair donation; high electron density on the metal atom—of necessity in low oxidation states—can thus be delocalized on to the ligands. The ability of ligands to accept electron density into low-lying empty π orbitals can be called π *acidity*, the word acidity being used in the Lewis sense.

There are many unsaturated organic molecules and ions capable of forming more or less stable complexes with transition metals in low oxidation states besides those to be discussed in this chapter. There are the ones which form the so-called π *complexes*: they will be discussed in the following chapter. The separation is justified, because there is a qualitative difference in the bonding, from a structural standpoint. The ligands

719

discussed here form bonds to the metal using σ orbitals and exercise their π acidity using π orbitals whose nodal planes include the axis of the σ bond. In π complexes, on the other hand, both donation and back-acceptance by the ligand are accomplished by use of ligand π orbitals. For the π complexes, therefore, the metal atom lies out of the molecular plane of the ligand, whereas for the complexes discussed here the metal lies along the axes of linear ligands or in the plane of the planar ones.

We can note at this point that the stoichiometries of many, though not all, of the complexes can be predicted by use of the *noble-gas formalism*. This requires that the number of valence electrons possessed by the metal atom plus the number of pairs of σ electrons contributed by the ligands be equal to the number of electrons in the succeeding noble-gas atom.

As explained later, this is simply a phenomenological way of formulating the tendency of the metal atom to use its valence orbitals, nd, $(n + 1)s$ and $(n + 1)p$, as fully as possible, in forming bonds to ligands. While it is of considerable utility in the design of new compounds, particularly of metal carbonyls, nitrosyls and isonitriles, and their substitution products, it is by no means infallible. It fails altogether for the dipyridyl and dithio-olefin type ligands and there are numerous exceptions even among carbonyls, such as $V(CO)_6$ and the stable $[M(CO)_2(diphos)_2]^+$ (M = Mo, W) ions.[1]

In general these compounds have to be prepared by indirect methods from other compounds although it is sometimes possible to combine metal and ligand directly.[2] Ni is most reactive, combining directly with CO, CH_3PCl_2 and 1,2-bis(diethylphosphino)benzene. Co and Pd also combine with the latter and the metals Fe, Co, Mo, W, Rh and Ru will also combine with CO, but with the exceptions of Ni and Fe the reactions are too sluggish to be of practical value.

CARBON MONOXIDE COMPLEXES

The most important π-acceptor ligand is carbon monoxide. Many of its complexes are of considerable structural interest as well as of importance industrially and in catalytic and other reactions. Carbonyl derivatives of at least one type are known for all of the transition metals with the exception of Zr and Hf, and it is possible that carbonyls of these elements will be made in due course.

27-1. Binary Molecular Metal Carbonyls

The important binary carbonyls, together with some of their properties, are listed in Table 27-1. The compounds are all hydrophobic and are

[1] J. Lewis and R. Whyman, *J. Chem. Soc.*, **1965**, 5486.
[2] J. Chatt, F. A. Hart and D. T. Rosevear, *J. Chem. Soc.*, **1961**, 5504.

TABLE 27-1

The More Important Binary Carbonyls[a]

Compound	Color and form	Melting point, °C	Comments
$V(CO)_6$	Black crystals	Decomposes at 70; sublimes *in vacuo*	Paramagnetic (1e); yellow-orange in solution; Na gives $V(CO)_6^-$
$Cr(CO)_6$ $Mo(CO)_6$ $W(CO)_6$	Colorless crystals	Sublime *in vacuo*	Octahedral; stable in air, soluble in organic solvents; decompose at 180–200°
$Mn_2(CO)_{10}$	Golden crystals	154–155; sublimes *in vacuo*	Slowly oxidized in air, especially in solution. Metal–metal bond cleaved by Na in THF giving green $Mn(CO)_5^-$; halogens give $Mn(CO)_5X$
$Re_2(CO)_{10}$	Colorless crystals	177; sublimes *in vacuo*	Stable in air, otherwise similar to $Mn_2(CO)_{10}$. $Tc_2(CO)_{10}$ is similar
$Fe(CO)_5$	Yellow liquid	–20; b 103	Ultraviolet on petrol solution gives $Fe_2(CO)_9$
$Fe_2(CO)_9$	Bronze mica-like platelets	Decomposes at 100	Nonvolatile; almost insoluble in organic solvents
$Fe_3(CO)_{12}$	Dark green crystals	Decomposes at ~140; sublimes *in vacuo* with decomposition	Soluble in organic solvents; more chemically reactive than $Fe(CO)_5$
$Co_2(CO)_8$	Orange crystals	51; sublimes *in vacuo*	Air sensitive; particularly in solution; decomposes at m.p. to $Co_4(CO)_{12}$ (black crystals; decompose at 60°)
$Ni(CO)_4$	Colorless liquid	–25; b 43	Toxic with musty smell; burns readily and decomposes to metal readily

[a] Less well-studied carbonyls are $Ru(CO)_5$ and $Os(CO)_5$. X-ray studies show that the $Os_2(CO)_9$ and $Ru_2(CO)_9$ reported in the literature are trinuclear species with formula $[M(CO)_4]_3$; other polynuclear carbonyls are $Co_4(CO)_{12}$ and $Rh_6(CO)_{16}$. The iridium carbonyls are of uncertain structure at present. A number of bimetallic carbonyls are known, e.g., $(CO)_5MnRe(CO)_5$ and $(CO)_5ReCo(CO)_4$.

inflammable liquids or readily combustible solids; with some exceptions they are soluble in nonpolar organic solvents. Vanadium carbonyl is rather air sensitive and so are the cobalt carbonyls, but the other carbonyls are fairly stable in air, especially the group VI and rhenium carbonyls. The liquids $Fe(CO)_5$ and $Ni(CO)_4$ must be handled with caution since they are highly toxic and their vapors can form explosive mixtures with air; they can be readily destroyed by bromine in an organic solvent.

Preparation. The preparative methods for carbonyls are numerous and varied. Only nickel tetracarbonyl and iron pentacarbonyl can be prepared by direct interaction of the finely divided reactive metal with carbon monoxide. Nickel carbonyl can be obtained at normal temperature and pressure. Since the reaction

$$Ni + 4CO = Ni(CO)_4$$

is reversible, the carbonyl decomposing readily on warming, it provides a method for obtaining very pure nickel. This method, which was developed by Mond, the discoverer of this first carbonyl, is now operated only at Clydach in South Wales. Iron pentacarbonyl is obtained only by using elevated temperatures and pressures.

Dicobalt octacarbonyl is prepared by the reaction at 250–300 atm pressure and 120–200°:

$$2CoCO_3 + 2H_2 + 8CO = Co_2(CO)_8 + 2CO_2 + 2H_2O$$

Other binary carbonyls are made from the metal halides. The general method is to treat them, usually in suspension in an organic solvent, such as tetrahydrofuran, with carbon monoxide at 200–300 atm pressure and temperatures up to 300° in presence of a reducing agent. A variety of reducing agents have been employed—electropositive metals like Na, Al or Mg, trialkyl aluminums, copper or the sodium ketyl of benzophenone (Ph_2CONa). The detailed course of the reactions is not well known, but when organometallic reducing agents are employed it is likely that unstable organo derivatives of the transition metal are formed as intermediates. Vanadium carbonyl is most easily obtained by the reaction:

$$VCl_3 + CO + Na \text{ (excess)} \xrightarrow[120° \, 5000 \, psi]{diglyme} [Na \text{ diglyme}_2][V(CO)_6] \xrightarrow[\text{then sublime } 50°]{H_3PO_4} V(CO)_6$$

Rhenium and technetium carbonyls can be obtained by the direct reaction under very high pressure of CO and the heptoxides or the potassium salt of the oxo anion. Since the carbon monoxide in $Fe(CO)_5$ is labile, exchange reactions can occur and the group VI carbonyls can be obtained from interaction of $Fe(CO)_5$ and their halides.

The binuclear carbonyl $Fe_2(CO)_9$ is obtained as orange mica-like plates by photolysis of $Fe(CO)_5$ in hydrocarbon solvents. The green $Fe_3(CO)_{12}$

is best made by acidification of a polynuclear carbonylate anion (see later) which in turn is obtained from $Fe(CO)_5$ by the action of organic amines such as triethylamine.

The bimetallic carbonyls are generally obtained by the method used for the first known example, $\pi\text{-}C_5H_5(CO)_3MoW(CO)_3\pi\text{-}C_5H_5$, namely, the interaction of a carbonyl halide with the sodium salt of a carbonylate anion (see later discussion).

Structures of Metal Carbonyls. The CO molecule is known to fulfil three different structural functions, as shown in Figure 27-1. Terminal CO

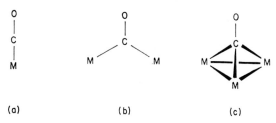

(a)   (b)   (c)

Fig. 27-1. The three types of metal–CO linkages: (a) terminal CO group; (b) doubly, or ketonic, bridging CO; (c) triply bridging CO. The various lines are drawn mainly to guide the eye and indicate the usual position of bonds but they are not intended to indicate the order of bonds.

groups are most common. Although there is direct evidence in only a few cases, there seems no doubt that they contain M—C and not M—O bonds. There is direct evidence in scores of cases that the M—C—O groups are linear. The ketonic, or doubly bridging, CO group occurs quite frequently in polynuclear carbonyls, but the triply bridging type has been found in only a few compounds. Metal–metal bonds also play an important part in the structures of the polynuclear carbonyls, some of which are good examples of metal atom cluster compounds.

The bonding in metal carbonyls will be discussed in detail after the structures have been reviewed. However, in order to consider structural relationships one aspect of the bonding problem must be established. The metal atoms have nine valence orbitals (nd^5, $(n + 1)s$, $(n + 1)p^3$) and in metal carbonyls and related compounds they show a strong tendency to utilize all of them in forming bonds. Purely for simplicity and not as an attempt to describe the actual electron distribution, we may assume that in a terminal MCO group, the CO donates 2 electrons to an empty metal orbital, while in a bridging M(CO)M group we assume that each M—C bond is formed by one metal electron and one carbon electron. Thus in $Fe(CO)_5$, five orbitals are used for the Fe—C σ bonds, the electrons of which "originate" in the CO groups, while the remaining four orbitals contain "Fe electrons" which are also used in π bonding. Because the terminal CO groups bring electrons in pairs, when the metal atom initially has an odd number of electrons (Mn, Co, for example), any mononuclear species, $M(CO)_n$, will still have an unpaired electron. In order to use this in bonding, the $M(CO)_n$ unit almost invariably combines with another to give a metal–metal bond. The sole exception is $V(CO)_6$, where steric factors may prevent dimerization. The above argument as to the utilization of all metal valence orbitals in bonds is, in effect, an explanatory reformulation of the "noble gas formalism" alluded to earlier.

Mononuclear Carbonyls. The characterized ones are listed in Table 27-2, together with the available structural data. The three structural types, octahedral, trigonal bipyramidal and tetrahedral, will be encountered

TABLE 27-2

Structures of Mononuclear Carbonyls

Compound	Structure	M—C bond lengths, Å[a]
$V(CO)_6$	Octahedral (?)	—
$Cr(CO)_6$	Octahedral	1.92 ± 0.04
$Mo(CO)_6$	Octahedral	2.06 ± 0.02[b]
$W(CO)_6$	Octahedral	2.06 ± 0.04[b]
$Fe(CO)_5$	Trigonal bipyramid[c]	1.797 ± 0.015(axial); 1.842 ± 0.015(trig.)
$Ni(CO)_4$	Tetrahedral	1.84 ± 0.04

[a] The intervals are standard deviations; the true value is about 70% certain to be within this range and about 99% certain to be within 3 times this range.

[b] See ref. 11 for discussion of $Mo(CO)_6$. The distance for $W(CO)_6$ may be even less reliable than indicated.

[c] Electron diffraction; M. I. Davis and H. P. Hanson, *J. Phys. Chem.*, **69**, 3405 (1965); C—O $= 1.136 \pm 0.003$Å. These authors also discuss the axial–trigonal bond differences in terms of MO theory.

repeatedly among derivatives of these carbonyls and in iso-electronic species, e.g., carbonylate anions, carbonyl halides, nitrosyls, etc., to be discussed below.

Binuclear Carbonyls. Several important structures are shown in Figure 27-2. The $Mn_2(CO)_{10}$ structure is also found in $Tc_2(CO)_{10}$ and $Re_2(CO)_{10}$. These dimers are held together by the metal–metal bonds alone, without help from bridging CO groups. In $Fe_2(CO)_9$, on the other hand, doubly bridging CO groups are present, but there is also an Fe—Fe bond since the molecule has no unpaired electrons and the Fe—Fe distance is quite short. $Co_2(CO)_8$ in the crystalline state has a structure which is essentially the same as that of $Fe_2(CO)_9$ with one one bridging CO group missing. The two electrons contributed by a bridging CO group are now unnecessary since each Co atom already has one more electron than an iron atom. The diamagnetism of the $Co_2(CO)_8$ molecule and the closeness of the Co atoms show that again there is a metal–metal bond.

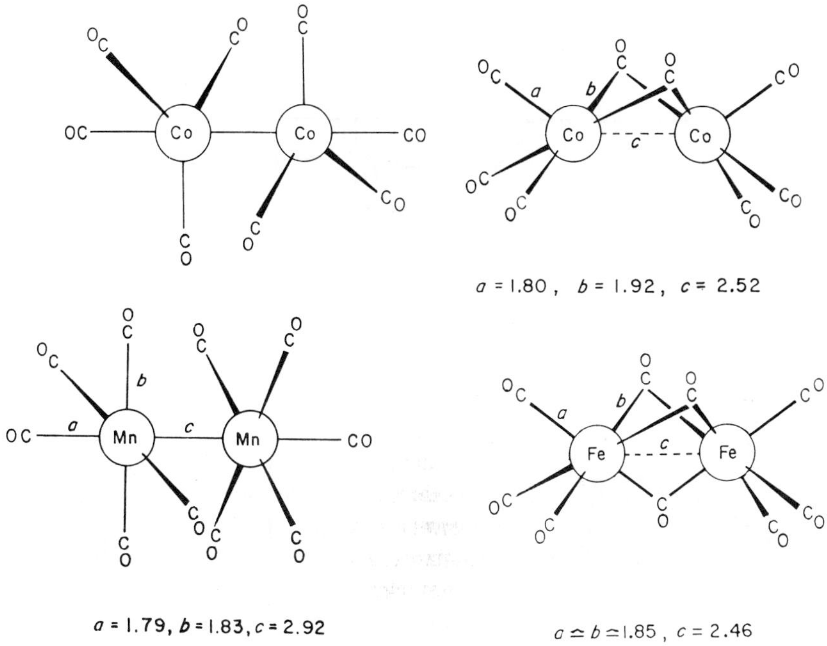

$a = 1.80$, $b = 1.92$, $c = 2.52$

$a = 1.79$, $b = 1.83$, $c = 2.92$ $a \simeq b \simeq 1.85$, $c = 2.46$

Fig. 27-2. The structures of some binuclear carbonyls; that of $Co_2(CO)_8$ in the crystalline state was only recently described (G. G. Summer, M. P. Klug and L. E. Alexander, *Acta Cryst.*, **17**, 732 (1964)). Note the staggered configuration (D_{4d} symmetry) for $Mn_2(CO)_{10}$ and also for $Fe_2(CO)_9$(D_{3h} symmetry). The non-bridged structure for $Co_2(CO)_8$ in solution is deduced from infrared spectra.

One might well wonder why the $M_2(CO)_{10}$ molecules dimerize without bridges while $Co_2(CO)_8$ has bridges. There is no qualitative reason why a bridged structure for the former, say, $(OC)_4M(CO)_2M(CO)_4$ (with an M—M bond), should be unstable nor is there any qualitative reason why a non-bridged structure, as shown in Figure 27-2 for $Co_2(CO)_8$ should not be stable enough to exist. In fact, the latter structure, of D_{3d} symmetry, evidently does exist[3] in equilibrium with the bridged structure in solution. Moreover the substituted cobalt carbonyls, $Co_2(CO)_7(PPh_3)$[4] and $Co_2(CO)_6(PPh_3)_2$[5] also appear to have nonbridged structures, but derived from that proposed for the unsubstituted carbonyl.

[3] K. Noack, *Helv. Chim. Acta*, **47**, 1555 (1964).
[4] G. Bor and L. Markó, *Chem. and Ind.*, **1963**, 912.
[5] O. Vohler, *Chem. Ber.*, **91**, 1235 (1958).

Trinuclear and Higher Polynuclear Carbonyls. For a trinuclear molecule either a linear or a cyclic structure might be expected. For $Os_3(CO)_{12}$, the cyclic (D_{3h}) structure without bridges is unequivocal (Fig. 27-3a).[6] This substance is the one long considered to be $Os_2(CO)_9$ and

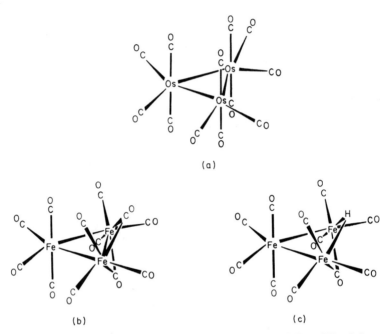

Fig. 27-3. (a) The trinuclear structure of $Os_3(CO)_{12}$ with which $Ru_3(CO)_{12}$ is isomorphous. (b) The proposed structure for $Fe_3(CO)_{12}$ based on analogy with that of (c) the anion in $[Et_3NH][HFe_3(CO)_{11}]$. Note that both (b) and (c) can be regarded as being derived from $Fe_2(CO)_9$ by substitution of one bridging CO group by $Fe(CO)_4$ in the former, and of a second by H^- in the latter.

there is now no evidence that $Os_2(CO)_9$ exists, although it may. $Ru_3(CO)_{12}$ is similar.

The structure of $Fe_3(CO)_{12}$ has presented a difficult problem. A linear structure was first proposed on the basis of IR spectra and an incomplete X-ray study appeared to support this. Later X-ray work seemed to require a cyclic structure, although crystal disorder prevented location of the CO groups. More recently, Mössbauer spectra (see page 847) and further IR studies were interpreted in favor of the linear model. Although full confirmation is still lacking, a structure proposed[7] on the basis of analogy with

[6] E. R. Corey and L. F. Dahl, *Inorg. Chem.*, **1**, 521 (1962).
[7] L. F. Dahl and J. F. Blount, *Inorg. Chem.*, **4**, 1373 (1965).

the known structure of the hydridocarbonylate ion $[HFe_3(CO)_{11}]^-$ appears to satisfy existing data. The two structures are shown in Figure 27–3b and c. They are both derived from the structure of $Fe_2(CO)_9$ by replacing one of the bridging CO groups by a *cis*-$Fe(CO)_4$ group; in $[HFe_3(CO)_{11}]^-$ a second CO group is replaced by a symmetrically bridging hydrogen atom (see later). This proposal for $Fe_3(CO)_{12}$ accommodates the solid state IR spectrum which shows stretches for both bridging and nonbridging CO's. Also it satisfies the Mössbauer spectrum[8] which showed that there were two types of Fe atom present; two atoms showed substantial quadrupole splitting and had shifts similar to the atoms in $Fe_2(CO)_9$ while the other had little splitting as expected for an octahedral environment.

Cobalt forms a tetranuclear carbonyl, $Co_4(CO)_{12}$, which contains a tetrahedron of Co atoms. In the crystal[9a] there is one $Co(CO)_3$ and three $Co(CO)_2$ groups with ketonic bridges on three edges, whereas infrared study indicates that in solution[9b] the structure is that shown in Figure 27-4a.

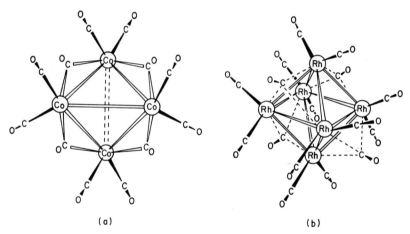

(a)   (b)

Fig. 27-4. (a) The D_{2d} structure proposed for $Co_4(CO)_{12}$ in solution on the basis of its infrared spectrum. (b) The structure (symmetry T_d) of $Rh_6(CO)_{16}$ determined entirely by X-ray crystallography.

Rhodium forms a polynuclear carbonyl, $Rh_6(CO)_{16}$, with the structure[10] shown in Figure 27-4b. It consists of an octahedron of Rh atoms with two terminal CO groups on each and triply bridging CO groups on four of the eight octahedral faces. Another compound that is known to

[8] N. E. Ericksen and A. W. Fairhall, *Inorg. Chem.*, **4**, 1320 (1965).
[9a] L. F. Dahl, private communication.
[9b] D. L. Smith, *J. Chem. Phys.*, **42**, 1460 (1965).
[10] E. R. Corey, L. F. Dahl and W. Beck, *J. Amer. Chem. Soc.*, **85**, 1202 (1963).

contain triply bridging CO groups is the trinuclear $(\pi\text{-}C_5H_5)_3Ni_3(CO)_2$ though several other likely possibilities, e.g., $(C_6H_6)_3Co_3(CO)_2{}^+$, exist.

Bonding. The fact that refractory metals, with high heats of atomization (~ 100 kcal/mol), and a generally inert molecule like CO are capable of uniting to form stable, molecular compounds must certainly be considered, at face value, surprising, especially when it is noted that the CO molecules remain as individuals in the resulting molecules. Moreover, it is known that the simple Lewis basicity (donor ability) of CO is negligible. However, the explanation lies in the multiple nature of the M—CO bond, for which there is much evidence, some of it semi-quantitative.

While it is possible to formulate the bonding in terms of a resonance hybrid of 27-Ia and 27-Ib, a molecular orbital formulation is more detailed,

$$\bar{M}\!-\!\overset{+}{C}\!\equiv\!O\!: \leftrightarrow M\!=\!C\!=\!\ddot{O}\!:$$

$$\text{(27-Ia)} \qquad \text{(27-Ib)}$$

graphic and probably more accurate (see page 745). The MO picture is as follows: There is first a dative overlap of the filled carbon σ orbital with an empty metal σ orbital (Fig. 27-5a) and second a dative overlap

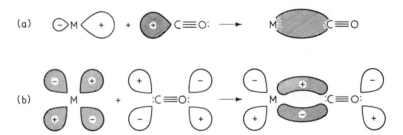

Fig. 27-5. (a) The formation of the metal←carbon σ bond using an unshared pair on C atom. (b) The formation of the metal→carbon π bond. The other orbitals on the CO are omitted for clarity.

of a filled $d\pi$ or hybrid $dp\pi$ metal orbital with an empty antibonding $p\pi$ orbital of the carbon monoxide (Fig. 27-5b). This bonding mechanism is *synergic*, since the drift of metal electrons into CO orbitals will tend to make the CO as a whole negative and hence to increase its basicity via the σ orbital of carbon; at the same time the drift of electrons to the metal in the σ bond tends to make the CO positive, thus enhancing the acceptor strength of the π orbitals. Thus, up to a point, the effects of σ bond formation strengthen the π bonding and vice versa. It may be noted here that dipole moment studies indicate that the moment of an M—C bond is only very low, about 0.5 D, suggesting a close approach to electroneutrality.

The main lines of physical evidence showing the multiple nature of the M—CO bonds are bond lengths and vibrational spectra. According to the preceding description of the bonding, as the extent of back donation from M to CO increases, the M—C bond becomes stronger and the C≡O bond becomes weaker. Thus, the multiple bonding should be evidenced by shorter M—C and longer C—O bonds as compared to M—C single bonds and C≡O triple bonds respectively. Actually very little information can be obtained from the CO bond lengths, because in the range of bond orders (2–3) concerned, CO bond length is relatively insensitive to bond order,[11] as shown in Figure 4-3 (page 113). The bond length in CO itself is 1.128 A, while the bond lengths in metal carbonyl molecules are ~1.15 A, a shift in the proper direction but of little quantitative significance due to its small magnitude and the uncertainties (~0.02 A) in the individual distances. For M—C distances, the sensitivity to bond order in the range concerned (1–2) is relatively high, probably about 0.3–0.4 A per unit of bond order,[11] and good evidence for multiple bonding can therefore be expected from such data. However, there is a difficulty in applying this criterion, in that the estimation of the length of an M—C single bond is difficult because zero valent metals do not form such bonds. By indirect schemes—often of questionable validity, though apparently giving reasonable answers— such estimates were made for Cr^0, Fe^0, Ni^0, etc., and from these results it was deduced that the M—C bonds in the carbonyls of these metals are some 0.15–0.30 A shorter than would be the single bonds. More recently,[11] estimates of M—C bond shortening have been made in a more direct and reliable way now to be illustrated.

In order to estimate the extent to which the metal–carbon bonds are "shortened" we measure the lengths of M—CO bonds in the same molecule in which some other bond, M—X, exists, such that this bond must be single. Then, using the known covalent radius for X, estimating the single bond covalent radius of C to be 0.70 A when an sp hybrid orbital is used (the greater s character makes this ~0.07 A shorter than that for sp^3 carbon), the length for a single M—CO bond in this molecule can be estimated and compared with the observed value. Unfortunately, few data suitable for this purpose are currently available, but the data shown in Figure 27-6 can be used to illustrate the argument.

From $Mo(dien)(CO)_3$ we take the mean Mo—N bond length to represent an Mo—N single bond, since the amine N atom has no orbitals available for π bonding. When the covalent radius of sp^3 N (~0.70 A) is subtracted and the covalent radius of sp C (also, by chance, 0.70 A) is added, the length of a single Mo—CO bond should be 2.32 ± 0.02 A. The observed length, 1.94 ± 0.01 A, shows that there is extensive Mo—C π bonding. Similarly,

---

[11] F. A. Cotton and R. M. Wing, *Inorg. Chem.*, **4**, 314 (1965).

in $(\pi\text{-}C_5H_5)Mo(CO)_3C_2H_5$ the $Mo\text{—}C_2H_5$ distance, less 0.77 (the radius for sp^3 carbon), plus 0.70 gives 2.32 ± 0.04 A for the single bond length. That observed is 1.97 ± 0.03 A; again, there is a large difference indicating appreciable π bonding. The good agreement in the numbers for these two cases is very satisfying and lends strength to the argument.

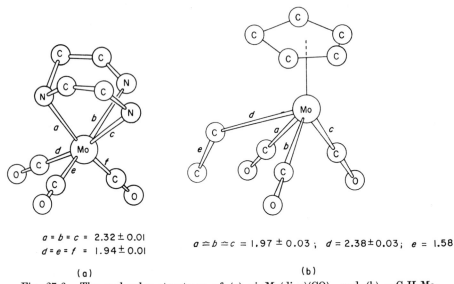

$a = b = c = 2.32 \pm 0.01$
$d = e = f = 1.94 \pm 0.01$

(a)

$a \simeq b \simeq c = 1.97 \pm 0.03 ;\quad d = 2.38 \pm 0.03;\quad e = 1.58$

(b)

Fig. 27-6. The molecular structures of (a) cis-$Mo(dien)(CO)_3$ and (b) $\pi\text{-}C_5H_5Mo$-$(CO)_3C_2H_5$. (Reproduced by permission from reference 11 and R. Mason, et al., Proc. Chem. Soc., **1963**, 273, respectively.)

From the vibrational spectra of metal carbonyls, to be discussed more fully below, it is possible to infer very directly, and even semi-quantitatively, the existence and extent of M—C multiple bonding. This is most easily done by studying the CO stretching frequencies rather than the MC stretching frequencies, since the former give rise to strong sharp bands well separated from all other vibrational modes of the molecules. MC stretching frequencies, on the other hand, are in the same range with other types of vibration (e.g., MCO bends) and therefore assignments are not easy to make, nor are the "MC stretching modes," so called, actually pure MC stretching motions. The inferring of M—C bond orders from the behavior of C—O vibrations depends only on the assumption that the valence of C is constant, so that a given increase in the M—C bond order must cause an equal decrease in the C—O bond order; this, in turn, will cause a drop in the CO vibrational frequency (see page 111).

From the direct comparison of CO stretching frequencies in carbonyl molecules with the stretching frequency of CO itself, certain useful qualitative conclusions can be drawn. The CO molecule has a stretching frequency of 2143 cm^{-1}. Terminal CO groups in neutral metal carbonyl molecules are found in the range 2125–1900 cm^{-1}, showing the reduction in CO bond orders. Moreover, when changes are made which should increase the extent of M—C back-bonding, the CO frequencies are shifted to even lower values. Thus, if some CO groups are replaced by ligands with low or negligible back-accepting ability, those CO groups which remain must accept $d\pi$ electrons from the metal to a greater extent in order to prevent the accumulation of negative charge on the metal atom. Thus, the frequencies for $Cr(CO)_6$ are $\sim$2100, $\sim$2000 and $\sim$1985 (exact values vary with phase and solvent) whereas, when three CO's are replaced by amine groups which have essentially no ability to back accept, as in the Cr analog of $Modien(CO)_3$ (Fig. 27-6), there are two CO stretching modes with frequencies of $\sim$1900 and $\sim$1760 cm^{-1}. Similarly, when we go from $Cr(CO)_6$ to the isoelectronic $V(CO)_6^-$, when more negative charge must be taken from the metal atom, a band is found at $\sim$1860 cm^{-1} corresponding to the one found at $\sim$2000 cm^{-1} in $Cr(CO)_6$. A series of these isoelectronic species illustrating this trend, with their IR-active CO stretching frequencies (cm^{-1}) is: $Ni(CO)_4$, ($\sim$2060); $Co(CO)_4^-$, ($\sim$1890); $Fe(CO)_4^{2-}$, ($\sim$1790). (The anionic species will be described in detail in the next section.) Conversely, a change which would tend to inhibit the shift of electrons from metal to CO π orbitals, such as placing a positive charge on the metal, should cause the CO frequencies to *rise*, and this effect has been observed in several cases, the following being representative:

$Mn(CO)_6^+$, $\sim$2090 $Mndien(CO)_3^+$, $\sim$2020, $\sim$1900
$Cr(CO)_6$, $\sim$2000 $Crdien(CO)_3$, $\sim$1900, $\sim$1760
$V(CO)_6^-$, $\sim$1860

In order to obtain semi-quantitative estimates of M—C π bonding from vibrational frequencies, it is necessary to carry out an approximate dynamical analysis of the CO stretching modes and thus derive force constants (page 112) for the CO groups. Though not difficult[12] this procedure involves some principles which are neither explained in this book nor assumed as prerequisites. Therefore, only a brief illustration will be given, omitting details.

For molecules of the type *cis*-$ML_3(CO)_3$, of which *cis*-$Modien(CO)_3$ is an example, each CO group shares the two metal $d\pi$ orbitals from which it receives electrons with the ligand, L, which is *trans* to it. In the hexacarbonyl itself (L = CO) each $d\pi$ orbital is thus contributing equally to all six ligands. Since there are three $d\pi$ orbitals (see page 706), each containing one electron pair, there can be, at most, $\frac{1}{2}$ of a π bond for each M—C pair, if the $d\pi$ electrons are fully used. Now in the case where L represents a

[12] F. A. Cotton, *Inorg. Chem.*, **3**, 702 (1964), and prior papers cited therein.

ligand incapable of accepting $d\pi$ electrons, each of the three CO groups has access to $\frac{1}{3}$ of the three pairs of $d\pi$ electrons. Thus, if the $d\pi$ electrons enter fully into the back bonding, each M—C pair will have a full π bond. Thus, assuming full participation by the metal $d\pi$ electrons in each case, the M—C bond orders go from 1.5 in $M(CO)_6$ to 2.0 in cis-$ML_3(CO)_3$ where L is a ligand atom without π-acceptor orbitals, such as an aliphatic amino nitrogen atom. The CO bond orders in these two cases should then be, respectively, 2.5 and 2.0. From data for CO groups in organic molecules, it can be estimated that for a change of 0.5 in CO bond order, the bond force constant should change by ~ 3.4 md/A. It has been found that the CO force constants in $Mdien(CO)_3$ molecules are 3.4 ± 0.4 md/A less than those in the corresponding $M(CO)_6$ molecules. Thus, the extensive, essentially complete participation of the metal $d\pi$ electrons in M—C π bonding is nicely demonstrated by these data.

Infrared Spectra. Because of the relative ease of observing and interpreting the CO stretching frequencies of metal carbonyls and their derivatives, the observation of these frequencies has become by far the single most potent physical aid in the study of metal carbonyl chemistry. While Raman data are sometimes obtained, and are equally useful, nearly all data, except for certain simple molecules, have been obtained from infrared spectra.

One general way in which infrared data can be used, namely, to infer and correlate changes in M—C bonding, has already been described. In addition to many purely empirical, though important uses, such as following the course of reactions, or testing for impurities, there is a second important general application of vibrational data, namely, the inference of molecular structure. This can be done in two ways, one depending on the *frequency range* in which the bands are found, the other depending on the *number* and, to some extent, the *relative intensities* of the observed bands. However, since several factors influence the frequencies of CO stretching, interpretation must be done *with caution*, and usually with the help of collateral data.

It is especially important to note that CO stretching frequencies (and NO frequencies in nitrosyls discussed later) show appreciable solvent shifts;[13] the use of nonpolar solvents such as hexane is hence desirable.

Because doubly bridging CO groups are similar to organic keto groups (having essentially double CO bonds) their stretching frequencies are to be expected at substantially lower values than those of terminal carbonyl groups in the same or similar molecules, namely 1700–1850 cm^{-1}. The appearance of bands in this region can therefore be taken as indicative of the presence of ketonic bridges, *provided* it is known that terminal CO

[13] W. Beck and K. Lottes, *Z. Naturforsch*, **19b**, 987 (1964).

frequencies have not been lowered into this range by the presence of many non-π-accepting ligands or negative charge on the metal, as discussed earlier. As examples, the spectra of $Fe_2(CO)_9$ and $Os_3(CO)_{12}$ are shown in Figure 27-7. The latter, which contains no bridging groups (see Fig. 27-3a),

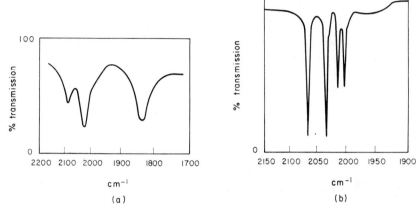

Fig. 27-7. The infrared spectra in the CO stretching region of (a) solid $Fe_2(CO)_9$ and (b) $Os_3(CO)_{12}$ in solution. Note the greater sharpness of the solution spectra. The most desirable spectra are those obtained in nonpolar solvents or in the gas phase. (Data from F. A. Cotton in *Modern Coordination Chemistry*, J. Lewis and R. G. Wilkins, eds., Wiley–Interscience, New York, 1960, and D. K. Huggins, N. Flitcroft and H. D. Kaesz, *Inorg. Chem.*, **4**, 166 (1965).)

has four CO bands, all in the terminal CO range, whereas $Fe_2(CO)_9$ has not only two bands in the terminal CO range, but also one in the bridging range ($\sim$1830 cm^{-1} in the solid). Since there is no reason to expect a terminal frequency as low as this, the inference can be drawn that one or more ketonic bridges are present. This, of course, is true (see Fig. 27-2).

Inferring structures from the number of CO bands observed in the infrared spectrum is a common and useful practice, though a certain amount of judgement and experience are necessary in order to consistently avoid errors. The procedure consists in first determining from the mathematical and physical requirements of symmetry how many CO stretching bands ought to appear in the infrared spectrum for each of several possible structures.[14] The experimental observations are then compared with the predictions and those structures for which the predictions disagree with observation are considered to be eliminated. In favorable cases there will be only one possible structure which remains. In carrying out this procedure, due regard must be given to the possibilities of bands being

[14] See, for example, K. Nakamoto, *Infrared Spectra of Inorganic and Coordination Compounds*, Wiley, New York, 1961, for an explanation of how this is done.

weak or superposed, and of course, the correct model must be among those considered. The reliability of the procedure can usually be increased if the behavior of approximate force constants[14] and the relative intensities of the bands[15] are also considered.

To illustrate the procedure, consider the *cis* and *trans* isomers of an $ML_2(CO)_4$ molecule. Figure 27-8 shows the approximate forms of the CO

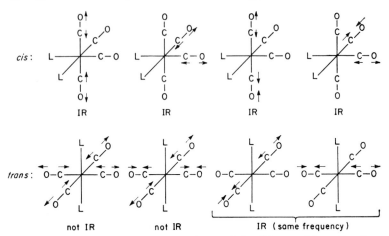

Fig. 27-8. Schematic indication of the forms of the CO stretching vibrations of *cis* and *trans* $ML_2(CO)_4$ molecules. For the *cis* isomer, all four are distinct and can absorb infrared radiation. For the *trans* isomer, two are equivalent and have the same frequency, forming a degenerate vibration; only this one can absorb infrared radiation.

stretching vibrations and also indicates which ones are expected to absorb infrared radiation, when only the symmetry of the $M(CO)_4$ portion of the molecule is considered. When $L = (C_2H_5)_3P$, the two isomeric compounds can be isolated. One has four infrared bands (2016, 1915, 1900, 1890 cm^{-1}) and is thus the *cis* isomer, while the other shows only one strong band (1890 cm^{-1}) and is thus the *trans* isomer.

It may also be noted that since no major interaction is to be expected between the CO stretching motions in two $M(CO)_4$ groups if they are connected only through the two heavy metal atoms, $Os_3(CO)_{12}$ should have the 4-band spectrum of a *cis*-$ML_2(CO)_4$ molecule, and as seen in Figure 27-7 it does.

The arrangement of CO groups in $Co_4(CO)_{12}$ (Fig. 27-4a) was determined from the infrared spectrum[9] and this provides an excellent example of both the utility of the procedure and its skilful use.

Finally we may note the very simple case in which there are two CO (or NO) groups present in an octahedral type molecule. If the groups are

[15] L. E. Orgel, *Inorg. Chem.*, **1**, 25 (1962).

trans there will be only one CO band in the infrared (see, for example, *trans*-[Cr(CO)$_2$ (diphos)$_2$]),[1] due to the antisymmetrically coupled stretching of the two groups, whereas when they are *cis* (as in *cis*-M(NO)$_2$L$_4$ complexes[16]), both the symmetric and the antisymmetric combinations cause infrared absorption and two strong bands are observed.

Reactions. The number of carbonyls and the number and variety of their reactions is so enormous that only a few types of reaction can be mentioned. For Mo(CO)$_6$ and Fe(CO)$_5$, Figure 27-9 gives a suggestion of

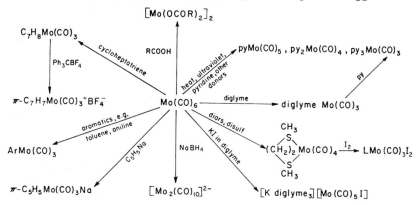

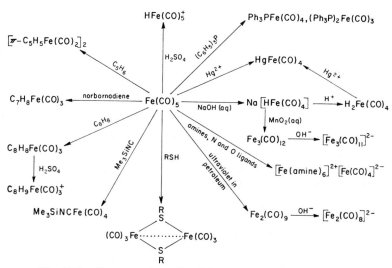

Fig. 27-9. Some reactions of molybdenum and iron carbonyls.

[16] F. A. Cotton and B. F. G. Johnson, *Inorg. Chem.*, **3**, 1609 (1964).

the extensive chemistry which any individual carbonyl typically has. Other examples will be encountered in succeeding chapters.

The most important general reactions of carbonyls are those in which CO groups are displaced by other ligands. These may be individual donor molecules, with varying degrees of back-acceptor ability themselves, e.g., PX_3, PR_3, $P(OR)_3$, SR_2, NR_3, OR_2, RNC, etc., or unsaturated organic molecules such as C_6H_6 or cycloheptatriene. Derivatives of the latter are discussed separately in the next chapter.

Another important general reaction is that with bases (OH^-, H^-, NH_2^-) leading to the carbonylate anions, which are discussed in the next section.

Although many of the substitution reactions with other π-acid ligands proceed thermally (temperatures up to 200° in some cases being required for the less reactive carbonyls) it is sometimes more convenient to obtain a particular product by photochemical methods;[17] in some cases, substitution proceeds readily only under irradiation. For example, the thermal reactions of $Fe(CO)_5$ and triphenylphosphine or triphenylarsine (L) give mixtures, whereas, photochemically, $Fe(CO)_4L$ and $Fe(CO)_3L_2$ can be obtained quite simply.[18] Manganese carbonyl and π-$C_5H_5Mn(CO)_3$ are usually quite resistant to substitution reactions, but the former under irradiation gives $[Mn(CO)_4PR_3]_2$.[19] In the very rapid photochemical production of acetylene and olefin complexes from $Mo(CO)_6$ and $W(CO)_6$[20] it is believed that $M(CO)_5$ radicals are the initiating species; even in absence of other ligands, bright yellow solutions are produced when Cr, Mo and W hexacarbonyls are irradiated in various solvents. Metal carbonyls in presence of organic halogen compounds such as CCl_4 have been found to act as initiators for the free radical polymerization of methyl methacrylate and other monomers.[21]

Kinetic and mechanistic studies of metal carbonyl reactions have been limited mainly to CO exchange processes.[22] In general these reactions seem to take place by an S_N1 mechanism, although some specific exceptions are known. In a general way, the rates of exchange—and reactivity in general—can be correlated with the degree of M—C π bonding, as would be expected for processes controlled by a dissociative step. For example, the rates of CO exchange for the manganese carbonyl halides, $XMn(CO)_5$

---

[17] W. Strohmeier, *Angew. Chem.* (*Internat.*), **3**, 730 (1964); a comprehensive review. D. T. Thompson, *J. Organomet. Chem.*, **4**, 74 (1965).

[18] J. Lewis, *et al.*, *J. Chem. Soc.*, **1964**, 2825.

[19] A. G. Osborne and M. H. B. Stiddard, *J. Chem. Soc.*, **1964**, 634.

[20] I. W. Stolz, G. R. Dobson and R. K. Sheline, *Inorg. Chem.*, **2**, 1265 (1963); G. R. Dobson, *et al.*, *Inorg. Chem.*, **1**, 526 (1962).

[21] See C. H. Bamford and G. C. Eastmond, *Ann. Rep. Chem. Soc.*, **1963**, 92.

[22] F. Basolo and R. G. Pearson, *Adv. Inorg. Chem. Radiochem.*, **3**, 68 (1961).

(X = Cl, Br, I), show two main features. (1) In each case four CO's exchange more rapidly than the fifth. This can be attributed to the fact that the CO which is *trans* to X has a greater degree of M—C π bonding because the X's are poorer back-acceptors than CO. (2) The overall rates of exchange decrease in the order Cl > Br > I. This is the order of decreasing electronegativity of X which means that it is also the order of decreasing partial positive charge on the metal and hence the order of increasing M—C π bonding.

27-2. Carbonylate Anions and Carbonyl Hydrides

It was first shown by Hieber, who has made many notable contributions to carbonyl chemistry, that if iron pentacarbonyl is treated with aqueous alkali it dissolves to give an initially yellow solution containing the ion $HFe(CO)_4^-$, which on acidification gives a thermally unstable gas $H_2Fe(CO)_4$. Carbonylate anions have been obtained from most of the carbonyls. Some do not give hydrides on acidification; however, the carbonylate ions of Mn, Re, Fe and Co certainly do.

The carbonylate anions can be obtained in a number of ways—by treating carbonyls with aqueous or alcoholic alkali hydroxide or with amines, sulfoxides or other Lewis bases, by cleaving metal–metal bonds with sodium, or in special cases by refluxing carbonyls with salts in an ether medium. Illustrative examples are:

$$Fe(CO)_5 + 3NaOH(aq) = Na[HFe(CO)_4](aq) + Na_2CO_3(aq) + H_2O$$

$$Co_2(CO)_8 + 2Na/Hg \xrightarrow{\text{THF}} 2Na[Co(CO)_4]$$

$$Mn_2(CO)_{10} + 2Li \xrightarrow{\text{THF}} 2Li[Mn(CO)_5]$$

$$Mo(CO)_6 + KI \xrightarrow{\text{diglyme}} [K(diglyme)_3]^+[Mo(CO)_5I]^- + CO$$

$$2Co^{2+}(aq) + 11CO + 12OH^- \xrightarrow{\text{KCN (aq)}} 2[Co(CO)_4]^- + 3CO_3^{2-} + 6H_2O$$

$$TaCl_5 + CO + Na(excess) \xrightarrow[\text{3000–5000 psi}]{\text{diglyme} \sim 100°} [Na(diglyme)_2]^+[Ta(CO)_6]^-$$

The carbonylate ions, like the binary carbonyls, can be said to obey the noble-gas formalism, and their stoichiometries can be readily predicted. The ions are usually fairly readily oxidized by air; the alkali metal salts are soluble in water, from which they can be precipitated by large cations such as $[Co(NH_3)_6]^{3+}$ or $[Ph_4As]^+$.

In addition to mononuclear carbonylate anions, a variety of polynuclear species have been obtained, though in several cases these are not fully established. The iron carbonylate ions have been studied carefully,

24 + A.I.C.

however.[23] The ions are obtained by the action of aqueous alkali or Lewis bases on binary carbonyls or in other ways, for example,

$$Fe_2(CO)_9 + 4OH^- = [Fe_2(CO)_8]^{2-} + CO_3^{2-} + 2H_2O$$
$$Fe_3(CO)_{12} + 4OH^- = [Fe_3(CO)_{11}]^{2-} + CO_3^{2-} + 2H_2O$$

$$Ni(CO)_4 \xrightarrow[NH_{3(l)}]{Na\ in} Na_2[Ni_4(CO)_9]$$

$$3Ni(CO)_4 + 3(phen) \rightarrow [Ni^{II}(phen)_3]^{2+}[Ni_2(CO)_6]^{2-} + 6CO$$
$$Cr(CO)_6 + 3KOH = K[HCr(CO)_5] + K_2CO_3 + H_2O$$
$$2K[HCr(CO)_5] + 4KOH + 3H_2O = K_2[Cr_2(CO)_6(OH)_3H] + 2H_2 + 6HCOOK$$

The structures are probably related to those of the polynuclear carbonyls themselves but are so far little known with the exception of $[HFe_3(CO)_{11}]^-$ discussed above. The ion $[Fe_2(CO)_8]^{2-}$ has been shown to have a structure with terminal CO groups and a metal–metal bond (cf. $Mn_2(CO)_{10}$). The group VI binuclear carbonylate anions, $[M_2(CO)_{10}]^{2-}$, and the manganese species,[24] $[Mn_2(CO)_8X_2]^{2-}$, are isoelectronic with $Mn_2(CO)_{10}$ and on the basis of their infrared spectra appear to have the same structure, without bridging CO groups.

The most important general reaction of the carbonylate anions (or of closely related ions such as $\pi\text{-}C_5H_5Fe(CO)_2^-$) is that with a halide, generally RX. Some examples where R is an alkyl or aryl group will be discussed in the next chapter, but R can also be groups such as R'_3Si, R'_2P, R'S, etc. The reactions are usually carried out in tetrahydrofuran solution in which the sodium carbonylate salts are soluble. Not all halides react with every carbonylate ion, of course, but a great variety of derivatives have been made. Two typical examples are

$$(CO)_5Mn^- + ClCH_2\text{---}CH{=}CH_2 = (CO)_5MnCH_2\text{---}CH{=}CH_2 + Cl^-$$
$$\pi\text{-}C_5H_5(CO)_3W^- + ClSiMe_3 = \pi\text{-}C_5H_5(CO)_3WSiMe_3 + Cl^-$$

A special case of this general reaction occurs when R is a complex of another transition (or nontransition) metal, in which case compounds with metal–metal bonds are obtained (see also page 652). Some examples[25] are

$$\pi\text{-}C_5H_5(CO)_3Mo^- + ClW(CO)_3\pi\text{-}C_5H_5 = \pi\text{-}C_5H_5(CO)_3MoW(CO)_3\pi\text{-}C_5H_5 + Cl^-$$
$$Ta(CO)_6^- + C_2H_5HgCl = C_2H_5HgTa(CO)_6 + Cl^-$$
$$Fe(CO)_4^{2-} + 2Ph_3PAuCl = (Ph_3Au)_2Fe(CO)_4 + 2Cl^-$$
$$Mn(CO)_5Br + Co(CO)_4^- = (OC)_4CoMn(CO)_5 + Br^-$$

[23] J. R. Case and M. C. Whiting, *J. Chem. Soc.*, **1960**, 4632; W. Hieber and H. Beutner, *Z. Naturforschg.*, **17b**, 211 (1962); W. F. Edgell, *et al.*, *J. Amer. Chem. Soc.*, **87**, 3080 (1965).

[24] E. W. Abel and I. S. Butler, *J. Chem. Soc.*, **1964**, 434.

[25] C. E. Coffey, J. Lewis and R. S. Nyholm, *J. Chem. Soc.*, **1964**, 1741; A. S. Kasenally, R. S. Nyholm and M. B. H. Stiddard, *J. Chem. Soc.*, **1965**, 5343; K. A. Keblys and M. Dubeck, *Inorg. Chem.*, **3**, 1646 (1964); J. Lewis and S. B. Wild, *J. Chem. Soc.*, **1966A**, 69.

There are also many compounds obtained by reaction of carbonylate anions, particularly $Fe(CO)_4{}^{2-}$, with compounds of As, Sb, Bi, Sn, Pb, Tl, etc. These often have formulas such as $PbFe_3(CO)_{12}$, $As_2Fe_3(CO)_{12}$ and $SbFe_2(CO)_8$ but aside from some speculative suggestions, the structures of these substances and their further chemical behavior are unknown.

Finally, it is convenient to mention here the *carbonylate cations* which are obtained by reactions of the type

$$Mn(CO)_5Cl + AlCl_3 + CO \overset{benzene}{=} [Mn(CO)_6]^+[AlCl_4]^-$$

$$\pi\text{-}C_5H_5Fe(CO)_2Cl + NaBPh_4 + CO \overset{THF}{=} [\pi\text{-}C_5H_5Fe(CO)_3]^+[BPh_4]^- + NaCl$$

The ions are usually known only as salts of comparatively large anions.

Carbonyl Hydrides. In some cases hydrides corresponding to the carbonylate anions can be isolated. Some of these are listed in Table 27-3 along with their main properties.

TABLE 27-3

Some Carbonyl Hydrides and their Properties

Compound	Form	Melting point, °C	M—H stretch, cm^{-1}	τ value[a]	Comment
$HMn(CO)_5$	Colorless liquid	-25	1783	17.5	Stable liquid at 25°; weakly acidic
$H_2Fe(CO)_4$	Yellow liquid, colorless gas	-70	?	21.1	Decomposes at $-10°$ giving H_2 + red $H_2Fe_2(CO)_8$
$H_2Fe_3(CO)_{11}$	Dark red liquid		?	25	
$HCo(CO)_4$	Yellow liquid, colorless gas	-26	~ 1934	20	Decomp. above m.p. giving H_2 + $Co_2(CO)_8$
$HW(CO)_3(\pi\text{-}C_5H_5)$	Yellow crystals	69	1854	17.5	Stable short time in air
$HFe(CO)_3(PPh_3)_2{}^+$	Yellow	—	?	17.6	Formed by protonation of $Fe(CO)_3(PPh_3)_2$ in H_2SO_4

[a] τ value is position of high-resolution proton magnetic resonance line in parts per million referred to tetramethylsilane reference as 10.00.

In general the carbonyl hydrides are rather unstable substances. They can be obtained by acidification of the appropriate alkali carbonylates or in other ways. Examples of the preparations are:

$$NaCo(CO)_4 + H^+(aq) = HCo(CO)_4 + Na^+(aq)$$

$$Fe(CO)_4I_2 \xrightarrow{\text{NaBH}_4 \text{ in THF}} H_2Fe(CO)_4$$

$$Mn_2(CO)_{10} + H_2 \xrightarrow[200°]{200 \text{ atm}} 2HMn(CO)_5$$

$$Co + 4CO + \tfrac{1}{2}H_2 \xrightarrow[150°]{50 \text{ atm}} HCo(CO)_4$$

The iron and cobalt carbonyl hydrides form pale yellow solids or liquids at low temperatures and in the liquid state begin to decompose above about -10 and $-20°$, respectively; they are relatively more stable in the gas phase, however, particularly when diluted with carbon monoxide. They both have revolting odors and are readily oxidized by air. $HMn(CO)_5$ is appreciably more stable.

The hydrides are not very soluble in water but in water they behave as acids, ionizing to give the carbonylate ions:

$$HMn(CO)_5 = H^+ + [Mn(CO)_5]^- \qquad pK \sim 7.1$$
$$H_2Fe(CO)_4 = H^+ + [HFe(CO)_4]^- \qquad pK_1 \sim 4.4$$
$$[HFe(CO)_4]^- = H^+ + [Fe(CO)_4]^{2-} \qquad pK_2 \sim 14$$
$$HCo(CO)_4 = H^+ + [Co(CO)_4]^- \qquad \text{strong acid}$$

It was reported many years ago on the basis of electron diffraction studies that for $H_2Fe(CO)_4$ and $HCo(CO)_4$ the $M(CO)_4$ skeletons are nearly tetrahedral; infrared spectra also suggested that the $Mn(CO)_5$ skeleton might be approximately the same as that of $Fe(CO)_5$. The question of where and how the hydrogen atoms are bound was a vexed one until quite recently. It was easily shown by infrared study that a suggestion that the hydrogen atom was bound to oxygen or carbon is incorrect. The abnormally high field proton nmr lines indicated metal–hydrogen bonding. Further, the large separation in the acid dissociation constants for $H_2Fe(CO)_4$ strongly suggests that the hydrogen atoms must be bound to the iron atom (cf. K_1 and K_2 for H_2S).

While the nature of carbonyl hydrides is still not completely settled, the picture has been clarified by the recognition that hydrogen can form an extensive series of hydrido complexes (see page 203) with transition elements, and by the partial determination of the structure of $HMn(CO)_5$. In the latter, the five CO groups are located at approximately five of the six vertices of an octahedron and it is assumed that the hydrogen atom lies at the sixth vertex.[26] Thus, $HMn(CO)_5$ is to be considered as a hydrido complex, structurally related to other $XMn(CO)_5$ compounds (X = alkyl, acyl, halide). It has also been suggested[27] that $H_2Fe(CO)_4$ is an octahedral molecule with the H atoms in *cis* positions. This is consistent with all available data though there is no direct proof and it incidentally implies that the electron diffraction study mentioned above is in error (which is certainly possible).

One feature of some carbonyl hydrides, notably $HCo(CO)_4$ and $H_2Fe(CO)_4$, which distinguishes them from all other hydrido complexes is their acidity. Indeed, it seems incongruous to formulate a compound which dissociates to give H^+ as a complex containing H^-, but the explanation doubtless lies in the great stability of the carbonylate anion which results upon acid dissociation.

Like hydride complexes in general, the carbonyl hydrides generally exhibit sharp M—H stretching bands in the infrared and proton nuclear resonance absorptions at very high τ values as shown in Table 27-3.

[26] S. J. La Placa, W. C. Hamilton and J. A. Ibers, *Inorg. Chem.*, **3**, 1491 (1964).
[27] L. L. Lohr and W. N. Lipscomb, *Inorg. Chem.*, **3**, 77 (1964).

The carbonyl hydrides undergo quite a variety of reactions in which they either add to a molecule or in which hydrogen is transferred. Some examples are

$$\pi\text{-}C_5H_5Mo(CO)_3H + CCl_4 = CHCl_3 + \pi\text{-}C_5H_5Mo(CO)_3Cl$$
$$\pi\text{-}C_6H_5Mo(CO)_3H + CH_2N_2 = \pi\text{-}C_5H_5Mo(CO)_3CH_3 + N_2.$$

They can also add across multiple bonds to give compounds with metal to carbon σ bonds (see page 786), e.g.,

$$HMn(CO)_5 + CF_3C{\equiv}CCF_3 = trans\text{-}CF_3CH{=}C(CF_3)Mn(CO)_5$$

This type of addition of $HCo(CO)_4$ to olefins is one step in the hydroformylation reaction of olefins to produce aldehydes (see page 790).

The carbonyl hydrides corresponding to the more complex carbonylate anions, e.g., $Ni_4(CO)_9{}^{2-}$ and $Mo_3(CO)_{14}{}^{2-}$, have not in general been isolated.

In addition to the ion $[HFe_3(CO)_{11}]^-$ discussed earlier, the structural evidence for several other hydrido species is now available. The compounds $HMn_3(CO)_{10}(BH_3)_2$, $\pi\text{-}C_5H_5Mo(CO)_3\text{-}\mu PMe_2\text{-}\mu HMo(CO)_3\pi\text{-}C_5H_5$, $[HM_2(CO)_{10}]^-$ (M = Cr, Mo, W) and $Re_3(CO)_{12}H_3$, like $[HFe_3(CO)_{11}]^-$ appear to have symmetrical bridging hydrogen atoms. The bonding can be described in terms of 3-center MO's just as in the boranes (page 279). In the ion $[HCr_2 (CO)_{10}]^-$ there appears to be a linear Cr—H—Cr group.[28a]

The first evidence[28b] for the association of a hydrogen atom with two metal atoms was obtained from nmr studies of the protonated species $[HM_2(CO)_6(\pi\text{-}C_5H_5)_2]^+$ (M = Mo, W). Although these could be formulated with a bridge H atom, the metal–metal bond is very long and nmr studies were most consistent with rapid intramolecular exchange of H between the metal atoms.

27-3. Carbonyl Halides and Related Compounds

Carbonyl halides, $M_x(CO)_yX_z$, are known for most of the elements forming binary carbonyls but also for Pd, Pt and Au which do not form binary carbonyls; Cu^I and Ag^I carbonyl complexes also exist.

The carbonyl halides are obtained either by the direct interaction of metal halides with carbon monoxide, usually at high pressure, or in a few

[28a] R. J. Doedens and L. F. Dahl, *J. Amer. Chem. Soc.*, **87**, 2576 (1965); H. D. Kaez, *et al.*, *J. Amer. Chem. Soc.*, **87**, 2753 (1965); J. M. Smith, *et al.*, *Inorg. Chem.*, **4**, 1361 (1965); U. Anders and W. A. G. Graham, *Chem. Comm.*, **1965**, 499; L. B. Handy, *et al.*, *J. Amer. Chem. Soc.*, **88**, 366 (1965).
[28b] A. Davison, W. McFarlane, L. Pratt and G. Wilkinson, *J. Chem. Soc.*, **1962**, 3653.

cases by the cleavage by halogens of polynuclear carbonyls, for example,

$$Mn_2(CO)_{10} + Br_2(l) \overset{40°}{=} 2Mn(CO)_5Br \underset{CO, 150\ atm}{\overset{in\ petrol\ at\ 120°}{\rightleftarrows}} [Mn(CO)_4Br]_2 + 2CO$$

$$RuI_3 + 2CO \overset{200°}{=} [Ru(CO)_2I_2]_n + \tfrac{1}{2}I_2$$

$$2PtCl_2 + 2CO = [Pt(CO)Cl_2]_2$$

A few examples of the halides and some of their properties are listed in Table 27-4. Carbonyl halide anions are also known. They are often derived

TABLE 27-4

Some Examples of Carbonyl Halides, Isocyanide Complexes, and Substituted Phosphine and Arsine Complexes

Compound	Form	Melting point, °C	Comment
$Mn(CO)_5Cl$	Pale yellow crystals	Sublimes	Loses CO at 120° in organic solvents; can be substituted by pyridine, etc.
$[Re(CO)_4Cl]_2$	White crystals	Decomposes > 250	Halogen bridges cleavable by donor ligands or by CO (pressure)
$[Ru(CO)_2I_2]_n$	Orange powder	Stable > 200	Halide bridges cleavable by ligands
$[Pt(CO)Cl_2]_2$	Yellow crystals	195; sublimes	Hydrolyzed H_2O; PCl_3 replaces CO
$Cr(CNPh)_6$	Red crystals	156 ⎫	
$[Mn(CNCH_3)_6]I$	White needles	263 ⎬	Stable to air; soluble in benzene
$Co(CO)NO(CNC_7H_7)_2$	Orange-red crystals	156 ⎭	
$RuCl_2(CNCH_3)_4$	Yellow-green crystals		
$Ni(PCl_3)_4$	Yellow crystals	Decomposes > 200	Soluble in benzene; stable in dry air
$Ni(PF_3)_4$	Colorless liquid	−55; b 70.7	Resembles $Ni(CO)_4$; stable to H_2O
$Fe(CO)_3(PPh_3)_2$	Yellow crystals	Decomposes > 265	Protonates in conc. H_2SO_4
$Mn(CO)_3Cl(AsPh_3)_2$	Yellow crystals	Decomposes > 200	Octahedral: stable to air
$Mo[o-C_6H_4(PEt_2)_2]_3$	Red-black needles	236	Very soluble in petrol and oxidized in air

by reaction of ionic halides with metal carbonyls or substituted carbonyls.

$$M(CO)_6 + R_4N^+X^- \overset{diglyme}{=} R_4N^+[M(CO)_5X]^- + CO \qquad M = Cr, Mo, W$$

$$Mn_2(CO)_{10} + 2R_4N^+X^- = (R_4N^+)_2[Mn_2(CO)_8X_2]^{2-} + 2CO$$

$$(R_4N^+)_2[Mn_2(CO)_8X_2]^{2-} + 2R_4N^+Y^- = 2(R_4N^+)_2[Mn(CO)_4XY]^{2-}$$

$$M(CO)_4(dipy) + 2KCN = K_2[M(CO)_4(CN)_2] + dipy \qquad M = Cr, Mo, W$$

The structures of the carbonyl halides present little problem; where they are dimeric or polymeric they are invariably bridged through the halogen atoms and *not* by carbonyl bridges, for example, in 27-I and 27-II. The

(27-I)   (27-II)

halogen bridges can be broken by numerous donor ligands such as pyridine, substituted phosphines, isocyanides, etc. The breaking of halogen bridges by other donor ligands is not of course confined to the carbonyl halides, and other bridged halides such as those given by olefins (see page 784) can be cleaved. As an example we may cite the reaction

$$[Mn(CO)_4I]_2 + 4py = 2Mn(CO)_3Ipy_2 + 2CO \qquad (27\text{-}1)$$

The initial product of the cleavage in reaction 27-1 is 27-III, but the

(27-III)   (27-IV)

reaction can proceed further and the product 27-IV is isolated. This occurs because in 27-III two of the CO groups are *trans* to each other and thus will be competing across the metal atom for the same metal π bonding orbitals. Hence in the presence of any ligand like a nitrogen, phosphorus or arsenic donor, of *lower* π bonding requirement or capacity compared to CO, one of the *trans* CO groups will be displaced. It follows that the two pyridine (or other) ligands inserted must appear in the *cis* position to each other. This type of labilization of groups in certain stereochemical situations has been discussed elsewhere under the *trans effect* (see page 175). We can also note that in 27-IV, which is resistant to further displacement of CO, three of the octahedral positions are occupied by essentially non-π bonding ligands, so that the remaining three CO groups must be responsible for the delocalization of the negative charge on the metal atom; they will, however, now have the exclusive use of the electrons in the d_{xy}, d_{yz} and d_{xz} metal orbitals for π bonding, and hence the metal–carbon bonding is about at a maximum in 27-IV and similar derivatives.

We may finally note that, although $Ni(CO)_4$ exists, there are no corresponding palladium and platinum carbonyls, while, on the other hand, carbonyl halides of Pd^{II} and Pt^{II} exist but there is no carbonyl halide of Ni^{II} (substituted phosphine halides of Ni^{II} do exist, however). The reasons for these differences probably lie in the electronic structures (Ni, d^8s^2; Pd, d^{10}; Pt, d^9s) and promotional energies involved in forming the complexes in the zero and II oxidation states; it would appear that Ni^0 can form π bonds more readily than Pd^0 or Pt^0, but Pd^{II} and Pt^{II} can form π bonds more readily than Ni^{II}. All three derivatives, $M(PF_3)_4$, (M = Ni, Pd, Pt) and complexes such as $PtCO(PPh_3)_3$ and $Pt_3(CO)_4(PMe_2Ph)_3$ are known however (Section 30-H-4).

COMPLEXES WITH OTHER π-ACCEPTOR LIGANDS

27-4. Isocyanide Complexes

Isocyanide complexes can be obtained by direct substitution reactions of the metal carbonyls and in other ways. Some examples are given in Table 27-4.

Isocyanides generally appear to be stronger σ donors than CO, and various complexes such as $[Ag(CNR)_4]^+$, $[Fe(CNR)_6]^{2+}$ and $[Mn(CNR)_6]^{2+}$ are known where π bonding is of relatively little importance; derivatives of this type are not known for CO. However, the isocyanides are capable of extensive back-acceptance of π electrons from metal atoms in low oxidation states. This is indicated qualitatively by their ability to form compounds such as $Cr(CNR)_6$ and $Ni(CNR)_4$, analogous to the carbonyls and more quantitatively by comparison of CO and CN stretching frequencies. As shown in Table 27-5 the extent to which CN stretching frequencies in

TABLE 27-5

Lowering of CO and CN Frequencies in Analogous Compounds, Relative to Values for Free CO and $CNAr^a$

Molecule[b]	Δv, cm^{-1} for each fundamental mode		
$Cr(CO)_6$	43	123	160
$Cr(CNAr)_6$	68	140	185
$Ni(CO)_4$	15	106	
$Ni(CNAr)_4$	70	125	

[a] Ar represents C_6H_5 and p-$CH_3OC_6H_4$.
[b] Data for isonitriles from F. A. Cotton and F. Zingales, *J. Amer. Chem. Soc.*, **83**, 351 (1961).

$Cr(CNAr)_6$ and $Ni(CNAr)_4$ molecules are lowered relative to the frequencies of the free CNAr molecules exceeds that by which the CO modes of the corresponding carbonyls lie below the frequency of CO. While these results are not to be taken in a literally quantitative sense, they do show that the back-acceptor capacity of isonitriles rivals that of CO. Various other infrared studies[29] have led to this or a similar conclusion.

Another indication of extensive back donation in isonitrile complexes of low valent metals comes from the Co—C distances found[30] in the Co^I complex, $[Co(CNCH_3)_5]^+$; the mean value, 1.87 A, is at least 0.17 and probably ~ 0.25 A shorter than that for a Co—C single bond, and indicates a bond order of 1.5–2.0.

[29] M. Bigorgne, *J. Organomet. Chem.*, **1**, 101 (1963); K. K. Joshi, P. L. Pauson and W. H. Stubbs, *J. Organomet. Chem.*, **1**, 51 (1963); R. C. Taylor and W. D. Horrocks, *Inorg. Chem.*, **3**, 584 (1964).

[30] F. A. Cotton, T. G. Dunne and J. S. Wood, *Inorg. Chem.*, **4**, 318 (1965).

As in the case of metal carbonyls, the back bonding might be considered either in terms of a resonance hybrid

$$\bar{M}-C\!\equiv\!\overset{+}{N}R \leftrightarrow M\!=\!C\!=\!\overset{..}{N} \diagdown R$$

or formulated as the flow of electron density in metal $d\pi$ orbitals into the CN $p\pi^*$ orbitals. In this case, however, there is a physical distinction between these processes, the first leading to a CNR angle bent from 180°, the other permitting retention of the linear CNR arrangement which occurs in the free isonitriles. It has been shown in one case[30] that a Co—C—N—C chain, unperturbed by intermolecular forces, is essentially linear, even though the Co—C distance implies that there is extensive back donation. This argues decisively for the MO formulation of the multiple bonding. It has also been shown that the electronic spectra of metal carbonyls can be interpreted on an MO basis.[31]

While bridging isonitrile groups appear to be uncommon, one has been reported[32] in the compound $(\pi\text{-}C_5H_5)_2Fe_2(CO)_3(CNC_6H_5)$.

27-5. Donor Complexes of Nitrogen, Phosphorus and Similar Ligands

A variety of trivalent phosphorus, arsenic and, to a lesser extent, antimony and bismuth compounds can also give complexes with transition metals; we may also include thio derivatives R_2S in this category. Some examples are given in Table 27-4. These donor molecules are of course quite strong Lewis bases and will give complexes with acceptors such as BR_3 compounds where d orbitals are not involved. However, the donor atoms do have empty $d\pi$ orbitals and back-acceptance into these orbitals is possible as shown in Figure 27-10.

The extent to which back donation occurs depends on the identity of the donor atom and on the electronegativity of the groups attached to it. Figure 27-11 shows some infrared data illustrating this. It can be seen that analogous PX_3, AsX_3 and SbX_3 compounds differ very little, while the ligands having a nitrogen atom which lacks π orbitals cause significantly lower frequencies for the CO vibrations. However, the importance of electronegativity is well illustrated by the series of $L_3Mo(CO)_3$ compounds in which L changes from PCl_3 to PPh_3.

[31] H. B. Gray and N. A. Beach, *J. Amer. Chem. Soc.*, **85**, 2922 (1963).
[32] K. K. Joshi, *et al.*, *Chem. Comm.*, **1965**, 181.

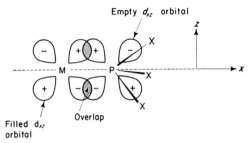

Fig. 27-10. Diagram showing the back bonding from a filled metal d orbital to an empty phosphorus $3d$ orbital in the PX_3 ligand, taking the internuclear axis as the z axis. An exactly similar overlap occurs in the yz plane using the d_{yz} orbitals.

On the basis of the data in Figure 27-11 and other studies,[33] the qualitative order of various ligands in their ability to function as π acceptors is the following:

$$NO \geqslant CO \sim RNC \sim PF_3 > PCl_3 \sim AsCl_3 \sim SbCl_3 > PCl_2(OR) > PCl_2R$$
$$> PCl(OR)_2 > PClR_2 \sim P(OR)_3 > PR_3 \sim AsR_3 \sim SbR_3 \sim SR_2$$
$$> RCN > NR_3 \sim OR_3 \sim ROH > H_2NCOR.$$

This kind of an ordering can be made somewhat quantitative by a procedure[12] which uses approximate values of the force constants for the CO

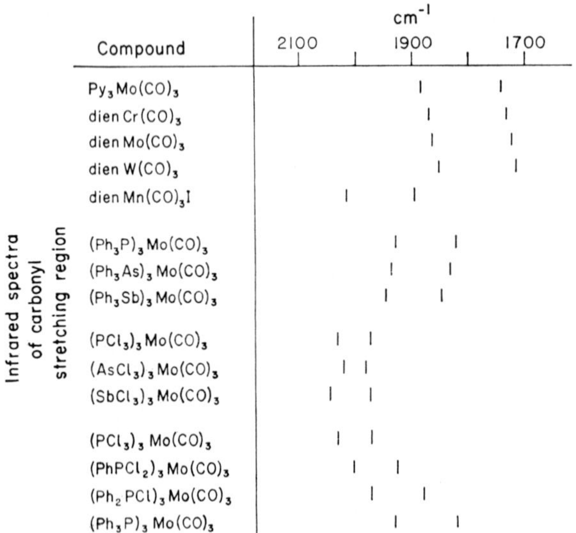

	Compound	2100	1900	1700
Infrared spectra of carbonyl stretching region	Py₃Mo(CO)₃		l	l
	dien Cr(CO)₃		l	l
	dien Mo(CO)₃		l	l
	dien W(CO)₃		l	l
	dien Mn(CO)₃I	l	l	
	(Ph₃P)₃Mo(CO)₃		l l	
	(Ph₃As)₃Mo(CO)₃		l l	
	(Ph₃Sb)₃Mo(CO)₃		l l	
	(PCl₃)₃Mo(CO)₃	l l		
	(AsCl₃)₃Mo(CO)₃	l l		
	(SbCl₃)₃Mo(CO)₃	l l		
	(PCl₃)₃Mo(CO)₃	l l		
	(PhPCl₂)₃Mo(CO)₃	l l		
	(Ph₂PCl)₃Mo(CO)₃	l l		
	(Ph₃P)₃Mo(CO)₃		l l	

(header: cm⁻¹)

Fig. 27-11. Chart of infrared spectra of various substituted carbonyls. (Reprnted with permission from E. W. Abel, M. A. Bennett and G. Wilkinson, *J. Chem. Soc.*, **1959**, 2325.)

[33] W. D. Horrocks, Jr., and R. C. Taylor, *Inorg. Chem.*, **2**, 723 (1963).

bonds in compounds where the various ligands are competing with CO for the available $d\pi$ electrons. Such semi-quantitative studies show that PF_3 is essentially equivalent to CO and RNC and that the trichlorides are only a little less effective.

Since CO and RNC are capable of forming complexes in which they alone are bonded to zero-valent metal atoms, it might be expected that ligands of similar π-acceptor ability would also be able to form such compounds and this, in fact, is true. Most of these compounds are formed by nickel, presumably because the ready reactivity of Ni with such ligands makes the compounds easier to prepare for kinetic rather than thermodynamic reasons. Thus, the NiL_4 compounds with L = PF_3, PCl_3, $P(OCN)_3$, $PCl_2C_6H_5$, etc., are known. With diphosphines and PF_3, ML_6 analogs of $M(CO)_6$ can be made, e.g., by reduction of higher valent complexes with sodium naphthalenide[34] or by interaction of dibenzene-chromium and -molybdenum[35a] with PF_3. However, the most common compounds of such ligands are those in which these replace some but not all of the CO groups of carbonyl molecules.

Trialkyl and arylphosphine and -arsine complexes are especially important for platinum group metals, for rhenium and for some other 2nd and or $Mo(CO)_6$[35b] 3rd row elements. Many examples will be discussed later in detail. Among the most important types of complex are halides, $(R_3P)_xM^nX_n$ where X = H, Cl, CH_3, etc.

The $SnCl_3^-$ ion is known to act as a ligand,[36] so far only for the platinum metals in complexes such as $[PtCl_2(SnCl_3)_2]^{2-}$, $[Rh_2Cl_2(SnCl_3)_4]^{4-}$, $[RhCOCl(SnCl_3)_2]^{2-}$, etc. It appears that $SnCl_3^-$ is a fairly weak σ donor but a moderately strong π-acid, using its vacant $5d$ orbitals for this purpose, and it has a high *trans* effect,[36,37] see Section 30-H-1.

Although the iso-electronic $SbCl_3$ forms substitution complexes with, e.g., $Fe(CO)_5$, it does not give platinum metal complexes. Presumably the negative charge on $SnCl_3^-$ results in orbital expansion and better $d\pi$–$d\pi$ overlap with the larger atoms.

27-6. Nitric Oxide Complexes

The nitric oxide molecule is very similar to the carbon monoxide molecule in forming complexes with transition metals but not with simple acceptors or nontransition metal atoms. However, NO has an additional electron

[34] J. Chatt and H. R. Watson, *J. Chem. Soc.*, **1962**, 2545.
[35a] T. Kruck, W. Lang and A. Engelman, *Angew. Chem. (Internat.)*, **4**, 148 (1965).
[35b] R. J. Clark and P. I. Hoberman, *Inorg. Chem.*, **4**, 1771 (1965).
[36] J. F. Young, R. D. Gillard and G. Wilkinson, *J. Chem. Soc.*, **1964**, 5176.
[37] R. V. Lindsay, Jr., G. W. Parshall and U. G. Stolberg, *J. Amer. Chem. Soc.*, **87**, 658 (1965).

in an antibonding π-MO which is readily lost to give the nitrosonium ion, NO^+ (page 343); the increased strength of the N—O bond caused by loss of this antibonding electron is shown by the increase in the N—O stretching frequency from 1878 cm^{-1} in free NO to 2200–2300 cm^{-1} in nitrosonium salts.

Complexes regarded as derived from the nitrosonium ion. The majority of NO complexes are best regarded as being formed by donation from the nitrosonium ion (NO^+) to the metal atom with M—N back bonding in a manner entirely analogous to that in the M—C bond in carbonyls. However, since we have initially neutral NO, it is first necessary formally to transfer one electron to the metal atom, reducing its valence by one unit, for example,

$$M + NO \rightarrow M^- + NO^+ \rightarrow M^{2-}\text{—}N^+\equiv O^+ \leftrightarrow M^-\text{=}N\text{=}O^+$$

Thus if we regard CO, PR_3, etc., as two-electron donors, NO can be considered formally as a three-electron donor; with this assumption, the formulas of NO compounds can often be predicted using the noble-gas rule. This rule is well exemplified by the formulas of the mixed carbonyl–nitrosyl compounds. There are two series of mononuclear ones corresponding to $Ni(CO)_4$ and $Fe(CO)_5$:

$$Ni(CO)_4, \; Co(NO)(CO)_3, \; Fe(NO)_2(CO)_2, \; Mn(NO)_3CO, \; [Cr(NO)_4]$$
$$Fe(CO)_5, \; Mn(NO)(CO)_4, \; [Cr(NO)_2(CO)_3], \; [V(CO)_2(NO)_3]$$

The compounds in square brackets have not yet been reported. It is interesting to note that there is a manganese compound in each series. Other compounds whose compositions can be interpreted in a similar way are $V(NO)(CO)_5$ and $Mn_2(NO)_2(CO)_7$, the latter being presumably analogous to $Fe_2(CO)_9$ with the arrangement $(NO)(CO)_2Mn(CO)_3Mn(CO)_2(NO)$.

It is a characteristic feature of the carbonyl–nitrosyl compounds that in the many derivatives containing phosphine, amine or isonitrile substituents which can be prepared, it is always the CO groups which are replaced. This is a piece of chemical evidence indicating the greater strength of M—NO as compared to M—CO bonding.

Physical evidence which points to the same conclusion is obtained from infrared and structural data. Relative to the NO^+ frequency, the NO frequencies in typical, neutral molecules are lowered by 300–500 cm^{-1}, whereas frequencies of terminal CO groups are lowered in comparable circumstances by only 100–300 cm^{-1}. Also, the Fe—NO bond distances in several compounds are 1.57–1.67 A, whereas Fe—CO bond distances have all been 1.70–1.90 A. The overall range, $\sim$1580 to $\sim$1900 cm^{-1} for NO frequencies brackets the free N—O value, suggesting that the average number of back-donated electrons is about one per NO group. The series of ions $[Fe(CN)_5NO]^{2-}$, $[Mn(CN)_5NO]^{3-}$, $[V(CN)_5NO]^{5-}$ illustrates a trend similar to the one found in carbonylate anions, in which increasing negative charge causes a marked increase in back donation with a resultant decrease in the N—O stretching frequency. The frequencies for the above complexes are, respectively, 1944, 1730 and 1575 cm^{-1}.

Structural studies of carbonyl nitrosyls show that the M—N—O groups are very nearly, and probably exactly, linear. In π-C_5H_5NiNO, the linearity of the Ni—N—O group is rigorous according to sensitive microwave spectral studies, and in the $[Fe(CN)_5NO]^{2-}$ ion any deviation from linearity cannot exceed a few degrees. Whether M—N—O groups are generally linear, however, is still not established, and some deviations from linearity have been reported. Definite cases of significantly bent MNO bonds are those of $(NO)_4Fe_2S_2Et_2$ and π-$C_5H_5CrCl(NO)_2$.[38a] In order to interpret esr data for $[Cr(CN)_5NO]^{3-}$ a nonlinear Cr—N—O group has been postulated but there is no direct evidence. In several NO complexes of ruthenium Ru—N—O angles of ca 150° have been reported, but the X-ray work is of uncertain but seemingly low accuracy.

There are a very large number of complexes which can be formulated as NO^+ complexes, and only a few examples are listed in Table 27-6. Nitric

TABLE 27-6

Some Nitric Oxide (NO^+) Complexes

Compound	Form	Melting point, °C.	Comment
$Mn(NO)_3CO$	Green solid or liquid	27	Unstable in air; soluble in organic solvents
$Co(CO)_3NO$	Red-brown liquid	-1; b 49	N—O str. 1832 cm^{-1}
π-C_5H_5NiNO	Red liquid	-41; b 144 at 715 mm	N—O str. 1820 cm^{-1}
$[Rh(NO)_2Cl]_{2\ (or\ 4)}$	Black solid		N—O str. 1703, 1605 cm^{-1}; insoluble in H_2O; halide bridges
$K_2[Fe(CN)_5NO]\cdot H_2O$	Red crystals		So-called nitroprusside; soluble in water; N—O str. 1944 cm^{-1}; OH^- converts NO to NO_2
$K_5[V(CN)_5NO]\cdot H_2O$	Orange crystals		Soluble in water; N—O str. 1575 cm^{-1}
$\left[(NO)_2Fe \underset{\diagdown}{\overset{Et}{\underset{S}{\diagup}}} \right]_2$	Red crystals		Roussin's red salt as ethyl ester

---

[38a] O. L. Carter, A. T. McPhail and G. A. Sim, *Chem. Comm.*, **1966**, 49.

oxide complexes can be prepared in many ways, the simplest being the direct replacement of CO or other ligands by NO gas, e.g.,

$$Co_2(CO)_8 + 2NO \xrightarrow{petrol} 2Co(CO)_3NO + 2CO$$

Nitrosyl halides, like carbonyl halides, can be obtained by direct interaction of the halide and the gas. In a few instances, special methods are available using nitrite, hydroxylamine or NOCl as the source of NO, e.g.,

$$K_2PtCl_4 + NOCl = K_2[PtNOCl_5]$$
$$K_2CrO_4 + NH_2OH + OH^- + CN^- \rightarrow K_3[Cr^I(CN)_5NO] \cdot H_2O$$

A few nitric oxide compounds merit further discussion.

Nitrosyl Halides. These are formed especially by Fe, Co and Ni but also by V, Mn, Mo, W, Pd, Pt, Os, Rh, Ir and Cu. For the most part they are polymeric with halogen bridges, and they react with additional donor molecules, such as phosphites, phosphines and amines, to give monomers. There is a remarkable paucity of structural data on the nitrosyl halide compounds and their addition products. Typical compounds and their reactions are:

$$[Fe(NO)_2X]_2 + 2L = 2Fe(NO)_2XL$$
$$\tfrac{1}{\infty}[Mo(NO)_2Cl_2]_\infty + 2L = Mo(NO)_2Cl_2L_2$$
$$[Ni(NO)X]_4 + 4L = 2[Ni(NO)XL]_2$$
$$[Ni(NO)XL]_2 + 2L = 2Ni(NO)XL_2$$

Roussin's Salts and Esters. There are many compounds, often with very complicated formulas, which contain both NO and sulfur. The best known are the two series of Roussin's salts, the red and black and their esters. The diamagnetic red salts, $M^I_2[Fe(NO)_2S]_2$, can be prepared in several ways and the esters obtained either directly or by treating the salts with alkyl halides:

$$[Fe(NO)_2I]_2 \xrightarrow{K_2S} K_2[Fe(NO)_2S]_2 \xrightarrow{RX} [Fe(NO)_2SR]_2$$
$$Fe(NO)_2(CO)_2 \xrightarrow{RSH} [Fe(NO)_2SR]_2$$

The structure of the ethyl ester is shown in Figure 27-12a. The black salts contain the anion $[Fe_4(NO)_7S_3]^-$ whose structure is shown in Figure 27-12b. The very short Fe—N distances (1.57, 1.67 A) indicate strong Fe—N bonding and the existence of highly delocalized molecular orbitals has been proposed to account for the diamagnetism and the structural and spectroscopic properties of this curious species. Carbonyl analogs to the red esters, viz., $[Fe(CO)_3SR]_2$ are known and have a similar structure.[38b] A related complex is $[Fe(CO)_3S]_2$ which has a structure[39] in which there is a μ-dithio, i.e., S—S bridge, symmetrically bound to two $Fe(CO)_3$ units. The S—S axis is in the plane perpendicular to the line joining the Fe atoms, and there is a "bent" Fe—Fe bond. This structure thus has some

[38b] L. F. Dahl and C. H. Wei, *Inorg. Chem.*, **2**, 328 (1963).
[39] C. H. Wei and L. F. Dahl, *Inorg. Chem.*, **4**, 1 (1965).

similarity to complexes which have bridging acetylene groups, e.g., $(CO)_3Co(PhCCPh)Co(CO)_3$ (see page 781).

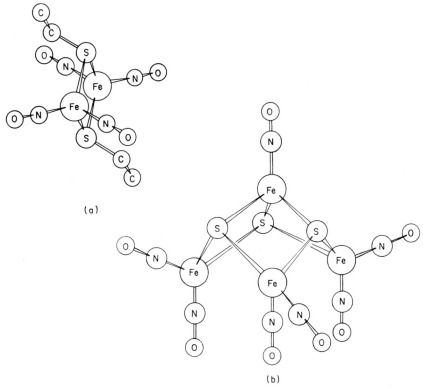

(a)

(b)

Fig. 27-12.   The structure of (a) the ethyl ester of Roussin's red salt, (b) the anion in the black salt.

Nitrosyl Cyanide Compounds. These are mostly of the type $[M(NO)$-$(CN)_5]^{n-}$, and their importance stems from the magnetic, spectroscopic and theoretical studies which have been made to determine their electronic structures. The weight of evidence indicates that there is very strong M—NO π bonding. However, more detailed interpretation of the electronic structures of these complexes is subject to controversy. According to the most recent suggestion,[40a] the order of the levels relevant to the outer electron configuration is: $(d_{xz}, d_{yz}) < d_{xy} < \pi^*NO < d_{x^2-y^2} < d_{z^2}$. The esr data[40b] for $[Cr(NO)(L)_5]^{3-}$ (L = CN, NH$_3$, H$_2$O) can be explained by the electron configuration $(d_{xz}, d_{yz})^4 d_{xy}{}^1$, making this a good example of the NO$^+$

[40a] H. B. Gray and P. T. Manoharan, *J. Amer. Chem. Soc.*, **87**, 3340 (1965).

[40b] I. Bernal, S. D. Robinson, L. S. Meriwether and G. Wilkinson, *Chem. Comm.*, **1965**, 571.

formalism (although considerable back donation occurs and the level called π^* NO has much d orbital character). For $[Fe(NO)(CN)_5]^{3-}$ the assignment is $(d_{xz}, d_{yx})^4 \, d_{xy}^2(\pi^*NO)^1$, which means that this complex is better described as containing Fe^{II} and $NO^{\cdot}$ than as an Fe^I—NO^+ complex (see below). Table 27-7 lists a number of $[M(NO)(CN)_5]^{n-}$ complexes according to their presumed[40a] electronic structures. The NO^- case will be discussed below.

TABLE 27-7

Some $[M(NO)(CN)_5]^{n-}$ Complexes and their Presumed Electronic Structures

Formal structures	Occupation of outer orbitals	Examples, M(n)
d^5-NO^+	$(d_{xz}, d_{yz})^4 d_{xy}^1$	Cr(3), Mn(2)
d^6-NO^+	$(d_{xz}, d_{yz})^4 d_{xy}^2$	V(5), Mn(3), Fe(2)
d^6-$NO^{\cdot}$	$(d_{xz}, d_{yz})^4 d_{xy}^2(\pi^* \; NO)^1$	Fe(3)
d^6-NO^-	$(d_{xz}, d_{yz})^4 d_{xy}^2(\pi^* \; NO)^2$	Co(3)

Brown-ring Compounds. The nature of these classical nitrosyl complexes, which were discovered in 1790 by Priestley and have long been used as a test for nitrates, has remained a problem until recently. The compounds can be obtained by direct interaction of aqueous solutions of ferrous salts with nitric oxide; the reaction

$$[Fe(H_2O)_6]^{2+} + NO = [Fe(H_2O)_5NO]^{2+} + H_2O$$

is reversible, and the equilibrium constant has been measured. The NO can be readily swept out of the solution by nitrogen. Infrared studies confirm the presence of a coordinated NO^+ group, since there is a band at 1745 cm^{-1} and susceptibility measurements give a value of 3.90 BM for the complex. The only formulation in keeping with these facts is that of a high spin d^7 octahedral complex with NO donating three electrons to give, formally, a complex of Fe^I, that is, $[Fe^INO(H_2O)_5]^{2+}$. The brown color is attributable to charge-transfer bands associated with the Fe—N—O system.

Ruthenium forms numerous NO complexes of exceptional stability (see Section 30-F-1).

Other Types of NO Complex. We have considered in the last section complexes where NO donates formally as NO^+. It is conceivable that instead of the electron in the antibonding orbital being transferred to the metal, it could stay on the NO which would then donate M ← N—O; since NO is paramagnetic, there should be an unpaired spin on the NO in such a complex. There are only two cases in which this seems to occur, the $[Fe(NO)(CN)_5]^{3-}$ ion already discussed, and the NO complex formed by heme where esr data[41] indicate that the electron resides mainly in NO.

[41] For references and detailed studies of Fe—NO compounds, see C. C. McDonald, W. D. Phillips and H. F. Mower, *J. Amer. Chem. Soc.*, **87**, 3319 (1965).

Although bridging CO groups are common, and at least one case of bridging RNC is known, there is no proved example of bridging NO. However, on the basis of indirect evidence the presence of such groups has been postulated, first in (π-C_5H_5)$_2$Mn$_2$(NO)$_3$ and more recently [42] in the similar compounds (π-C_5H_5)$_2$Mn$_2$(CO)$_2$(NO)$_2$ and [(π-C_5H_5)Cr(NO)]$_2$.

Finally, we come to the possibility that a metal atom may transfer an electron to NO, giving NO$^-$, which then would behave as an ordinary anionic ligand, donating two electrons. At one time there was thought to be evidence for the independent existence of the NO$^-$ ion, but it is now clear that the "M^{I}NO" compounds, such as "NaNO," do not contain such an ion. [43] It appears that they contain the *cis* isomer of the hyponitrite ion (ONNO)$^{2-}$. The complexes which have most generally been considered to contain NO$^-$ are [Co(NH$_3$)$_5$NO]$^{2+}$ and [Co(NO)(CN)$_5$]$^{3-}$. Two isomers, one red, the other black, of the former have long been known and a great many attempts have been made to assign structures to them. It is now virtually certain [44] that the red isomer is a dimer, containing an ONNO^{2-} ion of some configuration between the Co atoms (27-V). The black isomer is monomeric [45] with the structure 27-VI. Actually this structure is

$$a \sim 1.95 \qquad d \sim 1.26 \text{ or } \sim 1.41$$
$$b \sim 2.29 \qquad \angle \text{ N—Co—N } \sim 90°$$
$$c \sim 2.01 \qquad \angle \text{ Co—N—O } \sim 180°$$

(27-VI)

(27-V)

reasonable in some ways but puzzling in others, when considered as that of an NO$^-$ complex of Co^{III}. The Co—NO bond length is entirely reasonable for a Co^{3+} to NO$^-$ bond, but the diamagnetism of the compound is hard to explain in view of the linearity of the Co—N—O chain. For such a linear structure, the π^* NO orbitals should be doubly degenerate and the two electrons postulated to be occupying them should be unpaired (as in O$_2$). The great uncertainty in the N—O bond length (the two values quoted

[42] R. B. King and M. B. Bisnette, *Inorg. Chem.*, **3**, 791 (1964).

[43] N. Gee, D. Nicholls and V. Vincent, *J. Chem. Soc.*, **1964**, 5897.

[44] R. D. Feltham, *Inorg. Chem.*, **3**, 1038 (1964); M. Ardon, *Israel J. Chem.*, **2**, 181 (1964).

[45] D. Hall and A. A. Taggart, *J. Chem. Soc.*, **1965**, 1359; D. Dale and D. C. Hodgkin, *J. Chem. Soc.*, **1965**, 1364.

resulting from independent studies) makes discussion difficult. On addition of one electron to $O_2{}^+$ (isoelectronic with NO) the O—O distance increases only 0.09 A (see page 369). Since the distance in NO is 1.14 A, an NO$^-$ distance of only around 1.23 A would be expected, though this argument is not rigorous. A final point is that the exceptional length of the Co—NH$_3$ bond *trans* to NO is also quite surprising but not entirely unexpected in view of the high *trans* effect of NO. Since the crystals used to determine this structure were twinned and very possibly disordered, it may be that the structure reported is *very* inaccurate.

The assignment of $[Co(NO)(CN)_5]^{3-}$ as an NO$^-$ complex rests on the orbital diagram (see above) and the observation of an NO stretching frequency at 1150 cm^{-1}. The correctness of the assignment is proved by observation of an isotopic shift in the N^{15}O complex. This frequency is quite reasonable for an NO bond with an order of ~ 2. Since the complex is diamagnetic, it should have a bent Co—N—O chain but structural data are lacking.

27-7. Cyanide Complexes

The formation of cyanide complexes is restricted almost entirely to the transition metals of the d block and their near neighbours Zn, Cd and Hg. This appears to indicate that metal–CN π bonding is of importance in the stability of cyanide complexes and, as shown below, there is evidence of various types to support this. However, the π-accepting tendency of CN$^-$ does not seem to be nearly as high as for CO, NO$^+$ or RNC, which is, of course, reasonable in view of its negative charge. CN$^-$ is a strong nucleophile so that back bonding need not be invoked to explain the stability of its complexes with metals in normal (i.e., II, III) oxidation states. Nonetheless, because of the formal similarity of CN$^-$ to CO, NO and RNC, it is convenient to discuss its complexes in this chapter.

Types of Cyano Complex. The main class of cyano complexes have the general formula $[M^{n+}(CN)_x]^{(x-n)-}$ and are anionic, such as $[Fe(CN)_6]^{4-}$, $[Ni(CN)_4]^{2-}$, $[Mo(CN)_8]^{3-}$. Mixed complexes, particularly of the type $[M(CN)_5X]^{n-}$, where X may be H$_2$O, NH$_3$, CO, NO, H or a halogen are also well known.

Although bridging cyanide groups might be expected in analogy with those formed by CO, none have been definitely proved. However, linear bridges, M—CN—M, are well known and play an important part in the structures of many crystalline cyanides and cyano complexes. Thus AuCN, Zn(CN)$_2$ and Cd(CN)$_2$ are all polymeric with infinite chains.

The free anhydrous acids corresponding to many cyano anions can be isolated, examples being H$_3$[Rh(CN)$_6$] and H$_4$[Fe(CN)$_6$]. These acids are thus different from those corresponding to many other complex ions, such as $[PtCl_6]^{2-}$ or $[BF_4]^-$ which cannot be isolated except as hydroxonium (H_3O^+) salts, and they are also different from metal carbonyl hydrides in that they contain no metal–hydrogen bonds. Instead the hydrogen atoms are situated in hydrogen bonds between anions[46], i.e., MCN . . . H . . . NCM. Different sorts of structures arise depending on the stoichiometry. For example, in $H[Au(CN)_4]$ there are chains, while in $H_2[Pd(CN)_4]$ there are sheets. For octahedral anions there is a difference in structure depending on whether or not the number of protons equals half the number of cyanide ions. For $H_3[M(CN)_6]$ compounds an infinite, regular 3-dimensional array is formed in which the hydrogen bonds are perhaps symmetrical, whereas in other cases the structures appear to be more complicated.

Metal–Cyanide Bonding. The cyanide ion occupies a very high position in the spectrochemical series, gives rise to large nephelauxetic effects and produces a strong *trans* effect. All these properties are accounted for most easily by postulating M—CN π bonding, and semi-empirical MO calculations[31] support this. From close analysis of the vibrational spectra of cyanide complexes,[47] the existence of π bonding has been confirmed more directly, but it does not appear to be nearly as extensive as in carbonyls.

However, the cyanide ion does have the ability to stabilize metal ions in low formal oxidation states, and it presumably does this by accepting electron density into its π^* orbitals. The fact that cyano complexes of zero-valent metals are generally much less stable (in a practical as opposed to a well-defined thermodynamic or chemical sense) than similar metal carbonyls has often been taken to show the poor π-acidity of CN^-, but it should be noted that the cyano compounds, e.g., $[Ni(CN)_4]^{4-}$, are anionic and might thus tend to be more reactive for this reason alone. In some instances cyano complexes are known in two or even three successive oxidation states, $[M(CN)_n]^{x-}$, $[M(CN)_n]^{(x+1)-}$, $[M(CN)_n]^{(x+2)-}$, and in this respect they resemble the complexes to be discussed next.

LIGANDS WITH EXTENDED π SYSTEMS

27-8. Dipyridyl and Similar Amines

2,2′-Dipyridyl forms complexes with many metal ions in normal (e.g., $+2, +3$) oxidation states, in which the bonding can be formulated in much the same way as in all ordinary complexes of these same metal ions. Thus, there are presumably strong σ donor bonds, supplemented by some

[46] D. F. Evans, D. Jones and G. Wilkinson, *J. Chem. Soc.*, **1964**, 3174; A. P. Ginsberg and E. Koubek, *Inorg. Chem.*, **4**, 1186 (1965).
[47] L. H. Jones, *Inorg. Chem.*, **2**, 777 (1963); **3**, 1581 (1964); **4**, 1472 (1965).

moderate degree of π bonding. However, in contrast to nearly all of the other complexes formed by metal ions in normal oxidation states the *dipy complexes*, generally $[Mdipy_2]^{n+}$ or $[Mdipy_3]^{n+}$, can be reduced giving stable species with the same formulas but with charges of only $+1, 0$ or even -1. This is true of both transition and nontransition metals.[48]   The ones which have been obtained with a charge of 0 are those of the metals: Li, Be, Na, Mg, Al, Si, Sc, Y, Ti, Zr, V, Nb, Cr, Mo, W, Mn, Fe, Co, Zn and U.

The problem of meaningfully assigning oxidation states to the metals in these compounds is a very subtle one, and may not, in fact, admit of any simple solution involving whole numbers, even in a purely formal sense. One obvious extreme is to assume that the ligand, dipy, is always formally neutral, thus making the formal oxidation state of the metal equal to whatever charge is carried by the complex as a whole. Herzog, who has prepared most of the known complexes, uses this formalism, and it has been implicitly adopted here for the purpose of classifying dipy as a π-acid type ligand. When this formalism is used, it must be assumed that the dipy molecules manifest their π-acidity by absorbing electron density from filled metal orbitals into the π^* antibonding orbitals of the ring system. This view is perhaps preferable for the transition metal complexes (although direct support, as from esr or electronic spectral studies, is virtually absent), but for the nontransition metal complexes it seems less appropriate than the other extreme formalism.[49]   In this, the metal atom is assumed to remain always in a normal oxidation state while the dipy groups are assumed to be reduced to radical anions, dipy$^{\bar{\ }}$, with the extra electrons occupying antibonding π^* orbitals. When the number of unpaired electrons is found to be less than the number of dipy$^{\bar{\ }}$ groups, it is further postulated that there is sufficient dipy$^{\bar{\ }}$–dipy$^{\bar{\ }}$ interaction to cause coupling of spins.

Obviously there can be cases in which the distribution of electrons is about midway between those postulated in these two extreme formalisms, thus making them equally appropriate—or inappropriate—descriptions. In such cases an accurate description will be possible only in terms of LCAO expressions for the occupied MO's, showing how much metal character and how much ligand character each of them has.

27-9. Olefin Dithiol or Dithio-α-diketone Ligands

This relatively newly discovered category of complexes presents the same problems of ambiguity, or at least potential ambiguity, in the assignment

---

[48] See S. Herzog and H. Präkel, *Proc. 8th ICCC*, Vienna, 1964, p. 214 for references.
[49] L. E. Orgel, *J. Chem. Soc.*, **1961**, 3683.

of oxidation states as described in the preceding section, but in what is perhaps an even more elaborate and extensive way. The complexes in question here are mainly of the type 27-VII, although several other types

$$\left[\left(\begin{matrix}R \\ R\end{matrix}\ {C \atop C}\ \begin{matrix}S \\ S\end{matrix}\right)_n M\right]^x$$

R = H, alkyl, C_6H_5, CF_3, CN
n = 2; x = 0, −1, −2
n = 3; x = 0, −1, −2, −3

(27-VII)

$$\left[\left(\begin{matrix} \\ R\end{matrix}\ \begin{matrix}S \\ S\end{matrix}\right)_n M\right]^x$$

R = alkyl
n = 2; x = 0, −1, −2

(27-VIII)

$$\left(\ {N-H \atop S}\ \right)_2 Ni$$

(27-IX)

$$\left(\ {N-H \atop N-H}\ \right)_2 Ni$$

(27-X)

more limited in number such as 27-VIII, 27-IX and 27-X are closely related. It is stressed that all lines drawn between atoms in the formulas and equations used here are only for guidance and do *not* indicate valences or bond orders, since to do so would be to beg the question.

These compounds, particularly those of types 27-VII and 27-VIII, may be obtained for many of the transition metals by a variety of preparative methods.[50-52] A few representative reactions are the following:

$$NiCl_2 + Na^+{}_2[(NC)C(S)C(S)(CN)]^{2-} \xrightarrow{(C_2H_5)_4N^+} [(C_2H_5)_4N]^+{}_2 \left[\left(\begin{matrix}NC \\ NC\end{matrix}\ {C \atop C}\ \begin{matrix}S \\ S\end{matrix}\right)_2 Ni\right]^{2-}$$

$$Ni(CO)_4 + 2(C_6H_5)_2C_2 + 4S \rightarrow \left(\begin{matrix}C_6H_5 \\ C_6H_5\end{matrix}\ {C \atop C}\ \begin{matrix}S \\ S\end{matrix}\right)_2 Ni \xrightarrow[(C_2H_5)_4N^+]{p\text{-}H_2NC_6H_4NH_2}$$

$$[(C_2H_5)_4N]^+ \left[\left(\begin{matrix}C_6H_5 \\ C_6H_5\end{matrix}\ {C \atop C}\ \begin{matrix}S \\ S\end{matrix}\right)_2 Ni\right]^{-}$$

[50] G. N. Schrauzer and V. P. Mayweg, *J. Amer. Chem. Soc.*, **87**, 1483, 3585 (1965).
[51] A. Davison and D. V. Howe, *Chem. Comm.*, **1965**, 290; J. A. McCleverty, *et al.*, *Chem. and Ind.*, **1965**, 1300; *Chem. Comm.*, **1966**, 29.
[52] H. B. Gray, *et al.*, *Inorg. Chem.*, **5**, 78 (1966); *J. Amer. Chem. Soc.*, **88**, 43 (1966).

There have been extensive studies aimed at elucidating the electronic structures of these complexes by means of magnetic, redox and spectroscopic measurements.[53-56]   The molecular structures have been shown to be as indicated in 27-VII with square coordination of the metal ions in the ML_2^{x-} $(x = 0, 1, 2)$ complexes by X-ray studies of several compounds.[50,57]

The problem of assigning valence states and electronic structures, which at the present time (September 1965) still appears to be unresolved, is illustrated by the series of three complexes, NiL_2, NiL_2^- and NiL_2^{2-}, where L represents $CF_3C(S)C(S)CF_3$, whose preparations have been described above.   Similar series of complexes related by electron transfer reactions, though not generally including all three members, are known with other metals and other $RC(S)C(S)R$ ligands.

There appears to be general agreement that the ML_2^{2-} complexes are most realistically formulated as olefin dithiolate (i.e., $RC(S)=C(S)R^{2-}$) complexes of dipositive metal ions, M^{2+}.   However, the description of the ML_2^- and ML_2^{2-} species is controversial.   One proposal attributes the oxidation processes, $ML_2^{2-} \rightarrow ML_2^-$ and $ML_2^- \rightarrow ML_2$, entirely to the metal atoms and thus describes the neutral molecules as olefin dithiolate complexes of M^{4+} ions.   Another view is that the oxidations take place entirely by

[53] A. Davison, N. Edelstein, R. H. Holm and A. H. Maki, *J. Amer. Chem. Soc.*, **86**, 2799 (1964); *Inorg. Chem.*, **2**, 1226 (1963); **3**, 814 (1964).

[54] *Idem.*, *J. Amer. Chem. Soc.*, **86**, 4580 (1964).

[55] H. B. Gray, *et al.*, *J. Amer. Chem. Soc.*, **86**, 4594 (1964); *Inorg. Chem.*, **3**, 663 (1964).

[56] I. Stiefel, J. H. Waters, E. Billig and H. B. Gray, *J. Amer. Chem. Soc.*, **87**, 3016 (1965).

[57] J. H. Enemark and W. N. Lipscomb, *Inorg. Chem.*, **4**, 1729 (1965); A. E. Smith, *et al.*, *J. Amer. Chem. Soc.*, **87**, 5798 (1965).

removing electrons from the ligands and the ML^- and ML_2 compounds are thus assumed to contain M^{2+} with, respectively, one or two radical anion ligands, $RC(S)C(S)R^-$. Another extreme view, namely that the ML_2 complexes should be considered as zero-valent metal complexes of dithio-α-diketones is not generally considered plausible, particularly as there seems to be square coordination[50] in $[(C_6H_5)C(S)C(S)(C_6H_5)]_2Ni$, whereas an Ni^0 complex ought to be tetrahedral (cf. $Ni(CO)_4$ and its derivatives).

As noted before in respect to the dipyridyl complexes, the true electron distribution need not correspond exactly to any simple picture in which integral numbers of electrons are allocated to metal atoms, but it is permissible to try and determine whether one such picture is significantly closer to the truth than another. At present, there is considerable esr evidence which is alleged to support[54] the idea that the oxidation state of the metal varies in a series of electron transfer related compounds, while other evidence,[51,56] such as the fact that compound 27-X, in which the oxidation state of II for the metal seems rather certain, appears to have an electronic structure essentially similar to the electronic structures of the compounds of Ni of type 27-VII and compounds 27-VIII and 27-IX. Probably the only way in which to settle definitively the question of the electron distributions in these species is by study of hyperfine coupling in the esr spectra of appropriately isotopically substituted paramagnetic species.

In view of the controversy over assignment of oxidation states in these substances, they have not in general been considered as compounds representative of particular oxidation states in Chapters 29 and 30. However, in deference to the older tradition of treating dipyridyl complexes as though dipy is always a neutral ligand, the dipyridyl complexes are often mentioned later as examples of lower oxidation states, e.g., $Crdipy_3^-$ as a Cr^{-I} complex.

References*

Abel, E. W., *Quart. Rev.*, **17**, 133 (1963). Brief review on binary carbonyls.

Booth, G., *Adv. Inorg. Chem. Radiochem.*, **6**, 1 (1964). Comprehensive review of complexes of phosphines, arsines and stibines.

Chatt, J., P. L. Pauson and L. M. Venanzi in H. Zeiss, ed., *Organometallic Chemistry* (A.C.S. Monograph No. 147), Reinhold, New York, 1960. General review on carbonyls and related compounds.

Ford-Smith, M. H., *The Chemistry of Complex Cyanides*, H.M. Stationery Office, London, 1964. Comprehensive collection of data and references.

Ginsberg, A., *Progr. Transition Met. Chem.*, **1**, 111 (1965). Hydrido complexes.

Green, M. L. H., and D. J. Jones, *Adv. Inorg. Chem. Radiochem.*, **7**, 115 (1965). Hydrido complexes.

Griffith, W. P., *Quart. Rev.*, **16**, 188 (1962). Review of CN^- complexes.

* See also references for Chapter 28.

Hieber, W., W. Beck and G. Braun, *Angew Chem.*, **72**, 795 (1960). Early work on carbonylate ions.

Hileman, J. C., in W. F. Jolly, ed., *Preparative Inorganic Reactions*, Vol. I, p. 77, Interscience–Wiley, New York, 1964. Metal carbonyls.

Johnson, B. F. G., and J. A. McCleverty, *Progr. Inorg. Chem.*, Vol. 7, 1966. Comprehensive review on NO complexes.

King, R. B., *Adv. Organomet. Chem.*, **2**, 157 (1964). Catalog of carbonylate and substituted carbonylate ions and reactions.

Livingstone, S. E., *Quart. Rev.*, **19**, 386 (1965). Extensive review of complexes with S, Se and Te donor ligands.

Malatesta, L., *Progr. Inorg. Chem.*, **1**, 283 (1959). Isocyanide complexes.

Manuel, T. A., *Adv. Organomet. Chem.*, Vol. 3, 1965. Lewis base–metal carbonyl complexes.

Nyholm, R. S., *Proc. Chem. Soc.*, **1961**, 273. Electronic configuration and structure of complexes including carbonyls.

Sternberg, H. W., and I. Wender, *Proc. I.C.C. Spec. Pub. No. 13*, Chemical Society, London, 1959. Metal carbonyls as intermediates in organic reactions.

Venanzi, L. M., *Angew Chem. (Internat.)*, **3**, 453 (1964). Complexes of tetradentate P and As ligands.

Williams, H. E., *Cyanogen Compounds*, Arnold, London, 1948. Contains much early information on cyanide complexes.

28

Organometallic Compounds of Transition Metals

Although a few compounds with transition metal–carbon bonds have been known for a long time, it is only comparatively recently, principally during the years of intense activity following the discovery of the compound di-π-cyclopentadienyliron, $(\pi\text{-}C_5H_5)_2Fe$, that it has become clearly recognized that the formation of bonds to carbon is a general and characteristic property of all of the d-group transition metals. The metals can form a variety of compounds in which there is a normal σ bond to carbon, although the binary alkyls and aryls are usually less stable thermally and chemically than those in which other ligands, notably π-bonding ligands, are in addition bound to the metal atom. The unique characteristics of d orbitals also allow certain types of unsaturated hydrocarbons and some of their derivatives to be bound to metals in a nonclassical manner to give molecules or ions with structures which have no counterpart elsewhere in chemistry. Not only are a wide range of organo compounds of different types isolable, but labile species play an important role in many metal-complex catalyzed reactions of olefins, acetylenes and their derivatives. Many of these reactions also involve the incorporation of carbon monoxide and/or hydrogen into unsaturated molecules.

28-1. "Sandwich"-bonded Compounds

The first compound of this class, reported in 1951, is di-π-cyclopentadienyliron, $(\pi\text{-}C_5H_5)_2Fe$, *ferrocene*. Although it was at first supposed that this exceedingly thermally stable compound had C_5H_5 groups bound to iron by σ bonds, it was shown by a combination of chemical and physical studies, culminating with X-ray confirmation, that the correct structure is that shown in Figure 28-1. The designation $\pi\text{-}C_5H_5$ is made to distinguish such bonding from the normal alkyl type, i.e., σ-C_5H_5, where there is a metal to carbon σ bond. Although in the crystal of ferrocene, the two symmetrical five-membered rings are staggered, in the corresponding ruthenium compound (Fig. 28-1) they are eclipsed. From various lines

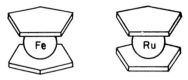

Fig. 28-1.   Staggered and eclipsed configurations found for ferrocene and ruthenocene, respectively, in their crystals.

of physical and chemical evidence, it is certain that the barrier to rotation of the rings about the metal to ring axis is very small. The relative orientation of the rings in crystals is probably mainly a reflection of packing forces in the lattice; moreover, transitions in the heat capacity of ferrocene at low temperatures suggest that the relative orientation of the rings is temperature dependent.[1]

The recognition of the "sandwich" concept of bonding stimulated a vast amount of work not only on cyclopentadienyl derivatives but also on similar carbocyclic systems. We discuss first the cyclopentadienyl system since this is by far the most important and forms the greatest variety of isolable compounds.

π-Cyclopentadienyl Metal Complexes.   Cyclopentadiene is a weak acid ($pK_a \sim 20$) and with a variety of bases can give salts of the symmetrical cyclopentadienide ion, $C_5H_5^-$; like other ring systems which give "sandwich" compounds, this ion has the "aromatic" sextet of π electrons. A general method for the preparation of all cyclopentadienyl compounds is the reaction of sodium cyclopentadienide with a metal halide or complex halide in tetrahydrofuran, ethyleneglycol dimethyl ether, dimethylformamide or similar solvent. A solution of sodium salt is obtained by treating dispersed sodium with the hydrocarbon in tetrahydrofuran:

$$2C_5H_6 + Na = C_5H_5^- + Na^+ + H_2 \text{ (main reaction)}$$
$$3C_5H_6 + 2Na = 2C_5H_5^- + 2Na^+ + C_5H_8$$
$$C_5H_5^- + MR^+ = C_5H_5MR$$

An alternative method useful in some cases employs a strong base, preferably diethylamine, for example,

$$2C_5H_6 + 2(C_2H_5)_2NH + FeCl_2 \xrightarrow[\text{amine}]{\text{in excess}} (\pi\text{-}C_5H_5)_2Fe + 2(C_2H_5)_2NH_2Cl$$

[1] J. Edwards, G. L. Kington and R. Mason, *Trans. Faraday. Soc.*, **56**, 660 (1960).

Since the $C_5H_5^-$ anion functions as a uninegative ligand, the di-π-cyclopentadienyl metal complexes are of the type $[(\pi\text{-}C_5H_5)_2M]X_{n-2}$, where the oxidation state of the metal M is n and X is a uninegative ion. Hence in the II oxidation state we obtain neutral, sublimable and organic solvent-soluble molecules like $(\pi\text{-}C_5H_5)_2Fe$ and $(\pi\text{-}C_5H_5)_2Cr$ and in III, IV and V oxidation states species such as $(\pi\text{-}C_5H_5)_2Co^+$, $(\pi\text{-}C_5H_5)_2TiCl_2$ and $(\pi\text{-}C_5H_5)_2NbBr_3$, respectively.

All of the $3d$ elements have been obtained in neutral molecules, and, with the exception of the manganese compound discussed below, they appear to have the same structure and essentially the same bonding as in ferrocene; however, only ferrocene is air stable, the others being sensitive to destruction or oxidation by air; the stability order is Ni > Co > V ≫ Cr > Ti.

The cationic species, several of which can exist in aqueous solutions provided these are acidic, behave like other large unipositive ions, e.g., Cs^+, and can be precipitated by silicotungstate, $PtCl_6^{2-}$, BPh_4^- and other large anions. The $(\pi\text{-}C_5H_5)_2Co^+$ ion is remarkably stable and is unaffected by concentrated sulfuric and nitric acids, even on heating.

Some typical π-cyclopentadienyl compounds are given in Table 28-1.

TABLE 28-1

Some Di-π-cyclopentadienyl Metal Compounds

Compound	Appearance; melting point, °C	Unpaired electrons	Other properties[a]
$(\pi\text{-}C_5H_5)_2Fe$	Orange crystals; 174	0	Oxidized by $Ag^+(aq)$, dil. HNO_3; $\pi\text{-}Cp_2Fe^+ = \pi\text{-}Cp_2Fe$, $E^0 = -0.3$ v (vs. SCE); stable thermally to $> 500°$.
$(\pi\text{-}C_5H_5)_2Cr$	Scarlet crystals; 173	2	Very air sensitive; soluble HCl giving C_5H_6 and blue cation, probably $[\pi\text{-}C_5H_5CrCl(H_2O)n]^+$
$(\pi\text{-}C_5H_5)_2Ni$	Bright green; 173 (d.)	2	Fairly air stable as solid; oxidized to Cp_2Ni^+; NO gives $\pi\text{-}CpNiNO$; Na/Hg in C_2H_5OH gives $\pi\text{-}CpNiC_5H_7$
$(\pi\text{-}C_5H_5)_2Co^+$	Yellow ion in aqueous solution	0	Forms numerous salts and a stable strong base (absorbs CO_2 from air); thermally stable to ~ 400°
$(\pi\text{-}C_5H_5)_2TiCl_2$	Bright red crystals; 230	0	Sl. sol. H_2O giving $\pi\text{-}Cp_2TiOH^+$; C_6H_5Li gives $\pi\text{-}Cp_2Ti(C_6H_5)_2$; reducible to $\pi\text{-}Cp_2TiCl$; Al alkyls give polymerization catalyst
$(\pi\text{-}C_5H_5)_2WH_2$	Yellow crystals; 163	0	Moderately stable in air, soluble benzene, etc.; soluble in acids giving $\pi\text{-}Cp_2WH_3^+$ ion

[a] $Cp = C_5H_5$

In addition to the di-π-cyclopentadienyls, many other sandwich-bonded compounds exist in which only one $\pi\text{-}C_5H_5$ ring is present, together with other ligands. A few of these compounds, their methods of production and reactions are shown in Figure 28-2.

The $\pi\text{-}C_5H_5$ ring has a resemblance to benzene in its C—C bond order and it was anticipated that the ring would have aromatic character. For compounds whose properties allow them to survive the reaction conditions, this possibility has been amply realized. The most extensive study has been made with ferrocene, which has been shown to undergo a large number of reactions such as Friedel–Crafts acylation, metalation by butyllithium, sulfonation, etc.; there is now an exceedingly extensive

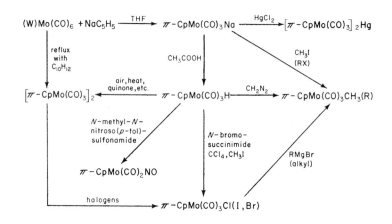

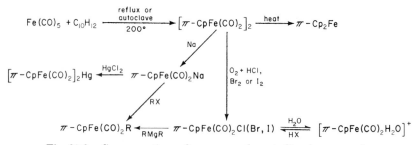

Fig. 28-2. Some reactions of mono-π-cyclopentadienyl compounds.

organic chemistry of ferrocene. A monocyclopentadienyl compound, π-$C_5H_5Mn(CO)_3$, behaves similarly. It is now known that in certain organic reactions of the molecules the metal atom is directly involved. One example is the intramolecular hydrogen bonding of ferrocene alcohols; another is the protonation of ferrocene (see later) in Friedel–Crafts reactions.

Bonding in π-Cyclopentadienylmetal Compounds. A detailed theoretical account of the bonding between the metal atoms and the C_5H_5 rings is beyond the scope of this text; although numerous different approaches have been made, there are still unsettled problems. However, the essential feature of the bonding is fairly easy to grasp. We can consider the ferrocene molecule to result from the combination of a ferrous ion with two $C_5H_5^-$ anions or from the combination of an iron atom with two C_5H_5 radicals.

There are advantages for the former, and it is more realistic in view of the methods of preparation. Each $C_5H_5^-$ anion is planar and is a symmetrical pentagon in shape. Each carbon atom of the ring has a p_z orbital perpendicular to the plane of the ring and these p_z (or $p\pi$) orbitals combine into π molecular orbitals. Five MO's are formed, and the lower three of these are occupied by three electron pairs. It is primarily the overlap of these filled MO's with empty orbitals on the iron atom which gives rise to the bonding, but there is also some back-bonding between filled orbitals on the iron atom and the two unfilled MO's of the $C_5H_5^-$ anion. "Back-bonding" is not essential, however, since in compounds such as $(\pi\text{-}C_5H_5)_2TaH_3$ there are no filled orbitals on the tantalum atom, but, where filled nonbonding orbitals exist, the "back-bonding" effect can enhance the metal to ring bonding.

As an example of the overlap of a filled π MO of the $C_5H_5^-$ ring with an empty d orbital of the iron atom—and in fact the one believed to be of major importance in the bonding—consider the diagrams in Figure 28-3.

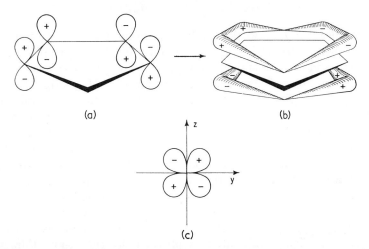

Fig. 28-3. Diagrams showing the molecular orbital view of the bonding in di-π-cyclopentadienyl compounds of the ferrocene type (see text).

In Figure 28-3a the p_z orbitals of four of the carbon atoms of a C_5H_5 ring are shown. In Figure 28-3b the general nature of the MO formed by overlap of these orbitals is sketched. This is one of the three π MO's which contains a pair of electrons. Figure 28-3c shows the d_{yz} orbital of the ferrous ion which is empty and which also has the xz plane as a nodal plane. The ring MO and the iron d_{yz} orbital are thus symmetrically compatible and can overlap to give a bond. The primary metal to ring bond is thus a two-electron covalent bond. The empty d_{zx} orbital of iron can overlap with a filled π MO similar to Figure 28-3b on another $C_5H_5^-$ ring, thus producing $(\pi\text{-}C_5H_5)_2Fe$ with the "sandwich" geometry. In order to account in detail for all features of the structure, all of the possible overlaps must be considered. In a very crude way we can envisage the existence of a circularly symmetric tube of π-electron density on the $C_5H_5^-$ anion overlapping with a cylindrically symmetric set of orbitals on the metal atom.

Although it was originally thought that there was some special feature of the bonding that gave the parallel ring, or ferrocene-like, structure, this view had to be modified to account for the monocyclopentadienyl compounds, and the subsequent observation that in several di-π-cyclopentadienyl compounds the rings are *not* parallel.

The non-planarity had to be postulated to account for the fact that the compounds $(\pi\text{-}C_5H_5)_2ReH$, $(\pi\text{-}C_5H_5)_2MoH_2$ and $(\pi\text{-}C_5H_5)WH_2$ appeared to have lone-pairs since they behaved as *bases*, comparable in strength to ammonia, dissolving in aqueous acids to give cations, e.g.,

$$(\pi\text{-}C_5H_5)_2WH_2 \underset{OH^-(aq)}{\overset{H^+(aq)}{\rightleftharpoons}} (\pi\text{-}C_5H_5)_2WH_3^+$$

Ferrocene itself is a very weak base but can be protonated by a propionic anhydride–boron trifluoride hydrate mixture; other cyclopentadienyl compounds, and arene metal carbonyls (see below), are also weak bases.[2]

In addition, nmr studies showed that for $(\pi\text{-}C_5H_5)_2WH_3^+$ and the nonbasic $(\pi\text{-}C_5H_5)_3TaH_3$, only two of the hydrogen atoms are equivalent, the three hydrogens constituting an A_2B system. These observations can be accounted for. If it is assumed that the rings are tilted as in Figure 28-4, and that in the bonding all nine s, p and d orbitals of the metal are utilized, it is possible to construct two identical sets of three hybridized orbitals which provide good overlap with the ring orbitals even if the angle ω is as low as $150°$ (Fig. 28-4c). The remaining three hybridized orbitals, only two of which, $spd_{x^2-y^2}$, d_{z^2} hybrids (A, in Fig. 28-4c), are equivalent, and the third, an sp hybrid, can then be used to house lone-pairs or to bond other groups. Final confirmation is provided by the X-ray diffraction study (Fig. 28-4b) of $(\pi\text{-}C_5H_5)_2MoH_2$.[3]

While the main bonding according to the MO view of ferrocene can be regarded as that due to a two-electron bond between the metal and ring, the more general treatment involving three spd hybridized orbitals suggests that it is possible to consider the $\pi\text{-}C_5H_5$ ring as occupying three coordination positions about the metal atom. This is an artificiality but has some use in that it can *sometimes* be used to predict the approximate molecular

[2] M. L. H. Green, J. A. McCleverty, L. Pratt and G. Wilkinson, *J. Chem. Soc.*, **1961**, 4854; A. Davison, W. McFarlane, L. Pratt and G. Wilkinson, *J. Chem. Soc.*, **1962**, 3653.
[3] M. Gerloch and R. Mason, *J. Chem. Soc.*, **1965**, 296.

structure. Thus $(\pi\text{-}C_5H_5)_2TaH_3$ or $(\pi\text{-}C_5H_5)_2MoH_2$ can be considered as 9-coordinate, the latter having a stereochemically important lone-pair. Finally, it may be noted that in a number of non-symmetrical mono-π-cyclopentadienyl compounds,[4] the bond lengths and angles in the $\pi\text{-}C_5H_5$

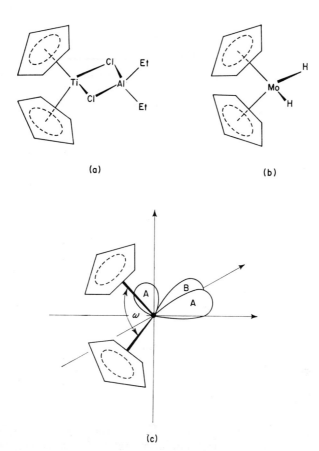

(a)   (b)

(c)

Fig. 28-4. The structures of (a) $(\pi\text{-}C_5H_5)_2TiCl_2Al(C_2H_5)_2$ and (b) $(\pi\text{-}C_5H_5)_2MoH_2$. Figure (c) shows the general structure of $(\pi\text{-}C_5H_5)_2MX_n$ ($n = 1, 2, 3$); ω can be between 150 and 180°. The orbitals A and B are nonbonding toward the rings and may be occupied by groups or by lone-pairs.

ring suggest that the five-fold symmetry is lost in the sense that the bond lengths vary approximately as shown in 28-I. This could arise because the d_{xz} and d_{yz} orbitals of the metal are not entirely equivalent and therefore do not overlap with the corresponding ring π orbitals in an entirely

[4] M. J. Bennett, M. R. Churchill, M. Gerloch and R. Mason, *Nature*, **201**, 1318 (1964).

equivalent way. Another way of interpreting the distortion of the five-fold symmetry is to assume that there is a tendency of the ring to behave as a combination of an olefin and an allyl anion (see later discussion) as indicated in 28-II. However, the idea lacks generality since there exist

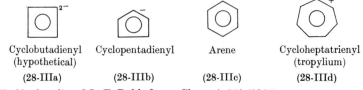

$$a = 1.29 - 1.44 \text{ A}$$
$$b = 1.42 - 1.49 \text{ A}$$
$$c = 1.34 - 1.43 \text{ A}$$

(28-I)   (28-II)

structures[5] in which no significant deviation from five-fold symmetry of the $\pi\text{-}C_5H_5$ ring occurs.

Tris π-cyclopentadienyls of U, Np and Pu are known;[6a] for $(\pi\text{-}C_5H_5)_3UCl$, the $\pi\text{-}C_5H_5$ rings have been found to be in a distorted tetrahedral arrangement with the chlorine occupying the fourth position but bound essentially ionically.[6b]

Ionic Cyclopentadienides. As noted above, the alkali metals give ionic derivatives such as $C_5H_5^-Na^+$. On electrostatic grounds, we could expect that for a dipositive metal, M^{2+}, in which there is little possibility of covalent bonding due to d overlap, the two $C_5H_5^-$ rings would align themselves on opposite sides of the metal atom to give a ferrocene-like structure. For $Mg(C_5H_5)_2$ and $Mn(C_5H_5)_2$, this appears to be so. The manganese compound is anomalous among the other neutral $(C_5H_5)_2M$ compounds; like C_5H_5Na, it reacts with water, and with ferrous chloride in tetrahydrofuran gives ferrocene quantitatively. Also the free molecule has five unpaired electrons like the Mn^{2+} ion, while the crystals show anomalous antiferromagnetic behavior similar to that of other Mn^{II} compounds.

The lanthanide elements form similar crystalline ionic derivatives, $M(C_5H_5)_3$, $MCl(C_5H_5)_2$ and, for Eu, $Eu(C_5H_5)_2$. They are thermally very stable, sublime *in vacuo* but are air- and water-sensitive. They undergo quantitative ionic reactions,

$$2Pr(C_5H_5)_3 + 3Fe^{2+} \xrightarrow{\text{THF}} 3(\pi\text{-}C_5H_5)_2Fe + 2Pr^{3+}$$

Other Symmetrically Delocalized Hydrocarbon Metal Complexes. It has been noted that the $C_5H_5^-$ ion has a sextet of π electrons. Other ring systems (28-III) with this sextet could be expected to give "sandwich"

Cyclobutadienyl (hypothetical)	Cyclopentadienyl	Arene	Cycloheptatrienyl (tropylium)
(28-IIIa)	(28-IIIb)	(28-IIIc)	(28-IIId)

[5] W. E. Oberhansli and L. F. Dahl, *Inorg. Chem.*, **4**, 150 (1965).
[6a] F. Baumgartner, *et al.*, *Angew. Chem.*, **77**, 866 (1965); *Naturwiss.*, **52**, 560 (1965).
[6b] C. Wong, T. Yen and T. Lee, *Acta Cryst.*, **18**, 340 (1965).

compounds similar to the π-C_5H_5 compounds. All four systems have indeed been bound to metals, although only $C_5H_5{}^-$ and arenes give L_2M type compounds.

Cyclobutadienylmetal Compounds. Before their isolation, complexes of this type were postulated to act as intermediates in reactions of acetylenes with metal carbonyls. Comparatively few established complexes exist. The first of these was the methyl-substituted nickel compound obtained as in Figure 28-5.

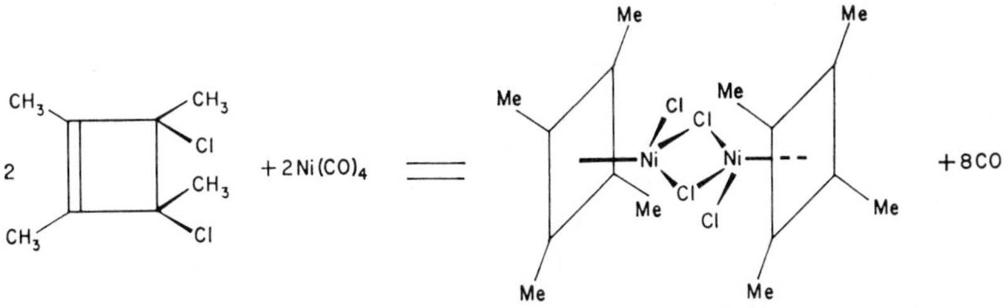

Fig. 28-5. The preparation and structure of $[(CH_3C)_4NiCl_2]_2$.

The interaction of diphenylacetylene with $Fe_3(CO)_{12}$ under specified conditions gives a complex $Ph_4C_4Fe(CO)_3$ in which there is an essentially square carbon ring bound to iron;[7] $Mo(CO)_6$ similarly gives $Ph_4C_4Mo(CO)_2$.[8] Tetraphenylcyclobutadiene complexes can often be synthesized by ligand transfer using tetraphenylcyclobutadiene-palladium(II) chloride as reagent.[9] It is not fully established whether some of the compounds obtained do in fact contain cyclobutadiene rings or whether they are tautomers containing two acetylene groups (cf. 28-XX). However, a molybdenum complex is postulated to have the structure 28-IV.

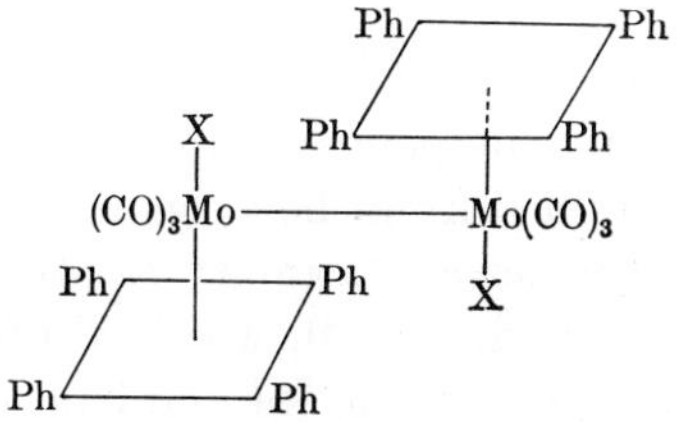

(28-IV)

A good example of the need for caution in postulating the existence of coordinated cyclobutadiene rings is provided by the compound of empirical

[7] R. P. Dodge and V. Schomaker, *Acta. Cryst.*, **18**, 614 (1965).
[8] W. Hübel and R. Merenyi, *J. Organomet. Chem.*, **1**, 213 (1964).
[9] P. M. Maitlis, A. Efraty and M. L. Games, *J. Amer. Chem. Soc.*, **87**, 719 (1965).

formula $C_4H_4AgClO_4$, which nmr evidence indicates is a cyclo-octatetraene derivative $C_8H_8 \cdot 2AgClO_4$. However, a true *unsubstituted* cyclobutadiene complex[10] has been obtained by the interaction of *cis*-3,4-dichloro-cyclobutene with $Fe_2(CO)_9$. Evidence for $C_4H_4Fe(CO)_3$, rather than a bis(acetylene)iron tricarbonyl formulation, is provided by the mass spectroscopic cracking pattern where no peaks due to loss of C_2H_2 fragments could be observed, and by the reaction with $FeCl_3$ in ethanol to give *trans*-3,4-dichlorocyclobutene. It undergoes aromatic substitution re-actions (cf. ferrocene).

Certain compounds obtained by the action of diphenylacetylene on $PdCl_2$ in ethanol, in which a molecule of this solvent becomes incorporated, have been shown[9,11] to be cyclobutenyl derivatives. In these, three carbon atoms of the four-membered ring are bound to the metal as in the allyl complexes discussed later.

Arene Metal Compounds. The chromium arene compounds were obtained by Hein over 30 years ago by the reaction of $CrCl_3$ and C_6H_5MgBr; acid hydrolysis of the reaction mixture gave yellow solutions which were believed to contain σ-bonded phenyl cationic derivatives such as $(C_6H_5)_3Cr^+$.

These "polyphenylchromium" compounds are now known to be diarene chromium cations with benzene, di- or triphenyl units "sandwich" bonded to the metal, such as 28-V.

(28-V)   (28-VI)   (28-VII)

The prototype neutral compound, dibenzenechromium, $(C_6H_6)_2Cr$ (28-VI), has also been obtained from the Grignard reaction of $CrCl_3$, but a more effective method of wider applicability to other metals is the direct interaction of an aromatic hydrocarbon with a transition metal halide in presence of Al powder as a reducing agent and halogen acceptor and $AlCl_3$ as a Friedel–Crafts type activator. Although the neutral species are formed directly in the case of chromium, the usual procedure is to hydrolyze the reaction mixture with dilute acid which gives the cations $(C_6H_6)_2Cr^+$, $(mesitylene)_2Ru^{2+}$, etc. In several cases these cations can be reduced to the neutral molecules by reducing agents such as hypophosphorous acid.

[10] R. Pettit, *et al.*, *J. Amer. Chem. Soc.*, **87**, 131, 3254 (1965).
[11] L. F. Dahl and W. E. Oberhansli, *Inorg. Chem.*, **4**, 629 (1965).

Dibenzenechromium, which forms dark brown crystals, is much more sensitive to air than ferrocene, with which it is isoelectronic; it does not survive the reaction conditions of aromatic substitution reactions. As with the π-C_5H_5 compounds, a variety of complexes with only one arene ring have been prepared, for example,

$$C_6H_5CH_3 + Mo(CO)_6 \overset{reflux}{=} C_6H_5CH_3Mo(CO)_3 + 3CO$$

$$C_6H_6 + Mn(CO)_5Cl + AlCl_3 = C_6H_6Mn(CO)_3{}^+AlCl_4{}^-$$

X-ray and electron diffraction measurements on dibenzenechromium and other arene complexes show that the carbon–carbon bond lengths are equivalent.[12]

π-Cycloheptatrienyl or Tropylium Compounds. The seven-membered ring complexes are few and not too stable; they have not been prepared directly from the $C_7H_7{}^+$ ion itself, but only indirectly, for example,

$$C_7H_8Mo(CO)_3 + (C_6H_5)_3C^+BF_4{}^- = \pi\text{-}C_7H_7Mo(CO)_3{}^+BF_4{}^- + (C_6H_5)_3CH$$

$$\pi\text{-}C_5H_5V(CO)_4 + C_7H_8 \overset{reflux}{\longrightarrow} \pi\text{-}C_5H_5V\pi\text{-}C_7H_7$$

Nmr studies show the equivalence of the seven hydrogen atoms in $[C_7H_7Mo(CO)_3]^+$ and the probable structure of this ion is shown in 28-VII.

Heterocyclic Sandwich Compounds. There is no reason, in principle, why certain heterocyclic rings which have a significant degree of aromatic character should not be able to form "sandwich"-type bonds to metals. Few such compounds are known and in some cases the failures are not explained, though in others, e.g., of pyridine, they are due to the fact that the heterocyclic atom has lone-pairs which are more basic than the π electrons. Compounds containing thiophen, e.g., $C_4H_4SCr(CO)_3$ and the anion of pyrrole, viz., $C_4H_4NMn(CO)_3$, are analogous to $C_6H_6Cr(CO)_3$ and π-$C_5H_5Mn(CO)_3$ respectively. Azaferrocene, π-cyclopentadienyl-π-pyrrolyliron, has also been obtained as red crystals, m 114°, of lower thermal stability than ferrocene;[13]

$$\pi\text{-}C_5H_5Fe(CO)_2I + C_4H_4NK \overset{\text{benzene}}{\searrow}$$
$$\pi\text{-}C_5H_5Fe\ \pi\text{-}C_4H_4N$$
$$FeCl_2 + C_5H_5Na + C_4H_4NNa \overset{\text{THF}}{\nearrow}$$

Azaferrocene appears to be isomorphous with ferrocene so that the N atoms must be randomly placed in any of the ten positions occupied by carbon in the ferrocene molecule in the crystal.

---

[12] A. Haaland, *Acta. Chem. Scand.*, **19**, 41 (1965); M. F. Bailey and L. F. Dahl, *Inorg. Chem.*, **4**, 1299, 1314 (1965).

[13] K. K. Joshi, P. L. Pauson, A. R. Qazi and W. H. Stubbs, *J. Organomet. Chem.*, **1**, 471 (1964); R. B. King and M. B. Bisnette, *Inorg. Chem.*, **3**, 796 (1964).

It has been shown recently[14a] that a carborane anion can give complexes which appear to be analogs of $(\pi\text{-}C_5H_5)_2Fe$, $\pi\text{-}C_5H_5Mn(CO)_3$ and $\pi\text{-}C_5H_5Re\text{-}$ $(CO)_3$. The $C_5H_5^-$ anion is replaced by an icosahedral $B_9C_2H_{11}^{2-}$ unit. The ferrocene analog, $[Fe(B_9C_2H_{11})_2]^{2-}$, which is obtained by interaction of $FeCl_2$ and a salt of the $B_9C_2H_{11}^{2-}$ ion, can be oxidized to the ferricinium ion analog, $[Fe(B_9C_2H_{11})_2]^-$. X-ray study[14b] of $\pi\text{-}C_5H_5Fe(B_9C_2H_{11})$ has confirmed the "sandwich" bonding of the CCBBB "ring" of an icosahedral face of the carborane to the metal atom.

28-2. Olefin Complexes

About 1830, Zeise, a Danish pharmacist, characterized a compound of stoichiometry $PtCl_2 \cdot C_2H_4$ which is now known to be a dimer with chlorine bridges; he also isolated, from the reaction products of chloroplatinate with ethanol, salts of the ion $[C_2H_4PtCl_3]^-$. Although the structures of these ethylene complexes were fully established only recently, they were the first organometallic derivatives of transition metals to be prepared.

It was later found that certain metal halides or ions other than Pt^{II}, notably Cu^I, Ag^I, Hg^{II} and Pd^{II}, formed complexes when treated with a variety of olefins. Thus cuprous chloride in aqueous suspension will absorb ethylene, both components dissolving well beyond their normal solubilities and in a 1:1 mole ratio. Solid cuprous halides also absorb some gaseous olefins, but the dissociation pressures of the complexes are quite high. The interaction of silver ions especially, with a variety of unsaturated substances, has been studied by physical measurements such as distribution equilibria between an aqueous and an organic solvent phase. The results can be accounted for in terms of equilibria of the type:

$$Ag^+(aq) + \text{olefin} = [Ag\ \text{olefin}]^+(aq)$$

For series of olefins, certain trends can be correlated with steric and inductive factors.[15] In some cases, the interaction of hydrocarbons with Ag^+ ions gives crystalline precipitates which are often useful for purification of the olefins. Thus cyclooctatetraene or bicyclohepta-2,5-diene on shaking with aqueous silver perchlorate (or nitrate) give white crystals of stoichiometry olefin$\cdot AgClO_4$ or 2olefin$\cdot AgClO_4$, depending on the conditions. Benzene with $AgNO_3$, $AgClO_4$ or $AgBF_4$ also gives crystalline complexes. In the structure of $[C_6H_6 \cdot Ag]^+ ClO_4^-$ the metal ion is asymmetrically located with respect to the ring.

[14a] M. F. Hawthorne, et al., J. Amer. Chem. Soc., **87**, 1818, 2496, 3987 (1965).

[14b] A. Zalkin, D. H. Templeton and T. E. Hopkins, J. Amer. Chem. Soc., **87**, 3988 (1965); A. H. Maki and T. E. Berry, J. Amer. Chem. Soc., **87**, 4437 (1965).

[15] W. Featherstone and A. J. S. Sorrie, J. Chem. Soc., **1964**, 5235; R. J. Cvetanovic, et al., J. Amer. Chem. Soc., **87**, 1827 (1965); W. H. Pritchard and W. J. Orville-Thomas, Theor. Chim. Acta, **3**, 426 (1965).

There is now an array of well-characterized olefin complexes of the elements of Groups VI–VIII, and there is evidence for rather unstable complexes of Ti and V. Some examples of olefin complexes are given in Table 28-2. In addition to hydrocarbons, other unsaturated compounds such as maleic acid or acrylonitrile, as well as perfluorinated olefins, may be bound to metals. While relatively few isolable species containing mono-olefins are known, there are a large number of complexes with chelating diolefins, e.g., bicyclohepta-2,5-diene, conjugated olefins, e.g., buta-1,3-diene, and especially cyclic olefins either nonconjugated, like *trans, trans,trans*-cyclododecatriene or conjugated like cycloheptatriene or cyclooctatetraene. Like carbonyls, olefin complexes are almost exclusively diamagnetic and the noble gas rule can usually be used to predict stoichiometries if each double bond is considered as a 2-electron donor.

Preparation. Olefin complexes are made in a variety of ways.

(a) The commonest method is direct interaction with a metal compound, commonly a halide or a carbonyl, viz.,

$$\underset{\text{cycloheptatriene}}{C_7H_8} + Mo(CO)_6 \xrightarrow{\text{reflux}} C_7H_8Mo(CO)_3 + 3CO$$

$$\underset{\text{butadiene}}{C_4H_6} + Fe(CO)_5 \xrightarrow{80° \text{ in bomb}} C_4H_6Fe(CO)_3 + 2CO$$

$$\underset{\substack{\text{cycloocta-}\\\text{1,5-diene}}}{C_8H_{12}} + RhCl_3(aq) \xrightarrow[\text{in ethanol}]{SnCl_2} C_8H_{12}Rh\underset{Cl}{\overset{Cl}{\diagdown}}RhC_8H_{12}$$

TABLE 28-2

Some Representative Olefin Complexes of Transition Metals

Olefin	Complex	Properties
Ethylene	$K[C_2H_4PtCl_3]$	Pale yellow, water-soluble salt
Cyclopentene	$\pi\text{-}C_5H_5Re(CO)_2C_5H_8$	Colorless crystals soluble in organic solvents; quite stable in air
Bicyclohepta-2,5-diene (norbornadiene)	$C_7H_8Fe(CO)_3$	Yellow distillable liquid
Cycloocta-1,5-diene	$[C_8H_{10}RhCl]_2$	Orange crystalline solid; halide bridge cleavable by *p*-toluidine, etc.
Cyclopentadiene	$\pi\text{-}C_5H_5CoC_5H_6$	Red crystals; gives $(\pi\text{-}C_5H_5)_2Co^+$ ion with acids
Octafluorocyclohex-1,3-diene	$C_6F_8Fe(CO)_3$	Colorless, air-stable and volatile crystalline solid
Cycloheptatriene	$C_7H_8Mo(CO)_3$	Red crystals; loses H^- with $(C_6H_5)_3C^+BF_4^-$ to give $C_7H_7Mo(CO)_3^+$
Cyclooctatetraene	$C_8H_8Fe(CO)_3$	Red crystals, m 72°; reversibly protonated by strong acids
Cyclododeca-1,5,9,-triene	$C_{12}H_{18}Ni$	Red crystals; air sensitive

For certain metal halides, a reducing agent must be used, as in the last example, where either ethanol alone or, more rapidly, stannous chloride will reduce the Rh^{III} to give a Rh^I complex. In other instances, e.g., with iridium, use of $SnCl_2$ gives olefin complexes containing an $SnCl_3$ group bound to the metal,[16] e.g.,

$$IrCl_6^{2-} + 2C_8H_{12} \xrightarrow[\text{in } C_2H_5OH]{SnCl_2} (C_8H_{12})_2IrSnCl_3$$

A special adaptation of the reductive procedure involves use of aluminum alkyls as in equation 28-1. With other metals, this type of reaction can lead to polymerization, e.g., of butadiene or acetylenes. These reactions involve unstable organometallic intermediates, some of which may be isolated (see later).

$$Ni\ acac_2 + C_{12}H_{18} \xrightarrow{AlEt_3 \text{ in ether}}$$

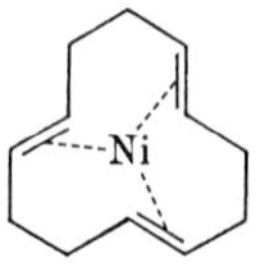

trans, trans, trans
cyclododeca-1,5,9,-triene

(28-1)

(*b*) Olefin complexes can also be obtained (i) by hydride ion addition to sandwich compounds, (ii) by hydride ion abstraction, or by protonation reactions of σ-bonded compounds.

Hydride ion addition to certain π-C_5H_5 compounds produces cyclopentadiene olefin complexes (equations 28-2, 28-3); addition to arene complexes give π-cyclohexadienyls (see later):

$$(\pi\text{-}C_5H_5)_2Co^+ + H^- \xrightarrow[\text{in THF}]{NaBH_4} \pi\text{-}C_5H_5CoC_5H_6$$

(28-2)

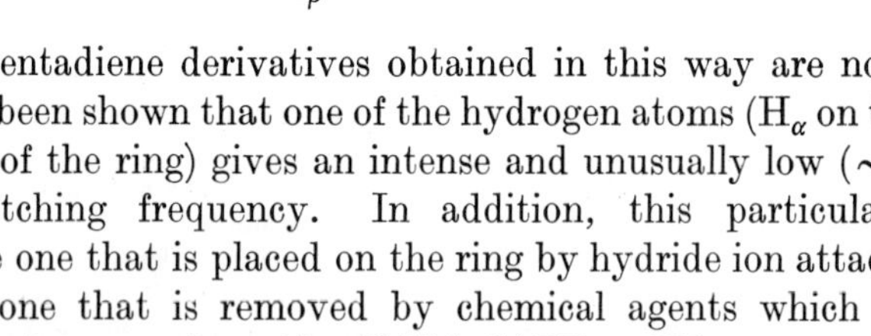

(28-3)

The cyclopentadiene derivatives obtained in this way are noteworthy in that it has been shown that one of the hydrogen atoms (H_α on the *endo*, i.e., metal side of the ring) gives an intense and unusually low (~ 2750 cm^{-1}) C—H stretching frequency. In addition, this particular hydrogen atom is the one that is placed on the ring by hydride ion attack, as well as being the one that is removed by chemical agents which can remove hydride ion, for example, acids, $(C_6H_5)_3C^+BF_4^-$, N-bromosuccinimide, etc. Thus we have reversible hydride ion transfer reactions such as that shown in equation 28-3.

Similar hydride transfer reactions are possible for certain complex

[16] J. F. Young, R. D. Gillard and G. Wilkinson, *J. Chem. Soc.*, **1964**, 5176.

alkyls,[17] where conversion to the olefin complex can be achieved by abstraction of H^- by triphenylmethyltetrafluoroborate:

$$\pi\text{-}C_5H_5(CO)_2Fe\text{—}CHRCH_2R' \xrightleftharpoons[BH_4^-]{Ph_3C^+BF_4^-} \left[\pi\text{-}C_5H_5(CO)_2Fe\cdots\underset{H}{\overset{H}{\underset{C}{\big|\big|}}}\overset{R}{\underset{R'}{C}} \right]^+ BF_4^- + Ph_3CH$$

There are related reactions[17] involving the addition to or abstraction of *protons* from the organic group. Thus acetonyl and other oxoalkyl compounds give olefin-coordinated ions in which the *enol* forms, e.g., of acetone, are stabilized by bonding to the metal atom:

$$\pi\text{-}C_5H_5(CO)Fe\text{—}\underset{CH_3}{\overset{H}{C}}\overset{H}{\underset{C=O}{\diagdown}} \xrightleftharpoons[base]{H^+} \left[\pi\text{-}C_5H_5(CO)_2Fe\cdots\underset{CH_3}{\overset{H}{\underset{C}{\big|\big|}}}\overset{H}{\underset{OH}{C}} \right]^+$$

A similar case occurs with cyanoalkyls, which may be reversibly protonated to ketenimine complexes:

$$\pi\text{-}C_5H_5(CO)_2Fe\text{—}\underset{CH_3}{\overset{C}{C}}\text{—H} \xrightleftharpoons[base]{H^+(D^+)} \left[\pi\text{-}C_5H_5(CO)_2Fe\cdots\underset{H\quad CH_3}{\overset{NH(D)}{\underset{C}{\big|\big|}}}C \right]^+$$

and, finally, σ-allylic complexes (see later) may be protonated:

$$\pi\text{-}C_5H_5(CO)_3Mo\text{—}CH_2\text{—}CH\text{=}CH_2 \xrightarrow{H^+} \pi\text{-}C_5H_5(CO)_3Mo\cdots\underset{H\quad H}{\overset{H\quad CH_3}{\underset{C}{\big|\big|}}}C$$

Structure and Bonding in Olefin Complexes. The nature of the bonding of olefins to metal atoms is still imperfectly understood, but it is quite clear that localized σ bonds between the metal atoms and carbon do not exist, except perhaps in certain compounds of tetrafluoroethylene and of cyclic unsaturated systems discussed below. The bonding is generally attributed to interaction between π electrons in the unsaturated molecule and hybrid orbitals of the metal.

Several olefin complexes have been studied by X-ray diffraction; two of the known structures are given in Figures 28-6 and 28-7. In ethylene complexes such as $[C_2H_4PdCl_2]_2$ and $[(C_2H_4)_2RhCl]_2$ the coordinated double bond is normal to the coordination plane, as shown in Figure 28-6. In

---

[17] M. L. H. Green, *et al.*, *J. Chem. Soc.*, **1963**, 889, 2976; **1964**, 1; *J. Organomet. Chem.*, **1**, 230 (1964).

[styrene PdCl$_2$]$_2$ the double bond is not normal to the plane, nor does this plane bisect the C=C bond (cf. discussion of allyl complexes); this sort of asymmetry may well occur in complexes of other unsymmetrical olefins. It is clearly not necessary that the metal atoms lie exactly along the direction

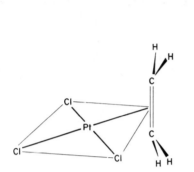

Fig. 28-6. The structure of the ion of Zeise's salt, [C$_2$H$_4$PtCl$_3$]$^-$.

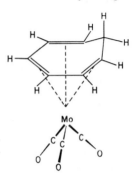

Fig. 28-7. The structure of cyclohepta-trienemolybdenum carbonyl.

of maximum π-electron density of the olefin, since the angles are quite different in the structures of chelate and cyclic olefin compounds, such as those shown in Figure 28-7 and equations 28-1 and 28-3.

The current view on the bonding is the MO approach illustrated in Figure 28-8. It assumes that the metal to olefin bond consists of two parts: (a)

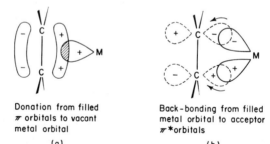

Donation from filled π orbitals to vacant metal orbital

(a)

Back-bonding from filled metal orbital to acceptor π*orbitals

(b)

Fig. 28-8. Diagrams showing the molecular orbital view of olefin–metal bonding according to Dewar. The donor part of the bond is shown in (a), and the back-bonding part in (b).

overlap of the π-electron density of the olefin with a σ-type acceptor orbital on the metal atom; (b) a "back-bond" resulting from flow of electron density from filled metal d_{xy} or other $d\pi$–$p\pi$ hybrid orbitals into anti-bonding orbitals on the carbon atoms. This view is thus similar to that discussed for the bonding of carbon monoxide and similar weakly basic ligands and involves some "double bond" character in the metal–olefin bond—though how much is uncertain.* The polarity of the donor bond (μ bond) is thus $(C_2H_4)^+$—M^-, whereas in the "back-bond" it is in the opposite direction so that these two modes of dative bonding mutually reinforce each other electrostatically and can lead to electroneutrality. The C—C distances which have been found in a number of olefin complexes lie in the range 1.40–1.47 A (whereas the C=C bond length is typically ~ 1.34 A) thus showing the reduction in bond order on coordination; this reduction is also shown by decreases of the order of 140–160 cm^{-1} in the C=C stretching frequencies where these can be observed.

There is no precise information concerning the extent to which electron density is located in the σ- and π-type bonds. For normal C=C bonds, there is a considerable barrier to free rotation so that in a metal–ligand "double bond" a barrier also might be anticipated. However, detailed nmr studies on the ethylene complexes $(C_2H_4)_2$Rhacac and $(C_2H_4)_2$Rh-(π-C_5H_5) indicate that the barrier to free rotation of the coordinated C_2H_4 about the metal–olefin axis is only about 6 kcal/mole.[18] This result is not actually surprising since back donation to the ethylene can take place not only from a $d\pi$ orbital perpendicular to the molecular plane (i.e., a d_{xz} or d_{yz} orbital) when the ethylene is in its normal perpendicular orientation, but also from the d_{xy} orbital when it lies in the plane of coordination. Thus the barrier to rotation measures only the difference between the strengths of these two bonds, or between the strength of the stronger one and that occurring at some intermediate rotational position, but it does not provide any absolute estimate of the strength of the $d\pi$–$p\pi$ interaction.

Although $(C_2H_4)_2$Rhacac is thermally stable, the exchange in solution

$$(C_2H_4)_2\text{Rhacac} + C_2D_4 \rightleftharpoons (C_2D_4)(C_2H_4)\text{Rhacac} + C_2H_4 \text{ etc.}$$

is very rapid, the average lifetime of a coordinated C_2H_4 molecule on Rh^I being *less* than 10^{-4} sec. at 25° This high lability contrasts with the inertness of π-C_5H_5Rh$(C_2H_4)_2$ and presumably reflects the more hindered condition of the Rh atom in the latter. Ethylene in $[PtCl_3(C_2H_4)]^-$ and in Rh$(C_2H_4)(PPh_3)_2$Cl also exchanges very rapidly—in the former[18] at a rate greater than 70 sec^{-1} even at $-75°$. There is similar lability in other square complexes, e.g., of CO in $(Ph_3P)_2$RhCl(CO).

Complexes of Cyclic Unsaturated Compounds. Certain of the numerous complexes of cyclic unsaturated compounds deserve special comment.

Cyclopentadiene and Cyclopentadienones.[19] It was mentioned earlier

---

[18] R. Cramer, *J. Amer. Chem. Soc.*, **86**, 217 (1964); *Inorg. Chem.*, **4**, 445 (1965).

[19] R. Mason and G. Wilkinson, in *Essays in Coordination Chemistry, Experientia Supplementa* No. 9, Birkhäuser Verlag, Basel, 1964, p. 233, and references therein.

* The bonding of C_2F_4 may involve metal–carbon σ bonding in some cases. See G. W. Parshall and F. N. Jones, *J. Amer. Chem. Soc.*, **87**, 5356 (1965) and M. J. Mays and G. Wilkinson, *J. Chem. Soc.*, **1965**, 6629.

that in C_5H_6 complex one of the hydrogen atoms on the CH_2 group has unusual properties. A variety of substituted compounds can be made, e.g., by the reaction with alkyl halides in tetrahydrofuran.

$$2(\pi\text{-}C_5H_5)_2Co^{II} + CF_3I = (\pi\text{-}C_5H_5)_2Co^{III}I + \pi\text{-}C_5H_5Co(C_5H_5CF_3)$$

The corresponding phenyl derivative has been shown to have the C_6H_5 group *exo* to the metal atom (i.e., replacing H_β, cf. eq. 28-3). This leads to a situation which has not yet been fully resolved, since for the *un*substituted C_5H_6 compounds, it is very difficult to explain the reactivity of one of the hydrogen atoms of the $> CH_\alpha H_\beta$ group or its anomalously low and intense C—H_α stretching frequency unless it is on *endo* side. The weakening of this C—H_α bond can then be attributed to some type of metal–hydrogen interaction comparable to hydrogen bonding (cf. page 208). It would seem, therefore, that the attack of H^- on, say, $(\pi\text{-}C_5H_5)_2Co^+$ gives an *endo*-H_α atom whereas the attack of C_6H_5Li gives an *exo*-C_6H_5 group.

Another important feature of these molecules is that nmr spectra suggest a structure in which two of the olefinic protons have become "aliphatic," as implied by 28-VIII, where there are two σ bonds plus a π bond, rather than two π bonds involved in bonding as in 28-IX. The structure 28-VIII

(28-VIII)   (28-IX)   (28-X)

could be regarded as one in which the metal atom has been involved in a Diels–Alder addition across a conjugated diene.

These nmr features are also shown by complexes of conjugated hydrocarbons, e.g., of butadiene, $C_4H_6Fe(CO)_3$, as well as by those of cyclopentadienone and other cyclic derivatives. Cyclopentadienone complexes can be made directly from interaction of the ligand and metal carbonyls, but are usually obtained by interactions with acetylenes:

$$\pi\text{-}C_5H_5Co(CO)_2 + 2CF_3C{\equiv}CCF_3 \longrightarrow \pi\text{-}C_5H_5Co{-} \qquad {=}O + CO$$

X-ray studies[19] of several such cyclic complexes have confirmed that there is a distinct tendency to approach the extreme bonding case of 28-VIII. The hybridization at C_2 and C_5 approaches tetrahedral so that C_1 bends away from the metal. This type of structure is also shown by a compound 28-X, where a hexakis(trifluoromethyl)benzene ring is bound by both olefinic and σ bonds.[20] Whether there is σ bonding from the terminal CH_2 groups in butadiene iron tricarbonyl is at present uncertain since available data indicate equal or nearly equal C—C bond lengths.

Cyclooctatetraene. This hydrocarbon can be bound by one or more of its double bonds. Thus in C_8H_8CuCl,[21] only one double bond is coordinated. Other complexes such as 28-XI have the olefin chelated in the boat form; the unused double bonds can be used for additional complexing in certain cases. A different type of complex (28-XII) is formed by interaction of $Fe_3(CO)_{12}$ with C_8H_8. In the crystal and in solution,[22a] the $Fe(CO)_3$ group is bound to four coplanar adjacent carbon atoms much as though these are acting like a butadiene unit. The conjugated nature of the remainder of the ring is shown by the formation of an adduct with tetracyanoethylene, and by the reversible protonation and hydride addition sequence:[22b]

(28-XI)   (28-XII)

A further unusual feature of $C_8H_8Fe(CO)_3$ is that despite the expectation based on 28-XII, in solution only *one* proton resonance line is observed. The single nmr line is believed to result from some rapid intramolecular exchange process. Similar phenomena have been discovered in other cases. At present, the tentative idea is that rotation of a ring relative to a metal atom to which it is bound unsymmetrically may occur with a relatively low activation energy—and hence rapidly—in cases where only redistribution of π electrons, and perhaps some alteration in bond angles, is required, but no bond breaking processes. Thus in 28-XIII we have a compound in which rotation does not occur, while in 28-XIV rotation does, the main evidence being nmr equivalence of all the ring protons.[23]

[20] R. S. Dickson and G. Wilkinson, *J. Chem. Soc.*, **1964**, 2699; M. R. Churchill and R. Mason, *Proc. Chem. Soc.*, **1964**, 226.

[21] N. C. Baenziger, G. F. Richards and J. R. Doyle, *Inorg. Chem.*, **3**, 1529 (1964).

[22a] R. T. Bailey, E. R. Lippincott and D. Steel, *J. Amer. Chem. Soc.*, **87**, 5346 (1965).

[22b] A. Davison, W. McFarlane, L. Pratt and G. Wilkinson, *J. Chem. Soc.*, **1962**, 4821.

[23] C. E. Keller, G. F. Emerson and R. Pettit, *J. Amer. Chem. Soc.*, **87**, 1389 (1965).

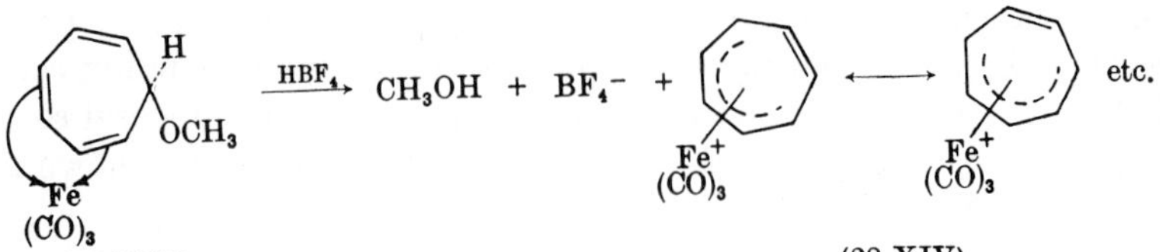

(28-XIII)   (28-XIV)

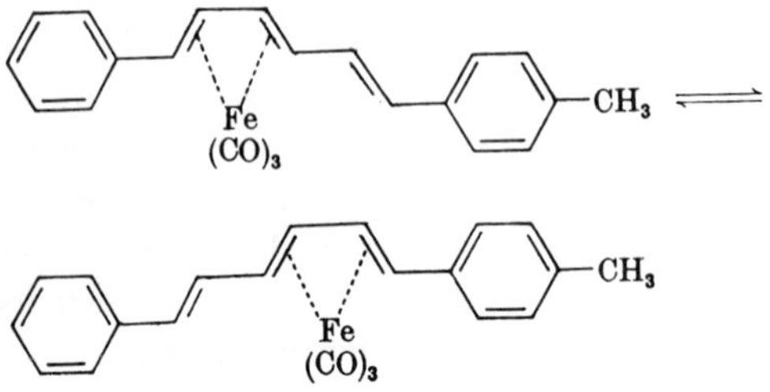

(28-XV)

Using a linear triene-iron tricarbonyl complex, it has proved possible to actually isolate two isomers (28-XV) which are interconverted at 120° but which are normally stable indefinitely.[24] It is not certain whether such isomerizations proceed by intermediates with only one double bond bound to the metal. A related phenomenon is the apparent equivalence of the protons in a σ-bound C_5H_5 ring in π-$C_5H_5Fe(CO)_2\sigma$-C_5H_5 where such equivalence would not be expected. Such rapid interconversions have some resemblances to valence isomerizations known in organic chemistry.[25] They are probably also related to intermediates in isomerization reactions of olefins catalyzed by metal species (see below).

28-3. Acetylene and Acetylene-derived Complexes

By analogy with the bonding of olefins, it might have been expected that for acetylenes, where there are two π bonds at right angles to each other, a metal atom could be bound to each. This possibility has been realized, for example, in the reaction of cobalt carbonyl with acetylenes of various types:

$$Co_2(CO)_8 + RC\equiv CR = Co_2(CO)_6(RC\equiv CR) \quad (R = CF_3, C_6H_5, \text{etc.})$$

The diphenylacetylene derivative has been studied by X-ray diffraction and it is indeed found (28-XVI) that two cobalt atoms (which also are

---

[24] H. W. Whitlock, Jr., and Y. N. Chuah, *J. Amer. Chem. Soc.*, **87**, 3605 (1965); *Inorg. Chem.*, **4**, 425 (1965).

[25] See E. Vogel, *Angew. Chem. (Internat.)*, **2**, 1 (1963) and G. Schröder in reference list.

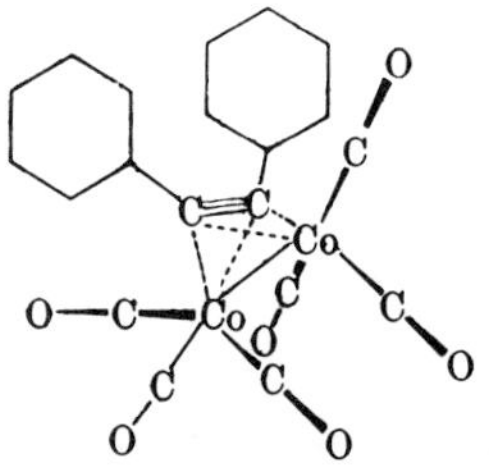

(28-XVI)

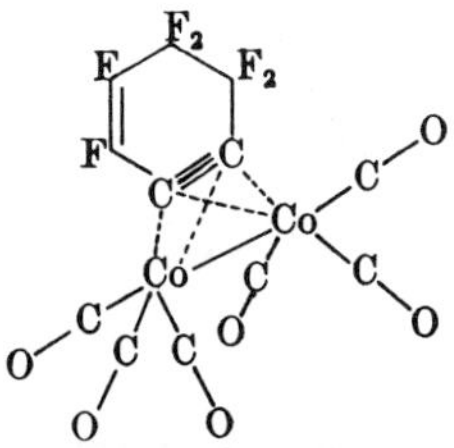

(28-XVII)

bound to each other by a metal–metal bond) are linked to the acetylene; the angle between the cobalt atoms and the C—C axis of the acetylene is about 90° as expected. A complex (28-XVII) which has a bridging acetylene-containing carbocyclic ring isomeric with perfluorobenzene (a kind of "benzyne") is obtained by interaction of $Co_2(CO)_8$ with perfluorocyclohexa-1,3-diene, which is partially defluorinated.[26] A number of complexes of a different type are known where the bound C—C bond appears to have considerable residual multiple bond character. Examples are 28-XVIII, where the carbon atoms are bound to a single metal atom, and 28-XIX where an alkyl type σ bond has been formed (cf. below). Finally some tungsten complexes $(RC{\equiv}CR)_3W(CO)$[27] appear to have three acetylene

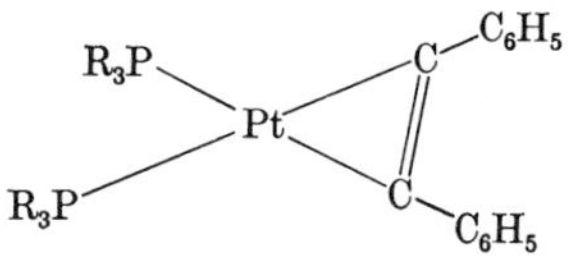

(28-XVIII)

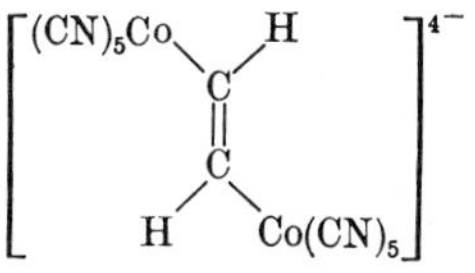

(28-XIX)

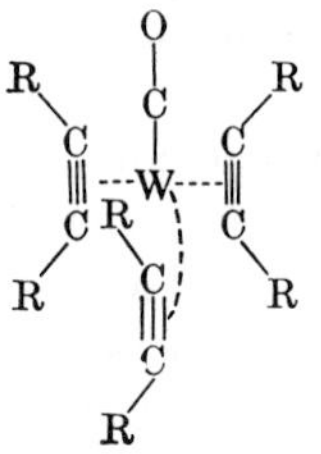

(28-XX)

ligands symmetrically arranged about the metal (28-XX) although precisely in what manner is not yet clear.

The majority of complexes derived from acetylenes (other than acetylides of monoacetylenes which have the grouping M—C≡CR and which are closely related to cyanide complexes, though they are often explosively unstable) are more complex products in which the identity of the acetylene has been lost.

The reaction of acetylenes with metal carbonyls, especially of iron, gives an array of complexes of various types, as well as ketones, quinones and

[26] R. L. Hunt and G. Wilkinson, *Inorg. Chem.*, **4**, 1270 (1965).
[27] D. P. Tate, J. M. Angl, W. M. Ritchey, B. L. Ross and J. G. Grasselli, *J. Amer. Chem. Soc.*, **86**, 3261 (1964). This gives references to various types of acetylene compounds.

other products. The course of the reactions depends very much on the conditions of temperature and pressure. We have already mentioned cyclobutadiene and cyclopentadienone metal compounds; others include those with quinones,[28] (28-XXI), and tropones,[29] and some with hetero-cyclic rings (28-XXII) or lactone rings (28-XXIII) .

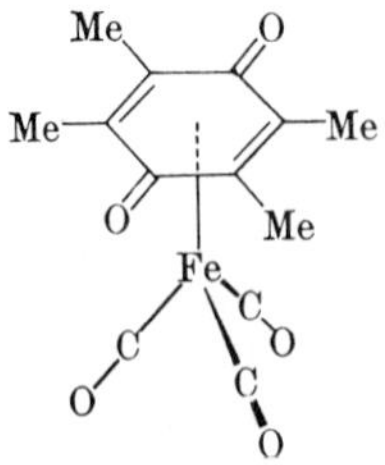

(28-XXI) 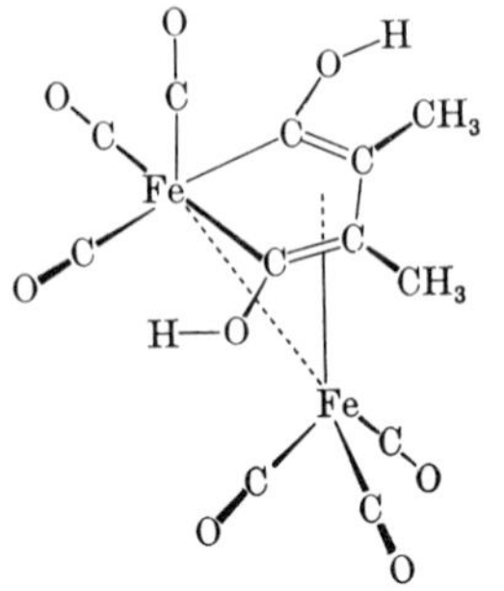   (28-XXII) 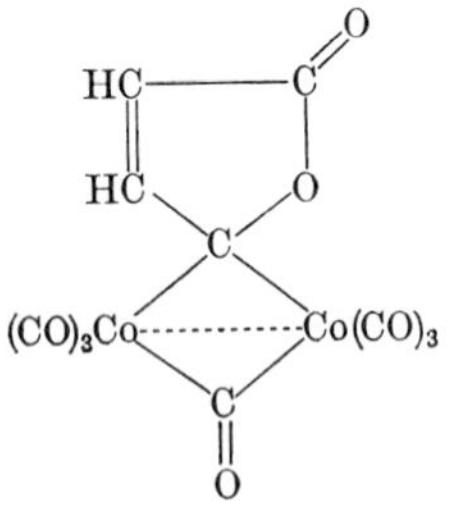   (28-XXIII)

28-4. Allyl and Related Metal Complexes

In π-cyclopentadienyl and arene complexes, leaving aside the question of distortion of five-fold symmetry in the former, there is symmetrical overlap between metal and ring orbitals. Although delocalization of electron density may occur to some extent in olefin complexes of conjugated and cyclic compounds, there is a well-characterized class of compounds, which are intermediate between the olefin and sandwich compounds. These have several carbon atoms, either in a ring or a chain over which electron density is delocalized.

π-Allyl Compounds. A number of compounds have been prepared in which a three-carbon delocalized allylic system $CH_2 \cdots CH \cdots CH_2$ can act as a sort of "half sandwich;" this system can be regarded, like NO, as a formal three-electron donor, or, if considered as an anion, as a four-electron donor.

The methods of preparation of the allyl complexes have been of the type:

$$CH_2 = CH - CH = CH_2 + HCo(CO)_4 \rightarrow \pi\text{-}CH_3 \cdot CHCHCH_2Co(CO)_3 + CO$$
Butadiene

$$CH_2 = CH - CH_2Cl + NaMn(CO)_5 \rightarrow CH_2 = CH - CH_2 - Mn(CO)_5 \xrightarrow{\text{heat}}$$
Allyl chloride   σ−Allyl compound

$$\pi\text{-}CH_2CHCH_2Mn(CO)_4 + CO$$
π−Allyl compound

$$CH_2 = CH - CH_2Cl + Ni(CO)_4 \rightarrow (\pi\text{-}CH_2CHCH_2NiCl)_2 + 4CO$$

$$2CH_2 = CH - CH_2MgBr + NiCl_2 \rightarrow (\pi\text{-}CH_2CHCH_2)_2Ni$$

[28] M. D. Glick and L. F. Dahl, *J. Organomet. Chem.*, **3**, 200 (1965).
[29] E. H. Braye and W. Hübel, *J. Organomet. Chem.*, **3**, 25 (1965).

The action of allyl alcohol on palladous halides also gives π-allyl, halide-bridged complexes.

For π-bonded, terminally substituted allyl compounds there are two isomers possible, as shown in Figure 28-9, where the stereochemistry is

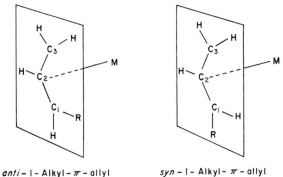

anti - I - Alkyl - π - allyl   *syn* - I - Alkyl - π - allyl

Fig. 28-9.   The idealized structure and stereochemistry of π-allyl compounds.

related to the middle hydrogen atom on C_2. Such isomers have been characterized, e.g., for $(\pi\text{-}CH_3CHCHCH_2)Co(CO)_3$.

X-ray studies of π-allyl complexes[30] indicate that the structure is somewhat different from the idealized one in Figure 28-9. In $[C_3H_5PdCl]_2$ the plane of the three allylic carbon atoms is *not* perpendicular to the plane of the $(PdCl)_2$ bridge system, being orientated so that the central carbon, C_2, although actually closest to Pd is tipped away from the metal (Fig. 28-10). Although the bonding of allyl groups can be described by non-classical overlaps of the sandwich-bond type, it is also possible, e.g., in the above Pd complex, in VB theory to regard the C_3H_5 group as occupying two bond positions in the usual square Pd^{II} geometry, delocalized π orbitals thus overlapping with two metal dsp^2 hybrids. In the interconversion of σ-allyl and π-allyl complexes, nmr and X-ray studies[31] show that there is an intermediate species which can be regarded as having the allyl group bound by a σ bond from the terminal carbon atom and a donor olefinic bond.

Cyclic allylic compounds include π-cyclobutenyls,[9,11] π-cyclopentenyls and π-cyclohexenyls prepared, for example, as follows:

$$(\pi\text{-}C_5H_5)_2Ni \xrightarrow[\text{EtOH}]{\text{Na/Hg}} \pi\text{-}C_5H_5Ni\pi\text{-}C_5H_7$$

$$\pi\text{-}C_6F_8Fe(CO)_3 + CsF \underset{}{\overset{\text{THF}}{\rightleftharpoons}} Cs[\pi\text{-}C_6F_9Fe(CO)_3]$$
Octafluorocyclo– π–Nonafluorocyclo–
hexa–1, 3–diene   hexenyl

[30] W. E. Oberhansli and L. F. Dahl, *J. Organomet. Chem.*, **3**, 43 (1965); M. R. Churchill and R. Mason, *Nature*, **204**, 777 (1964); A. E. Smith, *Acta Cryst.*, **18**, 331 (1965).

[31] J. Powell, S. D. Robinson and B. L. Shaw, *Chem. Comm.*, **1965**, 78; R. Mason and D. R. Russell, *Chem. Comm.*, **1966**, 26.

It appears that palladium especially readily forms allylic complexes, whereas with the same ligand, Pt gives olefin complexes, e.g., with mesityl oxide $PdCl_2$ and Na_2PtCl_4[32] give respectively 28-XXIV and 28-XXV.

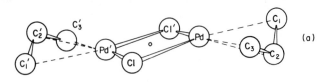

(a)

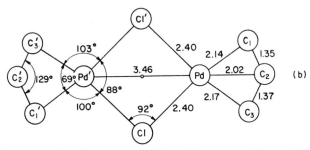

(b)

Fig. 28-10.   Structure of allylpalladium(II) chloride dimer.   (Reprinted by permission from *J. Organomet. Chem.*, **3**, 43 (1965).)

(28-XXIV)

(28-XXV)

(28-XXVI)

(28-XXVII)

Similarly with butadiene[33] palladium gives 28-XXVI and not an olefin complex.

[32] G. W. Parshall and G. Wilkinson, *Inorg. Chem.*, **1**, 896 (1962).
[33] S. D. Robinson and B. L. Shaw, *J. Chem. Soc.*, **1963**, 4806; **1964**, 5002.

The formation of allylic intermediates is believed to be of common occurrence in a variety of catalytic reactions such as the conversion of allyl alcohol into di-allyl ether by acidified Pd^{II} solutions, the carbonylation of allylic halides,[34] and in the isomerization of olefins by complexes of the platinum metals. The suggestion that allylic species such as 28-XXVII occur in the trimerization of butadiene to *trans,trans,trans*-cyclododeca-1,5,9-triene by Ni^0 catalysts[35] has been given substance by the isolation from the interaction of $RuCl_3$ and C_4H_6 in 2-methoxyethanol at 100°, of the complex $RuCl_2(C_4H_6)_3$ shown in 28-XXVIII. The carbon chain formed in

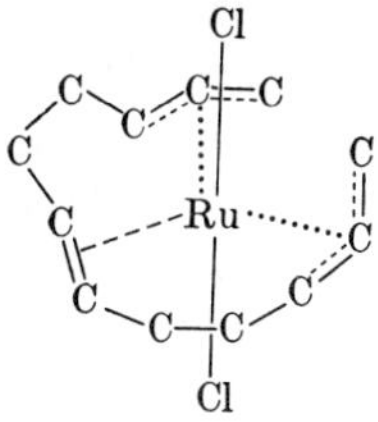

(28-XXVIII)   (28-XXIX) $R = tert\text{-}C_4H_9$

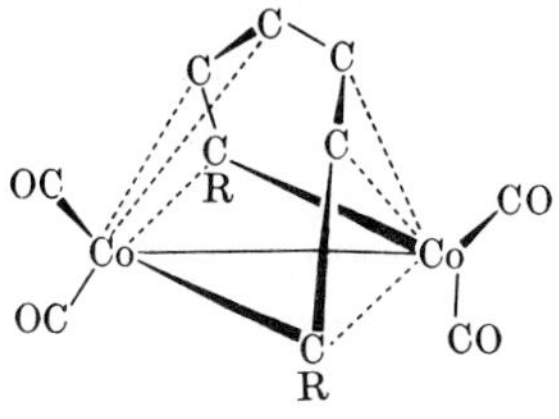

the polymerization of butadiene is stabilized by binding to a formally Ru^{IV} atom by one olefinic and two allylic bonds in a roughly trigonal bipyramidal configuration.[36]

A similar sort of bridged species[37] is that shown in 28-XXIX which can be interpreted as a diallyl.

π-Cyclohexadienyl Compounds. Another partially delocalized system, π-cyclohexadienyl, can act as a ligand formally analogous to $\pi\text{-}C_5H_5$. Hydride attack on suitable arene metal cations, or hydride ion abstraction from cyclohexa-1,3-diene olefin complexes, gives π-cyclohexadienyls, e.g.,

$$C_6H_8Fe(CO)_3 + Ph_3CBF_4 = C_6H_7Fe(CO)_3{}^+ + BF_4{}^- + Ph_3CH$$

while arene manganese tricarbonyl cations give the complex as in equation 28-4 where the H_α atom, as in C_5H_6 compounds discussed earlier, is chemically reactive.

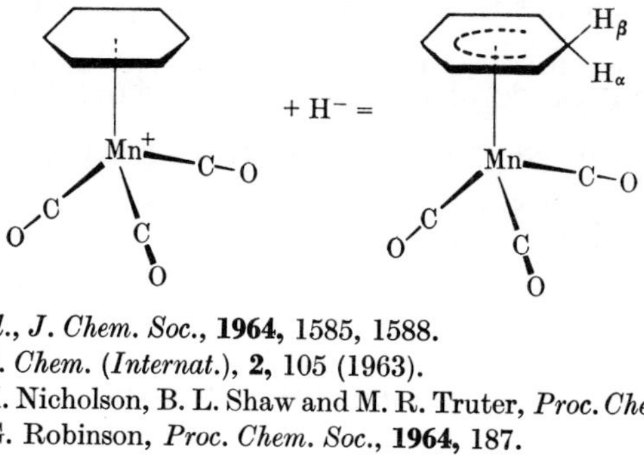

$+ H^- =$ (28-4)

---

[34] W. T. Dent, *et al.*, *J. Chem. Soc.*, **1964**, 1585, 1588.
[35] G. Wilke, *Angew. Chem. (Internat.)*, **2**, 105 (1963).
[36] J. E. Lydon, J. K. Nicholson, B. L. Shaw and M. R. Truter, *Proc. Chem. Soc.*, **1964**, 421.
[37] O. S. Mills and G. Robinson, *Proc. Chem. Soc.*, **1964**, 187.

For substituted derivatives, the R group also appears to be *exo* as in C_5H_5R complexes.

The species $C_8H_9Fe(CO)_3{}^+$, obtained by protonation of $C_8H_8Fe(CO)_3$, has been noted. Other olefin complexes which have one or more double bonds unused in metal bonding can similarly be protonated; a number of such metal-stabilized carbonium ion complexes exist, some of nonclassical nature.[38]

28-5. Transition Metal to Carbon σ-Bonds

Only a few binary alkyl or aryl compounds are known, examples being $Ti(CH_3)_4$ and $Cr(C_6H_5)_3$; there are also halides[39] such as $(CH_3)_3TaCl_2$ and $(\pi\text{-}C_5H_5)_2ZrClCH_3$. Most of these compounds are stable only at low temperatures and are air and water sensitive. Evidence for labile species such as $(C_2H_5)_2Ni$ can be obtained from chemical reactions in solution, and such intermediates are useful reagents for various organic syntheses using acetylenes.

However, if π-bonding ligands such as CO or $\pi\text{-}C_5H_5$, are present, quite thermally stable σ-alkyls and aryls can be obtained. The first extensive series to be prepared were ones such as $\pi\text{-}C_5H_5W(CO)_3CH_3$ but other types, especially those containing phosphine and arsine ligands, are well known. The methods of preparation are standard—the action of metal complex halides with RMgX or RLi, or of sodium salts with organic halides; a number of compounds are known in which —CR_3 groups may be replaced by —SiR_3, —GeR_3, —SnR_3, —SR, etc.

Examples of preparations are:

$$\pi\text{-}C_5H_5Fe(CO)_2Br + CH_3MgBr = \pi\text{-}C_5H_5Fe(CO)_2CH_3 + MgBr_2$$

$$Mn(CO)_5Na + RX = RMn(CO)_5 + NaX$$

$$TiCl_4 + LiCH_3 \xrightarrow{\text{cold}} (CH_3)_4Ti \xrightarrow{TiCl_4} CH_3TiCl_3$$

$$(R_3P)_2PtCl_2 + 2CH_3MgBr \longrightarrow (R_3P)_2Pt(CH_3)_2$$

Other methods of preparation involve addition of diazomethane, or unsaturated compounds to transition metal complex hydrides, e.g.,

$$trans\text{-}[Pt(PEt_3)_2ClH] + C_2H_4 \rightleftharpoons trans\text{-}[Pt(PEt_3)_2ClC_2H_5]$$

$$\pi\text{-}C_5H_5Mo(CO)_3H + CH_2N_2 = \pi\text{-}C_5H_5Mo(CO)_3CH_3 + N_2$$

Addition can also be effected using fluorinated compounds,[40a,b] e.g.,

$$[Co(CN)_5H]^{3-} + C_2F_4 = [Co(CN)_5CF_2CF_2H]^{3-}$$

$$HRe(CO)_5 + CF_3C{\equiv}CCF_3 = (CO)_5ReC(CF_3){=}CH(CF_3)$$

---

[38] T. N. Margulis, *et al.,* and S. Winstein, *et al., J. Amer. Chem. Soc.,* **87**, 3267, 3269 (1965).

[39] G. L. Juvinall, *J. Amer. Chem. Soc.,* **86**, 4202 (1964); J. R. Surtees, *Chem. Comm.,* **1965**, 567.

[40a] M. J. Mays and G. Wilkinson, *Nature,* **203**, 1167 (1964); *J. Chem. Soc.,* **1965**, 6629.

[40b] J. B. Wilford and F. G. A. Stone, *Inorg. Chem.,* **4**, 93 (1965).

Generally, for any given series of compounds L_nMR, the stability increases with increasing atomic number of the metal and with increasing electronegativity of the alkyl or aryl substituent R. In some cases the use of selected ligands can introduce steric factors which can stabilize the alkyls, presumably by protecting the M—R bond from attack. The fluoroalkyl species are particularly stable, not only thermally, but to metal–carbon bond cleavage reactions. Thus although iron and cobalt carbonyl alkyls are thermally unstable at room temperature, the perfluoroalkyls such as $(CO)_3Co(CF_2)_2Co(CO)_3$ or 28-XXX, which are obtained by reaction of metal carbonyls with C_2F_4, are very stable substances.

(28-XXX)

X-ray[41] and infrared[42] studies of fluoroalkyl complexes suggest that the metal to carbon distance is shorter than expected; the shortening could be attributed either to the effect of the highly electronegative fluoroalkyl group causing metal orbital contraction and stronger metal–carbon bonding than is the case for equivalent alkyls, or, more likely, to acceptance of $d\pi$ electrons by the fluoroalkyl group using its C—F antibonding orbitals.

A few compounds are known in which there are nitrogen or oxygen ligands, and some of these can be made in aqueous solutions,[43] e.g.,

$$[Co(CN)_5H]^{3-} + CH_2{=}CHCl = [Co(CN)_5CHClCH_3]^{3-}$$
$$[Cr(H_2O)_6]^{2+}_{aq} + C_6H_5CH_2Cl = [Cr(H_2O)_5CH_2C_6H_5]^{2+}$$
$$[Rh(NH_3)_5H]^{2+}_{aq} + C_2H_4 = [Rh(NH_3)_5C_2H_5]^{2+}$$

There is evidently one naturally occurring transition metal alkyl—the coenzyme of Vitamin B_{12} (cobalamin). A number of alkyl cobalamins have been made synthetically,[44] e.g., by the action of CH_3I on the reduced

[41] M. R. Churchill, *Inorg. Chem.*, **4**, 1734 (1965).

[42] F. A. Cotton and J. A. McCleverty, *J. Organomet. Chem.*, **4**, 490 (1965).

[43] J. Kwiatek and J. K. Seyler, *J. Organomet. Chem.*, **3**, 421, 433 (1965); R. G. Coombes, M. D. Johnson and N. Winterton, *J. Chem. Soc.*, **1965**, 7029; **1966A**, 177; J. Halpern and J. P. Maher, *J. Amer. Chem. Soc.*, **87**, 5361 (1965).

[44] For references see G. C. Hayward, *et al.*, *J. Chem. Soc.*, **1965**, 6485; D. Dolphin, A. W. Johnson and R. Rodrigo, *J. Chem. Soc.*, **1964**, 3186; D. Dolphin and A. W. Johnson, *J. Chem. Soc.*, **1965**, 2174.

$B_{12}(B_{12s})$. It is not completely certain whether B_{12s} contains Co^I or whether it contains a Co^{III}—H group; it reacts with C_2F_4 to give a Co—C_2F_4H group[40a] but other properties are consistent with spin-paired Co^I. A partial, simple analog for the B_{12} coenzyme appears to be provided by the dimethylglyoximecobalt complex 28-XXXI which can be alkylated by standard methods.[45]

(28-XXXI)

Finally, we note the preparation of a number of complexes which contain M—CRR' groups; the suggestion has been made[45a] that these complexes contain bound "carbenes." They have been obtained by nucleophilic attack of lithium alkyls or aryls at the carbon atom of carbon monoxide in compounds such as $W(CO)_6$ or π-$C_5H_5Mn(CO)_3$ to give ionic salts, which are converted to M—CRR' complexes by action of alkyl halides or by acid followed by diazomethane, e.g.,

$$W(CO)_6 + LiPh \xrightarrow{\text{ether}} Li[(CO)_5WC(O)Ph]$$

$$(CO)_5WC(OMe)Ph \xleftarrow{\text{CH}_2\text{N}_2} (CO)_5WC(OH)Ph$$

A related preparation[45b] involves protonation of an acyl complex, e.g.,

$$\pi\text{-}C_5H_5Fe(CO)_2COCH_3 \underset{\text{OH}^-}{\overset{\text{H}^+}{\rightleftharpoons}} [\pi\text{-}C_5H_5(CO)_2Fe\text{—}C(OH)CH_3]^+$$

The X-ray structure determination[45c] of the chromium complex (28-XXXII) indicates that the Cr—C(OMe)Ph distance is intermediate between that expected for a Cr—C single bond (~ 2.24, cf. page 729) and those found for the Cr—CO multiple bonds. Thus the bonding can be best described as a hybrid of both the M=CR_2 (carbene) and "ylide" (28-XXXIII) forms. Delocalization of the negative charge placed on the metal

[45] G. N. Schrauzer and J. Kohnle, *Chem. Ber.*, **97**, 3056 (1964); see also *Angew. Chem.* (*Internat.*), **4**, 147 (1965).

[45a] E. O. Fischer and A. Maasbol, *Angew. Chem.* (*Internat.*), **3**, 580, (1964).

[45b] R. M. Harley and M. L. H. Green, private communication.

[45c] O. S. Mills, private communication; O. S. Mills and A. D. Redhouse, *Angew. Chem.* (*Internat.*), **4**, 1082 (1965).

by the ylide form can be accomplished by the other π-acid ligands. The relative importance of the two contributions will influence the ease of rotation about the M—C bond, the ylide form introducing a negligible barrier, whereas in the carbene case, with restricted rotation, substitutional "*cis–trans*" isomers are possible.

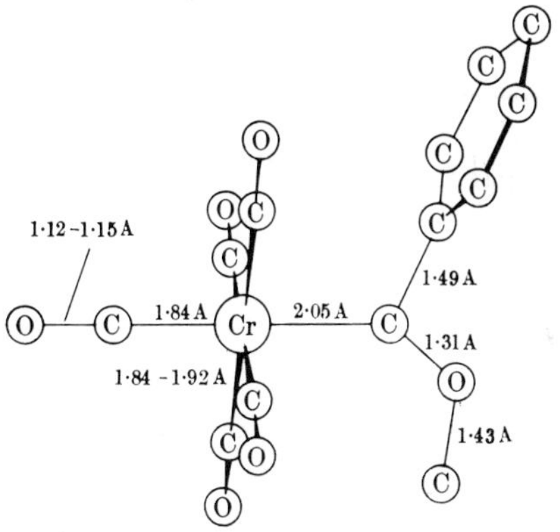

(28-XXXII)

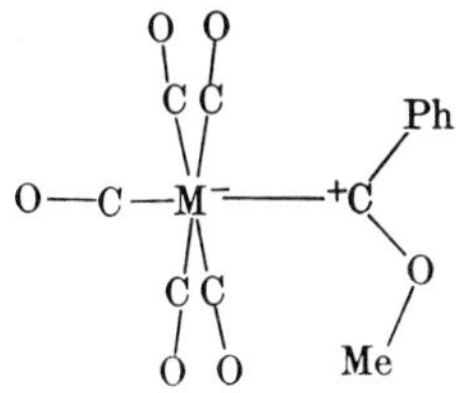

(28-XXXIII)

28-6. Transition Metal to Carbon Bonds in Catalysis.

There is little doubt that σ, π or delocalized bonding of some sort between organic radicals and transition metals at surfaces or in complex species in solution is an essential of all catalytic reactions. We cannot attempt to discuss these complicated matters but a few examples of the use of transition metal complexes in *homogeneous* catalytic reactions will illustrate the problems involved.

1. *Olefin oxidation.* An important catalytic process for the conversion of olefins into aldehydes is the so-called Wacker process which proceeds according to the equation:

$$RCH{=}CH_2 + PdCl_2 + H_2O = RCH_2CHO + Pd^0 + 2HCl$$

The palladium is re-dissolved in cupric chloride solution in the presence of air:

$$Pd^0 + 2HCl + \tfrac{1}{2}O_2 \xrightarrow{\text{CuCl}_2} PdCl_2 + H_2O$$

The mechanism of the reaction[46] is complicated but appears to involve initial reaction of the olefin with the $PdCl_4{}^{2-}$ ion present in Pd^{II} solutions to give the analog of the anion in Zeise's salt:

$$PdCl_4{}^{2-} + C_2H_4 \rightleftharpoons [PdCl_3C_2H_4]^- + Cl^-$$

The fact that this particular olefin complex hydrolyzes, with reduction to palladium metal, giving acetaldehyde, was known long before the practical

[46] P. M. Henry, *J. Amer. Chem. Soc.*, **86**, 3246 (1964); and references therein.

catalytic reaction was developed. The initial hydrolysis steps appear to be:

$$[PdCl_3C_2H_4]^- + H_2O \rightleftharpoons [PdCl_2(H_2O)C_2H_4] + Cl^-$$
$$[PdCl_2(H_2O)C_2H_4] + H_2O \rightleftharpoons [PdCl_2(OH)C_2H_4]^- + H_3O^+$$

The *trans* isomer of this hydroxo species is doubtless more stable than the *cis* isomer (see discussion of *trans* effect, page 175), but kinetically significant amounts of the latter will almost certainly be present so that further reaction occurs:

$$[PdCl_2(OH)C_2H_4]^- \xrightarrow{\text{slow}} Cl—Pd—CH_2CH_2OH + Cl^-$$

The hydride shift in the activated complex is of the same type as those involved in other platinum metal complex reactions where β-hydrogens of alcohols or aldehydes are activated (see Section 30-F-1).

The Wacker process can also be used to make acetone or methyl ethyl ketone from propylene or butene.[46a]

A different but probably mechanistically similar sequence of reactions of C_2H_4 occurs in acetic acid containing sodium acetate, where $PdCl_2$ reacts to give vinyl acetate and metal.[47]

2. *The hydroformylation or "oxo" process.* This important method for the manufacture of higher alcohols *via* the aldehyde (usually C_6—C_9) has the overall stoichiometry

$$RCH{=}CH_2 + CO + H_2 \rightarrow RCH_2CH_2CHO$$

It is usually carried out at high pressures and temperatures of 150° or above, using cobalt carbonyl catalyst; the latter is doubtless formed *in situ* from added cobalt salts.

Pertinent to the mechanism of the oxo reaction are carbon monoxide insertion reactions of the type observed for several complex metal alkyls, namely,

$$CH_3Mn(CO)_5 + CO = CH_3COMn(CO)_5$$
$$(R_3P)_2Pt(CH_3)_2 + 2CO = (R_3P)_2Pt(COCH_3)_2$$

These insertion reactions are reversible. Tracer studies on the manganese compound have shown that the entering CO does *not* become the one in the

---

[46a] *Chem. and Eng. News*, **1963**, July, page 50.
[47] E. W. Stern and M. L. Spector, *Proc. Chem. Soc.*, **1961**, 370.

acyl group. Similar reactions occur with other adding ligands, e.g., L = Ph_3P, or amines; with Ph_3P, both *cis* and *trans* isomers are formed[48]

$$CH_3Mn(CO)_5 + L \rightleftharpoons CH_3COMn(CO)_4L$$

It appears from study of a de-carbonylation[49] that certain of these reactions, such as the one above, may proceed more by way of a "methyl shift" than by a CO insertion, as shown in equation 28-5.

(28-5)

A mechanism which seems to fit the available kinetic and stoichiometric data for the oxo reaction is one involving the formation of a metal carbonyl hydride, addition of this across the olefin to give an alkyl, followed by carbonylation:[50]

$$Co_2(CO)_8 + H_2 \rightleftharpoons 2HCo(CO)_4$$
$$HCo(CO)_4 \rightleftharpoons HCo(CO)_3 + CO$$
$$RCH{=}CH_2 + HCo(CO)_3 \rightleftharpoons (RCH{=}CH_2)HCo(CO)_3 \rightleftharpoons RCH_2{-}CH_2Co(CO)_3$$
$$RCH_2CH_2Co(CO)_3 + CO \rightleftharpoons RCH_2CH_2Co(CO)_4$$
$$RCH_2CH_2Co(CO)_4 + CO \rightleftharpoons RCH_2CH_2COCo(CO)_4$$
$$RCH_2CH_2COCo(CO)_4 + H_2 \rightleftharpoons RCH_2CH_2CHO + HCo(CO)_4$$

Recent studies have shown that rhodium catalysts are more effective than cobalt ones, allowing the reaction to proceed at lower temperatures and pressures. The most active complex is $(Ph_3P)_3RhCl$ which, with CO, rapidly gives $(Ph_3P)_2RhCOCl$, the actual catalyst. This rhodium system[51] is also unusual in that it allows homogeneous hydrogenation of olefinic and acetylenic compounds to be carried out at ordinary temperatures and pressures. In this case, a solvated species $(Ph_3P)_2Rh(solvent)Cl$ is the active one; this species can take up separately a mole of molecular hydrogen or of olefin and the transfer of bound hydrogen to added olefin can be

[48] R. J. Mawby, F. Basolo and R. G. Pearson, *J. Amer. Chem. Soc.*, **86**, 3994 (1964); C. S. Kraihanzel and P. K. Maples, *J. Amer. Chem. Soc.*, **87**, 5267 (1965).

[49] R. J. Mawby, F. Basolo and R. G. Pearson, *J. Amer. Chem. Soc.*, **86**, 5043 (1964); see also W. D. Bannister, M. Green and R. N. Haszeldine, *Chem. Comm.*, **1965**, 54.

[50] R. F. Heck and D. S. Breslow, *J. Amer. Chem. Soc.*, **83**, 4023 (1961).

[51] J. A. Osborne, F. H. Jardine, J. F. Young and G. Wilkinson, *Chem. Comm.*, **17**, 131 (1965); *Chem. and Ind.*, **1965**, 560.

shown to occur by disappearance of the high-field nmr line of Rh—H. There are thus labile equilibria of the type:

$$(Ph_3P)_3RhCl + solvent \rightleftharpoons (Ph_3P)_2Rh(solvent)Cl + Ph_3P$$
$$(Ph_3P)_2Rh(solvent)Cl + C_2H_4 \rightleftharpoons (Ph_3P)_2Rh(C_2H_4)Cl + solvent$$
$$(Ph_3P)_2Rh(solvent)Cl + H_2 \rightleftharpoons (Ph_3P)_2RhH_2Cl + solvent$$

In the rapid catalytic hydrogenation it seems likely that both the olefin and hydrogen are bound to the same atom in the transition state, since the lifetime of an ethylene molecule bound to such a square complex is known to be very short (see page 777) and a single-step addition of a polarized H_2 molecule $H^{\delta+}\cdots H^{\delta-}$ to the activated double bond could occur. The rate depends on the basicity of the coordinated solvent—with a strongly bound molecule such as pyridine or CO, the rate is very much slower than with benzene or alcohols.

It may be noted also that sulfur dioxide can be inserted into metal-carbon bonds[52] to give a sulfinic ester, e.g.,

$$\pi\text{-}C_5H_5Fe(CO)_2CH_3 + SO_2 = \pi\text{-}C_5H_5Fe(CO)_2(OSOCH_3)$$

with the possibility of a hydroformylation type of reaction existing, and finally, that hydrosilation of olefins can be achieved using Pt^{II}, Rh^{I} and $Co_2(CO)_8$ catalysts.[53]

3. *Olefin isomerizations.* Under hydroformylation conditions, $HCo(CO)_4$ can isomerize olefins and such processes have been catalyzed also by platinum metal salts such as $RhCl_3(aq)$ or $PdCl_2$ in ethanol or similar solvents. There is still some discussion[54] concerning whether the reaction proceeds by way of an allylic intermediate, or whether, as seems more likely, a hydride ion transfer such as

$$-CH_2-CH=CH_2 \rightleftharpoons -CH_2-CH-CH_3 \rightleftharpoons -CH=CH-CH_3$$
$$\quad\quad | \quad\quad\quad\quad\quad\quad | \quad\quad\quad\quad\quad\quad \vdots$$
$$\quad\quad MH \quad\quad\quad\quad\quad\quad M \quad\quad\quad\quad\quad\quad MH$$

is involved. In some reactions of cyclic olefins with metals, coordination of the isomerized olefin can be observed, e.g.,

4. *Olefin and acetylene polymerizations.* Although olefins can be polymerized by lithium alkyls, one of the most widely used technical processes

[52] J. P. Bibler and A. Wojcicki, *J. Amer. Chem. Soc.*, **86**, 5051 (1964).

[53] A. J. Chalk and J. F. Harrod, *J. Amer. Chem. Soc.*, **87**, 16, 1133 (1965).

[54] J. F. Harrod and A. J. Chalk; N. R. Davies, *Nature*, **205**, 280 (1965); J. K. Nicholson and B. L. Shaw, *Tetrahedron Letters*, **1965**, 3533; L. Ross and M. Orchin, *J. Amer. Chem. Soc.*, **87**, 5502 (1965).

is that in which α-olefins are polymerized alone, or are incorporated into bi- or ter-polymers with other olefins such as styrene, butadiene or dicyclopentadiene. These processes stemmed from Ziegler's discovery that ethylene can be polymerized at ordinary temperature and pressure by hydrocarbon solutions of aluminum alkyls containing titanium chlorides. There has been a subsequent avalanche of publications adapting the procedure to other olefins or olefin mixtures and using other transition metal salts or complexes as co-catalysts. While most Ziegler catalyst systems are heterogeneous, the reaction probably occurring at sites on the surface of crystalline $TiCl_3$ or $TiCl_2$, polymerization of certain olefins can be achieved homogeneously using for example $(\pi\text{-}C_5H_5)_2TiCl_2$ as co-catalyst.

The first step appears to be the replacement of one of the chloride ions in a Ti^{3+} ion at the surface by an alkyl radical derived from the aluminum alkyl; the surface Ti atom has one of its six coordination sites vacant. An ethylene molecule is then bound to the vacant site. Following the promotion of an electron from the Ti–alkyl bond to a molecular orbital of the complex, a four-center transition state is produced which enables an ethylene to be inserted between the Ti atom and the alkyl group. A further molecule of ethylene is then bound to the vacant site and the process repeated. The mechanism[55] is then as follows:

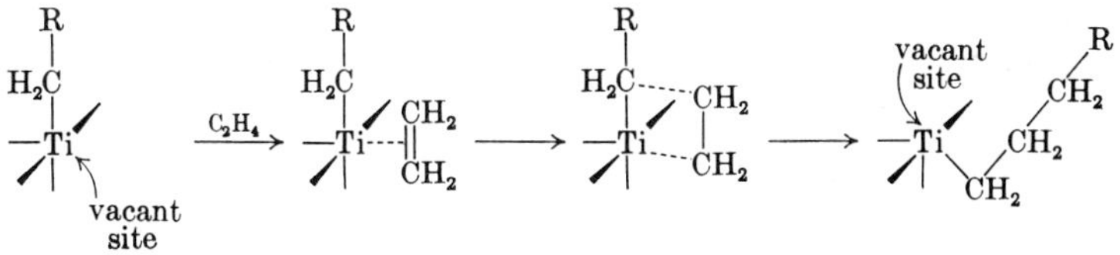

It will be noted that this is another example of a cis-ligand insertion reaction similar to that of CO discussed earlier. Many other cases involving this type of reaction are now being recognized.[56]

The trimerization of butadiene[35] has been referred to above. This olefin may also be dimerized, be converted to open chain products such as n-octatrienes, or be co-oligomerized with other unsaturated compounds.[57] Acetylenes may be cyclopolymerized to arenes and other products while acetylene itself can be converted to cyclooctatetraene. A variety of nickel,

[55] P. Cossee, J. Catalysis, 3, 80 (1964); P. Cossee and E. J. Arlman, J. Catalysis., 3, 89, 99 (1964). For general discussion of Ziegler polymerization see also C. E. H. Bawn and A. Ledwith, Quart. Rev., 16, 361 (1962); J. P. Kennedy and A. W. Langner, Adv. in Polymer Sci., 3, 508 (1964).

[56] See, e.g., articles by R. S. Nyholm and J. Halpern, 3rd Congress on Catalysis, pp. 25, 146. North-Holland Pub. Co., Amsterdam, 1965.

[57] H. Müller, et al., Angew. Chem. (Internat.), 4, 327 (1965).

cobalt carbonyl and Ziegler type catalysts may be utilized.[58]   In solutions of nickel complexes such as $NiCl_2(PR_3)_2$ containing also sodium boro-hydride,[59] acetylenes may be converted to linear polymers.

Finally we note a dimerization process for ethylene using rhodium tri-chloride in ethanol. Detailed studies[60] on the intermediates are possible by nmr and it appears that four steps are involved: (a) the protonation by HCl of a bis(ethylene)rhodium(I) anionic complex, $[(C_2H_4)_2RhCl_2]^-$, to give an ethyl–rhodium(III) complex, $[(C_2H_4)C_2H_5RhCl_3]^-$; (b) the inser-tion of C_2H_4 into the Rh—C_2H_5 bond to give Rh—C_4H_9; (c) collapse of the latter with loss of HCl to give butene and Rh^I; (d) coordination of C_2H_4 to reform the initial ethylene complex.

[58] A. J. Hubert and J. Dale, *J. Chem. Soc.*, **1965**, 3160 and references therein.
[59] L. B. Luttinger and E. C. Colthup, *J. Org. Chem.*, **27**, 3152 (1962).
[60] R. D. Cramer, *J. Amer. Chem. Soc.*, **87**, 4717 (1965).

References

Annual Reports, Chemical Society, London.   These contain excellent review sections, *inter alia* on alkyl, olefin, acetylene and π complexes.

Bennett, M. A., *Chem. Rev.*, **62**, 611 (1962).   A comprehensive review on olefin, acetylene and allyl complexes.

Bird, C. W., *Chem. Rev.*, **62**, 283 (1962).   Syntheses of organic compounds by carbonyla-tion reactions.

Birmingham, J. M., *Adv. Organomet. Chem.*, **2**, 365 (1965).   Synthesis of π-C_5H_5 com-pounds.

Cais, M., in S. Patai, ed., *The Chemistry of Alkenes*, Interscience—Wiley, New York, 1964.   Alkene metal complexes.

Fischer, E. O., and H. Werner, *Metal-π-Komplex mit di- und oligo-olefinischen Liganden*, Verlag Chemie, 1963.   Review on olefin complexes.

Fritz, H. P., *Adv. Organomet. Chem.*, **1**, 143 (1964).   Molecular spectra of π complexes.

Fritz, H. P., and E. O. Fischer, *Adv. Inorg. Chem. Radiochem.*, **1**, 55 (1959).   Chemistry of π-C_5H_5 and arene complexes.

Green, M. L. H., and P. L. I. Nagy, *Adv. Organomet. Chem.*, **2**, 325 (1965).   Allyl complexes.

Guy, R. G., and B. L. Shaw, *Adv. Inorg. Chem. Nucl. Chem.*, **4**, 78 (1962).   Review on olefin, acetylene and π-allyl complexes.

Halpern, J., *Ann. Rev. Phys. Chem.*, **16**, 103 (1965).   Review on homogeneous hydro-genation, olefin oxidation, acetylene hydration, etc.

Heck, R. F., *Adv. Chem. Series*, No. 49, A.C.S., Washington, D.C., 1965.   Extensive review on insertion reactions.

Huggins, D. K., and H. D. Kaez, in H. Reiss, ed., *Progr. Solid State Chem.*, **1**, 417 (1964).   Catalog of infrared and Raman spectra of organometallic compounds.

King, R. B., *Adv. Organomet. Chem.*, **2**, 157 (1965).   Reactions of carbonylate anions; includes many π-complex reactions.

———, *Organometallic Syntheses*, Vol. I, *Transition Metal Compounds*, Academic Press, New York, 1965.   Detailed preparative procedures.

Little, W. F., *Survey of Prog. in Chem.*, **1**, 133 (1963). Review on sandwich compounds, especially organic chemistry of ferrocene.

Pettit, R., and G. F. Emerson, *Adv. Organomet. Chem.*, **1**, 143 (1964). Diene-iron carbonyl and related complexes.

Plesske, K., *Angew. Chem. (Internat.)*, **1**, 312, 394 (1962). Ring substitution and organic reactions of aromatic π complexes. A comprehensive review.

Rausch, M. D., *Can. J. Chem.*, **41**, 1289 (1963); *Adv. Chem. Series*, No. 37, A.C.S., Washington, D.C., 1963. Reviews on π-C_5H_5 compounds including especially organic aspects.

Rosenblum, M., *The Iron Group Metallocenes: Ferrocene, Ruthenocene, Osmocene*, Vol. I. (The Chemistry of Organometallic Compounds), Wiley, New York, 1965.

Schrauzer, G. N., *Adv. Organomet. Chem.*, **2**, 1 (1965). Organometallic chemistry of nickel.

Schröder, G., J. F. M. Oth and R. Merenyi, *Angew. Chem. (Internat.)*, **4**, 752 (1965). Review of valence bond isomerism.

Skinner, M. A., *Adv. Organomet. Chem.*, **2**, 49 (1965). Strengths of metal to carbon bonds.

Smidt, J., *et al.*, *Angew. Chem. (Internat.)*, **1**, 80 (1962). Oxidation of olefins by Pd catalysts.

Sternberg, H. W., and I. Wender, *Proc. I.C.C. Spec. Publ.* No. 13, 35 (1959), *Chem. Soc.* (London). Metal complexes in organic synthesis.

Treichel, P. M., and F. G. A. Stone, *Adv. Organomet. Chem.*, **1**, 143 (1964). Fluorocarbon derivatives of transition metals.

Wilkinson, G., and F. A. Cotton, *Prog. Inorg. Chem.*, **1**, 1 (1959). A comprehensive review of early work on sandwich compounds.

Zeiss, H., ed., *Organometallic Chemistry* (A.C.S. Monograph No. 147), Reinhold, New York, 1960. Several sections on transition metal compounds.

29

The Elements of the First Transition Series

GENERAL REMARKS

The main features of the transition elements and of their complex chemistry have been presented in the preceding chapters. In describing in more detail the individual elements and their chemistries, familiarity with this material will be assumed.

We discuss in this chapter the elements of the first transition series, titanium through copper. There are two main reasons for considering these elements apart from their heavier congeners of the second and third transition series: (1) in each group, for example, V, Nb, Ta, the first series element always differs appreciably from the heavier elements, and there is little to be gained by comparisons; and (2) the aqueous chemistry of the first series elements is much simpler, and the use of ligand-field theory in explaining both the spectra and magnetic properties of compounds has been far more extensive. The ionization potentials for the first series atoms are listed in Table 29-1. Under the sections for each element the oxidation states and stereochemistries are summarized; we do not specify except in special cases of interest distortions from perfect geometries which can be expected in octahedral d^1 and d^2 (slight), octahedral d^4 spin-free (two long coaxial bonds), octahedral d^4 spin-paired (slight), octahedral d^6, d^7 spin-free (slight) or octahedral d^7, d^8 spin-paired (two long coaxial bonds). A few other general features of the elements can be mentioned here.

The energies of the $3d$ and $4s$ orbitals in the neutral atoms are quite similar, and their structures are $3d^n4s^2$ with the exception of Cr, $3d^54s^1$, and Cu, $3d^{10}4s^1$, which are attributable to the stabilities of the half-filled and filled d shells, respectively. Since the d orbitals become stabilized relative

TABLE 29-1

Ionization Potentials of the Elements of the First Transition Series

(In electron volts)

Element	Configuration	Ionization potential,							
		1st	2nd	3rd	4th	5th	6th	7th	8th
Sc	$3d^1 4s^2$	6.54	12.80	24.75	73.9	92	111	138	159
Ti	$3d^2 4s^2$	6.83	13.57	27.47	43.24	99.8	120	141	171
V	$3d^3 4s^2$	6.74	14.65	29.31	48	65.2	128.9	151	174
Cr	$3d^5 4s^1$	6.76	16.49	30.95	49.6	73.2	90.6	161	185
Mn	$3d^5 4s^2$	7.43	15.64	33.69	52	76	98	119	196
Fe	$3d^6 4s^2$	7.90	16.18	30.64	57.1	78	102	128	151
Co	$3d^7 4s^2$	7.86	17.05	33.49	53	83.5	106	132	161
Ni	$3d^8 4s^2$	7.63	18.15	35.16	56	78	110	136	166
Cu	$3d^{10} 4s^1$	7.72	20.29	36.83	58.9	82	106	140	169
Zn	$3d^{10} 4s^2$	9.39	17.96	39.7	62	86	112	142	177

to the s orbital when the atoms are charged, the predominant oxidation states in ionic compounds and complexes of non-π-bonding ligands are II or greater. Owing to its electronic structure, copper has a higher second ionization potential than the other elements and the univalent state is important for copper. The high values of third ionization potentials also indicate why it is difficult to obtain oxidation states for nickel and copper greater than II. Although ionization potentials give some guidance concerning the relative stabilities of oxidation states, this problem is a very complex one and not amenable to facile generalization. Indeed it is often futile to discuss relative stabilities of oxidation states as some oxidation states may be perfectly stable under certain conditions, for example, in solid compounds, in fused melts, in the vapor at high temperatures, in absence of air, etc., and non-existent in aqueous solutions or in air. Thus there is no aqueous chemistry of Ti^{2+}, yet crystalline $TiCl_2$ is stable up to about 400° in absence of air; also in fused potassium chloride, titanium and titanium trichloride give Ti^{II} as the main species and Ti^{IV} is in vanishingly small concentrations. On the other hand, in aqueous solutions in air only Ti^{IV} species are stable.

However, it is sometimes profitable to compare the relative stabilities of ions differing by unit charge when surrounded by similar ligands with similar stereochemistry, as in the case of the Fe^{3+}–Fe^{2+} potentials (page 853) or with different anions. In these cases, as elsewhere, many factors are usually involved; some of these have already been discussed, but they include (a) ionization potentials of the metal atoms, (b) ionic radii of the metal ions, (c) electronic structure of the metal ions, (d) the nature of the anions or ligands involved with respect to their polarizability, donor $p\pi$- or acceptor $d\pi$-bonding capacities, (e) the stereochemistry either in a complex ion or a crystalline lattice and (f) nature of solvents or other media. In spite of the complexities there are a few trends which can be found, namely:

1. From Ti to Mn the highest valence, which is usually found only in oxo compounds or fluorides or chlorides, corresponds to the total number of d and s electrons in the atom. The stability of the highest state decreases from Ti^{IV} to Mn^{VII}. After Mn, that is, for Fe, Co and Ni, the higher oxidation states are difficult to obtain.

2. In the characteristic oxo anions of the valence states IV to VII, the metal atom is tetrahedrally surrounded by oxygen atoms, whereas in the oxides of valences up to IV the atoms are usually octahedrally coordinated.

3. The oxides of a given element become more acidic with increasing oxidation state and the halides more covalent and susceptible to hydrolysis by water.

4. In the II and III states, complexes in aqueous solution or in crystals are usually either in four or six coordination and, across the first series, generally of a similar nature in respect to stoichiometry and chemical properties.

5. The oxidation states less than II, with the exception of Cu^{I}, are found only with π-acid type ligands.

Finally we re-emphasize that the occurrence of a given oxidation state as well as its stereochemistry depends very much on the experimental conditions and that species which cannot have independent existence under ordinary conditions of temperature and pressure in air may be the dominant species under others. As a final point in this connection we may note that transition metal ions may be obtained in a particular configuration difficult to produce by other means through incorporation by isomorphous substitution in a crystalline host lattice, for example, tetrahedral Co^{3+} in other oxides, V^{3+} tetrahedral in the $NaAlCl_4$ lattice, as well as by using ligands of fixed geometry such as phthalocyanins.

Although some discussion of the relationships between the first, second and third transition series is useful, we defer this until the next chapter.

In the following discussion of individual chemistries of elements we have kept to the traditional order, i.e., elemental chemistries are considered separately, with reference to their oxidation state. However, it is possible to organize the subject matter from the standpoint of the d^n electronic configuration of the metal. While this can bring out useful similarities in spectra and magnetic properties in certain cases, and has a basis in theory (Chap. 26) nevertheless the differences in chemical properties of d^n species due to differences in the nature of the metal, its energy levels and especially the charge on the ion, often exceed the similarities. Nonetheless such cross-considerations, as for example in the d^6 series V^{-I}, Cr^0, Mn^I, Fe^{II}, Co^{III}, Ni^{IV}, can provide a useful exercise for students.

29-A. TITANIUM

Titanium is the first member of the d-block transition elements and has four valence electrons, $3d^2 4s^2$. Titanium(IV) is the most stable and common oxidation state; compounds in lower oxidation states, $-I$, 0, II and III, are quite readily oxidized to Ti^{IV} by air, water or other reagents. The energy for removal of four electrons is high so that the Ti^{4+} ion does not have a real existence and Ti^{IV} compounds are generally covalent in nature. In this IV state, there are some resemblances to the elements Si, Ge, Sn and Pb, especially Sn. The estimated ionic radii ($Sn^{4+} = 0.71$, $Ti^{4+} = 0.68$ A) and octahedral covalent radii ($Sn^{IV} = 1.45$, $Ti^{IV} = 1.36$ A) are similar; thus TiO_2 (rutile) is isomorphous with SnO_2 (cassiterite) and is similarly yellow when hot. Titanium tetrachloride, like $SnCl_4$, is a distillable liquid readily hydrolyzed by water and behaving as a Lewis acid, giving adducts with donor molecules; $SiCl_4$ and $GeCl_4$ do not give stable, solid, molecular addition compounds with ethers although $TiCl_4$ and $SnCl_4$ do so, a difference which may be attributed to ability of the halogen atoms to fill the coordination sphere of the smaller Si and Ge atoms. There are also similar halogeno anions such as $TiF_6{}^{2-}$, $GeF_6{}^{2-}$, $TiCl_6{}^{2-}$, $SnCl_6{}^{2-}$, $PbCl_6{}^{2-}$, some of whose salts are isomorphous. There are other similarities such as the behavior of the tetrachlorides on ammonolysis to give amido species. It is a characteristic of Ti^{IV} compounds to undergo hydrolysis to give species with Ti—O bonds, in many of which there is octahedral coordination by oxygen; Ti—O—C bonds are well known, and compounds with Ti—O—Si and Ti—O—Sn bonds are known.

The stereochemistry of titanium compounds is summarized in Table 29-A-1.

29-A-1. The Element

Titanium is relatively abundant in the earth's crust (0.6%). The main ores are *ilmenite*, $FeTiO_3$, and *rutile*, one of the several crystalline varieties of TiO_2. It is not possible to obtain the metal by the common method of reduction with carbon because a very stable carbide is produced and, moreover, the metal is rather reactive toward oxygen and nitrogen at elevated temperatures. However, because the metal appears to have certain uniquely useful metallurgical properties, the following rather expensive process (Kroll process) has been developed commercially.

TABLE 29-A-1

Oxidation States and Stereochemistry of Titanium

Oxidation state	Coordination number	Geometry	Examples
Ti^{-I}	6	Octahedral	Tidipy$_3^-$
Ti^0	6	Octahedral	Tidipy$_3$
Ti^{II}, d^2		π-Complex	$(\pi$-C$_5$H$_5)_2$Ti, $(\pi$-C$_5$H$_5)_2$Ti(CO)$_2$
	6	Octahedral	TiCl$_2$
Ti^{III}, d^1	6	Octahedral	TiF$_6^{3-}$, [Ti(H$_2$O)$_6$]$^{3+}$, TiCl$_3 \cdot$3THF
Ti^{IV}, d^0	4^a	Tetrahedral	TiCl$_4$
		π-Complex	$(\pi$-C$_5$H$_5)_2$TiCl$_2$
	5	Distorted TBP	K$_2$Ti$_2$O$_5$
		Square pyramid	TiO(acac)$_2$ (?)
		?	TiX$_4 \cdot$NMe$_3$
	6^a	Octahedral	TiF$_6^{2-}$, Ti(acac)$_2$Cl$_2$, [(Cl$_3$PO)TiCl$_4$]$_2$, [Ti(OC$_2$H$_5)_4$]$_4$, TiO$_2^b$
	7	ZrF$_7^{3-}$ type	[Ti(O$_2$)F$_5$]$^{3-}$
	8	Dodecahedral	TiCl$_4$(diars)$_2^c$

^{a} Most common states.

^{b} Distortions occur in some forms of TiO$_2$ and in BaTiO$_3$.

^{c} diars = o-phenylenebis(dimethylarsine). As atoms form the elongated tetrahedron, Cl atoms the flattened one.

Ilmenite or rutile is treated at red heat with carbon and chlorine to give TiCl$_4$, which is fractionated to free it from impurities such as FeCl$_3$. The TiCl$_4$ is then reduced with molten magnesium at $\sim 800°$ in an atmosphere of argon. This gives metallic titanium as a spongy mass from which excess Mg and MgCl$_2$ are removed by volatilization at $\sim 1000°$. The sponge may then be fused in an atmosphere of argon or helium, using an electric arc, and cast into ingots.

Extremely pure titanium can be made on the laboratory scale by the van Arkel–de Boer method (also used for other metals) in which TiI$_4$, which has been carefully purified, is vaporized and decomposed on a hot wire in vacuum.

The metal has a hexagonal close-packed lattice and resembles other transition metals such as iron, nickel, etc., in being hard, refractory (m 1680 $\pm$ 10°, b 3260°), and a good conductor of heat and electricity. It is, however, quite light in comparison to other metals of similar mechanical and thermal properties and unusually resistant to certain kinds of corrosion and has therefore come into demand for special applications in turbine engines and industrial chemical and marine equipment.

Although rather unreactive at ordinary temperatures, titanium combines directly with most nonmetals, for example, hydrogen, the halogens, oxygen, nitrogen, carbon, boron, silicon and sulfur, at elevated temperatures. The resulting nitride, TiN, carbide, TiC, and the borides, TiB and TiB_2, are interstitial compounds which are very stable, hard and refractory.

As noted, corrosion resistance is one of the technologically desirable properties of titanium. The metal is not attacked by mineral acids at room temperature or even by hot aqueous alkali. It dissolves in hot HCl giving Ti^{III} species, whereas hot nitric acid converts it to a hydrous oxide which is rather insoluble in acid or base. The best solvents are HF or acids to which fluoride ions have been added. Such media dissolve titanium and hold it in solution as fluoro complexes.

29-A-2. Compounds of Tetravalent Titanium

Titanium(IV) Halides. Titanium tetrachloride is normally prepared in the laboratory by passing chlorine over a hot mixture of the dioxide and carbon:

$$TiO_2 + C + 2Cl_2 = TiCl_4 + CO_2$$

$TiCl_4$ is a colorless liquid, m $-23°$, b $137°$, with a pungent odor. It fumes strongly in moist air and is vigorously, though not violently, hydrolyzed by water:

$$TiCl_4 + 2H_2O = TiO_2 + 4HCl$$

With some HCl present or a deficit of H_2O, partial hydrolysis occurs giving oxochlorides, whereas in concentrated HCl the titanium remains in solution due to formation of chloro complexes, namely, $[TiCl_5(H_2O)]^-$ and $[TiCl_6]^{2-}$. Salts of the latter may be precipitated on addition of cations such as NH_4^+ or Cs^+. By direct reaction of $TiCl_4$ vapor at 1 atm with KCl, RbCl and CsCl the solid green to yellow $M^I_2TiCl_6$ compounds can be prepared directly.[1] $TiCl_4$ is a strong Lewis acid and forms addition compounds of the types R_2OTiCl_4 and $(R_2O)_2TiCl_4$ with various oxygen donors such as ethers, alcohols and esters. Adducts are also given by P, As and S donors and are in general 6-coordinate;[2] many are so insoluble that their coordination numbers are not known with certainty. Trimethylamine adducts, $TiX_4 \cdot NMe_3$ (page 806) are presumably 5-coordinate while the o-phenylene-bisdimethylarsine complex is 8-coordinate. The crystalline adduct $TiCl_4 \cdot OPCl_3$ has been shown to be dimeric with two chlorine bridges between the octahedral titanium atoms and with oxygen bound to titanium.

$TiBr_4$ and TiI_4 are similar to the chloride, but they are crystalline at room temperature and are isomorphous with SiI_4, GeI_4 and SnI_4 having molecular lattices.

---

[1] R. L. Lister and S. N. Flengas, *Can. J. Chem.*, **41**, 1548 (1963).
[2] G. W. A. Fowles and R. A. Walton, *J. Chem. Soc.*, **1964**, 4330; R. J. H. Clark, *J. Chem. Soc.*, **1965**, 5699.

TiF_4, which may be obtained by treatment of $TiCl_4$ with HF, is a white, powdery, presumably ionic substance, although this is not known with certainty. However, it acts as a Lewis acid, forming complexes similar to those given by $TiCl_4$, and it readily adds F^- ions to give the hexafluoro-titanate ion, $[TiF_6]^{2-}$, of which various salts are known. The TiF_6^{2-} ion is stable in aqueous solution, and has been characterized by nmr and Raman spectra.[3a]

Titanium Oxide; Complex Oxides. The dioxide, TiO_2, is known in three crystal modifications, rutile, anatase and brookite, all of which occur in nature. In rutile, the commonest, the titanium is octahedrally coordinated, and this structure has been illustrated and discussed earlier (page 48), as it is a common one for MX_2 compounds. In anatase and brookite there are very distorted octahedra of oxygen atoms about each titanium, two being relatively close. Although rutile has been assumed to be the most stable form because of its common occurrence, recent thermochemical data indicate that anatase is 2–3 kcal/mole more stable than rutile.[3b]

Under the name *titania*, the dioxide finds some commercial use as a white pigment. Naturally occurring forms are usually colored, sometimes even black, owing to the presence of impurities such as iron. Pigment grade material is generally made by hydrolysis of $TiOSO_4$ or vapor phase oxidation of $TiCl_4$. The solubility of TiO_2 depends a good deal on its chemical and thermal history. Strongly roasted specimens are quite inert.

No definite hydroxide, $Ti(OH)_4$, appears to exist, and the precipitates obtained on adding base to Ti^{IV} solutions are best regarded as hydrous TiO_2. This substance dissolves in concentrated alkali hydroxide to give solutions from which hydrated "titanates" having formulas such as $M^I_2TiO_3 \cdot nH_2O$ and $M^I_2Ti_2O_5 \cdot nH_2O$ but of unknown structure may be obtained.

A considerable number of materials called "titanates" are known, some of which are of technical importance. Nearly all of them have one of the three major mixed metal oxide structures discussed in Chapter 2 (page 51), and indeed the names of two of the structures are those of the titanium compounds which were first found to possess them, namely, $FeTiO_3$, ilmenite, and $CaTiO_3$, perovskite. Other titanites with the ilmenite structure are $MgTiO_3$, $MnTiO_3$, $CoTiO_3$ and $NiTiO_3$, while others with the perovskite structure are $SrTiO_3$, and $BaTiO_3$. There are also titanates with the spinel structure such as Mg_2TiO_4, Zn_2TiO_4 and Co_2TiO_4. Barium titanate is of particular interest, since it shows remarkable ferroelectric behavior. The reason for this is understood in terms of the structure. Here the

[3a] P. A. W. Dean and D. F. Evans, Imperial College, private communication.
[3b] J. L. Margrave, Rice University, private communication.

ion, Ba^{2+}, is so large relative to the small ion, Ti^{4+}, that the latter can literally "rattle around" in its octahedral hole. When an electric field is applied to a crystal of this material, it can be highly polarized because the Ti^{4+} ions are drawn over to one side of their octahedra, thus causing an enormous electrical polarization of the crystal as a whole.

The only compound in which there is evidence for discrete titanate ions is Ba_2TiO_4. This compound has a structure of the β-K_2SO_4 type to which that of β-Ca_2SiO_4 is closely related. It contains discrete TiO_4 groups which are moderately distorted tetrahedra. Sr_2TiO_4 has quite a different structure (but not the spinel structure) in which there are layers of TiO_6 octahedra sharing oxygen atoms.

Aqueous Chemistry; Oxo Salts. There is no simple aquated Ti^{4+} ion because of the extremely high charge to radius ratio, and in aqueous solutions hydrolyzed species occur and basic oxo salts or hydrated oxides may precipitate. Although there have been claims for a titanyl ion, TiO^{2+}, this ion does *not* appear to exist in either solutions or in crystalline salts such as $TiOSO_4 \cdot H_2O$. The latter has been shown to have $(TiO)_n^{2n+}$ chains

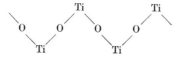

which are joined together in the crystal by sulfate groups, each of which is in contact with three metal ions; the water molecule is associated with the titanium atoms so that the latter are approximately octahedrally coordinated by oxygen.

The TiO group is, however, believed to exist[4] in several $TiO(\beta$-diketonate$)_2$ compounds. $TiO(acac)_2$ appears to exist not only in this monomeric form but also as a dimer with Ti—O—Ti bridges. Another compound with such an oxo bridge is $[Ti(OCOCH_3)_3]_2O$.

In dilute perchloric acid solutions, there appears to be an equilibrium between the main species

$$Ti(OH)_3^+ + H^+ = Ti(OH)_2^{2+} + H_2O$$

each of which is almost certainly octahedrally coordinated, as, for example, $[Ti(OH)_2(H_2O)_4]^{2+}$. In sulfuric acid, these and other species such as $Ti(OH)_3HSO_4$ and $Ti(OH)_2HSO_4^+$ have been invoked. On increasing the pH, polymerization and further hydrolysis eventually give colloidal or precipitated hydrous TiO_2.

When halide or other coordinating anions are present in solution, various complex species exist; in HF solutions the predominant ion is TiF_6^{2-}.

---

[4] M. Cox, J. Lewis and R. S. Nyholm, *J. Chem. Soc.*, **1965**, 2840.

A characteristic reaction of acidified titanium solutions is the development of an intense yellow-orange color on addition of hydrogen peroxide. This reaction can be used as a colorimetric method of analysis for either Ti^{IV} or hydrogen peroxide. The colored species, which is destroyed by fluoride ion, appears to be the peroxotitanyl group TiO_2^{2+}(aq). Peroxo complexes such as $(NH_4)_3[TiF_5O_2]$ and $K_2[TiO_2(SO_4)_2]\cdot 3H_2O$ have been isolated.[5]

Simple salts with oxo anions are relatively few. The sulfate can be made by the reaction

$$TiCl_4 + 6SO_3 = Ti(SO_4)_2 + 2S_2O_5Cl_2$$

The anhydrous nitrate is a very interesting volatile compound (m 58°), best made[6a] by the action of N_2O_5 on hydrated Ti^{IV} nitrate. It is very reactive toward organic substances, often causing inflammation or explosion. It has been proposed[6b] that it reacts by releasing the very reactive NO_3 radical. It has the eight-coordinate structure shown in Figure 29-A-1. This is a special case of the dodecahedral structure as explained earlier (page 137).

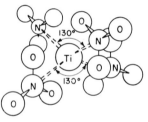

Fig. 29-A-1.   The structure of titanium(IV) nitrate. Each NO_3 group is bidentate and they are disposed so that the N atoms form a slightly distorted tetrahedron with D_{2d} symmetry (from ref. 6b by permission).

Alkoxides.   Many metal chlorides undergo solvation and/or partial solvolysis with alcohols, but replacement of chloride is incomplete in absence of a base such as the ethoxide ion, ammonia, pyridine, etc. The titanium alkoxides have been much studied and are generally typical of many other transition metal alkoxides, such as those of Hf, Ce, V, Nb, Fe, U, which will not be discussed in detail. The compounds can be obtained by reactions such as:

$$TiCl_4 + 4ROH + 4NH_3 = Ti(OR)_4 + 4NH_4Cl$$
$$TiCl_4 + 3EtOH = 2HCl + TiCl_2(OEt)_2\cdot EtOH$$

[5] For references see W. P. Griffith, *J. Chem. Soc.*, **1965**, 5248.
[6a] B. O. Field and C. J. Hardy, *J. Chem. Soc.*, **1963**, 5278.
[6b] C. C. Addison, *et al.*, *Proc. Chem. Soc.*, **1964**, 367.

The titanium alkoxides are liquids or solids which can be distilled or sub-limed and are soluble in organic solvents such as benzene. They are exceed-ingly readily hydrolyzed by even traces of water, the ease decreasing with increasing chain length of the alkyl group. The initial hydrolytic step probably involves coordination of water to the metal; a proton on H_2O could then interact with the oxygen of an —OR group through hydrogen bonding, leading to hydrolysis:

$$
\begin{array}{c}
H \\
\diagdown \overset{+}{O}-\overset{-}{M}(OR)_x \\
H \diagup
\end{array}
\longrightarrow
\begin{array}{c}
H \\
\diagdown \overset{+}{O}-\overset{-}{M}(OR)_{x-1} \\
H \cdots\cdots :O \\
\diagdown \\
R
\end{array}
\longrightarrow M(OH)(OR)_{x-1} + ROH
$$

Probably the most important structural feature of the titanium and other alkoxides is that, although monomeric species can in certain cases exist, especially in very dilute solution, these compounds are in general polymers. Solid $Ti(OC_2H_5)_4$ is a tetramer,[7] with the structure shown in Figure 29-A-2.

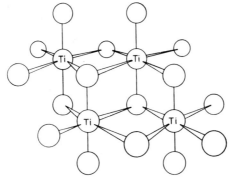

Fig. 29-A-2.   The tetrameric structure of crystalline $Ti(OC_2H_5)_4$. Only Ti and O atoms are shown.

This compact structure neatly allows each Ti atom to attain octahedral coordination. However, in benzene solution[8a] this compound, and most other $Ti(OR)_4$ compounds, is a trimer. The susceptibility of the polymers to hydrolytic degradation by even minute traces of water makes it difficult to obtain accurate measurements of molecular weight in solution, but the existence of trimers seems fairly certain. The alkoxides also undergo scrambling reactions.[8b] Partially hydrolyzed polymer species could have OH or O bridges.

[7] J. A. Ibers, *Nature*, **197**, 686 (1963); R. L. Martin and G. Winter, *Nature*, **197**, 687 (1963).
[8a] D. C. Bradley and C. E. Holloway, *Inorg. Chem.*, **3**, 1163 (1963).
[8b] H. Weingarten and J. R. Van Wazer, *J. Amer. Chem. Soc.*, **87**, 724 (1965).

It is convenient to note here when dealing with oxygen ligands that titanium gives an acetylacetonate $Ti(acac)_2Cl_2$ which is a normal six-coordinate, monomeric nonelectrolyte. This compound reacts with $FeCl_3$ giving $[Ti(acac)_3]^+[FeCl_4]^-$ as the main product.[9]

Nitrogen Compounds. Nitrogen ligands appear to react with titanium halides initially to give an adduct from which hydrogen halide is eliminated by base catalysis. Thus the action of diluted gaseous ammonia on $TiCl_4$ gives addition, but with excess ammonia, ammonolysis occurs and up to three Ti—Cl bonds are converted to Ti—NH_2 bonds. With increasing substitution, the remaining Ti—Cl bonds become more ionic and even liquid ammonia ammonolyzes only three bonds. Primary and secondary amines react in a similar way to give orange or red solids such as $TiCl_2$-$(NHR)_2$ and $TiCl_3NR_2$ which can be further solvated by the amine.

The action of lithium alkylamides, $LiNR_2$, on $TiCl_4$ leads to liquid or solid compounds of the type $Ti[N(C_2H_5)_2]_4$, which, like the alkoxides, are readily hydrolyzed by water with liberation of amine.

With a tertiary amine simple adduct formation should be more likely, and $N(CH_3)_3$, for example, affords $TiCl_4 \cdot N(CH_3)_3$ and $TiBr_4 \cdot N(CH_3)_3$ which are monomers in benzene.[10] Reduction also occurs, however, in a manner not well understood giving Ti^{III} compounds.

29-A-3. Lower Valent Titanium Compounds

Valence states of -1 and 0 are known only in the special case of the 2,2'-dipyridyl complexes, $Li[Ti(dipy)_3] \cdot 3.5C_4H_8O$ and $[Ti(dipy)_3]$, which are formed as black plates or purple needles, respectively, by the lithium reduction of $TiCl_4$ in presence of dipyridyl in tetrahydrofuran. These compounds, which are presumably stabilized by delocalization of electron density over the aromatic rings (with some attendant doubt as to the significance of the formal oxidation states; see page 756) are readily oxidized by air.

Divalent compounds are few in number and Ti^{II} has no aqueous chemistry, because of its oxidation by water, although it has been reported that ice-cold solutions of TiO in dilute HCl contain Ti^{II} ions which persist for some time. The well defined compounds are $TiCl_2$, $TiBr_2$, TiI_2 and TiO. The halides are best obtained by reduction of the tetrahalides with titanium:

$$TiX_4 + Ti = 2TiX_2$$

[9] R. J. Woodruff, J. L. Marini and J. P. Fackler, Jr., *Inorg. Chem.*, **3**, 687 (1963); M. Cox, J. Lewis and R. S. Nyholm, *J. Chem. Soc.*, **1964**, 6113.

[10] G. W. A. Fowles and R. A. Hoodless, *J. Chem. Soc.*, **1963**, 33.

or by disproportionation of the trihalides,

$$2TiX_3 = TiX_2 + TiX_4$$

the volatile tetrahalides being removed by distillation.

TiO is obtained by heating TiO_2 with Ti. It has the rock salt structure, but it has a marked tendency to have lattice vacancies so that the precise stoichiometry TiO is seldom found.

Titanium(III) has a fairly extensive chemistry. On reduction of aqueous titanium(IV) either electrolytically or chemically (e.g., with zinc and acid), violet solutions containing the $[Ti(H_2O)_6]^{3+}$ ion are obtained. These solutions are fairly rapid, mild reducing agents and are used in certain quantitative analyses.

$$\text{``}TiO^{2+}\text{''(aq)} + 2H^+ + e = Ti^{3+} + H_2O \qquad E^0 = ca\ 0.1\ v$$

The solutions reduce atmospheric oxygen and must therefore be stored in sealed containers and handled in hydrogen or nitrogen atmospheres.

From aqueous solutions of Ti^{III} and chloride ions, the violet hexahydrate, $[Ti(H_2O)_6]Cl_3$, may be crystallized. If, however, the aqueous solution is covered with a layer of ether and saturated with HCl, a green hexahydrate is obtained. It is probable that this is a hydration isomer similar to one of those known for $CrCl_3 \cdot 6H_2O$ (see page 149). Anhydrous $TiCl_3$, as a violet powder, is prepared by passing the vapors of $TiCl_4$ together with excess of hydrogen through a red-hot tube ($\sim 650°$) and rapidly quenching the hot gases. When heated to above $500°$, $TiCl_3$ disproportionates as above.

The other titanium(III) halides, including TiF_3, are also known.

Ti^{III} is decidedly more basic than Ti^{IV}, as would be expected, and the purple precipitate obtained on addition of base to Ti^{III} solutions shows no amphoteric behavior. It is usually written as $Ti(OH)_3$, but is probably the hydrous oxide, $Ti_2O_3 \cdot nH_2O$. The anhydrous oxide, Ti_2O_3, which has the corundum structure, can be obtained by heating TiO_2 to $1000°$ in a stream of hydrogen and $TiCl_4$. It is quite stable and is attacked only by oxidizing acids.

Ti^{III} forms a number of double or complex sulfate salts such as $NH_4Ti_3(SO_4)_5 \cdot 9H_2O$, $RbTi_3(SO_4)_5 \cdot 12H_2O$ and $NaTi(SO_4)_2 \cdot 2.5H_2O$ of unknown structure, as well as two alums, $RbTi(SO_4)_2 \cdot 12H_2O$ and $CsTi(SO_4)_2 \cdot 12H_2O$, which contain $[Ti(H_2O)_6]^{3+}$ ions. It also forms a green, anhydrous sulfate, $Ti_2(SO_4)_3$, of unknown structure.

The best-known halo complexes of Ti^{III} are the pentachloroaquotitanium-(III), $[TiCl_5(H_2O)]^{2-}$, and hexafluorotitanium(III), $[TiF_6]^{3-}$, both found in crystals with alkali metal cations. There are also the $M^I_2TiF_5$ compounds whose structures are unknown. It seems likely that they contain octahedral TiF_6 units as a result of sharing F^- ions.

$TiCl_3$ reacts with many donors such as ethers, nitriles, alcohols, ketones and amines, to form substances with the formula $TiCl_3 \cdot nL$, where $n = 1$, 2 or 3 depending upon L and the reaction conditions.[11] The structures are not in general known. Those with $n = 3$ are probably octahedral. The $TiX_3 \cdot 2N(CH_3)_3$ compounds, unlike their V analogs, which are five-coordinate monomers, are too insoluble to permit molecular weight studies. The compound $TiCl_3 \cdot 3THF$ loses two THF below 100° and the resulting $TiCl_3 \cdot THF$ disproportionates to $TiCl_4 \cdot 2THF$ (as a yellow sublimate) and $TiCl_2$ at 150–200°, which is several hundred degrees below the disproportionation temperature for $TiCl_3$ itself.[12]

$Ti(acac)_3$ and the benzoylacetone analog are also fairly well characterized Ti^{III} complexes;[4] they are readily oxidized in air to $TiO(diketonate)_2$.

The Ti^{III} ion is a d^1 system, and in an octahedral ligand field the configuration must be t_{2g}. One absorption band is expected ($t_{2g} \rightarrow e_g$ transition), and this has been observed in several compounds. The spectrum of the $[Ti(H_2O)_6]^{3+}$ ion is shown and discussed on page 674. The violet color of the hexaquo ion is attributable to this band which is so placed as to permit some blue and most red light to be transmitted.

The magnetic properties of Ti^{III} compounds have been investigated to some extent.[13] Although a d^1 ion in an electrostatic field of perfect O_h symmetry should show a highly temperature dependent moment as a result of spin-orbit coupling, with μ_{eff} going to 0 at 0°K, the combined effects of distortion and covalence (which causes delocalization of the electron) cause a leveling out of μ_{eff}, and it has in general been found to vary from not less than about 1.5 BM at 80°K to ~ 1.8 BM at about 300°K. Room temperature values of μ_{eff} are generally close to 1.7 BM.

In $[\pi\text{-}C_5H_5TiCl]_2$ there appears to be a thermal equilibrium between singlet and triplet states, probably associated with Ti—Ti bonding interactions via bridging chlorine atoms.[14]

29-B. VANADIUM

The maximum valence shown by vanadium is $+5$. There is little similarity in this state to the chemistries of the phosphorus group elements. Although V^V does indeed form vanadates, these have little in common

[11] G. W. A. Fowles, R. A. Hoodless and R. A. Walton, *J. Chem. Soc.*, **1963**, 5873; G. W. A. Fowles and R. A. Walton, *J. Chem. Soc.*, **1965**, 4983; G. W. A. Fowles, R. A. Hoodless and R. A. Walton, *J. Inorg. Nucl. Chem.*, **27**, 391 (1965).

[12] R. J. Keen, *J. Inorg. Nucl. Chem.*, **24**, 1105 (1962).

[13] R. J. H. Clark, J. Lewis, D. J. Machin and R. S. Nyholm, *J. Chem. Soc.*, **1963**, 379; B. N. Figgis, J. Lewis and F. Mabbs, *J. Chem. Soc.*, **1963**, 2473.

[14] R. L. Martin and G. Winter, *J. Chem. Soc.*, **1965**, 4709.

chemically or structurally with phosphates; the oxochlorides, $OVCl_3$ and $OPCl_3$, are both readily hydrolyzed liquids, however.

The oxidation states and stereochemistries for vanadium are summarized in Table 29-B-1.

TABLE 29-B-1
Oxidation States and Stereochemistry of Vanadium

Oxidation state	Coordination number	Geometry	Examples
V^{-I}	6	Octahedral	$K_5[V(CN)_5NO]$, $V(CO)_6{}^-$, $Li[V(dipy)_3]\cdot 4C_4H_8O$
V^0	6	Octahedral	$V(CO)_6$, $Vdipy_3$, $V[C_2H_4(PMe_2)_2]_3$
V^I, d^4	6	Octahedral	$[V(dipy)_3]^+$
		π-Complex	$[V(CO)_4\ arene]^+$
	7	?	$Ph_3PAuV(CO)_6$
V^{II}, d^3	6	Octahedral	$[V(H_2O)_6]^{2+}$, $[V(CN)_6]^{4-}$
V^{III}, d^2	4	Tetrahedral	$[VCl_4]^-$
	5	Trigonal bipyramidal	$trans$-$VCl_3(SMe_2)_2$
	6^a	Octahedral	$[V(NH_3)_6]^{3+}$, $[V(C_2O_4)_3]^{3-}$, VF_3
V^{IV}, d^1	4	Tetrahedral	VCl_4
	5	Tetragonal pyramidal	$VO(acac)_2$
		?	$[VO(SCN)_4]^{2-}$
	6^a	Octahedral	VO_2 (rutile), K_2VCl_6, $VO(acac)_2py$
	8	Dodecahedral	$VCl_4(diars)_2$
V^V, d^0	4	Tetrahedral	$VOCl_3$
	5	Trigonal bipyramidal	VF_5
	6^a	Octahedral	$VF_6{}^-$; V_2O_5 (very distorted; almost trigonal bipyramidal with one distant O)

^a Most important states.

29-B-1. The Element

Vanadium has an abundance of about 0.02%. It is widely spread—over sixty minerals being known—but there are few concentrated deposits. The more important minerals are a complex sulfide called *patronite*, *vanadinite* ($Pb_5(VO_4)_3Cl$), and *carnotite* ($K(UO_2)VO_4\cdot\frac{3}{2}H_2O$). The latter is more important as a uranium ore, but the vanadium is usually recovered as well.

Very pure vanadium is rather rare because, like titanium, it is quite reactive toward oxygen, nitrogen and carbon at the elevated temperatures used in conventional thermometallurgical processes. Since its chief commercial use is in alloy steels and cast iron, to which it lends ductility and shock resistance, commercial production is mainly as an iron alloy called *ferrovanadium*. The very pure metal can be prepared by the de Boer–van Arkel process (page 800).

26*

The pure metal is reported to melt at $\sim 1700°$, but addition of small percentages of carbon (interstitially) raises the melting point markedly: vanadium containing 10% carbon melts at $\sim 2700°$. The pure, or nearly pure, metal resembles titanium in being corrosion resistant, hard and steel grey in color. In the massive state it is not attacked by air, water, alkalies or nonoxidizing acids other than HF at room temperature. It does dissolve in nitric acid, concentrated sulfuric acid and in aqua regia.

At elevated temperatures it combines with most nonmetals. With oxygen it gives V_2O_5 contaminated with lower oxides, and with nitrogen the interstitial nitride, VN. Arsenides, silicides, carbides and other such compounds, many of which are definitely interstitial and nonstoichiometric, are also obtained by direct reaction of the elements.

29-B-2. Vanadium Halides

These are listed in Table 29-B-2 together with some of their reactions.

TABLE 29-B-2

The Halides of Vanadium

VF_5[a] white m 19.5°	VF_4 brown $\xrightarrow{\sim 325°[b]}$	VF_3 green	VF_2 pale green
$\uparrow$ HF(g) 25°		$\uparrow$ HF(g) 600°	$\uparrow$ HF(g) 600°
VCl_4[a] red-brown b 154°	$\underset{Cl_2}{\overset{reflux}{\rightleftharpoons}}$	VCl_3 violet $\xrightarrow{>450°[b]}$	VCl_2 green
VBr_4[c] magenta	$\underset{Br_2}{\overset{>-23°}{\rightleftharpoons}}$	VBr_3[a] black $\xrightarrow{>280°}$	VBr_2 brown
		VI_3[a] black $\xrightarrow{>280°}$	VI_2 red

[a] Made by direct interaction at elevated temperatures, F_2, 300°; Cl_2, 500°; Br_2, I_2, 150°.
[b] Disproportionation reaction, e.g., $2VCl_3 = VCl_2 + VCl_4$ (see ref. 2).
[c] Isolated from vapor at $\sim 550°$ by rapid cooling to $-78°$ (see ref. 2).

The *tetrachloride* is obtained not only from $V + Cl_2$ but also by the action of CCl_4 on red hot V_2O_5 and by chlorination of ferrovanadium (followed by distillation to separate VCl_4 from Fe_2Cl_6). It is an oily liquid which is immediately and violently hydrolyzed by water to give solutions of oxo-vanadium(IV) chloride; its magnetic and spectral properties confirm its non-associated tetrahedral nature.[1] It has a high dissociation pressure

[1] R. J. H. Clark and D. J. Machin, *J. Chem. Soc.*, **1963**, 4430.

and loses chlorine slowly on standing and rapidly on boiling, leaving VCl_3. The thermal behavior of VCl_3 and VBr_3 is complex but well understood.[2] For both, the following reactions occur:

$$2VX_3(s) = VX_2(s) + VX_4(g)$$
$$VX_3(s) = VX_2(s) + \tfrac{1}{2}X_2(g)$$

Thus the ultimate product of heating VCl_3, VBr_3 and VI_3 and removing the halogen is the dihalide; VCl_2 is thermally stable to $1110°$. VCl_3 and VBr_3 have non-molecular BI_3 type lattices.

Like SbF_5, VF_5 has a high viscosity and may be associated through fluorine bridging.[3]

Some *complex halides* are known. Salts of $VF_6{}^-$ can be made by treating VCl_3 + alkali metal chloride with BrF_3; K_2VCl_6 is formed by interaction of VCl_4 with KCl in ICl. Complex fluorides of V^{III} are of types $VF_6{}^{3-}$, $VF_5(H_2O)^{2-}$ and $VF_4(H_2O)_2{}^-$; thus treatment of the stable alum $(NH_4)V(SO_4)_2 \cdot 12H_2O$ with KHF_2 gives $K_2VF_5 \cdot H_2O$ as green crystals. The green crystals of "$K_2VCl_5 \cdot nH_2O$", obtained by treating VCl_3 in concentrated HCl with KCl have been shown to be fortuitous mixtures of KCl and $KVCl_4 \cdot nH_2O$.[4] In the latter, as well as in hydrated halides such as $VCl_3 \cdot 6H_2O$ (which gives green crystals from acid solution), V^{III} appears to be octahedrally coordinated by four water molecules and two chloride ions. The ion $VCl_6{}^{3-}$ has also been characterized.

29-B-3. The Chemistry of Vanadium(V)

Vanadium(V) Oxide and the Vanadates. Vanadium(V) oxide is obtained on burning the finely divided metal in excess of oxygen, although some quantities of lower oxides are also formed. The usual method of preparation is by heating so-called ammonium meta-vanadate:

$$2NH_4VO_3 = V_2O_5 + 2NH_3 + H_2O$$

It is thus obtained as an orange powder which melts at about $650°$ and solidifies on cooling to orange, rhombic needle crystals. Addition of dilute H_2SO_4 to solutions of NH_4VO_3 gives a brick red precipitate of V_2O_5. It has a slight solubility in water (~ 0.007 g/liter) to give pale yellow acidic solutions. Although mainly acidic in character, and hence readily soluble in bases, V_2O_5 also dissolves in acids. That the V^V species so formed are moderately strong oxidizing agents is indicated by the fact that chlorine is evolved when V_2O_5 is dissolved in hydrochloric acid, V^{IV} being produced.

[2] R. E. McCarley and J. W. Roddy, *Inorg. Chem.*, **3**, 50, 54, 60 (1964).
[3] R. G. Cavell and H. C. Clark, *Inorg. Chem.*, **3**, 1789 (1964).
[4] S. M. Horner and S. Y. Tyree, *Inorg. Chem.*, **3**, 1173 (1964).

It is also reduced by warm sulphuric acid. The following standard potential has been estimated:

$$VO_2{}^+ + 2H^+ + e = VO^{2+} + H_2O \qquad E^0 = 1.0 \text{ v}$$

Solutions of V_2O_5 in base have been extensively studied to determine the species present and the pH-dependent equilibria among them.[5] The available data are satisfied by the following equilibrium expressions and constants:

$$\begin{aligned}
VO_4{}^{3-} + H^+ &= [VO_3(OH)]^{2-} & K &= 10^{12.6} \\
2[VO_3(OH)]^{2-} + H^+ &= [V_2O_6(OH)]^{3-} + H_2O & K &= 10^{10.6} \\
[VO_3(OH)]^{2-} + H^+ &= [VO_2(OH)_2]^- & K &= 10^{7.7} \\
3[VO_3(OH)]^{2-} + 3H^+ &= V_3O_9{}^{3-} + 3H_2O & K &= 10^{30.7}
\end{aligned}$$

Before discussing these equilibria, it must be noted—and this comment will apply to all similar equilibria discussed later—that equilibrium measurements in dilute aqueous solutions cannot establish the extent of hydration of the various species so that the formulas given are arbitrary in this regard. In general, though not always, we write the simplest possible formula, that is, the one containing no water. Thus $[VO_3(OH)]^{2-}$ probably is $[VO_2(OH)_3]^{2-}$ or $[VO_2(OH)_3(H_2O)]^{2-}$, etc.

The above equilibria show that in the most basic solutions, mononuclear, tetrahedral vanadate ions, $VO_4{}^{3-}$, are formed and that, as the basicity is reduced, these first protonate and then aggregate into dinuclear and trinuclear species, written above as $[V_2O_6(OH)]^{3-}$ and $[V_3O_9]^{3-}$. It has been suggested that these several anions may be built up from dioxo-vanadium ions $VO_2{}^+$ (which are discussed further below) and OH^- ions as indicated in 29-B-I, 29-B-II and 29-B-III, but this is only speculative at present.

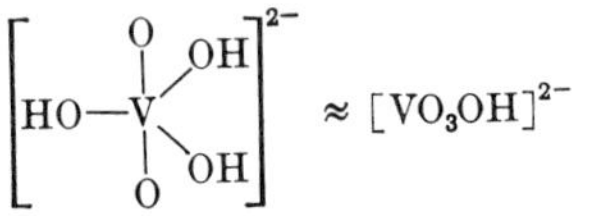

(29-B-I) 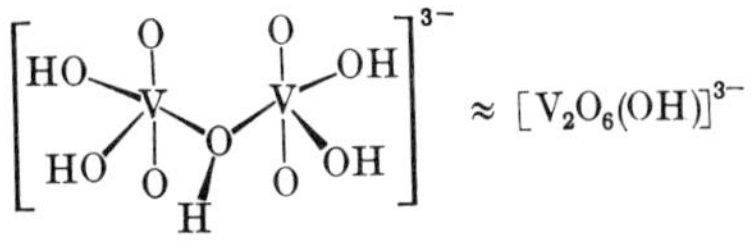   (29-B-II)

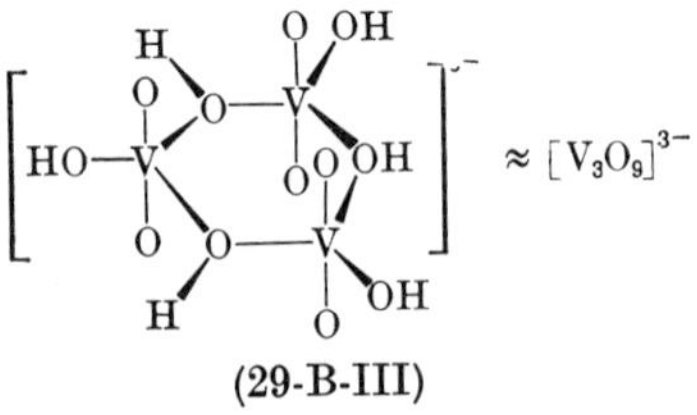

(29-B-III)

[5] O. W. Howarth and R. E. Richards, *J. Chem. Soc.*, **1965**, 864; A. W. Naumann and C. J. Hallada, *Inorg. Chem.*, **3**, 70 (1964); D. B. Copley, A. K. Banerjee and S. Y. Tyree, *Inorg. Chem.*, **4**, 1480 (1965).

At very high pH the solutions are essentially colorless, but they become yellow and then orange as the pH is lowered. When the pH is lowered below about 6.8, hydrous V_2O_5 precipitates. Even at the higher pH's solid "vanadates" can be crystallized from the solutions. These solids have a great variety of compositions, such as, $M^I_3V_5O_{14}$, $M^I_4HV_5O_{15}$, etc., and their structures are almost entirely unknown. It is very important to bear in mind that from the compositions of these precipitates *nothing* can be inferred as to the polyvanadate ions which are present in the solutions from which they were obtained. Failure to recognize that an equilibrium can exist between such solids and the solutions without the same species being present in both phases is responsible for a great deal of confusion in the older literature in this field.

When V_2O_5 is dissolved in acid, complex solutions are again obtained. The most recent data can be accounted for by the following equilibria:

$$10VO_2^+ + 8H_2O = [H_2V_{10}O_{28}]^{4-} + 14H^+ \qquad K = 10^{-6.75}$$
$$[H_2V_{10}O_{28}]^{4-} = [HV_{10}O_{28}]^{5-} + H^+ \qquad K = 10^{-3.6}$$
$$[HV_{10}O_{28}]^{5-} = [V_{10}O_{28}]^{6-} + H^+ \qquad K = 10^{-5.8}$$

Again, simplest formulas are used; the actual species may contain more water. It is also possible that other species may exist in small amounts, but the data can be fitted within experimental error by these equilibria so that such other species are, in effect, undetectable. The data are sufficiently accurate to make the V_{10} species rather certain; equilibria with V_9, V_{11} or V_{12} species cannot be devised so as to be in as good accord with the experimental measurements over the entire ranges of pH and total V concentration as are those given above. The possible importance of hexavanadate species has often been suggested and there is some supporting data. However, the above equilibria involving mainly decavanadates are most probable. These equilibrium expressions show that from the lowest pH's studied (~ 1) up to pH's of 1.3–2.0, depending on total V concentrations, the dioxovanadium(V) ion, VO_2^+ is the main species, with the decanuclear species $[H_nV_{10}O_{28}]^{(6-n)-}$, arising as the pH is raised. In the pH region 4–7, there appear to be three V_{10} species protonated to different degrees.

In solid compounds, namely $Ca_3V_{10}O_{28} \cdot 16H_2O$ and $K_2Zn_2V_{10}O_{28} \cdot 16H_2O$, which can be crystallized from orange solutions at pH 2–6, the existence of the $V_{10}O_{28}^{6-}$ ion, consisting of ten VO_6 octahedra fused together, has been demonstrated by X-ray data.[6]

The dioxovanadium(V) group occurs in some complex vanadium(V) salts, for example, $M^I_3[VO_2(C_2O_4)_2]$ and $M^I[VO_2(SO_4)]$.

[6] H. T. Evans, A. G. Swallow and W. H. Barnes, *J. Amer. Chem. Soc.*, **86**, 4209 (1964).

Vanadium(V) Oxohalides. A number of oxohalides and oxohalo complex anions of V^V are known. Vanadium oxotrichloride, $VOCl_3$, and oxotribromide, $VOBr_3$, can be prepared by halogenation of V_2O_3,

$$V_2O_3 + 3X_2 = 2VOX_3 + \tfrac{1}{2}O_2$$

and the chloride also by chlorination of V_2O_5. Both are rather volatile substances, suggesting that they are simple molecular compounds, at least in the vapor state, and for $VOCl_3$ this is confirmed by electron diffraction study which has shown the molecule to be essentially tetrahedral. Vanadium oxotrifluoride is also known, being obtained by treatment of the oxotrichloride with cold concentrated hydrofluoric acid or by oxidation of VF_3 with molecular oxygen at 500–600°. All three oxotrihalides are rapidly hydrolyzed by water.

Several salts containing fluorovanadate(V) anionic complexes have been reported, although their exact structures are not known. They are obtained by reactions between vanadium pentoxide and an alkali metal fluoride, usually in hydrofluoric acid solution. They are of the type $M^I[VOF_4]$, $M^I_2[VOF_5]$ and $M^I_2[VO_2F_3]$.

With pyridinium chloride, (pyH)Cl, in alcoholic solution, $VOCl_3$ forms the salt (pyH)[VOCl$_4$], which is hydrolyzed by water.

Other Vanadium(V) Compounds. A sulfide, V_2S_5, has been claimed, but its existence seems doubtful at present. The metal reacts with N_2O_4 in acetonitrile to give a brick-red solid, VO_2NO_3, which is very soluble in water and on heating gives V_2O_5 and N_2O_5.

There is a series of peroxo compounds of V^V of which the solid salts $KH_2[VO_2(O_2)_2]\cdot H_2O$, $(NH_4)_2H[VO_2(O_2)_2]\cdot nH_2O$ and $M^I_3[V(O_2)_4]\cdot nH_2O$ are insoluble. In these, two or all of the oxygen atoms of $[VO_4]^{3-}$ are replaced by peroxo groups, O_2.

29-B-4. The Chemistry of Vanadium(IV)

This important oxidation state of vanadium is the most stable one under ordinary conditions. V^{III} is oxidized to V^{IV} by molecular oxygen, and V^V is reduced to V^{IV} by fairly mild reducing agents. The dark blue oxide, VO_2, can be obtained by mild reduction of V_2O_5, a classic method being by fusion of the latter with oxalic acid; it is amphoteric, being about equally readily soluble in both acids and bases. In strongly basic solutions vanadate(IV) ions, VO_4^{4-}, probably not of this simple nature, exist and from these solutions, and less basic ones, various vanadate(IV) compounds, also called *hypovanadates* are obtainable. They are of the type $M^I_2V_4O_9\cdot 7H_2O$. By fusion of VO_2 with alkaline earth oxides, other vanadate(IV) compounds, for example, $M^{II}VO_3$, $M^{II}_2VO_4$ and $M^{II}_3VO_5$, have been obtained. Virtually nothing is known of their structures.

Aside from a few compounds such as VCl_4, the chemistry of V^{IV} is almost entirely of *oxovanadium*, or *vanadyl*, compounds. These contain the VO unit which can persist through a variety of chemical reactions. Oxovanadium(IV) compounds[7] may, depending on the nature of the ligands, be cationic, neutral or anionic and be either penta- or hexa-coordinate, e.g., $[VOdipy_2Cl]^+$, $VOacac_2$, $[VO(NCS)_4]^{2-}$.

The VO bond has been shown to be essentially a double bond V=O. Thus (a) in $VOSO_4 \cdot 5H_2O$ there are four water molecules in a plane with the V—O distance 2.3 A, while perpendicular to this plane is the V—O bond of length 1.67A; the position *trans* to the oxygen is occupied by one oxygen atom of the SO_4 group. The structure of the acetylacetonate (29-B-IV) is similar with V—O = 1.56 A and the vanadium atom is above the center of the base square. Even in VO_2, which has a distorted rutile structure, one bond is conspicuously shorter, 1.76 A, than the others in the VO_6 unit (note that in TiO_2 all Ti—O bonds are essentially equal).

(29-B-IV)

(b) All oxovanadium(IV) compounds have infrared bands in the region 900–1100 cm^{-1}, even $VO(OH)_2$.

(c) Electronic, esr and vibrational spectra[8] of the vanadyl ion are consistent with the formulation $[VO(H_2O)_5]^{2-}$.

The VO bonds can be regarded as multiple ones, the π-component arising from flow of electron density $O(p\pi) \to V(d\pi)$. The pentacoordinate complexes have been shown to take up a sixth ligand quite readily,[9] becoming octahedral, with donors such as pyridine or triphenylphosphine. The V=O stretching frequency is quite sensitive to the nature of the *trans* ligand, and donors which increase the electron density on the metal thereby reduce its acceptor properties toward O, and hence cause lowering of the

---

[7] For examples see: J. Selbin and L. H. Holmes, *J. Inorg. Nucl. Chem.*, **24**, 1111 (1962); S. M. Horner, S. Y. Tyree and D. L. Venezky, *Inorg. Chem.*, **1**, 844 (1962).

[8] C. J. Ballhausen and H. B. Gray, *Inorg. Chem.*, **1**, 111 (1962); I. Bernal and D. H. Rieger, *Inorg. Chem.*, **2**, 256 (1963); J. C. Evans, *Inorg. Chem.*, **2**, 372 (1963).

[9] R. L. Carlin and F. A. Walker, *J. Amer. Chem. Soc.*, **87**, 2128 (1965).

V—O multiple bond character and the stretching frequency.[10] The esr and electronic spectra of VO^{2+} species are sensitive also to solvents for the same reason.

Because of the strong VO π bonding in oxovanadium(IV) compounds, the interpretation of the electronic spectra is not as simple as it would be for an ordinary octahedral complex and at present there are some unresolved differences of opinion as to the interpretation of the spectra and of the exact ordering of the orbitals.[11]

The commercial salt $VOSO_4 \cdot 2H_2O$ is soluble in water, the solution probably containing a weak sulfato complex $[VO(H_2O)_4OSO_3H]^+$. Addition of base gives yellow $VO(OH)_2$ which dissolves in $HClO_4$ and other acids to give the blue aquo ion, $[VO(H_2O)_5]^{2+}$. The oxalato complex $(NH_4)_2$-$[VO(C_2O_4)_2] \cdot 2H_2O$ is readily obtained as blue crystals by boiling NH_4VO_3 solutions with ammonium oxalate. Neutral oxalato complexes VO-$(C_2O_4) \cdot 2H_2O$ and $VO(C_2O_4) \cdot 4H_2O$ have been prepared,[12] the former appearing to be 5-coordinate (cf. $VO(acac)_2$).

Oxovanadium chloride, $VOCl_2$, is best made by reduction of $VOCl_3$ with hydrogen; it is a bright green deliquescent substance, soluble in water. Solutions of $VOCl_2$ and $VOBr_2$ are readily obtained by heating V_2O_5 in in the aqueous acid with ethanol.

Vanadium tetrafluoride and VCl_4 give adducts with a number of O, N and other ligands to give complexes of the types VCl_4L, VCl_4L_2. All of the complexes are readily hydrolyzed and oxidized in air.[13]

29-B-5. The Chemistry of Vanadium(III)

This oxidation state is of moderate importance. The oxide, V_2O_3, is a black, refractory substance made by reduction of V_2O_5 with moderately powerful reducing agents such as hydrogen or carbon monoxide. It has the corundum structure, but it is difficult to obtain in an exactly stoichiometric condition since it has a marked tendency to become oxygen deficient without change in structure. Compositions as low in oxygen as $VO_{1.35}$ are reported to retain the corundum structure.

V_2O_3 is entirely basic in nature and dissolves in acids to give solutions of the V^{III} aquo ion or its complexes. The same solutions may also be obtained by electrolytic reduction of acid solutions containing vanadium in the IV or V state. In solutions free of complexing agents, V^{III} exists as the

[10] J. Selbin, L. M. Holmes, Jr., and S. P. McGlynn, *J. Inorg. Nucl. Chem.*, **25**, 1359 (1963).
[11] J. Selbin and L. Morpurgo, *J. Inorg. Nucl. Chem.*, **27**, 673 (1965).
[12] D. N. Sathyanarayana and C. C. Patel, *J. Inorg. Nucl. Chem.*, **27**, 297 (1965).
[13] B. E. Bridgland, G. W. A. Fowles and R. A. Walton, *J. Inorg. Nucl. Chem.*, **27**, 383 (1965) and references therein.

blue hexaquo ion, $[V(H_2O)_6]^{3+}$. Such solutions, and also others, of V^{III} are subject to air oxidation in view of the potential:

$$VO^{2+} + 2H^+ + e = V^{3+} + H_2O \qquad E^0 = 0.36 \text{ v}$$

Hydrous V_2O_3 can be precipitated by addition of hydroxide to these solutions; it is very easily oxidized.

When solutions of V^{2+} and VO^{2+} are mixed, V^{3+} is formed but a brown intermediate species which has an oxo bridge, VOV^{4+}, occurs;[14] this is similar to a chromium(III) species $CrOCr^{4+}$ obtained when Cr^{2+} is oxidized under conditions where a Cr^{IV} complex might be expected—by the two-electron oxidant Tl^{3+}.

Vanadium(III) forms a fair number of complexes, mostly anionic. Salts of the trioxalato ion, $[V(C_2O_4)_3]^{3-}$, the hexacyano ion, $[V(CN)_6]^{3-}$, and the hexathiocyanato ion, $[V(NCS)_6]^{3-}$, are also known. In addition to its occurrence in aqueous solutions, where partial hydrolysis to $V(OH)^{2+}$ and VO^+ occurs, and its probable occurrence in hexaquovanadium(III) chloride, the $[V(H_2O)_6]^{3+}$ ion occurs in the vanadium alums, M^IV-$(SO_4)_2 \cdot 12H_2O$. The ammonium alum is obtained as air-stable blue-violet crystals by electrolytic reduction of NH_4VO_3 in H_2SO_4. V^{III} does not appear to form simple ammine complexes; reaction of VCl_3 with liquid ammonia yields what seems to be $VCl_2(NH_2) \cdot 4NH_3$. An alleged simple ammine has been shown to be a mixture of $[V(NH_2)(NH_3)_5]Br_2$ and NH_4Br.[15]

The electronic structure of an octahedrally coordinated d^2 ion, of which V^{III} is the example *par excellence*, has already been discussed at some length in Chapter 26. It need only be added here that experimental data for a number of V^{III} octahedral complexes, such as $V(H_2O)_6^{3+}$, VF_6^{3-}, $V(C_3H_2O_4)_3^{3-}$ and V^{3+} substituted into α-Al_2O_3 have been interpreted satisfactorily in terms of the ligand field model, although in general it has been found necessary to take account of the effects of a small trigonal distortion (to symmetry D_{3d}) of the basically octahedral field.

29-B-6. The Chemistry of Vanadium(II)

This is decidedly the least stable or important of the oxidation states of vanadium. The black oxide, VO, has a crystal lattice of the rock salt type, but it shows a marked tendency to nonstoichiometry, being obtainable with anywhere from ~ 45 to ~ 55 atom % oxygen. It has a metallic luster and rather good electrical conductivity of a metallic nature. There is

[14] T. W. Newton and F. B. Baker, *Inorg. Chem.*, **3**, 569 (1964); J. H. Espenson, *Inorg. Chem.*, **4**, 1533 (1965).
[15] D. Nicholls, *J. Inorg. Nucl. Chem.*, **24**, 1001 (1962).

doubtless a good deal of direct metal–metal bonding. It is an entirely basic substance, dissolving in acids to give V^{II} solutions.

Violet, air sensitive aqueous solutions of V^{II} are usually obtained by reduction of acidic solutions of V^{IV} electrolytically or using zinc. The oxidation of V^{2+} by air is complicated[16] and proceeds in part by direct oxidation to VO^{2+} and part by way of the intermediate VOV^{4+} noted above.

V^{II} is isoelectronic with Cr^{III} and therefore has an analogous energy level diagram (see page 827 for the Cr^{III} diagram). From the spectrum of V^{II} solutions of non-complexing anions, it can be deduced that they contain octahedral $[V(H_2O)_6]^{2+}$ ions, as might be expected. Solutions of V^{II} are strongly reducing, even attacking the solvent water with the evolution of hydrogen. It may be noted that this attack on neutral water ought to require an oxidation potential of ≤ 0.414 v (see page 198), although the reported standard potential for the V^{3+}–V^{2+} couple is only -0.25 v. No complexing between V^{2+} and Cl^-, Br^-, I^- or $SO_4{}^{2-}$ occurs but there are weak complexes with CNS^- and F^-; there is some suggestion[17] that at 5mM concentration the V^{II} ion is a hydrated dimer V_2O^{2+}. However, blue mono-, bis- and triacetyl acetonates are formed in solution although they are readily oxidized by air.[18]

There are few crystalline V^{II} salts. The Tutton salts, $M^I_2SO_4 \cdot VSO_4 \cdot 6H_2O$, containing $[V(H_2O)_6]^{2+}$ ions, and the sulfate, $VSO_4 \cdot 7H_2O$, isomorphous with the corresponding Cr^{II} and Fe^{II} compounds, exist. A complex cyanide, $K_4[V(CN)_6] \cdot 3H_2O$, is also known.

29-C. CHROMIUM

For chromium, as for Ti and V, the highest oxidation state continues to be the one corresponding to the total number of $3d$ and $4s$ electrons. Although Ti^{IV} is the most stable state for titanium and V^V is only mildly oxidizing, chromium(VI), which exists only in oxo species such as CrO_3, $CrO_4{}^{2-}$ and CrO_2F_2, is rather strongly oxidizing. Apart from stoichiometric similarities, chromium resembles the group VI elements of the sulfur group only in the acidity of the trioxide and the covalent nature and ready hydrolysis of CrO_2Cl_2.

Although Cr^V and Cr^{IV} are formed as transient intermediates in the reduction of Cr^{VI} solutions, these oxidation states have no stable aqueous chemistry because of their ready disproportionation to Cr^{III} and Cr^{VI}. Some solid and gaseous compounds do exist, however.

[16] J. H. Swinehart, *Inorg. Chem.*, **4,** 1069 (1965).
[17] W. J. Biermann and W-K. Wong, *Can. J. Chem.*, **41,** 2510 (1963).
[18] W. P. Schaefer, *Inorg. Chem.*, **4,** 642 (1965).

The most stable and important state is Cr^{III}, d^3, which in an octahedral complex has each t_{2g} level singly occupied giving a sort of half-filled shell stability. The lower oxidation states are strongly reducing; in aqueous solution only the divalent state, Cr^{2+}, is known. Since for Cr and also for the following elements of the first transition series the more important oxidation states are the lower ones, we discuss them first.

The oxidation states and stereochemistry are summarized in Table 29-C-1.

TABLE 29-C-1

Oxidation States and Stereochemistry of Chromium

Oxidation state	Coordination number	Geometry	Examples
Cr^{-II}		?	$Na_2[Cr(CO)_5]$
Cr^{-I}		Octahedral	$Na_2[Cr_2(CO)_{10}]$
Cr^0	6	Octahedral	$Cr(CO)_6$, $[Cr(CO)_5I]^-$, $Cr(dipy)_3$
Cr^I, d^5	6	Octahedral	$K_3[Cr(CN)_5NO]$, $[Cr(dipy)_3]^+$
Cr^{II}, d^4	6	Distorted[b] octahedral	CrF_2, $CrCl_2$, CrS
	7	?	$[Cr(CO)_2(diars)_2X]X$
Cr^{III}, d^3	4	Distorted tetrahedral?	$[PCl_4]^+[CrCl_4]^-$(?)
	6[a]	Octahedral	$[Cr(NH_3)_6]^{3+}$, $Cr(acac)_3$, $K_3[Cr(CN)_6]$
Cr^{IV}, d^2	4	Tetrahedral	$Cr(OC_4H_9)_4$, Ba_2CrO_4
	6	Octahedral	K_2CrF_6
Cr^V, d^1	4	Tetrahedral	CrO_4^{3-}
	6	Octahedral	$K_2[CrOCl_5]$
	8	Quasi-dodecahedral	K_3CrO_8 (see text)
Cr^{VI}, d^0	4	Tetrahedral	CrO_4^{2-}, CrO_2Cl_2, CrO_3 (two more distant O)

[a] Most stable state.
[b] Four short and two long bonds.

29-C-1. The Element

The chief ore is *chromite*, $FeCr_2O_4$, which is a spinel with Cr^{III} on octahedral sites and Fe^{II} on the tetrahedral ones. If pure chromium is not required—as for use in ferrous alloys—the chromite is simply reduced with carbon in a furnace affording the carbon-containing alloy ferrochromium:

$$FeCr_2O_4 + 4C = Fe + 2Cr + 4CO$$

When pure chromium is required, the chromite is first treated with molten alkali and oxygen to convert the Cr^{III} to chromate(VI) which is dissolved in water and eventually precipitated as sodium dichromate. This is then reduced with carbon to Cr^{III} oxide:

$$Na_2Cr_2O_7 + 2C = Cr_2O_3 + Na_2CO_3 + CO$$

This oxide is then reduced with aluminum:

$$Cr_2O_3 + 2Al = Al_2O_3 + 2Cr$$

Chromium is a white, hard, lustrous and brittle metal, m 1890 $\pm$ 10°. It is extremely resistant to ordinary corrosive agents, which accounts for its extensive use as an electroplated protective coating. The metal dissolves fairly readily in nonoxidizing mineral acids, for example, hydrochloric and sulfuric, but not in cold aqua regia or nitric acid, either concentrated or dilute. These latter reagents passivate the metal in a manner which is not well understood. The electrode potentials of the metal are:

$$Cr^{2+} + 2e = Cr \qquad E^0 = -0.91 \text{ v}$$
$$Cr^{3+} + 3e = Cr \qquad E^0 = -0.74 \text{ v}$$

so that it is rather active when not passivated. Thus it readily displaces copper, tin and nickel from aqueous solutions of their salts.

At elevated temperatures, chromium unites directly with the halogens, sulfur, silicon, boron, nitrogen, carbon and oxygen.

29-C-2. The Chemistry of Chromium(II)

A fair number of Cr^{II} compounds are known, all of them strong and rapid reducing agents. The chromous ion in aqueous solution has a sky-blue color and is very easily oxidized:

$$Cr^{3+} + e = Cr^{2+} \qquad E^0 = -0.41 \text{ v}$$

Thus it is easily oxidized by molecular oxygen, and solutions can only be preserved by exclusion of air. Even then they decompose, at rates varying with the acidity and the anions present, by reducing the water with liberation of hydrogen. The mechanism by which O_2 oxidation of the perchlorate solution occurs is thought to involve an initial CrO_2Cr group which becomes protonated to give $[(H_2O)_4Cr(OH)_2Cr(H_2O)_4]^{4+}$, since all atoms of the O_2 consumed are ultimately found in the substitution-inert $[Cr(H_2O)_6]^{3+}$, which is the final product.[1]

While there are various ways to prepare Cr^{II} solutions, the best is by dissolving very pure electrolytic chromium metal in dilute aqueous acid.[2] Less pure metal is unsatisfactory, however, since considerable oxidation to Cr^{III} then occurs.

Various hydrated salts can be crystallized from the aqueous solutions,[3]

---

[1] R. W. Kolaczkowski and R. A. Plane, *Inorg. Chem.*, **3**, 323 (1964).

[2] H. Lux, *et al.*, *Chem. Ber.*, **91**, 2143 (1958); **97**, 503 (1964).

[3] J. P. Fackler, Jr., and D. G. Holah, *Inorg. Chem.*, **4**, 954 (1965).

for example, $CrSO_4 \cdot 5H_2O$, $CrCl_2 \cdot 4H_2O$, $CrBr_2 \cdot 6H_2O$, $Cr(ClO_4)_2 \cdot 6H_2O$ and $[Cr(OCOCH_3)_2]_2 \cdot 2H_2O$.

The acetate of Cr^{II} is one of the commonest, most stable and most easily prepared chromous compounds. It comes down as a sparingly soluble, red crystalline precipitate when a solution of Cr^{II} chloride is run into a fairly concentrated solution of sodium acetate. 'It has the dimeric structure shown in Figure 29-C-1; which is analogous to the structures of

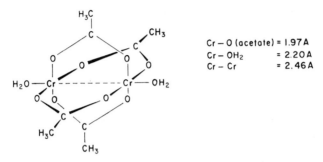

Cr – O (acetate) = 1.97 A
Cr – OH₂ = 2.20 A
Cr – Cr = 2.46 A

Fig. 29-C-1. The structure of Cr^{II} acetate hydrate.

Cu^{II} and Rh^{II} acetates. The very short Cr—Cr distance would imply that the interaction between the two metal ions is strong, and, indeed, it is so great that the four d electrons of each metal ion become fully paired and the substance is diamagnetic at room temperature. However, the strength of the interaction is apparently not as great as in the similar Mo^{II} acetate (page 952), where the metal–metal distance is extremely short (2.13 A) and a multiple bond has been postulated. It is to be noted that the diamagnetism does not mean that all the electron–electron interactions must correspond to genuine chemical bonds, but only that the singlet (spin-paired) state lie several times kT (~ 210 cm^{-1} at 300°K) below the triplet state. Thus an interaction energy of only a few kilocalories—not a very respectable bond—is sufficient.

There are a large number of other nearly diamagnetic Cr^{II} alkanoates known[4] all of which are assumed to have dimeric structures similar to that of the acetate.

Anhydrous Cr^{II} compounds are best obtained by dry procedures. The four halides are known and can be prepared by reaction of HF, HCl or HBr on the metal at 600–700° or by reduction of the anhydrous trihalides with hydrogen at 500–600°. The iodide and the sulfide, CrS, are prepared by direct combination of the elements at elevated temperatures. The

[4] S. Herzog and W. Kalies, Z. anorg. Chem., 329, 83 (1964).

halides rather readily take up gaseous ammonia to form addition compounds, $CrX_2 \cdot nNH_3$ ($n = 6, 5, 3, 2, 1$). The hexammoniate of $CrCl_2$ has been reported to contain octahedral $[Cr(NH_3)_6]^{2+}$ ions but presumably there is some distortion.

Cr^{II} also forms other complexes, such as those of hydrazine and dipyridyl. The hydrazine complexes, of the type $CrCl_2 \cdot 2N_2H_4$ and $CrI_2 \cdot 2N_2H_4$, are unusually stable toward oxidation and rather insoluble in water. The dipyridyl complex, as the perchlorate, is black-violet; it forms a wine-red solution which can be fairly easily oxidized, reduced or caused to disproportionate:

$$2[Cr(dipy)_3]^{2+} = [Cr(dipy)_3]^+ + [Cr(dipy)_3]^{3+}$$

There are also complexes known with ethylenediamine, thiocyanate (e.g., $K_4[Cr(NCS)_6]$) and cyanide (e.g., $K_4[Cr(CN)_6]$).

The only examples of complexes of Cr^{II} with a coordination number other than 6 are salts such as $[Cr(CO)_2 diars_2 X]X$ with di- and triarsines.[5] These are made by halogen oxidation, e.g., of $Cr(CO)_2(diars)_2$, which is in turn obtained by diarsine substitution in $Cr(CO)_6$. The salts are isomorphous with similar Mo and W salts, but are less stable.

Apart from these the only coordination number reported for Cr^{II} is 6, the geometry being that of a distorted octahedron (see next paragraph). In an octahedral environment two electron distributions, $t_{2g}^3 e_g$ and t_{2g}^4, are possible. The magnetic data available for chromium(II) compounds[3,6] show that in general they are of the high-spin type. The Curie–Weiss law is usually obeyed and the moments are ~ 4.95, i.e., close to the spin-only value. Aside from the alkanoates and the benzoate, there is a red form of the formate which is nearly diamagnetic, but a blue paramagnetic formate exists also; the structures are probably different from that of the acetate (cf. page 904). The $[Cr(CN)_6]^{4-}$ ion has a moment of only ~ 3.2 BM and is thus a low-spin complex.

For the mononuclear high-spin complexes only one spin-allowed absorption band, an $^5E_g \rightarrow {}^5T_{2g}(t_{2g}^3 e_g \rightarrow t_{2g}^2 e_g^2)$ transition, is to be expected in O_h symmetry. The blue color of the aquo Cr^{II} ion is attributable to the existence of such a band, which is rather broad, at about 700 mμ. However, because of the distortion of the octahedron, to be discussed presently, the band is actually attributable to several nearly superposed transitions and there is also another band in the near infrared.[3]

As noted earlier (page 685), an ion with a d^4 high-spin configuration should cause Jahn–Teller distortion of an octahedral environment. In several instances precise X-ray studies have shown marked distortions, of the type found so commonly in Cu^{II} compounds (page 898), where two

[5] R. S. Nyholm, M. R. Snow and M. H. B. Stiddard, *J. Chem. Soc.*, **1965**, 6570.
[6] A. Earnshaw, L. F. Larkworthy and K. S. Patel, *Proc. Chem. Soc.*, **1963**, 281.

ligands are much farther from the metal ion than are the other four. For example[7] in $CrCl_2$ there are four Cl^- at 2.39 A and two at 2.90 A, and quite similar distortions have been observed in CrF_2, $CrBr_2$ and CrS. The compound Cr_2F_5 contains both Cr^{2+} and Cr^{3+} ions in octahedral environments, but the octahedra about the Cr^{2+} ion are highly distorted with four short (1.96–2.01 A) and two long (2.57 A) bonds.[8]

29-C-3. The Chemistry of Chromium(III)

This is the most stable and important oxidation state of the element in general and particularly in its aqueous chemistry. The foremost characteristic of this state is the formation of a large number of relatively kinetically inert complexes. Ligand displacement reactions of Cr^{III} complexes are only about 10 times faster than those of Co^{III}, with half-times in the range of several hours. It is largely because of this kinetic inertness that so many complex species can be isolated as solids and that they persist for relatively long periods of time in solution, even under conditions where they are thermodynamically quite unstable.

Chromium(III) Oxide. The parent oxide is green Cr_2O_3 which has the corundum structure (page 439). It is formed on burning the metal in oxygen, on thermal decomposition of Cr^{VI} oxide or ammonium dichromate or on roasting the hydrous oxide, $Cr_2O_3 \cdot nH_2O$. The latter, commonly called chromic hydroxide, although its water content is variable, is precipitated on addition of hydroxide to solutions of Cr^{III} salts. The oxide, if ignited too strongly, becomes inert toward both acid and base, but otherwise it and its hydrous form are amphoteric, dissolving readily in acid to give aquo ions, $[Cr(H_2O)_6]^{3+}$, and in concentrated alkali to form chromites. The species present in these chromite solutions have not been identified with certainty, but they are most probably $[Cr(OH)_6]^{3-}$ and perhaps $[Cr(OH)_5(H_2O)]^{2-}$. From such solutions crystalline compounds such as $M^I{}_nCr(OH)_{3+n}$ ($n = 3$–5) and similar alkaline earth salts can be obtained.

On fusing Cr_2O_3 with the oxides of a number of bivalent metals, well-crystallized compounds of the composition $M^{II}O \cdot Cr_2O_3$ are obtained. These compounds have the spinel structure with the Cr^{III} ions occupying the octahedral interstices.

Chromium(III) Sulfide. Like aluminum sulfide, chromium(III) sulfide cannot be precipitated from aqueous solution because of its instability toward hydrolysis to $Cr_2O_3 \cdot nH_2O$ and H_2S. It can be made by treatment of $CrCl_3$ with H_2S at red heat or directly from the elements. It is a black solid which is quite stable toward nonoxidizing acids.

[7] J. W. Tracy, et al., Acta Cryst., **14**, 927 (1961); **15**, 460 (1962).
[8] H. Steinfink and J. H. Burns, Acta Cryst., **17**, 823 (1964).

Chromium(III) Halides. The fluoride, chloride and bromide are known in the anhydrous state, and all four halides are known in one or more hydrated forms. The chlorides are by far the commonest and most important. The anhydrous chloride can be prepared by many of the general preparative methods for anhydrous metal chlorides (page 577). It is a red-violet substance which can be sublimed in a stream of chlorine at about 600°, but if heated to such a temperature in the absence of chlorine it decomposes to Cr^{II} chloride and chlorine. The flaky or leaflet form of $CrCl_3$ is a consequence of its crystal structure, which is of an unusual type. It consists of a cubic close-packed array of chlorine atoms in which two thirds of the octahedral holes between *every other* pair of Cl planes are occupied by metal atoms. Those alternate layers of chlorine atoms with no metal atoms between them are held together only by van der Waals' forces and thus the crystal has pronounced cleavage parallel to the layers. $CrCl_3$ is the only substance known to have this exact structure, but $CrBr_3$, as well as $FeCl_3$ and triiodides of As, Sb and Bi have one which differs only in that the halogen atoms are in hexagonal rather than cubic close packing.

Chromic chloride does not dissolve at a significant rate in pure water, but in presence of Cr^{II} ion or reducing agents such as $SnCl_2$ which can generate some Cr^{II} from the $CrCl_3$ it dissolves readily. This is because the process of solution can then take place by electron transfer from Cr^{II} in solution via a Cl bridge to the Cr^{III} in the crystal. This Cr^{II} can then leave the crystal and act upon a Cr^{III} ion elsewhere on the crystal surface, or perhaps it can act without moving. At any rate, the "solubilizing" effect of reducing agents must be related in this or some similar way to the mechanism by which chromous ions cause decomposition of otherwise inert Cr^{III} complexes in solution (page 182). The reaction of $CrCl_3$ with ethers to form etherates, such as the useful reagent $CrCl_3 \cdot 3THF$, is similarly catalyzed by reducing agents.

From aqueous solution, Cr^{III} chloride may be crystallized as one or another of the three hydration isomers of $CrCl_3 \cdot 6H_2O$ (page 149).

The other halides of Cr^{III} are generally similar to the chloride. The fluoride occurs in various hydrated forms, $CrF_3 \cdot 3H_2O$ and $CrF_3 \cdot 6H_2O$ being best known; the bromide forms two hydration isomers, a violet one which is most probably $[Cr(H_2O)_6]Br_3$ and a green one thought to be $[Cr(H_2O)_4Br_2]Br \cdot 2H_2O$. The iodide is known only as a nonahydrate of unknown structure.

Other Simple and Hydrated Chromium(III) Salts. Only a few of these are of much importance. Chromium(III) sulfate is known as $Cr_2(SO_4)_3 \cdot 18H_2O$ and with a variety of lower degrees of hydration including the anhydrous substance obtained only by prolonged heating at low pressure.

The nitrate can be crystallized from water with various amounts of water of hydration. The anhydrous nitrate can be obtained only by action of N_2O_5 on $Cr(CO)_6$; it is a pale green very deliquescent solid which decomposes above 60°.[9] Hydrated forms of the oxalate, acetate and other salts are also known.

29-C-4. Complexes of Chromium(III)

Literally thousands of these are known, and only a brief outline of them can be given here. There are no authenticated exceptions to the rule that Cr^{III} is always hexacoordinate. It has been proposed that the long known compound $PCrCl_8$ may be $[PCl_4^+][CrCl_4^-]$, with a tetrahedral anion. While magnetic data agree very well with this, a polymeric octahedral structure cannot yet be ruled out.[10]

The chromium(III) ammines are perhaps the most numerous and most extensively studied. They include the pure ammines, $[CrAm_6]^{3+}$, the mixed amine–aquo types, that is, $[CrAm_{6-n}(H_2O)_n]^{3+}$ ($n = 0–4, 6$), the mixed amine–acido types, that is, $[CrAm_{6-n}R_n]^{(3-n)+}$ ($n = 1–4, 6$), and mixed amine–aquo–acido types, for example, $[CrAm_{6-n-m}(H_2O)_nR_m]^{(3-m)+}$. In these general formulas, Am represents the monodentate ligand NH_3 or half of a polydentate amine such as ethylenediamine, and R represents an acido ligand such as a halide, nitro or sulfate ion. These ammine complexes provide examples of virtually all of the kinds of isomerism possible in octahedral complexes (see pages 144–150).

The hexaquo ion occurs in aqueous solution under many circumstances as well as in various crystalline compounds. Among these are the violet hexahydrates of the chloride and bromide and an extensive series of alums, $M^ICr(SO_4)_2 \cdot 12H_2O$.

Many complex anions of the type $[CrX_6]^{3-}$, where X is a monodentate acido ligand such as F^-, Cl^-, NCS^- and CN^-, or part of a polydentate anion such as oxalate, are known. There are, of course, many mixed amine–acido and aquo–acido complexes. A particularly common one is Reinecke's salt, $NH_4[Cr(NCS)_4(NH_3)_2] \cdot H_2O$. The anion in this salt is widely used to precipitate large cations, both organic and inorganic. The existence of the $CrCl_6^{3-}$ ion has only recently been demonstrated conclusively.[11]

[9] C. C. Addison and D. J. Chapman, *J. Chem. Soc.*, **1964**, 539.
[10] D. J. Machin, D. F. C. Morris and E. L. Short, *J. Chem. Soc.*, **1964**, 4658.
[11a] C. M. Cook, Jr., *J. Inorg. Nucl. Chem.*, **25**, 123 (1963).
[11b] W. E. Hatfield, R. C. Fay, C. E. Pfluger and T. S. Piper, *J. Amer. Chem. Soc.*, **85**, 265 (1963).

Polynuclear Complexes. A large number of these are also known. In fact, the formation of the hydroxo and oxo bridged polynuclear complexes frequently causes difficulties in carrying out reactions in basic or neutral solutions. There are also amino and thiocyanato bridged polynuclear complexes. Some representative polynuclear complexes whose structures are fairly certain are shown below.

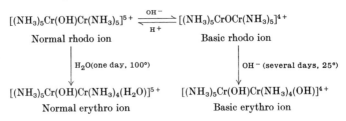

$$[(NH_3)_5Cr(OH)Cr(NH_3)_5]^{5+} \underset{H^+}{\overset{OH^-}{\rightleftharpoons}} [(NH_3)_5CrOCr(NH_3)_5]^{4+}$$

Normal rhodo ion   Basic rhodo ion

H_2O(one day, 100°) OH^- (several days, 25°)

$[(NH_3)_5Cr(OH)Cr(NH_3)_4(H_2O)]^{5+}$ $[(NH_3)_5Cr(OH)Cr(NH_3)_4(OH)]^{4+}$

Normal erythro ion   Basic erythro ion

The $[Cr_2Cl_9]^{3-}$ ion, which occurs as the Cs and K salts,[11a] has a structure similar to that of the $[W_2Cl_9]^{3-}$ ion (page 444) but the Cr^{3+} ions remain at the centers of their octahedra and the magnetic moments are normal, thus showing that little if any metal–metal interaction occurs in this case.

Chromium(III) forms trinuclear basic acetate compounds of unusual structure.[12] The basic unit is $[Cr_3(CH_3COO)_6O]^+$ in which there is an equilateral triangle of Cr atoms with an O atom at the center. There are two bridging CH_3COO groups across each edge of the triangle. Finally, a water molecule is coordinated to each Cr so that it is surrounded by a distorted octahedron of oxygen atoms.

Electronic Structures of Chromium(III) Complexes. The magnetic properties of the octahedral Cr^{III} complexes are quite uncomplicated. From the simple orbital splitting diagram (page 669) it follows that all such complexes must have three unpaired electrons irrespective of the strength of the ligand field, and, in all known mononuclear complexes, this has been confirmed. More sophisticated theory further predicts that the magnetic moments should be very close to, but slightly below, the spin-only value of 3.88 BM; this, too, is observed experimentally.

The spectra of Cr^{III} complexes are also well understood in their main features. A partial energy level diagram is shown in Figure 29-C-2. It is seen that three spin-allowed transitions are expected, and these have been observed in a considerable number of complexes. Indeed, the spectrochemical series was originally established by Tsuchida using data for Cr^{III} and Co^{III} complexes. In the aquo ion, the bands are found at 17,400, 24,700 and 37,000 cm^{-1}.

Ruby, natural or synthetic, is α-Al_2O_3 containing occasional Cr^{III} ions in place of Al^{III} ions. The environment of the Cr^{III} in ruby is thus a slightly

[12] B. N. Figgis and G. B. Robertson, *Nature*, **205**, 694 (1965).

distorted (D_{3d}) octahedron of oxide ions. The frequencies of the spin-allowed bands of Cr^{III} in ruby indicate that the Cr^{III} ions are under considerable compression, since the value of Δ_0 calculated is significantly higher than it is in the $[Cr(H_2O)_6]^{3+}$ ion or in other oxide lattices and glasses.

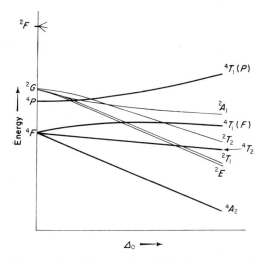

Fig. 29-C-2.   Partial energy level diagram for a d^3 ion in an octahedral field (also for a d^7 ion in a tetrahedral field). The quartet states are drawn with heavier lines.

Also, in ruby, spin-forbidden transitions from the $^4A_2$ ground state to the doublet states arising from the ^2G state of the free ion are observed. The transitions to the ^2E and $^2T_1$ states give rise to extremely sharp lines because the slopes of the energy lines for these states are the same as that for the ground state (except in extremely weak fields). This relationship is explained more fully on page 843 in connection with Mn^{II} complexes.

These same doublet states play a key role in the operation of the ruby laser. In this device a large single crystal of ruby is irradiated with light of the proper frequency to cause excitation to the $^4T_2(F)$ state. The exact magnitudes of certain energy differences and relaxation times are such, in the ruby, that the system rapidly makes a radiationless transition (i.e., by loss of energy to the crystal lattice in the form of vibrations) to the ^2E and $^2T_1$ states, instead of decaying directly back to the ground state. The systems then return from these doublet states to the ground state by stimulated emission of very sharp lines which are in phase with the stimulating radiation. Thus, bursts of extremely intense, monochromatic and coherent (all emitters in phase) radiation are obtained which are of use in communication and as sources of energy.

HIGHER OXIDATION STATES

29-C-5. The Chemistry of Chromium(VI)

In its highest oxidation state, chromium forms compounds which, with the exception of CrF_6, are all oxo compounds, and all are potent oxidizing agents. The parent oxide, chromic oxide, CrO_3, can be obtained as an orange-red precipitate on adding sulfuric acid to aqueous solutions of sodium or potassium dichromates. Chromium(VI) oxide is readily soluble in water. It is highly poisonous. It is not thermally stable above its melting point (197°), losing oxygen to give, after a series of intermediate stages, Cr_2O_3. It oxidizes most forms of organic matter vigorously; potentially highly explosive chromate esters can be formed with alcohols.

It is the aqueous chemistry of Cr^{VI} which is most important. In basic solution it exists as the yellow tetrahedral chromate ion, CrO_4^{2-}. Insoluble chromates such as those of Ba^{2+}, Pb^{2+} and Ag^+ can be precipitated from these solutions. As the pH is lowered, solutions of chromate ions turn orange, giving the *dichromate* ion, $Cr_2O_7^{2-}$. The steps involve first protonation to give $HCrO_4^-$ and then dimerization of the latter:

$$CrO_4^{2-} + H^+ = CrO_3(OH)^-$$
$$CrO_3(OH)^- + H^+ = H_2CrO_4$$
$$2CrO_3(OH)^- = Cr_2O_7^{2-} + H_2O$$

These pH dependent equilibria have been studied in detail;[13a,b] the equilibria are labile and on adding cations which form insoluble chromates, the chromates, and not dichromates are precipitated. Further, the species present depend on the nature of the acid used and only for HNO_3 and $HClO_4$ are the equilibria as given above.[13a] Using hydrochloric acid, there is essentially quantitative conversion to the chlorochromate ion, while with sulfuric acid a sulfate complex results:

$$CrO_3(OH)^- + H^+ + Cl^- = CrO_3Cl^- + H_2O$$
$$CrO_3(OH)^- + HSO_4^- = CrO_3(OSO_3)^{2-} + H_2O.$$

Orange potassium chlorochromate can be prepared simply by dissolving $K_2Cr_2O_7$ in hot $6M$ HCl and crystallizing. It can be recrystallized from HCl but is hydrolyzed by water

$$2CrO_3Cl^- + H_2O = Cr_2O_7^{2-} + 2H^+ + 2Cl^-$$

The potassium salts of CrO_3F^-, CrO_3Br^- and CrO_3I^- are obtained similarly. They owe their existence to the fact that dichromate, though a powerful

[13a] G. P. Haight, Jr., D. C. Richardson and N. H. Coburn, *Inorg. Chem.*, **3**, 1777 (1964).
[13b] J. Y. Tong, *Inorg. Chem.*, **3**, 1804 (1964).

oxidizing agent, is kinetically slow in its oxidizing action toward halide ions.

Acid solutions of dichromate are powerful oxidizing agents:

$$Cr_2O_7^{2-} + 14H^+ + 6e = 2Cr^{3+} + 7H_2O \qquad E^0 = 1.33 \text{ v}$$

The chromate ion in basic solution is much less oxidizing, however:

$$CrO_4^{2-} + 4H_2O + 3e = Cr(OH)_3(s) + 5OH^- \qquad E^0 = -0.13 \text{ v}$$

Chromium(VI) does not give rise to the extensive and complex series of poly acids and anions characteristic of the somewhat less acidic oxides of V^V, Mo^{VI} and W^{VI}. The reason for this is perhaps the greater extent of multiple bonding, Cr=O, for the smaller chromium ion. Other than the chromate and dichromate ions there are no oxo acids or anions of major importance, although trichromates, $M^I_2Cr_3O_{10}$, and tetrachromates, $M^I_2Cr_4O_{13}$, have been reported. The dichromate ion in the ammonium salt has the structure shown in Figure 29-C-3.

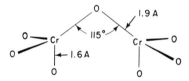

Fig. 29-C-3.   The structure of the dichromate ion as found in $(NH_4)_2Cr_2O_7$.

Another type of chromium(VI) compound of note is exemplified by chromyl chloride, CrO_2Cl_2, a deep red liquid (b 117°). It is formed by the action of hydrogen chloride on chromium(VI) oxide:

$$CrO_3 + 2HCl = CrO_2Cl_2 + H_2O$$

by warming dichromate with alkali metal chloride in concentrated sulfuric acid:

$$K_2Cr_2O_7 + 4KCl + 3H_2SO_4 = 2CrO_2Cl_2 + 3K_2SO_4 + 3H_2O$$

and in other ways. It is photosensitive but otherwise rather stable, although it vigorously oxidizes organic matter. It is hydrolyzed by water to chromate ion and hydrochloric acid.

Chromyl fluoride, CrO_2F_2, obtained by the action of fluorine on chromyl chloride or by treatment of CrO_3 with anhydrous HF, is a red-brown gas condensing to a deep red-violet solid at 30°. Some other chromyl compounds such as the acetate have also been reported.

Chromium(VI) fluoride is obtained, along with CrF_5, by fluorination of the metal at 400° with F_2 at 350 atm. The presence of some Mn powder appears to promote the reaction.[14] It is a very unstable, lemon yellow powder which decomposes to CrF_5 above about $-100°$ in a vacuum. Direct fluorination of the metal has also been reported[15] to give dark red $CrOF_4$ (along with CrF_5) as a deep red solid.

29-C-6. Chromium(V) Compounds

Rather few Cr^V compounds are known. The only binary compound[14,15] is CrF_5, a crimson solid, m 30°, with a red liquid and red vapor. It is obtained by the direct action of fluorine on the metal at high temperature and under pressure. It is instantly hydrolyzed by water, presumably with concomitant disproportionation. The oxofluoride, $CrOF_3$, has been prepared in impure form by the action of ClF_3, BrF_3 or BrF_5 on CrO_3 or $K_2Cr_2O_7$. $CrOCl_3$ is made by reduction of CrO_2Cl_2 with BCl_3.[16] Some halo and oxohalo complexes are also known. The moisture sensitive oxofluoro-chromates(V), $KCrOF_4$ and $AgCrOF_4$, can be obtained by treating CrO_3 mixed with KCl or AgCl with BrF_3. Oxochloro compounds with the general formula $M^I_2[CrOCl_5]$, are obtained by reduction of CrO_3 with concentrated hydrochloric acid in the presence of alkali metal ions at 0°.

Alkali and alkaline earth chromates(V) have been prepared and characterized.[17] They are black or blue-black solids which are hygroscopic; they hydrolyze with disproportionation to Cr^{III} and Cr^{VI}. Na_3CrO_4 has a magnetic susceptibility corresponding to one unpaired electron and both Li_3CrO_4 and Na_3CrO_4 as well as the $M^{II}_3(CrO_4)_2$ compounds appear to contain discrete, tetrahedral CrO_4^{3-} ions.

The only evidence for a persisting Cr^V species in solution is obtained by dissolution of chromates(VI) in 65% oleum.[18] The quantity of O_2 evolved and the magnetic properties of the blue solution are consistent with the formation of Cr^V but the nature of the species is uncertain.

29-C-7. Chromium(IV) Compounds

Chromium(IV) compounds are perhaps slightly more numerous and stable than those of chromium(V), but still relatively rare.

The halides, CrF_4, $CrCl_4$ and $CrBr_4$ are known. The fluoride is made by the action of F_2 on CrF_3 or $CrCl_3$ or on the metal at 300–350°. It is a dark

[14] O. Glemser, H. Roesky and K.-H. Hellberg, *Angew. Chem. (Internat.)*, **2**, 266 (1963).
[15] A. J. Edwards, *Proc. Chem. Soc.*, **1963**, 205.
[16] R. B. Johannesen and H.-L. Kraus, *Chem. Ber.*, **97**, 2094 (1964).
[17] R. Scholder and H. Schwarz, *Z. anorg. Chem.*, **326**, 1, 11 (1963).
[18] H. C. Mishra and M. C. R. Symons, *Proc. Chem. Soc.*, **1962**, 23.

green-black solid[19] insoluble in organic solvents. It is rapidly hydrolyzed by water, but otherwise rather inert. It follows the Curie–Weiss law with $\mu = 3.0$ BM. $CrCl_4$ and $CrBr_4$ are not stable as solids but exist in the vapors when the trihalides are heated with an excess of the halogen.

Complex fluoride salts of the types M^ICrF_5 and $M^I_2CrF_6$ are known. The former,[19] prepared by reaction of CrF_4 with MF in 1:1 mole ratio in BrF_3, have $\mu \approx 3.1$ BM, but their structures are unknown. The latter, obtained either by reaction of $CrF_4 + 2MF$ in BrF_3 or by the fluorination of a mixture of $CrCl_3$ and MCl, also have $\mu \approx 3.1$ BM and are known to contain octahedral $[CrF_6]^{2-}$.

Blue, volatile and monomeric alkoxides, $Cr(OR)_4$, can be prepared by treating $Cr(NEt_2)_4$ with alcohols[20] or, for the t-butyl compound, by the action of the peroxide, ROOR, on dibenzenechromium. They have μ_{eff} values of ~ 2.8 BM at 300°K and their colors are due to an absorption band with ν_{max} at $\sim 15,500$ cm^{-1} and $\epsilon \approx 600$. It is believed that these are tetrahedral molecules. The assignment of the absorption band is uncertain, but it is probably due to the $^3A_2 \rightarrow {}^3T_1$ transition (see the diagram for octahedral d^8, page 678).

CrO_2 at room temperature has an undistorted rutile structure (cf. MoO_2, where there is a distortion to give Mo—Mo bonds) with two unpaired electrons per Cr. However, it is ferromagnetic and has metallic conductance, and the proper understanding of its electronic structure requires consideration of electron delocalization into energy bands, formed by cation–anion–cation exchange coupling via the oxygen π orbitals.[21]

Finally some mixed oxides, $M^{II}_2CrO_4$, $M^{II}_3CrO_5$ and $M^{II}_4CrO_6$ where M^{II} is an alkaline earth ion may be mentioned. Of these only the blue-black $M^{II}_2CrO_4$ compounds containing Ba and Sr are well characterized.[22] These air-stable compounds contain discrete CrO_4^{4-} ions with magnetic moments of ~ 2.8 BM.

29-C-8. Peroxo Complexes

These are formed by chromium in several of its higher oxidation states (IV, V and VI) and are better discussed as a class than separately. They are all more or less unstable, both in and out of solution, decomposing slowly with the evolution of oxygen, and some of them are explosive or inflammable in air. The main ones are the adducts of the deep blue

[19] H. C. Clark and Y. N. Sadana, *Can. J. Chem.*, **42**, 50 (1964).
[20] J. S. Basi and D. C. Bradley, *Proc. Chem. Soc.*, **1963**, 305.
[21] J. B. Goodenough, *Magnetism and the Chemical Bond*, Interscience–Wiley, N.Y., 1963.
[22] K. A. Wilhelmi and O. Jenssen, *Acta Chem. Scand.*, **15**, 1415 (1961).

chromium peroxide, CrO_5, the violet peroxochromates, the red peroxochromates and the addition compounds of CrO_4.

When acid dichromate solutions are treated with hydrogen peroxide, a deep blue color rapidly appears but does not persist long.[23] The species responsible for it decomposes yielding Cr^{III} aquo ions. However, the blue species may be extracted into ether where it is more stable and, on addition of pyridine to the ether solution, the compound $pyCrO_5$, a monomer in benzene and essentially diamagnetic, is obtained. These facts lead to the formulation of the blue species as aquo, ether or pyridine adducts of the molecule $CrO(O_2)_2$ containing Cr^{VI}. In aqueous solution, the main equilibrium is

$$HCrO_4^- + 2H_2O_2 + H^+ = CrO(O_2)_2 + 3H_2O$$

In the case of the pyridine adduct, X-ray crystallographic study[24] has confirmed this formulation and revealed the structure shown in Figure 29-C-4.

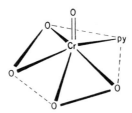

Fig. 29-C-4. The structure of $CrO(O_2)_2 \cdot py$. The coordination polyhedron is approximately a pentagonal pyramid with the oxide oxygen atom at the apex.

The action of H_2O_2 on neutral or slightly acidic solutions of K^+, NH_4^+ or Tl^+ dichromates leads to diamagnetic blue-violet, violently explosive salts. Although there has been some question about their nature, they are now believed[25] to contain the ion $[Cr^{VI}O(O_2)_2OH]^-$. The salts are thus related to CrO_5 since they contain the same number, 2, of peroxo groups; CrO_5 can be converted to the violet salts merely by addition of OH^-.

On treatment of alkaline chromate solutions with 30% hydrogen peroxide—and after further manipulations—the red-brown peroxochromates, $M^I_2CrO_8$, can be isolated. They are paramagnetic with one unpaired electron per formula unit and K_3CrO_8 forms mixed crystals with K_3NbO_8 and K_3TaO_8, in both of which the heavy metals are pentavalent. Thus it

[23] See D. G. Tuck and R. M. Walters, *J. Chem. Soc.*, **1964**, 3405.

[24] R. Stomberg, *Arkiv för Kemi*, **22**, 29 (1964).

[25] W. P. Griffith, *J. Chem. Soc.*, **1962**, 3948; references to many other peroxo compounds are given.

may be formulated as a quasi dodecahedral (D_{2d}) tetraperoxo complex of Cr^V (Fig. 29-C-5).

When the reaction mixture used in preparing $(NH_4)_3CrO_8$ is heated to 50° and then cooled to 0°, brown crystals of $(NH_3)_3CrO_4$ are obtained. From

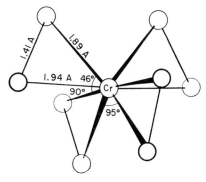 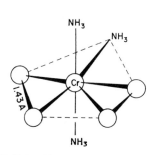

Fig 29-C-5. The dodecahedral (D_{2d}) structure of the CrO_8^{3-} ion.

Fig. 29-C-6. The pentagonal bipyramidal structure of $(NH_3)_3CrO_4$.

this, on gentle warming with KCN solutions, $K_3[CrO_4(CN)_3]$ is obtained. An X-ray study[26] of the ammonia compound has revealed the structure shown in Figure 29-C-6. It has been suggested that it contains Cr^{II} coordinated by two superoxide ions. In view of the magnetic data which show the presence of two unpaired electrons, this would require the rather unlikely assumption that the Cr^{II} is here diamagnetic. It seems more natural to consider that the compound contains Cr^{IV}, with two unpaired electrons, coordinated by peroxide ions, which may be abnormal however.[27]

The bonding of the peroxo group in peroxo compounds of Ti, Cr, Nb and Ta has been discussed in terms of "bent" bonds.[28] For the compounds for which there is information, the structures are dodecahedral (K_3CrO_8) or pentagonal bipyramidal $(K_2W_{12}O_{11}, CrO_4(NH_3)_3, CrO_5py)$, with the peroxo group(s) in the ring. In both structures, the normal metal–ligand orbitals lie at 71 to 72°, while the peroxo group, with the O—M—O angle of 45°, lies between these metal–ligand directions. Assuming normal angles for the metal hybrids used in σ bonding, the σ orbitals on the oxygen atoms in the MO_2 triangle can subtend angles of 15–20° outward from the M—O and O—O directions so that "bent" bond overlap occurs. This model is similar to that used to explain the stability of other small rings, notably of cyclopropane and ethylene oxide. This bonding

[26] R. Stomberg, *Arkiv. för Kemi.*, **22**, 49 (1964).
[27] J. E. Fergussen, C. J. Williams and J. F. Young, *J. Chem. Soc.*, **1962**, 2136.
[28] W. P. Griffith, *J. Chem. Soc.*, **1964**, 5248.

27 + A.I.C.

implies a somewhat shortened O—O distance—cf. O—O in BaO_2, 1.49 A, O—O in CrO_5py, 1.40 A. These figures can be compared with the O—O distance of 1.30 A found in $[(NH_3)_5CoO_2Co(NH_3)_5]^{5+}$ and $O_2IrClCO(PPh_3)_2$, (see pages 868 to 1021) which is however characteristic of O_2^-.

It has been predicted[28] that stable peroxo compounds will form where the normal ligand–bond angles are *ca* 70°.

29-D. MANGANESE

As with Ti, V and Cr, the highest oxidation state of manganese corresponds to the total number of $3d$ and $4s$ electrons. This VII state occurs only in the oxo compounds MnO_4^-, Mn_2O_7 and MnO_3F, and these compounds show some similarity with corresponding compounds of the halogens, in the instability of the oxide, for example. Manganese(VII) is powerfully oxidizing, usually being reduced to Mn^{II}. The intermediate oxidation states are known, but only a few compounds of Mn^V have been characterized; nevertheless, Mn^V species are frequently postulated as intermediates in the reduction of permanganates. Although Mn^{II} is the most stable state, it is quite readily oxidized in alkaline solution. The oxidation states and stereochemistry of manganese are summarized in Table 29-D-1.

29-D-1. The Element

Manganese is relatively abundant, constituting about 0.085% of the earth's crust. Among the heavy metals, only iron is more abundant. Although widely distributed, it occurs in a number of substantial deposits of good ores, the most important being *pyrolusite*, MnO_2. The other ores are mainly oxides, hydrous oxides or the carbonate, and from all these, or the Mn_3O_4 obtained by roasting them, the metal can be obtained by reduction with aluminum.

Manganese is roughly similar to iron in its physical and chemical properties, the chief difference being that manganese is harder and more brittle but less refractory (m 1247°). It is fairly electropositive, and readily dissolves in dilute, nonoxidizing acids. It is not particularly reactive toward nonmetals at ordinary temperatures, but at elevated temperatures it reacts vigorously with many. Thus it burns in chlorine to give $MnCl_2$, reacts with fluorine to give MnF_2 and MnF_3, burns in nitrogen above 1200° to give Mn_3N_2, and, of course, combines with oxygen, giving Mn_3O_4 at high temperatures. It also combines directly with boron, carbon, sulfur, silicon and phosphorus, but not with hydrogen.

TABLE 29-D-1

Oxidation States and Stereochemistry of Manganese

Oxidation state	Coordination number	Geometry	Examples
Mn^{-III}	4	Tetrahedral	Mn(NO)$_3$CO
Mn^{-II}	4 or 6	Square	[Mn(phthalocyanine)]$^{2-}$ [b]
Mn^{-I}	5	Trigonal bipyramid	Mn(CO)$_5{}^-$, [Mn(CO)$_4$PR$_3$]$^-$
	4 or 6	Square	[Mn(phthalocyanine)]$^-$ [b]
Mn^0	6	Octahedral	Mn$_2$(CO)$_{10}$
Mn^I, d^6	6	Octahedral	Mn(CO)$_5$Cl, K$_5$[Mn(CN)$_6$], [Mn(CNR)$_6$]$^+$
Mn^{II}, d^5	4	Tetrahedral	MnCl$_4{}^{2-}$, MnBr$_2$(OPR$_3$)$_2$
	4	Square	[Mn(H$_2$O)$_4$]SO$_4$·H$_2$O
	6^a	Octahedral	[Mn(H$_2$O)$_6$]$^{2+}$, [Mn(SCN)$_6$]$^{4-}$
	5	?	[Mn(dienMe)X$_2$]^c
	7	NbF$_7{}^{2-}$ structure	[Mn(EDTA)(H$_2$O)]$^{2-}$
Mn^{III}, d^4	5?	Square pyramidal?	[Et$_4$N]$_2$[MnCl$_5$]
	6^a	Octahedral	Mn(acac)$_3$, [Mn(C$_2$O$_4$)$_3$]$^{3-}$, MnF$_3$ (distorted)
Mn^{IV}, d^3	6	Octahedral	MnO$_2$, Mn(SO$_4$)$_2$, MnCl$_6{}^{2-}$
Mn^V, d^2	4	Tetrahedral	MnO$_4{}^{3-}$
Mn^{VI}, d^1	4	Tetrahedral	MnO$_4{}^{2-}$
Mn^{VII}, d^0	3	Planar	MnO$_3{}^+$
	4	Tetrahedral	MnO$_4{}^-$, MnO$_3$F

[a] Most common states.

[b] R. Taube and H. Munke, *Angew. Chem.*, **75**, 299 (1962).

[c] dienMe = Me$_2$N(CH$_2$)$_2$NMe(CH$_2$)$_2$NMe$_2$

29-D-2. The Chemistry of Divalent Manganese

This is the most important and, generally speaking, the most stable oxidation state for the element. In neutral or acid aqueous solution it exists as the very pale pink hexaquo ion, [Mn(H$_2$O)$_6$]$^{2+}$, which is quite resistant to oxidation as shown by the potentials:

$$\text{MnO}_4{}^- \qquad \text{Mn}^{3+} \underline{\quad 1.5\ v \quad} \text{Mn}^{2+} \underline{\quad -1.18\ v \quad} \text{Mn}$$
$$\underline{\hspace{6cm}}$$
$$1.5\ v$$

In basic media however, the hydroxide, Mn(OH)$_2$, is formed and this is more easily oxidized, by air for example, as shown by the potentials:

$$\text{MnO}_2 \cdot y\text{H}_2\text{O} \underline{\quad 0.2\ v \quad} \text{Mn}_2\text{O}_3 \cdot x\text{H}_2\text{O} \underline{\quad 0.1\ v \quad} \text{Mn(OH)}_2$$

Manganese(II) oxide is a grey-green to dark green powder made by roasting the carbonate in hydrogen or nitrogen or by reduction of higher oxides with hydrazine. It has the rock salt structure and is insoluble in water. It is not a very common or important compound. Manganese(II) hydroxide is precipitated from Mn^{2+} solutions by alkali metal hydroxides as a gelatinous white solid which rapidly darkens because of oxidation by atmospheric oxygen. $Mn(OH)_2$ is a well-defined compound—not an indefinite hydrous oxide—having the same crystal structure as magnesium hydroxide. It is only very slightly amphoteric,

$$Mn(OH)_2 + OH^- = Mn(OH)_3^- \quad K \sim 10^{-5}$$

Manganous sulfide is a salmon-colored substance precipitated by alkaline sulfide solutions. It has a relatively high K_{sp} (10^{-14}) and redissolves easily in dilute acids. It is a hydrous form of MnS and turns brown on standing in air owing to oxidation. If air is excluded, the salmon-colored material changes on long standing, or more rapidly on boiling, into a green substance, which is crystalline, anhydrous MnS.

MnS, MnSe and MnTe have the rock salt structure. They are all strongly antiferromagnetic as are also the anhydrous halides. The super-exchange mechanism (page 697) is believed responsible for their antiferromagnetism.

Manganese(II) forms an extensive series of salts with all common anions. Most are soluble in water, although the phosphate and carbonate are only slightly so. Most of the salts crystallize from water as hydrates. The anhydrous salts must in general be obtained by dry reactions or using nonaqueous solvents. Thus $MnCl_2$ is made by reaction of chlorine with the metal or of HCl with the metal, the oxide or the carbonate. The sulfate, $MnSO_4$, is obtained on fuming down sulfuric acid solutions. It is quite stable and may be used for manganese analysis provided no other cations giving nonvolatile sulfates are present.

Manganese(II) forms many complexes, but the equilibrium constants for their formation in aqueous solution are not high as compared to those for the divalent cations of succeeding elements (Fe^{II}–Cu^{II}) as noted earlier (page 690), because the Mn^{II} ion is the largest of these and it has no ligand field stabilization energy in its complexes (except in the few of low spin). Many hydrated salts, $Mn(ClO_4)_2 \cdot 6H_2O$, $MnSO_4 \cdot 7H_2O$, etc., contain the $[Mn(H_2O)_6]^{2+}$ ion, and the direct action of ammonia on anhydrous salts leads to the formation of ammoniates, some of which have been shown to contain the $[Mn(NH_3)_6]^{2+}$ ion. Chelating ligands such as ethylenediamine, EDTA, oxalate ions, etc., form complexes isolable from aqueous solution. Some EDTA complexes, e.g. $[Mn(OH_2)EDTA]^{2-}$, are 7-coordinate,[1a] while certain tridentate amines give 5-coordinate species.[1b] The formation constants for halo complexes are extremely low (e.g., 3.8 l mole^{-1} for $MnCl^+$). While no hexahalo complexes have been isolated, $M^I_4[Mn(SCN)_6]$ salts can be crystallized as hydrates from aqueous solutions.

Manganese(II) acetylacetonate is trimeric[2] and it is likely that octahedral coordination is achieved by sharing of oxygen atoms as in the Co^{II}

[1a] S. Richards, B. Pederson, J. V. Silverton and J. L. Hoard, *Inorg. Chem.*, **3**, 27 (1964).
[1b] M. Ciampolini and G. Speroni, *Inorg. Chem.*, **5**, 45 (1966).
[2] D. P. Graddon and G. M. Mockler, *Aust. J. Chem.*, **17**, 1119 (1964)

and Ni^{II} cases, but the structure has not been established. It readily reacts with H_2O and other donors, L, forming octahedral $Mn(acac)_2L_2$ species.

A number of tetrahedral complexes are also known. These are not stable in contact with water or other donor solvents, but they exist in crystals and in solvents of only low or moderate polarity such as $CHCl_3$, CH_3CN, $C_6H_5NO_2$, etc. They include salts of the tetrahalo anions, $[MnX_4]^{2-}$, with large cations such as R_4N^+, R_4P^+ or R_4As^+, as well as neutral complexes containing triphenylphosphine oxide or triphenylarsine oxide and halide ions, for example, $[Mn(Ph_3PO)_2Br_2]$. Manganese(II) ions are also known to occupy tetrahedral holes in certain glasses and to substitute for Zn^{II} in ZnO. In tetrahedral environments, Mn^{II} has a green-yellow color, far more intense than the pink of the octahedrally coordinated ion, and it very often exhibits intense yellow-green fluorescence. Indeed most commercially used phosphors are manganese-activated zinc compounds wherein Mn^{II} ions are substituted for some of the Zn^{II} ions in tetrahedral surroundings, as for example in Zn_2SiO_4.

All of the complexes so far mentioned have five unpaired electrons. There are also some, such as $[Mn(CN)_6]^{4-}$ and $[Mn(CN)_5NO]^{3-}$, and the isonitrile complexes, $[Mn(CNR)_6]^{2+}$, which have only one unpaired electron.

29-D-3. The Chemistry of Manganese(III)

The chemistry of Mn^{III} is not extensive. In aqueous solution it is quite unstable, being easily reduced to Mn^{II}, and even in the absence of reducing agents the Mn^{III} aquo ion is subject to disproportionation:

$$2Mn^{3+} + 2H_2O = Mn^{2+} + MnO_2(s) + 4H^+ \qquad K = 10^9$$

Mn_2O_3 occurs in nature as the mineral braunite and can be prepared by heating MnO_2 in air at temperatures of about $550-900°$. The product of oxidation of precipitated manganous hydroxide is hydrous manganese(III) oxide, $Mn_2O_3 \cdot nH_2O$, which on drying at $100°$ gives $Mn(OH)O$, which is also found in nature as the mineral manganite. Manganese(III) also occurs in the oxide Mn_3O_4, which is obtained on heating Mn_2O_3 above $950°$ in air or above $1100°$ in oxygen. This substance is correctly formulated as $Mn^{II}Mn^{III}_2O_4$ and has a distorted spinel structure (see page 51).

The only simple halide known is MnF_3, which is a red solid obtained by the action of fluorine on manganese(II) iodide. This dissolves in water to give a red-brown solution which may also be obtained by dissolving the oxide Mn_2O_3 in hydrofluoric acid; from this solution the hydrate $MnF_3 \cdot 2H_2O$ may be crystallized as ruby red crystals. Dark red complex salts[3] of

---

[3] For references see R. Dingle, *Inorg. Chem.*, **4**, 1287 (1965).

the types $M^I MnF_4$ and $M^I_2 MnF_5$ may be crystallized on addition of alkali metal fluorides to the solution.

No simple chloride, bromide or iodide of manganese(III) is known, but dark red salts of chloro complexes, of the formula $M^I_2 MnCl_5$, are known. The absence even of complexes with Br^- and I^- may be attributed to their being able to reduce Mn^{III}.

Manganese(III) acetate, $Mn(C_2H_3O_2)_3 \cdot 2H_2O$, is one of the best-known manganese(III) compounds since it is easy to prepare, relatively stable and serves as a good starting point for the preparation of other Mn^{III} compounds. It is obtained by oxidizing a solution of manganese(II) acetate in hot glacial acetic acid with permanganate or chlorine.

Several phosphates and an acid sulfate of Mn^{III} are also known. The $[Mn(H_2O)_6]^{3+}$ ion occurs in the alum $CsMn(SO_4)_2 \cdot 12H_2O$.

In addition to the fluoro and chloro complexes mentioned, Mn^{III} forms several others of fair stability. Tris(acetylacetonato)manganese(III) is best prepared by reaction of Mn^{II} with permanganate in the presence of excess acetylacetone; even air will oxidize Mn^{II} in the presence of this ligand, making the preparation of pure bis(acetylacetonato)manganese(II) tedious. The tris(oxalato)- and tris(malonato)manganese(III) complex anions are also known, but they are not very stable toward heat, light or water.

The only low-spin manganese(III) compounds reported are the salts of the $[Mn(CN)_6]^{3-}$ ion. Manganese(II) in the presence of excess CN^- is readily oxidized, even by a current of air, with the production of this ion which is first isolated from the solution as the Mn^{II} salt, $Mn^{II}_3[Mn(CN)_6]_2$, from which other salts are obtained.

29-D-4. The Chemistry of Manganese(IV)

This is very limited; aside from MnO_2, MnF_4 and $Mn(SO_4)_2$ the only stable compounds are a few complexes.

MnF_4 can be prepared by direct fluorination of the metal under specific conditions.[4] It is an extremely reactive, volatile, blue-grey solid.

MnO_2 is a grey to grey-black solid, usually nonstoichiometric. It occurs extensively in nature and is one of the chief manganese ores. It can be prepared by mild ignition ($\sim 530°$) of $Mn(NO_3)_2$ in air, and it also arises in a hydrated form by reduction of permanganate in basic solution. Its stability is due primarily to its insolubility, but it is readily attacked by reducing agents in acid solution. It is rather inert to most acids except on heating and then it does not dissolve to give Mn^{IV} in solution but instead

[4] H. Roesky and O. Glemser, *Angew. Chem.*, **75**, 920 (1963).

functions as an oxidizing agent, the exact manner of this depending on the acid. With HCl, chlorine is evolved:

$$MnO_2 + 4HCl = MnCl_2 + Cl_2 + 2H_2O$$

and this reaction is often used for small-scale generation of the gas in the laboratory. With sulfuric acid at 110°, oxygen is evolved and an Mn^{III} acid sulfate formed. MnO_2 can be fused with other metal oxides to give substances called *manganites*. With alkaline earth oxides, MO, for instance, substances of the compositions $MO \cdot \frac{1}{2}MnO_2$, $MO \cdot MnO_2$, $MO \cdot 2MnO_2$, $MO \cdot 3MnO_2$ and $MO \cdot 5MnO_2$ have been reported. Little is known of their structures, and they are in general not well characterized. MnO_2 dissolves in concentrated KOH to give a blue solution which contains equimolar amounts of Mn^V and Mn^{III}; Mn^{IV} is thermodynamically unstable in such solutions.

If $MnSO_4$ in sulfuric acid is oxidized with permanganate, black crystals of $Mn(SO_4)_2$ may be obtained on cooling. This substance is quickly hydrolyzed by treatment with water or dilute sulfuric acid to deposit hydrous MnO_2.

Complex salts include the chloro and fluoro salts, $M^I_2[MnX_6]$, which can be obtained by reduction of $KMnO_4$ in fuming HCl or HF_1 respectively, with ether,[5] the iodates, $M^I_2[Mn(IO_3)_6]$, and some curious glyceryl complexes such as $Na_2[Mn(C_3H_5O_3)_2]$.

29-D-5. The Chemistry of Manganese(VI) and -(VII)

Manganese(VI) is known in only one environment, namely, as the deep green *manganate* ion, $[MnO_4]^{2-}$. This ion is formed on oxidizing MnO_2 in fused KOH with potassium nitrate, air or other oxidizing agents. Only two salts, K_2MnO_4 and several hydrated forms of Na_2MnO_4, have been isolated in completely pure condition. Both are very dark green, in fact nearly black, in color.

The manganate ion is stable only in very basic solutions. In acid, neutral or only slightly basic solutions it readily disproportionates according to the equation:

$$3MnO_4^{2-} + 4H^+ = 2MnO_4^- + MnO_2(s) + 2H_2O \qquad K \sim 10^{58}$$

Manganese(VII) is best known in the form of salts of the permanganate ion, $[MnO_4]^-$, of which the potassium salt is by far the commonest, being widely used as a laboratory oxidizing agent. $KMnO_4$ is manufactured on a large scale by electrolytic oxidation of a basic solution of potassium manganate. Aqueous solutions of MnO_4^- may be prepared by oxidation of solutions of Mn^{II} ion with very powerful oxidizing agents such as PbO_2 or $NaBiO_3$. The ion has an intense purple color, and crystalline salts look

5 P. C. Moews, Jr., *Inorg. Chem.*, **5**, 5 (1966).

almost black. Solutions of permanganate are intrinsically unstable, and decomposition according to the equation

$$4MnO_4^- + 4H^+ = 3O_2(g) + 2H_2O + 4MnO_2(s)$$

takes place slowly but observably in acid solution. In neutral or slightly alkaline solutions in the dark, decomposition is immeasurably slow. It is, however, catalyzed by light so that standard permanganate solutions should be stored in dark bottles.

In basic solution permanganate functions as a powerful oxidizing agent:

$$MnO_4^- + 2H_2O + 3e = MnO_2(s) + 4OH^- \qquad E^0 = +1.23 \text{ v}$$

In very strong base and with excess MnO_4^-, however, manganate ion is produced:

$$MnO_4^- + e = MnO_4^{2-} \qquad E^0 = +0.56 \text{ v}$$

In acid solution permanganate is reduced to Mn^{2+} by excess of reducing agent,

$$MnO_4^- + 8H^+ + 5e = Mn^{2+} + 4H_2O \qquad E^0 = +1.51 \text{ v}$$

but because MnO_4^- oxidizes Mn^{2+},

$$2MnO_4^- + 3Mn^{2+} + 2H_2O = 5MnO_2(s) + 4H^+ \qquad E^0 = +0.46 \text{ v}$$

the product in presence of excess permanganate is MnO_2.

The addition of small amounts of potassium permanganate to concentrated sulfuric acid gives a clear green solution. If a little water is added, or if a large amount of $KMnO_4$ is added, manganese heptoxide, Mn_2O_7, separates as an unstable oil which is red by transmitted and green by reflected light. The oxide decomposes explosively on heating into oxygen and MnO_2 and with water gives a solution of permanganic acid.

The green solutions of $KMnO_4$ in concentrated sulfuric acid are unstable, but cryoscopic measurements on dilute solutions are consistent with the ionization

$$KMnO_4 + 3H_2SO_4 = K^+ + MnO_3^+ + H_3O^+ + 3HSO_4^-$$

At higher concentrations, MnO_3HSO_4 or MnO_4SO_3H may be formed. The visible and ultraviolet absorption spectra are consistent with a planar trigonal ion, MnO_3^+.

The only other manganese(VII) compound which has been reported is the oxofluoride, MnO_3F.

29-D-6. Electronic Structures of Manganese Compounds

High-Spin Manganese(II) Complexes. The electronic structures of manganese(II) compounds are of unusual interest since they exemplify some important fundamental principles very clearly. Figure 29-D-1 shows the visible spectrum of the $[Mn(H_2O)_6]^{2+}$ ion. Mn^{II} in other octahedral environments has a very similar spectrum. Its most striking features are (a) the weakness of the bands, (b) the large number of bands and (c) the great variation in the widths of the bands, with one being extremely narrow indeed. All of these main features of the spectrum are easily understood in terms of ligand field theory.

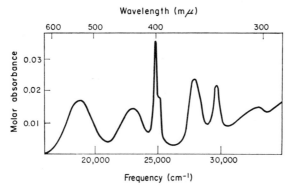

Fig. 29-D-1.   The visible spectrum of the $[Mn(H_2O)_6]^{2+}$ ion obtained using an aqueous solution of the perchlorate.

Let us consider first the weakness of the bands. It is because of their extreme weakness that the ion has such a pale color, and the many other salts and complexes of Mn^{II} in which the ion finds itself in octahedral surroundings are also very pale pink in color; finely ground solids often appear to be white. The reason for the weakness of the bands is very simple. The ground state of the d^5 system in a weak octahedral field has one electron in each d orbital, and their spins are parallel, making it a spin sextuplet. This corresponds to the ^6S ground state of the free ion, which is not split by the ligand field. This, however, is the only sextuplet state possible, for every conceivable alteration of the electron distribution $t_{2g}^3 e_g^2$, with all spins parallel, results in the pairing of two or four spins thus making quartet or doublet states. Hence, all excited states of the d^5 system have different spin multiplicity from the ground state, and transitions to them are spin forbidden. Because of weak spin-orbit interactions, such transitions are not totally absent, but they give rise only to very weak absorption bands. As a rough rule such spin-forbidden transitions give absorption bands ~ 100 times weaker than those for similar but spin-allowed transitions.

In order to understand the number and widths of the spin-forbidden bands, we must refer to an energy level diagram. Figure 29-D-2 shows a

27*

simplified one for the d^5 system in which all spin-doublet states are omitted. Most of these are of very high energy, and transitions to them from the sextuplet ground state are doubly spin-forbidden and hence never observed. It is seen that there are four Russell–Saunders states of the free ion which

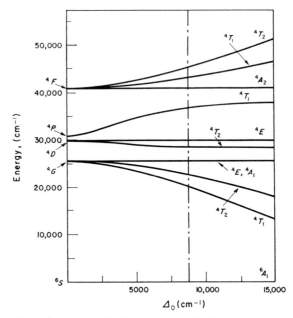

Fig. 29-D-2.   Partial energy level diagram for the Mn^{II} ion, showing only the ^6S state and the quartet states. The separations of the Russell–Saunders states at $\Delta = 0$ are those appropriate for the $[Mn(H_2O)_6]^{2+}$ ion (*not* the actual free Mn^{2+} ion) and the vertical line (—·—·—) is at the Δ value (8600 cm^{-1}) for this species.

are quartets, and their splittings as a function of ligand field strength are shown.   It is found that the observed bands of $[Mn(H_2O)_6]^{2+}$ can be fitted by taking Δ equal to about 8600 cm^{-1}.   This is indicated by the vertical dashed line in the diagram.   The diagram shows that to the approximation used to calculate it the ^4E and $^4A_1$ states arising from the ^4G term are degenerate.   This is very nearly but not exactly so, as the slight shoulder on the sharp band at $\sim 25{,}000$ cm^{-1} shows.   It may also be pointed out that the energies of the Russell–Saunders states shown in this diagram are all lower than those for the free ion, an allowance being made for the nephelauxetic effect (page 697).   It will also be noted that there are three states, the $^4A_2$ state from ^4F, the ^4E state from ^4D, and the ($^4E_1$, $^4A_1$) state from ^4G, whose energies are independent of the strength of the ligand field.   Such a situation, which never occurs for upper states of the same spin multiplicity as the ground state, makes it unusually easy to measure accurately the decrease in the interelectronic repulsion parameters.

Theoretical considerations show that the widths of spectral bands due to d–d transitions should be proportional to the slope of the upper state relative to that of the ground state. In the present case, where the ground state energy is independent of the ligand field strength, this means that the band widths should be proportional to the slopes of the lines for the respective upper states as they are seen in Figure 29-D-2. Comparison of the spectrum of $[Mn(H_2O)_6]^{2+}$ with the energy level diagram shows that this expectation is very well fulfilled indeed. Thus the narrowest bands are those at $\sim 25{,}000$ and $\sim 29{,}500$ cm^{-1}, which correspond to the transitions to upper states with zero slope. The widths of the other lines are also seen to be greater in proportion to the slopes of the upper state energy lines.

The reason why the band widths are proportional to the slopes is easy to grasp in a qualitative way. As the ligand atoms vibrate back and forth, the strength of the ligand field, Δ, also oscillates back and forth about a mean value corresponding to the mean position of the ligands. Now, if the separation between the ground and excited states is a sensitive function of Δ, then the energy difference will vary quite a bit over the range in Δ which corresponds to the range of metal–ligand distances covered in the course of the vibrational motion. If, on the other hand, the energy separation of the two states is rather insensitive to Δ, only a narrow range of energy will be encompassed over the range of the vibration. This argument is illustrated in Figure 29-D-3.

As we have already noted, tetrahedral complexes of Mn^{II} are yellow-green, and the coloration is more intense than that of the octahedral complexes. A typical spectrum is shown in Figure 29-D-4. First it will be noted that the molar absorbance values are in the range 1.0–4.0, whereas for octahedral Mn^{II} complexes (see Fig. 29-D-1), they are in the range 0.01–0.04. This factor of about 100 in the intensities of tetrahedral complexes over octahedral ones is entirely typical and will be seen again, especially for complexes of Ni^{II} and Co^{II}. The reasons for it are not known with complete certainty, but it is thought to be due in part to mixing of metal p and d orbitals in the tetrahedral environment which is facilitated by overlap of metal d orbitals with ligand orbitals in the tetrahedral complexes.

It may also be seen in Figure 29-D-4 that there are six absorption bands in two groups of three, just as there are in $[Mn(H_2O)_6]^{2+}$, but they are here much closer together. This is to be expected since the Δ value for the tetrahedral complex, $[MnBr_4]^{2-}$, should be less than that for $[Mn(H_2O)_6]^{2+}$.

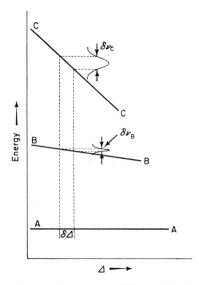

Fig. 29-D-3. Diagram showing how band width is related to the slope of the upper state relative to that of the ground state. A–A gives the energy of the ground state, B–B and C–C the energies of two upper states as functions of the ligand field strength, Δ. $\delta\Delta$ represents the range of variation of Δ due to ligand vibrations, and $\delta\nu_B$ and $\delta\nu_C$ are the widths of the bands due to the transitions $A \rightarrow B$ and $A \rightarrow C$.

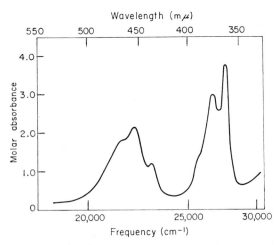

Fig. 29-D-4. The visible absorption spectrum of the tetrahedral manganese(II) complex, $[MnBr_4]^{2-}$.

From the energy level diagram (Fig. 29-D-2) it can be seen that the upper-most band in the group at lower energy should be due to the transition to the field-strength-independent ($^4E_1$, $^4A_1$) level, and this band does seem to be quite narrow, although it is partly overlapped by the other two in the group. The fact that this band occurs at $\sim 22{,}000$ cm^{-1}, whereas the corresponding band occurs at $\sim 25{,}000$ cm^{-1} in $[Mn(H_2O)_6]^{2+}$, shows there is a greater nephelauxetic effect in the tetrahedral than in the octahedral complexes. This is in accord with the suggestion made above that the greater intensity of the bands is due at least in part to greater orbital overlap.

Low-Spin Manganese(II) Complexes. Inspection of Figure 29-D-2 shows that a quartet state is destined to drop below the ^6S ground state. As noted above, however, we have omitted all of the doublet states from the diagram for clarity, and it turns out that one of these will cut the ^6S state first and will remain the ground state thereafter. Using a simple splitting diagram of the d orbitals we have already (page 669) reached the same conclusion, namely, that if Δ_0 becomes sufficiently large, the ground configuration will be t_{2g}^5, with one unpaired electron. It turns out that the pairing energy for Mn^{II} is quite high so that only a few of the strongest ligands, especially those which can increase Δ_0 by π bonding are capable of causing spin pairing. Among the better-known low-spin complexes of Mn^{II} are $[Mn(CN)_6]^{4-}$, $[Mn(CN)_5NO]^{3-}$ and several isonitrile complexes of the type $[Mn(CNR)_6]^{2+}$.

Manganese(III) Compounds. The ground state, $^5E_g(t_{2g}^3 e_g)$, for Mn^{III} in octahedral surroundings is subject to a Jahn–Teller distortion. Because of the odd number of e_g electrons this distortion should be appreciable (page 685), and it might be expected to resemble the distortions in Cr^{II} and Cu^{II} compounds, namely, a considerable elongation of two *trans* bonds with little difference in the lengths of the other four. In several cases this has been observed. Thus, MnF$_3$ has the same basic structure as VF$_3$, in which each V^{3+} ion is surrounded by a regular octahedron of F$^-$ ions, except that two Mn—F distances are 1.79 A, two more are 1.91 A, and the remaining two are 2.09 A. In Mn(OH)O, each Mn^{3+} has four near oxygens in a plane at distances of 1.85 and 1.92 A and two more at 2.30 A. There is also the distortion of the spinel structure of Mn$_3$O$_4$. Here Mn^{2+} ions are in tetrahedral interstices and Mn^{3+} ions in octahedral interstices. Each of the latter tends to distort its own octahedron and the cumulative effect is that the entire lattice is distorted from cubic to elongated tetragonal. However, in the case of Mn(acac)$_3$ the arrangement of the six oxygen atoms does not show this kind of distortion, nor any large deviation from an octahedral disposition.[6] The reason for this is not clear,

[6] B. Morosin and J. R. Brathorde, *Acta Cryst.*, **17**, 705 (1964).

but in this case the chelate rings with their π systems introduce a significant low symmetry (D_3) component into the ligand field and this may influence the operation of the Jahn–Teller effect here in a manner which remains to be investigated.

A simplified energy level diagram for d^4 systems is shown in Figure 29-D-5. It is consistent with the existence of both high-spin and low-spin

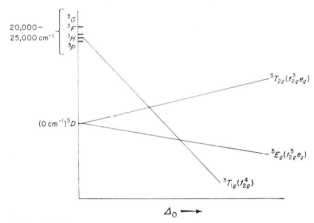

Fig. 29-D-5. Simplified energy level diagram for the d^4 system Mn^{III} in octahedral surroundings.

octahedral complexes. Because the next quintet state (^5F, derived from the d^3s configuration) lying $\sim 110,000$ cm^{-1} above the ^5D ground state of the free ion is of such high energy, only one spin-allowed absorption band ($^5E_g \rightarrow {}^5T_{2g}$) is to be expected in the visible region. For $[Mn(H_2O)_6]^{3+}$ and tris(oxalato)- and tris(acetylacetonato)manganese-(III) a rather broad band appears around 20,000 cm^{-1} and the red or red-brown colors of high-spin Mn^{III} compounds may be attributed to such absorption bands. However, the spectra of some six coordinate Mn^{III} complexes are not so simple and they are difficult to interpret in all their details, presumably because both static and dynamic Jahn–Teller effects perturb the simple picture based on fixed and perfect O_h symmetry.[7] For the low-spin complex $[Mn(CN)_6]^{3-}$, there appear to be no transitions likely below frequencies where they would be obscured by strong ultraviolet bands, and none have been observed.

Manganese(VI) and -(VII) Compounds. In the manganate ion there is one unpaired electron, but its behavior cannot be predicted by a ligand field treatment because the overlap of metal and oxygen orbitals is too great. Instead, a molecular orbital approach must be used. This is, of

[7] J. P. Fackler, Jr., and I. D. Chawla, *Inorg. Chem.*, **3**, 1130 (1964).

course, in no way surprising, for we surely could not expect to have an Mn^{6+} ion surrounded by O^{2-} ions without a great deal of electron density being drawn from the oxide ions to the Mn orbitals.

The permanganate ion has no unpaired electrons, but it does have a small paramagnetism which is temperature independent (see page 637).

Attempts to provide a complete description of the electronic structures of MnO_4^{2-} and MnO_4^-, capable of accounting for both their spectra and their magnetic properties have been made using semi-empirical MO theory (see page 709). While some success has been achieved, there remain certain difficulties, some of which may be due to inherent inconsistencies in the methods of treatment.[8]

29-E. IRON

With this element, the trends already noted in the relative stabilities of oxidation states continue, except that there are now no compounds or chemically important circumstances in which the oxidation state equal to the total number of valence shell electrons—eight in this case—is found. The highest oxidation state known is VI, and it is rare and of little importance. Even the trivalent state which rose to a peak of importance at chromium now loses ground to the divalent state. We shall see later that this trend continues, Co^{III} being stable only in complexes (of which, however, there are many) and Ni^{III} being found only in a few very special circumstances.

Iron compounds are amenable to study by a type of nuclear resonance spectroscopy which depends on a phenomenon known as the *Mössbauer effect*.[1] Although it can be observed with some 28 nuclides besides iron, chemical information from Mössbauer effects has been obtained only for tin, but the use is much more limited in this case than with iron. With reference to iron, the effect depends on the fact that the nuclide ^{57}Fe which is formed in the decay of ^{57}Co, has an excited state ($t_{\frac{1}{2}} \approx 10^{-7}$ sec) at 14.4 kev above the ground state; this can lead to a very sharp resonance absorption peak. Thus if γ radiation from the ^{57}Co source falls on an absorber where the iron nuclei are in an environment identical with that of the source atoms, then resonant absorption of γ rays will occur. However, if the Fe nuclei are in a different environment, no absorption occurs and the

---

[8] R. W. Fenske and C. C. Sweeney, *Inorg. Chem.*, **3**, 1105 (1964); A. Viste and H. B. Gray, *Inorg. Chem.*, **3**, 1113 (1964).

[1] E. Flucke, *Adv. Inorg. Chem. Radiochem.*, **6**, 433 (1964); J. F. Duncan and R. M. Golding, *Quart. Rev.*, **19**, 36 (1965); G. K. Wertheim, *Mössbauer Effect: Principles and Applications*, Academic Press, N.Y., 1964.

radiation is transmitted and can be measured. In order to obtain resonant absorption, it is then necessary to impart a velocity to the absorber, relative to the source. This motion changes the energy of the incident quanta (Doppler effect) so that at a certain velocity there is correspondence with the excitation energy of the nuclei in the absorber. The shifts in the absorption position relative to stainless steel as arbitrary zero, are customarily expressed in velocities (mm/sec) rather than in energies. The shift in the resonance absorption depends both on the chemical environment and on temperature. The chemical or isomer shift is a linear function of s electron density at the nucleus; thus Fe^{2+} has a more positive shift than Fe^{3+} since the $4s$ electrons in Fe^{2+} are more strongly screened by the additional d electron. There are two other types of information that can be obtained:

(a) Even when all nuclei in an absorber are in identical environments, splitting of the resonance absorption peak may occur. This is due to interaction of an electric field gradient at the nucleus with the nuclear quadrupole. The field gradient depends upon the asymmetry of the electronic charge distribution. Thus $Fe^{3+}(d^5)$, or Fe^{II} in $[Fe(CN)_6]^{4-}$ have a spherically symmetrical distribution of charge, but $Fe^{2+}(d^6)$ is asymmetric and hence a quadrupole splitting results.

(b) There may be line splitting due to magnetic dipole interactions thus providing a sensitive tool for the detection of magnetically ordered states (i.e., ferromagnetic and antiferromagnetic states).

Some examples of useful results are the following:

1. In Berlin blues, e.g., $Fe_4[Fe(CN)_6]_3$, it has been shown that discrete Fe^{2+} and Fe^{3+} ions exist, in agreement with other lines of evidence.

2. In $[Fe(CN)_6]^{4-}$, the removal of charge from the Fe atom by π bonding leads to isomer shifts in the region for Fe^0. In substituted complexes, $Fe(CN)_5X$, if X is a better π acid than CN^-, the $3d$ occupation is reduced and the s density at the nucleus accordingly raised because the $4s$ level contracts when less shielded. The π-acid order derived this way is: $NO^+ > CN^- > SO_3^{2-} > NO_2^- \sim NH_3$.

3. In the case of the FeO_4^{2-} ion, the isomer shift cannot be explained in terms of the value expected for a d^2 Fe^{VI} ion using sp^3 hybrid orbitals. Instead, considerable use of the $3d$ orbitals, resulting in their occupation by bonding electrons, must be involved.

4. The broad but single resonance peak of $[Fe(CN)_6]^{4-}$ is replaced by a well-resolved doublet in the isoelectronic $[Fe(CN)_5NO]^{2-}$, thus confirming that asymmetry is introduced by the greater degree of FeNO π bonding compared to FeCN π bonding.

The oxidation states and stereochemistry of iron are summarized in Table 29-E-1.

TABLE 29-E-1

Oxidation States and Stereochemistry of Iron

Oxidation state	Coordination number	Geometry	Examples
Fe^{-II}	4	Tetrahedral	$Fe(CO)_4{}^{2-}$, $Fe(CO)_2(NO)_2$
Fe^0	5	Trigonal bipyramidal	$Fe(CO)_5$, $(Ph_3P)_2Fe(CO)_3$, $Fe(PF_3)_5$
	6	Octahedral (?)	$Fe(CO)_5H^+$, $Fe(CO)_4PPh_3H^+$
Fe^I, d^7	6	Octahedral	$[Fe(H_2O)_5NO]^{2+}$
Fe^{II}, d^6	4	Tetrahedral	$FeCl_4{}^{2-}$
	5	?	$Fe(dienMe)X_2{}^b$
	6^a	Octahedral	$[Fe(H_2O)_6]^{2+}$, $[Fe(CN)_6]^{4-}$
Fe^{III}, d^5	4	Tetrahedral	$FeCl_4{}^-$, Fe^{III} in Fe_3O_4
	6^a	Octahedral	Fe_2O_3, $[Fe(C_2O_4)_3]^{3-}$, $Fe(acac)_3$
	7	Approx. pentagonal bipyramidal	$[FeEDTA(H_2O)]^-$
Fe^{IV}, d^4	6	Octahedral	$[Fe(diars)_2Cl_2]^{2+}$
Fe^V, d^3	4	Tetrahedral	$FeO_4{}^{3-}$
Fe^{VI}, d^2	4	Tetrahedral	$FeO_4{}^{2-}$

^{a} Most common states.

^{b} See footnote to Table 29-D-1, page 835.

29-E-1. The Element

Iron is the second most abundant metal, after aluminum, and the fourth most abundant element in the earth's crust. The core of the earth is believed to consist mainly of iron and nickel, and the occurrence of many iron meteorites suggests that it is abundant throughout the solar system. The major iron ores are *hematite*, Fe_2O_3, *magnetite*, Fe_3O_4, *limonite*, FeO(OH), and *siderite*, $FeCO_3$.

The technical production and metallurgy of iron constitute a vast subject which will not be discussed here (see Remy in reference list). Chemically pure iron can be prepared by reduction of pure iron oxide (which is obtained by thermal decomposition of ferrous oxalate, carbonate or nitrate) with hydrogen, by electrodeposition from aqueous solutions of iron salts, or by thermal decomposition of iron carbonyl.

Pure iron is a white, lustrous metal, m 1528°. It is not particularly hard, and it is quite reactive. In moist air it is rather rapidly oxidized to give a hydrous oxide which affords no protection since it flakes off, exposing fresh metal surfaces. In a very finely divided state, metallic iron is pyrophoric. It combines vigorously with chlorine on mild heating and also with a variety of other nonmetals including the other halogens, sulfur, phosphorus, boron, carbon and silicon. The carbide and silicide phases play a major role in the technical metallurgy of iron.

The metal dissolves readily in dilute mineral acids. With nonoxidizing acids and in the absence of air, Fe^{II} is obtained. With air present or when warm dilute nitric acid is used, some of the iron goes to Fe^{III}. Very strongly oxidizing media such as concentrated nitric acids or acids containing dichromate passivate iron. Air-free water and dilute air-free hydroxides have little effect on the metal, but hot concentrated sodium hydroxide attacks it.

At temperatures up to 906° the metal has a body-centered lattice. From 906 to 1401°, it is cubic close-packed, but at the latter temperature it again becomes body-centered. It is ferromagnetic up to its Curie temperature of 768° where it becomes simply paramagnetic.

29-E-2. The Oxides of Iron

Because of the fundamental structural relationships between them, we discuss these compounds together, rather than separately under the different oxidation states. Three iron oxides are known. They all tend to be nonstoichiometric, but the ideal compositions of the phases are FeO, Fe_2O_3 and Fe_3O_4.

Iron(II) oxide can be obtained as a black pyrophoric powder when iron(II) oxalate is heated in vacuum. If heated to a higher temperature for a short time, it becomes less reactive. Crystalline FeO can only be obtained by preparing it under equilibrium conditions at quite high temperatures and quenching the system rapidly, for at lower temperatures it is unstable with respect to Fe and Fe_3O_4. If the high temperature FeO system is cooled slowly, disproportionation into these two substances takes place. FeO has the rock salt structure.

The brown hydrous ferric oxide, FeO(OH), exists in several forms depending on the method of preparation, e.g., by hydrolysis of iron(III) chloride solutions at elevated temperatures or by oxidation of iron(II) hydroxide. On heating at 200° the final product is the red-brown α-Fe_2O_3.[2] This oxide occurs in nature as the mineral hematite. It has corundum structure where the oxide ions form a *hexagonally* close-packed array with Fe^{III} ions occupying octahedral interstices. However, by careful oxidation of Fe_3O_4 or by heating one of the modifications of FeO(OH) (lepidocrocite) one obtains another type of Fe_2O_3 called γ-Fe_2O_3. The structure of this phase may be regarded as a *cubic* close-packed array of oxide ions with the Fe^{III} ions distributed randomly over both the octahedral and tetrahedral interstices.

Finally, there is Fe_3O_4, a mixed Fe^{II}–Fe^{III} oxide which occurs in nature in the form of black, octahedral crystals of the mineral magnetite. It can be made by strong ignition of Fe_2O_3 (above 1400°) or by heating Fe_2O_3 to 250° *in vacuo*. It has the inverse spinel structure (page 51). Thus the Fe^{II} ions are all in octahedral interstices, whereas the Fe^{III} ions are half in tetrahedral and half in octahedral interstices of a cubic close-packed array of oxide ions.

[2] G. Butler and H. C. K. Ison, *Chem. Comm.*, **1965**, 264.

The tendency of each of these oxides to be nonstoichiometric is due to some extent to the intimate relationship between their structures. In each case (except α-Fe_2O_3) the structure may be visualized by starting with a cubic close-packed array of oxide ions and distributing a certain number of Fe^{II} and/or Fe^{III} ions among the octahedral and tetrahedral holes. Thus, when all of the octahedral holes are filled by Fe^{II} ions, we have the ideal FeO structure. If a small portion, $3x$, of these Fe^{II} ions are replaced by two-thirds their number of Fe^{III} ions, we get the usual defect structure for ferrous oxide, for example, $Fe_{1-x}O$, where x is commonly ~ 0.05. If this process is continued until two-thirds of the iron atoms are Fe^{III} and half of these migrate to tetrahedral sites, we have Fe_3O_4. Conversion of the remaining Fe^{II} to Fe^{III} gives γ-Fe_2O_3. The fact that each of these oxides can alter its composition in the direction of one or two of the others without there being any major structural change—only a redistribution of ions among the tetrahedral and octahedral interstices—accounts for their ready interconvertibility, their tendency to be nonstoichiometric, and, in general, the complexity of the Fe–O system.

29-E-3. The Chemistry of Iron(II), d^6

Halides. All four are known in both anhydrous and hydrated forms. The iodide and bromide can be prepared by direct reaction of the elements, though when iron is burned in bromine there must be an excess of metal present to prevent formation of $FeBr_3$. The direct reaction of chlorine and fluorine with iron yields the iron(III) halides, but the action of hydrogen fluoride and hydrogen chloride on the metal affords FeF_2 and $FeCl_2$. Iron(II) chloride is also conveniently prepared by reduction of the heated trichloride with hydrogen, by reduction of a solution of the trichloride in tetrahydrofuran with excess iron filings or by refluxing $FeCl_3$ in chlorobenzene.

The metal dissolves in the aqueous hydrohalic acids (and also slowly in water containing iodine), and from these solutions the hydrated iron(II) halides, $FeF_2 \cdot 8H_2O$ (colorless), $FeCl_2 \cdot 6H_2O$ (pale green), $FeBr_2 \cdot 6H_2O$ (pale green) and $FeI_2 \cdot 4H_2O$ (pale green), may be crystallized. The anhydrous fluoride and chloride may be obtained by heating the hydrates in a stream of the appropriate hydrogen halide. An X-ray structural study has shown that $FeCl_2 \cdot 6H_2O$ contains *trans* octahedral $[FeCl_2(H_2O)_4]$ units and not hexaquo ions.

Other Salts. Iron(II) forms salts with virtually every stable anion. These are almost invariably obtained as green hydrated substances by evaporating aqueous solutions of the appropriate composition. Typical ones are $FeSO_4 \cdot 7H_2O$, $Fe(ClO_4)_2 \cdot 6H_2O$, $Fe(SCN)_2 \cdot 3H_2O$ and $FeC_2O_4 \cdot \frac{3}{2}H_2O$.

It has been shown that the sulfate and perchlorate contain octahedral $[Fe(H_2O)_6]^{2+}$ ions. An important double salt is Mohr's salt, $(NH_4)_2SO_4 \cdot FeSO_4 \cdot 6H_2O$, which is fairly stable toward both air oxidation and loss of water. It is commonly used in volumetric analysis to prepare standard solutions of iron(II) and as a calibration substance in magnetic measurements. Many other ferrous compounds are more or less susceptible to superficial oxidation by air and/or loss of water of crystallization, thus making them unsuitable as primary standards. This behavior is particularly marked for $FeSO_4 \cdot 7H_2O$, which slowly effloresces and turns yellow-brown on standing.

Iron(II) carbonate, hydroxide and sulfide may be precipitated from aqueous solutions of ferrous salts. Both the carbonate and the hydroxide are white, but in presence of air they quickly darken due to oxidation. On long standing in contact with air, precipitated $Fe(OH)_2$ is eventually converted entirely into $Fe_2O_3 \cdot nH_2O$. The sulfide also undergoes slow oxidation.

$Fe(OH)_2$ is somewhat amphoteric. It readily redissolves in acids, but also in concentrated sodium hydroxide. On boiling 50% NaOH with finely divided iron and cooling, fine, blue-green crystals of $Na_4[Fe(OH)_6]$ are obtained. The strontium and barium salts may also be precipitated.

Iron(II) hydroxide can be obtained as a definite crystalline compound having the brucite, $Mg(OH)_2$, structure.

Iron(II) sulfide has already been discussed along with FeS_2 with regard to their structures (page 531).

Aqueous Chemistry. Aqueous solutions of iron(II), not containing other complexing agents, contain the hexaquoiron(II) ion, $[Fe(H_2O)_6]^{2+}$, which has a pale blue-green color. The potential of the $Fe^{3+}-Fe^{2+}$ couple, 0.771 v, is such that molecular oxygen can convert ferrous to ferric ion in acid solution,

$$2Fe^{2+} + \tfrac{1}{2}O_2 + 2H^+ = 2Fe^{3+} + H_2O \qquad E^0 = 0.46 \text{ v}$$

In basic solution, the oxidation process is still more favorable,

$$\tfrac{1}{2}Fe_2O_3 \cdot 3H_2O + e = Fe(OH)_2(s) + OH^- \qquad E^0 = -0.56 \text{ v}$$

Thus, ferrous hydroxide almost immediately turns dark when precipitated in presence of air. Neutral and acid solutions of ferrous ion oxidize *less* rapidly with increasing acidity (despite the fact that the potential of the oxidation reaction will become more positive). This is because Fe^{III} is actually present in the form of hydroxo complexes, except in extremely acid solutions, and there may also be kinetic reasons.

The oxidation of Fe^{II} to Fe^{III} species by molecular oxygen appears to involve the initial formation of an ion FeO_2^+ in which the oxygen may be bound as in $O_2Ir(PPh_3)_2(CO)Cl$ (see page 368 and hemoglobin discussed below). The reaction kinetics also suggest that a binuclear species is a transient intermediate formed by attack of Fe^{2+} on FeO_2^{2+}. The overall reaction

$$FeO_2^{2+} + Fe(H_2O)^{2+} \rightarrow Fe(OOH)^{2+} + Fe(OH)^{2+}$$

leads to the hydroperoxo ion which rapidly decomposes to give Fe^{III} and HO_2^-, which itself either oxidizes Fe^{2+} or decomposes to O_2. The hydroperoxo ion has been detected in reactions of H_2O_2 with Fe^{3+}.

Complexes. Iron(II) forms a number of complexes, most of them octahedral. Ferrous complexes can normally be oxidized to ferric complexes and the Fe^{II}–Fe^{III} aqueous system provides a good example of the effect of complexing ligands on the relative stabilities of oxidation states,

$$[Fe(CN)_6]^{3-} + e = [Fe(CN)_6]^{4-} \qquad E^0 = 0.36 \text{ v}$$
$$[Fe(H_2O)_6]^{3+} + e = [Fe(H_2O)_6]^{2+} \qquad E^0 = 0.77 \text{ v}$$
$$[Fe(phen)_3]^{3+} + e = [Fe(phen)_3]^{2+} \qquad E^0 = 1.12 \text{ v}$$

The ferrous halides combine with gaseous ammonia, forming several ammoniates of which the highest are the hexammoniates. X-ray studies have shown that these contain the hexammine ion, $[Fe(NH_3)_6]^{2+}$. Other anhydrous ferrous compounds also absorb ammonia. The ammine complexes are not stable in water, however, except in saturated aqueous ammonia. With chelating amine ligands, many complexes stable in aqueous solution are known. For example, ethylenediamine forms the entire series:

$$[Fe(H_2O)_6]^{2+} + en = [Fe(en)(H_2O)_4]^{2+} + 2H_2O \qquad K = 10^{4.3}$$
$$[Fe(en)(H_2O)_4]^{2+} + en = [Fe(en)_2(H_2O)_2]^{2+} + 2H_2O \qquad K = 10^{3.3}$$
$$[Fe(en)_2(H_2O)_2]^{2+} + en = [Fe(en)_3]^{2+} + 2H_2O \qquad K = 10^2$$

β-Diketones (dike) form stable, inner-salt complexes, $Fe(dike)_2$, but considering the polymeric nature of the analogous Mn^{II}, Co^{II} and Ni^{II} species, together with the small tendency of Fe^{II} to form 4-coordinate complexes, polymerization to give octahedral coordination seems very likely.

The famous brown ring test for nitrates and nitrites depends on the fact that, under the conditions of the test, nitric oxide is generated. This combines with ferrous ion to produce a brown complex, $[Fe^I(H_2O)_5NO]^{2+}$, in which the iron is formally in the $+1$ oxidation state (see page 752 for further discussion).

The hexacyanoferrate(II) ion, commonly called ferrocyanide, is an extremely stable and well-known complex of iron(II). It forms a vast number of salts with various cations. The free acid, $H_4[Fe(CN)_6]$, can be precipitated as an ether addition compound (probably containing oxonium ions, R_2OH^+) by adding ether to a solution of the ion in strongly acid solution. The ether can be removed to leave the acid as a white powder. It is a strong tetrabasic acid when dissolved in water; in the solid, the protons are bound to the nitrogen atoms of the CN groups with intermolecular hydrogen bonding (see page 212).

With several diphosphines the *trans*-[FeCl$_2$(diphos)$_2$] species can be prepared, and by treatment of these with LiAlH$_4$ in THF the hydrido complexes *trans*-[FeHCl(diphos)$_2$] and *trans*-[FeH$_2$(diphos)$_2$] can be obtained. These hydrido complexes are easily oxidized by air but have good thermal stability.

Fe^{II} has a lower tendency to form tetrahedral complexes than Co^{II} or Ni^{II}, but a number of these are known, and others doubtless can be made. The [FeX$_4$]$^{2-}$ ions exist in salts with several large cations[3a] while neutral, FeL$_2$X$_2$, and cationic, FeL$_4^{2+}$, complexes, e.g., with (Me$_2$N)$_3$PO or Ph$_3$PO, have been characterized.[3b]

Finally, we discuss briefly the most important iron(II) complex, namely the oxygen-carrying protein molecule of blood, hemoglobin. The molecule consists of a protein, globin, with four *heme* units attached to it. Heme is a complex of protoporphyrinIX, which has the basic porphin nucleus (29-E-I) with certain substituents on the periphery of the ring; the actual system should be thought of as a resonance hybrid of 29-E-I and other double bond arrangements. In hemoglobin, where the order of the amino acid units in the protein is now known, the hemes are bound *via* the imidazole rings of histidine molecules. It is usually assumed that only one iron–histidine link is involved as in 29-E-II, so that the coordination of the

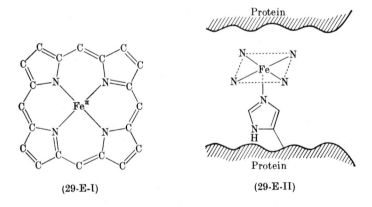

(29-E-I)   (29-E-II)

[3a] C. Furlani, E. Cervone and V. Valenti, *J. Inorg. Nucl. Chem.*, **25**, 159 (1963).
[3b] J. T. Donoghue and R. S. Drago, *Inorg. Chem.*, **2**, 1158 (1963); D. Foster and D. M. L. Goodgame, *J. Chem. Soc.*, **1965**, 268, 454.

Fe^{II} atom is octahedral with a vacant site, which can be occupied by O_2, CO, PF_3, etc. However, there is recent evidence[4] to suggest that three histidines may be involved to give 7-coordinate Fe^{II} as in 29-E-III, and there is X-ray evidence that the iron atom in hemoglobin is slightly out of the porphyrin plane, which would be implied by such a structure.

The details of the binding of oxygen to the heme unit are not fully understood. The heme groups are enclosed in pockets in the protein mole-

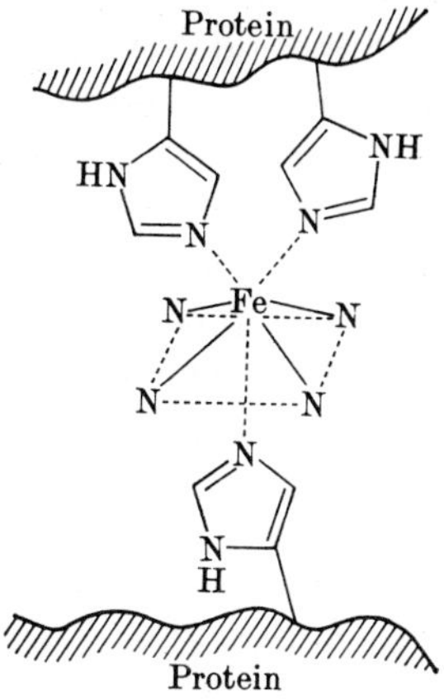

(29-E-III)

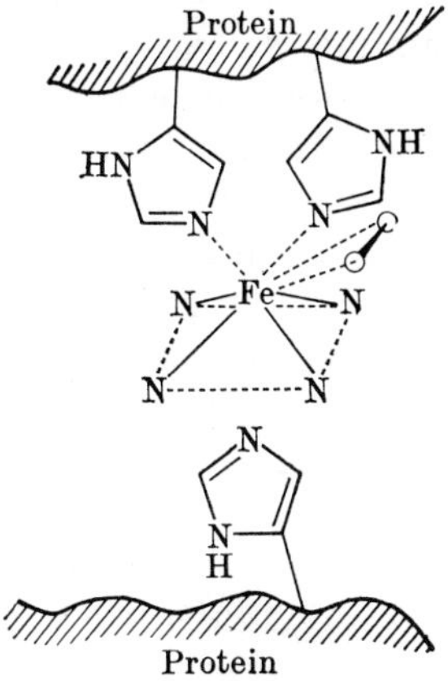

(29-E-IV)

cule and are shielded by hydrophobic portions of the protein. In the absence of this protection, heme is exceedingly readily oxidized by air to the corresponding Fe^{III} complex and the unique reversible oxygen-carrying capacity of hemoglobin is lost. It appears probable that the oxygen molecule is bound "sideways" as in $O_2Ir(PPh_3)_2(CO)Cl$ (see page 1021). There is some evidence that one iron–imidazole link is broken on oxygenation and if this is so then an 8-coordinate, formally Fe^{IV} atom would result in 29-E-IV; the oxygen molecule could, of course, be below the plane. The low-lying d levels of such an 8-coordinate structure could account for the radical change in magnetism from the high-spin value of 5.4 BM for hemoglobin to diamagnetism for oxyhemoglobin.

Hemoglobin can also combine with CO, CN^- and other ligands; though it is improbable that they attack the iron atom in the same position as O_2, oxygenation is inhibited. This is the reason for the toxic nature of, e.g., CO or PF_3. Heme also occurs in myoglobin, and other important hemoproteins are the cytochromes, which differ from hemoglobin in the way

---

[4] A. H. Corwin, quoted in *Chem. and Eng. News*, **1965**, May 31, 36.

the heme ring is substituted and in protein structure. They also differ in function in that they reduce oxygen rapidly rather than transport it as does hemoglobin.

There are a number of other biologically important non-heme complexes of iron whose constitution is not yet fully understood. Among the most important are the sulfur-containing ferridoxins which participate in the redox cycle and may also play a part in nitrogen and carbon dioxide fixation.

Electronic Structures of Iron(II) Complexes. The ground state for a d^6 configuration is ^5D. This is the only quintet state, the higher states being triplets and singlets. Hence in weak octahedral ligand fields, the ground state is $^5T_{2g}$, and the only excited state of the same spin multiplicity is the ^5E_g state, also originating from ^5D. In sufficiently strong fields, however, it is possible for a singlet state arising from one of the excited free-ion states to drop far enough to become the ground state. These features of the energy level diagram (and a few others which will be of interest later in connection with the other well-known d^6 ion, Co^{III}) are indicated in Figure 29-E-1.

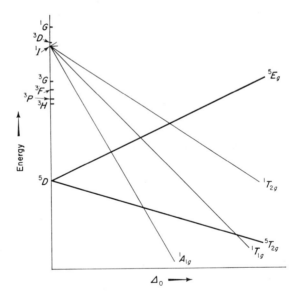

Fig. 29-E-1. Simplified energy level diagram for a d^6 ion in an octahedral ligand field.

For iron(II) quite strong ligand fields are required to cause spin-pairing. Thus practically all iron(II) complexes are high spin, but some, such as the $[Fe(CN)_6]^{4-}$, $[Fe(CNR)_6]^{2+}$ and $[Fe(phen)_3]^{2+}$, are low spin (diamagnetic).

Fephen$_2$(CN)$_2$ is also diamagnetic, though most other Fephen$_2$X$_2$ complexes are high spin. When X = SCN or SeCN a curious temperature dependence of the moment is observed, with a change from ~ 5.1 BM at room temperature to ~ 1.5 BM at $\leq 150°$ K. It has been proposed that these two compounds are polymerization isomers (page 150) of Fephen$_2$X$_2$, namely [phen$_2$FeX$_2$Fephen$_2$]$^{2+}$X$_2$, with a temperature-dependent anti-ferromagnetic interaction between the two Fe^{II} ions,[5] but there is no direct evidence for this.

The spectra of the high-spin complexes consist of only the $^5T_{2g} \rightarrow {}^5E_g$ transition which in the aquo ion occurs around 1000 mμ. A tail of the absorption band runs into the visible at the red end, thus causing the characteristic, very pale, blue-green color of [Fe(H$_2$O)$_6$]$^{2+}$. This absorption band is actually a doublet. As mentioned earlier (page 685), this is perhaps due to a Jahn–Teller effect in the ^2E_g state, but other explanations are possible.

For tetrahedrally coordinated Fe^{II} the ground state should be ^5E. There should be only one absorption band, $^5E \rightarrow {}^5T_2$, and there should be only a small, second order orbital contribution to the magnetic moment. In good accord these expectations, magnetic moments of 5.0–5.2 BM and absorption spectra consisting of single bands at ~ 4000 cm^{-1} have been reported.

29-E-4. The Chemistry of Iron(III), d^5

Halides. The fluoride, chloride and bromide are known, but the iodide does not exist in the pure state, although some of it may be formed in equilibrium with iron(II) iodide and iodine. In effect, iron(III) is too strong an oxidizing agent to coexist with a good reducing agent like I$^-$. In aqueous solution Fe^{3+} and I$^-$ react quantitatively,

$$Fe^{3+} + I^- = Fe^{2+} + \tfrac{1}{2}I_2$$

The three stable iron(III) halides can be obtained by direct halogenation of the metal. The chloride and bromide are quite similar in their properties, both being red-brown, very hygroscopic (forming yellow-brown liquids) and volatile. If heated in vacuum, they both decompose with loss of halogen to give the iron(II) halides. In the gaseous state iron(III) chloride exists as dimers with a structure[6] geometrically the same as those of the aluminum halide dimers up to about 700°, where monomers begin to predominate. Ferric chloride, however, does not preserve this structure

[5] W. A. Baker, Jr., and H. M. Bobonich, *Inorg. Chem.*, **3**, 1184 (1964).
[6] E. Z. Zasorin, N. G. Rambidi and P. Akishin, *Zhur. Strukt. Khim.*, **4**, 910 (1963).

in the solid state. It has instead a semicovalent layer structure similar to that of $CrCl_3$ (page 824). Ordinarily, iron(III) chloride is encountered as the hexahydrate, $FeCl_3 \cdot 6H_2O$, in the form of yellow lumps obtained by evaporating aqueous solutions on steam baths. The fluoride is obtained from aqueous solution as either the $4\frac{1}{2}$ or 3 hydrate, both pink. The anhydrous compound is green.

Other Salts. Iron(III) occurs in salts with most anions except those which are incompatible with it because of their character as reducing agents. The nitrate, perchlorate and sulfate are obtained as pale pink to nearly white hydrates from aqueous solutions, namely, $Fe(ClO_4)_3 \cdot 10H_2O$, $Fe(NO_3)_3 \cdot 9(or\ 6)H_2O$ and $Fe_2(SO_4)_3 \cdot 10H_2O$. Other hydrates are also known.

Aqueous Chemistry. One of the most conspicuous features of ferric iron in aqueous solution is its tendency to hydrolysis and/or formation of complexes. It has been established that the hydrolysis (equivalent in the first stage to acid dissociation of the aquo ion) is governed in its initial stages by the following equilibrium constants:

$$[Fe(H_2O)_6]^{3+} = [Fe(H_2O)_5(OH)]^{2+} + H^+ \qquad K = 10^{-3.05}$$
$$[Fe(H_2O)_5(OH)]^{2+} = [Fe(H_2O)_4(OH)_2]^+ + H^+ \qquad K = 10^{-3.26}$$
$$2[Fe(H_2O)_6]^{3+} = [Fe(H_2O)_4(OH)_2Fe(H_2O)_4]^{4+} + 2H^+ \qquad K = 10^{-2.91}$$

In the last of these equations the binuclear species is written to imply the structure 29-E-V for the dimer, which, though plausible, is quite unproved.

(29-E-V)

From the constants for these equilibria it can be seen that even at the rather acid pH's of 2–3, the extent of hydrolysis is very great, and in order to have solutions containing Fe^{III} mainly (say $\sim 99\%$) in the form of the pale purple hexaquo ion the pH must be around zero. As the pH is raised above 2–3, more highly condensed species than the dinuclear one noted above are formed, attainment of equilibrium becomes sluggish, and soon colloidal gels are formed. Ultimately, as on addition of dilute aqueous ammonia to Fe^{III} solution, hydrous ferric oxide is precipitated as a red-brown gelatinous mass.

There is no evidence that any definite hydroxide, $Fe(OH)_3$, exists, and the red-brown precipitate commonly called ferric hydroxide is best described as hydrous ferric oxide, $Fe_2O_3 \cdot nH_2O$. At least a part of such precipitates seems to be $FeO(OH)$, which exists in at least two definite crystalline forms (page 850).

The various hydroxo species, such as $[Fe(OH)(H_2O)_5]^{2+}$, are yellow in color because of charge transfer bands in the ultraviolet which have tails coming into the visible. Thus aqueous solutions of ferric salts even with noncomplexing anions are yellow unless strongly acid.

Hydrous iron(III) oxide is readily soluble in acids but also to a slight extent in strong bases. On boiling concentrated solutions of strontium or barium hydroxide with ferric perchlorate, the hexahydroxoferrates(III), $M^{II}_3[Fe(OH)_6]_2$, are obtained as white crystalline powders. With alkali metal hydroxides, substances of composition M^IFeO_2 can be obtained. The latter can also be made by fusion of Fe_2O_3 with the alkali metal hydroxide or carbonate in the proper stoichiometric proportion. Moderate concentrations of what is presumably the $[Fe(OH)_6]^{3-}$ ion can be maintained in strongly basic solutions.

Just as the aquo ion readily loses protons to form the mono- and dihydroxo species, so too are halo complexes, also yellow in color, readily formed,

$$\begin{aligned}
Fe^{3+} + Cl^- &= FeCl^{2+} & K &\sim 30 \\
FeCl^{2+} + Cl^- &= FeCl_2^+ & K &\sim 5 \\
FeCl_2^+ + Cl^- &= FeCl_3 & K &\sim 0.1
\end{aligned}$$

The nature of more concentrated aqueous solutions of $FeCl_3$ is complex. Solutions dilute in Fe^{3+} and concentrated in HCl contain mainly $FeCl_4^-$, but at higher Fe^{3+} and/or lower H^+ concentrations octahedral species such as $[FeCl_4(H_2O)_2]^-$ and polymers of uncertain nature arise.[7]

Perhaps the best-known reaction of aqueous Fe^{III} is with thiocyanate ion to form one or more thiocyanate complexes which have an intense red color and are therefore of use in the detection and quantitative estimation of trace quantities of Fe^{III}. The red color is destroyed by fluoride ion. Although salts of the FeF_6^{3-} ion can be prepared by dry methods, in aqueous solution the main equilibria appear to be

$$\begin{aligned}
Fe^{3+} + F^- &= FeF^{2+} & K &\sim 10^5 \\
FeF^{2+} + F^- &= FeF_2^+ & K &\sim 10^4 \\
FeF_2^+ + F^- &= FeF_3 & K &\sim 10^3
\end{aligned}$$

Ferric iron in aqueous solution is rather readily reduced by many reducing agents, such as I^-, as already noted. It also oxidizes sulfide ion so that no ferric sulfide can be precipitated. On adding H_2S or a sulfide to Fe^{III} solution, a precipitate consisting of iron(II) sulfide and colloidal sulfur is obtained.

It may also be noted that ferric carbonate cannot be precipitated either; addition of carbonate or bicarbonate to an iron(III) solution precipitates the hydrous oxide.

---

[7] G. W. Brady, M. B. Robin and J. Varimbi, *Inorg. Chem.*, **3**, 1168 (1964).

Iron(III) Complexes. Iron(III) forms a large number of complexes, mostly octahedral ones, and the octahedron may be considered its characteristic coordination polyhedron. It does also form a few tetrahedral complexes, of which $FeCl_4^-$ is the most important.

The hexaquo ion exists in very strongly acid solutions of ferric salts and presumably also in the highly hydrated crystalline ones. It is known to occur in the several ferric alums, $M^IFe(SO_4)_2 \cdot 12H_2O$.

The affinity of iron(III) for amine ligands is very low. No simple ammine complexes exist in aqueous solution; addition of aqueous ammonia only precipitates the hydrous oxide. Chelating amines, for example, EDTA, do form some definite complexes among which is the 7-coordinate $[Fe(EDTA)H_2O]^-$ ion.[8] Also, those amines such as 2,2'-dipyridyl and 1,10-phenanthroline which produce ligand fields strong enough to cause spin-pairing form fairly stable complexes, isolable in crystalline form with large anions such as perchlorate.

Iron(III) has its greatest affinity for ligands which coordinate via oxygen, especially monophosphate ions, $H_nPO_4^{(3-n)-}$, polyphosphates and polyols such as glycerine, sugars, etc. With oxalate the trisoxalato complex, $[Fe(C_2O_4)_3]^{3-}$, and with β-diketones the neutral $[Fe(dike)_3]$ complexes are formed. Formation of complexes with β-diketones is the cause of the intense colors that develop when they are added to solutions of ferric ion, and this serves as a useful diagnostic test for them.

Important complexes are formed with halide and pseudohalide ions. The formation of FeX^{2+} and FeX_2^+ species in aqueous solution has already been noted. A number of compounds long assumed to contain $Fe_2Cl_9^{3-}$ and $Fe_2Br_9^{3-}$ ions have been shown to contain instead only the FeX_4^- ions, although there is a form of $Cs_3Fe_2Cl_9$ which does contain the $Fe_2Cl_9^{3-}$ ion, isostructural with the $Cr_3Cl_9^{3-}$ ion.[9] The hexachloro- and hexathiocyanatoferrate(III) complexes can be isolated; the more common halo complexes appear to be the penta species, for example, $[FeF_5H_2O]^{2-}$. With cyanide ion only the hexacyanoferrate(III) ion, commonly called the ferricyanide ion, and some pentacyano species, $[Fe(CN)_5X]$ ($X = H_2O$, NO_2, etc.) are known. All of these are of low spin (one unpaired electron). $[Fe(CN)_6]^{3-}$ is quite poisonous, in contrast to $[Fe(CN)_6]^{4-}$, which is not; this is a kinetic effect, the former dissociating or reacting rapidly and the latter only slowly. The free acid, $H_3[Fe(CN)_6]$, is known as well as many salts of which the potassium one is most common.

It has long been known that on treating a solution of Fe^{III} with hexacyanoferrate(II) a blue precipitate called *Prussian blue* is formed, and that on treating a solution of Fe^{II} with hexacyanoferrate(III) a blue precipitate

---

[8] M. D. Lind, M. J. Hamor, T. A. Hamor and J. L. Hoard, *Inorg. Chem.*, **3**, 34 (1964).
[9] A. P. Ginsberg and M. B. Robin, *Inorg. Chem.*, **2**, 817 (1963).

called *Turnbull's blue* is formed. It appears probable that these substances are actually identical, having the formulas $M^IFeFe(CN)_6$, where M^I is Na, K, Rb, but not Li or Cs. Their structure is closely related to those of brown ferric ferricyanide, $FeFe(CN)_6$, the white, insoluble potassium ferrous ferrocyanide, $K_2FeFe(CN)_6$, and a number of similar compounds such as $KCu^{II}Fe(CN)_6$ and $Cu^{II}_2Fe(CN)_6$. In all cases the basic structural feature seems to be a cubic array of iron ions with CN^- ions along cube edges between them. In $Fe^{III}Fe^{III}(CN)_6$ this is the complete structure, except for water molecules inside some of the cubes. In $M^IFe^{II}Fe^{III}(CN)_6$ every other cube contains an M^I ion at its center, and in $M^I_2Fe^{II}Fe^{II}(CN)_6$ every cube contains an M^I ion at its center. Other compounds such as the Cu^{II} salts appear to have the same sort of structure. It has been proposed that in Prussian blue itself, the Fe^{II} ions are surrounded by the C atoms while the Fe^{III} ions are surrounded by N atoms, and that the absorption spectrum is due mainly to charge transfer bands.[10]

Iron(III) like Cr^{III} forms basic acetate compounds which contain the $[Fe_3(CH_3COO)_6O]^+$ cation, isostructural with that of Cr^{III} (see page 826).

Electronic Structures of Iron(III) Compounds. Iron(III) is isoelectronic with manganese(II), discussed on page 840. Although the energy level diagrams of Fe^{III} and Mn^{II} are identical except for exact energies of the states of the free ions and for the somewhat larger Δ values to be expected for the trivalent ion, much less is known of the details of Fe^{III} spectra. This is because of the very much greater tendency of the trivalent ion to have charge transfer bands in the near ultraviolet which have sufficiently strong low energy wings in the visible to obscure almost completely—or completely in many cases—the very weak, spin-forbidden *d–d* bands. Insofar as they are known, however, the spectral features of iron(III) ions in octahedral surroundings are in accord with theoretical expectations.

Magnetically, iron(III), like manganese(II), is high spin in nearly all of its complexes except those with the strongest ligands, of which $[Fe(CN)_6]^{3-}$, $[Fe(dipy)_3]^{3+}$ and $[Fe(phen)_3]^{3+}$ are well-known examples. In the high-spin complexes, the magnetic moments are always very close to the spin-only value of 5.9 BM because the ground state (derived from the ^6S state of the free ion) has no orbital angular momentum and there is no effective mechanism for introducing any by coupling with excited states. The low-spin complexes, with t_{2g}^5 configurations, usually have considerable orbital contributions to their moments at around room temperature, values of ~ 2.3 BM being obtained. The moments are, however, intrinsically temperature dependent, and at liquid nitrogen temperature (77°K) they decrease to ~ 1.9 BM.

[10] M. B. Robin, *Inorg. Chem.*, **1**, 337 (1962); D. F. Shriver, S. A. Shriver and S. E. Anderson, *Inorg. Chem.*, **4**, 725 (1965).

It has been shown that in certain tris-dithiocarbamate complexes, $Fe(S_2CNR_2)_3$, the ligand field strength is such that the ^6A, and $^2T_2$ states are of nearly equal stability. The dependence of the magnetic suscepti-bility and the electronic spectra therefore exhibit quite complicated behavior as a function of temperature.[11]

29-E-5. Compounds of Iron(IV), d^4, and Iron(VI), d^2

Iron (IV). The best-known compounds of iron in this oxidation state are Sr_2FeO_4 and Ba_2FeO_4. Both are made by oxidation of the hexa-hydroxoferrates(III) with molecular oxygen at elevated temperatures:

$$M^{II}_3[Fe(OH)_6]_2 + M^{II}(OH)_2 + \tfrac{1}{2}O_2 \xrightarrow{800-900^\circ} 2M^{II}_2FeO_4 + 7H_2O$$

X-ray studies have shown that these do not contain any discrete ferrate(IV) ions, although the compounds are commonly called ferrates(IV), but that they are mixed metal oxides, the barium one having the spinel structure (page 51).

The only established discrete cationic species are salts of the ions $[Fe^{IV}(diars)_2X_2]^{2+}$, X = Cl, Br, which are obtained by oxidation of the corresponding $[Fe^{III}(diars)_2X_2]^+$ ions by $15M$ nitric acid.[12] They have magnetic moments indicating two unpaired electrons, consistent with a spin-paired d_ε^4 octahedral configuration having a large tetragonal distor-tion, as is expected from the *trans* positions of the halogens.

Iron (VI). The ferrate(VI) ion, FeO_4^{2-}, can be obtained by oxidizing suspensions of $Fe_2O_3 \cdot nH_2O$ in concentrated alkali with chlorine or by anodic oxidation of metallic iron in concentrated alkali. It is also reported that when iron filings are fused with potassium nitrate, the melt becomes incandescent and on cooling dissolves in water to give a violet solution of K_2FeO_4. The red-purple ferrate(VI) ion is most easily precipitated with barium ion, but the very soluble sodium and potassium salts are also known.

The ferrate(VI) ion is relatively stable in basic solution, but in neutral or acidic solution it decomposes according to the equation:

$$2FeO_4^{2-} + 10H^+ = 2Fe^{3+} + \tfrac{3}{2}O_2 + 5H_2O$$

It is an extremely potent oxidizing agent, even stronger than permanganate. Thus it oxidizes ammonia to nitrogen, Cr^{III} to chromate and arsenite to arsenate.

There is a discrete, tetrahedral ferrate(VI) ion; the potassium salt has been shown to be isomorphous with potassium sulfate and chromate. It has, as expected, two unpaired electrons, exhibiting a magnetic moment of 3.06 BM at room temperature.

[11] A. H. Ewald, R. L. Martin, I. G. Ross and A. H. White, *Proc. Roy. Soc.*, **A280**, 235 (1964).

[12] G. S. F. Hazeldean, R. S. Nyholm and R. V. Parish, *J. Chem. Soc.*, **1966A**, 162.

29-F. COBALT

The trends toward decreased stability of the very high oxidation states and increased stability of the II state, relative to the III state, which have been noted through the series Ti, V, Cr, Mn and Fe, persists with cobalt. Indeed, the former trend culminates in the complete absence of oxidation states higher than IV under chemically significant conditions. The III state is stable relative to the II state in hydroxides, in the fluoride, but mainly in complexes, of which, however, there are a great many. There are also some important complexes of Co^I; this oxidation state is better known for cobalt than for any other element of the first transition series except copper.

The oxidation states and stereochemistry are summarized in Table 29-F-1.

TABLE 29-F-1

Oxidation States and Stereochemistry of Cobalt

Oxidation state	Coordination number	Geometry	Examples
Co^{-I}	4	Tetrahedral	$Co(CO)_4{}^-$, $Co(CO)_3NO$
Co^0	4	Tetrahedral(?)	$K_4[Co(CN)_4]$
Co^I, d^8	4	Tetrahedral(?)	$[Co(CN)_3CO]^{2-}$, $Co\{C_2H_4(PPh_2)_2\}_2$
	5	Trigonal bipyramidal	$[Co(NCR)_5]^+$, $[Co(CO)_3(PR_3)_2]^+$
		Tetragonal pyramidal	$(R_2CS_2)_2CoNO$
	6	Octahedral	$[Co(dipy)_3]^+$
Co^{II}, d^7	4[a]	Tetrahedral	$[CoCl_4]^{2-}$, $CoBr_2(PR_3)_2$, Co^{II} in Co_3O_4
	4	Square	$[Co(CH_3SCH_2CH_2SCH_3)](ClO_4)_2$, $[Coen_2](AgI_2)_2$
	5	Trigonal bipyramidal	$[Co(N\text{-methylsalicylaldimine})_2]_2$
	6[a]	Octahedral	$CoCl_2$, $[Co(NH_3)_6]^{2+}$, $[Co(diars)_3]^{2+}$
Co^{III}, d^6	4	Tetrahedral	In a 12-heteropolytungstate
	6[a]	Octahedral	$[Co(en)_2Cl_2]^+$, $[Cr(CN)_6]^{3-}$, $ZnCo_2O_4$, $[CoF_6]^{3-}$
Co^{IV}, d^5	6	Octahedral	$[CoF_6]^{2-}$

[a] Most common states.

29-F-1. The Element

Cobalt always occurs in nature in association with nickel and usually also with arsenic. The most important cobalt minerals are *smaltite*, $CoAs_2$, and *cobaltite*, CoAsS, but the chief technical sources of cobalt are residues called "speisses," which are obtained in the smelting of arsenical ores of nickel, copper and lead. The separation of the pure metal is somewhat complicated and of no special relevance here.

Cobalt is a hard, bluish white metal, m 1490°, b 3100°. It is ferromagnetic with a Curie temperature of about 1150°. It dissolves slowly in dilute mineral acids, the Co^{2+}/Co potential being -0.277 v, but it is relatively unreactive. It does not combine directly with hydrogen or nitrogen, and, in fact, no hydride or nitride appears to exist. The metal will combine with carbon, phosphorus and sulfur on heating. It also is attacked by atmospheric oxygen and by water vapor at elevated temperatures, giving CoO.

29-F-2. Simple Salts and Compounds of Cobalt(II), d^7, and Cobalt(III), d^6

In its ordinary aqueous chemistry, cobalt has two important oxidation states, II and III. In aqueous solutions containing no complexing agents, the oxidation to Co^{III} is very unfavorable:

$$[Co(H_2O)_6]^{3+} + e = [Co(H_2O)_6]^{2+} \qquad E^0 = 1.84 \text{ v}$$

although in the presence of complexing agents, such as NH_3, which form stable complexes with Co^{III} the stability of trivalent cobalt is greatly improved:

$$[Co(NH_3)_6]^{3+} + e = [Co(NH_3)_6]^{2+} \qquad E = 0.1 \text{ v}$$

Trivalent cobalt is also more stable in basic than in acid media:

$$CoO(OH)(s) + H_2O + e = Co(OH)_2(s) + OH^- \qquad E_0 = 0.17 \text{ v}$$

It will be noted that the potential for the oxidation in acid solutions containing no complexing anion is so high that Co^{III} in appreciable concentrations rapidly oxidizes water. Hence aqueous solutions of uncomplexed Co^{III} are of little importance. This relative instability of uncomplexed Co^{III} is evidenced by the rarity of simple salts and binary compounds, whereas Co^{II} forms such compounds in abundance.

Cobalt(II) oxide, an olive-green substance, is easily prepared by reaction of the metal with oxygen at high temperature, by pyrolysis of the carbonate or nitrate, and in other ways. It has the rock salt structure and is antiferromagnetic at ordinary temperatures. On firing it at 400–500° in an atmosphere of oxygen, the oxide Co_3O_4 is obtained. This is a normal spinel containing Co^{II} ions in tetrahedral interstices and diamagnetic Co^{III} ions in octahedral interstices. There is no evidence for the existence of the pure cobaltic oxide Co_2O_3.

Few simple Co^{III} salts are known. The anhydrous fluoride is prepared by fluorination of the metal or of $CoCl_2$ at 300–400°. It is a brown powder instantly reduced by water. The hydrate, $CoF_3 \cdot 3.5H_2O$, is of uncertain nature. It separates as a green powder on electrolysis of Co^{II} in 40% HF solution. The blue sulfate, $Co_2(SO_4)_3 \cdot 18H_2O$, which is stable when dry but decomposed by water, is precipitated when Co^{II} in $8N$ H_2SO_4 is oxidized either electrolytically or by ozone or fluorine. Co^{III} also occurs in the alums $MCo(SO_4)_2 \cdot 12H_2O$ (M = K, Rb, Cs, NH$_4$), which are also dark blue and reduced by water. Presumably there are $[Co(H_2O)_6]^{3+}$ ions in the sulfate as there are known to be in the alum. It is noteworthy that the alums are diamagnetic. Cobaltic acetate precipitates from a solution of cobaltous acetate in glacial acetic acid on electrolytic oxidation. Its constitution is not known, but it perhaps involves some relatively stable complex of Co^{III}, since it dissolves in water but is only slowly reduced. There are also various forms of the black hydroxide, $CoO(OH)$, which can be obtained by mild oxidation of cobalt(II) hydroxide.

Cobalt(II) forms an extensive group of simple and hydrated salts. The parent base, cobaltous hydroxide, may be precipitated by strong bases as either a blue or a pink solid, depending on conditions, but only the pink form is permanently stable. It is rather insoluble ($K_{SP} = 2.5 \times 10^{-16}$) but somewhat amphoteric, dissolving in very concentrated alkali to give a deep blue solution of $[Co(OH)_4]^{2-}$ ions, from which $Na_2Co(OH)_4$ and $Ba_2Co(OH)_6$ may be precipitated. Addition of sulfide ions or H_2S to solutions of Co^{2+} ion causes precipitation of a black solid, usually taken to be CoS and assigned a K_{SP} of about 10^{-22}. However, after standing a short while, this substance becomes far less soluble in acid than the above K_{SP} would indicate since oxidation occurs in air to give the less soluble Co(OH)S.

The anhydrous halides of Co^{II} are all known. They may be obtained by direct union of the elements at elevated temperatures, or from hydrates by dehydration procedures. All of the anhydrous halides have structures in which the Co^{II} ion is octahedrally coordinated.

Hydrated cobaltous salts with all common anions are known. They are easily obtained by reaction of $Co(OH)_2$ with the appropriate acid or by metathetical reactions. So far as is known, all such hydrated salts are red or pink in color and contain octahedrally coordinated Co^{II}. In many there are $[Co(H_2O)_6]^{2+}$ ions.

29-F-3. Complexes of Cobalt(II), d^7

Divalent cobalt forms numerous complexes of various stereochemical types. Octahedral and tetrahedral ones are most common, but there are a fair number of square ones as well as some which are five-coordinate.[1,2] Co^{II} forms more tetrahedral complexes than any other transition metal ion.

[1] A. Sacco and M. Freni, *Gazz. Chim. Ital.*, **89**, 1800 (1959).

[2a] P. L. Orioli, M. Di Vaira and L. Sacconi, *Chem. Comm.*, **1965**, 103, 590; L. Sacconi, P. L. Orioli and M. Di Vaira, *J. Amer. Chem. Soc.*, **87**, 2059 (1965); M. Ciampolini, *et al.*, *Inorg. Chem.*, **5**, 41, 45 (1966).

[2b] P. Pauling, G. B. Robertson and G. A. Rodley, *Nature*, **207**, 73 (1965).

28 + A.I.C.

This is in accord with the fact that for a d^7 ion, ligand field stabilization energies disfavor the tetrahedral configuration relative to the octahedral one to a smaller extent than for any other d^n ($1 \leq n \leq 9$) configuration,[3a] although it should be carefully noted that this argument is valid only in *comparing* the behavior of one metal ion to another and not for assessing the absolute stabilities of the configurations for any particular ion (see page 691). Co^{2+} is the only d^7 ion of common occurrence.

Because of the small stability difference between octahedral and tetrahedral Co^{II} complexes, there are several cases in which the two types with the same ligand, are both known and may be in equilibrium.[3b] The existence of some $[Co(H_2O)_4]^{2+}$ in equilibrium with $[Co(H_2O)_6]^{2+}$ has already been noted (page 152). There is also a tetrahedral $[Co(NH_3)_4]^{2+}$ ion in $[Co(NH_3)_4](ReO_4)_2$ although in all other cases the hexammine ion, $[Co(NH_3)_6]^{2+}$, is formed.

Tetrahedral complexes, $[CoX_4]^{2-}$, are generally formed with monodentate anionic ligands, such as Cl^-, Br^-, I^-, SCN^-, N_3^- and OH^-; with a combination of two such ligands and two neutral ones, L, tetrahedral complexes of the type CoL_2X_2 are formed. With ligands which are bidentate mono anions, tetrahedral complexes are formed in some cases, e.g., with *n*-alkylsalicylaldiminato and bulky β-diketonate anions. With the less hindered ligands of this type association to give a higher coordination number often occurs. Thus in bis-(*N*-methylsalicylaldiminato)cobalt(II) a dimer[2b] with five-coordinate Co atoms is formed (Fig. 29-F-1) while $Co(acac)_2$ is a tetramer[4] in which each Co atom is six-coordinate, as shown in Figure 29-F-2.

Planar complexes are formed with several bidentate mono anions such as dimethylglyoximate, aminooxalate, *o*-aminophenolate and the disulfur ligands discussed in Section 27–9. Several neutral bidentate ligands also give planar complexes although it is either known or reasonable to presume that the accompanying anions are coordinated *to some degree* so that these complexes could also be considered as very distorted octahedral ones. Examples are $[Coen_2](AgI_2)_2$[5] and $[Co(CH_3SC_2H_4SCH_3)_2](ClO_4)_2$.[6] With the tetradentate ligands bis-salicylaldehydeethylenediiminato ion and porphyrins, planar complexes are also obtained.

Apparently certain organocobalt(II) derivatives of the type CoR_2L_2, where R is bulky, are planar, such a structure having been proved for $Co(mesityl)_2(PEt_2Ph)_2$ by X-ray crystallography.[7]

[3a] A. B. Blake and F. A. Cotton, *Inorg. Chem.*, **3**, 5 (1964).

[3b] S. M. Nelson and T. M. Shepherd, *J. Chem. Soc.*, **1965**, 3284.

[4] F. A. Cotton and R. C. Elder, *Inorg. Chem.*, **4**, 1145 (1965).

[5] A. B. P. Lever, J. Lewis and R. S. Nyholm, *J. Chem. Soc.*, **1963**, 2552.

[6] F. A. Cotton and D. L. Weaver, *J. Amer. Chem. Soc.*, **87**, 4189 (1965).

[7] P. G. Owston and J. M. Rowe, *J. Chem. Soc.*, **1963**, 3411.

An important feature of the chemistry of Co^{II} is the very ready oxidation by molecular oxygen in the presence of a variety of complexing ligands, especially nitrogen donors. Although oxidation to normal Co^{III} complexes

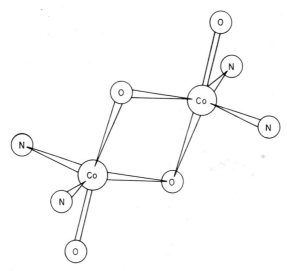

Fig. 29-F-1. The structure of the dimer of bis-(N-methylsalicylaldiminato)cobalt(II). Each Co^{II} is surrounded by a distorted trigonal bipyramid of ligand atoms. The Mn^{II} and Zn^{II} complexes have analogous structures.

eventually occurs, particularly when activated charcoal is present as a catalyst, due to the instability of the intermediates, the action of oxygen normally gives initially a binuclear peroxo species of Co^{III}. The first

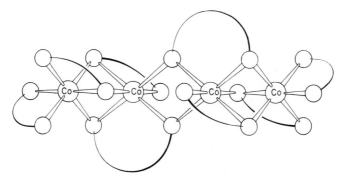

Fig. 29-F-2. Schematic representation of the structure of the tetramer of bis-acetylacetonatocobalt(II). Unlabeled open circles represent oxygen atoms, and the chelate rings are indicated by the heavy curved lines.

step may well involve coordination of O_2 (see page 368) to give a transient Co^{IV} species which is then converted by reaction with more Co^{II} to give the binuclear Co^{III} complex. Thus air oxidation of $CoCl_2$ solutions gives brown, diamagnetic complexes $[(NH_3)_5Co(O_2)Co(NH_3)_5]^{4+}$ in presence of ammonia, and $[(CN)_5Co(O_2)Co(CN)_5]^{6-}$ in presence of cyanide ion. These complexes are reasonably stable as dry solids but are usually fairly readily decomposed by water and acids. It seems most reasonable to assume that they consist of low-spin pentamminocobalt(III) groups bridged by peroxide ions, O_2^{2-}, as discussed below.

The Co^{III} peroxo complexes can sometimes be oxidized in a one-electron step, the above pentammine, for example, giving the green ion $[(NH_3)_5Co(O_2)Co(NH_3)_5]^{5+}$. This ion was formerly thought to contain Co^{III} and Co^{IV}, but esr and X-ray structural studies (Fig. 29-F-3) show that the two cobalt atoms are entirely equivalent and that the single unpaired electron is distributed equally over both of them; the assignment of integral oxidation numbers is thus meaningless. This type of delocalization of unpaired electrons is known to occur in other polynuclear complexes with symmetrical structures. It seems best to assume that the oxidized species also contain Co^{III} ions, now bridged by a superoxide ion, O_2^-. Thus in the $[(NH_3)_5CoO_2Co(NH_3)_5]^{5+}$ ion shown in Figure 29-F-3, the O—O distance, 1.31 A, is nearly the same as that (1.28 A) of the superoxide ion, whereas the distance for the peroxide ion is much longer, viz., ~ 1.48 A.[8]

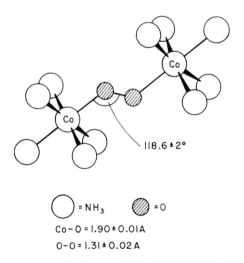

= NH_3 = O

Co–O = 1.90 ± 0.01A
O–O = 1.31 ± 0.02 A

Fig. 29-F-3. The structure of the ion $[(NH_3)_5CoO_2Co(NH_3)_5]^{5+}$ as it is found in $[(NH_3)_5CoO_2Co(NH_3)_5]SO_4(HSO_4)_3$. (Adapted from ref. 8.)

[8] W. P. Shaefer and R. E. Marsh, *J. Amer. Chem. Soc.*, **88**, 178 (1966).

The cobalt(II) complexes of a number of chelating ligands such as bissalicylaldehydeethylenediimine, glycylglycine and histidine can act as *reversible* oxygen carriers in either the solid state or in solution; the oxygen adducts are presumably best formulated as Co^{IV} species.[9]

Finally, the cobalt(II) cyanide system deserves mention. On addition of KCN to Co^{II} solutions, a dark green solution is obtained from which ethanol precipitates a purple salt. The latter is believed to have a Co—Co bond and to be $K_6[Co_2(CN)_{10}]$. The green solution unquestionably contains the 5-coordinate ion $[Co(CN)_5]^{2-}$ probably in equilibrium with a small concentration of $[Co(CN)_4]^{2-}$. The solution absorbs molecular hydrogen giving the yellow hydrido ion $[HCo^{III}(CN)_5]^{3-}$ but both this ion and the green ion are subject to further changes of a complicated nature on standing in solution. The solutions are of interest since they provide one of the more effective catalysts for the homogeneous hydrogenation of conjugated (but not non-conjugated) olefins, a reaction in which allylic intermediates (cf. page 782) are held to be involved.[10a] Other substances such as nitrobenzene and aldehydes can also be reduced. The cyanide also undergoes insertion reactions with C_2F_4, C_2H_2, O_2, SO_2 and $SnCl_2$ to give species[10b] such as $[(CN)_5Co(SnCl_2)Co(CN)_5]^{6-}$.

29-F-4. Electronic Structures, Spectra and Magnetism of Cobalt(II) Compounds

Octahedral Coordination. The Co^{II} ion, with the electron configuration d^7, may have for its ground state configuration in an octahedral ligand field either $t_{2g}^5 e_g^2$ in weaker fields or $t_{2g}^6 e_g$ in stronger fields. Figure 29-F-4 shows a portion of the energy level diagram for Co^{II} in an octahedral field. It is seen that at a sufficiently high value of the octahedral field a ^2E state originating in the ^2G state of the free ion will become the ground state. However, it can be estimated that rather high values of ligand field strength ($\Delta_0 \geq 15{,}000$ cm^{-1}) will be required, and thus low spin octahedral Co^{II} complexes can be expected only with ligands lying very far to the strong end of the spectrochemical series. Moreover, because a $t_{2g}^6 e_g$ configuration should give rise to a large Jahn–Teller distortion (page 685), a *truly* octahedral complex may not be expected. In actual fact, the situation is complicated and poorly understood. A few complexes which appear to be six-coordinate and which have one unpaired electron, have been reported, viz.,

[9] L. H. Vogt, Jr., H. M. Faigenbaum and S. E. Wiberley, *Chem. Rev.*, **63**, 269 (1963); J. A. Connor and E. A. V. Ebsworth, *Adv. Inorg. Chem. Radiochem.*, **6**, 279 (1964).

[10a] J. Kwiatek and J. K. Seyler, *J. Organomet. Chem.*, **3**, 421, 433 (1965).

[10b] A. A. Vlcek and F. Basolo, *Inorg. Chem.*, **5**, 156 (1966).

$[Co(NO_2)_6]^{4-}$, $[Co(diars)_3]^{2+}$ and $[Co(triars)_2]^{2+}$, but in no case has the structure been investigated in detail. In certain other cases, namely with the ligands CN^- and CH_3NC, simple "octahedral" complexes are not obtained. With CH_3NC two compounds of empirical formula $Co(CNH_3)_5(ClO_4)_2$

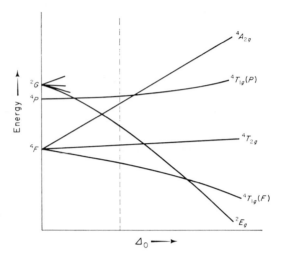

Fig. 29-F-4. A partial energy level diagram for a d^7 ion (e.g., Co^{II}) in an octahedral field. All of the quartet states are shown along with the $^2E_g(G)$ state which becomes the ground state in sufficiently high fields. The dashed line shows the position of Δ_0 for $[Co(H_2O)_6]^{2+}$.

can be obtained. One is yellow and diamagnetic and has been shown[11] to contain the dimeric cation $[(CH_3NC)_5Co—Co(CNCH_3)_5]^{4+}$, isostructural (and isoelectronic) with $Mn_2(CO)_{10}$ (page 725). The other compound, to which the yellow one changes in solution, is blue and has one unpaired electron. It is too unstable as a solid to permit structure determination, but it is presumably a five-coordinate complex. The cyanide complexes $K_6[Co_2(CN)_{10}]$ and $[Co(CN)_5]^{3-}$ mentioned above are presumably similar.

The high-spin octahedral compounds have magnetic moments ranging from 4.7 to 5.2 BM, that is, they have very high orbital contributions since the spin-only moment for three unpaired electrons is only 3.89 BM. This high orbital contribution is attributable to the three-fold orbital degeneracy of the $^4T_{1g}$ ground state, and can be understood quantitatively using detailed ligand field theory.

It will be seen from Figure 29-F-4 that an octahedrally coordinated Co^{II} ion should have three spin-allowed d–d transitions, those from the ground state, $^4T_1(F)$, to the states $^4T_{2g}$, $^4A_{2g}$ and $^4T_{1g}(P)$. The hexaquocobalt(II)

[11] F. A. Cotton, T. G. Dunne and J. S. Wood, *Inorg. Chem.*, **3**, 1495 (1964).

ion has the visible absorption shown as curve A in Figure 29-F-5. Note that the visible absorption is rather weak and placed in the blue part of the spectrum, thus accounting for the pale pink color of the aquocobalt(II) ion.

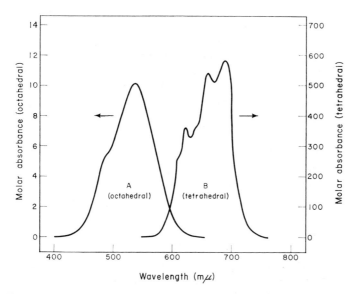

Fig. 29-F-5.   The visible spectra of $[Co(H_2O)_6]^{2+}$ (curve A) and $[CoCl_4]^{2-}$ (curve B). The molar absorbance scale at the left applies to curve A, and the one at the right applies to curve B.

The absorption band which is seen is due to the $^4T_{1g}(F) \rightarrow {}^4T_{1g}(P)$ transition, the shoulder on the high frequency side being a consequence of spin-orbit coupling in the $^4T_{1g}(P)$ state.   The $^4T_{1g}(F) \rightarrow {}^4T_{2g}$ transition occurs at 8350 cm^{-1} (1200 mμ, not shown in Figure 29-F-5).   Using these two assignments and the appropriate algebraic expressions for the energies of the quartet levels, it is calculated that the $^4T_{1g}(F) \rightarrow {}^4A_{2g}$ transition should occur at just slightly lower energy than the $^4T_{1g}(F) \rightarrow {}^4T_{1g}(P)$ band (~ 560 mμ).   However, since the $^4A_{2g}$ state is derived from a $t_{2g}^3 e_g^4$ configuration, while the $^4T_{1g}(F)$ state is derived in the main from the $t_{2g}^5 e_g^2$ configuration, the $^4T_{1g}(F) \rightarrow {}^4A_{2g}$ transition is essentially a two-electron process and for this reason it should be weaker (by $\sim 10^{-2}$) than the other transitions.   This weakness combined with the closeness of the $^4T_{1g}(F) \rightarrow {}^4T_{1g}(P)$ band results in the $^4T_{1g}(F) \rightarrow {}^4A_{2g}$ transition being unobserved.

Tetrahedral Coordination.   The energy level diagram for tetrahedral cobalt(II) is qualitatively the same as the one for octahedral Cr^{III} (see

Table 26-3), and this has already been given (Fig. 29-C-2). From this it follows that tetrahedral Co^{II} complexes must have high spin regardless of the strength of the ligand field. This same conclusion may, of course, be reached by a simple orbital occupancy argument.

Figure 29-F-5, curve B, shows the visible absorption spectrum of the $[CoCl_4]^{2-}$ ion, which is a representative tetrahedral species. Note that this absorption is placed in the red part of the spectrum and is very intense compared to the absorption of the $[Co(H_2O)_6]^{2+}$ ion. This accounts for the deep blue color of this and most other tetrahedral Co^{II} complexes. This absorption band is due to the transition from the $^4A_2$ ground state to the $^4T_1(P)$ state. The fine structure is caused by spin-orbit coupling which both splits the $^4T_1(P)$ state itself and allows the transitions to the neighboring doublet states to gain some intensity. The other transitions, $^4A_2 \rightarrow {}^4T_2$ and $^4A_2 \rightarrow {}^4T_1(F)$, lie outside of the visible region. The former lies around 3000–5000 cm^{-1} in most instances but is seldom observed since it is inherently weak due to an orbital selection rule, while the latter can generally be observed in the region 4000–8000 cm.[12]

Despite the fact that tetrahedral Co^{II} has a ground state, $^4A_2$, which has no inherent orbital angular momentum, magnetic moments considerably in excess of the spin-only value (3.89 BM), namely in the range 4.4 to 4.8 BM, are observed. An explanation of this was actually one of the earliest successes (Schlapp and Penney, 1932) of the crystal field theory. First order perturbation theory shows that spin-orbit coupling causes the $^4T_2$ state which is separated by Δ_t from the ground state to be mixed into the ground state, thus introducing orbital angular momentum, and making the actual magnetic moment, μ, greater than the spin-only moment, μ_{SO}. The quantitative expression is:

$$\mu = \mu_{SO} - \frac{15.59\lambda'}{\Delta_t} = 3.89 - \frac{15.59\lambda'}{\Delta_t}$$

λ' represents the effective value of the spin-orbit coupling constant in the complex (λ' is less than the free ion value, λ, see page 700) and is defined to be a negative quantity. Hence the correction to μ_{SO} is positive. Since λ' varies only a little from one complex to another, the magnitude of the orbital contribution is, approximately, an inverse function of Δ_t, that is of the position of the ligands in the spectrochemical series. Thus the magnetic moments for some CoX_4^{2-} complexes are as follows, where the X's are listed in their order in the spectrochemical series: CoI_4^{2-}, 4.77 BM; $CoBr_4^{2-}$, 4.69 BM; $CoCl_4^{2-}$, 4.59 BM; $Co(NCS)_4^{2-}$, 4.40 BM. Several other

---

[12] F. A. Cotton, D. M. L. Goodgame and M. Goodgame, *J. Amer. Chem. Soc.*, **83**, 4690 (1961).

common types of complexes, for example those of octahedral Cr^{III} and octahedral Ni^{II}, behave in the same way in principle, but because of the relatively large values of Δ_0 the pattern is less clearly shown.

Square and Tetragonal Complexes. Practically nothing is known in detail of the electronic structures of these complexes. All of the square complexes and the strongly tetragonal ones are of the low spin type, having one unpaired electron. However, there is a very large orbital contribution to the magnetic moment, so that the effective moments for these compounds around room temperature are in the range 2.4–2.8 BM. It may be noted that while the existence of high-spin square complexes of Co^{II} has been proposed and certain compounds so described, all such reports have later been found incorrect or unfounded.

29-F-5. Complexes of Cobalt(III), d^6

The complexes of cobalt(III) are exceedingly numerous. Because they generally undergo ligand exchange reactions slowly, but not too slowly, they have, from the days of Werner and Jørgensen, been extensively studied and a large fraction of our knowledge of the isomerism, modes of reaction and general properties of octahedral complexes as a class is based upon studies of Co^{III} complexes. All known Co^{III} complexes are octahedral, and a considerable number of representative ones have been mentioned in Chapter 5 as examples in general discussions. The Co^{III} and Cr^{III} complexes are very similar in many ways. Tetrahedral Co^{III} is known in one heteropolytungstate, however.

Co^{III} shows a particular affinity for nitrogen donors and the majority of its complexes contain ammonia, amines such as ethylenediamine, nitro groups, nitrogen-bonded SCN groups, as well as halide ions and water molecules. In general, these complexes are synthesized in several steps beginning with one in which the aquo Co^{II} ion is oxidized in solution, typically using molecular oxygen or hydrogen peroxide and often a surface active catalyst such as activated charcoal, in the presence of the ligands. For example, on drawing a vigorous stream of air for several hours through a solution of a cobalt(II) salt, CoX_2 (X = Cl, Br or NO_3), containing ammonia, the corresponding ammonium salt and some activated charcoal, good yields of the hexammine salts are obtained:

$$4CoX_2 + 4NH_4X + 20NH_3 + O_2 = 4[Co(NH_3)_6]X_3 + 2H_2O$$

In the absence of charcoal, substitution usually occurs to give, for example, $[Co(NH_3)_5Cl]^{2+}$ and $[Co(NH_3)_4(CO_3)]^+$. Similarly, on air oxidation of a solution of $CoCl_2$, ethylenediamine and an equivalent quantity of its

28*

hydrochloride salt, tris(ethylenediamine)cobalt(III) chloride is obtained.

$$4CoCl_2 + 8en + 4en \cdot HCl + O_2 = 4[Co(en)_3]Cl_3 + 2H_2O$$

However, a similar reaction in acid solution using the hydrochloride gives the green *trans*-dichlorobis(ethylenediamine)cobalt(III) ion as the salt *trans*-$[Coen_2Cl_2][H_5O_2]Cl_2$ which loses HCl on heating. This *trans* isomer may be isomerized to the red racemic *cis* isomer on evaporation of a neutral aqueous solution at 90–100°. Both the *cis* and *trans* isomers are aquated on heating in water.

$$[Co(en)_2Cl_2]^+ + H_2O = [Co(en)_2Cl(H_2O)]^{2+} + Cl^-$$
$$[Co(en)_2Cl(H_2O)]^{2+} + H_2O = [Co(en)_2(H_2O)_2]^{3+} + Cl^-$$

and on treatment with solutions of other anions are converted into other $[Co(en)_2X_2]^+$ species, for example,

$$[Co(en)_2Cl_2]^+ + 2NCS^- = [Co(en)_2(NCS)_2]^+ + 2Cl^-$$

These few reactions are illustrative of the very extensive chemistry of Co^{III} complexes with nitrogen-coordinating ligands.

In addition to the numerous mononuclear ammine complexes of Co^{III}, there are a number of polynuclear ammine complexes in which hydroxo (OH^-), peroxo (O_2^{2-}), amido (NH_2^-) and imido (NH^{2-}) groups function as bridges. Some typical complexes of this class are $[(NH_3)_5Co\!-\!O\!-\!O\!-\!Co(NH_3)_5]^{4+}$ (page 868), $[(NH_3)_3Co(OH)_3Co(OH)_3Co(NH_3)_3]^{3+}$ and $[(NH_3)_4Co(OH)\text{-}(NH_2)Co(NH_3)_4]^{4+}$.

An important Co^{III} complex which occurs in nature is vitamin B_{12}. This enzyme contains the cobalt ion in a porphyrin-like ring coordinated by four nitrogen atoms, with the fifth position in the octahedron filled by an adenine nitrogen. The sixth position is often filled by a CN^- ion, but the ligand occupying this position, which seems to be the active site of the enzyme, is variable[13] and in the coenzyme is an alkyl group. (See also discussion on page 787).

Some other Co^{III} complexes of significance are the hexacyano complex, $[Co(CN)_6]^{3-}$, the oxygen-coordinated complexes such as cobalt(III) acetylacetonate and salts of the tris(oxalato)cobalt(III) anion. There is some evidence that the so-called cobaltinitrite, $[Co(NO_2)_6]^{3-}$, is a mixture of nitrito and nitro species in solution.

29-F-6. Electronic Structures of Cobalt(III) Complexes

The free Co^{III} ion, d^6, has qualitatively the same energy level diagram as does Fe^{II} (see page 856). However, with Co^{III} the $^1A_{1g}$ state origin-

---

[13] R. Bonnett, *Chem. Rev.*, **63**, 573 (1963); J. M. Pratt and G. Thorp, *J. Chem. Soc.*, **1966A**, 187.

ating in one of the high energy singlet states of the free ion drops very rapidly and crosses the $^5T_{2g}$ state at a very low value of Δ. Thus all Co^{III} complexes known, including even $[Co(H_2O)_6]^{3+}$ and $[Co(NH_3)_6]^{3+}$, have diamagnetic ground states, with the one exception of $[CoF_6]^{3-}$, which is paramagnetic with four unpaired electrons.

The visible absorption spectra of Co^{III} complexes may thus be expected to consist of transitions from the $^1A_{1g}$ ground state to other singlet states. Although the entire energy level pattern for Co^{III} is not known in detail, the two absorption bands found in the visible spectra of regular octahedral Co^{III} complexes represent transitions to the upper states $^1T_{1g}$ and $^1T_{2g}$. In complexes of the type CoA_4B_2, which can exist in both *cis* and *trans* configurations, there are certain spectral features which are diagnostic of the *cis* or *trans* configurations, as shown in Figure 29-F-6. For a regular octa-

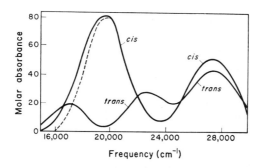

Fig. 29-F-6.   The visible spectra of *cis*- and *trans*-$[Co(en)_2F_2]^+$. The dotted line shows where the low frequency side of the $^1A_{1g} \rightarrow {}^1T_{1g}$ band of the *cis* isomer would be if the band were completely symmetrical. The asymmetry is caused by slight splitting of the $^1T_{1g}$ state.

hedral Co^{III} complex, for example, $[Co(en)_3]^{3+}$, the energy level diagram will be as in Figure 29-F-7b, and two absorption bands will be found in the visible at $\sim 20{,}000$ and $\sim 28{,}000$ cm^{-1}. When two of the six ligands are replaced by different ones, the lowering of the octahedral symmetry causes a splitting of the two upper states. Theory shows that the $^1T_{2g}$ state is not split observably, whereas the splitting of the $^1T_{1g}$ state should be at least twice as great for the *trans* compound as for the *cis*. These results are indicated in Figure 29-F-7a and Figure 29-F-7c. Moreover, because the *cis* isomer lacks a center of symmetry, it may be expected that if there is any difference in the intensities of absorption in the two isomers the greater intensity will be found in the *cis* isomer. It will be seen in Figure 29-F-6 that qualitatively these predictions are nicely borne out by the spectra of *cis*- and *trans*-$[Co(en)_2F_2]^+$. More extensive studies have shown that so long as the two ligands, A and B, in complexes of the types $[CoA_4B_2]$ and $[CoA_3B_3]$, which also form *cis* and *trans* isomers, differ somewhat in their positions in the spectrochemical series, behavior of this kind is observed. Thus spectra provide a useful criterion for identifying *cis* and *trans* isomers of Co^{III} complexes.

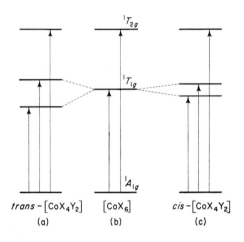

Fig. 29-F-7.   Diagrammatic representation (not to scale) of the energy levels involved in the transitions responsible for observed absorption bands of octahedral Co^{III} complexes.   In the center, (b), are the levels for a regular octahedral complex, $[CoX_6]$.   In (a) and (c) the splittings caused by the replacement of two ligands X by two ligands Y are indicated.

29-F-7. Tetravalent Cobalt, d^5

Compounds in this class are few and on the whole not well characterized. It has been reported that fluorination of Cs_2CoCl_4 gives Cs_2CoF_6, with a crystal structure isomorphous to that of Cs_2SiF_6 and a magnetic moment of 2.9 BM.   The latter value is difficult to explain, however, since the Co^{IV} ion would be expected to have either one or five unpaired electrons and the compound can be regarded as needing further characterization.   The action of powerful oxidizing agents (e.g., Cl_2) on strongly alkaline Co^{II} solutions produces a material believed to be hydrous CoO_2, at least in part, but it is ill characterized. Ba_2CoO_4, a red-brown substance obtained by oxidation of $2Ba(OH)_2$ and $2Co(OH)_2$ at $1050°$ and a heteropolymolybdate of Co^{IV}, namely, $3K_2O \cdot CoO_2 \cdot 9MoO_3 \cdot 6\frac{1}{2}H_2O$, have been reported but not further investigated.   It would appear at present that Co^{IV} is too unstable to have any very extensive chemistry.

29-F-8. Complexes of Cobalt(I), d^8

Only a few of these are known, and all involve π-acid type ligands. The characteristic coordination number of Co^I seems to be 5, and all available evidence indicates that the trigonal bipyramid is the preferred coordination polyhedron. However, in a few cases octahedral and square pyramidal complexes are also formed. Cobalt carbonyl reacts with isonitriles, disproportionating to Co^I and Co^{-I}:

$$Co_2(CO)_8 + 5RNC = [Co(CNR)_5]^+[Co(CO)_4]^- + 4CO$$

The ionic nature of the product, as indicated in this equation, is confirmed by the preparation of the same substance by the following reaction:

$$Na[Co(CO)_4] + [Co(CNR)_5]ClO_4 = [Co(CNR)_5][Co(CO)_4] + NaClO_4$$

Various salts of the $[Co(CNR)_5]^+$ cations, such as the perchlorate used above, can be prepared by the action of an excess of isonitrile on a Co^{II} salt or by first preparing the $Co(CNR)_4X_2$ compound and then reducing it with RNC or another reducing agent such as N_2H_4, $S_2O_4^{2-}$ or an active metal. In the case of $[Co(CNCH_3)_5]ClO_4$ the cation has been shown to be TBP.[14]

In polar solvents and at elevated temperatures triphenylphosphine reacts with cobalt carbonyl to give the cation $[Co(CO)_3(Ph_3P)_2]^+$ in the following disproportionation reaction:

$$Co_2(CO)_8 + 2Ph_3P = [Co(CO)_3(Ph_3P)_2]^+[Co(CO)_4]^- + CO$$

However, at a low temperature ($\sim 0°$) in nonpolar solvents a genuine substituted cobalt carbonyl, $[Co_2(CO)_6(Ph_3P)_2]$, is produced. $[Co(CO)_3-(Ph_3P)_2]^+$ has been shown by infrared study to be TBP with the phosphines occupying the apical positions.

The reduction of $[Cophen_3](ClO_4)_2$ with borohydride in ethanol at $-5°$ produces $[Cophen_3]ClO_4$.[15]

The melon-shaped phosphite, $P(OCH_2)_3CCH_3$, which has good π acidity, affords several Co^I compounds. On reaction with Co^{II} perchlorate, a disproportionation occurs giving $[Co^{III}L_6](ClO_4)_3$ and $[Co^IL_5]ClO_4$, where L represents the phosphite ligand. $[Co^IL_5]NO_3$ has also been prepared. Both are yellow diamagnetic solids and 1:1 electrolytes.[16]

Finally, there are several cases in which Co^{II} complexes add NO to form substances conventionally formulated as NO^+—Co^I complexes. Examples are $Co(S_2CNEt_2)_2NO$, where a square-pyramidal structure has been established by X-ray work, and $Co(acac)_2NO$.

[14] F. A. Cotton, T. G. Dunne and J. S. Wood, *Inorg. Chem.*, **4**, 318 (1965).
[15] N. Maki, M. Yamagami and H. Itatani, *J. Amer. Chem. Soc.*, **86**, 514 (1964).
[16] J. G. Verkade, *et al.*, *Inorg. Chem.*, **4**, 950 (1965) and references therein.

It has also been reported that Co^{II} is reduced by CO in strongly alkaline solution containing CN^- to give $[Co(CN)_3CO]^{2-}$:

$$2Co^{2+} + 3CO + 6CN^- + 4OH^- = 2[Co(CN)_3CO]^{2-} + CO_3^{2-} + 2H_2O$$

29-G. NICKEL

The trend toward decreased stability of higher oxidation states continues with nickel so that only Ni^{II} occurs in the ordinary chemistry of the element, although Ni^{III} and Ni^{IV} occur in certain oxide systems and in a few complexes.   Nickel(0) and Ni^I compounds are also scarce.   However, despite the fact that only one oxidation state occurs commonly, the chemistry of nickel is not simple because of the existence of complex inter-conversions of various structures, i.e., octahedral, tetrahedral and square, as well as the formation of polymers by sharing of ligand atoms.

The oxidation states and stereochemistry of nickel are summarized in Table 29-G-1.

TABLE 29-G-1

Oxidation States and Stereochemistry of Nickel

Oxidation state	Coordination number	Geometry	Examples
Ni^{-I}	4 ?	?	$[Ni_2(CO)_6]^{2-}$
Ni^0	4	Tetrahedral	$Ni(PF_3)_4$, $[Ni(CN)_4]^{4-}$, $Ni(CO)_4$
Ni^I, d^9	4 ?	?	$K_4[Ni_2(CN)_6]$
Ni^{II}, d^8	4[a]	Square	$NiBr_2(PEt_3)_2$, $[Ni(CN)_4]^{2-}$
	4[a]	Tetrahedral	$NiCl_4^{2-}$, $NiCl_2(PPh_3)_2$
	5	Square pyramid(?)	$[Ni(CN)_5]^{3-}$
	5	TBP	$[NiX(QAS)]^+$, $[NiP\{CH_2CH_2\text{-}CH_2AsMe_2\}_3CN]^+$
	6[a]	Octahedral	NiO, $[Ni(NCS)_6]^{4-}$, $KNiF_3$ $Ni(DMGH)_2$,[b] $[Ni(dipy)_3]^{2+}$
	6	Trigonal prism	NiAS
Ni^{III}, d^7	?	?	$Ni_2O_3 \cdot 2H_2O$
	5	TBP	$NiBr_3(PEt_3)_2$
	6	Octahedral	$[Ni(diars)_2Cl_2]^+$
Ni^{IV}, d^6	6	Octahedral	K_2NiF_6, $[Ni(diars)_2Cl_2]^{2+}$

[a] Most common state.
[b] Square set of nitrogen atoms about Ni with long Ni—Ni bonds.

29-G-1. The Element

Nickel occurs in nature mainly in combination with arsenic, antimony and sulfur, for example, as *millerite*, NiS, red nickel ore which is mainly NiAs, as well as in deposits consisting chiefly of $NiSb$, $NiAs_2$, NiAsS or

NiSbS. The most important deposits commercially are *garnierite*, a magnesium–nickel silicate of variable composition, and certain varieties of the iron mineral *pyrrhotite* (Fe_nS_{n+1}) which contain 3–5% Ni. Elemental nickel is also found alloyed with iron in many meteors, and the central regions of the earth are believed to contain considerable quantities. The metallurgy of nickel is complicated in its details, many of which vary a good deal with the particular ore being processed. In general, the ore is transformed to Ni_2S_3 which is roasted in air to give NiO, and this is then reduced with carbon to give the metal. Some high purity nickel is made by the *carbonyl process*. Carbon monoxide reacts with impure nickel at 50° and ordinary pressure or with nickel–copper matte under more strenuous conditions, giving volatile $Ni(CO)_4$, from which metal of 99.90–99.99% purity is obtained on thermal decomposition at 200°.

Nickel is silver-white with typically metallic properties. It has high electrical and thermal conductivities (both ~15% of those of silver), m 1452°, and it can be drawn, rolled, forged and polished. It is quite resistant to attack by air or water at ordinary temperatures when compact and is therefore often electroplated as a protective coating. It is also ferromagnetic but not so much as iron. The finely divided metal is reactive to air, and it may be pyrophoric under some conditions.

The metal is moderately electropositive,

$$Ni^{2+} + 2e = Ni \qquad E^0 = -0.25 \text{ v}$$

and dissolves readily in dilute mineral acids. Like iron, it does not dissolve in concentrated nitric acid because it is rendered passive by this reagent.

29-G-2. The Chemistry of Divalent Nickel, d^8

In the divalent state nickel forms a very extensive series of compounds. This is the only oxidation state of importance in the aqueous chemistry of nickel, and, with the exception of a few special complexes of nickel in other oxidation states, Ni^{II} is also the only important oxidation level in its non-aqueous chemistry.

Binary Compounds. *Nickel(II) oxide* is a green solid, which has the rock salt structure. It is formed on heating the hydroxide, carbonate, oxalate or nitrate of nickel(II). It is insoluble in water but dissolves readily in acids.

The *hydroxide*, $Ni(OH)_2$, may be precipitated from aqueous solutions of Ni^{II} salts on addition of alkali metal hydroxides as a voluminous green gel which becomes crystalline on prolonged standing. It is readily soluble in acid ($K_{SP} = 2 \times 10^{-16}$) and also in aqueous ammonia owing to the formation of ammine complexes. The crystalline substance is a definite hydroxide which, like the other hydroxides of divalent metals of the first transition series, has the $Mg(OH)_2$ structure. $Ni(OH)_2$ has little or no amphoteric tendency, and no nickelate(II) species of any kind have been reported.

Addition of sulfide ions to aqueous solutions of nickel(II) ions precipitates black NiS. This is initially freely soluble in acid, but, like CoS, on exposure to air it soon becomes insoluble due to oxidation to $Ni(OH)S$.

All four nickel *halides* are known in the anhydrous state. Except for the fluoride, which is best made by heating the double salt $(NH_4)_2NiF_4$, they can be prepared by direct reaction of the elements. All of the halides are soluble in water (the fluoride only moderately so), and from aqueous solutions they can be crystallized as the hexahydrates, except for the fluoride which gives $NiF_2 \cdot 3H_2O$. Lower hydrates are obtained from these on standing or on heating.

On addition of CN^- ions to aqueous Ni^{II} the *cyanide* is precipitated in a green hydrated form. On heating at 180–200° the hydrate is converted to the yellow-brown, anhydrous $Ni(CN)_2$. The green precipitate readily redissolves in excess cyanide to form the yellow $[Ni(CN)_4]^{2-}$ ion, and many hydrated salts of this ion, for example, $Na_2[Ni(CN)_4] \cdot 3H_2O$, may be crystallized from such solutions. In strong cyanide solutions a further CN^- is taken up to give the red $[Ni(CN)_5]^{3-}$ ion, but this weak complex exists only in solutions, attempts to precipitate the ion giving only $[Ni(CN)_4]^{2-}$ salts; infrared studies[1] indicate that it is square pyramidal (C_{4v}). Nickel(II) thiocyanate is also known, as a yellow-brown (probably hydrated) precipitate obtained on concentrating the green solutions resulting from the reaction:

$$NiSO_4(aq) + Ba(SCN)_2(aq) = BaSO_4(s) + Ni(SCN)_2(aq)$$

It reacts with excess SCN^- to form complex ions, $[Ni(NCS)_4]^{2-}$ and $[Ni(NCS)_6]^{4-}$, which can be isolated in crystalline complexes.

Other Binary Nickel (II) Compounds. A number of binary nickel compounds, probably all containing Ni^{II} but not all stoichiometric, may be obtained by direct reaction of nickel with various nonmetals such as P, As, Sb, S, Se, Te, C and B. Nickel appears to form a nitride Ni_3N. The existence of a hydride is uncertain, although the finely divided metal absorbs hydrogen in considerable amounts.

Salts of Oxo Acids. A large number of these are known. They occur most commonly as hydrates, for example, $Ni(NO_3)_2 \cdot 6H_2O$, $NiSO_4 \cdot 7H_2O$, and most of them are soluble in water. Exceptions are the carbonate,

---

[1] J. S. Coleman, H. Petersen, Jr., and R. A. Penneman, *Inorg. Chem.*, **4**, 135 (1965).

$NiCO_3 \cdot 6H_2O$, which precipitates on addition of alkali bicarbonates to solutions of Ni^{II}, and the phosphate, $Ni_3(PO_4)_2 \cdot 7(?)H_2O$.

The Hexaquonickel(II) Ion. Aqueous solutions of Ni^{II} not containing strong complexing agents contain the green hexaquonickel(II) ion, $[Ni(H_2O)_6]^{2+}$. This ion also occurs in a number of hydrated nickel(II) salts, for example in $Ni(NO_3)_2 \cdot 6H_2O$, $NiSO_4 \cdot 6H_2O$, $NiSO_4 \cdot 7H_2O$, $Ni(ClO_4)_2 \cdot 6H_2O$, but not in $NiCl_2 \cdot 6H_2O$ which contains instead *trans*-$[NiCl_2(H_2O)_4]$ units. The aquo ion is quite labile as are nickel(II) complexes in general.

29-G-3. Stereochemistry and Electronic Structures of Nickel(II) Complexes

Nickel(II) forms a large number of complexes, the main structural types being octahedral, tetrahedral or square. However, it is characteristic of Ni^{II} complexes that complicated equilibria, which are generally temperature dependent and sometimes concentration dependent, often exist between these structural types. In this section we shall describe the characteristics of the octahedral, tetrahedral and square complexes separately, using as examples mainly those compounds which exist completely or practically completely in one form or another. In the next section we shall describe the configurational equilibria of the three major forms which account for most of the so-called "anomalous" behavior of Ni^{II} complexes.

Octahedral Complexes. The maximum coordination number of nickel(II) is 6. A considerable number of neutral ligands, especially amines, displace some or all of the water molecules in the octahedral $[Ni(H_2O)_6]^{2+}$ ion to form complexes such as *trans*-$[Ni(H_2O)_2(NH_3)_4](NO_3)_2$, $[Ni(NH_3)_6]$-$(ClO_4)_2$, $[Ni(en)_3]SO_4$, etc. Such ammine complexes characteristically have blue or purple colors in contrast to the bright green color of the hexaquonickel ion. This is because of shifts in the absorption bands when H_2O ligands are replaced by others lying toward the stronger end of the spectrochemical series. This can be seen in Figure 29-G-1, where the spectra of $[Ni(H_2O)_6]^{2+}$ and $[Ni(en)_3]^{2+}$ are shown. These spectra can readily be interpreted by referring to the energy level diagram for d^8 ions (Fig. 26-14, page 678). It is seen that three spin-allowed transitions are expected, and the three observed bands in each spectrum may thus be assigned as shown in Table 29-G-2. It is a characteristic feature of the spectra of octahedral nickel(II) complexes, exemplified by those of $[Ni(H_2O)_6]^{2+}$ and $[Ni(en)_3]^{2+}$, that molar absorbances of the bands are at the low end of the range (1–100) for octahedral complexes of the first transition series in general, namely, between 1 and 10. The splitting of the middle band in the $[Ni(H_2O)_6]^{2+}$ spectrum is due to spin-orbit coupling which mixes the $^3T_{1g}(F)$ and ^1E_g

TABLE 29-G-2

Spectra of Octahedral Nickel(II) Complexes

(Approximate band positions in cm^{-1})

Transition	$[Ni(H_2O)_6]^{2+}$	$[Ni(en)_3]^{2+}$
$^3A_{2g} \rightarrow {}^3T_{2g}$	9000	11,000
$^3A_{2g} \rightarrow {}^3T_{1g}(F)$	14,000	18,500
$^3A_{2g} \rightarrow {}^3T_{1g}(P)$	25,000	30,000

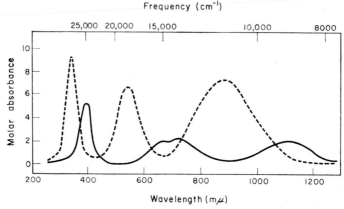

Fig. 29-G-1. Absorption spectra of $[Ni(H_2O)_6]^{2+}$ (———) and $[Ni(en)_3]^{2+}$ (– – – – – –).

states which are very close in energy at the Δ_0 value given by $6H_2O$, whereas in the stronger field of the 3en they are so far apart that no significant mixing occurs.

Magnetically, octahedral nickel(II) complexes have relatively simple behavior. From both the simple d-orbital splitting diagram (page 669) and the energy level diagram (page 678), it follows that all of them should have two unpaired electrons, and this is found always to be the case, the magnetic moments ranging from 2.9 to 3.4 BM depending on the magnitude of the orbital contribution. One possible exception to the above rule is the diamagnetic $[Ni(diars)_3]^{2+}$. It is possible that in an extremely intense ligand field, such as this ligand might give, a singlet level originating in a Russell–Saunders state of a d^7s or d^7p configuration could drop down and become the ground state.

Five Coordinate Complexes. There are a number of these known for Ni^{II} with polydentate ligands such as $N[CH_2CH_2NMe_2]_3$,[2a] $P(CH_2CH_2CH_2AsMe_2)_3$ or $P(o\text{-}C_6H_4SMe)_3(TSP)$. The latter, for example,[2b] gives

[2a] M. Ciampolini, et al., Inorg. Chem., **5**, 35, 41, 45 (1966).
[2b] G. Dyer and D. W. Meek, Inorg. Chem., **4**, 1398 (1965) and references therein.

complexes of the type $[NiTSPX]^+ (X = Cl, Br, I, CNS)$ and $[NiTSPL]^{2+}$, $(L = PPh_3, PPh_2Me$ or thiourea); they are diamagnetic and have characteristic electronic spectra. The stereochemistry appears to be trigonal bipyramidal and X-ray studies have confirmed this in two cases.

Tetrahedral Complexes. The literature prior to about 1959 contains very little reliable information on such compounds. However, since then the preparation and positive identification of tetrahedral complexes have been reported frequently. There are several stoichiometric classes, the main ones being NiX_4^{2-}, NiL_3X^-, NiL_2X_2 and $Ni(L—L)_2$, where X represents a halogen, L a neutral ligand such as an amine, phosphine, arsine, phosphine oxide or arsine oxide and L—L represents a uninegative, bidentate chelate such as a salicylaldiminato ion, with a very bulky N-substituent.[3a] There are three identifying characteristics of tetrahedral nickel(II) complexes.[3b]

First, there are two features of their spectra. Practically all tetrahedral complexes have a rather intense blue color due to the presence of an absorption band in the red part of the visible region. This may be seen in the spectrum of $[Ni(Ph_3AsO)_2Br_2]$ (Fig. 29-G-2). There is also a second absorption band around 7000–8000 cm^{-1}. A simple energy level diagram for a d^8 ion in a tetrahedral field is given in Figure 29-G-3. The visible absorption band, at $\sim 15,000$ cm^{-1} is assigned to the $T_1(F) \rightarrow T_1(P)$ transition, the one at 7000–8000 cm^{-1} to the $T_1(F) \rightarrow A_2$ transition. The occasional appearance of a green or even red color in a tetrahedral nickel(II) complex is attributable to charge transfer absorption tailing into the visible region from the ultraviolet; it has been observed mainly in those complexes having coordinated iodide or bromide ions. The splitting of the visible band is caused by spin-orbit coupling which lifts the degeneracy of the $T_1(P)$ state.

The second feature of the spectra of tetrahedral nickel(II) complexes is the relatively high intensities of the absorption bands. We have already noted that for octahedral complexes the bands have molar absorbances at the peaks of only 1–10 whereas tetrahedral complexes typically have molar absorbances of ~ 200 at the peak of the visible band.

The final distinguishing characteristic of tetrahedral nickel(II) complexes is the common occurrence of very high orbital contributions to their magnetic moments. It can be shown (page 671) that a d^8 system in a tetrahedral field must have two unpaired electrons, however strong the field. Although octahedral and high-spin tetragonal complexes have moments between 2.83 (the spin-only value) and ~ 3.4 BM, theory shows

[3a] See, e.g., L. Sacconi, M. Ciampolini and U. Campigli, *Inorg. Chem.*, **4**, 407 (1965).
[3b] D. M. L. Goodgame, M. Goodgame and F. A. Cotton, *J. Amer. Chem. Soc.*, **83**, 4161 (1961).

that a regular tetrahedral complex with four identical ligands should have a moment between 3.5 and 4.2 BM. This is because in octahedral and square complexes the ground state does not have orbital degeneracy, and the orbital contribution arises from a second-order process, whereas (Fig.

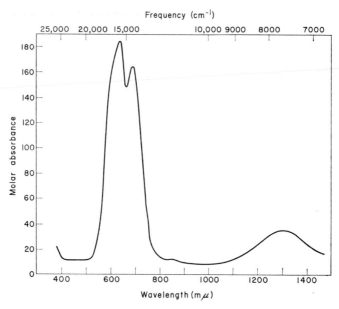

Fig. 29-G-2.   The visible and near-infrared absorption spectrum of a typical tetrahedral complex of nickel(II), [Ni(Ph₃AsO)₂Br₂].

29-G-3) tetrahedral complexes have orbitally degenerate ground states and an orbital contribution to the magnetic moment is, as it were, built in. In agreement with this expectation, those tetrahedral complexes in which the ligands are all identical or come close together in the spectrochemical series (e.g., the halide ions and Ph_3PO or Ph_3AsO) have moments of 3.7–4.0 BM. In those complexes containing ligands which are well separated in the spectrochemical series (e.g., Ph_3P and halide or NO^+ and OH^-), the degeneracy of the ground state is lost, and only second-order orbital contributions are possible. Such tetrahedral complexes thus have moments in the same lower range as those of octahedral ones.

Planar Complexes.   As shown on page 672, a square complex of nickel(II) may be diamagnetic or have two unpaired electrons depending on whether the energy separation of the two uppermost d orbitals is greater or less than the energy necessary to cause electron pairing. This separation in the energies of the uppermost d orbitals is determined by the nature of the four ligands and by the degree to which surrounding molecules—either solvent molecules or others in a crystal lattice—contribute to the ligand field by approaching the nickel atom along the two ends of the axis passing through the nickel atom and perpendicular to the plane of the other four ligand atoms.

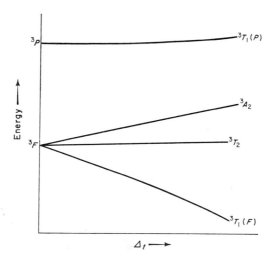

Fig. 29-G-3. Diagram showing the triplet levels of a d^8 ion (e.g., Ni^{II}) in a tetrahedral field.

Experimental data indicate that only in the presence of two additional molecules which are relatively good donors does the energy separation become small enough to give a paramagnetic complex. In short, all *truly square*, that is four-coordinate complexes of nickel(II) are of the low-spin (diamagnetic) type. They are frequently red, yellow or brown in color due to the presence of an absorption band of medium intensity ($\epsilon \approx 60$) in the range 450–600 mμ. In many cases, other bands also occur in the visible region so that green or blue colors result. The interpretation of the spectra and detailed accounting of the electronic energy levels of the square complexes has been undertaken,[4] but significant uncertainties still remain. Deviations from strict diamagnetism or changes in color are generally indicative of one of the types of so-called anomalous behavior which will be discussed in the next section.

Some representative square complexes are the well-known pale orange $[Ni(CN)_4]^{2-}$, the deep red bis(dimethylglyoximato)nickel(II), 29-G-I, the red β-ketonenolate complex shown as 29-G-II, *some* N-alkyl salicylaldiminato complexes, 29-G-III, *some* NiL_2X_2 complexes (in which L is an

---

[4] H. B. Gray and C. J. Ballhausen, *J. Amer. Chem. Soc.*, **85**, 260 (1963).

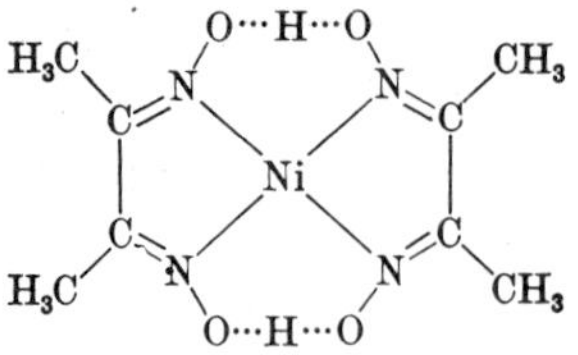

(29-G-I)

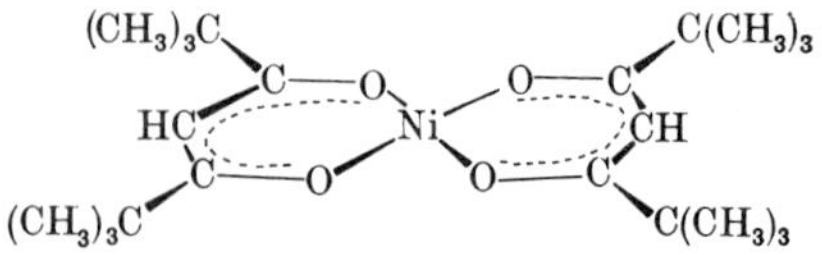

(29-G-II)

amine, phosphine or arsine) and some bis-chelate complexes in which the ligands are substituted ethylenediamines such as N,N,N',N'-tetramethylethylenediamine or the stilbenediamine shown as 29-G-IV. It will be

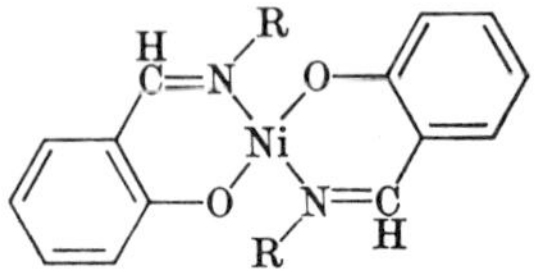

(29-G-III)

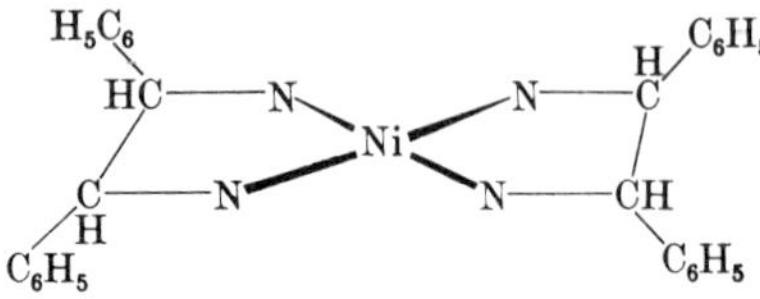

(29-G-IV)

noted that several types of complexes in this list, e.g., NiL_2X_2 and N-salicylaldiminato complexes, were also mentioned earlier as sometimes having tetrahedral structures. This relationship will be developed in the next section.

29-G-4. The So-called Anomalous Behavior of Nickel(II) Complexes

A considerable number of nickel(II) complexes do not behave entirely or under all conditions according to expectation for any *one* of the three structural types described above. Therefore they have in the past been described as anomalous, but in recent years, with the advent of ligand field theory and the wide spread use of powerful physical methods such as X-ray structure determination, most of the "anomalies" have been satisfactorily explained. There are three main forms of structural variation which embrace nearly all recognized types of "anomalous" behavior, and each of these will now be described and illustrated. A few other phenomena of infrequent occurrence will be omitted from this discussion.

1. Formation of Octahedral Complexes by Addition of Ligands to Square Ones. For any square complex, NiL_4, the following equilibrium with additional ligands, L', may exist:

$$NiL_4 + 2L' = trans\text{-}NiL_4L_2'$$

In many cases, where L' represents a very good donor such as pyridine, H_2O or C_2H_5OH, such equilibria lie far to the right and the six-coordinate complexes may be isolated as pure crystalline compounds. Thus, the complex 29-G-II is normally prepared in the presence of water and/or alcohol and is first isolated as the green, paramagnetic dihydrate or dialcoholate, from which the red, square complex is then obtained by heating to drive off the H_2O or C_2H_5OH. Similarly, various diamagnetic, square complexes of the salicylaldiminato type, 29-G-III, become paramagnetic to the degree expected for the presence of two unpaired electrons when dissolved in pyridine, and the dipyridinates can be isolated as stable, paramagnetic, octahedral complexes. There are, however, cases in which solutions of square complexes attain only a fraction of the paramagnetism expected for complete conversion to octahedral species, thus indicating that the above equilibrium reaction proceeds only part way to the right.

Well-known examples of the square–octahedral ambivalence are provided by the Lifschitz salts, which are complexes of nickel(II) with substituted ethylenediamines, especially the stilbenediamines, one of which is illustrated in 29-G-IV. Many years ago, Lifschitz and others observed that such complexes were sometimes blue and paramagnetic and other times yellow and diamagnetic depending upon many factors, such as temperature, identity of the anions present, the solvent in which they are dissolved or from which they were crystallized, exposure to atmospheric water vapor and the particular diamine involved. The bare experimental facts—the complicated "tale of the blue and the yellow"—bewildered chemists for several decades and many hypotheses were promulgated in an effort to explain some or all of the facts. It is now believed that all of the yellow species are square complexes, as typified by 29-G-IV, while the blue ones are octahedral complexes, derived from the square ones by coordination of two additional ligands—solvent molecules, water molecules or anions— above and below the plane of the square complex. This view is supported by spectral and magnetic data [5a] and by X-ray results.[5b]

One of the compounds studied by X-rays, a yellow form of bis(*meso*-stilbenediamine)nickel(II) dichloroacetate, was found to contain both square, diamagnetic entities (29-G-IV) and octahedral ones in which the octahedra are completed by oxygen atoms of the $CHCl_2COO^-$ ions, in a 1:2 ratio.

It is in principle possible that the degree of tetragonality achieved by adding two ligands near the weak end of the spectrochemical series to a square complex in which the four ligand atoms lie nearer the strong end of the series might lead to a situation in which the energy difference between the high-spin and low-spin states would be about equal to thermal energies at or near room temperature. In such a case, the magnetism and spectrum

[5a] W. C. E. Higginson, S. C. Nyburg and J. S. Wood, *Inorg. Chem.*, **3**, 463 (1964).
[5b] S. C. Nyburg and J. S. Wood, *Inorg. Chem.*, **3**, 468 (1964).

should depend on temperature according to a relationship derivable from the Boltzmann distribution law. It has been reported[6] that the compound Ni(N,N'-diethylthiourea)$_4$Cl$_2$ exemplifies this situation.

2. Monomer–Polymer Equilibria. In many cases, four-coordinate complexes associate or polymerize, to give species in which the nickel ions become five- or six-coordinate. In some cases, the association is very strong and the four-coordinate monomers are observed only at high temperatures, while in others, the position of the equilibrium is such that both red, diamagnetic monomers and green or blue, paramagnetic polymers are present in a temperature- and concentration-dependent equilibrium around room temperature.

One of the clearest examples of this situation is provided by various β-ketoenolate complexes. When the β-ketoenolate is the acetylacetonate ion, the trimeric structure shown in Figure 29-G-4 is adopted. As a result

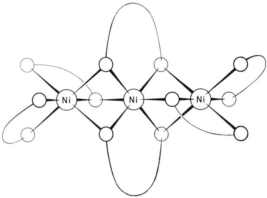

Fig. 29-G-4. Sketch indicating the trimeric structure of nickel acetylacetonate. (J. G. Bullen, R. Mason and P. Pauling, *Inorg. Chem.*, **4**, 456 (1965).) The unlabeled circles represent oxygen atoms, and the curved lines connecting them in pairs represent the remaining portions of the acetylacetonate rings. This structure may be compared with that of [Co(acac)$_2$]$_4$ shown on page 567.

of the sharing of some oxygen atoms, each nickel atom achieves octahedral coordination; the situation is comparable to, but different in its details, from that found for [Co(acac)$_2$]$_4$. This trimer is very stable and only at temperatures around 200° (in a non-coordinating solvent) do detectable quantities of monomer appear. It is, however, readily cleaved by donors such as H$_2$O or pyridine, to give six-coordinate monomers.

It can be seen from inspection of a scale model of the trimer that replacement of the methyl groups of the acetylacetonate rings by very bulky groups, such as tertiary butyl groups, should completely prevent formation

[6] S. L. Holt, Jr., R. J. Bouchard and R. L. Carlin, *J. Amer. Chem. Soc.*, **86**, 519 (1964).

of the trimer because of steric repulsion, and it is for precisely this reason that 29-G-II is a diamagnetic, square monomer under all known conditions. It is interesting to note that the related tetramer of $Co(acac)_2$ is also destroyed when the CH_3 groups are replaced by $—C(CH_3)_3$ groups, but in this case the monomers obtained are tetrahedral.

The most interesting situation results when the methyl groups of $[Ni(acac)_2]_3$ are replaced by groups of intermediate size such as $CH(CH_3)_2$ or when the hydrogen atom of the central carbon atom of the ring is replaced by a phenyl group.[7]   In these circumstances, the degree of steric hindrance is such as to interfere partially but not completely with the formation of the trimer, and the spectral and magnetic behavior of the compounds when dissolved in noncoordinating solvents is a function of temperature and concentration.

There are various other cases in which monomer–polymer equilibria are known to be responsible for "anomalous" behavior, though these systems are not understood in such detail as are the β-ketoenol ones. Some important examples are provided by the salicylaldiminato systems, 29-G-III, in which R = H, OH or one of a number of primary alkyl groups. It has been suggested that in these cases the polymers are dimers in which each nickel ion is five-coordinate.

3. Square–Tetrahedral Equilibria and Isomerism. We have already indicated that nickel(II) complexes of certain stoichiometric types, namely the bishalo–bisphosphino and bis-salicylaldiminato types may have either square or tetrahedral structures, depending on the identity of the ligands. For example, in the NiL_2X_2 cases, when L is triphenylphosphine, tetrahedral structures are found, whereas the complexes with trialkyl phosphines generally give square complexes. Perhaps it is then not very surprising that a number of NiL_2X_2 complexes in which L represents a mixed alkyl–aryl phosphine exist in solution in an equilibrium distribution between the tetrahedral and square forms.[8] Moreover, in some cases[9] it is possible to isolate two crystalline forms of the compound, one yellow to red and diamagnetic, the other green or blue with two unpaired electrons. There is even a case, $Ni[(C_6H_5CH_2)(C_6H_5)_2P]_2Br_2$, in which both tetrahedral and square complexes are found together in the same crystalline substance.[10] Since the square and tetrahedral structures of a complex differ chiefly in the angles subtended by ligand atoms at the metal atom, it has been proposed[10] that such isomers be called *allogons* (from *allos* meaning different and *gonia* meaning angle).

[7] F. A. Cotton and J. P. Fackler, Jr., *J. Amer. Chem. Soc.*, **83**, 2818, 3775 (1961).

[8] L. M. Venanzi, *et al.*, *J. Chem. Soc.*, **1961**, 4816; **1962**, 693.

[9] R. G. Hayter and F. S. Humiec, *Inorg. Chem.*, **4**, 1701 (1965).

[10] B. T. Kilbourn, H. M. Powell and J. A. C. Darbyshire, *Proc. Chem. Soc.*, **1963**, 207.

The most important and thoroughly examined examples of square–tetrahedral equilibria are provided by the salicylaldiminato complexes, 29-G-III, in which R is a secondary alkyl group[11] and the aminotropone-imine complexes,[12] 29-G-V. In the tetrahedral forms unpaired electron

(29-G-V)

spin density from the nickel atoms is introduced into the ligand π system, which results in large shifts in the positions of the various proton nuclear magnetic resonances. The various shifts are in proportion to the spin density at the carbon atom to which the proton is attached, so that from the nmr spectra much can be learned of the nature of the π orbitals into which the spin density is introduced. Such studies have therefore proved to be very important in respect to the electronic structures of a wide variety of aromatic systems which can be attached to the basic ring systems of these complexes, but the detailed results[12b] are outside the scope of this book. However, in the course of these studies, the square–tetrahedral equilibria themselves have been studied carefully.

To a certain extent the position of the equilibrium is a function of steric factors, that is of the repulsion between the R groups on the nitrogen atoms of one ligand and various parts of the other ligand, the greater degree of repulsion encountered in the square configuration tending to shift the equilibrium to the tetrahedral side. However, some ring substituents affect the equilibrium by means of electronic effects as well. The ΔH values for the square–tetrahedral conversion are generally of the order of a few kilocalories per mole and are positive, meaning that the proportion of tetrahedral form increases with increasing temperature. In a few cases, however, when extremely bulky substituents are used, the equilibrium lies predominantly on the tetrahedral side. For example in the salicylaldiminato complex with R = t-butyl, ΔH is negative.

[11] R. H. Holm and K. Swaminathan, *Inorg. Chem.*, **2**, 181 (1963); for interconversions of tetrahedral and discrete octahedral species see also L. Sacconi, *et al.*, *Inorg. Chem.*, **4**, 818 (1965), A. Chakravorty, *et al.*, *Inorg. Chem.*, **4**, 26 (1965) and S. M. Nelson and T. M. Shepherd, *J. Chem. Soc.*, **1965**, 3284.

[12] (a) D. R. Eaton, W. D. Phillips and D. J. Caldwell, *J. Amer. Chem. Soc.*, **85**, 397 (1963). (b) D. R. Eaton and W. D. Phillips, *J. Chem. Phys.*, **43**, 392 (1965).

29-G-5. Higher Oxidation States of Nickel

Hydroxides and Oxides. There is no evidence for anhydrous oxides of Ni^{III} and Ni^{IV} but there are a number of hydrous oxides and mixed metal oxides, some of considerable complexity, which contain Ni^{III} and Ni^{IV}.

The best defined hydroxide is β-NiO(OH), which is obtained as a black powder by the oxidation of nickel(II) nitrate solutions with bromine in aqueous potassium hydroxide below 25°. It is readily soluble in acids; on aging, or by oxidation in hot solutions, a Ni^{II}–Ni^{III} hydroxide of stoichiometry $Ni_3O_2(OH)_4$ is obtained. The oxidation of strongly alkaline nickel nitrate solutions by peroxodisulfate gives a black oxide, "$NiO_2 \cdot nH_2O$" which is unstable, being readily reduced by water.

The electrochemical oxidation[13] of $Ni(OH)_2$ in alkaline solution gives a black oxide which does not have a unique stoichiometry and which retains alkali metal ions; its X-ray pattern is related to that of $LiNiO_2$. Further oxidation gives a grey metallic material which contains both Ni^{III} and Ni^{IV}.

The Edison or nickel–iron battery which operates using KOH as the electrolyte and which produces about 1.3 v, is based on the reaction

$$Fe + 2NiO(OH) + 2H_2O \xrightleftharpoons[\text{charge}]{\text{discharge}} Fe(OH)_2 + 2Ni(OH)_2$$

but the mechanism and the true nature of the oxidized nickel species are not fully understood.

There are also a variety of mixed oxides obtained in dry ways. Thus $LiNiO_2$ is made by bubbling oxygen through molten alkali metal hydroxides contained in nickel vessels at about 800°. Other oxides and oxide phases can be made by heating NiO with alkali or alkaline earth oxides in oxygen.[14] These mixed oxides evolve oxygen on treatment with water or acids.

Complexes of Tetravalent Nickel. There are not a great number of these, but several of those known are quite well characterized and establish beyond doubt that this oxidation state can be stabilized by appropriate coordination. Complexes in which the high oxidation state is stabilized by coordination with ions derived from highly electronegative elements are the purple heteropoly salt $3BaO \cdot NiO_2 \cdot 9MoO_3 \cdot 12H_2O$, the dark purple periodate $Na(K)NiIO_6 \cdot nH_2O$ and the red complex fluoride K_2NiF_6. The first and the last of these are diamagnetic, but the periodate complex shows weak paramagnetism (leading to a calculated magnetic moment of only ~ 1.2 BM), which is believed to be caused by impurities (e.g., Ni^{III}).

[13] D. Tuomi, *J. Electrochem. Soc.*, **112**, 1 (1965), and references therein.
[14] H. Bade, W. Bronger and W. Klemm, *Bull. Soc. Chim. France*, **1965**, 1124.

Diamagnetism in these cases can be attributed to d orbital splitting by octahedral fields sufficient to produce t_{2g}^6 ground state configurations. That this can happen even with F^- ions as ligands is not too surprising when it is recalled that the d^6 configuration seems especially prone to spin pairing (cf. Co^{III} complexes) and that the magnitudes of Δ values increase sharply with increasing positive charge of the cation (page 680).

Complexes of Trivalent Nickel. It has often been alleged that oxidation of four-coordinate Ni^{II} complexes produces Ni^{III} complexes, but in many cases, particularly with amine or oxime ligands, the available experimental data do not adequately support the claims. Oxidation of $[Ni(diars)_2Cl_2]$ by oxygen in presence of excess chloride ion gives a greenish yellow precipitate of $[Ni(diars)_2Cl_2]Cl$, which has been well characterized by various physical measurements, particularly by magnetic measurements which show the presence of one unpaired electron (~ 1.9 BM). Analogous bromide and thiocyanate complexes exist.

Similarly,[15] when certain complexes of the type $Ni(R_3P)_2X_2$ ($X = Cl, Br$) are treated with ClNO or BrNO, the compounds $Ni(R_3P)_2X_3$ are obtained. These are intensely colored substances, easily soluble in common organic liquids, which are monomeric in solution and have one unpaired electron. Since their electric dipole moments are effectively zero, they are believed to have symmetrical trigonal bipyramidal structures (D_{3h} symmetry).

29-G-6. Lower Oxidation States of Ni

The oxidation states $-I$, 0 and I are each represented; the compounds of Ni^0 are decidedly the most numerous. In all cases, however, the ligands involved are of the types with strong π-acid properties and thus the formal oxidation numbers should not be interpreted as having much physical significance.

The oxidation state $-I$ is represented by the carbonylate anion, $[Ni_2(CO)_6]^{2-}$, of unknown structure. There is also a carbonylate anion $[Ni_4(CO)_9]^{2-}$ in which the formal oxidation state of Ni is $-\frac{1}{2}$. This second case serves very well to emphasize that extensive delocalization of electrons and probably Ni—Ni bonds are important in such compounds, thus rendering the classification in terms of oxidation state a pure formality.

The Ni^0 complexes, apart from the organo derivatives which are described in Chapter 28, are all tetrahedral molecules in which the nickel atom is surrounded by four π-acid type ligands. The pre-eminent example is, of course, nickel carbonyl, $Ni(CO)_4$, which has been described in Chapter 27, along with various derivatives, $NiL_x(CO)_{4-x}$, and some analogous NiL_4

[15] K. A. Jensen, B. Nygaard and C. T. Pedersen, *Acta Chem. Scand.*, **17**, 1126 (1963).

molecules in which L is a strongly π-acidic ligand such as PF_3, PCl_3, $P(OCN)_3$ or $P(OR)_3$.[16]   There are also the anionic complexes found in copper-colored $K_4[Ni(CN)_4]$, which is obtained by treating $K_2[Ni(CN)_4]$ with excess potassium in liquid ammonia and the acetylide complex $K_4[Ni(C\equiv CH)_4]$.   Both of these are extremely unstable toward air and hydroxylic solvents.   On the basis of the NO^+ formalism, various nitrosyl complexes, e.g., $[NiX(NO)]_4$, $[NiLX(NO)]_2$ and $NiL_2X(NO)$ (see Chapter 27), are also to be regarded as Ni^0 complexes.

Nickel(I) complexes are very rare indeed. $K_4[Ni_2(CN)_6]$ has been reported; it is an unstable reactive compound of uncertain structure.   The $[Ni(S_2C_2X_2)_2]^-$ ions are also formally Ni^I complexes if the ligands are considered to be radical anions, $[S_2C_2X_2]^-$ (but see page 756).   The reaction of ClNO and $Ni(CO)_4$ in the gas phase produces a grey-green powder, $NiCl_2(NO)$, which is stable to 150°.   It appears to be polymeric and has two unpaired electrons per atom of Ni.[17]

29-H. COPPER

Copper has a single s electron outside a completed d shell and accordingly has sometimes been classed in group I.   This is unwise, since Cu has little in common with the alkalies except with regard to formal stoichiometries in the $+$ I oxidation state.   The filled d shell is much less effective than is a noble-gas shell in shielding the s electron from the nuclear charge so that the first ionization potential of Cu is higher than those of the alkalies.   Since the electrons of the d shell are also involved in metallic bonding, the heat of sublimation and the melting point of copper are also much higher than those of the alkalies.   These factors are responsible for the more noble character of copper, and the effect is to make the compounds more covalent and to give them higher lattice energies, which are not offset by the somewhat smaller radii of the unipositive ion compared to the alkali ions in the same period—Cu^+, 0.93; Na^+, 0.95; and K^+, 1.33 A.

The second and third ionization potentials of Cu are very much lower than those of the alkalies and account in part for the transition metal character shown by the existence of colored paramagnetic ions and complexes in the II and III oxidation states.   Even in the I oxidation state numerous transition metal-like complexes, for example, those with olefins, are formed.

There is only moderate similarity between copper and the heavier

[16] R. S. Vinal and L. T. Reynolds, *Inorg. Chem.*, **3**, 1062 (1963).
[17] C. C. Addison and B. F. G. Johnson, *Proc. Chem. Soc.*, **1962**, 305.

elements Ag and Au, but some points are noted in the later discussions of these elements (Chapter 30).

The oxidation states and stereochemistry of copper are summarized in Table 29-H-1.

TABLE 29-H-1

Oxidation States and Stereochemistry of Copper

Oxidation state	Coordination number	Geometry	Examples
Cu^I, d^{10}	2	Linear	Cu_2O, $[Cu(NH_3)_2]^+$
	3	Planar	$K[Cu(CN)_2]$
	4ᵃ	Tetrahedral	CuI, $[Cu(CN)_4]^{3-}$
Cu^{II}, d^9	4	Tetrahedral (distorted)	$Cs_2[CuCl_4]$, $Cu(N$-isopropyl-salicylaldiminato$)_2$
	5	Trigonal bipyramidal	$[Cu(dipy)_2I]^+$
	5	Square pyramidal	$[Cu(DMGH)_2]_2(s)$
	4ᵃ	Square	CuO, $[Cu(py)_4]^{2+}$, $(NH_4)_2[CuCl_4]$
	6ᵃ	Distorted octahedral	K_2CuF_4, $K_2[CuEDTA]$, $CuCl_2$
Cu^{III}, d^8	4 ?	Square (?)	$KCuO_2$
	6	Octahedral	K_3CuF_6

ᵃ Most common states.

29-H-1. The Element

Copper is widely distributed in nature in the free state, in sulfides, arsenides, chlorides and carbonates. It is extracted by oxidative roasting and smelting, followed by electrodeposition from sulfate solutions.

Copper is a tough, soft and ductile reddish metal second only to silver in its high thermal and electrical conductivities. The metal is completely miscible with Au. It is only superficially oxidized in air, sometimes giving a green coating of hydroxo carbonate and hydroxo sulfate.

Copper reacts at red heat with oxygen to give CuO and, at higher temperatures, Cu_2O; with sulfur it gives Cu_2S or a nonstoichiometric form of this phase. It is attacked by halogens but is unaffected by nonoxidizing or noncomplexing dilute acids in absence of air. Copper readily dissolves in nitric acid and sulfuric acid in presence of oxygen. It is also soluble in ammonia or potassium cyanide solutions in the presence of oxygen, as indicated by the potentials

$$Cu + 2NH_3 \xrightarrow{-0.12 \text{ v}} [Cu(NH_3)_2]^+ \xrightarrow[+2NH_3]{-0.01 \text{ v}} [Cu(NH_3)_4]^{2+}$$

29-H-2. Copper(I) Compounds

The cuprous ion has the electronic structure $3d^{10}$ so that its compounds are diamagnetic and, except where color results from the anion or charge-transfer bands (page 713), colorless.

The relative stabilities of the cuprous and cupric states are indicated by the following potential data:

$$Cu^+ + e = Cu \qquad E^0 = 0.52 \text{ v}$$
$$Cu^{2+} + e = Cu^+ \qquad E^0 = 0.153 \text{ v}$$

whence

$$Cu + Cu^{2+} = 2Cu^+ \qquad E^0 = -0.37 \text{ v}; \; K = [Cu^{2+}]/[Cu^+]^2 = \sim 10^6$$

The relative stabilities of Cu^I and Cu^{II} depend very strongly on the nature of anions or other ligands present, on the dielectric constant of the solution and on the nature of neighboring atoms in a crystal.

It is obvious that in aqueous solution the free Cu^+ ion can exist only in exceedingly low concentrations, and the only cuprous compounds which are stable to water are the highly insoluble ones like CuCl or CuCN; cuprous salts of oxo anions can be obtained in nonaqueous media, but such salts as Cu_2SO_4 are at once decomposed by water to give copper and the cupric salt. This instability toward water is due partly to the greater lattice and solvation energies of the cupric ion so that ionic Cu^I derivatives are unstable.

The equilibrium $2Cu^I = Cu + Cu^{II}$ can be displaced in either direction depending on the conditions. Thus with CN^-, I^- and Me_2S, Cu^{II} reacts to give the Cu^I compound; with anions that cannot give covalent bonds or bridging groups, for example, ClO_4^- and SO_4^{2-}, or with complexing agents which have their greater affinity for Cu^{II}, the Cu^{II} state is favored—thus ethylenediamine reacts with cuprous chloride in aqueous potassium chloride solution:

$$2CuCl + 2en = [Cu(en)_2]^{2+} + 2Cl^- + Cu^0$$

That the latter reaction also depends on the geometry of the ligand, that is on its chelate nature, is shown by differences in the $[Cu^{2+}]/[Cu^+]^2$ equilibrium with chelating and nonchelating amines. Thus for ethylenediamine, K is $\sim 10^5$, for pentamethylenediamine (which does not chelate) 3×10^{-2} and for ammonia 2×10^{-2}. Hence in the last case the reaction is

$$[Cu(NH_3)_4]^{2+} + Cu^0 = 2[Cu(NH_3)_2]^+$$

Cuprous Oxide and Sulfide. These solids are the most stable copper compounds at high temperatures, and the corresponding cupric compounds are thermally unstable toward them. The oxide is readily made as a yellow powder by controlled reduction of an alkaline solution of a cupric salt by hydrazine, or as red crystals by thermal decomposition of CuO. It is soluble in ammonia to give the ammine. The sulfide is a black crystalline solid obtained by heating copper and sulfur in absence of air.

Cuprous Halides. The fluoride is unknown. The chloride and bromide are made by boiling the cupric salt with excess copper in acid solution and, on addition of water to the CuX_2^- solutions so obtained, the white chloride and pale yellow bromide are precipitated. On addition of iodide ion to a cupric salt, a precipitate is formed which rapidly decomposes by a quantitative redox reaction to give cuprous iodide and iodine.

The three halides have the zinc blende structure with the metal atom tetrahedrally surrounded by halogen atoms. The chloride and bromide are associated in the vapor state, and for CuCl the principal species appears to be a cyclic trimer with alternating Cu and Cl atoms and a Cu—Cl distance of 2.16 A. The white CuCl becomes deep blue at 178° and gives a deep green liquid.

The halides are highly insoluble in water, the iodide being least soluble ($K_{SP} = 10^{-12}$). They are soluble to varying extents in complexing media such as CN^-, NH_3, $S_2O_3^{2-}$; excess of the halide ion gives species such as $CuCl_2^-$, $CuCl_3^{2-}$, $CuCl_4^{3-}$ depending on the conditions; in $1M$ KCl the main species is $CuCl_2^-$.

Cuprous Cyanide. This compound is similar to CuI and is made similarly in a redox reaction which also provides a convenient preparation of cyanogen:

$$2Cu^{2+}(aq) + 4CN^-(aq) = 2CuCN(s) + (CN)_2$$

The cyanide is soluble in solutions of complexing ions; cyanide gives $[Cu(CN)_4]^{3-}$ as the main species. The latter has such a large formation constant that copper metal will dissolve in potassium cyanide solution with evolution of hydrogen.

Cuprous Sulfate. Although cuprous oxo salts are usually complex, there are a few simple salts, of which the sulfate is the best known. It is obtained as a greyish solid, stable in the absence of moisture, by the reaction

$$Cu_2O + (CH_3)_2SO_4 \xrightarrow{160°} Cu_2SO_4 + CH_3OCH_3$$

Cuprous Complexes. Cuprous complexes with non-π-bonding as well as $p\pi$ and $d\pi$ bonding ligands, olefins and acetylenes are known.

With ammonia, halide ions and monodentate ligands, the cuprous complexes usually have the highest stability for $n = 2$ (e.g., $[Cu(NH_3)_2]^+$). However, in general, the complexes from $n = 1$ to $n = 4$ can exist under appropriate conditions. The two-coordinate complexes apparently all have linear structures, $[ClCuCl]^-$, and occur quite frequently. The four-coordinate complexes are invariably tetrahedral, although the tetrahedra may be distorted.[1]

The cyanide complex $K[Cu(CN)_2]$ has been shown to have an unusual spiral polymeric structure where the copper atom has coordination number

[1] M. R. Truter and K. W. Rutherford, *J. Chem. Soc.*, **1962**, 1748.

3; the carbon and nitrogen atoms bound to copper are almost coplanar with the metal atom (Fig. 29-H-1). The corresponding silver and gold ions are discrete, $[NC—M—CN]^-$.

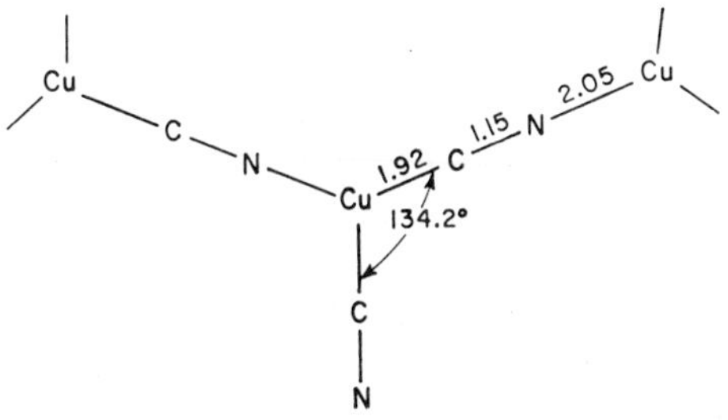

Fig. 29-H-1. A portion of the spiral chain in $K[Cu(CN)_2]$.

Acetylene complexes are readily formed. Thus cuprous chloride in concentrated hydrochloric acid absorbs acetylene to give colorless species such as $CuCl \cdot C_2H_2$ and $[CuCl_2C_2H_2]^-$. In neutral potassium chloride solution, sparingly soluble compounds such as $K_2[Cu_2C_2(CuCl)_8]$ can be obtained. These halide solutions can also catalyze the conversion of acetylene to vinyl acetylene (in strong alkali chloride) or to vinyl chloride (high HCl), and the reaction of acetylene with hydrogen cyanide to give acrylonitrile is also catalyzed.

If cuprous ammine solutions are treated with acetylenes containing the $HC≡C—$ group, yellow or red precipitates, insoluble in solvents with which they do not react, are obtained. Acetylene itself gives $Cu_2C_2 \cdot H_2O$ quantitatively. The thermal stability and insolubility of these alkynyl complexes has been attributed to polymerization through π bonding (29-H-I).

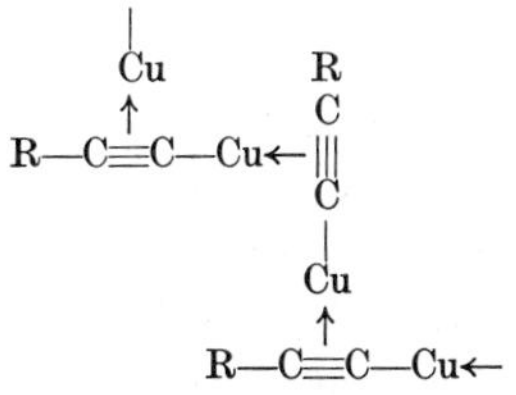

(29-H-I)

Propynyl copper dissolves in triethylphosphine in toluene to give $[Et_3PCuC≡CMe]_3$, which is probably a cyclic polymer of similar type.

Olefins form cuprous complexes which are less stable than their silver analogs. Thus CuCl absorbs ethylene and other olefins under pressure, but the products have high dissociation pressures.

29 + A.I.C.

Carbon Monoxide and Related Complexes. Cuprous ammines or chloro-cuprates(I) absorb carbon monoxide giving colorless solutions. From the latter solutions the halogen-bridged dimer $[CuCOCl_2]_2$ can be obtained as crystals. The gas is absorbed quantitatively by $[Cu(NH_3)_2]^+$ and can be regenerated on acidification.

Substituted phosphines, arsines and sulfides give stable complexes, notably with the iodide. The alkyl phosphine complexes are organic-soluble tetramers, $[R_3PCuI]_4$; the copper atoms lie at the corners of a tetrahedron and are tetrahedrally coordinated since the iodine atoms lie on the tetrahedral faces. When the anion is noncomplexing, tetracoordinated cations can be obtained as in $[(Ph_3P)_4Cu]^+ClO_4^-$.

Another group of polymeric cuprous complexes are the dithiocarbamates, $[Cu(S_2CNR_2)]_n$. When $R = CH_3$, the polymerization number is apparently quite large, while for $R = C_2H_5$ tetramers containing nearly regular Cu_4 tetrahedra have been found by X-ray study.[2] The Cu—Cu distances, averaging 2.71 A, are short enough to indicate the existence of significant metal–metal bonding, thus making these metal atom cluster compounds (see page 656).

Rather unstable cuprous *alkyls* can be made by the action of Grignard reagents or lithium alkyls on cuprous halides. Methylcopper is a polymeric yellow solid which decomposes in boiling ether and explodes in the dry state. Phenylcopper is stable to about 80°.

29-H-3. Copper(II) Compounds

The dipositive state is the most important one for copper. Most cuprous compounds are fairly readily oxidized to cupric compounds, but further oxidation to Cu^{III} is difficult. There is a well-defined aqueous chemistry of Cu^{2+}, and a large number of salts of various anions, many of which are water soluble, exist in addition to a wealth of complexes.

Stereochemistry. As pointed out earlier (page 683), the Cu^{II} ion with its d^9 configuration, provides one of the best opportunities for observation of the Jahn–Teller effect. For a d^9 ion in would-be octahedral surroundings, appreciable distortions should occur, and for Cu^{II} there are extensive data which bear this out very convincingly. Some representative data are given in Table 29-H-2. In $CuCl_2$, $CuBr_2$, CuF_2 and $CsCuCl_3$ the structures are distorted cubic ones in which the Cu^{II} ions are found in distorted octahedra. In each case the distortion is such that two *trans* metal–ligand distances are greater than the other four. Analogous compounds containing metal ions (e.g., Ni^{II} or Zn^{II}) which are not subject to Jahn–Teller effects give cubic

---

[2] R. Hesse, *Arkiv för Kemi*, **20**, 481 (1963).

TABLE 29-H-2

Interatomic Distances in Some Cupric Coordination Polyhedra

Compound	Distances, A
$CuCl_2$	4Cl at 2.30, 2Cl at 2.95
$CsCuCl_3$	4Cl at 2.30, 2Cl at 2.65
$CuCl_2 \cdot 2H_2O$	2O at 2.01, 2Cl at 2.31, 2Cl at 2.98
$CuBr_2$	4Br at 2.40, 2Br at 3.18
CuF_2	4F at 1.93, 2F at 2.27
$[Cu(H_2O)_2(NH_3)_4]$ in	
$CuSO_4 \cdot 4NH_3 \cdot H_2O$	4N at 2.05, 1O at 2.59, 1O at 3.37
K_2CuF_4	2F at 1.95, 4F at 2.08

crystals with regular octahedra about the metal ions. It may be noted that in the two chlorine compounds the four short bonds are of the same length in both cases, whereas the long bonds are of quite different lengths. It is also true in other compounds that the short bonds are those to be expected for a fairly constant "radius" for the Cu^{II} ion in these directions, but the long bonds vary from only slightly longer than the short ones to much longer. Theoretically, this is to be expected since the degree of distortion will depend in detail on many forces within each particular compound. Thus, it might be argued that the case of square coordination as found in CuO and in many discrete complexes of Cu^{II} should be regarded as the extreme of Jahn–Teller distorted octahedral coordination rather than as a different type of coordination.

In the salt K_2CuF_4 (and also in several M^ICuF_3 compounds) each Cu^{II} ion is surrounded by six F^- ions in the form of an octahedron flattened along one axis. Although there are calculations to show that a distortion of this type might occur here solely because of the Jahn–Teller effect, the case is uncertain because the general nature of the crystal structure is such that perfectly regular octahedral coordination would not be expected even in the absence of a Jahn–Teller effect.

In addition to the square merging into tetragonally distorted octahedral complexes formed by Cu^{II}, which class includes the vast majority, there are some other stereochemistries known, of which the most important is distorted tetrahedral. The $M_2^ICuX_4$ compounds, M^I representing a univalent cation and X representing Cl^- or Br^-, contain non-planar CuX_4^{2-} ions provided the cations are large. Thus $(NH_4)_2CuCl_4$ contains planar $CuCl_4^{2-}$ ions,[3] but Cs_2CuCl_4 and Cs_2CuBr_4,[4] as well as several salts with still larger cations have been shown to contain CuX_4^{2-} ions which are squashed tetrahedra as indicated in Figure 29-H-2. The reason for the

[3] R. D. Willett, *J. Chem. Phys.*, **41**, 2243 (1964).
[4] B. Morosin and E. C. Lingafelter, *Acta Cryst.*, **13**, 807 (1960).

distortion of the tetrahedra is not well understood. While a d^9 ion in tetrahedral surroundings is subject to a Jahn–Teller effect, it is also to be noted that the large spin-orbit coupling constant for copper might produce sufficient splitting of the ground state (T_2) to render the Jahn–Teller effect

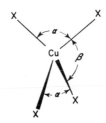

Fig. 29-H-2.   Squashed tetrahedral structures of $[CuX_4]^{2-}$ ions in Cs_2CuX_4 salts; $\alpha > \beta$.

inoperative. Probably the two perturbations, that is Jahn–Teller vibrational-electronic interaction and spin-orbit splitting, are of comparable magnitude. This situation leads to enormous computational difficulties with the result that a definitive answer has thus far eluded theoreticians.

There are various other examples of distorted tetrahedral coordination, in many of which it is possible that the tetrahedral environment is more or less determined by the steric properties of the ligands. In the spinel, $CuCr_2O_4$, the preference of Cr^{3+} for the octahedral interstices is so great that the copper ions have no choice but to enter the tetrahedral ones.[5] In the polymeric imidazole complex, $Cu(C_3N_2H_3)_2$, the approximately tetrahedral arrangement[6] may be forced by the steric interactions between the ligands. Interligand repulsion may also play a role in the case of the distorted tetrahedral bis-(N-R-salicylaldiminato)Cu^{II} complexes in which R represents isopropyl and *sec*-butyl,[7] since several analogous complexes with less bulky N-substituents are planar.

Tetrahedral configurations have also been shown to occur in some $Cu(Ph_3PO)_2X_2$ type compounds, but structural details are unknown.[8]

Finally, there is a wide range of *pentacoordinated species* of Cu^{II}. Both trigonal bipyramidal and square pyramidal configurations are known, the latter being most common.

The TBP configuration appears to occur in $CuCl_5^{3-}$, $Cu(terpy)Cl_2$ and $[Cu(dipy)_2I]I$, the data for the last mentioned being most accurate.[9]

The square pyramidal configuration occurs in diaquoacetylacetonato-

[5] E. Prince, *Acta Cryst.*, **10**, 554 (1957).

[6] J. A. J. Jarvis and A. F. Wells, *Acta Cryst.*, **13**, 1027 (1960).

[7] L. Sacconi and M. Ciampolini, *J. Chem. Soc.*, **1964**, 276; L. Sacconi, M. Ciampolini and U. Campigli, *Inorg. Chem.*, **4**, 407 (1965).

[8] D. M. L. Goodgame and F. A. Cotton, *J. Chem. Soc.*, **1961**, 2298.

[9] G. A. Barclay, B. F. Hoskins and C. H. L. Kennard, *J. Chem. Soc.*, **1963**, 5691.

copper(II) picrate[10] and commonly in adducts of complexes such as bis-acetylacetonatocopper(II)[10] and bissalicylaldimatocopper(II)[11a] with pyridine and other bases. It also occurs in the copper(II) complex of β-alanyl-L-histidine, which is a model compound for metal–protein interactions.[11b]

It also occurs in the crystal of dimethylglyoximatocopper(II), which in contrast to $Ni(DMGH)_2$, is soluble in water. In the copper compound the chelate rings are non-planar and one oxygen of the ligand in one $Cu(DMGH)_2$ molecule occupies the fifth position of the copper atom in the other component of the dimer; there are accordingly two free —OH groups. The bis(N,N'di-n-propyldithiocarbamato)copper(II) complex is similar, but with two bridging sulfur atoms. There are many other examples of copper(II) compounds, others being N,N'disalicylideneethylenediiminecopper and acetylacetonemono(o-hydroxoanilate)copper, which are dimeric in the crystalline state with oxygen bridges between the copper atoms.

Spectral and Magnetic Properties. As a result of the distorted octahedral or square coordination of Cu^{II}, a detailed interpretation of its electronic absorption spectrum is somewhat complicated. Virtually all complexes and compounds of Cu^{II} are blue or green. Exceptions are generally caused by strong ultraviolet bands—charge-transfer bands—tailing off into the blue end of the visible spectrum and thus causing the substances to appear red or brown. The blue or green colors are due to the presence of an absorption band in the 600–900 mμ region of the spectrum. However, close study of these somewhat asymmetric bands in a variety of complexes and salts has shown that they are made up of at least two, and possibly three or four, overlapping, symmetrical bands. Now we have already seen (page 666) that tetragonal distortion splits the e_g and t_{2g} levels so that more than one d–d transition, in fact three, are to be expected for Cu^{II} in its complexes. There is still some uncertainty as to whether all of the bands are really under the envelope of the absorption observed in the visible, but if this is so, as some workers believe, then the splitting pattern must be similar to that shown in Figure 26-7 except that the d_{xy} level is even closer to the d_{z^2} level and the (d_{zx}, d_{yz}) pair. Then, since Cu^{II} is a one-positron case (see page 675), this diagram can be inverted and it predicts that the following transitions of the positron

$$d_{x^2-y^2} \to d_{xy}$$
$$d_{x^2-y^2} \to d_{z^2}$$
$$d_{x^2-y^2} \to (d_{zx}, d_{yz})$$

[10] R. D. Gillard and G. Wilkinson, *J. Chem. Soc.*, **1963**, 5399; R. D. Gillard, *et al.*, *Acta Cryst.*, **16**, A67 (1963).

[11a] D. Hall, S. V. Sheat and T. N. Waters, *Chem. and Ind.*, **1965**, 1428 and references therein.

[11b] H. C. Freeman and J. J. Szymanski, *Chem. Comm.*, **1965**, 598; J. F. Blount, *et al.*, *Chem. Comm.*, **1966**, 23.

will give absorption bands lying very close together. It is also possible, however, that the visible absorption consists only of the first and second of these with the $d_{x^2-y^2} \rightarrow (d_{zx}, d_{yz})$ transition being placed further out in the ultraviolet where it might escape detection. In complexes of less than full cubic symmetry (that is fully regular octahedral or tetrahedral ones) completely definitive assignments of the spectra can be quite difficult to achieve. Thus, despite considerable effort[12] uncertainties still remain for most copper(II) complexes.

From the point of view of magnetic properties, copper(II) complexes fall into two broad classes. First there are those having essentially temperature-independent magnetic moments in the range 1.75–2.20 BM. Those exhibiting such moments are mononuclear complexes having no major interaction between the unpaired electrons on different copper ions. Although theory suggests that there should be some correlations between the magnitude of the orbital contribution and the coordination geometry, in practice they are not observed, presumably because of distortions and other variable factors such as covalence. As a rule the moments fall in the range 1.9–2.1 BM. The second class,[13] in which the moments are substantially below the spin-only value and markedly temperature-dependent, is composed of those in which pairs of Cu^{II} ions are held close together, usually by carboxylate anions, though in at least one case, the spins of the two Cu^{II} ions are so strongly coupled that the dimer is diamagnetic. Certain of these magnetically anomalous dimeric complexes will be described more fully below.

Esr studies of the planar bis-chelate complexes, e.g., the acetylacetonate, have shown that these characteristically have only two significantly different g values, even though in principle all three should be different. Typical values are $g_{\parallel} = 2.20$–2.35 and $g_{\perp} = 2.05$–2.10.

Cupric Oxide and Hydroxide. On heating the nitrate or other oxo salts, the black crystalline *oxide* CuO is obtained. It is unstable above 800° toward cuprous oxide and oxygen and is readily reduced to the metal by hydrogen or carbon monoxide at about 250°.

The *hydroxide*, $Cu(OH)_2$, is obtained as a blue bulky precipitate on addition of alkali hydroxide to cupric solutions; it can also be obtained as crystals. On warming in aqueous solution, the hydroxide is dehydrated to the oxide. It is soluble in moderately strong acids, but is also feebly acidic and dissolves in concentrated alkali hydroxide to give deep blue anions. These are believed to be of the type $[Cu_n(OH)_{2n-2}]^{2+}$. In ammoniacal solutions the deep blue tetrammine complex is formed.

[12] J. Ferguson, R. L. Belford and T. S. Piper, *J. Chem. Phys.*, **37**, 1569 (1962); W. E. Hatfield and T. S. Piper, *Inorg. Chem.*, **3**, 841 (1964).
[13] M. Kato, H. B. Jonassen and J. C. Fanning, *Chem. Rev.*, **1964**, 99.

Cupric Halides and Halide Complexes. The *fluoride* is colorless and has a distorted rutile lattice. By contrast, the yellow *chloride* and the almost black *bromide* form layer lattices in which there are halogen-bridged chains with the coordination of the copper atom being square. However, unlike some other similar polymeric halides, for example, $PdCl_2$, the packing of the copper chloride and bromide chains is such that two halogen atoms in one chain occupy the "long" octahedral positions to copper atoms in other chains. The chloride and bromide are readily soluble in water, hydrated salts being crystallizable, and also in donor organic solvents such as acetone, alcohol or pyridine.

The existence of both tetragonal (that is square or tetragonally distorted octahedral) and distorted tetrahedral halo complexes has been mentioned already. In addition, the existence of interesting low polymers, shown schematically in 29-H-II, III and IV, has been demonstrated.[14] There

(29-H-II)

(29-H-III)

(29-H-IV)

appears to be a general correlation between the structures and the colors of the chlorocuprate(II) complexes as follows:[3]

Simple planar $CuCl_4{}^{2-}$ (as in $(NH_4)_2CuCl_4$): yellow

Distorted tetrahedral: orange

Polymeric ($Cu_2Cl_6{}^{2-}$ or higher polymers such as 29-H-II to 29-H-IV): dark red.

Cupric Oxo Acid Salts. Perhaps the commonest cupric salt is the hydrated sulfate, $CuSO_4 \cdot 5H_2O$. Here the cupric ion has its usual coordination with four oxygen atoms in a plane, and oxygen atoms from sulfate groups occupying each axial position. The additional water molecule is hydrogen bonded between a second sulfate oxygen and a bound water molecule in the plane. The hydrated nitrate is a common salt, but of more interest is the unusual anhydrous nitrate. Copper metal is vigorously dissolved by a solution of N_2O_4 in ethyl acetate, and from this solution can be crystallized the salt $Cu(NO_3)_2 \cdot N_2O_4$, the infrared spectrum of

[14] R. D. Willett and R. E. Rundle, *J. Chem. Phys.*, **40**, 838 (1964).

which suggests that it is $[NO]^+[Cu(NO_3)_3]^-$. On heating at 90° this solvate gives the blue anhydrous $Cu(NO_3)_2$ which can be sublimed without decomposition in vacuum at 150–200°. There are two forms of the solid anhydrous nitrate both possessing complex structures in which Cu^{II} ions are linked together by nitrate ions in an infinite array. However, discrete molecules with the kind of structure[15] shown in 29-H-V occur in the vapor phase. It is not certain whether the molecule is entirely planar, however.

(29-H-V)

Several *cupric carboxylates* are dimeric either in the crystalline state, in solution, or both. Thus the acetate, $[Cu_2(OCOCH_3)_4] \cdot 2H_2O$, is dimeric in the crystal, although it is partially dissociated in solution;[16a] the monochloroacetate is dimeric also in solution. Magnetic studies have shown that in these dimers there is extensive quenching of the spin moment of the cupric ion.[16b] In the acetate which has the same structure as that of its Cr^{II} analog (see page 821), each metal atom is surrounded in a square plane, or approximately so, by the four oxygens of the bridging acetato groups. Each copper also has a water oxygen bound to it, and the Cu—Cu distance is only 2.64 A. The water molecules may be replaced by various other donors such as amines or a phosphine oxide, without any significant change[17] in the structure. Thus each copper atom has its usual distorted octahedral coordination. The metal atoms are sufficiently close to allow lateral overlap of the $3d_{xy}$ orbitals; this type of metal–metal interaction is called δ bonding. By contrast, the hydrated and anhydrous forms of the formate and benzoate have polymeric structures with bridging carboxylate groups. The trihydrate, $Cu(O_2CC_6H_5)_2 \cdot 3H_2O$ has a normal magnetic moment (1.87 BM) at 25° and in the crystal there are linear chains of $[CuO_2C_6H_5 \cdot 2H_2O]_x$ (29-H-VI) between which are sandwiched hydrated benzoate ions.[18]

The cupric salt of diazoaminobenzene, $C_6H_5NH—N{=}N—C_6H_5$ (29-H-VII), is also dimeric with bridging groups as indicated in the dia-

[15] R. E. LaVilla and S. H. Bauer, *J. Amer. Chem. Soc.*, **85**, 3597 (1963).

[16a] J. K. Kochi and R. V. Subramian, *Inorg. Chem.*, **4**, 1527 (1965).

[16b] J. Lewis, *et al.*, *J. Chem. Soc.*, **1965**, 6464; L. Dubicki, *et al.*, *Inorg. Chem.*, **5**, 93 (1966); B. N. Figgis and D. J. Martin, *Inorg. Chem.*, **5**, 100 (1966); D. Royer, *Inorg. Chem.*, **4**, 1830 (1965).

[17] G. A. Barclay and C. H. L. Kennard, *J. Chem. Soc.*, **1961**, 5244; E. Kokat and R. L. Martin, *Inorg. Chem.*, **3**, 1306 (1964).

[18] M. Inoue, M. Kishita and M. Kubo, *Inorg. Chem.*, **4**, 626 (1965).

gram. In this case the molecule is diamagnetic, the spins being completely coupled in the metal–metal bond.

(29-H-VI)   (29-H-VII)

Aqueous Chemistry. Most cupric salts dissolve readily in water and give the aquo ion, which may be written $[Cu(H_2O)_6]^{2+}$, keeping in mind, however, that two of the water molecules are farther from the metal atom than the other four. Addition of ligands to such aqueous solutions leads to the formation of complexes by successive displacement of water molecules. With NH_3, for example, the species $[Cu(NH_3)(H_2O)_5]^{2+}\ldots[Cu(NH_3)_4-(H_2O)_2]^{2+}$ are formed in the normal way, but the addition of the fifth and sixth molecules of NH_3 is difficult. In fact, the sixth cannot be added to any significant extent in aqueous media; $[Cu(NH_3)_6]^{2+}$ can be obtained in liquid ammonia, however. The reason for this unusual behavior is connected with the Jahn–Teller effect. Because of it, the Cu^{II} ion does not bind the fifth and sixth ligands strongly (even the H_2O). When this intrinsic weak binding of the fifth and sixth ligands is added to the normally expected decrease in the stepwise formation constants (page 155) the formation constants, K_5 and K_6, are very small indeed. Similarly, it is found with ethylenediamine that $[Cuen(H_2O)_4]^{2+}$ and $[Cu(en)_2(H_2O)_2]^{2+}$ form readily, but $[Cu(en)_3]^{2+}$ forms only at extremely high concentrations of en. Many other amine complexes of Cu^{II} are known, and all are much more intensely blue than the aquo ion. This is because the amines produce a stronger ligand field which causes the absorption band to move from the far red to the middle of the red region of the spectrum. For example, in the aquo ion the absorption maximum is at ~ 800 mμ, whereas in $[Cu(NH_3)_4-(H_2O)_2]^{2+}$ it is at ~ 600 mμ, as shown in Figure 29-H-3. The reversal of the shifts with increasing take-up of ammonia for the fifth ammonia is to be noted, indicating again the weaker bonding of the fifth ammonia molecule.

Halide ion complexes are also formed in aqueous solution on addition of HCl, HBr, LiCl or LiBr to the solutions. These range in color from green to brown, and on addition of large cations, for example, Cs^+ or $[(CH_3)_4N]^+$,

29*

the yellow and brown crystalline salts of $[CuCl_4]^{2-}$ and $[CuBr_4]^{2-}$ can be isolated. These have flattened tetrahedral structures as noted above.

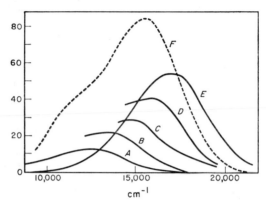

Fig. 29-H-3. Absorption spectra of $[Cu(H_2O)_6]^{2+}$ (*A*) and of the ammines in $2M$ ammonium nitrate at 25°, $[Cu(NH_3)(H_2O)_5]^{2+}$ (*B*), $[Cu(NH_3)_2(H_2O)_4]^{2+}$ (*C*), $[Cu(NH_3)_3(H_2O)_3]^{2+}$ (*D*), $[Cu(NH_3)_4(H_2O)_2]^{2+}$ (*E*), and $[Cu(NH_3)_5(H_2O)]^{2+}$ (*F*).

Many other Cu^{II} complexes may be isolated by treating aqueous solutions with ligands. When the ligands are such as to form neutral, water-insoluble complexes, as in the following equation, the complexes precipitate

$$Cu^{2+}(aq) + 2 \quad \text{(structure)} \longrightarrow Cu\text{(structure)}_2$$

and can be purified by recrystallization from organic solvents. The bis(acetylacetonato)copper(II) complex is another example of this type.

Some ligands which coordinate through oxygen form a large number of cupric complexes, often of considerable complexity. Thus the well-known blue solutions formed by addition of tartrate to Cu^{2+} solutions (Fehling's solution) are still far from understood, but it seems clear that polynuclear complexes must be present. Oxalate, glycerol and various thio compounds also give cupric complexes; thus addition of potassium oxalate to cupric sulfate solutions gives stable crystalline $K_2[Cu(C_2O_4)_2]\cdot 2H_2O$ with the chelated oxalate oxygens in the plane and the two water oxygen atoms normal to it.

It may be noted finally that the cupric ion in complexes plays an important role, probably second only to iron among the transition metals, as a catalyst in many oxidation and other processes; in many systems, Cu^{I}–Cu^{II} oxidation–reduction cycles are involved. Copper occurs in several enzymes such as phenolase and, as Cu^I in hemocyanin.[19]   Both of these metallo-proteins carry oxygen like hemoglobin, so that oxo species such as CuO_2^+ or CuO_2Cu^{2+} may be involved.   A comparatively simple system involving Cu^{2+}–amine–H_2O_2 mixtures acts as a model for phenolase in that *ortho* hydroxylation of phenols can be achieved.

A non-catalytic use of copper(II) acetate in pyridine solution is the oxidative coupling of acetylenes:

$$2RC{\equiv}CH + 2Cu^{2+} + 2py = RC{\equiv}C{-}C{\equiv}CR + 2pyH^+ + 2Cu^+$$

29-H-4. Copper(III) Compounds

There is good evidence that Cu^{III} can occur in crystalline compounds and in complexes.   It should be noted that Cu^{III}, with a d^8 shell, is isoelectronic with Ni^{II}.

If cupric hydroxide is treated with alkaline hypochlorite, it dissolves to give oxidizing solutions, which on acidification liberate oxygen.   Some alkaline earth and alkali cuprates can be obtained, for example, by heating the mixed oxides in oxygen; $KCuO_2$ is steel blue in color and is diamagnetic, suggesting square planar coordination.

By treatment of a mixture of potassium and cupric chlorides with fluorine, a pale green crystalline solid, K_3CuF_6, is obtained.   This is para-magnetic with $\mu = 2.8$ BM.

The oxidation of alkaline cupric solutions containing periodate or tellu-rate by hypochlorite or other oxidizing agents leads to diamagnetic complex salts such as $K_7[Cu(IO_6)_2]\cdot 7H_2O$.   These salts are strong oxidizing agents and liberate oxygen on acidification.

[19] See D. Kertesz, R. Zito and F. Ghiretti in O. Hayaishi, ed., *Oxygenases*, Academic Press, London, 1962.

References*

The following books provide many general references to the less recent literature on the chemistry of the first transition series elements.   For detailed coverage of the older literature, Gmelin and Pascal are the standard works.   For the most recent references, the *Annual Reports of the Chemical Society*, London, should be consulted.

Bailar, J. C., ed., *The Chemistry of Coordination Compounds* (American Chemical Society Monograph, No. 131), Reinhold, New York. 1956.
Calvin, M., *Rev. Pure Appl. Chem.*, **15**, 1 (1965).   Coordination chemistry of manganese porphyrins.

* See also references for Chapters 5, 25, 27, 28.

Falk, J. E., and J. N. Phillips in F. P. Dwyer and D. P. Mellor, eds., *Chelating Agents and Metal Chelates*, Academic Press, New York, 1964. Coordination chemistry of pyrrole pigments (heme, etc.).

Ives, D. J. G., *Principles of the Extraction of Metals*, Royal Institute of Chemistry, London, 1960. A valuable discussion on thermodynamic background with examples.

M. Kato, H. B. Jonassen and J. C. Fanning, *Chem. Rev.*, **64**, 99 (1964). Review on Cu complexes with subnormal magnetic moments.

Latimer, W. M., *The Oxidation States of the Elements and their Potentials in Aqueous Solutions*, 2nd ed., Prentice-Hall, New York, 1952.

Lewis, J., and R. Wilkins, eds., *Modern Coordination Chemistry*, Interscience, New York–London, 1959.

Meijer, H. J. de L., M. J. Janssen and G. J. M. van der Kerk, *Studies in Organic Chemistry of Vanadium*, Institute for Organic Chemistry, Utrecht, 1963. Metal–carbon chemistry, polymerization catalysts, etc.

Miller, J. R., *Adv. Inorg. Chem. Radiochem.*, **4**, 133 (1962). Extensive comparison of chemistry of Ni, Pd and Pt.

Nyholm, R. S., and M. L. Tobe, *Adv. Inorg. Chem. Radiochem.*, **5**, 1 (1963). The stabilization of oxidation states of the transition metals.

Remy, H., *Treatise on Inorganic Chemistry* (translated and amended by J. S. Anderson), Vol. II, Elsevier, Amsterdam, 1956.

Schrauzer, G. N., *Adv. Organomet. Chem.*, **2**, 2 (1964). Organometallic chemistry of nickel and utilization in catalysis.

Selbin, J., *Chem. Rev.*, **65**, 153 (1965). Exhaustive review of oxovanadium(IV) compounds.

Sidgwick, N. V., *The Chemical Elements and their Compounds*, Vols. I and II, Oxford University Press, London, 1950.

Stewart, R., *Oxidation Mechanisms; Applications to Organic Chemistry*, Benjamin, New York, 1964. Contains discussion of mechanism of oxidation of organic compounds by Cr^{VI}, Mn^{VII}, UO_2^+ and other metal ions.

30

The Elements of the Second and Third
Transition Series

GENERAL COMPARISONS WITH THE FIRST TRANSITION SERIES

In general, the second and third transition series elements of a given group have similar chemical properties but both show definite differences from their light congeners. A few examples will illustrate this generalization. Although Co^{II} forms a considerable number of tetrahedral and octahedral complexes and is the characteristic state in ordinary aqueous chemistry, Rh^{II} and Ir^{II} are rare and relatively unimportant states. Similarly, the Mn^{2+} ion is very stable, but for Tc and Re the II oxidation state is known only in a few complexes. Cr^{III} forms an enormous number of cationic ammine complexes which comprise one of the best known aspects of its chemistry, whereas Mo^{III} and W^{III} are not particularly stable states for these elements under any conditions and form only a few complexes, none of which are especially stable. Again, Cr^{VI} species are powerful oxidizing agents with no very extensive chemistry, whereas Mo^{VI} and W^{VI} are quite stable and give rise to an extensive series of polynuclear oxo anions.

This is not to say that there are no valid analogies between the chemistry of the three series of transition elements. For example, the chemistry of Rh^{III} complexes is in general quite similar to that of Co^{III} complexes, and here, as elsewhere, the ligand field bands in the spectra of complexes in corresponding oxidation states are similar. On the whole, however, there are certain consistent differences of which the above-mentioned comparisons are particularly obvious manifestations.

The ionization potentials of the second and third series elements are given in Table 30-1.

Some important features of the elements and comparison of these with the corresponding features of the first series are the following:

909

1. *Radii.* The radii of the heavier transition atoms and ions are not very well known except in a few cases. An important feature is that the filling of the 4f orbitals through the lanthanide elements causes a steady contraction, called the *lanthanide contraction,* in atomic and ionic sizes. Thus the expected size increases of the third transition series elements relative to those of the second transition series, due to increased number of electrons and the higher principal quantum numbers of the outer ones, are almost exactly offset, and there is in general little difference in atomic and ionic sizes between the two heavy atoms of a group whereas the corresponding atom and ions of the first transition series are significantly smaller. (The lanthanide contraction is fully discussed on page 1055.)

2. *Oxidation states.* For the heavier transition elements, higher oxidation states are in general much more stable than for the elements of the first transition series. Thus the elements Mo, W, Tc and Re form oxo anions in high valence states which are not especially easily reduced, for example, MoO_4^{2-}, whereas the analogous compounds of the first transition series elements, when they exist, are strong oxidizing agents. Indeed, the heavier elements form many compounds such as RuO_4, WCl_6 and PtF_6 which have no analogs among the lighter ones. At the same time, the chemistry of complexes and aquo ions of the lower valence states, especially II and III, which plays such a large part in the chemistry of the lighter elements, is of relatively little importance for most of the heavier ones.

TABLE 30-1

Ionization Potentials of the Elements of the Second and Third Transition Series

(In electron volts)

Element	Atomic number	1st	2nd	3rd	4th	5th	6th	7th	8th	9th	10th
Zr	40	6.95	14.03	24.11	33.99	83	98.8	118	143	163	181
Nb	41	6.77	13.5	28.1	38.3	49.5	103	125	145	172	193
Mo	42	7.18	15.2	27.0	40.5	56	72	125	153	174	204
Tc	43	7.45	15	29	43	59	76	94	162	184	206
Ru	44	7.5	16.4	28.6	46.5	63	81	100	119	194	217
Rh	45	7.7	18.1	31.0	45.6	67	85	105	126	147	228
Pd	46	8.33	19.9	33.4	48.8	66	90	110	132	155	178
Ag	47	7.574	22.0	39.7	52	70	89	116	139	167	187
Hf	72	5.5	14.9	21	31						
Ta	73	6		22.3	33.1	45					
W	74	7.98	14	24.1	35.4	48	61				
Re	75	7.87	13.1	26.0	37.7	51	64	79			
Os	76	8.7	15	25	40	54	68	83	99		
Ir	77	9.2	16	27	39	57	72	88	104	121	
Pt	78	8.96	18.56	28.5	41.1	55	75	92	109	127	146
Au	79	9.223	20.1	30.5	43.5	58	73	96	114	133	153

3. *Aqueous chemistry.* Aquo ions of the low and medium valence states are not in general well defined or important for any of the heavier transition elements, and some, such as Zr, Hf and Re, do not seem to form any simple cationic complexes. For most of them anionic oxo and halo complexes play a major role in their aqueous chemistry although some, such as Ru, Rh, Pd and Pt, do form important cationic complexes as well.

4. *Magnetic properties.* Whereas a simple interpretation of magnetic susceptibilities of the compounds of first transition series elements usually gives the number of unpaired electrons and hence the valence state and d orbital configuration, more complex behavior is often encountered in compounds of the heavier elements.

One important characteristic of the heavier elements is that they tend to give *low-spin* compounds, which means that in oxidation states where there is an odd number of d electrons there is frequently only one unpaired electron, and ions with an even number of d electrons are very often diamagnetic. There are two main reasons for this intrinsically greater tendency to spin-pairing. First, the $4d$ and $5d$ orbitals are spatially larger than $3d$ orbitals so that double occupation of an orbital produces significantly less interelectronic repulsion. Second, a given set of ligand atoms produces larger splittings of $5d$ than of $4d$ orbitals and in both cases larger splittings than for $3d$ orbitals (see page 680).

In cases where there are unpaired electrons, the susceptibility data are often less easily interpreted. For instance, low-spin octahedral Mn^{III} and Cr^{II} complexes have t_{2g}^4 configurations and hence two unpaired electrons. They have magnetic moments in the neighborhood of 3.6 BM which can be correlated with the presence of the two unpaired spins, these alone being responsible for a moment of 2.83 BM, plus a contribution from unquenched orbital angular momentum. Now, Os^{IV} also forms octahedral complexes with t_{2g}^4 configurations, but these commonly have moments of the order of 1.2 BM. Such a moment taken at face value has little meaning and certainly does not give any simple indication of the presence of two unpaired electrons. Indeed, in older literature it was naively taken to imply that there was only one unpaired electron from which the erroneous conclusion was drawn that the osmium ion was in an odd oxidation state instead of the IV state.

Similar difficulties arise in other cases, and their cause lies in the *high spin-orbit coupling constants* of the heavier ions. Figure 30-1 shows how the effective magnetic moment of a t_{2g}^4 configuration depends on the ratio of the thermal energy, kT, to the spin-orbit coupling constant, λ. For Mn^{III} and Cr^{II}, λ is sufficiently small that at room temperature ($kT \approx 200$ cm^{-1}) both of these ions fall on the plateau of the curve where their behavior is of the familiar sort. Os^{IV}, however, has a spin-orbit coupling constant which is an order of magnitude higher, and at room temperature kT/λ is still quite small. Thus at ordinary temperatures, octahedral Os^{IV} compounds should (and do) have low, strongly temperature-dependent magnetic moments. Obviously, if measurements on Os^{IV} compounds could be

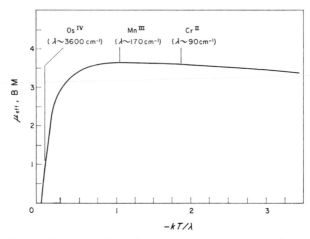

Fig. 30-1.   Curve showing the dependence on temperature and on the spin-orbit coupling constant, λ, of the effective magnetic moment of a d^4 ion in octahedral coordination.

made at sufficiently high temperatures—which is usually impossible—they would have "normal" moments, and, conversely, at very low temperatures Mn^{III} and Cr^{II} compounds would show "abnormally" low moments.

The curve shown in Figure 30-1 for the t_{2g}^4 case arises because of the following effects of spin-orbit coupling. First, the spin-orbit coupling splits the lowest triplet state in such a way that in the component of lowest energy the spin and orbital moments cancel one another completely. When λ and hence this splitting are large compared to the available thermal energy, the Boltzmann distribution of systems among the several spin-orbit split components is such that most of the systems are in the lowest one which makes no contribution at all to the average magnetic moment. At $0°K$, of course, all systems would be in this nonmagnetic state and the substance would become entirely diamagnetic. Second, however, the spin-orbit coupling causes an interaction of this lowest, nonmagnetic state with certain high-lying excited states so that the lowest level is not actually entirely nonmagnetic at all temperatures, and in the temperature range where kT/λ is much less than 1 the effective magnetic moment varies with the square root of the temperature.

Similar difficulties arise for d^1 ions in octahedral fields, when the spin-orbit coupling constant is large. For example, if $\lambda = 500$ (as for Zr^{III}) the nonmagnetic ground state, which splits off from the $^2T_{2g}$ term under the influence of spin-orbit coupling, will be so low that a temperature-independent susceptibility corresponding to an effective moment of only ~ 0.8 BM at room temperature will be observed. Again, this moment as such has no unique interpretation in terms of the number of unpaired electrons for the ion.

It is beyond the scope of this text to go more deeply into this subject,* but it should be borne in mind, as the examples given demonstrate, that the high spin-orbit coupling constants can cause metal ions of the second and third transition series to have magnetic moments at room temperature which cannot be simply interpreted in terms of the number of unpaired electrons present unless measurements are made over a considerable temperature range on magnetically dilute specimens and the results compared with theoretical calculations such as those represented by the curve in Figure 30-1 for the low-spin d^4 system. Other systems for which fairly complicated behavior is expected (only octahedral coordination being considered here) are d^1, d^2, d^7, d^8, and d^9. The d^6 systems have no paramagnetism (unless there is some of the temperature-independent type) since they have t_{2g}^6 configurations with no unpaired electrons. The d^3 systems have magnetic moments which are rigorously temperature independent regardless of the magnitude of λ. The d^5 systems have moments which vary with temperature only for very low values of kT/λ, and even then the temperature dependence is not severe; nevertheless, these systems can show complicated behavior because of intermolecular magnetic interactions in compounds which are not magnetically dilute.

30-A. ZIRCONIUM AND HAFNIUM

Because of the effects of the lanthanide contraction, both the atomic radii of Zr and Hf (1.45 and 1.44 A, respectively) and the radii of the Zr^{4+} and Hf^{4+} ions (0.74 and 0.75 A, respectively) are virtually identical. This has the effect of making the chemical behavior of the two elements extremely similar, more so than for any other pair of congeneric elements.

The oxidation states and stereochemistries are summarized in Table 30-A-1.

The chemistry of hafnium has been studied much less than that of zirconium, but so far as it has been examined it differs little from that of zirconium. Hence few specific references to hafnium chemistry need be

* For thorough summary of theory and fact see J. Lewis and B. N. Figgis, *Prog. Inorg. Chem.*, **6**, 37 (1964).

TABLE 30-A-1

Oxidation States and Stereochemistry of Zirconium and Hafnium

Oxidation state	Coordination number	Geometry	Examples
Zr^0	6	Octahedral(?)	$[Zr(dipy)_3]$?
Zr^{II}, d^2	?	?	$ZrCl_2$
Zr^{III}, Hf^{III}, d^1	?	?	$ZrCl_3$, $HfBr_3$
Zr^{IV}, Hf^{IV}, d^0	4	Tetrahedral	$ZrCl_4(g)$
	6	Octahedral	Li_2ZrF_6, $Zr(acac)_2Cl_2$, $ZrCl_6{}^{2-}$, $ZrCl_4(s)$
	7	Pentagonal bipyramidal	Na_3ZrF_7, Na_3HfF_7
		As $TaF_7{}^{2-}$, page 135	$(NH_4)_3ZrF_7$
		See text, Fig. 30-A-1	ZrO_2, HfO_2 (monoclinic)
	8	Square antiprism	$Zr(acac)_4$, $[Zr_4(OH)_8(H_2O)_{16}]^{8+}$, $Zr(SO_4)_2 \cdot 4H_2O$
		Dodecahedron	$[Zr(C_2O_4)_4]^{4-}$, $[ZrX_4(diars)_2]$

given, the small differences being largely in solubilities or volatilities of compounds, and in ion-exchange and solvent extraction behavior.[1]

The most important difference from titanium is that lower oxidation states are of minor importance. There are few authenticated compounds of these elements except in their tetravalent states. Like titanium, they form interstitial borides, carbides, nitrides, etc., but of course these are not to be regarded as having the metals in definite oxidation states. Increased size also makes the oxides more basic, the aqueous chemistry somewhat more extensive, and permits the attainment of coordination numbers 7 and, commonly, 8 in a number of compounds.

30-A-1. The Elements

Zirconium occurs widely over the earth's crust but not in very concentrated deposits. The major minerals are *baddeleyite*, a form of ZrO_2, and *zircon*, $ZrSiO_4$. The chemical similarity of zirconium and hafnium is well exemplified in their geochemistry, for hafnium is found in nature in all zirconium minerals in the range of fractions of a percent of the zirconium content. Separation of the two elements is extremely difficult, even more so than for adjacent lanthanides, but it can now be accomplished satisfactorily by ion exchange or solvent extraction fractionation methods.

Zirconium metal, m 1855 ± 15°, like titanium, is hard and corrosion resistant, resembling stainless steel in appearance. It is made by the Kroll process (page 799). Hafnium metal, m 2222 ± 30°, is similar. Like titanium, these metals are fairly resistant to acids, and they are best dissolved in HF where the formation of anionic fluoro complexes is im-

[1] See, e.g., W. Fischer, *et al.*, *Angew. Chem.* (*Internat.*), **5**, 15 (1966).

portant in the stabilization of the solutions. Zirconium will burn in air at high temperatures, reacting more rapidly with nitrogen than with oxygen, to give a mixture of nitride, oxide and oxonitride, Zr_2ON_2.

30-A-2. Compounds of Zirconium and Hafnium

Halides. $ZrCl_4$ is a white solid, subliming at 331°; it is monomeric and tetrahedral in the vapor. The structure in the crystal is not certain although there is some evidence to suggest that $ZrBr_4$ and ZrI_4, which are similar in properties to $ZrCl_4$, have a cubic close-packed arrangement of halide ions with Zr atoms in octahedral holes. It resembles $TiCl_4$ in its chemical properties. It may be prepared by chlorination of heated zirconium, zirconium carbide or a mixture of ZrO_2 and charcoal; it fumes in moist air, and it is hydrolyzed vigorously by water. Hydrolysis proceeds only part way at room temperature, affording the stable oxochloride,

$$ZrCl_4 + 9H_2O = ZrOCl_2 \cdot 8H_2O + 2HCl$$

$ZrCl_4$ also combines with donors such as ethers, esters, $POCl_3$ and CH_3CN, and with Cl^- ions to form six-coordinate species.

Hexachlorozirconates can be obtained by adding CsCl or RbCl to solutions of $ZrCl_4$ in concentrated HCl. The $ZrCl_6^{2-}$ ion is unstable in solutions and even $15M$ HCl solutions contain some cationic hydroxo species and the oxochloride can be crystallized from such solutions.

$ZrCl_4$ also combines with two moles of certain diarsines (as do $TiCl_4$, $HfCl_4$, and several other tetrahalides of these group IV elements) to form $ZrCl_4(diars)_2$, which has the dodecahedral type of eight-coordinate structure;[2a] 1:1 complexes are also formed but these are probably dimeric with octahedral Zr. Two moles of several nitrogen ligands are also added but the coordination numbers in these complexes are uncertain.[2b]

$ZrBr_4$ and ZrI_4 are similar to $ZrCl_4$. ZrF_4 is a white crystalline solid subliming at 903° which, unlike the other halides, is insoluble in donor solvents; it has an eight-coordinate structure with square antiprisms joined by sharing fluorines. Hydrated fluorides, $ZrF_4 \cdot 1$ or $3H_2O$, can be crystallized from $HF-HNO_3$ solutions.[3] The trihydrate has an eight-coordinate structure with two bridging fluorines, $(H_2O)_3F_3ZrF_2ZrF_3(H_2O)_3$.[4]

Zirconium Oxide and Mixed Oxides. Addition of hydroxide to zirconium(IV) solutions causes the precipitation of white gelatinous

[2a] R. J. H. Clark, J. Lewis and R. S. Nyholm, *J. Chem. Soc.*, **1962**, 2460.
[2b] G. W. A. Fowles and R. A. Walton, *J. Chem. Soc.*, **1964**, 4330.
[3] S. Maričič, P. Strohal and Z. Veksli, *J. Inorg. Nucl. Chem.*, **25**, 791 (1963).
[4] T. N. Waters, *Chem. and Ind.*, **1964**, 713.

$ZrO_2 \cdot nH_2O$, where the water content is variable;[5] no true hydroxide, $Zr(OH)_4$, exists. On strong heating, this hydrous oxide gives hard, white, insoluble ZrO_2. This has an extremely high melting point (2700°), exceptional resistance to attack by both acids and alkalies, and good mechanical properties; it is used for crucibles and furnace cores. ZrO_2 in its monoclinic (baddeleyite) form and one form of HfO_2 are isomorphous and have a structure in which the metal atoms are seven coordinate, but in a very irregular way as shown in Figure 30-A-1. ZrO_2 also has two cubic forms in which Zr is eight-coordinate.

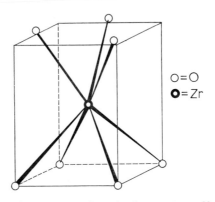

$O = O$
$\bullet = Zr$

Fig. 30-A-1.   Diagram showing approximately the structure of baddeleyite, monoclinic ZrO_2. The Zr—O distances range from 2.04 to 2.26 A, and the O—Zr—O angles from 72 to 91°. The next nearest oxygen atoms are 3.77 A from Zr.

A number of compounds called "zirconates" may be made by combining oxides, hydroxides, nitrates, etc., of other metals with similar zirconium compounds and firing the mixtures at 1000–2500°. These, like their titanium analogs, are mixed metal oxides; there are no discrete zirconate ions known. $CaZrO_3$ is isomorphous with perovskite, and there are a number of $M^{II}_2ZrO_4$ compounds having the spinel structure.

Aqueous Chemistry and Complexes. ZrO_2 is more basic than TiO_2 and is virtually insoluble in excess base. There is a more extensive aqueous chemistry of zirconium because of a lower tendency toward complete hydrolysis. Nevertheless hydrolysis does occur and it is very doubtful indeed if Zr^{4+} aquo ions exist even in strongly acid solutions. The hydrolyzed ion is often referred to as the "zirconyl" ion and written ZrO^{2+}. However, there is little, if any, reliable evidence for the existence of such an oxo ion either in solution or in crystalline salts. The most important "zirconyl" salt is $ZrOCl_2 \cdot 8H_2O$ which crystallizes from dilute hydrochloric

[5] A. Clearfield, *Inorg. Chem.*, **3**, 146 (1964).

acid solutions. Like the isomorphous bromide, it contains[6] the ion $[Zr_4(OH)_8(H_2O)_{16}]^{8+}$. Here the Zr atoms lie in a distorted square and are linked by pairs of hydroxo bridges. They are also bound to four water molecules so that the Zr atom is coordinated by eight oxygen atoms in a distorted square antiprismatic arrangement. There is at present no X-ray data on other salts, but there is *no* evidence for "ZrO^{2+}" or "HfO^{2+}" ions in compounds such as $ZrO(NO_3)_2 \cdot 2H_2O$, $ZrO(C_2H_3O_2)_2$, $HfOF_2$, $ZrOC_2O_4 \cdot nH_2O$,[7] etc. While some compounds have infrared spectra with bands at 850–900 cm^{-1} close to the region characteristic of M=O groups, these bands probably arise from the anti-symmetric modes of Zr—O—Zr groups.

In acid solutions Zr^{IV} ions are polymeric; at $2.8M$ HCl the main species is a trimer,[8] probably $[Zr_3(OH)_6Cl_3]^{3+}$ but the degree of polymerization increases with decreasing acid strength and is influenced by the age of the solutions. The studies are also complicated by slowness in attaining equilibrium in the solutions. The stable phase which crystallizes from chloride solutions is the tetramer and in concentrated Zr and Hf solutions there is some X-ray scattering evidence for the tetrameric species, probably $[M_4(OH)_8(H_2O)_{16}]^{8+}$. In 1–$2M$ perchloric acid solutions up to $0.02M$ Zr, the major species also appear to be $[Zr_3(OH)_4]^{8+}$ and $[Zr_4(OH)_8]^{8+}$, and all available evidence is consistent with trimeric or tetrameric ions at low acidities from 0.5–$2.5M$ for both HCl and $HClO_4$.

Some seemingly simple zirconium salts are best regarded as essentially covalent molecules, or as complexes; examples are the carboxylates $Zr(OCOR)_4$, the acetylacetonate[9] and the nitrate. Like its Ti analog, the latter is made by heating the initial solid adduct of N_2O_5 and N_2O_4 obtained in the reaction:

$$ZrCl_4 + 4N_2O_5 \xrightarrow{30°} Zr(NO_3)_4 \cdot xN_2O_5 \cdot yN_2O_4 + 4NO_2Cl$$

It forms colorless sublimable crystals. It is soluble in water but insoluble in toluene, whose ring it nitrates. Hafnium gives only $Hf(NO_3)_4 \cdot N_2O_5$.[10a] Nitrato complexes, $M(NO_3)_6^-$ are also known but neither the structure of these ions, nor of the nitrates, is certain although chelate nitrate groups may be involved.[10b]

Zirconium solutions with sulfate as anion show considerable difference from Cl^-, NO_3^- or ClO_4^- solutions. Even at low acidities, strong neutral and anionic complexes, some of which may be polymeric, are formed.

[6] A. Clearfield and P. A. Vaughan, *Acta Cryst.*, **9**, 555 (1956).

[7] L. M. Zaitsev, *Russ. J. Inorg. Chem.*, **9**, 1279 (1964).

[8] R. L. Angstadt and S. Y. Tyree, *J. Inorg. Nucl. Chem.*, **24**, 917 (1962).

[9] J. V. Silverton and J. L. Hoard, *Inorg. Chem.*, **2**, 243 (1963); M. Cox, J. Lewis and R. S. Nyholm, *J. Chem. Soc.*, **1964**, 6113.

[10a] B. O. Field and C. J. Hardy, *J. Chem. Soc.*, **1964**, 4428, and references therein.

[10b] K. W. Bagnall, D. Brown and J. G. H. du Preez, *J. Chem. Soc.*, **1965**, 5532.

From $6M$ H_2SO_4, crystals of $Zr(SO_4)_2 \cdot 4H_2O$ can be grown; this complex has square antiprism Zr with each Zr bound to four water molecules and four sulfate groups which act as bridges to give infinite sheets.[11] Under other conditions, basic salts which have coordinated sulfate as well as hydroxo groups can be obtained and also anions in salts like $(NH_4)_2$-$[Zr(SO_4)_3] \cdot 3H_2O$ and $M^I_4[Zr(SO_4)_4] \cdot nH_2O$.

Like Ce^{IV}, Pu^{IV} and other similar ions, Zr^{IV} gives an insoluble iodate which can be crystallized from nitric acid solution; it has an antiprism structure with bridging IO_3 groups.[12] The oxalate, $Na_4[Zr(C_2O_4)_4] \cdot 3H_2O$ and its Hf analog are isomorphous with dodecahedral coordination;[13] although isomers are theoretically possible, the anions lose oxalate by hydrolysis and/or aquation so that racemization occurs rapidly.[14] There are complexes with EDTA and similar ligands.[15]

Among the best-known complex salts of Zr^{IV} are the halogeno anions. A number of salts of the type $M^I_2ZrF_6$ have long been assumed to contain octahedral $[ZrF_6]^{2-}$ ions, analogous to the $[ZrCl_6]^{2-}$ ions noted above. However, K_2ZrF_6 contains ZrF_8 units formed by sharing of F^- ions, although Li_2ZrF_6 does contain the octahedral ion. $[ZrF_7]^{3-}$ ions also apparently occur with two different structures, depending on the cations present. Na_3ZrF_7 and Na_3HfF_7 contain $[MF_7]^{3-}$ ions which are pentagonal bipyramids (IF_7 structure), whereas, in $(NH_4)_3ZrF_7$, the $[ZrF_7]^{3-}$ ion has the structure shown on page 135 for the $[TaF_7]^{2-}$ ion. In aqueous solution ZrF_7^{3-} dissociates completely to give ZrF_6^{2-}. A number of compounds of the types $M^{II}_2ZrF_8$ ($M = Zn^{2+}$, Cd^{2+}, Cu^{2+}, Ni^{2+}) are known but their structures have not been investigated. $[ZrF_8]^{4-}$ ions may be present, but this cannot necessarily be assumed.

Lower Oxidation States. $ZrBr_2$ and $ZrBr_3$, prepared by passing a mixture of $ZrBr_4$ and H_2 over aluminum wire at $450°$, and ZrI_2 and ZrI_3, made by reducing ZrI_4 with Zr, are known. $ZrCl_4$, but not $HfCl_4$, is reduced by Zr metal at about $450°$ so that the relatively involatile $ZrCl_3$ remains while $HfCl_4$ sublimes; further reduction of $ZrCl_3$ by Zr at $675°$ gives black $ZrCl_2$.[16] ZrF_3 also seems authentic. These compounds have not been extensively studied, but $ZrCl_3$, $ZrBr_3$, ZrI_3 and HfI_3 appear to have chain structures involving metal–metal bonding and MX_6 octahedra.[17] There is no evidence for lower oxidation states in aqueous

[11] J. D. Singer and D. T. Cromer, *Acta Cryst.*, **12**, 719 (1959).

[12] A. C. Larson and D. T. Cromer, *Acta Cryst.*, **14**, 128 (1961).

[13] G. L. Glen, J. V. Silverton and J. L. Hoard, *Inorg. Chem.*, **2**, 250 (1963).

[14] F. A. Johnson and E. M. Larson, *Inorg. Chem.*, **1**, 159 (1962).

[15] B. J. Intome and A. E. Martell, *Inorg. Chem.*, **3**, 81 (1964); L. P. Varga and D. N. Hume, *Inorg. Chem.*, **2**, 201 (1963).

[16] B. Swaroop and S. N. Flengas, *Can. J. Chem.*, **43**, 2115 (1965).

[17] L. F. Dahl, T. Chiang, P. W. Seabaugh and E. M. Larson, *Inorg. Chem.*, **3**, 1236 (1964).

solution. The violet zirconium(0) compound, $[Zr(dipy)_3]$, is formed by reduction of $ZrCl_4$ with lithium in presence of 2,2'-dipyridyl in tetrahydrofuran solution.

30-B. NIOBIUM AND TANTALUM

These elements, though metallic in many respects, have chemistries in the V oxidation state which are very similar to those of typical nonmetals. They have virtually no cationic chemistry, but form numerous anionic species. Their halides and oxohalides, which are their most important simple compounds, are mostly volatile and are readily hydrolyzed. The oxidation states and stereochemistries are summarized in Table 30-B-1.

30-B-1. The Elements

Niobium and tantalum are of about equal abundance and frequently occur together in nature. They are often found as $Fe(NbO_3)_2$, $Fe(TaO_3)_2$ or an intermediate composition. Manganese sometimes replaces the iron.

The two elements are separated by fractional crystallization of fluoro complexes or fractional distillation of the pentachlorides; the alkali metal salts of complex halides can be used as electrolytes for the electrolytic deposition of the metals. Niobium and tantalum are bright, high-melting metals (Nb, 1950°; Ta, 3010°) which are very resistant to acids. The best solvent is a mixture of nitric and hydrofluoric acids, which gives a solution containing fluoro complexes. The metals are slowly attacked by fused alkalies and will react with various nonmetals at elevated temperatures.

TABLE 30-B-1
Oxidation States and Stereochemistries of Niobium and Tantalum

Oxidation State	Coordination Number	Geometry	Examples
Nb^{-I}, Ta^{-I}	6	Octahedral(?)	$[M(CO)_6]^-$
Nb^I, Ta^I		π-Complex	$(\pi\text{-}C_5H_5)M(CO)_4$
Nb^{II}, Ta^{II}, d^3	?	?	NbO(?); $TaCl_2$(?)
Nb^{III}, Ta^{III}, d^2	?	?	MCl_3, MBr_3
Nb^{IV}, Ta^{IV}, d^1	6	Octahedral	MO_2, MX_4, MCl_4py_2
	8	Dodecahedral	$NbX_4(diars)_2$
Nb^V, Ta^V, d^0	5(?)	?	$MF_5(g)$
		Trig. bipyramid	MCl_5(vapors)
	6	Octahedral	$NaMO_3$(perovskite), $NbCl_5 \cdot OPCl_3$, $TaCl_5 \cdot S(CH_3)_2$, TaF_6^-, $NbOCl_3$, M_2Cl_{10}, MCl_6^-
	7	?	TaX_5(diars)
	7	See text, p. 135	K_2MF_7, K_3NbOF_6
	8	Sq. antiprism	Na_3TaF_8
	8	?	$Nb(troponate)_4^+$
		π-Complex	$(\pi\text{-}C_5H_5)_2TaH_3$

30-B-2. Pentavalent Niobium and Tantalum

Oxygen Compounds. The oxides Nb_2O_5 and Ta_2O_5 are white powders obtained by dehydration of the hydrous oxides (so-called "niobic" and "tantalic acids"), by roasting compounds with other elements (e.g., sulfur, carbon) which can be driven off as oxides in excess oxygen, or, in the case of Ta_2O_5, by heating the metal in oxygen.

They are dense, relatively inert substances which can be brought into solution by fusing them with alkali hydrogen sulfate, alkali carbonate or hydroxide, or by treatment with concentrated hydrofluoric acid. They are not attacked by other acids.

The product of fusing Nb_2O_5 with excess sodium carbonate is the so-called orthoniobate,

$$Nb_2O_5 + 3Na_2CO_3 = 2Na_3NbO_4 + 3CO_2$$

Tantalum(V) oxide reacts more sluggishly but in the same manner. The formulas of the niobate or tantalate are inferred from the amount of CO_2 displaced. On leaching the carbonate melt with water, a residue is obtained which is not the orthoniobate, however, but the metaniobate, $NaNbO_3$, which has the perovskite structure (page 51). A number of other metaniobates, such as those of iron, manganese and other divalent metals, $M(NbO_3)_2$, are also known. These also are not niobates in the sense of containing any discrete "niobate" ions but are mixed metal oxides.[1] Similar perovskite-type mixed oxides containing tantalum are also known, as well as mixed oxides with the tungsten bronze structure[2] (page 935).

Both Nb and Ta form polymeric oxo anions in aqueous solution. These polyanions have a general similarity to those of Mo and W discussed in some detail later (page 938). The tantalate polyanion, which exists both in crystalline salts and in solution, has been most extensively studied,[3,4,5] and there is evidence that the species $H_2Nb_6O_{19}^{6-}$, $HNb_6O_{19}^{7-}$ and $Nb_6O_{19}^{8-}$ exist and acidity constants have been estimated.[6]

When Ta_2O_5 is fused with KOH, the aqueous extract precipitated with ethanol and the precipitate crystallized from dilute KOH, a crystalline salt of composition $K_8Ta_6O_{19} \cdot 16H_2O$ is obtained, which X-ray studies have shown to contain a discrete $Ta_6O_{19}^{8-}$ ion. Each tantalum atom is surrounded by an octahedron of oxygen atoms and there are six TaO_6

[1] F. Galasso and J. Pyle, *Inorg. Chem.*, **2**, 482 (1963); G. Blasse, *J. Inorg. Nucl. Chem.*, **26**, 1191 (1964).

[2] E. Sawaguchi and A. Kikuchi, *J. Phys. Soc.*, *Japan*, **19**, 579 (1964).

[3] W. H. Nelson and R. S. Tobias, *Inorg. Chem.*, **2**, 985 (1963).

[4] W. H. Nelson and R. S. Tobias, *Inorg. Chem.*, **3**, 653 (1964).

[5] J. Aveston and J. S. Johnson, *Inorg. Chem.*, **3**, 1051 (1964).

[6] G. Neumann, *Acta Chem. Scand.*, **18**, 278 (1964).

octahedra packed together to form a larger octahedron within which is an octahedral arrangement of tantalum atoms (Fig. 30-B-1). Essentially the same ion exists in alkaline solutions where, in contrast to the Mo and W

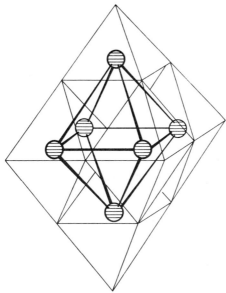

Fig. 30-B-1.   Structure of the $Ta_6O_{19}^{8-}$ ion. The central O atom is shared by all six octahedra. (Reprinted with permission from ref. 3).

polyanions, it does not depolymerize. Presumably the highly charged TaO_6^{7-} and the tetrahedral TaO_4^{3-} are relatively unstable. The reluctance of $Ta_6O_{19}^{8-}$ to protonate beyond $HTa_6O_{19}^{7-}$ and the appearance of an infrared band at about 950 cm^{-1} suggest that the peripheral oxygen atoms may be multiply bonded to the tantalum atoms. On acidification, the Nb and Ta polyanions are degraded to the hydrous pentoxides.

The hydrous pentoxides are also obtained, as gelatinous white precipitates, when the Nb^V and Ta^V halides are treated with water. They redissolve in strong base or in hydrofluoric acid.

Fluorides and Fluoride Complexes. The pentafluorides are made by direct fluorination of the metals, the pentoxides or the pentachlorides. They are both volatile white solids (Nb, m 80°, b 235°; Ta, m 95°, b 229°) giving colorless liquids and vapors. They have the tetrameric structure shown in Figure 30-B-2; they also appear to be polymeric when molten.

The interaction of TaF_5 with SiO_2 at high temperatures gives $TaOF_3$; oxofluorides of Nb are also known.[7]

[7] (a) H. Schafer, et. al., Naturwiss., **51**, 241 (1964); (b) F. P. Gortsema and R. Didchenko, Inorg. Chem., **4**, 182 (1965).

The metals and the pentoxides dissolve in aqueous HF to give fluoro complexes, whose composition depends markedly on the conditions. Addition of CsF to niobium in 50% HF precipitates $CsNbF_6$, while in weakly acidic solutions hydrolyzed species, $[NbO_xF_y \cdot 3H_2O]^{5-2x-y}$, occur

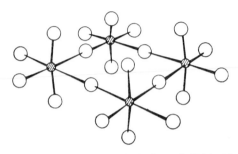

Fig. 30-B-2. The tetrameric structures of NbF_5 and TaF_5 (also MoF_5 and, with slight distortion, RuF_5 and OsF_5); M—F bridge = 2.06 A, non-bridge = 1.77 A. (Adapted from A. J. Edwards, *J. Chem. Soc.*, **1964**, 3714 by permission.)

and compounds such as $K_2NbOF_5 \cdot H_2O$ may be isolated. Although $[Nb(OH)_2F_5]^{2-}$ is as consistent as $[NbOF_5]^{2-}$ with this formula, there is no evidence for such hydroxo species either in solution or in crystalline compounds. Raman spectra show that up to about 35% HF, $[NbOF_5]^{2-}$ is present, while at about 25% HF, $[NbF_6]^-$ begins to form.[8] The hexafluoro complexes of both Nb^V and Ta^V can be made by dry reactions, such as

$$M_2O_5 + 2KCl \xrightarrow{BrF_3} 2KNbF_6$$

Nuclear magnetic resonance studies[9] have shown that the highest fluoro complex in solution is NbF_6^- (see Fig. 30-B-3). However, from solutions with very high F^- concentrations, salts which contain NbF_7^{2-} ions, can be crystallized. This ion is stabilized by crystal forces; both this and TaF_7^{2-} are true 7-coordinate species (see page 135).

From solutions of low acidity and high F^- concentration salts of the $[NbOF_6]^{3-}$ ion can be obtained; salts of this ion and also of $[TaOF_6]^{3-}$ can be made by bromination of the metal in methanol followed by addition of NH_4F or KF.[10]

The Ta^V fluoride system differs somewhat from that of Nb^V in that species up to TaF_8^{3-} and possibly TaF_9^{4-} exist in solution. In $1M$ $HClO_4$ there is some evidence to suggest that TaF_4^+ and TaF_5 may be present.[11]

[8] O. L. Keller, Jr., *Inorg. Chem.*, **2**, 783 (1963).
[9] K. J. Packer and E. L. Muetterties, *J. Amer. Chem. Soc.*, **85**, 3035 (1963).
[10] A. E. Baker and H. M. Haendler, *Inorg. Chem.*, **1**, 127 (1962).
[11] L. P. Varga and H. Freund, *J. Phys. Chem.*, **66**, 21, 187 (1962).

Salts of $[TaOF_5]^{2-}$, $[TaOF_6]^{3-}$, $[TaF_6]^-$, $[TaF_7]^{2-}$ and $[TaF_8]^{3-}$ are known, the latter ion having a square antiprismatic configuration. The higher fluoro complexes hydrolyze in water to oxofluorides, and eventually to Ta_2O_5.

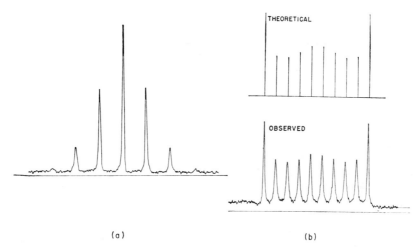

THEORETICAL

OBSERVED

(a)   (b)

Fig. 30-B-3. Nuclear magnetic resonance spectra of NbF_6^-; (a), the ^{93}Nb (spin $\frac{9}{2}$) spectrum at 14.2 Mc/sec., (b), comparison of theoretical ^{19}F (spin $\frac{1}{2}$) spectrum with that observed at 54.6 Mc/sec. (Reproduced by permission from ref. 9.)

In addition to accepting F^-, the fluorides also give adducts with various donor ligands,[12] e.g., $NbF_5 \cdot OEt_2$, $TaF_5 \cdot SEt_2$.

Other Halides of Niobium(V) and Tantalum(V). All six of these are yellow to brown or purple-red solids prepared by direct reaction of the metals with excess of the halogen, or in other ways, for example,

$$2Nb + 5I_2 \xrightarrow{300-400°} 2NbI_5$$
$$Ta_2O_5 + 5C + 5Cl_2 \xrightarrow{ca\ 400°} 2TaCl_5 + 5CO$$

The pentachlorides are conveniently made by action of $SOCl_2$ on the hydrous oxides.[13] The halides melt and boil at 200–300° and are soluble in various organic liquids such as ethers, CCl_4, etc. They are quickly hydrolyzed by water to the hydrous pentoxides and the hydrohalic acid, although the chlorides at least form clear solutions in concentrated hydrochloric acid, presumably by formation of chloro complexes. The chlorides behave as effective Friedel–Crafts catalysts, and also polymerize acetylenes to arenes;

[12] F. Fairbrother, K. H. Grundy and A. Thompson, *J. Chem. Soc.*, **1965**, 765.
[13] K. W. Bagnall and D. Brown, *J. Chem. Soc.*, **1964**, 3021.

their Lewis acid behavior is also shown by the formation of 1:1 complexes with chloride ions[13] and various donor molecules, such as $OPCl_3$,[14] ethers, diarsines and dialkyl sulfides.[15]   When the chlorides are heated with alcohols or alkali metal alkoxides, the dimeric niobium and tantalum alkoxides $[M(OR)_5]_2$ are formed. With lithium amides, $LiNR_2$, amides and imides such as $Ta[N(CH_3)_2]_5$ and $Ta(NCH_3)[N(CH_3)_2]_3$ are formed. Treatment of the chlorides with amines can lead to reduction, e.g., with pyridine $NbCl_4py_2$ is obtained.[16]   The halides (Cl, Br) can also abstract oxygen from certain oxygen donors,[17] e.g.,

$$NbCl_5 + 3(CH_3)_2SO = NbOCl_3 \cdot 2(CH_3)_2SO + (CH_3)_2SCl_2$$
$$(CH_3)_2SCl_2 = ClCH_2SCH_3 + HCl$$

VCl_4 and $MoCl_5$ undergo similar oxygen abstraction reactions.

All of the pentahalides can be sublimed without decomposition in an atmosphere of the appropriate halogen; in the vapor they are monomeric. Electron diffraction studies indicate, but do not conclusively establish that they are trigonal bipyramidal. Crystalline $NbCl_5$ has the dimeric structure shown in Figure 30-B-4a; $NbBr_5$, $TaCl_5$ and $TaBr_5$ are isostructural. In CCl_4 and $MeNO_2$, both $NbCl_5$ and $TaCl_5$ are dimeric but in coordinating solvents, adducts are formed.[18a]   It appears probable that NbI_5 has a hexagonal close-packed array of iodine atoms with niobium atoms in octahedral interstices;[18b] TaI_5 is not isomorphous and its structure is unknown.

Aside from their probable existence in solutions of the pentachlorides in

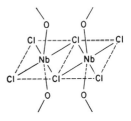

Fig. 30-B-4a.   The dinuclear structure of $NbCl_5$ in the solid. The octahedra are distorted as shown.

Fig. 30-B-4b. The structure of $NbOCl_3$ in the crystal. The oxygen atoms form bridges between infinite chains of the planar Nb_2Cl_6 groups.

[14] C.-I. Brandén and L. G. Sillén, *Acta Chem. Scand.*, **17**, 353 (1963).

[15] D. B. Copley, F. Fairbrother and A. Thompson, *J. Chem. Soc.*, **1964**, 315; K. Feenan and G. W. A. Fowles, *J. Chem. Soc.*, **1965**, 2449; R. T. H. Clark, D. L. Kepert and R. S. Nyholm, *J. Chem. Soc.*, **1965**, 2877.

[16] M. Albrutt, K. Feenan and G. W. A. Fowles, *J. Less Common Metals*, **6**, 299 (1964).

[17] D. B. Copley, F. Fairbrother, K. H. Grundy and A. Thompson, *J. Less Common Metals*, **6**, 407 (1964).

[18a] D. L. Kepert and R. S. Nyholm, *J. Chem. Soc.*, **1965**, 2871.

[18b] W. Littke and G. Brauer, *Z. anorg. Chem.*, **325**, 122 (1963).

concentrated hydrochloric acid, the $[MCl_6]^-$ ions appear also to exist in fused mixtures of the pentachlorides with all of the alkali metal chlorides except LiCl. There are compounds of the composition M^INbCl_6 or M^ITaCl_6, and it seems reasonable to suppose that they contain $[MCl_6]^-$ ions.[13]

Oxohalides. $NbOCl_3$, $TaOCl_3$, $NbOBr_3$, $TaOBr_3$, $NbOI_3$ and NbO_2I are known.[7,19] The chlorides are white, and the bromides yellow, volatile solids; they are, however, less volatile than the corresponding pentahalides, and small amounts of the oxohalides which often arise in the preparation of the pentahalides in systems not scrupulously free of oxygen can be rather easily separated by fractional sublimation.

The best methods of preparation are by pyrolysis of the monoetherate of $TaCl_5$ for $TaOCl_3$ and by controlled reaction between the pentahalides and molecular oxygen for the others. They are all hydrolyzed to the hydrous pentoxides by water.

It has been reported that from their solutions in concentrated hydrohalic acids and alkali metal cations, complex oxohalides such as M^INbOCl_4 and $M^I_2NbOCl_5$ can be crystallized; the latter ion has an Nb=O group.[20]

The oxotrihalides are monomeric in the vapor state but the lower volatility, compared to the corresponding pentahalides, is understandable in view of the structure of $NbOCl_3$ (Fig. 30-B-4b).

The pentahalides also react with N_2O_4 in ionizing solvents such as CH_3CN to give solvated oxonitrates, e.g., $NbO_2NO_3 \cdot 0.67CH_3CN$, which appear to be polymeric with oxo bridges. In the absence of solvent, $NbO(NO_3)_3$ and $TaO(NO_3)_3$ can be obtained.[21]

Other Compounds. These include nitrides, sulfides, silicides, selenides and phosphides, as well as many alloys.[22] Definite hydride phases also appear to exist.

There are no simple salts such as sulfates, nitrates, etc. Sulphates such as $Nb_2O_2(SO_4)_3$ probably have oxo bridges and coordinated sulfato groups.[23a] In HNO_3, H_2SO_4 or HCl solutions, Nb^V can exist as cationic, neutral and anionic species, hydrolyzed, polymeric and colloidal forms in equilibrium, depending on the conditions.[23b]

The tropolonate ion gives 8-coordinate complexes,[24] with both Nb and Ta of formula $[(C_7H_5O_2)_4M]^+$.

[19] H. Schäfer and R. Gerken, *Z. anorg. Chem.*, **317**, 705 (1962).

[20] D. Brown, *J. Chem. Soc.*, **1964**, 4944.

[21] K. W. Bagnall, D. Brown and P. J. Jones, *J. Chem. Soc.*, **1964**, 2396.

[22] L. H. Brixner and G. Teufer, *Inorg. Chem.*, **2**, 992 (1963); E. Bjerkelund and A. Kjekshus, *Z. anorg. Chem.*, **328**, 235 (1964); F. Jellinek, *J. Less Common Metals*, **4**, 9 (1962).

[23a] Ya. G. Goroschenko and M. I. Andreava, *Russ. J. Inorg. Chem.*, **8**, 505 (1963).

[23b] B. I. Nabivanets, *Russ. J. Inorg. Chem.*, **9**, 590 (1964).

[24] E. L. Muetterties and C. M. Wright, *J. Amer. Chem. Soc*, **87**, 4706 (1965).

The volatile, white, crystalline compound, $(\pi\text{-}C_5H_5)_2TaH_3$, is obtained by the action of $TaCl_5$ on a solution of sodium cyclopentadienide containing $NaBH_4$; its proton resonance spectrum shows that there are three hydrogen atoms bound to Ta, only two of which are equivalent (see page 767).

30-B-3. Lower Oxidation States

Niobium(IV) and Tantalum(IV) Oxides. NbO_2 and TaO_2 are dark grey to black powders; they are insoluble in water or acids, but they dissolve with oxidation in hot aqueous alkalies. NbO_2 is obtained on heating Nb_2O_5 to a white heat in a stream of hydrogen; TaO_2, by reduction of Ta_2O_5 with carbon at high temperature. The dioxides have distorted rutile lattices, with metal ions in adjacent MO_6 octahedra drawn toward each other, and the magnetic susceptibilities are low. Evidently metal–metal bonds are present,[25] both here and in the disulfides, MS_2.

The Lower Halides. By reduction of the pentahalides with either the metal (Nb or Ta) or with aluminum many lower-valent halides can be obtained,[26-28] some of which are non-stoichiometric, and many of which are metal atom cluster compounds (see page 656). The known anhydrous compounds—or phases—are summarized[28] in Tables 30-B-2 and 30-B-3.

TABLE 30-B-2
Lower Halides of Niobium

X/Nb	F	Cl	Br	I
2		a	$NbBr_2$	NbI_2?
2.33		$NbCl_{2.33}$		
2.50	$NbF_{2.5}$			
2.67		$NbCl_{2.67}$—	$NbBr_{2.67}$—	$NbI_{2.67}$—
3	NbF_3	—$NbCl_{3.13}$	—$NbBr_3$	—NbI_3
4	NbF_4	$NbCl_4$	$NbBr_4$	NbI_4

a The $NbCl_2$ reported earlier is now [28] recognized to be $NbCl_{2.33}$.

In addition, there are the hydrated $M_6X_{14}\cdot 7H_2O$ compounds. We shall discuss the anhydrous compounds first.

The only dihalides found are $NbBr_2$ and, with some uncertainty, NbI_2. The structures of these are unknown. The compound once thought to be $NbCl_2$ is now known[28] to be $NbCl_{2.33}$ or Nb_6Cl_{14}. It is built up of

[25] B-O. Marinder, *Acta Chem. Scand.*, **15**, 707 (1961).

[26] R. E. McCarley, *et. al.*, *Inorg. Chem.*, **2**, 540, 547 (1963); **3**, 1232 (1964); **4**, 1482, 1486, 1491 (1965); P. W. Seabaugh and J. D. Corbett, *Inorg. Chem.*, **4**, 176 (1965).

[27] H. Schäfer, *et. al.*, *Z. anorg. Chem.*, **300**, 1 (1959); **311**, 134 (1961); **331**, 154 (1964).

[28] H. Schäfer and H. G. Schnering, *Angew. Chem.*, **76**, 833 (1964); M. B. Robin and N. A. Kuebler, *Inorg. Chem.*, **4**, 978 (1965); H. Schäfer, *et. al.*, *J. Less Common Metals*, **8**, 95 (1965).

TABLE 30-B-3
Lower Halides of Tantalum

X/Ta	F	Cl	Br	I
2			$TaBr_{2.33}$	
2.33				$TaI_{2.33}$
2.50		$TaCl_{2.5}$	$TaBr_{2.5}$	
2.67				
3		$TaCl_{2.9}–TaCl_{3.1}$	$TaBr_{2.9}–TaBr_{3.1}$	TaI_3
4		$TaCl_4$	$TaBr_4$	TaI_4

$Nb_6Cl_{12}^{2+}$ ions (see Fig. 30-B-6) connected by bridging Cl^- ions. $TaI_{2.33}$ appears to be similarly constituted.[28a]

The three $MX_{2.5}$ compounds also appear[28] to be built of M_6X_{12} groups connected in a different manner by bridging X^- groups.

The so-called trihalides are all known except TaF_3. They can be prepared in various ways, e.g., by thermal decomposition, by disproportionation of higher halides or by reduction of higher halides with H_2. The course of the reactions depends very much on the temperatures used and on the presence of temperature gradients, arranged so that the products condense in certain parts of the apparatus while more volatile substances pass on.

The most remarkable thing about the "trihalides" is their lack of stoichiometry, for which the following tentative explanation has been suggested.[28] The crystal structure of $NbCl_{2.67}$ (Nb_3Cl_8) consists of a distorted *hcp* array of Cl^- ions, with niobium atoms occupying octahedral interstices in such a way that there are triangular groups of niobium atoms in adjacent octahedra, close enough to be bonded together into metal atom clusters. The arrangement is essentially the same as that of the Mo and O atoms in $Zn_2Mo_3O_8$ and is depicted schematically on page 657. Thus $NbCl_{2.67}$ (and presumably other niobium halides with this stoichiometry) are structurally well-defined phases in a perfect condition. Moreover, according to a study[28] of $NbCl_4$, this compound has a closely related structure, derived by removal of one third of the niobium atoms from $NbCl_{2.67}$ in such a way that each Nb_3 triangle becomes an Nb_2 pair. It is then postulated that solid solutions of $NbCl_4$ in $NbCl_{2.67}$ are stable up to about the composition $NbCl_{3.13}$, beyond which the pure $NbCl_4$ phase separates. A similar explanation would evidently be appropriate for the "$NbBr_3$" and "NbI_3" systems, and possibly also for the tantalum "trihalides." However, there is at present a need for further studies, before this interesting problem can be regarded as definitively solved.

[28a] D. Bauer, H. G. Schnering and H. Schäfer, *J. Less Common Metals*, **8**, 388 (1965).

The *tetrahalides* can be obtained by reduction of the pentahalides with metal or aluminum in a temperature gradient at 300–600°,[26] e.g.,

$$4NbBr_5(g) + Nb(s) = 5NbBr_4(g)$$

TaI_4 is probably easiest made by thermal decomposition of its pyridine complex:

$$2TaI_5 + 5py = 2TaI_4py_2 + pyI_2$$
$$TaI_4py_2 \xrightarrow{200°} TaI_4 + 2py$$

NbI_5 may be thermally decomposed to NbI_4.

The tetrahalides are all dark solids, and, with the exception of NbF_4,[7b] volatile above about 300°. They are diamagnetic despite the fact that the M^{IV} ions have one d electron. For NbI_4 the structure is known (Fig. 30-B-5). The diamagnetism is clearly attributable to Nb—Nb bonding. It has

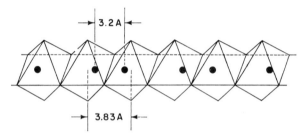

Fig. 30-B-5.   The structure of NbI_4. The iodine atoms are at the apices of the octahedra, and the filled circles represent Nb atoms.

been reported[27] that $TaCl_4$ and $NbBr_4$ are isomorphous with $NbCl_4$, the structure of which has been mentioned above. NbF_4 appears[7b] to have octahedral coordination of Nb by F.

The compounds $Nb_6Cl_{14}\cdot7H_2O$, $Nb_6Br_{14}\cdot7H_2O$, $Ta_6Cl_{14}\cdot7H_2O$ and $Ta_6Br_{14}\cdot7H_2O$ are best obtained in the following reactions (X = Cl or Br)

$$NbX_5 + Cd \xrightarrow[\text{heat}]{\text{red}} Nb_6X_{14}(?) + CdX_2 \xrightarrow[\text{dil. HX}]{\text{diss. in warm}} \xrightarrow{H_2S} CdS + Nb_6X_{14}\cdot7H_2O$$

$$TaX_5 + Pb \xrightarrow[\text{heat}]{\text{red}} Ta_6X_{14}(?) + PbX_2 \xrightarrow[\text{dil. HX}]{\text{warm}} Ta_6X_{14}\cdot7H_2O$$

They are soluble in water and alcohols, and only two of the halogens are immediately precipitated by Ag^+. From an X-ray diffraction study of the alcohol solutions, it was shown that these substances ionize in solution to give the kinetically inert $[M_6X_{12}]^{2+}$ ions which have the structure shown for $[Ta_6Cl_{12}]^{2+}$ in Figure 30-B-6. These $[M_6X_{12}]^{2+}$ groups are one of the more important types of metal atom cluster compounds.

Some lower oxohalides, e.g., $TaOCl_2$ and $NbOI_2$, are known, and these also appear to have metal–metal bonds.

Niobium(IV) and Tantalum(IV) Complexes.   Only Nb^V can be reduced in aqueous acid solutions by active metals or electrolytically, giving blue solutions of uncertain nature.   The ion $[Nb_6O_3(SO_4)_{12}]^{8-}$, containing both Nb^{IV} and Nb^{III}, has been alleged to arise in sulfuric acid.

Fig. 30-B-6.   The structure of the complex ion $[Ta_6Cl_{12}]^{2+}$.   (Reprinted with permission from L. Pauling, *The Nature of the Chemical Bond*, 3rd ed., Cornell University Press, Ithaca, New York, 1960, p. 440.)

When solutions of $NbCl_5$ in HCl-saturated alcohols are electrolytically reduced, very air-sensitive, orange to brown solutions are obtained, from which salts of the $[NbCl_5(OR)]^{2-}$ ions can be precipitated.[29]   Other species have also been isolated using ethanol:

$$NbCl_5 \xrightarrow[+e]{C_2H_5OH/HCl} NbCl_4? \xrightarrow{py/C_2H_5OH} [NbCl(OC_2H_5)_3py]_2$$

red–purple   red

$$[Nb(OEt)_4]_n \xleftarrow{NaOC_2H_5} \qquad \Big\downarrow \begin{smallmatrix}HCl/C_2H_5OH \\ \text{and} \\ pyH+\end{smallmatrix}$$

$$\xrightarrow{py/HCl/C_2H_5OH} (pyH)_2[NbCl_5(OC_2H_5)]$$

The $[NbCl_5(OR)]^{2-}$ compounds have magnetic moments corresponding to one unpaired electron, but $[NbCl(OC_2H_5)_3py]_2$ is diamagnetic, indicating an Nb–Nb interaction.   The diamagnetic tetraethoxide is polymeric and very readily hydrolyzed.

NbX_5 (X = Cl, Br, I) and TaI_5 are readily reduced by pyridine to give MX_4py_2 complexes.[26]   They are non-electrolytes and can exist in two forms, e.g., red and green $NbBr_4py_2$.   It is possible that these are *cis* and *trans* isomers, but there is some evidence against this explanation.   These complexes have low magnetic moments, e.g., 1.05 BM for NbI_4py_2 and 0.43 BM for $TaBr_4py_2$, which is a consequence of the combined effects of spin-orbit coupling and distortions of the ligand field from full octahedral symmetry.

[29] R. A. D. Wentworth and C. H. Brubaker, Jr., *Inorg. Chem.*, **2**, 551 (1963); **3**, 47 (1964).

30 + A.I.C.

A series of diarsine complexes of Nb (but not Ta) have been made, e.g., by interaction of $NbCl_5$ with the arsine; these are isomorphous with similar complexes of Ti, V, Zr and Hf. They are paramagnetic but the magnetic behavior is complicated.[30]

Aliphatic amines also reduce the pentahalides, and some π-cyclopentadienyl complexes of M^{IV} are also known.

Oxidation States I and $-$ I. These are found only in CO and π-C_5H_5 complexes, e.g., $[M(CO)_6]^-$ and π-$C_5H_5M(CO)_4$.[31] Reduction of diglyme solutions of MCl_5 by sodium, in presence of CO and a catalytic amount of $Fe(CO)_5$, affords the yellow $[Na(diglyme)_2][M(CO)_6]$ compounds. By reaction of these compounds with NaC_5H_5 and $HgCl_2$ (as oxidant), the π-C_5H_5 carbonyls are obtained. π-$C_5H_5Ta(CO)_4$, for example, is a red solid (m 171°) which sublimes and is soluble in hydrocarbons.

$$[Na(diglyme)_2][M(CO)_6] + NaC_5H_5 + HgCl_2 =$$
$$\pi\text{-}C_5H_5M(CO)_4 + 2CO + 2NaCl + Hg + 2 \text{ diglyme} \quad [M = V, Nb, Ta]$$

The diglyme salt of $[Ta(CO)_6]^-$ also reacts with C_2H_5HgCl to give a compound $C_2H_5HgTa(CO)_6$ which appears to be 7-coordinate with a Hg—Ta bond.[32]

30-C. MOLYBDENUM AND TUNGSTEN

Molybdenum and tungsten are quite similar chemically, although there are differences between them in various types of compounds which are not easy to explain. Some compounds of the same type, for example, the hexacarbonyls, also can differ quite noticeably in their reactivities toward various reagents and, again, no simple explanations are possible; for example, $Mo(CO)_6$ but not $W(CO)_6$ will react with acetic acid to give a diacetate.

Except for compounds with π-acid ligands, there is not a great deal of similarity to chromium. The divalent state, well defined for Cr, is not well known for Mo and W, and the high stability of Cr^{III} in its complexes has no counterpart in Mo or W chemistry. For the heavier elements, the higher oxidation states are more common and more stable to reduction.

Both Mo and W have a wide variety of stereochemistries in addition to the variety of oxidation states, and their chemistry is among the most complex of the transition elements. Uranium has sometimes been classed with Mo and W in group VI, and indeed there are some valid, though often rather superficial, similarities; the three elements form volatile hexa-

[30] R. J. H. Clark, et al., J. Chem. Soc., **1965**, 2865.
[31] R. P. M. Werner, A. M. Filbey and S. A. Manastyrsky, Inorg. Chem., **3**, 298 (1964).
[32] K. A. Keblys and M. Dubeck, Inorg. Chem., **3**, 1646 (1964).

fluorides, oxohalides and oxo anions which are similar in certain respects. There is little resemblance to the sulfur group except in regard to stoichiometric similarities, for example, SeF_6, WF_6, $SO_4{}^{2-}$, $MoO_4{}^{2-}$, and such comparisons are not profitable.

Although we do not discuss them in this order, the chemistries of Mo and W can be classed broadly as follows:

1. *Aqueous chemistry of oxo compounds:* (a) Both Mo^{VI} and W^{VI} give tetrahedral oxo anions $MO_4{}^{2-}$ whose alkali metal salts are water soluble. These anions polymerize on acidification giving rise to a very complicated series of isopolyanions, the nature of which depends on the circumstances; in the presence of other elements, heteropolyanions can be obtained.

(b) Mo^{VI} and W^{VI} can give a variety of complexes, whose constitution is not especially well known, with organic hydroxo compounds such as sugars, tartaric acid, etc. Interest in such species derives in part from the fact that Mo is thought to be one of the essential elements in biological systems, e.g., in nitrogen-fixing bacteria; there has accordingly been much study of aqueous Mo^{VI} complexes but the precise nature of many of the species is hard to ascertain.[1]

(c) The reduction of aqueous Mo^{VI} and W^{VI} species can lead to a variety of oxo species of Mo^V and W^V. This formation of oxo species with M=O and/or M—O—M bonds is a characteristic property of these elements. While Mo^V and W^V solutions are usually air sensitive, these states can be stabilized by suitable complexing.

(d) The lower oxidation states III and IV can be obtained in aqueous solution but the species are invariably complex and are air sensitive. There is essentially no cationic chemistry.

2. *Compounds existing in the solid state only:* There are extensive studies on oxides, carbides, sulfides, etc., especially of the oxides which can give highly colored non-stoichiometric compounds.

3. *Compounds of oxidation states II and below:* These are extensive and diverse but are almost exclusively ones involving π-acid ligands and/or metal–carbon bonds. Most compounds have been obtained from the hexacarbonyls $Mo(CO)_6$ and $W(CO)_6$ as source materials (see Chapter 27).

4. *Nonaqueous chemistry:* Apart from compounds such as those in (3), the chemistry is mainly of halides, oxohalides and their derivatives. The source materials here are usually the halides $MoCl_5$ and WCl_6 which can be handled in organic solvents such as acetonitrile and benzene or in liquid SO_2. The halides can be reduced by amines and will abstract oxygen from oxygen donors to give oxo compounds. Most of the fluorine chemistry of Mo and W is of necessity nonaqueous.

---

[1] See, e.g., J. T. Spence and J. Y. Lee, *Inorg. Chem.*, **4**, 385 (1965), for complexes and references to Mo enzymes.

The oxidation states and stereochemistry are summarized in Table 30-C-1.

TABLE 30-C-1

Oxidation States and Stereochemistry of Molybdenum and Tungsten

Oxidation state	Coordination number	Geometry	Examples
Mo^{-II}, W^{-II}	5	?	$[Mo(CO)_5]^{2-}$
Mo^0, W^0, d^6	6	Octahedral	$W(CO)_6$, $py_3Mo(CO)_3$, $[W(CO)_5X]^-$
			$Mo(diphosphine)_3$, $[Mo(CO)_5I]^-$, $[Mo(CN)_5NO]^{4-}$
Mo^I, W^I, d^5		π-Complex	$(C_6H_6)_2Mo^+$, π-$C_5H_5MoC_6H_6$,
			$[\pi$-$C_5H_5Mo(CO)_3]_2$
Mo^{II}, W^{II}, d^4		π-Complex	π-$C_5H_5W(CO)_3Cl$
	5	See text	$[Mo(OCOCH_3)_2]_2$
	6	Octahedral	$Mo(diars)_2X_2$, $Mo(CO)_2$ diars I_2, $[Mo(CN)_6]^{4-}$
	7	?	$[Mo(diars)_2(CO)_2X]^+$, $[W$ diars$(CO)_4I]^+$
	9	See text	Mo_6Cl_{12}, W_6Cl_{12}
Mo^{III}, W^{III}, d^3	6	Octahedral	$[Mo(NCS)_6]^{3-}$, $[MoCl_6]^{3-}$, $[Mo(CN)_6]^{3-}$
	7	?	$[W$ diars $(CO)_3Br_2]^+$
	8	Dodecahedral(?)	$[Mo(CN)_7(H_2O)]^{4-}$
Mo^{IV}, W^{IV}, d^2		π-Complex	$(\pi$-$C_5H_5)_2WH_2$, $(\pi$-$C_5H_5)_2MoH_2$
		,,	$(\pi$-$C_5H_5)_2WH_3^+$
	6	Octahedral	$[Mo(NCS)_6]^{2-}$, $[Mo(diars)_2Br_2]^{2+}$, $WBr_4(MeCN)_2$
	6	Trigonal prism	MoS_2
	8	Dodecahedral[a]	$[Mo(CN)_8]^{4-}$, $[W(CN)_4(OH)_4]^{4-}$, $MoCl_4(OAsPh_3)_4$
Mo^V, W^V, d^1	5	TBP	$MoCl_5(g)$
	6	Octahedral	$Mo_2Cl_{10}(s)$, $[MoOCl_5]^{2-}$, WF_6^-
	8	Dodecahedral(?)	$[Mo(CN)_8]^{3-}$, $[W(CN)_8]^{3-}$
Mo^{VI}, W^{VI}, d^0	4	Tetrahedral	MoO_4^{2-}, MoO_2Cl_2, WO_4^{2-}, WO_2Cl_2
	5?	?	$WOCl_4$, $MoOF_4$
	6	Octahedral	MoO_6, WO_6 in poly acids,
			WCl_6, MoF_6, $[MoO_2F_4]^{2-}$
			MoO_3 (distorted), WO_3 (distorted)
	8?		MoF_8^{2-}, WF_8^{2-}, WF_7^-

[a] The Raman spectrum of $[Mo(CN)_8]^{4-}$ in water has been interpreted in terms of an Archimedean antiprism. A dodecahedral structure for this ion and similar eight-coordinate ions is based on X-ray work on crystalline salts.

30-C-1. The Elements

In respect to occurrence (abundance $\sim 10^{-4}$ %), metallurgy and properties of the metals, molybdenum and tungsten are remarkably similar.

Molybdenum occurs chiefly as *molybdenite*, MoS_2, but also as molybdates such as $PbMoO_4$ (*wulfenite*) and $MgMoO_4$. Tungsten is found almost exclusively in the form of tungstates, the chief ones being *wolframite* (a solid solution and/or mixture of the isomorphous substances $FeWO_4$ and $MnWO_4$), *scheelite*, $CaWO_4$, and *stolzite*, $PbWO_4$.

Molybdenum ores contain relatively small amounts of MoS_2, but this is concentrated by the foam flotation process; the concentrate is then converted, usually by roasting, to MoO_3. After extraction with aqueous ammonia, ammonium molybdate, $(NH_4)_2MoO_4$, is isolated and roasted to yield relatively pure MoO_3 which is finally reduced with hydrogen to the metal. Reduction with carbon must be avoided because this yields carbides rather than the metal.

Tungsten ores are concentrated by mechanical and magnetic processes and the concentrates attacked by fusion with NaOH. The cooled melts are leached with water giving solutions of sodium tungstate from which hydrous WO_3 is precipitated on acidification. The hydrous oxide is dried and reduced to metal using hydrogen.

In the powder form in which they are first obtained both metals are dull grey, but when converted to the massive state by fusion are lustrous, silver-white substances of typically metallic appearance and properties. They have electrical conductances approximately 30% that of silver. They are extremely refractory; Mo melts at $2610°$ and W at $3380°$.

Neither metal is readily attacked by acids. Concentrated nitric acid initially attacks molybdenum, but the metal surface is soon passivated. Both metals can be dissolved—tungsten only slowly, however—by a mixture of concentrated nitric and hydrofluoric acids. Oxidizing alkaline melts such as fused KNO_3–NaOH or Na_2O_2 will attack them rapidly, but aqueous alkalies are without effect.

Both metals are inert to oxygen at ordinary temperatures, but at red heat they combine with it readily to give the trioxides. They both combine with chlorine when heated, but they are attacked by fluorine, yielding the hexafluorides, at room temperature.

The chief uses of both metals are in the production of alloy steels; even small amounts cause tremendous increases in hardness and strength. "High-speed" steels which are used to make cutting tools which remain hard even at red heat, contain W and Cr. Tungsten is also extensively used for lamp filaments.

30-C-2. Oxides, Sulfides and Simple Oxo Anions

Oxides. An enormous number of molybdenum and tungsten oxides are known. The simple ones are MoO_3, WO_3; Mo_2O_5; MoO_2, WO_2. Other non-stoichiometric ones have been characterized and have definite, though complicated structures; [2] thus $M_2^{II}Mo_3O_8$ is known to contain Mo_3O_{13} metal clusters (see page 656). The coordination is usually octahedral, but MoO_7 pentagonal bipyramidal units occur in some oxides.

[2] See, e.g., L. Kihlborg, *Arkiv för Kemi*, **21**, 443 (1964); E. Gebert and R. J. Ackermann, *Inorg. Chem.*, **5**, 136 (1966).

The *trioxides* are the ultimate products of heating the metals or other compounds such as the sulfides in oxygen. They are not attacked by acids but dissolve in bases to form molybdate and tungstate solutions, which are discussed later.

MoO_3 is a white solid at room temperature but becomes yellow when hot and melts to a deep yellow liquid at 795°. It is the anhydride of molybdic acid, but it does not form hydrates directly. The hydrates $MoO_3 \cdot 2H_2O$ and $MoO_3 \cdot H_2O$ can, however, be precipitated from approximately neutral solutions of molybdates. The crystal structure of MoO_3 is a rare type of layer structure in which each molybdenum atom is surrounded by a distorted octahedron of oxygen atoms.

WO_3 is a lemon yellow solid, m 1200°. Like CrO_3, it has a slightly distorted form of the cubic rhenium trioxide structure (page 965).

Mo_2O_5, a violet solid soluble in warm acids, is prepared by heating the required quantity of finely divided molybdenum with MoO_3 at 750°. When ammonia is added to solutions containing Mo^V, brown $MoO(OH)_3$ is precipitated; this gives Mo_2O_5 on heating.

Molybdenum(IV) oxide, MoO_2, is obtained by reducing MoO_3 with hydrogen or NH_3 below 470° (above this temperature reduction proceeds to the metal) and by reaction of molybdenum with steam at 800°. It is a brown-violet solid with a coppery luster, insoluble in nonoxidizing mineral acids but soluble in concentrated nitric acid with oxidation of the molybdenum to Mo^{VI}. The structure of MoO_2 is similar to that of rutile but so distorted that strong Mo—Mo bonds are formed (cf. page 653). WO_2 is similar.

The Blue Oxides. These are also called *molybdenum blue* and *tungsten blue* and are obtained by mild reduction, for example, by Sn^{II}, SO_2, N_2H_4, H_2S, etc., of acidified solutions of molybdates and tungstates or of suspensions of MoO_3 and WO_3 in water. Moist tungsten(VI) oxide will acquire a blue tint merely on exposure to ultraviolet light.

The "blue oxides" of Mo actually contain both oxide and hydroxide. Some blue compounds which have been identified and more or less characterized as distinct substances are listed in Table 30-C-2.

TABLE 30-C-2

"Blue Oxides" of Molybdenum

Mean oxidation number of Mo	Crystalline	Non-crystalline (amorphous)
5.76	$MoO_{2.88} \cdot H_2O$	$MoO_{2.88} \cdot xH_2O$
5.66		$H[Mo_3O_9]$
5.50	$MoO_{2.5}(OH)_{0.5}$	$MoO_{2.75} \cdot xH_2O$
5.20	$MoO_{2.60} \cdot xH_2O$	
5.00	$MoO_{2.0}(OH)$	

There appears to be an entire series of "genotypic" compounds (i.e., having the same basic structure but differing in the charges on cations and anions), with (olivegreen) $MoO(OH)_2$ as one limit and MoO_3 as the other. The compounds in which the mean oxidation state of Mo is between 5 and 6 are the blue ones, e.g., $MoO_{2.0}(OH)$ and $MoO_{2.5}(OH)_{0.5}$. A detailed electronic explanation for the blue color has not been found, although the general idea that Mo_3 metal atom clusters might be responsible has been suggested.

In the case of the "blue oxides" of W, similar general results have been obtained. Specific substances which have been reported are $WO_{2.67}$-$(OH)_{0.33}$, and $WO_{2.7}(OH)_{0.1}$, although in a genotypic series it is not clear why particular compositions such as the latter, in which the ratio of the different types of anions has no relationship to the multiplicities of crystallographic positions, should be stable. Probably all compositions within the genotypic range are likely to be isolable.

Tungsten Bronzes. The reduction of acid sodium tungstate at red heat with hydrogen gives a chemically inert substance with a bronze-like appearance. Other methods giving similar materials are heating sodium, potassium or alkaline earth tungstates or polytungstates in hydrogen, electrolytic reduction of fused tungstates and reduction of sodium tungstate with sodium, tungsten or zinc.

The tungsten bronzes are nonstoichiometric substances of general formula Na_nWO_3 ($0 < n \leq 1$) when sodium is present. The colors vary greatly with composition from golden-yellow for $n \sim 0.9$ to blue-violet for $n \sim 0.3$. Tungsten bronzes are extremely inert and have semimetallic properties, especially metallic luster and good electrical conductivity in which the charge carriers are electrons.[3] They are insoluble in water and resistant to all acids except hydrofluoric. They can reduce ammoniacal silver nitrate to metallic silver, and they can be oxidized by oxygen in presence of base to give tungstates(VI):

$$4NaWO_3 + 4NaOH + O_2 = 4Na_2WO_4 + 2H_2O$$

Structurally, the sodium tungsten bronzes may be regarded as defective $NaWO_3$ phases having the perovskite structure. It will be recalled (page 51) that for mixed oxides, ABO_3, where one cation is much larger than the other, a common structure is the perovskite structure in which the O^{2-} ions and large cations (Na^+ in $NaWO_3$) form a cubic close-packed array with the small cations occupying octahedral interstices. In the defective phase, Na_nWO_3, there are $(1 - n)$ W^{VI} atoms and $(1 - n)$ of the Na sites of the pure $NaWO_3$ phase are unoccupied. It appears that completely pure $NaWO_3$ has not been prepared, although heating phases with $n \sim 0.85$

---

[3] W. McNeill and L. E. Conroy, *J. Chem. Phys.*, **36**, 87 (1962); see also M. J. Sienko and S. M. Morehouse, *Inorg. Chem.*, **2**, 485 (1963).

with metallic sodium does result in sodium enrichment up to perhaps $n \sim 0.95$. In the other direction, it is found that the cubic structure collapses to rhombic and then triclinic for $n < \sim 0.3$. In the limit of $n = 0$ we have, of course, WO_3, which, as already noted, has a triclinically distorted ReO_3 structure. The cubic ReO_3 structure is just the same as the perovskite structure with all of the large cations removed. Thus the practical range (as opposed to the theoretical range) of composition of the tungsten bronzes is approximately $Na_{0.3}WO_3$–$Na_{0.9}WO_3$.

The semimetallic properties of the tungsten bronzes are associated with the fact that no distinction can be made between W^V and W^{VI} atoms in the lattice, all W atoms appearing equivalent. Thus the n "extra" electrons per mole (over the number for WO_3) are distributed throughout the lattice, delocalized in energy bands somewhat similar to those of metals.

The electrolytic reduction of alkali metal molybdate–MoO_3 melts can give not only crystals of MoO_2 but, under appropriate conditions, blue and red plate-like bronzes. The red bronze $K_{0.26}Mo_{1.01}O_3$ is a semi-conductor.[4]

Sulfides.[5] Of the known sulfides, Mo_2S_3, MoS_4, Mo_2S_5, MoS_3 and MoS_2, only the last three are important. The only tungsten sulfides, WS_2 and WS_3, appear to be similar to their molybdenum analogs.

MoS_2 can be prepared by direct combination of the elements, by heating molybdenum(VI) oxide in hydrogen sulfide, or by fusing molybdenum(VI) oxide with a mixture of sulfur and potassium carbonate. It is the most stable sulfide at higher temperatures, and the others which are richer in sulfur revert to it upon heating in vacuum. It dissolves only in strongly oxidizing acids such as aqua regia and boiling concentrated sulfuric acid. Chlorine and oxygen attack it at elevated temperatures giving $MoCl_5$ and MoO_3, respectively.

MoS_2 has layer structure in which the repeating unit is a sandwich consisting of a hexagonal sheet of molybdenum atoms between two hexagonal sheets of sulfur atoms. The stacking in this sandwich is such that the sulfur sheets are superposed and the molybdenum shifted so as to put each molybdenum at the center of a trigonal prism formed by six sulfur atoms. The forces between these sandwich-like layers are relatively weak ones between the sulfur atoms of adjacent layers, and MoS_2 therefore has lubricating properties similar to those of graphite, which it also resembles in general appearance.

Hydrated, brown MoS_3 is precipitated when hydrogen sulfide is passed into slightly acid solutions of molybdates; tungstates do not react similarly.

[4] A Wold, W. K. Kunnmann, R. I. Anholt and A. Ferretti, *Inorg. Chem.*, **3**, 545 (1964).
[5] J. C. Wildervande and F. Jellinek, *Zeit. anorg. Chem.*, **328**, 309 (1964). A summary paper with data and references.

Hydrous MoS_3 dissolves on digestion with alkali sulfide solution to give brown-red thiomolybdates. Hydrated Mo_2S_5 is precipitated from Mo^V solutions. Both hydrous sulfides can be dehydrated.

Thiomolybdates and thiotungstates are known. The discrete tetrahedral ions MS_4^{2-} occur in salts which are isostructural with one form of K_2SO_4.[6]

Simple Molybdates and Tungstates. The trioxides of molybdenum and tungsten dissolve in alkali metal hydroxides, and from these solutions the simple or normal molybdates and tungstates can be crystallized. They have the general formulas $M^I_2MoO_4$ and $M^I_2WO_4$ and contain the discrete tetrahedral ions MoO_4^{2-} and WO_4^{2-} in crystals. These are regular in alkali metal and a few other salts, but may be distorted in salts of other cations. It is now quite certain that the MoO_4^{2-} and WO_4^{2-} ions are also tetrahedral in aqueous solution.[7] Although both molybdates and tungstates can be reduced in solution (see below), they lack the powerful oxidising property so characteristic of chromates(VI). The normal tungstates and molybdates of many other metals can be prepared by metathetical reactions. The alkali metal, ammonium, magnesium and thallous salts are soluble in water, whereas those of other metals are nearly all insoluble.

When solutions of molybdates and tungstates are made weakly acid, polymeric anions are formed, but from more strongly acid solutions substances often called molybdic or tungstic acids are obtained. At room temperature the yellow $MoO_3 \cdot 2H_2O$ and $WO_3 \cdot 2H_2O$ crystallize, the former very slowly. From hot solutions, monohydrates are obtained rapidly.[8] These compounds are hydrates and do not contain discrete H_2MoO_4 molecules; broad line nmr study of these compounds indicates that all of the hydrogen is present in the form of water molecules; the same conclusion then follows for the tungsten compounds since they are isomorphous with those of molybdenum. A partial X-ray study of $MoO_3 \cdot 2H_2O$ shows the presence of sheets of MoO_6 octahedra sharing corners.

The oxo anions also give complexes with sulfate and with hydroxo compounds such as glycerol, tartrate ion and sugars. In base solution, hydrogen peroxide gives peroxo anions believed to be of the type $M_2O_{11}^{2-}$.[9]

Amines generally give ill-defined complexes or salts with molybdates but with diethylenetriamine a unique octahedral complex, $MoO_3 \cdot dien$, is obtained; the oxygen atoms here are mutually cis[10] (Fig. 27-6a).

---

[6] K. Sasvári, *Acta Cryst.*, **16**, 719 (1964).

[7] R. H. Busey and O. L. Keller, Jr., *J. Chem. Phys.*, **41**, 215 (1964).

[8] See M. L. Freedman, *J. Amer. Chem. Soc.*, **81**, 3834 (1959); *J. Inorg. Nucl. Chem.*, **25**, 575 (1963).

[9] W. P. Griffith, *J. Chem. Soc.*, **1963**, 5345.

[10] W. F. Marzluff, *Inorg. Chem.*, **3**, 395 (1964); F. A. Cotton and R. C. Elder, *Inorg. Chem.* **3**, 397 (1964).

30-C-3. Iso- and Heteropoly Acids and their Salts

An important and characteristic feature of the chemistry of molybdenum and tungsten is the formation of a large number of polymolybdate(VI) and polytungstate(VI) acids and their salts. Although some analogies exist between these polymolybdates and polytungstates and the poly acids or anions of elements such as Si, P, B, etc., they are of only a very general nature and hence of little help in developing detailed knowledge of the molybdenum and tungsten compounds. Of the other transition elements only V^V, Nb^V, Ta^V and U^{VI} show somewhat similar behavior. Comparatively little is known of these species and the extent to which they resemble the molybdenum and tungsten compounds.

The poly acids of molybdenum and tungsten are of two types: (a) the *isopoly acids* and their related anions, which contain only molybdenum or tungsten along with oxygen and hydrogen, and (b) the *heteropoly acids* and anions, which contain one or two atoms of another element in addition to molybdenum or tungsten, oxygen and hydrogen. All of the polyanions contain octahedral MoO_6 or WO_6 groups so that the conversion of MoO_4^{2-} or WO_4^{2-} into poly anions requires an increase in coordination number. It is still not clear why only certain metal oxo ions can polymerize, or why for these metals only certain species, e.g., $Mo_7O_{24}^{6-}$, $HW_6O_{21}^{5-}$ or $Ta_6O_{18}^{6-}$, predominate under a given set of conditions, or why for chromate, polymerization stops at $Cr_2O_7^{2-}$. The ability of the metal and oxygen orbitals to overlap to give substantial π bonding, M=O, must surely be involved (see page 364), as must the base strength of the oxygen atoms and the ability of the initial protonated species $MO_3(OH)^-$ to expand its coordination sphere by coordination of water molecules. The size of the metal ion is clearly important since this influences not only π-bonding capability but also, according to the radius ratio concept, the coordination number; the latter effect is shown by the fact that RuO_4^{2-} is tetrahedral in solution while the larger osmate ion is $[OsO_2(OH)_4]^{2-}$. The protonation of one oxygen atom to give, say, $WO_3(OH)^-$ could weaken the W—O bond, lengthening it and increasing the radius ratio so that octahedral coordination can occur. For larger metals the M—O bonds will be more ionic and π-bonding overlap less favorable and it is noteworthy that the larger metal ions of U, Nb and Ta give species which are polymerized even in base solution whereas the oxo anions of V, Cr, Mo and W are monomeric at high pH and polymerize only in acid. The somewhat smaller metals of the Tc and Re group and the platinum metals give only monomeric anions in solution where these exist at all.

The properties of the condensed species and their equilibria in aqueous solution have been studied by acid–base titration, cryoscopy, spectrophotometry, thermometric titration, diffusion and ion-exchange measurements, ultracentrifugation, light scattering, Raman spectra and X-ray diffraction. The conclusions drawn from diffusion measurements—and these figure importantly in the older literature—are very unreliable because certain invalid assumptions were made in the interpretation, especially assumptions about the relation between mobility and weight of the poly anions. The data from other types of study can often be—and indeed have been—interpreted in different ways and until comparatively recently there has been considerable confusion. X-ray studies of crystalline compounds of a number of salts of iso- and heteropoly anions have been made and will be discussed below. Using these structures as a guide, considerable headway has been made in the interpretation of solution studies, and, especially in recent work, reliable, internally consistent data have been obtained. It is to be noted however that the X-ray studies do not show positions of hydrogen atoms and that while the basic units determined crystallographically often persist in solutions, hydration and protonation in solution depends on the conditions. It must also be noted that the fact that a salt with a particular structure crystallizes from solution under certain conditions does not necessarily mean that the same anion is the major species in solution—or, in fact, that it even exists in solution. There are clear cases where the ions in solution and the crystals obtained from them are substantially different.

Iscpolymolybdates. When a basic solution, containing only $[MoO_4]^{2-}$ and alkali metal or ammonium ions, is acidified, the molybdate ions condense in definite steps to form a series of polymolybdate ions. It is known that at the pH where condensation begins for both CrO_4^{2-} and MoO_4^{2-} the species $MoO_3(OH)^-$ are formed:

$$MoO_4^{2-} + H^+ = MoO_3(OH)^-$$

Presumably coordination of water molecules occurs at this point, perhaps to give $[MoO(OH)_5]^-$. The OH group *trans* to a double-bonded oxygen is known to be labilized in certain rhenium complexes (page 975), and groups *trans* to Mo=O bonds are often more weakly bound[11] so that the next step could be the formation of an oxo bridge:

$$2[MoO(OH)_5]^- = [(HO)_4OMo—O—MoO(OH)_4]^{2-} + H_2O$$

The subsequent steps must be more complicated and as the pH of the solution is lowered to about pH 6, polymerization is detectable. It was proposed by Lindqvist, primarily because of its existence in crystals, that the first main reaction at this stage is to form the *paramolybdate* ion:

$$7MoO_4^{2-} + 8H^+ = Mo_7O_{24}^{6-} + 4H_2O$$

[11] F. A. Cotton, S. M. Morehouse and J. S. Wood, *Inorg. Chem.*, **3**, 1603 (1964).

Recent studies[12] have demonstrated more or less conclusively that this is the case; in somewhat more acid solutions, the *octamolybdate* ion, $[Mo_8O_{26}]^{4-}$, is formed. These two species in equilibrium seem to be able to account for most of the observed phenomena. There is no reliable evidence that there are any species containing more than one but less than seven Mo atoms in the polymolybdate system. However there is some evidence that higher polymers may exist. These two main polymeric anions may of course exist in hydrated forms or be partially protonated, e.g., $[H_8Mo_7O_{28}]^{6-}$, and there is evidence to suggest that the highly charged ions can also bind counter-ions such as Li^+ or Na^+. In very strong acid solutions, depolymerization occurs and, when hydrochloric acid is used, the species formed above $6M$ HCl appears to be MoO_2Cl_2.

The so-called dimolybdates, such as $Na_2O \cdot 2MoO_3 \cdot nH_2O$, which sometimes crystallize from solutions in the pH range of 5–6, are probably mixtures of normal molybdates and paramolybdates. Anhydrous dimolybdates, such as $Na_2Mo_2O_7$, can be obtained from molten alkali oxide-molybdenum oxide systems, but they contain no simple $Mo_2O_7^{2-}$ ion. They contain instead an infinite chain anion of rather complicated structure. Also, the various trimolybdates of general formula $M^I_2O \cdot 3MoO_3 \cdot nH_2O$ appear to contain acid paramolybdate ions or other ions with seven or more Mo atoms.

Tetramolybdates or *metamolybdates*, of general formula $M^I_2O \cdot 4MoO_3 \cdot nH_2O$, are formed from concentrated solutions of alkali molybdates treated with 1.5 moles per mole of hydrochloric acid. *Octamolybdates* are obtained similarly from solutions containing 1.75 moles per mole of hydrochloric acid or by adding the calculated amount of MoO_3 to ammonium paramolybdate solution. Both the tetra- and octamolybdates are derived from the ion $[Mo_8O_{26}]^{4-}$.

The structures of both the heptamolybdate and octamolybdate ions in crystals are discussed on page 944 in relation to other hetero- and isopoly anion structures.

Isopolytungstates. The behavior of the tungstate systems is similar to that of the molybdate systems.[13] Again, the degree of aggregation in solution increases as the pH is lowered, and numerous tungstates $M^I_2O \cdot nWO_3 \cdot mH_2O$, differing in the value of n have been crystallized from the solutions at different pH's.

In solution, the relationships appear to be those in Figure 30-C-1. There is some evidence that there may be intermediate stages between paratungstate A and Z and between the former and metatungstate. The

[12] J. Aveston, E. W. Anacker and J. S. Johnson, *Inorg. Chem.*, **3**, 735 (1964). This paper contains extensive references and a critique of experimental techniques.

[13] J. Aveston, *Inorg. Chem.*, **3**, 981 (1964).

species given may be hydrated; e.g., $W_{12}O_{41}{}^{10-}$ may be also written $H_{10}W_{12}O_{46}{}^{10-}$. The most important species is paratungstate Z, and crystallization of Na_2WO_4, acidified by addition of 1.167 moles HCl per mole of W, gives large glassy crystals. Aqueous solutions of this salt

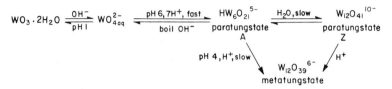

Fig. 30-C-1.   Isopolytungstates in aqueous solution.

contain mainly $W_{12}O_{41}{}^{10-}$ which slowly hydrolyzes giving a mixture of this species and $HW_6O_{21}{}^{5-}$ similar to that formed on direct acidification of $WO_4{}^{2-}$. The dodecatungstate predominates at high concentrations.

It should be noted that the X-ray crystallographic formula of the dodecatungstate ion is $W_{12}O_{46}{}^{20-}$ (Fig. 30-C-2d). This has no direct relation to the analytical formula which requires a $W_{12}O_{41}{}^{10-}$ ion for the neutral sodium salt. It is hence probably more correct to write the formula as $Na_{10}[W_{12}O_{36}(OH)_{10}]\cdot23H_2O$ rather than $Na_{10}W_{12}O_{41}\cdot28H_2O$, since the hydrogen present is not acidic and nmr spectra indicate the presence of OH groups.[14] The solution species is commonly written $W_{12}O_{41}{}^{10-}$ since the degree of hydration is indeterminate. The essential point is that there are twelve linked WO_6 octahedra in the ion. It has recently been proposed that a formula $W_{12}O_{42}{}^{12-}$, or protonated form such as $H_2W_{12}O_{42}{}^{10-}$, are more consistent with the X-ray and other data.[15]

Heteropoly Acids and their Salts. These are formed when molybdate and tungstate solutions containing other oxo anions (e.g., $PO_4{}^{3-}$, $SiO_4{}^{4-}$) or metal ions are acidified. At least 35 elements are known to be capable of functioning as the hetero atoms. The free acids and most salts of the heteropoly anions are extremely soluble in water and in various oxygenated organic solvents, such as ethers, alcohols and ketones. When crystallized from water, the heteropoly acids and salts are always obtained in highly hydrated condition. Like the isopoly acids they are decomposed by strong base:

$$34OH^- + [P_2Mo_{18}O_{62}]^{6-} = 18MoO_4{}^{2-} + 2HPO_4{}^{2-} + 16H_2O$$
$$18OH^- + [Fe_2W_{12}O_{42}]^{6-} = 12WO_4{}^{2-} + Fe_2O_3\cdot nH_2O + 9H_2O$$

In contrast to the isopoly acids, many of the heteropoly acids are stable without depolymerization in quite strongly acid solutions; they are often

[14] E. Schwarzmann, *Naturwiss.*, **50**, 519 (1963).
[15] W. N. Lipscomb, *Inorg. Chem.*, **4**, 133 (1965).

themselves strong acids. In general, heteropolymolybdates and tungstates of small cations, including those of some heavy metals, are water soluble, but with larger cations insolubility is frequently found. Thus Cs^+, Pb^{2+} and Ba^{2+} salts are usually insoluble, and NH_4^+, K^+ and Rb^+ salts are sometimes insoluble; salts of $[(\pi\text{-}C_5H_5)_2Fe]^+$, R_4N^+, R_4P^+ and alkaloids are invariably insoluble. Table 30-C-3 lists the principle types of hetero-

TABLE 30-C-3

Principal Types of Heteropolymolybdates

Ratio of hetero atoms to Mo atoms	Principal hetero atoms occurring	Anion formulas
1:12	Series A: P^V, As^V, Si^{IV}, Ge^{IV}, $Sn^{IV}(?)$, Ti^{IV}, Zr^{IV}	$[X^{n+}Mo_{12}O_{40}]^{(8-n)-}$
	Series B: Ce^{IV}, Th^{IV}, $Sn^{IV}(?)$	$[X^{n+}Mo_{12}O_{42}]^{(12-n)-}$
1:11	P^V, As^V, Ge^{IV}	$[X^{n+}Mo_{11}O_{39}]^{(12-n)-}$ (possibly dimeric)
1:10	P^V, As^V, Pt^{IV}	$[X^{n+}Mo_{10}O_x]^{(2x-60-n)-}$ (possibly dimeric)
1:9	Mn^{IV}, Ni^{IV}	$[X^{n+}Mo_9O_{32}]^{(10-n)-}$
1:6	Te^{VI}, I^{VII}, Co^{III}, Al^{III}, Cr^{III}, Fe^{III}, Rh^{III}	$[X^{n+}Mo_6O_{24}]^{(12-n)-}$
2:18	P^V, As^V	$[X_2^{n+}Mo_{18}O_{62}]^{(16-2n)-}$
2:17	P^V, As^V	$[X_2^{n+}Mo_{17}O_x]^{(2x-102-2n)-}$
$1m:6m^a$	Ni^{II}, Co^{II}, Mn^{II}, Cu^{II}, Se^{IV}, P^{III}, As^{III}, P^V	$[X^{n+}Mo_6O_x]_m^{m(2x-36-n)-}$

[a] For the tungstate analog of the Co^{II} compound it has been found that $m = 2$.

polymolybdates, many of which have exact or similar heteropolytungstate analogs. Table 30-C-4 illustrates the nomenclature according to the IUPAC system.

TABLE 30-C-4

Some Representative Heteropoly Salts and Their Nomenclature[a]

Formula	IUPAC names
$Na_3[P^VMo_{12}O_{40}]$	Sodium 12-molybdophosphate; sodium dodecamolybdophosphate
$H_3[P^VMo_{12}O_{40}]$	12-Molybdophosphoric acid; dodecamolybdophosphoric acid
$K_8[Co_2^{II}W_{12}O_{42}]$	Dimeric potassium 6-tungstocobaltate; dimeric potassium hexatungstocobaltate(II)
$Na_8[Ce^{IV}Mo_{12}O_{42}]$	Sodium 12-molybdocerate(IV); sodium dodecamolybdocerate(IV)

[a] International Union of Pure and Applied Chemistry recommendations

Structures of Iso- and Heteropoly Anions. In all cases so far studied definitively by X-ray diffraction, *the tungsten and molybdenum atoms lie at the centers of octahedra of oxygen atoms and the structures are built up of these octahedra by means of shared corners and shared edges (but not shared faces.)*

In the structural diagrams we use here, an MoO_6 or WO_6 octahedron will be represented by the sort of sketch shown in Figure 30-C-2a. Note that in the complete structures of the poly anions the octahedra are frequently distorted.

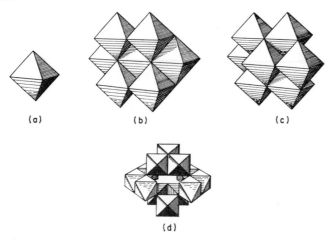

(a)   (b)   (c)

(d)

Fig. 30-C-2.   (a) The diagrammatic representation of MoO_6 and WO_6 octahedra to be used in showing structures of some isopoly and heteropoly anions. (b) The structure of the paramolybdate anion, $[Mo_7O_{24}]^{6-}$. (c) The structure of the octamolybdate anion, $[Mo_8O_{26}]^{4-}$ (note that one MoO_6 octahedron is completely hidden by the seven which are shown). (d) The structure of the $W_{12}O_{46}$ unit in the dodecatungstate ion.

The isopoly anion structures definitely known from X-ray studies of crystals are the paramolybdate ion, $[Mo_7O_{24}]^{6-}$ in $(NH_4)_6Mo_7O_{24} \cdot 4H_2O$, and the octamolybdate ion, $[Mo_8O_{26}]^{4-}$ in $(NH_4)_4Mo_8O_{26} \cdot 5H_2O$, both of whose structures are shown in Figure 30-C-2b and 30-C-2c. The meta-

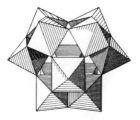

Fig. 30-C-3.   The structure of the series A 12-molybdo- and 12-tungstoheteropoly anions of general formula $[X_n{}^+Mo_{12}O_{40}]^{(8-n)-}$.

tungstate ion, best formulated[14] in its sodium salt as $Na_6[H_2W_{12}O_{40}] \cdot 3H_2O$ or $Na_6[W_{12}O_{38}(OH)_2]$, has the same structure as the 12-tungsto- and 12-molybdohetero anions of type A (see Fig. 30-C-3) to be discussed

944 THE TRANSITION ELEMENTS

shortly. The paratungstate ion in $Na_{10}[W_{12}O_{36}(OH)_{10}] \cdot 23H_2O$ is shown in Figure 30-C-2d.

All of the 12-molybdohetero anions with P^V, As^V, Ti^{IV} and Zr^{IV} and of the isomorphous 12-tungsto species containing the hetero atoms B^{III}, Ge^{VI}, P^V, As^V and Si^{IV} have the structure shown in Figure 30-C-3. It may be thought of as consisting of four groups of three MoO_6 or WO_6 octahedra. In each group there is one oxygen atom common to all three octahedra. In the complete structure these groups are so oriented by sharing of oxygen atoms between groups that the four triply shared oxygen atoms are placed at the corners of a central tetrahedron. The hetero atom sits in the center of this tetrahedron in the heteropoly ions and in the meta-tungstate ion there is no hetero atom. It will be noted that all of the hetero species occurring in the A series (Table 30-C-3) of 12-heteropoly anions are small enough to make a coordination number of four toward oxygen appropriate.

In the 12-hetero acids of type B, the hetero species are larger than those in the ones of type A, and it might be expected that their structures would be such as to have the hetero atoms in central octahedra of oxygen atoms. Their structures are not known, but it is noteworthy that the dodecatungstate structure (Fig. 30-C-2d) has just such a central octahedron.

The 9-molybdoheteropoly anions are built by packing MoO_6 octahedra so as to produce a central octahedron of oxygen atoms. The structure is shown in Figure 30-C-4. Closer inspection of this structure reveals that it is asymmetric and these anions should exist in enantiomorphic forms. No resolution has as yet been reported, however.

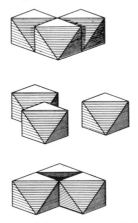

Fig. 30-C-4. An exploded view of the structure of the 9-molybdoheteropoly anion $[X_n{}^+Mo_9O_{32}]^{(10-n)-}$, showing the nine MoO_6 octahedra. When the upper and lower sets of three are moved in so as to share some corners with the equatorial set, a central octahedron of oxygen atoms occupied by the hetero atom is created.

The structure of the $[TeMo_6O_{24}]^{6-}$ anion is shown in Figure 30-C-5. Six MoO_6 octahedra share edges in such a way as to create a ring with a central octahedron of oxygen atoms which is occupied by the tellurium atom. Although the paramolybdate ion, $[Mo_7O_{24}]^{6-}$, might be formally regarded as a 6-molybdomolybdate ion, $[MoMo_6O_{24}]^{6-}$, it is structurally different in detail from the $[TeMo_6O_{24}]^{6-}$ ion.

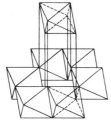

Fig. 30-C-5. The structure of the $[TeMo_6O_{24}]^{6-}$ ion with the central TeO_6 octahedron lifted out to show the ring of six MoO_6 octahedra.

Fig. 30-C-6. The structure of the dimeric anion $[P_2W_{18}O_{62}]^{6-}$.

It is probable that the various dimeric 9-molybdo- and 9-tungstoheteropoly anions, of general formula $[X_2Mo_{18}O_{62}]^{6-}$, have the same structure as the $[P_2W_{18}O_{62}]^{6-}$ ion shown in Figure 30-C-6. This structure can be thought of as consisting of two half units, each of which is derived from the series A 12-molybdoheteropoly anion structure (Fig. 30-C-3) by removal of three MoO_6 anions. The 11-molybdo- and 10-molybdoheteropoly anions may also be dimeric and consist of appropriate fragments of the 12-molybdo structure, but nothing is definitely known of their structures.

As for the isopoly acids, there have been extensive studies of heteropoly anions in solutions. X-ray studies of solutions of $12WO_3SiO_2 \cdot 2H_2O$ have demonstrated the ion $[SiW_{12}O_{40}]^{4-}$ with the structure shown in Figure 30-C-7, which is consistent with the crystal structure (Fig. 30-C-3).

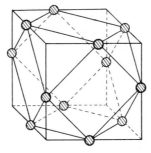

Fig. 30-C-7. Arrangement of W atoms in the $[SiW_{12}O_{40}]^{4-}$ ion in $0.3M$ aqueous solution (H. A. Levy, P. A. Agron and M. D. Danford, *J. Chem. Phys.*, **30**, 1486 (1959)).

We may finally note that despite the very bulky tungsten–oxygen cages surrounding the central atoms, it has been found that oxidation–reduction reactions of certain central atoms can be carried out, and the electron exchange between the 12-tungstocobaltates(II) and -(III), which have a central tetrahedral cobalt atom, has been studied.[16]

30-C-4. Halides and Oxohalides

Both molybdenum and tungsten form compounds with all of the halogens, Table 30-C-5.

TABLE 30-C-5

The Fluorides and Chlorides of Molybdenum and Tungsten[a]

II	III	IV	V	VI
	MoF_3 yellow-brown non-volatile	MoF_4 green non-volatile	$(MoF_5)_4$ yellow m 67°, b 213°	MoF_6 colorless m 17.5°, b 35.0°
		WF_4 red-brown non-volatile	—	WF_6 colorless m 2.3°, b 17.0°
$MoCl_2$[b] yellow	$MoCl_3$ dark red	$MoCl_4$ dark red	$(MoCl_5)_2$ green-black m 194°, b 628°	—
WCl_2[b] grey	—	WCl_4 black	$(WCl_5)_x$ green-black	WCl_6 blue-black m 275°, b 346°

[a] *Other halides:* $MoBr_2$, $MoBr_3$, $MoBr_4$; MoI_2, MoI_3, MoI_4; WBr_2, WBr_3, WBr_4, WBr_5, WBr_6; WI_2, WI_3, WI_4.

[b] Cluster compounds.

Fluorides. Direct fluorination of the metals yields in both cases the volatile, diamagnetic hexafluorides. Their chemical properties are not known in great detail. They are readily hydrolyzed and must be handled in scrupulously dry vacuum lines. Although the dry gases do not attack glass, attack is rapid in presence of traces of moisture which generate traces of HF by hydrolysis. MoF_6 is rather easily reduced and attacks organic matter; WF_6 is less reactive in both these respects. WF_6 exhibits Lewis acidity as indicated by the reactions

$$WF_6 + 4NH_3 = WF_6 \cdot 4NH_3$$
$$WF_6 + 3Am = WF_6 \cdot 3Am \qquad \text{(Am = pyridine or } CH_3NH_2)$$

The structures and hence the true coordination numbers of tungsten in these compounds are unknown. WF_6 also reacts with SO_3 to yield a compound of the composition $WF_4(SO_3F)_4$. Both MoF_6 and WF_6 react

[16] P. G. Rasmussen and C. H. Brubaker, *Inorg. Chem.*, **3**, 977 (1963).

slowly and incompletely with NaF (although UF_6 reacts completely) to give crystalline solids $MF_6 \cdot 2NaF$ which may contain 8-coordinate anions.[17]

MoF_3, obtained by treatment of MoF_6 with Mo at $\sim 400°$, has the molybdenum atoms surrounded by octahedra of fluorines similar to the trifluorides of V, Cr, Fe, Ru and Ga.

The treatment of molybdenum carbonyl with fluorine diluted in nitrogen at $-75°$ gives a product of composition Mo_2F_9. The nature of this substance has not been investigated, but when it is heated to $150°$ it yields the nonvolatile MoF_4 as a residue and the volatile MoF_5 condenses in cooler regions of the apparatus. MoF_5 is also obtained by the action of dilute F_2 on Mo at $400°$ or by the reaction:

$$5MoF_6 + Mo(CO)_6 \overset{25°}{=} 6MoF_5 + 6CO$$

Crystalline MoF_5 appears from X-ray studies to be tetrameric, Figure 30-B-2 (page 922). Some other pentafluorides appear to be similar.[18] Thus NbF_5 and TaF_5 are isostructural with MoF_5 while RuF_5 is a distorted version. ReF_5 is not yet known but α-UF_5 has infinite chains of UF_6 units linked by U—F—U bonds. These compounds clearly exemplify the tendency of the relatively small F atom to form single bridges rather than the double ones commonly formed by the larger chlorine and bromine atoms (see page 576).

The only lower fluoride of tungsten, WF_4, is obtained by reduction of WF_6 with benzene at $110°$.

Chlorides. Direct chlorination of the metals at elevated temperatures produces WCl_6 or $MoCl_5$. The hexachloride of molybdenum does not appear to exist.

WCl_6 is moderately volatile and the vapor is monomeric. It is soluble in many organic solvents such as CS_2, CCl_4, alcohol and ether. It is slightly soluble in cold water with which it slowly reacts, whereas warm water hydrolyzes it quickly to tungstic acid. It is reduced by primary amines to give amido complexes in lower oxidation states.

$MoCl_5$ is also moderately volatile and monomeric in the vapor, probably having a trigonal bipyramidal structure. In the crystal, however, chlorine-bridged dimers are formed so that each molybdenum is hexacoordinate. The structure is virtually identical with that of Nb_2Cl_{10} (page 924). Mo_2Cl_{10} is paramagnetic, the magnetic moment indicating only negligible coupling of electron spins of the two molybdenum atoms (Mo—Mo = 3.84 A). Mo_2Cl_{10} is soluble in benzene and also in more polar organic solvents. It is monomeric in solution and is presumably solvated. It can readily

[17] S. Katz, *Inorg. Chem.*, **3**, 1598 (1964).
[18] A. J. Edwards, R. D. Peacock and R. W. H. Small, *J. Chem. Soc.*, **1962**, 4488.

abstract oxygen from oxygenated solvents to give oxo species, and it is also reduced by amines to give amido complexes. It is rapidly hydrolyzed by water. Some of its reactions are shown in Figures 30-C-8 and 30-C-9, which set out the preparative methods for lower chlorides and

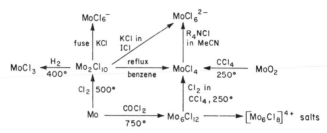

Fig. 30-C-8.   Preparation of molybdenum chlorides and chloro complexes.

oxochlorides. The tetrachloride is especially sensitive to air oxidation and hydrolysis.

The chlorides can be regarded as the parents of complex chlorides such as $[Mo^{III}Cl_6]^{3-}$ by additional coordination of halide ions. These complexes are discussed later.

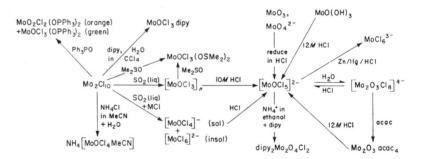

Fig. 30-C-9.   Some preparations and reactions of molybdenum pentachloride and of oxomolybdenum compounds.

The lower chlorides of tungsten can all be prepared by reduction of WCl_6 in hydrogen under appropriate conditions of temperature, pressure and reaction time. Mild conditions maximize the yield of WCl_5, which forms volatile black-green needles and a monomeric vapor. It does not seem to have been established whether or not crystalline WCl_5 is isomorphous with its molybdenum analog.

More drastic conditions in the reduction process lead to the formation of WCl_4 and WCl_2, but no WCl_3 appears to exist under conditions so far used. Use of very high temperature in the reduction reaction will lead to the production of metallic tungsten.

The tetrachloride is best[19] obtained by thermal gradient reduction with Al, and on heating disproportionates to give the dichloride:

$$WCl_6 + Al \xrightarrow{475 \to 225°} WCl_4$$

$$3WCl_4 \xrightarrow{500 \to 25°} WCl_2(s) + 2WCl_5$$

WCl_4 and WBr_4 made similarly form black needles isomorphous with NbX_4 or TaX_4. They are diamagnetic but, although d^2 does not require it, metal–metal bonds may be present.

The "dihalides" of molybdenum and tungsten are not simple compounds. It has been found[20] that $MoCl_2$ contains $[Mo_6Cl_8]^{4+}$ groups, of the kind discussed in the following paragraphs. The additional Cl^- ions occupy coordination positions on the Mo atoms, some serving as bridges between the $[Mo_6Cl_8]^{4+}$ units. This $[Mo_6Cl_8]^{8+}$ group is a typical example of a metal atom cluster compound. However, it is from the derivatives of the "dihalides" that the greatest amount of data on the $[M_6X_8]^{4+}$ species has been obtained. Several derivatives of them are well characterized and are also known to be metal atom cluster compounds.

The molybdenum compounds are best known. Solutions of "$MoCl_2$" contain the $[Mo_6Cl_8]^{4+}$ group, whose structure is shown in Figure 30-C-10. This is a persisting entity capable of binding six additional ligands, one to each Mo atom. From a fresh solution of Mo_6Cl_{12} only four chloride ions may be precipitated with Ag^+. From aqueous and alcoholic solutions such compounds as the following may be obtained.[21, 22]

$(H_3O)_2[Mo_6Cl_{14}]\cdot 6H_2O$, $[(Mo_6Cl_8)(OH)_4(H_2O)_2]\cdot 12H_2O$ and
$[(Mo_6Cl_8)L_6](ClO_4)_4$: $L = (CH_3)_2SO$, $(CH_3)_2NCHO$

In these the presence of the six coordinated groups is definite, while there are a great many other compounds such as $(Mo_6Cl_8)Cl_4\cdot 2C_5H_5N$, $(Mo_6Cl_8)Br_4\cdot 6H_2O$, $(Mo_6Cl_8)I_4\cdot 6H_2O$ and $[(CH_3)_4N]_2[(Mo_6Cl_8)Cl_6]$ in which a similar structural arrangement presumably occurs. The $[Mo_6Cl_8]^{4+}$ group is unstable toward strongly nucleophilic groups such as OH^-, CN^- and S^{2-}, and is not ordinarily a reducing agent. Presumably a series of $[Mo_6Br_8]^{4+}$ compounds exists but they are much less characterized.

The tungsten "dihalides" appear to be similar to their molybdenum analogs, but have been relatively little studied.[22a] $[(CH_3)_4N]_2[(W_6Cl_8)Cl_6]$ is isomorphous[22b] with the molybdenum analog. The tungsten compounds

[19] R. E. McCarley and T. M. Brown, *Inorg. Chem.*, **3**, 1232 (1964).

[20] H. Schäfer and H. G. Schnering, *Angew. Chem.*, **76**, 833 (1964). See esp. Table 7.

[21] See J. C. Sheldon, *J. Chem. Soc.*, **1964**, 1287 and references therein.

[22a] R. Siepmann and H. Schäfer, *Naturwiss.* **52**, 345 (1965).

[22b] F. A. Cotton and N. F. Curtis, *Inorg. Chem.*, **4**, 241 (1965) and unpublished work.

are far less stable; "WCl_2" behaves as an active reducing agent attacking water with liberation of hydrogen.

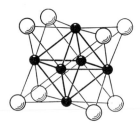

Fig. 30-C-10.   The structure of the $[Mo_6Cl_8]^{4+}$ group in $[Mo_6Cl_8(OH)_4(H_2O)_2]\cdot 12H_2O$. (Reprinted with permission from L. Pauling, *The Nature of the Chemical Bond*, 3rd ed., Cornell University Press, Ithaca, New York, 1960, p. 440.)

30-C-5. Interstitial Compounds with Nonmetals

Both Mo and W give hard, refractory and chemically inert compounds of nonmetals, especially B, C, N and Si. Their properties make them useful, or potentially so, for internal structural elements of kilns, gas turbines, jet engines, in sand-blast nozzles, cutting tools, etc.

All of these various interstitial compounds or phases can be prepared by direct reaction of the elements at high temperatures in inert or reducing (H_2) atmospheres. The relative quantities of the constituents used and the temperature of reaction determine the phase formed. The nitrides can be made by heating the metals in ammonia.

Among the well-characterized borides are those of the compositions M_2B, MB, MB_2 and M_2B_5. In all cases save the M_2B_5 compounds the corresponding Mo and W phases are isostructural. These borides are good examples of the various types of interstitial borides cited earlier (page 260). Thus the M_2B phases have close-packed arrays of metal atoms with isolated boron atoms in tetrahedral holes; the MB compounds exist in both high- and low-temperature polymorphs, but in both of these there are zigzag chains of boron atoms running through an array of metal atoms. In the MB_2 and M_2B_5 phases (which are generally encountered in non-stoichiometric condition) there are two-dimensional hexagonal nets of boron atoms penetrating the array of metal atoms.

The carbides and nitrides of a given metal are quite similar to one another, and both metals form the following well-studied phases: M_2C, M_2N, MC and MN. All of them are interstitial. For the M_2C and M_2N phases there are two closely related structures which involve the C or N atoms occupying octahedral (or slightly distorted octahedral) holes in hexagonal or cubic close-packed arrays of metal atoms. In the MC and MN phases the metal atoms form cubic close-packed arrays and the C or N atoms occupy octahedral interstices.

Both metals form a series of isomorphous silicide phases, the best known being M_3Si, M_3Si_2, M_5Si_3 and MSi_2. The structures of the M_3Si and M_5Si_3 phases are based upon cubic and hexagonal arrays of metal atoms with silicon atoms in the interstices. The structure of the M_3Si_2 phases is unknown. In the MSi_2 phases there are interpenetrating hexagonal nets of silicon atoms forming polyhedra which are square prisms with pyramidal ends. A metal atom is at the center of each of these polyhedra.

30-C-6. Complexes

As in all other phases of their chemistry, molybdenum and tungsten are sharply differentiated from chromium in the number and kinds of complexes they form. Whereas chromium forms an enormous number of kinetically inert, cationic complexes in the trivalent state, molybdenum and tungsten form relatively few cationic complexes.

Complexes in Oxidation States 0 and I. These are entirely with π-bonding ligands; they have been discussed in general in Chapters 27 and 28 and a few specific examples are listed in Table 30-C-1. The compound $K_4[Mo(CN)_5NO]$ has been the subject of some uncertainty but appears to have this formula. There is an extensive series[23] of complexes of the general formula $M(NO)_2Cl_2L_2$. These are Mo^0 and W^0 compounds if NO is regarded as NO^+.

Molybdenum(II) and Tungsten(II) Complexes, d^4. These complexes, apart from those containing $[M_6X_8]$ groups discussed earlier, are mainly ones derived from hexacarbonylmolybdenum as starting material. They usually have CO and other π-bonding ligands present and they can be either 6- or 7-coordinate. The π-cyclopentadienyl compounds, π-$C_5H_5M(CO)_3R$ (M = Mo and W, R = Cl, H, CH_3, etc.), are also divalent complexes; their structure can be regarded either as trigonal bipyramidal, or, considering π-C_5H_5 as occupying three bond positions, as 7-coordinate approximating to the $NbOF_6^{3-}$ structure. The nonorganometallic complexes can be obtained by reactions[24a,b] such as

$$Mo(CO)_6 + MeSCH_2CH_2SMe(L) \xrightarrow{heat} Mo(CO)_4L \xrightarrow{I_2} Mo(CO)_3LI_2$$

$$W(CO)_6 \xrightarrow{I_2, 120°} WI_3 \xrightarrow{diars} W(diars)_2I_2 \xrightarrow{CO} [W(CO)_2(diars)_2I]I$$

[23] F. A. Cotton and B. F. G. Johnson, *Inorg. Chem.*, **3**, 1609 (1964).
[24a] C. Mannerskantz and G. Wilkinson, *J. Chem. Soc.*, **1962**, 4454.
[24b] R. S. Nyholm, *et al.*, *J. Chem. Soc.*, **1965**, 6570; **1966A**, 16.

The diamagnetic, 7-coordinate complexes are presumed to have paired electrons in low-lying d_{xz} and d_{yz} orbitals. Other Mo^{II} complexes of o-phenylenebisdimethylarsine have been made by treating $[Mo^{III}(H_2O)Cl_5]^{2-}$ or $[Mo^{III}Cl_6]^{3-}$ with the diarsine in ethanolic hydrochloric acid. The bright yellow, octahedral neutral chloride, $Mo(diars)_2Cl_2$, probably has *trans*-chlorines. It is isomorphous with similar complexes of Tc^{II}, Re^{II} and Fe^{II} and is paramagnetic, the moment being close to that for the spin-only value for a t_{2g}^4 configuration with two unpaired electrons.[25] The simultaneous formation of Mo^V in the reaction suggests that the diarsine promotes the disproportionation: $3Mo^{III} \rightarrow 2Mo^{II} + Mo^V$.

Molybdenum gives diamagnetic, binuclear carboxylates,[26a] $[Mo(OCOR)_2]_2$ which are formed as yellow needles by interaction of acids with $Mo(CO)_6$. They are thermally very stable, the acetate for example subliming at over 300°. The acetate has a copper acetate type structure with four bridging carboxylate groups and a remarkably short Mo—Mo bond,[26b] which is presumably due to Mo—Mo multiple bonding as in the isoelectronic $[Re_2X_8]^{2-}$ species (pages 655 and 969).

Molybdenum(III) and Tungsten(III) Complexes, d^3. The cationic complexes are of mainly Mo. Molybdenum(III) can be obtained in aqueous solution by reduction of the higher states; the nature of the species depends on conditions but such solutions, which are usually red, are air-sensitive. On treatment of K_3MoCl_6 in aqueous ethanolic hydrochloric acid with 1,10-phenanthroline or 2,2'dipyridyl the compounds $[Mo(phen)_3]Cl_3$ and $[Mo(dipy)_3]X_3$ are obtained.[27] The only mononuclear cationic W^{III} complex is the 7-coordinate $[W(CO)_3(diars)Br_2]^+$ obtained[24b] by bromine oxidation of the corresponding W^{II} species; it has $\mu_{eff} = 1.54$ corresponding to spin-paired d^3.

Molybdenum(III) forms complexes of the type $[MoX_6]^{3-}$ with several halogens and pseudohalogens. Prolonged electrolytic reduction of a solution of MoO_3 in concentrated hydrochloric acid gives a green solution of Mo^{III} in the form of chloro complexes, of which $[MoCl_6]^{3-}$ and $[MoCl_5(H_2O)]^{2-}$ can be precipitated with the larger alkali metal cations. The salts are red, fairly stable in dry air, but rapidly hydrolyzed and oxidized in the presence of water. They are strong reducing agents.

K_3MoCl_6 reacts with molten KHF_2 to produce brown, cubic K_3MoF_6. It reacts with an oxygen-free solution of potassium cyanide to give black crystalline $K_4Mo(CN)_7 \cdot 2H_2O$, but in the presence of oxygen the molybdenum(IV) complex $K_4Mo(CN)_8 \cdot 2H_2O$ is obtained. With solutions of

[25] J. Lewis, R. S. Nyholm and P. W. Smith, *J. Chem. Soc.*, **1963**, 2592.
[26a] T. A. Stephenson and G. Wilkinson, *J. Chem. Soc.*, **1964**, 2538.
[26b] D. Lawton and R. Mason, *J. Amer. Chem. Soc.*, **87**, 921 (1965).
[27] W. M. Carmichael, D. A. Edwards and R. A. Walton, *J. Chem. Soc.*, **1966A**, 97.

alkali metal thiocyanates even in the presence of oxygen, it gives salts of the general formula $M^I_3[Mo(NCS)_6] \cdot nH_2O$. The N-bonded $[Mo(NCS)_6]^{3-}$ ion can be prepared directly by electrolytic reduction of a solution of ammonium molybdate at a bright platinum cathode in presence of an excess of NH_4SCN. Both Mo^{III} and W^{III}, as well as the divalent hexacyanides, can be obtained by dry hydrogen reduction of the octacyanides.[28]

The tris(acetylacetonate) is an air-sensitive dark brown-purple compound prepared by heating $Mo(CO)_6$ or K_3MoCl_6 in acetylacetone. A red crystalline $K_2Mo(CN)_5$ has a low magnetic moment and may have Mo—Mo bonds in a binuclear anion.

The magnetic and spectral properties of Mo^{III} complexes, to the extent that they are known, can be accounted for satisfactorily by ligand field theory. The octahedral complexes should have three unpaired electrons and the magnetic moments, like those of octahedral Cr^{III}, should be slightly below the spin-only value (3.86 BM) because of spin-orbit coupling. Thus values in such complexes as $[Mo(phen)_3]^{3+}$, $[Mo(dipy)_3]^{3+}$, $[MoCl_6]^{3-}$, $[MoF_6]^{3-}$ and $[Mo(NCS)_6]^{3-}$ are in the range 3.7–3.85 BM. In the spectrum of $[MoCl_6]^{3-}$ the $^4A_2 \to {}^4T_2$ and $^4A_2 \to {}^4T_1$ transitions have been observed, and from their energies the value of the ligand field parameter Δ is found to be 19,200 cm^{-1}, while the Racah parameter B is found to be 435 cm^{-1}. For $[CrCl_6]^{3-}$ the Δ value is only 13,600, which provides a good illustration of the generalization (page 680) that there is a general increase of $\sim 30\%$ in Δ values on passing from analogous complexes of one transition series to those of the next heavier one. The B value is about 70% of that for the free Mo^{3+} ion; this degree of reduction in B is quite typical (see page 701).

The only nonoctahedral complex of Mo^{III} which has been studied magnetically is $K_4Mo(CN)_7 \cdot 2H_2O$, and this has a moment of 1.75 BM, indicating the presence of just one unpaired electron. For either of the two formulations which have been proposed for the complex anion, that is, $[Mo(CN)_7]^{4-}$ or $[Mo(CN)_7(H_2O)]^{4-}$, the symmetry of the ligand field would be low. The presence of only a single unpaired electron could then be due to the presence of one or two d orbitals lying well below the others.

Apart from the cationic complex noted above, the only W^{III} complex is the ion $[W_2Cl_9]^{3-}$, which can be isolated in yellow green salts, obtained by the reduction of strong hydrochloric acid solutions of K_2WO_4 electrolytically or chemically. The $W_2Cl_9^{3-}$ ion has the structure of two octahedra sharing a triangular face with chlorine atoms at each of the nine distinct apices. Thus three of the chlorine atoms are bridging. The magnetism of $K_3W_2Cl_9$ has been studied by two groups, one reporting it to be diamagnetic, the other stating that it was very weakly paramagnetic, with a susceptibility corresponding to a moment of only 0.46 BM per tungsten

[28] J. S. Yoo, E. Griswold and J. Kleinberg, *Inorg. Chem.*, **4**, 365 (1965).

atom. From these results it is clear that there is considerable if not complete pairing of electron spins of adjacent tungsten atoms. It seems that earlier claims of another polynuclear ion, the red $W_3Cl_{14}^{3-}$, are incorrect and that the color was due to admixture of $[W^{IV}Cl_5OH]^{2-}$.[29a]

Molybdenum(IV) and Tungsten(IV) Complexes, d^2. Molybdenum(IV) species are postulated labile intermediates in the reduction of Mo^{VI} by Sn^{II} or other agents and in oxidation of Mo^{III}, and they can be obtained under certain conditions in aqueous solution by mixing Mo^{III} and Mo^{VI} solutions.[29b] There are also some isolable anionic complexes of both elements. The dark-green alkali metal salts, e.g., K_2MoCl_6, are made by the interaction of $MoCl_5$ and MCl in ICl as solvent; the yellow tetra-alkylammonium salts can be made in liquid SO_2. Similar red tungsten salts are made by heating WCl_6 and KI at $130°$. These compounds evidently contain octahedral halide anions since they appear to have the K_2PtCl_6 structure.[30] Amine salts are formed by reduction of WCl_6 with aliphatic amines. The salt $K_2[WCl_5OH]$ and similar salts can be made by reduction of tungstates in hydrochloric acid.

The W^{IV} salts and also the orange complex, WCl_4py_2, obtained from K_2WCl_6 by action of pyridine or by treating WCl_4 with pyridine, have magnetic moments which are much below the spin-only value for two unpaired electrons. Some compounds are certainly antiferromagnetic and since WCl_6^{2-} salts have crystal structures similar to $IrCl_6^{2-}$ salts where antiferromagnetic interaction occurs through neighboring chlorine atoms, this explanation is probably general.

An 8-coordinate, diamagnetic, non-conducting complex, $MoCl_4(OAsPh_3)_4$, made by interaction of $MoCl_4$ with the oxide is the only example of this type so far.[31] A number of other complexes, generally $MoCl_4L_2$, have been made but the coordination number is not known with certainty.[27, 32]

Hexafluoromolybdates, for example, the dark brown Na_2MoF_6, can be obtained by reduction of MoF_6 with an excess of NaI; the hexafluoro-molybdates(IV) are much more stable with respect to hydrolysis than are the Mo^V species.

The most important complexes of Mo^{IV} and W^{IV} are the octacyanides, $[Mo(CN)_8]^{4-}$ and $[W(CN)_8]^{4-}$. The molybdenum one forms in solutions of Mo^{III} or Mo^V on treatment with a large excess of potassium cyanide. In the former case it appears, as noted earlier, that molecular oxygen must

[29a] E. König, Inorg. Chem., **2**, 1238 (1963).

[29b] Cf. A. A. Bergh and G. P. Haight, Inorg. Chem., **1**, 688 (1962).

[30] A. J. Edwards, R. D. Peacock and A. Said, J. Chem. Soc., **1962**, 4643; C. D. Kennedy and R. D. Peacock, J. Chem. Soc., **1963**, 3392.

[31] S. M. Horner and S. Y. Tyree, Inorg. Chem., **1**, 947 (1962).

[32] E. A. Allen, K. Feenan and G. W. A. Fowles, J. Chem. Soc., **1965**, 1636.

be present as the oxidizing agent; in the latter case the manner of reduction has not been established.   Both $[Mo(CN)_8]^{4-}$ and $[W(CN)_8]^{4-}$ are remarkably stable species, thermally, toward hydrolysis, and toward acids and oxidizing agents.   They can be oxidized by very powerful oxidants, for example, Ce^{IV} or MnO_4^-, to the corresponding yellow octacyano complexes of Mo^V and W^V which, like the IV-valent complexes, can be isolated as either salts or as free acids such as $H_4[W(CN)_8]\cdot6H_2O$. Both the Mo^{IV} and W^{IV} anions, as well as the corresponding V complexes, undergo facile photolysis involving loss of CN^-; neither the mechanism nor the nature of the products is well known.[33a]

The structure of the $[Mo(CN)_8]^{4-}$ ion has already been discussed (page 932).   The diamagnetism of the octacyanides suggests that the distortion of the arrangement of the eight CN^- ions from that of a cube splits the d_{z^2} and $d_{x^2-y^2}$ orbitals sufficiently so that the two d electrons become paired in the one of lower energy.   An investigation of the Raman spectrum of $[Mo(CN)_8]^{4-}$ has been reported to provide evidence that this complex has the configuration of a square antiprism rather than the dodecahedral structure (page 136) previously deduced from X-ray study.   Whether there is an error in the experimental work or whether there is a change in configuration when the crystalline salt is dissolved in water remains to be determined.   The latter seems most probable, however, considering the small difference in inherent stability of the two arrangements (page 137).

Molybdenum(V) and Tungsten(V) Complexes, d^1.   Apart from some chloroalkoxides, blue, paramagnetic $WCl_3(OEt)_2$ and $WCl_4(OEt)_6$, which is red and diamagnetic,[33b] these are all anionic and contain oxygen, halogens, thiocyanate or cyanide groups as ligands.   The hexafluoromolybdate(V) and hexafluorotungstate(V) anions can be obtained as Na, K, Rb or Cs salts by the reaction:

$$W(Mo)(CO)_6 + M^I I + IF_5 \rightarrow M^I W(Mo)F_6 + 6CO + \text{other unidentified products}$$

Here, IF_5 serves both as the fluorinating agent and the solvent.   In these complexes there is considerable interionic electron spin coupling which makes them antiferromagnetic (Neél temperatures of the order of 100–150°K).   These couplings must take place by overlap of orbitals of the fluoride ions of adjacent $[MF_6]^-$ units in the crystals, that is, by a superexchange process similar in principle to that in halides and chalconides of some divalent metals of the first transition series (see page 697).   Such an explanation of course requires the assumption of significant overlap of metal $d\pi$ (t_2) orbitals with fluoride ion $p\pi$ orbitals.

[33a] J. R. Perumareddi, Mellon Institute, *Theoretical Chemistry Preprint*, No. 19, Dec. 1964, and references therein.
[33b] O. J. Klejnot, *Inorg. Chem.*, **4**, 1668 (1965).

It is also possible to isolate K_3MoF_8 and K_3WF_8 from the above reaction system under certain conditions. It is not known whether these compounds contain octacoordinated metal ions or not.

Black crystals of the tetraethylammonium salt of $MoCl_6^-$ result from the interaction of $MoCl_5$ with Et_4NCl in CH_2Cl_2. Corresponding green WCl_6^- and WBr_6^- salts can be made similarly or in other ways.[34] The magnetic moments of these complexes are lower than the spin-only value and Et_4NWCl_6 is actually antiferromagnetic. The salts are thermally decomposed to the red W^{IV} complex,

$$2M^IWCl_6 \underset{\text{green}}{\overset{280–300°}{\rightleftarrows}} M_2^IWCl_6 + WCl_6$$
$$\text{red}$$

Molybdenum(VI) and Tungsten(VI) Complexes, d^0. Most complexes are anionic with fluorine and/or oxygen as the ligand atoms.

By reaction of $W(CO)_6$ with IF_5 (as the reaction medium) in presence of KI the compound K_2WF_8 is obtained. The unit cell of this compound and of $CsWF_7$ and $RbWF_7$ is cubic, but the shape of the coordination polyhedra about the tungsten atom is not yet known. Similar MF_7^- species of uncertain structure are formed by interaction of MF_6 with NOF and NO_2F as the NO^+ and NO_2^+ salts.[35]

30-C-7. Oxo Complexes

There are many compounds of molybdenum in the V and VI oxidation states in which there are one or more oxygen atoms bound to the molybdenum by multiple bonds, which can be represented Mo=O, since they are evidently approximately double bonds. The nature of such bonds has been considered earlier (page 364). There are also oxo species which have linear bridges M—O—M and non-linear oxo bridges appear to exist also. While there are certain resemblances in this oxo chemistry to that of Cr, and while tungsten also forms some analogous compounds, by far the most extensive chemistry is known for molybdenum. Some important relationships are summarized in Figure 30-C-9 (page 948).

Molybdenum(V) Compounds. The *oxochloride*, $MoOCl_3$, is a dark-brown, non-volatile solid best obtained by solvolysis of $MoCl_5$ by liquid SO_2 or by reducing $MoOCl_4$ with refluxing chlorobenzene;[36] it probably has[36] the $NbOCl_3$ structure (Fig. 30-B-5). Since $MoCl_5$ can abstract oxygen not

---

[34] B. J. Brisdon and R. A. Walton, *J. Inorg. Nucl. Chem.*, **27**, 1101 (1965); *idem.*, *J. Chem. Soc.*, **1965**, 2274; K. W. Bagnall, D. Brown and G. M. du Preez, *J. Chem. Soc.*, **1964**, 2603; R. N. Dickinson, *et. al.*, *Inorg. Chem.*, **3**, 1600 (1964).

[35] J. R. Geichman, E. A. Smith and P. R. Ogle, *Inorg. Chem.*, **2**, 1012 (1963).

[36] M. L. Larson and F. W. Moore, *Abstract 149th A.C.S. Meeting*, Detroit, 1965; D. A. Edwards, *J. Inorg. Nucl. Chem.*, **25**, 1198 (1963).

only from SO_2 but from other donors such as Me_2SO, Ph_3PO, etc., inter-action with such ligands leads to octahedral complexes such as $MoOCl_3$-$(OSMe_2)_2$;[37] these mononuclear compounds appear to have Mo=O bonds. The $MoOCl_4^-$ ion can be regarded as being derived from $MoOCl_3$ by coordination of Cl^- (see below).

An extensive range of Mo^V compounds can be obtained by reduction of molybdates or MoO_3 in acid solutions either chemically, e.g., by shaking with mercury, or electrolytically. The nature of the resultant species depends critically on the anions present and on conditions of pH and concentration. Probably the most important species, and one which is often used as a source material for preparation of other Mo^V compounds, is the emerald green ion $[MoOCl_5]^{2-}$ which can be isolated as a variety of salts. The salts can be obtained by reduction of hydrochloric acid solutions of Mo^{VI} or from $MoCl_5$. Solutions of $MoCl_5$ in oxygenated solvents contain oxo species, as we have seen, and green solutions in ethanol or methanol can be used; when $MoCl_5$ is put into concentrated hydrochloric acid containing a univalent chloride MCl and the solution saturated with HCl gas, crystalline salts such as $K_2[MoOCl_5]$ are obtained. Such salts are paramagnetic with μ_{eff} ca 1.67, indicating a single unpaired electron with slight antiferromagnetic or other effects.[38a] The $MoOCl_5^{2-}$ has been studied extensively in solution and in crystals and its spectral lines assigned on the basis of strong tetragonal distortion of octahedral symmetry.[38b] If solutions of $MoOCl_5^{2-}$ are less than ca $10M$ HCl, the color deepens and the paramagnetism of Mo^V is decreased. Absorption and esr spectra together with the pH dependence of the system suggest that dimerization through the formation of oxo bridges is occurring. There appears to be a paramagnetic dimer in the region 4–$10M$ HCl as well as a diamagnetic dimer, but below $2M$ HCl the solutions are completely diamagnetic; $MoOCl_5^{2-}$ does not exist below $4M$ HCl. The nature of these species is not fully established. The first step is probably of the type

$$[MoOCl_5]^{2-} \rightleftharpoons [MoOCl_4 \cdot H_2O]^- + Cl^- \rightleftharpoons [MoOCl_4OH]^{2-} + H^+$$

where the chloride opposite the oxygen may be labilized by the *trans* effect, followed by condensation to give Mo—O—Mo bonds:

$$2[MoOCl_4OH]^{2-} \rightleftharpoons [Cl_4OMoOMoOCl_4]^{4-} + H_2O$$

$$[Cl_4OMoOMoOCl_4]^{4-} \underset{HCl}{\overset{H_2O}{\rightleftharpoons}} [Cl_3OMoO_2MoOCl_3]^{4-} + 2H^+ + 2Cl^-$$
$$(Mo_2O_3 \text{ unit}) \qquad\qquad (Mo_2O_4 \text{ unit})$$

[37] K. Feenan and G. W. A. Fowles, *Inorg. Chem.*, **4**, 310 (1965).

[38a] D. Brown, *J. Chem. Soc.*, **1964**, 4944.

[38b] G. P. Haight, *J. Inorg. Nucl. Chem.*, **24**, 663, 673 (1962); H. B. Gray and C. R. Hare. *Inorg. Chem.*, **1**, 363, 831 (1962).

In HBr, there is no evidence for $[MoOBr_5]^{2-}$ and the Mo^V and Mo^{VI} species in the solution appear to be dimeric.[39]

While there is little information about the geometry of such oxo-bridged complexes, essentially all Mo^V oxo complexes contain MoO, Mo_2O_3 or Mo_2O_4 units; there is little evidence for cationic species, e.g., MoO^{3+}, but anionic and neutral complexes are widespread.[40] For example there are complexes such as $MoOCl_3(dipy)$, $Mo_2O_3Cl_4dipy_2$ and $Mo_2O_4Cl_2dipy_2$ and oxalato complexes such as $\{[MoO(ox)H_2O]_2O_2\}^{2-}$. The latter binuclear anion[40b] has a double oxygen bridge and the diamagnetism is clearly due to the existence of an Mo—Mo bond (2.51 A). An ethylxanthate complex, $[(C_2H_5OCS_2)_2MoO]_2O$, has been shown to have a structure with two distorted octahedra linked by a linear Mo—O—Mo bond with *cis* double-bonded oxygen atoms on each Mo.[40c] The action of acetylacetone on $[MoOCl_5]^{2-}$ gives a brown diamagnetic compound $[O{=}Mo(acac)]_2O$;[41] in this case at least there must be $d\pi$–$p\pi$ bonding in presumably a linear Mo—O—Mo bridge, similar to that in the xanthate species.

Some quite stable oxomolybdenum(V) species can be obtained with certain anions,[42] notably ethylenediaminetetraacetate and its derivatives— thus diethylenetriaminepentaacetic acid with Mo^V in $3M$ HCl gives a crystalline product reported as $H_3[Mo_2O_2(OH)_4DPTA]$ which is indefinitely stable in air; 8-hydroxyquinoline-5-sulfonic acid also gives stable species.

We have noted above the occurrence of $[MoOCl_4]^-$ salts[43] related to both $MoOCl_3$ and $[MoOCl_5]^{2-}$. They are best prepared in liquid sulfur dioxide, e.g.,

$$MoCl_5 + R_4NCl \xrightarrow{SO_2} R_4N^+[MoOCl_4]^- + SOCl_2$$

The color varies with the cation; Rb and Cs salts are pale green, the pyridinium salt yellow. Since crystal and solution spectra (in SO_2) differ, the crystals could contain octahedral Mo^V through interaction of the type $Mo{=}O \rightarrow Mo{=}O$, while solutions doubtless contain solvated ions

[39] J. F. Allen and H. M. Neumann, *Inorg. Chem.*, **3**, 1611 (1964).

[40a] P. C. H. Mitchell and R. J. P. Williams, *J. Chem. Soc.*, **1962**, 4570; P. C. H. Mitchell, *J. Inorg. Nucl. Chem.*, **25**, 963 (1963); **26**, 1967 (1964) and references therein; H. Funk, M. Hesselbart and F. Schmeil, *Zeit. anorg. Chem.*, **318**, 318 (1962); D. A. Edwards, *J. Inorg. Nucl. Chem.*, **27**, 303 (1965).

[40b] F. A. Cotton and S. M. Morehouse, *Inorg. Chem.*, **4**, 1377 (1965); see also *idem.*, *Inorg. Chem.*, **4**, 922 (1965).

[40c] A. B. Blake, F. A. Cotton and J. S. Wood, *J. Amer. Chem. Soc.*, **86**, 3024 (1964).

[41] M. L. Larson and F. W. Moore, *Inorg. Chem.*, **2**, 88 (1963).

[42] R. E. Sievers and J. C. Bailar, *Inorg. Chem.*, **1**, 174 (1962); J. T. Spence and E. R. Peterson, *Inorg. Chem.*, **2**, 277 (1962); D. J. Sawyer and J. M. McKinnie, *J. Amer. Chem. Soc.*, **82**, 4191 (1960).

[43] A. E. Allen, *et al.*, *J. Chem. Soc.*, **1963**, 4649.

[$MoOCl_4OSO$]$^-$. Corresponding solvated salts such as K[$MoOCl_4 \cdot MeCN$] are known.

Tungsten(V) forms a number of corresponding derivatives. Thus when $WO_4{}^{2-}$ in 12M HCl is reduced, crystalline salts of [$WOCl_5$]$^{2-}$ can be obtained from the blue solutions; [$WOCl_4$]$^-$ and [$WOCl_4 \cdot H_2O$]$^-$ salts are also known.

Compounds of Mo^{VI} and W^{VI}. The oxohalides are volatile molecular compounds of the types MOX_4 and MO_2X_2. The molybdenum compounds are less stable than those of tungsten but are all fairly rapidly hydrolyzed by water. They are obtained as by-products in the halogenation of the metals unless the metal is first scrupulously reduced and the reaction system vigorously purged of oxygen.

$MoOCl_4$ is best obtained as green crystals (m 101–103°) by evaporation of the red solutions obtained by refluxing MoO_3 with $SOCl_2$;[44] it decomposes to $MoOCl_3$ and Cl_2 even at 25° and is readily reduced by organic solvents to Mo^V species.

$MoOF_4$ and WOF_4 can both be prepared by the same types of reaction,

$$\left.\begin{array}{l} M + O_2 + F_2 \\ MO_3 + F_2 \\ MOCl_4 + HF \end{array}\right\} \rightarrow MOF_4 \qquad (M = Mo \text{ or } W)$$

They are both colorless, volatile solids, not as reactive as the hexafluorides.

WO_2F_2 has been reported but there is some doubt of its actual existence. MoO_2F_2 can be obtained by the action of HF on MoO_2Cl_2; it is a white solid subliming at 270° at 1 atm.

MoO_2Cl_2 is best made by the action of chlorine on heated, dry MoO_2. It is fairly volatile and dissolves with hydrolysis in water. An electron diffraction study of MoO_2Cl_2 vapor has shown the existence of tetrahedral molecules.

A substance of the formula $MoO_2Cl_2 \cdot H_2O$ is obtained when MoO_3 is treated with dry hydrogen chloride at 150–200°. It is a pale yellow, very volatile compound soluble in various polar organic solvents. Its molecular structure is not known, but the formulation $MoO(OH)_2Cl_2$ seems reasonable.

The two tungsten oxochlorides are formed together when WO_3 is heated in CCl_4, phosgene or PCl_5 vapor. They are easily separated since $WOCl_4$ is much more volatile than WO_2Cl_2. On strong heating above 200° the following reaction occurs

$$2WO_2Cl_2 = WO_3 + WOCl_4$$

$WOCl_4$ forms scarlet crystals, a red monomeric vapor, and is in general

---

[44] R. Colton, I. B. Tompkins and P. W. Wilson, *Aust. J. Chem.*, **17**, 496 (1964).

highly reactive. It is violently hydrolyzed by water. WO_2Cl_2 occurs as yellow crystals and is not nearly so reactive as $WOCl_4$; it is hydrolyzed only slowly by cold water.

A number of *dioxo complexes* are known, some of which have been shown by infrared study to have the two oxygen atoms *trans*; examples are $[MoO_2Cl_4]^{2-}$ and $[WO_2Cl_4]^{2-}$. Other dioxo complexes of uncertain configuration include $MoO_2(acac)_2$ made by refluxing MoO_3 with acetylacetone and complexes of the type $MoO_2Cl_2L_2$[45] and $MoO_2(S_2CNMe_2)_2$. Several sulfato-oxo complexes of unknown structure, e.g., MoO_2SO_4, obtained by heating MoO_3 with concentrated sulfuric acid, and salts apparently containing $[Mo_2O_6SO_4]^{2-}$ and $[MoO_4SO_4]^{4-}$, which are obtained from it by heating with metal sulfates, are also known.

Mo^{VI} forms various binuclear oxo complexes having both $Mo{=}O$ and $Mo{-}O{-}Mo$ groups. The best characterized structurally is the anion in $K_2[Mo_2O_5(C_2O_4)_2(H_2O)_2]$ which has[11] the centrosymmetric structure shown in Figure 30-C-11; the bridge group $Mo{-}O{-}Mo$ is linear and symmetrical.

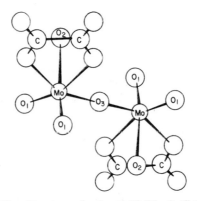

Fig. 30-C-11.   Structure of anion in $K_2[Mo_2O_5(C_2O_4)_2(H_2O)_2]$.

A number of π-cyclopentadienyloxomolybdenum complexes such as $\pi\text{-}C_5H_5MoO_2Cl$ and $[\pi\text{-}C_5H_5MoO_2]_2O$ are also known.[46]

30-D. TECHNETIUM AND RHENIUM

Technetium and rhenium resemble each other closely in chemistry and differ noticeably from manganese, although there are similarities in stoichiometries, for example, MnO_4^- and ReO_4^-, and in some complexes,

[45] H.-L. Kraus and W. Huber, *Chem. Ber.*, **94**, 2865 (1961).
[46] M. Cousins and M. L. H. Green, *J. Chem. Soc.*, **1964**, 1567.

such as carbonyls, with π-bonding ligands. The most stable and characteristic oxidation state for manganese is the II state, and manganese generally gives high-spin complexes, forming low-spin compounds or complexes rather reluctantly. Technetium and rhenium in most of their compounds and complexes have low spin. There is no evidence for any simple $2+$ cationic species for either element—indeed there is little evidence for simple cationic species at all, although green, readily oxidized solutions of Tc^{III} can be obtained by cathodic reduction of TcO_4^- in phosphate buffer and similar observations have been made for Re. In general, the higher oxidation states are the most stable. For technetium, the IV and VII states are the best known with the III, V and VI difficult to prepare and poorly characterized and the II state known only in a few complexes; for rhenium, the VI state is difficult to obtain, and the III, IV, V and VII states are the commonest. A characteristic feature of Re^{III} in its halide compounds is the formation of metal atom clusters.

While there is very little cationic aqueous chemistry, the oxo anions TcO_4^- and ReO_4^- are well known in aqueous solution. Polarographic studies of the reduction of these ions in aqueous solution containing different anions have been made,[1] but, although standard potential values can be associated with the observed reduction steps, the precise nature of the species present is obscure. The final reduction appears to involve the formation of hydride species (page 978). Some potential data—of limited reliability—are as shown in Figure 30-D-1. The oxidation states and stereochemistry of the elements are summarized in Table 30-D-1.

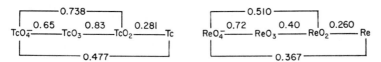

Fig. 30-D-1. Electrode potential data for technetium and rhenium.

30-D-1. The Elements

Although its existence was predicted much earlier from the periodic table, rhenium was first detected by its X-ray spectrum only in 1925. Several prior attempts to isolate the element failed mainly because of its low abundance ($\sim 1 \times 10^{-9}\%$) in the earth's crust. The discoverers, Noddack, Berg and Tacke, later isolated about a gram of rhenium from molybdenite. Rhenium is now recovered on a fairly substantial scale from the flue dusts in the roasting of molybdenum sulfide ores and from residues in the smelting

[1] G. B. S. Salaria, C. L. Rulfs and P. J. Elving, *J. Chem. Soc.*, **1963**, 2479.

of some copper ores. The element is usually left in oxidized solution as perrhenate ion, ReO_4^-. After concentration, the perrhenate is precipitated by addition of potassium chloride as the sparingly soluble salt, $KReO_4$.

TABLE 30-D-1

Oxidation States and Stereochemistry of Technetium and Rhenium

Oxidation state	Coordination	Geometry	Examples
Tc^{-I}, Re^{-I}	5	?	$[Re(CO)_5]^-$
Tc^0, Re^0, d^7	6	Octahedral	$Tc_2(CO)_{10}$, $Re_2(CO)_{10}$
Tc^I, Re^I, d^6		π-Complex	π-$C_5H_5Re(CO)_2C_5H_8$, π-$C_5H_5Re(CO)_3$
	6	Octahedral	$Re(CO)_5Cl$, $K_5[Re(CN)_6]$, $Re(CO)_3py_2Cl$, $[(CH_3C_6H_4NC)_6Re]^+$
Tc^{II}, Re^{II}, d^5	5	?	ReX_2TAS
	6	Octahedral	$Re(diars)_2Cl_2$, $Tc(diars)_2Cl_2$
Tc^{III}, Re^{III}, d^4		π-Complex	$(\pi$-$C_5H_5)_2ReH$, $(\pi$-$C_5H_5)_2ReH_2^+$
	5	TBP?	$(Ph_3PO)_2ReCl_3$
	6	Octahedral	$[Tc(diars)_2Cl_2]^+$, $ReCl_2acac(PPh_3)_2$
		Trigonal prism	$Re(S_2C_2Ph_2)_3$
	?	Metal atom clusters[a]	$Re_2X_8^{2-}$, $Re_3X_{9+n}^{n-}$, $Re_3X_9L_3$
Tc^{IV}, Re^{IV}, d^3	4?	Metal atom clusters(?)	ReF_4, $ReCl_4$
	6[a]	Octahedral	K_2TcI_6, K_2RtCl_6, ReI_4py_2, $TcCl_4$, $[Re_2OCl_{10}]^{4-}$, $ReCl_4diars$
	7	?	$[ReCOdiars_2I_2]ClO_4$
Tc^V, Re^V, d^2	5	TBP?	$ReCl_5$, ReF_5, $NReCl_2(PPh_3)_2$
		Square pyramid	$[ReOX_4]^-$
	6[a]	Octahedral	$ReOCl_3(PPh_3)_2$, $[ReOCl_5]^{2-}$
	7	?	$ReOCl_3TAS$
	8	Dodecahedral(?)	$[Re(diars)_2Cl_4]^+$, $K_3[Re(CN)_8]$
Tc^{VI}, Re^{VI}, d^1	6	Octahedral	ReO_3, ReF_6
	7	?	$ReOCl_6^{2-}$
	8	Dodecahedral(?)	$[Re(CN)_8]^{2-}$
Tc^{VII}, Re^{VII}, d^0	4[a]	Tetrahedral	ReO_4^-, TcO_4^-, ReO_3Cl, Re_2O_7
	6	Octahedral	$ReO_3Cl_3^{2-}$
	7	?	ReF_7
	8	Archimedean antiprism	$KReF_8$
	9	See page 978	ReH_9^{2-}

[a] Most common states.

The discoverers of rhenium also believed that they had detected element 43 to which they gave the name masurium. However, it is now known that all isotopes of this element are unstable toward β decay or electron capture and traces exist in nature only as fragments from the spontaneous fission of uranium. The element was named technetium by the discoverers of the first radioisotope—Perrier and Segré. Three isotopes have half-lives greater than 10^5 years, but the only one which has been obtained on a macro scale is ^{99}Tc (β^-, 2.12×10^5 years). Technetium is recovered from waste fission product solutions after removal of plutonium and uranium. It is recovered by precipitation of tetraphenylarsonium pertechnetate, $(Ph_4As)TcO_4$, using perchlorate ion as carrier. The precipitate is dissolved in alcohol and passed through an anion exchange resin in the chloride form; the TcO_4^- ion is absorbed while the soluble tetraphenylarsonium chloride is eluted and recovered. The TcO_4^- ion is eluted with $2N$ perchloric acid and is purified by distillation (as Tc_2O_7) from perchloric acid solution. Other extraction procedures, such as solvent extraction with methyl ethyl ketone, can be used.

The metals resemble platinum in appearance but are usually obtained as grey powders; Re has a higher melting point ($3180°$) than any metal except W ($3400°$). They are obtained by thermal decomposition of NH_4MO_4 or $(NH_4)_2MCl_6$ in H_2. Technetium can also be made by electrolysis of NH_4TcO_4 in $2N$ H_2SO_4, with continuous addition of H_2O_2 to re-oxidize a brown solid also produced; Re can also be electrodeposited from H_2SO_4 solutions but special conditions are required to obtain coherent deposits. Both metals crystallize in a hexagonal close-packed arrangement. They burn in oxygen on heating above $400°$ to give the oxides M_2O_7 which sublime away; in moist air the metals are slowly oxidized to the oxo acids. The latter are also obtained by dissolution of the metals in concentrated nitric acid or hot concentrated sulfuric acid. The metals are insoluble in hydrofluoric and hydrochloric acids but are conveniently dissolved by warm bromine water. Rhenium, but not technetium, is soluble in hydrogen peroxide.

At the present time rhenium has only minor uses, as in an alloy with tungsten for flash bulb filaments, and its alloys suffer from their reactivity toward oxygen; with inert gas protection a very useful Pt–Re thermocouple can be made. The TcO_4^- ion in very low concentrations has been shown to be a powerful corrosion inhibitor for steels, but there does not seem to be commercial utilization of this property.

BINARY COMPOUNDS OF TECHNETIUM AND RHENIUM

30-D-2. Oxides and Sulfides

The known *oxides* are shown in Table 30-D-2. The *heptoxides*, obtained by burning the metals, are quite volatile. If acid solutions containing TcO_4^- are evaporated, the oxide is driven off, a fact which can be utilized to isolate and separate technetium; rhenium is not lost from acid solutions

TABLE 30-D-2

Oxides of Rhenium and Technetium[a]

Rhenium		Technetium	
Oxide	Color	Oxide	Color
$Re_2O_3 \cdot xH_2O$	Black		
ReO_2	Brown	TcO_2	Black
ReO_3	Red	TcO_3	Purple
Re_2O_5	Blue		
Re_2O_7	Yellow (m 220°)	Tc_2O_7	Yellow (m 119.5°)

[a] Lower hydrated oxides formulated as $ReO \cdot H_2O$ and $Re_2O \cdot 2H_2O$, are obtained by Zn reduction of weakly acid ReO_4^- solutions; they are not fully investigated.

on evaporation, i.e., at 100°, but can be distilled from hot conc. H_2SO_4. The heptoxides readily dissolve in water giving acidic solutions, and Re_2O_7 is deliquescent. The oxides are not isomorphous and differ in other respects; for example, solid Tc_2O_7 conducts electricity just below its melting point, although the liquid is non-conducting—Re_2O_7 shows just the opposite behavior for reasons obscure.

The lower oxides can be obtained by either thermal decomposition of NH_4MO_4 or by heating $M_2O_7 + M$, at 200–300°. The hydrated dioxides, $MO_2 \cdot 2H_2O$, can be obtained by addition of base to M^{IV} solutions, for instance, of $ReCl_6^{2-}$, or, for Tc, by reduction of TcO_4^- in hydrochloric acid with zinc. For rhenium a hydrated sesquioxide, $Re_2O_3 \cdot xH_2O$ has been obtained by addition of base to a solution of Re_3Cl_9 in water; this oxide is readily oxidized by water to $ReO_2 \cdot xH_2O$. The pentoxide has been made by electrolytic reduction of perrhenate in sulfuric acid solution; it decomposes above 200°.[2a]

Rhenium(VI) oxide has a structure which is also found in other trioxides, such as CrO_3 and WO_3. This structure is commonly called the ReO_3 structure and is shown in Figure 30-D-2. A variety of mixed oxides[2b] containing Re are known, some of which have the perovskite structure.

The *sulfides* TcS_2, ReS_2 and Tc_2S_7, Re_2S_7 are isomorphous. The black heptasulfides are obtained by saturation of 2–6N hydrochloric acid solution of TcO_4^- or ReO_4^- with hydrogen sulfide. The precipitation is sensitive to conditions and is often incomplete. The treatment of neutral solutions of the oxo anions with thioacetamide or sodium thiosulfate followed by acidification gives a better yield. Excess sulfur in the precipitates may be extracted with CS_2. ReS_3 is obtained[3a] by hydrogen reduction of Re_2S_7.

[2a] S. Tribalat, D. Delafosse and C. Piolet, *Comptes Rendus*, **261**, 1008 (1965).
[2b] J. M. Longo, L. Katz and R. Ward, *Inorg. Chem.*, **4**, 235 (1965).
[3a] K. Traore, G. Coeffier and J. Brenet, *Bull. Soc. Chim.*, **1962**, 361

The disulfides are obtained by heating the heptasulfides with sulfur in vacuum; they have a tendency to be nonstoichiometric.

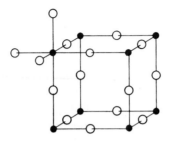

Fig. 30-D-2.   The ReO_3 structure.   Each metal atom lies at the center of an octahedron of oxygen atoms.   This structure is closely related to the perovskite structure (page 51) since the latter is obtained from this one by insertion of a large cation in the center of the cube shown.

Rhenium sulfides are effective catalysts for hydrogenation of organic substances and they have the advantage over heterogeneous platinum metal catalysts in that they are not poisoned by sulfur compounds.   An inorganic reduction which they catalyze is that of NO to N_2O at 100°.[3b]

30-D-3. Halides

The known halides of the elements are shown in Table 30-D-3. TcF_6 results from the fluorination of technetium at 400°; it is stable in nickel or dry pyrex vessels for an extended period of time.   On hydrolysis, like

TABLE 30-D-3

The Halides of Technetium and Rhenium

			$TcCl_4$ blood red		$TcCl_6$ green	
			ReF_4 blue, sub. >300°	ReF_5 greenish yellow, m 48°	TcF_6 golden yellow, m 33°	ReF_7 pale yellow
		Re_3Cl_9 dark red	$ReCl_4$ black	$ReCl_5$ dark red-brown	ReF_6 pale yellow, m 18.7°	
		Re_3Br_9 red-brown	$ReBr_4$ dark red	$ReBr_5$ green-blue	$ReCl_6$ green-brown, m ~22°	
ReI_2 black		Re_3I_9 black	ReI_4 black			

[3b] L. H. Slaugh, *Inorg. Chem.*, **3**, 920 (1964).

ReF_6, it gives a black precipitate, presumably of hydrous TcO_2. $TcCl_4$ is obtained as paramagnetic red crystals by the action of carbon tetrachloride on Tc_2O_7 in a bomb, or by thermal decomposition of $TcCl_6$, which is obtained on direct chlorination of the metal. $TcCl_4$ consists of octahedral $TcCl_6$ units linked into linear chains by bridging Cl atoms. The Tc—Tc distance (3.59 A) indicates little if any metal–metal interaction.[4a]

ReF_6, is obtained by direct interaction of the elements at 120°. Spectroscopic studies have shown that it is an octahedral molecule and the absorption spectrum of its d^1 system, which is influenced by strong spin-orbit coupling, has been analyzed. Both ReF_6 and TcF_6 have moments much lower than the spin-only value for the same reason. The compound is very sensitive to moisture and on hydrolysis gives ReO_2, $HReO_4$ and HF. The heptafluoride, ReF_7, is also obtained by direct interaction of the metal at 400° with fluorine under slight pressure. ReF_5 is obtained along with ReF_4 and oxofluorides by the reduction of ReF_6 with metal carbonyls. The nonvolatile ReF_4 is best made[4b] by reduction of ReF_6 with Re at 500°.

On heating rhenium metal (freshly prepared by thermal decomposition of ammonium perrhenate in hydrogen) in oxygen-free chlorine, the hexachloride is obtained as a green vapor which condenses to a green-brown solid. $ReCl_6$ is hydrolyzed, with disproportionation, to ReO_4^- and hydrated ReO_2; unlike $TcCl_6$, it does not give the tetrachloride on heating.[5] If rhenium metal powder (contaminated with KCl) is heated in chlorine at 500° mainly $ReCl_5$ is obtained as a dark red-brown vapor which condenses to a dark red-brown solid; chlorination at higher temperatures gives a mixture of $ReCl_5$ and $ReCl_6$. $ReCl_5$ is also obtained by extraction of various salts of $ReCl_6^{2-}$ with boiling CCl_4. Since these salts can be readily obtained from the corresponding perrhenates by reduction with CCl_4 at 400°, or in other ways, this is a useful preparation not needing metal.[6] $ReCl_5$ is rapidly hydrolyzed by water or moist air. If it is heated in a nitrogen atmosphere, it loses chlorine and the relatively nonvolatile "trichloride," is obtained as dark red crystals (see below). The only preparative method reported for the tetrachloride is treatment of the hydrated dioxide with $SOCl_2$.[7a] Magnetic susceptibility measurements indicate that $ReCl_4$ may actually consist of Re_3Cl_{12} molecules containing metal atom clusters, with a structure similar to that of the Re_3Cl_9 groups in Re^{III} chloride (see below). Direct proof is lacking, however, since the

[4a] M. Elder and B. R. Penfold, *Chem. Comm.*, **1965**, 308.

[4b] D. E. Lavalle, R. M. Steele and W. T. Smith, Jr., *J. Inorg. Nucl. Chem.*, **28**, 260 (1966).

[5] R. Colton, *Nature*, **194**, 374 (1962).

[6] W. W. Horner, F. N. Collier, Jr., and S. Y. Tyree, Jr., *Inorg. Chem.*, **3**, 1388 (1964).

[7a] D. Brown and R. Colton, *J. Chem. Soc.*, **1964**, 714.

compound has yet to be obtained in crystalline form.[7b] $ReCl_5$ and $ReCl_6$ also have unusual magnetic properties,[7a] the latter having a high moment for d^1.

The pentabromide, obtained by bromination of Re at 650°, decomposes readily to Re_3Br_9 on heating.[8] The tetrabromide and tetraiodide can be made by careful evaporation of solutions of $HReO_4$ in excess HBr or HI. The iodide is unstable and on heating at 350° in a sealed tube gives ReI_3. At 110° in nitrogen, ReI_2 is obtained; it is diamagnetic and is believed to be polymeric with Re—Re bonds.[9]

Re^{III} *Halides.* Little is known of the iodide. The chloride particularly and the bromide have been extensively studied and their true molecular formulas are Re_3X_9. They are not isomorphous, but both[10,11] consist of Re_3X_9 units connected by sharing of X atoms as shown for Re_3Cl_9 in Figure 30-D-3. The Re_3X_9 units are metal atoms cluster compounds;

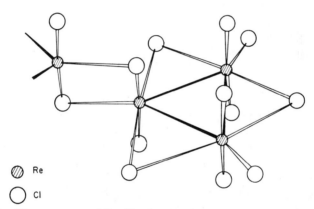

Re

Cl

Fig. 30-D-3. The structure of Re_3Cl_9 showing how the trinuclear molecules are linked by chlorine bridges.

the Re_3 groups are equilateral triangles within experimental error (exactly so in Re_3Cl_9) with Re—Re distances of ~ 2.48A. The metal–metal bonding is strong, the bond orders being about 2 according to molecular orbital theory.[12] The Re_3X_9 units are very stable, persisting in the vapors of both compounds[13] at temperatures around 600°. As will be seen presently,

[7b] R. Colton and R. L. Martin, *Nature,* **205,** 239 (1965).

[8] R. Colton, *J. Chem. Soc.,* **1962,** 2078.

[9] J. E. Fergusson, B. H. Robinson and W. R. Roper, *J. Chem. Soc.,* **1962,** 2113.

[10] F. A. Cotton, S. S. Lippard and J. T. Mague, *Inorg. Chem.,* **4,** 508 (1965).

[11] F. A. Cotton and J. T. Mague, *Inorg. Chem.,* **3,** 1402 (1964).

[12] F. A. Cotton and T. E. Haas, *Inorg. Chem.,* **3,** 10 (1964); J. E. Fergussen, *et al.,* *J. Chem. Soc.,* **1965,** 5500.

[13] K. Rinke and H. Schäfer, *Angew. Chem. (Internat.)* **4,** 148 (1965), Re_3Cl_9; A. Buchler, private comm., Re_3Cl_9 and Re_3Br_9.

the Re_3X_9 units also persist in many complexes. Earlier work suggesting dimers, Re_2X_6, is in error. Re_3Cl_9 absorbs water vapor from the atmosphere, up to ~ 1–2 H_2O per Re, but this can be easily pumped off. After such treatment, the Re_3Cl_9 becomes much more easily soluble; this may be attributed to the fact that the H_2O molecules break the Re—Cl—Re bridges forming weak Re—OH_2 bonds. On removal of the water, the Re_3Cl_9 units do not link up to reconstitute the original structure in its entirety.

Complex Halides. Both Tc^{IV} and Re^{IV} form a series of stable hexahalo complex ions MX_6^{2-}. No fluorotechnetates are known so far, although they doubtless can be made; the hexafluororhenate ion, ReF_6^{2-}, is an exceedingly stable ion in aqueous solution, even when alkaline. The salts can be made in several ways, by heating K_2ReBr_6 with MF or K_2ReI_6 with KHF_2, by reducing ReF_6 in liquid SO_2 with KI, or by heating $KReO_4$ with aqueous HF and KI. The salt K_2ReF_6 forms green octahedra. Interaction of liquid ReF_6 with alkali fluorides gives salts of the ReF_8^{2-} ion.[14]

The most important and useful complexes are the hexachloro salts, which are obtained by reducing TcO_4^- or ReO_4^- with 8–13M hydrochloric acid, preferably with the addition of KI as reductant. The salts K_2TcCl_6 (yellow) and K_2ReCl_6 (yellow-green) form large octahedral isomorphous crystals. The solubilities of these and other salts are similar to those of the $PtCl_6^{2-}$ ion in that large unipositive ions give insoluble salts. In water, K_2ReCl_6 is hydrolyzed to give $ReO_2 \cdot xH_2O$. In the reduction of TcO_4^- or ReO_4^- by hydrochloric acid, the intermediate V oxidation state complexes can be isolated (see later). The hexabromo complexes of Tc and Re are made by the action of HBr on the chloro complex, and the hexaiodo by heating the bromide with HI.

The halides Re_3Cl_9 and Re_3Br_9 can be dissolved in concentrated HCl or HBr respectively. The exact species present in solution are not known, but using various large univalent cations, M^I, substances of the following types have been obtained:[10,15–18] $M_3Re_3X_{12}$, $M_2Re_3X_{11}$, MRe_3X_{10} and $M_2Re_4Br_{15}$. The explanation of the unusual stoichiometries of the first three is simple in terms of the persisting Re_3X_9 unit. The three outer positions (see Fig. 30-D-4) are sites for the attachment of additional X^- ions, and, depending on the cation, crystal packing considerations and the equilibria in solution, 1, 2 or all three of these may be filled in the complex anion which is precipitated. The last-mentioned compound

[14] E. G. Ippolitov, *Russ. J. Inorg. Chem.*, **7**, 485 (1962); P. A. Koz'min, *Zhur. Struct. Khim.*, **5**, 70 (1964).

[15] J. A. Bertrand, F. A. Cotton and W. A. Dollase, *Inorg. Chem.*, **2**, 1166 (1963).

[16] F. A. Cotton and S. J. Lippard, *Inorg. Chem.*, **4**, 59 (1965).

[17] B. H. Robinson and J. E. Ferguson, *J. Chem. Soc.*, **1964**, 5683.

[18] J. E. Fergusson, B. R. Penfold and B. R. Robinson, *Nature*, **201**, 181 (1964).

consists of Re_3Br_9 groups and $ReBr_6{}^{2-}$ ions, the latter having arisen by partial oxidation of the Re^{III}; this compound can be precipitated directly from solutions containing equal molar quantities of Re_3Br_9 and $ReBr_6{}^{2-}$. It is to be noted that X-ray data show that the additional ligands (X^- or others) are bound less strongly than the X atoms which form part of the Re_3X_9 group.

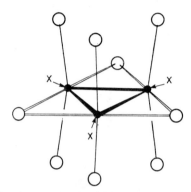

Fig. 30-D-4. A sketch of an isolated Re_3X_9 unit which has D_{3h} symmetry. The three positions where additional ligands may be attached are indicated by $X \rightarrow$.

By reduction of $ReO_4{}^-$ in HCl or HBr solution using H_2 or H_3PO_2, the extraordinary $Re_2X_8{}^{2-}$ ions ($X = Cl$, Br) can be obtained.[19] They have been shown by X-ray studies[20,21] to have the sort of structure shown in Figure 30-D-5 for $Re_2Cl_8{}^{2-}$. The two most remarkable features of the structure, namely, the extremely short Re—Re bond and the *eclipsed* rotomeric configuration (symmetry D_{4h}) have been explained in terms of a quadruple Re—Re bond (see page 655 for details). A Tc compound, $(NH_4)_3Tc_2Cl_8$, has been shown[22] to contain a similar anion, but the reason for the fractional mean oxidation state (2.5) is obscure.

30-D-4. Oxo Acids and Oxohalides

The formation of the pertechnetate and perrhenate ions is one of the most important aspects of the chemistry of technetium and rhenium. The aqueous acids or their salts are formed on oxidation of all technetium or rhenium compounds by nitric acid, hydrogen peroxide or other strong

[19] F. A. Cotton, N. F. Curtis, B. F. G. Johnson and W. R. Robinson, *Inorg. Chem.*, **4**, 326 (1965).
[20] B. G. Kuznetsov and P. A. Koz'min, *Zhur. Strukt. Khim.*, **4**, 55 (1963).
[21] F. A. Cotton and C. H. Harris, *Inorg. Chem.*, **4**, 330 (1965).
[22] F. A. Cotton and W. K. Bratton, *J. Amer. Chem. Soc.*, **87**, 921 (1965).

oxidizing agents. Pure perrhenic acid has not been isolated, but a red crystalline product, claimed to be $HTcO_4$, has been obtained; both acids are strong acids in aqueous solution. The solubilities of alkali perrhenates generally resemble those of the perchlorates, but pertechnetates are more soluble in water than either (cf. $KReO_4$, 9.8g/l, $KTcO_4$, 126g/l, at 20°). Highly insoluble precipitates, suitable for gravimetric determination, are given by tetraphenylarsonium chloride and nitron with both anions.

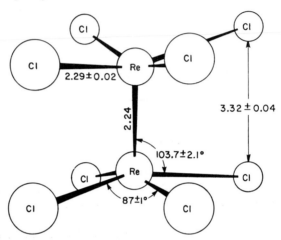

Fig. 30-D-5. The structure of the $Re_2Cl_8{}^{2-}$ ion.

The $TcO_4{}^-$ and $ReO_4{}^-$ ions are tetrahedral both in crystals and in solution.[23] Unlike $MnO_4{}^-$, both $TcO_4{}^-$ and $ReO_4{}^-$ are quite stable in alkaline solution. They are also much weaker oxidizing agents than $MnO_4{}^-$, but they are reduced by HCl, HBr or HI. In acid solutions, the ions can be extracted into various organic solvents such as tributyl-phosphate, and cyclic amines will extract them from basic solution. Such extraction methods of purification suffer from difficulties due to reduction of the ions by organic material. The anions can be readily absorbed by anion exchange resins, from which they can be eluted by perchloric acid.

For rhenium, some less well-characterized oxo anions exist but not in aqueous solution. Thus on fusing ReO_2 with NaOH, the sodium salt of the ion $ReO_3{}^{2-}$ is obtained, and color changes occurring when rhenium metal is fused with KOH in air show that there are intermediate stages in the oxidation to the colorless $ReO_4{}^-$ ion. In excess hydroxide perrhenate takes up oxygen on heating, and a greenish yellow salt, $Ba_3(ReO_5)_2$, has been isolated. The natures and structures of these oxo anions are not known.

[23] R. H. Busey and O. L. Keller, Jr., *J. Chem. Phys.*, **41**, 215 (1964).

Oxohalides, all of which are readily hydrolyzed by water are shown in Table 30-D-4.

TABLE 30-D-4

Oxo Halides of Rhenium and Technetium

V	VI	VII	
$ReOF_3$	$ReOF_4$	TcO_3F?	
black, nonvolatile	blue, t.p. 107.8°	yellow, m 18.3	
	$ReOCl_4$	TcO_3Cl	
	green-brown, m 30°	colorless	
	$ReOBr_4$	ReO_3F	$ReOF_5$
	blue, d. > 80°	yellow, m 147°	cream, t.p. 40.8°
		ReO_3Cl	ReO_2F_3
		colorless liquid,	pale yellow,
		b 131°	m 90°
		ReO_3Br	
		colorless, m 39.5°	

Pertechnetylfluoride, TcO_3F, has a melting point intermediate between that of MnO_3F and ReO_3F to which it is structurally and chemically similar. It is made by fluorination of TcO_2 with F_2 at 150°.[24] The chloride is obtained by adding 12M hydrochloric acid to $KTcO_4$ in 18M sulfuric acid and extracting the product into chloroform from which it is removed by evaporation of the solvent.

There are several oxofluorides of rhenium. The most important one, perrhenylfluoride, ReO_3F, is obtained by the action of IF_5 on $KReO_4$,

Related compounds are oxofluorosulfates, $ReO_2(SO_3F)_3$ and $ReO_3(SO_3F)$, obtained by action of $S_2O_6F_2$ on Re.[25] The action of $SOCl_2$ on Re_2O_7 and NH_4ReO_4 gives respectively red $(ReO_3Cl)_2SO_2Cl_2$ and $NH_4ReO_2Cl_4SO_2Cl_2$. The former probably has an —O—SCl_2—O— bridge.[26]

Oxohalogeno anions. Coordination of X^- to the oxohalides can, in principle, give the oxo anions and a number of these are known.

$KRe^{VI}OF_5$ and other salts of this blue ion are obtained by hydrolysis of K_2ReF_8; they are soluble in some ethers and ketones but are hydrolyzed by water.[14]

The Re^V oxohalide anions $[ReOX_4]^-$ ($X = Cl^-$, Br^-, I^-, SCN^-) and $[ReOCl_5]^{2-}$ are known.[27a,b] The Cl and Br species of the former are prepared by reduction of ReO_4^- in a mixture of CH_3OH and conc. H_2SO_4

[24] H. Selig and J. G. Malm, *J. Inorg. Nucl. Chem.,* **25**, 349 (1963).
[25] G. C. Kleinkopf and Jean'ne M. Shreeve, *Inorg. Chem.,* **3**, 607 (1964).
[26] K. W. Bagnall, D. Brown and R. Colton, *J. Chem. Soc.,* **1964**, 3017.
[27a] F. A. Cotton and S. J. Lippard, *Inorg. Chem.,* **4**, 162 (1965); **5**, 9 (1966).
[27b] R. Colton, *Austral. J. Chem.,* **18**, 435 (1965).

by granular zinc.[27a] They can be interconverted by metathetical reactions. X-ray studies show that the ions are square pyramidal (C_{4v}) with oxygen at the apex. The Re—O bond is short (1.72 ± 0.02A) indicating multiple bonding. Salts of $[\mathrm{ReOCl_5}]^{2-}$ are best prepared by treating $\mathrm{ReCl_5}$ in conc. hydrochloric acid with tetraalkylammonium or other chlorides.

The $\mathrm{Re^{VI}}$ ion can also be obtained by addition of CsCl to $\mathrm{ReOCl_4}$ in $\mathrm{SOCl_2}$.[27b]

The oxo-bridged species, $[\mathrm{Re_2OCl_{10}}]^{4-}$, is discussed later.

COMPLEX CHEMISTRY OF TECHNETIUM AND RHENIUM

The chemistry of Tc in complexes has been relatively little studied and even that of Re is less well known than that of its neighboring elements. Low spin complexes predominate and where paramagnetism occurs, large spin-orbit coupling effects render the interpretation difficult (except for the d^3 species).

We shall discuss mainly the chemistry of rhenium, noting some technetium behavior where it is known and of special interest. Complex halides have been described earlier.

30-D-5. Rhenium- and Technetium(—I, 0, I)

The complexes in these states are mainly those with π-bonding ligands (see page 719).

The only other species are cyanides. The reduction of $\mathrm{K_2ReCl_6}$ in KCN solution by K/Hg, or by $\mathrm{BH_4}^-$ leads to a green salt, $\mathrm{K_5[Re^I(CN)_6]}$. The corresponding Tc complex is obtained by reduction of $\mathrm{TcO_4}^-$ in KCN by K/Hg.[29] By contrast, however, reduction[30] of $\mathrm{ReO_4}^-$ thus gives $[\mathrm{Re(CN)_5H_2O}]^{3-}$ which, provided this complex does not contain a Re—H bond (this is quite possible), appears to be a $\mathrm{Re^{II}}$ species.

30-D-6. Rhenium(II), d^5

Few complexes are fully established, and these are with polydentate arsines. $\mathrm{Re^{II}Cl_2(diars)}$ is obtained by stannite reduction of the $\mathrm{Re^{III}}$ species (see below), while with tri- and quadridentate arsines, TAS and QAS, the complexes $\mathrm{ReX_2QAS}$ and $\mathrm{ReX_2TAS}$ can be made.[31] These complexes may be respectively octahedral and 5-coordinate, but they are

[28] P. H. L. Walter, J. Kleinberg and E. Griswold, *Inorg. Chem.*, **1**, 10 (1962).
[29] K. Schwochau and H. Herr, *Z. anorg. Chem.*, **319**, 148 (1962).
[30] S. Sen, *Z. anorg. Chem.*, **333**, 160 (1964).
[31] R. J. Mawby and L. M. Venanzi, *J. Chem. Soc.*, **1962**, 4447.

too insoluble for molecular weight determinations and could be poly-nuclear. They have magnetic moments lower than the spin-only value for a low-spin d^5 configuration.

The reported phosphine complexes[32] "$ReX_2(PPh_3)_2$" have been shown to be nitrido complexes of Re^V (see below).

The reduction of Tc^{IV} by hydroxylamine has been alleged[33] to give a complex, possibly $[Tc(NH_2OH)_2(NH_3)_3(H_2O)]^{2+}$ but its constitution is not certain.

30-D-7. Rhenium(III), d^4

This is a fairly common oxidation state for rhenium complexes, and many types are known. Perhaps the best understood types are those derived directly from Re_3Cl_9, Re_3Br_9 or their hydrates, or acetone sol-vates.[10,34a] Most, if not all such complexes, provided the conditions of preparation are relatively mild, contain the Re_3X_9 group intact. While their simplest formulas are $LReX_3$, their true molecular formulas are thus $Re_3X_9L_3$, and they are structurally similar to the $Re_3X_{12}{}^{3-}$, $Re_3X_{11}{}^{2-}$ and $Re_3X_{10}{}^-$ ions discussed earlier. The ligands L occupy the positions marked X→ in Figure 30-D-4.

However, there do appear to be some monomeric Re^{III} complexes derived from Re_3X_9, and obtainable also in other ways.[34b] There are for example[35,36] some complexes of the type $ReX_3(PR_3)_3$ obtainable from Re_3X_9, as well as a solvate $(CH_3COOH)_2ReCl_3$[37] and a complex $(Ph_3PO)_2ReCl_3$.[38] Whether the latter diamagnetic substances have trigonal pyramidal structure or not is unknown. Octahedral species with arsine ligands are well characterized; for example reduction of $HReO_4$ in ethanolic hydrochloric acid in presence of o-phenylenebisdimethylarsine by H_3PO_2 gives $[Re(diars)_3]Cl_3$; it can be oxidized to Re^V or reduced to Re^{II} species. A seven-coordinate diarsine complex is known.[42b] The interaction of β-diketones with $ReO(OEt)Cl_2(PPh_3)_2$ (see page 975) gives a series of complexes such as $ReCl_2acac(PPh_3)_2$ and $ReCl(acac)_2PPh_3$.[39] These complexes are paramagnetic but show the effects of spin-orbit coupling.

[32] J. Chatt and G. Rowe, *J. Chem. Soc.*, **1962**, 4019.

[33] J. D. Eakins, D. G. Humphrey and C. E. Mellish, *J. Chem. Soc.*, **1963**, 6012.

[34a] F. A. Cotton and J. T. Mague, *Inorg. Chem.*, **3**, 1094 (1964).

[34b] F. A. Cotton, N. F. Curtis and W. R. Robinson, *Inorg. Chem.*, **4**, 1696 (1966).

[35] R. Colton, R. Levitus and G. Wilkinson, *J. Chem. Soc.*, **1960**, 4121.

[36] J. Chatt and G. Rowe, *J. Chem. Soc.*, **1962**, 4109.

[37] F. I. M. Taha and G. Wilkinson, *J. Chem. Soc.*, **1963**, 5406.

[38] N. P. Johnson, C. J. L. Lock and G. Wilkinson, *J. Chem. Soc.*, **1964**, 1054.

[39] D. E. Grove, N. P. Johnson, C. J. L. Lock and G. Wilkinson, *J. Chem. Soc.*, **1965**, 490.

Prolonged interaction of Re_3Cl_9 with carboxylic acids in absence of air gives a number of orange, crystalline carboxylates[37] such as [ClRe-$(OCOCH_3)_2]_2$. These molecules can also be obtained by refluxing $ReOCl_3$-$(PPh_3)_2$ with acetic acid and by treatment of the $Re_2X_8^{2-}$ species with RCOOH, and there exists the following reversible equilibrium:[19]

$$Re_2X_8^{2-} + 4RCOOH = Re_2(RCOO)_4X_2 + 4HX + 2X^-$$

These carboxylates presumably have the Cr^{II} acetate structure with chlorine end groups, since the Cl^- groups can be readily replaced by SCN^-. In presence of air, the reaction gives two types of oxo compounds, purple $[ReOCl(OCOR)_2]_2$ and $[ReO_2(OCOR)_2]_2$. The former appears to have a Re—O—Re bridge in addition to bridging carboxylate, while the latter has an additional Re=O end group; they must be Re^{IV} or Re^V complexes.

A dark blue salt $K_3[Re^{III}(OH)_3(CN)_3]$ is obtained by BH_4^- reduction of $K_4[ReO_2(CN)_4]$.[28]

One of the best characterized monomeric Re^{III} complexes is $(\pi-C_5H_5)_2ReH$. This complex was of importance as it was the first compound for which the characteristic high field nmr line for H bound to a transition metal was detected. It was also the first transition metal complex to be shown to undergo protonation of the metal atom; the hydride is about as strong a base as NH_3 and gives salts of the ion $(\pi-C_5H_5)_2ReH_2^+$ (see page 766). Corresponding halides and other derivatives are now known.[40] Technetium behaves differently giving only $[(\pi-C_5H_5)_2Tc]_2$.

Other Re^{III} hydrides of the type $ReH_3(PPh_3)_4$ have been claimed; they are converted by HCl to $ReCl_4(PPh_3)_2$.[41]

30-D-8. Rhenium(IV), d^3

The well characterized halogeno complexes have been discussed earlier.

The addition of halogens to $ReX_3(PR_3)_3$ (X = Cl, Br) gives $ReX_4(PR_3)_2$.[42a] The Ph_3P compounds can also be made by interaction of acetic acid with $ReOCl_3(PPh_3)_2$. $Trans$-$[ReCl_4(PEt_2Ph)_2]$ has $\mu_{eff} = 3.64$ BM at $20°$, which is in accord with its being an octahedral complex of a d^3 ion. The diarsine complex, $ReCl_4$diars, is made by chlorinating $Re(CO)$diarsCl which itself is made by direct substitution in $Re(CO)_5Cl$ by diarsine.[42b]

[40] R. L. Cooper and M. L. H. Green, *Z. Naturforsch.*, **19b**, 652 (1964); R. L. Cooper, M. L. H. Green and J. T. Moelwyn-Hughes, *J. Organometal. Chem.*, **3**, 261 (1965).
[41] M. Freni and V. Valenti, *Gazetta*, **91**, 1357 (1961).
[42a] J. Chatt, J. G. Garforth, N. P. Johnson and G. A. Rowe, *J. Chem. Soc.*, **1964**, 601.
[42b] W. J. Kirkham, *et al.*, *J. Chem. Soc.*, **1965**, 550.

A grey-black, readily oxidized complex $K_4[ReO_2(CN)_4]$ is obtained by action of aqueous KCN on K_2ReCl_6.[28] However, the addition of KCN to methanolic K_2TcI_6 leads to dark red $K_2[Tc(CN)_6]$, which is soluble in, but rapidly hydrolyzed by water. A similar reaction using K_2ReI_6 gives $K_3[Re^V(CN)_8]$ (see page 978).

30-D-9. Rhenium(V), d^2

The complexes of Re^V are among the most extensive and best known rhenium species. They are of several types, the ones with Re—O bonds predominating. All are diamagnetic.

Oxo Complexes. The simple oxohalide species, $ReOX_4^-$ and $ReOX_5^{2-}$, have already been mentioned. In all studies of oxorhenium complexes, the appearance of medium to strong Re—O stretching bands in the infrared spectra is of great assistance. In $ReOX_4^-$ ions the frequencies are around 1000 cm^{-1} while in other complexes are in the range 920–970 cm^{-1}.

The interaction of $HReO_4$ or perrhenates with tertiary phosphines, arsines or stibines in ethanol or acetic acid solutions containing hydrochloric acid gives complexes[36,38] such as $ReOCl_3(PR_3)_2$. The oxygen atom has a strong *trans* effect[38] and hence halide groups *trans* to it are labile, the order being $Cl < Br < I$. One result of this effect is that when ethanol is used as solvent, ethanolysis can occur; the iodides, merely on washing with ethanol, give $ReO(OEt)I_2(PR_3)_2$. The labilizing tendency of Re=O is also shown by the fact that the $[ReOX_4]$ ions bind additional ligands (H_2O, CH_3CN) only weakly and lose them easily again.

The dichloroethoxo and trichloro complexes are very useful sources for the preparation of other rhenium complexes (Fig. 30-D-6). The complexes have distorted octahedral structures and can exist in isomeric forms; these can be obtained by crystallization from differing solvents although in solutions it appears that equilibration occurs quite rapidly.[39] Green $ReOCl_3(PEt_2Ph)_2$ has been shown to have *trans* PR_3 groups and to have a short Re—O bond.[43] The reported distance of 1.6A is quite uncertain and it seems likely that the value is too small, but it does suggest a bond order of 2 or greater. The involvement of oxygen lone-pairs in π bonding is also indicated by the fact that the Re=O compounds cannot be protonated to give Re—OH groups, although in the oxo species discussed below, protonation can occur.

One of the more unusual reactions of $ReOCl_3(PPh_3)_2$, $ReO(OEt)Cl_2$-$(PPh_3)_2$, or $[ReOX_4]^-$ is that with moist pyridine where the final product is the orange salt $[ReO_2py_4]Cl \cdot 2H_2O$. An intermediate complex

---

[43] H. W. W. Erlich and P. G. Owston, *J. Chem. Soc.*, **1963**, 4368.

$Re_2O_3Cl_4py_4$, which is similar to some complexes of Mo (page 956), can be isolated.[44] This suggests that the displacement of the labile Cl *trans* to Re=O leads to an unisolated hydroxo species which can condense to the

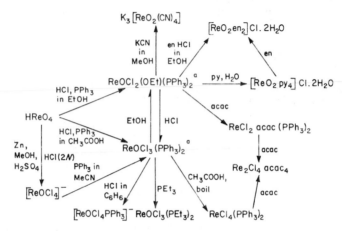

Fig. 30-D-6.   Some reactions of oxorhenium(V) complexes.

[a] The isomers have different colors.   Although reactions involving Ph_3P are generally typical of R_3P or R_3As, there may be specific differences depending on the nature of the ligand.

bridged oxo complex.   This mechanism is also indicated by the fact that the final product is the *trans* dioxo species and by the stability of a corresponding *trans* oxoethoxo compound (Fig. 30-D-7).

The best characterized bridged oxo species is the Re^{IV} ion $[Cl_5ReOReCl_5]^{4-}$, which can be isolated as an intermediate in the reduction of $KReO_4$ to K_2ReCl_6 by aqueous HCl.   The crystal structure shows a linear Re—O—Re bond,[45] as in similar ruthenium (page 1003) and molybdenum (page 958) complexes.   The dimeric ion has only weak temperature independent paramagnetism.

Dioxo Species.   Various *trans* dioxo complexes exist, examples being $[ReO_2(CN)_4]^{3-}$, $[ReO_2py_4]^+$ and $[ReO_2en_2]^+$.   In such complexes, the observed antisymmetric O—Re—O stretching frequency is relatively low because both oxygen atoms use the same metal $d\pi$ orbitals for π bonding.   Thus as one bond is stretched the other can more easily contract by taking advantage of the increased availability of the $d\pi$ orbitals.   This antisymmetric motion thus becomes easier and of lower frequency.   Similar effects have been noted in *trans* dioxo complexes of other metals.

[44] N. P. Johnson, F. I. M. Taha and G. Wilkinson, *J. Chem. Soc.*, **1964**, 2614.
[45] J. C. Morrow, *Acta. Cryst.*, **15**, 851 (1962).

In the monoxo species, two Re—O $p\pi$–$d\pi$ interactions can occur simultaneously giving stronger ReO bonds, and as noted above $ReOL_5$ or $ReOL_4$ species are not protonatable. However, in the *trans* dioxo species, protonation can readily occur.[27b,38,46] Thus for $[ReO_2en_2]^+$, both $[ReO(OH)en_2]^{2+}$ and $[Re(OH)_2en_2]^{3+}$ salts can be isolated, although the second base constant is very small.[46]

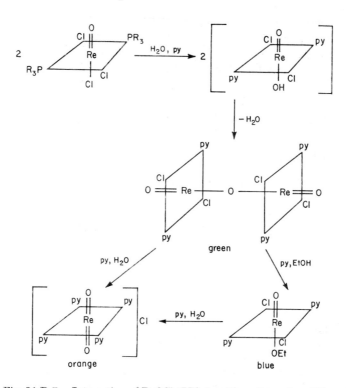

Fig. 30-D-7.   Interaction of $ReOCl_3(PPh_3)_2$ with water and pyridine.

Nitrido Complexes of Re^V. Like Os, which readily gives compounds with Os—N bonds (page 1008), Re has the ability to form Re=N and Re≡N bonds, as in $[NReO_3]^{2-}$. A number of compounds of the general types $ArN=ReX_3(PR_3)_2$, $N=ReX_2(PR_3)_2$ and $N=ReX_2(PR_3)_3$ can be made, e.g., in selected cases, by hydrazine reduction:[47]

$$Re_2O_7 + Ph_3P + N_2H_4 \cdot 2HCl \xrightarrow{\text{EtOH}} NReCl_2(PR_3)_2$$

[46] R. K. Murman and D. R. Foerster, *J. Phys. Chem.*, **67**, 1383 (1964); J. H. Beard, J. Casey and R. K. Murman, *Inorg. Chem.*, **4**, 797 (1965).

[47] J. Chatt, J. D. Garforth, N. P. Johnson and G. A. Rowe, *J. Chem. Soc.*, **1964**, 1012.

or by the following condensation reaction which is reminiscent of the Schiff base reaction of organic $C=O$ compounds:

$$C_6H_5NH_2 + O=ReCl_3(PPh_3)_2 = C_6H_5N=ReCl_3(PPh_3)_2 + H_2O$$

Another example of a nitrido complex, the pink salt, $K_2[NRe^V(CN)_4H_2O]$, is obtained[48] together with $K_3[ReO_2(CN)_4]$ by action of KCN and N_2H_5OH on $KReO_4$.

Other Complexes of Re^V. Addition of KCN to K_2ReI_6 in methanol gives the diamagnetic salt $K_3[Re(CN)_8]$;[48] the oxidation Re^{IV}–Re^V occurs presumably because an 8-coordinate Re^{IV} complex would be paramagnetic with an electron in a high lying orbital (cf. Co^{II}–Co^{III}).

This octacyano complex is rapidly oxidized in acid solution by air to a purple paramagnetic ion, $[Re^{VI}(CN)_8]^{2-}$, which, though it can be isolated as salts, hydrolyzes with reduction to $[ReO(OH)(CN)_4]^{2-}$.

30-D-10. Rhenium(VI), d^1, and Rhenium(VII), d^0 Complexes

Complexes of Re^{VI} are quite rare; the octacyanide has just been mentioned and the only other examples are fluoro complexes like ReF_8^{2-} discussed earlier. Others can doubtless be made.

For Re^{VII}, salts of the ion ReF_8^- are known, but the only other species, which is of much greater interest, is the hydrido anion ReH_9^{2-}.

In 1937, Lundell and Knowles found that when acid solutions of ReO_4^- are reduced with Zn/Hg in a Jones reductor, the resulting reduced species had a formal oxidation state of -1. They considered the species to be the "rhenide" ion, Re^-. Subsequent polarographic studies indicated an 8-electron reduction:

$$Re^{VII} + 8e = Re^{-I}$$

Later, a number of white crystalline "rhenide" salts, thought to be KRe or $K[Re(H_2O)_n]$, were isolated by a complex procedure involving addition of concentrated aqueous solutions of ReO_4^- to potassium in ethylenediamine. However, nmr studies showed that the reduction of aqueous alkaline ReO_4^- solutions by Na/Hg gave species with Re—H bonds. Although there has been some controversy over the precise stoichiometry of the hydrido anion it appears that it is now unequivocally ReH_9^{2-}, on the basis of X-ray and neutron diffraction studies.[49] Although this ion is evidently the one present in reduced alkaline aqueous solutions, the Lundell and Knowles species obtained in acid solution is not the same; it is probably

[48] C. J. L. Lock and G. Wilkinson, *J. Chem. Soc.*, **1964**, 2281.
[49] K. Knox and A. P. Ginsberg, *Inorg. Chem.*, **3**, 555 (1964); S. C. Abrahams, A. P. Ginsberg and K. Knox, *Inorg. Chem.*, **3**, 528 (1964).

also hydridic, but has not been obtained in high enough concentrations for definitive identification.

A technetium analog, TcH_9^{2-}, which is similar to ReH_9^{2-} but more reactive, has been obtained by reduction of TcO_4^- with potassium in ethylenediamine–ethanol mixtures.[50]

The structure of K_2ReH_9 (symmetry D_{3h}) is shown in Figure 30-D-8(a).

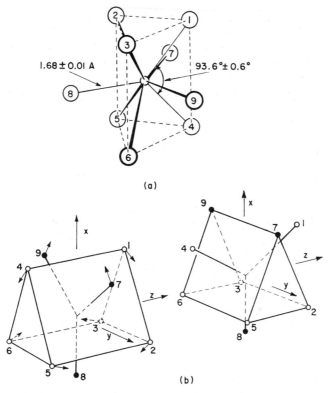

(a)

(b)

Fig. 30-D-8.   (a) Structure of ReH_9^{2-}; Re—H distance of 1.68A is consistent with the sum of single bond radii (Re = 1.28A).   (b) Diagrams showing how a deformation mode can interchange the prism and equatorial H atoms.   (Reproduced by permission from ref. 49.)

The nmr spectra of solutions of the salt show only a single line although this is inconsistent with the structure since three of the H's are not symmetrically equivalent to the other six.   Deformation modes such as those shown in Figure 30-D-8(b), which in effect interchange the prism and equatorial positions, can probably occur readily, thus making all nine H atoms equivalent on the nmr time-scale.

[50] A. P. Ginsberg, *Inorg. Chem.*, **3**, 567 (1964).

30-E. THE PLATINUM METALS

30-E-1. General Remarks

These elements, ruthenium, osmium, rhodium, iridium, palladium and platinum, are the six heavier members of Group VIII. They are rare elements; platinum itself is the commonest with an abundance of about $10^{-6}\%$ whereas the others have abundances of the order of $10^{-7}\%$ of the earth's crust. The elements occur in nature, often as alloys such as osmiridium, which is one of the few sources of osmium. Although platinum-rich ores contain little osmium, the elements are usually associated not only with one another but also with other noble metals such as copper, silver and gold. They also occur in arsenide, sulfide and other ores. The main suppliers of platinum metals are Canada, South Africa and the USSR.

Since the relative concentrations of individual elements and associated elements differ widely, the extraction methods vary considerably. An important source is the nickel–copper sulfide of South Africa; the ore is physically concentrated by gravitation and flotation, after which it is smelted with lime, coke and sand and bessemerized in a convertor. The resulting Ni–Cu sulfide "matte" is smelted with sodium sulfate to give a top layer of Cu_2S and Na_2S and a bottom layer of NiS. The latter is roasted to oxide, reduced with coal and the metal cast into anodes. The copper layer is similarly converted to a copper anode. The anode slimes from electrolysis contain the platinum metals, silver and gold. The refining of platinum metals, also varied and complicated, is highly developed and the metals can be obtained in purities of over 99.5% (see references).

Some of the chemical steps in the separation of the elements depend on specific reactions, such as the following:

1. Os and Ru are unattacked by any acids up to the boiling point, whereas Pd is fairly readily soluble in nitric acid and the others are more or less readily soluble in aqua regia.

2. Os and Ru are attacked by alkaline oxidizing fusion, for example, with Na_2O_2 or $NaOH + NaClO_3$, and the melts dissolve in water to give osmates and ruthenates. Ruthenates are reduced to black, insoluble $RuO_2 \cdot nH_2O$ by aqueous alcohol, whereas osmium remains in solution as osmate(VI) which can be precipitated as the ammonium salt. The elements are purified by distillation of their tetroxides.

3. On reduction of the oxidized chloride solutions of the other elements with $FeSO_4$, gold is precipitated, lower oxidation states of Rh, Ir and Pd are obtained, while $PtCl_6^{2-}$, which is the most stable chloro anion with respect also to hydrolysis, can be precipitated as the ammonium salt.

4. Rhodium and iridium can be precipitated as hydrated oxides by treatment of solutions of Rh^{III} and Ir^{IV} with ClO_2^- or BrO_3^- in $NaHCO_3$ buffered solution.

5. A useful laboratory separation of platinum, probably not used commercially, is the ether or ethyl acetate extraction of the red $SnCl_3^-$ complex (page 1034), obtained by reduction of $PtCl_6^{2-}$ with $SnCl_3^-$ in aqueous solution.

6. Sodium hexachlororhodate(III), either hydrated or anhydrous, is insoluble in ethanol and can be separated from the sodium salts of the hexachloro anions of palladium(IV), platinum(IV) and iridium(IV), all of which are readily soluble in ethanol.

30-E-2. The Metals

Some properties are collected in Table 30-E-1. The metals are obtained

TABLE 30-E-1

Some Properties of the Platinum Metals

Element	Melting point °C	Form	Best solvent
Ru	~2310	Grey-white, brittle, fairly hard	Alkaline oxidizing fusion
Os	~3050	,,	,, ,, ,,
Rh	1960	Silver-white, soft ductile	Hot conc. H_2SO_4 Conc. HCl + $NaClO_3$ at 125–150°
Ir	2443	Silver-white, hard, brittle	Conc. HCl + $NaClO_3$ at 125–150°
Pd	1552	Grey-white, lustrous, malleable, ductile	Conc. HNO_3, HCl + Cl_2
Pt	1769	,,	Aqua regia

initially as sponge or powder by ignition of ammonium salts of the hexachloro anions. Almost all complex and binary compounds of the elements give the metal on heating above 200° in air or oxygen; osmium is oxidized to the volatile OsO_4, and at dull red heat ruthenium gives RuO_2, so that reduction in hydrogen is necessary. The metals are also obtained by reduction of acidic solutions of salts or complexes by magnesium, zinc, molecular hydrogen or other reducing agents such as oxalic acid or formic acid, or by electrolysis under proper conditions.

The metals are widely used as catalysts and there are special techniques for reduction of platinum metal salts on various supports; the compacted metals as gauze or foil are also used and the use of the metals for electrical contacts, etc., is extensive.

Ru and Os are unaffected by mineral acids below $\sim 100°$ and are best dissolved by alkaline oxidizing fusion, e.g., $NaOH + Na_2O_2$, $KClO_3$, etc. Rh and Ir are extremely resistant to attack by acids, neither one dissolving even in aqua regia when in the massive state. Finely divided rhodium (rhodium sponge) can be dissolved in aqua regia or hot concentrated H_2SO_4. Both metals also dissolve in concentrated HCl under pressure of oxygen or in presence of sodium perchlorate in a sealed tube at 125–150°. At red heat Cl_2 gives the trichlorides.

Pd and Pt are rather more reactive than the other metals. Pd is dissolved by nitric acid; in the massive state the attack is slow, but is accelerated by oxygen and oxides of nitrogen. As sponge, Pd also dissolves slowly in HCl in presence of chlorine or oxygen. Platinum is considerably more resistant to acids and is not attacked by any single mineral acid although it readily dissolves in aqua regia and even slowly in HCl in presence of air since

$$PtCl_4{}^{2-} + 2e = Pt + 4Cl^- \qquad E^0 = 0.73 \text{ v}$$
$$PtCl_6{}^{2-} + 2e = PtCl_4{}^{2-} + 2Cl^- \qquad E^0 = 0.68 \text{ v}$$

Platinum is certainly not the inert material that it is often considered to be. There are at least seventy oxidation–reduction and decomposition reactions which are catalyzed by metallic platinum. Examples are the Ce^{IV}–Br^- reaction and the decomposition of N_2H_4 to N_2 and NH_3. It is possible to predict whether catalysis can occur or not from a knowledge of the electrochemical properties of the reacting couples.[1]

Both Pd and Pt are rapidly attacked by fused alkali oxides, and especially peroxides, and by F_2 and Cl_2 at red heat. It is of importance in the use of platinum for laboratory equipment that on heating it combines with, e.g., elemental P, Si, Pb, As, Sb, S and Se, so that when compounds of these elements are heated in contact with platinum under reducing conditions, the platinum is also attacked.

Both Pd and Pt are capable of absorbing large volumes of molecular hydrogen. At 80° and 1 atm Pd will absorb up to 900 times its own volume corresponding to a composition ca $PdH_{0.7}$. At higher temperatures the volumes absorbed at a given pressure become smaller. The absorption causes both the electrical conductivity and magnetic susceptibility to fall and these and other observations lead to the general belief that there is a definite hydride phase although the limiting composition and structure are not definitely established. Heated massive palladium will allow H_2 to diffuse through it.

[1] M. Spiro and A. B. Ravnö, *J. Chem. Soc.*, **1965**, 78.

30-E-3. Platinum Metal Chemistry

The chemistries of these six elements have some common features but there are nevertheless wide variations depending on differing stabilities of oxidation states, stereochemistries, etc. The principal areas of general similarity are as follows.

1. *Binary compounds.* There are a large number of oxides, sulfides, phosphides, etc., but by far the most important binary compounds are the halides.

2. *Aqueous chemistry.* This chemistry is almost exclusively that of complex compounds. Aquo ions of Ru^{II}, Rh^{III} and Pd^{II} exist but in presence of anions other than ClO_4^-, complex ions are formed. The precise nature of many supposedly simple solutions, e.g., of $RhCl_3 \cdot 3H_2O$, is complicated and often unknown.

A vast array of complex ions, predominantly with halide or nitrogen donor ligands, are water soluble. Exchange and kinetic studies have been made with many of these because of interest in (a) *trans* effects especially with square Pt^{II}, (b) differences in substitution mechanisms between the ions of the three transition metal series, and (c) the unusually rapid electron transfer processes with heavy metal complex ions.[2]

3. *Compounds with π-bonding ligands.* (a) In addition to binary carbonyls formed by all but Pd and Pt, the elements give carbonyl halides and other carbonyl complexes. (b) For Ru, nitric oxide complexes are an essential feature of the chemistry. (c) All of the elements have a notable tendency to form bonds to carbon especially with olefins and acetylenes and Pt forms many compounds in which it is σ-bonded to carbon (see page 786). (d) An especially widely studied aspect is the formation of complexes with R_2S, R_3P and R_3As ligands; such ligands have been particularly useful in allowing the isolation of stable alkyl and hydrido complexes. (e) The formation of hydrido complexes is a characteristic feature of the platinum metals when compounds in higher oxidation states are reduced in the presence of certain ligands.

We shall treat the binary compounds as a group, and thereafter discuss other chemistry under the particular individual elements.

BINARY COMPOUNDS OF PLATINUM METALS

30-E-4. Oxides

The anhydrous oxides and some of their properties are given in Table 30-E-2; the tetraoxides of Ru and Os are discussed later (page 1005). The

[2] N. Sutin, *Ann. Rev. Nucl. Sci.*, **12**, 285 (1962); P. Hurwitz and J. K. Kustin, *Inorg. Chem.*, **3**, 823 (1964).

TABLE 30-E-2

Anhydrous Oxides of Platinum Metals[a]

Oxide	Color/form	Structure	Comment
RuO_2	Blue-black	Rutile	From O_2 on Ru, RuS_2 or $RuCl_3$, at 500–700°. Loses O_2 above 700°.
RuO_4	Orange-yellow cryst. m 25°, b 100°	Tetrahedral molecules	See page 1005.
OsO_2	Brown-black	Rutile	Heat Os in NO or OsO_4 or dry $OsO_2 \cdot 2H_2O$.
OsO_4	Colorless cryst. m 40°, b 101°	Tetrahedral molecules	Normal product of heating Os in air; see page 1005
Rh_2O_3	Brown	Corundum (α-Al_2O_3)	Heat Rh^{III} nitrate or Rh_2O_3 (aq). Dissociates > 1100°.
Ir_2O_3	Brown		Impure by heating K_2IrCl_6 + Na_2CO_3
IrO_2	Black	Rutile	Normal product of Ir + O_2. Dissociates > 1100°.
$IrO_{2.7}$?	Black	Possibly peroxide	Ir fused with Na_2O_2. Powerful oxidant.
PdO	Black		From Pd + O_2; dissociates 875°. Insol. all acids.
PtO_2	Brown		Dehydrate PtO_2 (aq). Dissociates > 200°

[a] In oxygen at 800–1500°, gaseous oxides exist: RuO_3, OsO_3, RhO_2, IrO_3, PtO_2. A number of other solids of uncertain nature exist: RuO_3, OsO_3, Ru_2O_5, Rh_2O_5, Os_2O_3, Ru_2O_3.

oxides are usually inert to aqueous acids, are reduced to the metal by hydrogen, and dissociate to the metal and oxygen on heating.

RuO_2 is seldom, if ever, obtained entirely pure but is usually defective in oxygen with a corresponding amount of Ru^{III} in place of Ru^{IV}. The reactivity of OsO_2 depends on its method of preparation but generally it is readily oxidized on heating in air and is soluble in HCl(aq) to give a solution of chloroosmates(IV).

Mixed oxide systems are also known for these elements and some have been studied in detail.[3] Thus $BaRuO_3$ has close-packed BaO_3 layers and RuO_6 octahedra and intermetallic bonding between Ru atoms.

Hydrous Oxides. The addition of alkali hydroxide to platinum metal halide or nitrate solutions precipitates hydrous oxides. These are seldom pure being difficult to free from alkali ions and sometimes readily become colloidal. They are soluble in acids when freshly precipitated.

A black solid, probably $Ru_2O_3 \cdot nH_2O$, obtained from Ru^{III} chloride solutions, is readily oxidized by air, probably to $RuO_2 \cdot nH_2O$, which can also be obtained by reduction of RuO_4 or RuO_4^{2-} solutions. Reduction of aqueous RuO_4 by H_2 gives $RuO_2 \cdot H_2O$. $OsO_2 \cdot 2H_2O$ is obtained by reduction of OsO_4 or by addition of OH^- to $OsCl_6^{2-}$ solutions.

[3] P. C. Donohue, L. Katz and R. Ward, *Inorg. Chem.*, **4**, 306 (1965).

$Rh_2O_3 \cdot 5H_2O$ is formed as a yellow precipitate from Rh^{III} solutions. In base solution, powerful oxidants convert it to the only known Rh^{IV} oxide, $RhO_2 \cdot nH_2O$; the latter loses oxygen on dehydration. $Ir_2O_3 \cdot nH_2O$ can be obtained only in moist atmospheres; it is at least partially oxidized by air to $IrO_2 \cdot nH_2O$ which is formed either by action of mild oxidants on $Ir_2O_3 \cdot nH_2O$ or by addition of OH^- to $IrCl_6^{2-}$.

$PdO \cdot nH_2O$ is a yellow gelatinous precipitate which dries in air to a brown, less hydrated form and on heating at $100°$ loses more water, eventually becoming black; it cannot be dehydrated completely without loss of oxygen.

When $PtCl_6^{2-}$ is boiled with Na_2CO_3, red-brown $PtO_2 \cdot nH_2O$ is obtained. It dissolves in acids and also in strong alkalies to give what can be regarded as solutions of hexahydroxoplatinate, $[Pt(OH)_6]^{2-}$. The hydrous oxide becomes insoluble on heating to *ca* $200°$.

A very unstable Pt^{II} hydrous oxide is obtained by addition of OH^- to $PtCl_4^{2-}$; after drying in CO_2 at $120\text{–}150°$ it approximates to $Pt(OH)_2$, but at higher temperatures gives PtO_2 and Pt.

Poorly characterized hydrous oxides of Pt^{III}, Pd^{III} and Pd^{IV} have been reported.

30-E-5. Sulfides, Phosphides, etc.

All of the platinum metals give very complex systems with non- or semi-metallic elements like S, Se, Te, P, As, Bi, Sn and Pb. The chalconides and phosphides are generally rather similar to those of other transition metals; indeed many of the phosphides for example are isostructural with those of the iron group, viz., Ru_2P with Co_2P; RuP with FeP and CoP; RhP_3, PdP_3 with CoP_3 and NiP_3. In addition to stoichiometric compounds there are phases subject to non-stoichiometry; both may be stable at different temperatures and system compositions. The complexity is illustrated by palladium–sulfur where there are the phases Pd_4S, $Pd_{14}S_5$, $Pd_{11}S_5$, PdS and PdS_2.

The various compounds are made by direct interaction of the elements in suitable proportions under specific conditions. They are usually dark colored substances resistant to acids other than HNO_3 or aqua regia. Some have semimetallic properties.

Sulfides can also be obtained by passing H_2S into platinum metal salt solutions. Thus from $PtCl_4^{2-}$ and $PtCl_6^{2-}$ are obtained PtS and PtS_2 respectively; from Pd^{II} solutions PdS, which on heating with S gives PdS_2; the Rh^{III} and Ir^{III} sulfides are assumed to be $M_2S_3 \cdot nH_2O$ but exact compositions are uncertain.

A few examples of nonmetallic compounds are given in Table 30-E-3.

TABLE 30-E-3

Some Compounds of Platinum Metals with Nonmetallic Elements

Structure type	Examples
Pyrite (page 531)	PtP_2, $PtAs_2$, $PbSb_2$, MS_2, MSe_2, MTe_2 (M = Ru, Os)
Marcasite (page 531)	RuP_2, OsP_2
NiAs structure (page 530)	PdTe, RuP
$Cd(OH)_2$ structure	$PdTe_2$, PtS_2, $PtSe_2$, $PtTe_2$
Square coordination	PtS

30-E-6. Fluorides

The platinum metal fluorides and some properties are listed in Table 30-E-4. Many of these materials have unusual magnetic properties.

TABLE 30-E-4

Platinum Metal Fluorides

II	III	IV	V	VI
—	RuF_3 brown	RuF_4 sandy-yellow	$[RuF_5]_4$ dark green[b] m 86.5°, b 227°	RuF_6 dark brown m 54°
—	—	OsF_4 yellow	$[OsF_5]_4$ green[b] m 70° b 225.9°	OsF_6 yellow-green[b] m 33.2°, b 47°
—	RhF_3 red	RhF_4 blue	$[RhF_5]_4$ red	RhF_6 yellow
—	IrF_3 black	—[c]	$[IrF_5]_4$ yellow m 104°	IrF_6 yellow m 44.0°, b 53°
PdF_2 pale violet	—	PdF_4 brick-red	—	—
—[a]	—[a]	PtF_4 yellow-brown	$[PtF_5]_n$ deep red m 80°	PtF_6 dark red m 61.3°, b 69.1°

[a] Early claims disproved by N. Bartlett and D. H. Lohmann, *J. Chem. Soc.*, **1964**, 619.
[b] Vapor is colorless.
[c] Alleged IrF_4 is IrF_5, N. Bartlett and P. R. Rao, *Chem. Comm.*, **1965**, 252.

Hexafluorides. Perhaps the most interesting of these compounds are the hexafluorides of which only that of palladium is still unknown. While

OsF_6 is the normal product of fluorination of Os at 300° and is the most stable compound of the group, the other fluorides are the initial products of the fluorinations but, due to their thermal instability, must be chilled from the gas phase in order to collect them. Platinum wire ignited in fluorine by an electron current continues to react exothermically to give red vapors of PtF_6.

The hexafluorides decrease in stability W > Re > Os > Ir > Pt, and Ru > Rh, dissociating into fluorine and lower fluorides, RuF_5, RhF_5, PtF_4. PtF_6 is quite unstable and is one of the most powerful oxidizing agents known; its reactions with oxygen and xenon to give $O_2^+PtF_6^-$ and $Xe(PtF_6)_n$ have been previously discussed (page 369 and page 593). The volatility of the compounds also decreases with increasing mass.

All of the hexafluorides are reactive and corrosive substances and normally must be handled in Ni or Monel apparatus although quartz can be used if necessary. Only PtF_6 and RhF_6 actually react with glass (even when rigorously dry) at room temperature. In addition to thermal dissociation, ultraviolet radiation causes decomposition to lower fluorides, even OsF_6 giving OsF_5. The vapors hydrolyze with water vapor and liquid water reacts violently, e.g., IrF_6 gives HF, O_2, O_3 and IrO_2(aq), while OsF_6 gives OsO_4, HF and OsF_6^-. All of the hexafluorides are octahedral. Their magnetic and spectral properties have been studied in detail and their interpretation often requires the use of ligand field theory in its more sophisticated forms.

Pentafluorides. These are obtained by thermal dissociation of MF_6 or by fluorination reactions under conditions where this is unstable. Thus the usual product of fluorination of Ru at 300° is RuF_5 and of $PtCl_2$ at 350°, PtF_5. OsF_5 is usually obtained by UV dissociation of OsF_6 or by reduction using I_2 in IF_5. Fluorination of Rh at 400° gives RhF_5 and of Ir at $\sim$360°, IrF_5.[4a]

The pentafluorides also are reactive and very readily hydrolyzable substances; PtF_5 readily disproportionates to PtF_4 and PtF_6. The most unusual feature is the polymerization which has been conclusively shown for RuF_5.[4b] This is tetrameric with nonlinear M—F—M bridges similar to the pentafluorides Nb, Ta and Mo (page 992) but somewhat distorted. IrF_5 and OsF_5 are isomorphous with RuF_5 and thus probably tetrameric. Some of the color changes on heating, e.g., of green $[OsF_5]_4 \rightarrow$ green liquid $\rightarrow$ blue liquid $\rightarrow$ colorless vapor, are probably due to depolymerization.

[4a] N. Bartlett and P. R. Rao, *Chem. Comm.*, **1965**, 252; J. H. Holloway, P. R. Rao and N. Bartlett, *Chem. Comm.*, **1965**, 306.

[4b] J. H. Holloway and R. D. Peacock, *J. Chem. Soc.*, **1963**, 527; J. H. Holloway, R. D. Peacock and R. W. H. Small, *J. Chem. Soc.*, **1964**, 645.

Tetrafluorides. These are obtained by reactions such as:

$$10RuF_5 + I_2 = 10RuF_4 + 2IF_5$$

$$OsF_6 \xrightarrow{W(CO)_6} OsF_4$$

$$RhCl_3 \xrightarrow{BrF_3(l)} RhF_4 \cdot 2BrF_3 \xrightarrow{heat} RhF_4$$

$$Pt \xrightarrow{BrF_3(l)} PtF_4 \cdot 2BrF_3 \xrightarrow{heat} PtF_4 \xleftarrow{F_2} PtBr_4$$

$$PdBr_2 \xrightarrow{BrF_3(l)} Pd^{II}Pd^{IV}F_6 \xrightarrow{F_2, 100 lb/sq in., 150°} PdF_4$$

The formation of BrF_3 adducts as above is a fairly common feature in the preparation of heavy metal fluorides in this way: such adducts may be ionic, i.e., $[BrF_2^+]_2 \cdot MF_6^{2-}$, but it is more likely that they are fluoride bridged species of the type 30-E-I or singly bridged polymers. Similar

(30-E-I)

adducts of SeF_4, which is a better F^- donor, appear to be ionic,[5] viz., $(SeF_3^+)_2 \cdot PtF_6^{2-}$. The tetrafluorides are violently hydrolyzed by water. The structures[6] of PdF_4 and PtF_4 appear to be similar to the structure of UCl_4; the metal is 8-coordinate at the center of two flattened tetrahedra.

Trifluorides. RuF_3 is best obtained by reduction

$$5RuF_5 + I_2 \overset{250°}{=} 2IF_5 + 5RuF_3$$

For rhodium, direct fluorination of Rh or $RhCl_3$ at 500–600° gives RhF_3; the solid is unaffected by water or bases. Hydrates $RhF_3 \cdot 6H_2O$ and $RhF_3 \cdot 9H_2O$ can be crystallized from fluoride solutions of Rh^{III}. IrF_3, which can be obtained only indirectly by reduction of IrF_6, e.g., by Ir at 50°, is also relatively inert to water. The Rh and Ir trifluorides have a slightly distorted ReO_3 structure.

The supposed palladium trifluoride has been shown[6] to be $Pd^{II}Pd^{IV}F_6$.

Difluorides. Palladous fluoride can be obtained by the reaction

$$Pd^{II}Pd^{IV}F_6 + SeF_4 \xrightarrow{reflux} 2PdF_2 + SeF_6$$

It is the only simple compound of Pd^{II} which is paramagnetic and the moment is consistent with the observed octahedral coordination. The Pd^{2+} ion also occurs in $Pd^{II}Pd^{IV}F_6$, $Pd^{II}Sn^{IV}F_6$ or $Pd^{II}Ge^{IV}F_6$, which can be obtained by addition of BrF_3 to mixtures of $PdBr_2$ and, e.g., $SnBr_4$.[6]

[5] N. Bartlett and D. H. Lohmann, *J. Chem. Soc.*, **1964**, 619.
[6] N. Bartlett and P. R. Rao, *Proc. Chem. Soc.*, **1964**, 393.

Oxofluorides. Colorless $RuOF_4$ is formed in the interaction of Ru with BrF_3,[4a] the oxygen coming from attack on glass. The action of BrF_3 on OsO_4 in presence of KBr gives an orange solid $KOsO_3F_3$ which is stable when dry; in presence of excess OsO_4 at 100° or by direct fluorination of OsO_4, the orange volatile OsO_3F_2, m 170°, is formed. Direct fluorination of OsO_2 gives $OsOF_5$,[7] emerald green, m 59.8°, which is isomorphous with UF_6 and hence presumably octahedral; like other oxofluorides it is stable when dry. $OsOF_4$ and $PtOF_3$ exist and $PtOF_4$ a deep red solid, m 75°, obtained by fluorination of Pt in silica apparatus.[5] No Rh or Ir oxofluorides are known.

30-E-7. Chlorides, Bromides and Iodides

The anhydrous halides are listed in Table 30-E-5. In addition to these there are a number of hydrated halides; since these are closely related to

TABLE 30-E-5

Anhydrous Halides of Platinum Metals[a]

Oxidation state	Ru	Os	Rh	Ir	Pd	Pt
II	$RuCl_2$	$OsCl_2$	—	—	$PdCl_2$ red	$PtCl_2$ black-red
		—			$PdBr_2$ red-black	$PtBr_2$ brown
		OsI_2 black			PdI_2 black	PtI_2 black
III	$RuCl_3$ black	$OsCl_3$ brown	$RhCl_3$ red	$IrCl_3$ brown-red	—	—
	$RuBr_3$? green	$OsBr_3$ dark grey	$RhBr_3$ dark red	$IrBr_3$ brown	—	—
	RuI_3 black	OsI_3 black	RhI_3 black	IrI_3 black	—	PtI_3?
IV	—	$OsCl_4$ black	—	—	—	$PtCl_4$ red-brown
	—	$OsBr_4$ black	—	$IrBr_4$?	—	$PtBr_4$ brown-black
	—	—[b]	—	IrI_4?	—	PtI_4 brown-black

[a] *Other halides:* there is some evidence for grey metallic OsI, and lower halides of Rh and Ir.
[b] Early claims of OsI_4 are not substantiated (J. E. Fergusson, B. H. Robinson and W. R. Roper, *J. Chem. Soc.*, **1962**, 2113).

[7] N. Bartlett, N. K. Tha and J. Trotter, *Proc. Chem. Soc.*, **1962**, 277.

aqueous complex ions we deal with them separately under the appropriate elements. Oxochlorides are also considered later.

Ruthenium. The trichloride,[8] as β-$RuCl_3$, a dark fluffy brown powder, is one of the most important ruthenium compounds and is best obtained by action of Cl_2, with added carbon monoxide, on the metal at 370° or by evaporating ethanolic solutions of Ru^{IV} chloro complexes. It is soluble in ethanol. Above 450° in chlorine it is converted to black lustrous leaflets of α-$RuCl_3$, which is insoluble in water and ethanol. α-$RuCl_3$ has a layer lattice structure and is antiferromagnetic. The tribromide has not been obtained pure but only as green hygroscopic crystals by evaporation of $Ru_2O_3 \cdot nH_2O$ in HBr; it gives an unstable solution in water and dissolves in HBr or Br^- solutions to give complex ions. The iodide is precipitated from Ru^{III} chloride solutions by KI. It is insoluble in common solvents, rather easily oxidized with liberation of iodine, and almost invariably contains strong OH bands in its infrared spectrum indicating contamination or incorporation of OH bridges in the lattice.

Osmium. Chlorination of Os gives a mixture of $OsCl_3$ and $OsCl_4$, the trichloride predominating only below 500° in a limited supply of Cl_2; pure $OsCl_4$ is given in excess Cl_2 above 650°. $OsCl_3$ is best made by thermal decomposition of $(NH_4)_2OsCl_6$ in Cl_2; it is a hygroscopic powder, soluble in water and ethanol, which sublimes above *ca* 350° and disproportionates to non-volatile $OsCl_2$ and volatile $OsCl_4$ above 550°. The inert dichloride can be made only in this way and is freed from other chlorides by boiling with HCl(aq) and water. $OsCl_4$ sublimes at *ca* 650° but is insoluble in common reagents other than oxidizing ones such as HNO_3(aq); it reacts with water slowly, eventually giving $OsO_2 \cdot nH_2O$. The similar tetrabromide is obtained by direct interaction in sealed tubes.[9]

Osmium iodides have been recently studied[10] by the reactions:

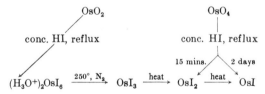

The monoiodide has an effective magnetic moment at room temperature of about 0.5 BM suggesting Os—Os interaction.

Rhodium. $RhCl_3$ is obtained by chlorination of Rh and can be sublimed above 900° to give red leaflets; it is isostructural with $AlCl_3$ forming a

[8] K. R. Hyde, E. W. Hooper, J. Waters and J. M. Fletcher, *J. Less Common Metals*, **8**, 428 (1965).

[9] I. Semenov and N. I. Kolbin, *Russ. J. Inorg. Chem.*, **7**, 111 (1962); **6**, 638 (1961).

[10] J. E. Fergusson, B. H. Robinson and W. R. Roper, *J. Chem. Soc.*, **1962**, 2113.

pseudohexagonal layer lattice with defective stacking of the layers.[11a] Dehydration of $RhCl_3(aq)$ at 180° in dry HCl gives a red $RhCl_3$ which is much more reactive, dissolving in water; on heating to above 300° this property is lost. The structural nature of these modifications are not known.

Iridium. The only important halide is $IrCl_3$, best obtained by chlorination of Ir at ~600°; it has two forms, brown and dark red.[11b] It is insoluble in water. The bromide and iodide can be obtained by dehydration of hydrates and a hydrated tetrachloride of somewhat uncertain nature also exists. In the pyrolysis of the trihalides to metal there is evidence for intermediate di- and monohalides.

Palladium and Platinum. Palladous chloride is probably the most important simple compound of palladium. It is made by the action of chlorine on the metal at red heat and is obtained as red crystals or an orange-red powder which is hygroscopic and soluble in water. From the aqueous solution crystals of the dihydrate, $PdCl_2 \cdot 2H_2O$, are obtained. In the anhydrous substance, there are infinite flat chains of the form 30-E-II. Palladium(II) chloride is quite soluble in hydrochloric acid or

(30-E-II)

alkali metal chloride solutions owing to formation of $[PdCl_4]^{2-}$ ions. The chloride reacts with many ligands, L, such as amines, phosphines, sulfides, etc., to give complexes of the types L_2PdCl_2 and $[LPdCl_2]_2$.

$PdBr_2$ is made from the elements in presence of nitric acid; it is obtained as a brown mass, insoluble in water but soluble in hydrobromic acid. PdI_2 can be precipitated from solutions of Pd^{II} chloride on addition of iodide ions. It is dark red to black, very insoluble in water, but slightly soluble in excess potassium iodide to give a red solution which evidently contains $[PdI_4]^{2-}$ ions. $K_2[PdI_4]$ can be isolated from the solution. Neither $PdBr_2$ nor PdI_2 have been characterized structurally.

Pt^{II} halides are relatively less stable than those of Pd^{II}. $PtCl_2$ can be made by heating the metal in chlorine at 500° or by thermal decomposition of the tetrachloride. X-ray study of black-red crystals has shown the presence of Pt_6Cl_{12} metal clusters. There is an octahedron of Pt atoms with the chlorides bridged so that the coordination of Pt by Cl is square.[11c] Normally $PtCl_2$ is a brownish green solid, insoluble in water but soluble

---

[11a] H. Bärnighausen and B. K. Handa, *J. Less Common Metals*, **6**, 225 (1964).

[11b] K. Broderson, F. Moers and H. G. Schnering, *Naturwiss.*, **52**, 205 (1965).

[11c] K. Broderson, G. Thiele and H. G. Schnering, *Zeit. anorg. Chem.*, **337**, 120 (1965).

in hydrochloric acid to give a solution containing $[PtCl_4]^{2-}$ ions. Many salts containing this ion are known. The brown dibromide and black diiodide are both formed by thermal decomposition of the tetrahalides, trihalides being possible intermediates. The dihalides have narrow thermal stability ranges and it is extremely difficult to obtain pure compounds.

Pt^{IV} chloride is a red-brown crystalline substance which can be made by heating platinum with chlorine at 250–300° or by heating platinum with $AsCl_3$ and $SeCl_4$ in a sealed tube. It is also often prepared by heating chloroplatinic acid, $(H_3O)_2PtCl_6 \cdot nH_2O$, to 300°. It is easily soluble in water and acetone, and from aqueous solutions it crystallizes in several hydrated forms, some of which probably contain mixed chlorohydroxo complexes such as $[PtCl_4(OH)_2]^{2-}$.

$PtBr_4$ and PtI_4, obtained by direct interaction at $\sim 150°$, are both brown-black powders only slightly soluble in water but moderately soluble in alcohol and ether. They decompose on heating to $\sim 180°$ into the halogen and the Pt^{II} halide. The addition of KI to cold $PtCl_6^{2-}$ solutions gives a black precipitate of stoichiometry PtI_3; this gives PtI_2 at 270°. Although "PtI_3" is diamagnetic[12] its nature is not certain, but it appears not to be a mixture of PtI_2 and PtI_4; it may well be some sort of cluster compound.

30-F. RUTHENIUM AND OSMIUM

The chemistry of these elements bears little resemblance to the chemistry of iron except in certain solid state compounds such as sulfides or phosphides, and in complexes with π-bonding ligands such as CO or π-C_5H_5. The higher oxidation states, VI and VIII, are much more readily obtained than for iron and there is an extensive and important chemistry of the tetroxides, MO_4, oxohalides and oxo anions. There are quite close analogies between the chemistries of Ru, Os and Re especially in oxo compounds. Ruthenium forms a unique series of nitrosyl compounds which have neither Re nor Os analogs.

For both elements the nature of so-called "simple" solution species is far from simple. There is little evidence for simple aquo ions and virtually all aqueous solutions, whatever the anion, may be considered to contain complex ions.

The oxidation states and stereochemistries of Ru and Os are given in Table 30-F-1.

30-F-1. Ruthenium(II) and Osmium(II), d^6

Apart from osmium dihalides no simple salts or compounds are known but both elements give numerous complexes. The usual method of

12 G. R. Argue and J. J. Banewicz, *J. Inorg. Nucl. Chem.*, **25**, 923 (1963).

TABLE 30-F-1

Oxidation States and Stereochemistry of Ruthenium and Osmium

Oxidation state	Coordination number	Geometry	Examples
Ru^{-II}	4	Tetrahedral(?)	$Ru(CO)_4^{2-}$ (?), $[Ru(diphos)_2]^{2-}$
Ru^0, Os^0	5	TBP?	$Ru(CO)_5$, $Os(CO)_5$, $Ru(CO)_3(PPh_3)_2$
Ru^I, d^7	?	?	$NORu(S_2CNEt_2)_3$(?)
Ru^{II}, Os^{II}, d^6	5	See text	$RuCl_2(PPh_3)_3$
	6^a	Octahedral	$[RuNOCl_5]^{2-}$, $[Ru(dipy)_3]^{2+}$, $[Ru(NH_3)_6]^{2+}$, $[Os(CN)_6]^{4-}$, $RuCl_2CO(PEtPh_2)_3$, $OsHCl(diphos)_2$
Ru^{III}, Os^{III}, d^5	6^a	Octahedral	$[Ru(NH_3)_5Cl]^{2+}$, $[RuCl_5H_2O]^{2-}$ $[Os(dipy)_3]^{3+}$, K_3RuF_6, $[OsCl_6]^{3-}$
Ru^{IV}, Os^{IV}, d^4	$6^{a,b}$	Octahedral	K_2OsCl_6, K_2RuCl_6, $[Os(diars)_2X_2]^{2+}$,
	8		RuO_2(rutile)
Ru^V, Os^V, d^3	5 in vapor(?)		RuF_5
	6	Octahedral	$KRuF_6$, $NaOsF_6$, $(RuF_5)_4$
Ru^{VI}, Os^{VI}, d^2	4	Tetrahedral	RuO_4^{2-}
	5	?	$OsOCl_4$
	6^b	Octahedral	RuF_6, OsF_6, $[OsO_2Cl_4]^{2-}$, $[OsO_2(OH)_4]^{2-}$, $[OsNCl_5]^{2-}$
Ru^{VII}, Os^{VII}, d^1	4	Tetrahedral	RuO_4^-
	6	Octahedral	$OsOF_5$
Ru^{VIII}, Os^{VIII}, d^0	4	Tetrahedral	RuO_4, OsO_4, $[OsO_3N]^-$
	5	?	OsO_3F_2
	6	Octahedral	$[OsO_3F_3]^-$, $[OsO_4(OH)_2]^{2-}$

[a] Most common states for Ru.
[b] Most common states for Os.

preparation is the reduction of Ru^{III}, Os^{III}, Ru^{IV} or Os^{IV} halides or halogeno complexes in the presence of ligands. In some cases the ligand itself may act as a reductant. All complexes of Ru^{II} and Os^{II} are octahedral, diamagnetic and usually kinetically inert; these characteristics are consistent with a t_{2g}^6 configuration of d electrons. The only apparent exception is the complex $RuCl_2(PPh_3)_3$, which is formally 5-coordinate;[1] however, the sixth position is actually blocked by a hydrogen atom of the phenyl ring so that a quasi-octahedral complex results. The occupancy of a coordination position by a nonbonding ligand atom in order to achieve a preferred coordination number is known in other cases (see page 1024).

When ruthenium chloride solutions are treated with hydrogen under pressure, with Ti^{3+}, or are electrolytically reduced, blue solutions of chloro complexes are obtained. Using tetrafluoroborate or p-toluenesulfonate solutions however, the hexaquo ion, $[Ru(H_2O)_6]^{2+}$, may be obtained.

[1] S. J. LaPlaca and J. A. Ibers, *Inorg. Chem.*, **4**, 778 (1965).

In the presence of other ions, even trifluoroacetate, complexes are formed, while ClO_4^- is reduced. The Ru^{III}/Ru^{II} couple is estimated to be 0.22 v (cf. also ref. 15), and the solutions are readily oxidized by air.[2a] The blue chloro complexes are reduced even by water.[2b]

Nitrogen Ligands. The reduction of any ruthenium compound of a mineral acid in ammoniacal NH_4Cl solution with zinc dust yields a solution from which orange crystals of $[Ru(NH_3)_6]Cl_2$ separate. This salt forms yellow crystalline double salts with Zn or Cd halides. It is a powerful reducing agent. Extensive series of related compounds are known.[3,15]

Although $[Ru(dipy)_3]Cl_2$ and its osmium analog were first obtained by fusing Ru^{III} chloride or K_2OsCl_6 respectively, with dipyridyl at 250°, the cations are more conveniently obtained by heating aqueous $K_2[Ru^{III}Cl_5H_2O]$ or $(NH_4)_2OsBr_6$ with the ligand plus a reducing agent. The use of sucrose or sodium d-tartrate as reducing agent leads to a remarkable asymmetric synthesis in high yields of the levo-isomers.[4a] The reductant must be functioning not only as such but as a complexing agent in an intermediate, thus directing the stereochemistry of the reaction; such asymmetric syntheses are rare but examples for Co^{III} and Cu^{II} complexes are known. Extensive series of salts of these ions and the corresponding 1,10-phenanthroline complexes can be made metathetically. The oxalato complex,[4b] $[Rudipy_2ox]\cdot 4H_2O$, obtained by reduction of $K[Ru^{IV}Cl_5H_2O]$ with potassium oxalate, is a convenient source for the preparation of Ru^{III} complexes, e.g., by chlorine oxidation.

The $[Ru(dipy)_3]^{2+}$ ion, which lends an intense red color to all of its compounds, is extremely stable (the chloride is not decomposed at 300° or on boiling in concentrated HCl or 50% KOH). Its optical antimers do not racemize in cold aqueous solution and only slowly at 90°. The enantiomorphs of $[Os(dipy)_3]^{2+}$ are quite stable and a most remarkable feature of the ion is that it can be oxidized to $[Os(dipy)_3]^{3+}$, which can then be reduced to regenerate $[Os(dipy)_3]^{2+}$ without loss of optical activity

Both Ru^{II} and Os^{II} form very stable hexacyano anions. The complexes are obtained in various ways such as

$$Ru + (NaOH\text{--}NaNO_3, \text{ fused}) \longrightarrow RuO_4^{2-} \xrightarrow[100°]{KCN/H_2O} K_4[Ru(CN)_6]$$

by evaporating $RuCl_3$ repeatedly on a steam bath with excess KCN until a colorless residue is obtained, or by evaporating K_2OsO_4 with KCN and igniting the residue. From the potassium salts obtained by these pro-

[2a] E. E. Mercer and R. R. Buckley, *Inorg. Chem.*, **4**, 1692 (1965).

[2b] G. A. Rechnitz and H. A. Catherino, *Inorg. Chem.*, **4**, 112 (1965).

[3] F. M. Lever and A. R. Powell, *Special Publication No. 13*, Chemical Society, London, 1959.

[4a] C. F. Liu, N. C. Liu and J. C. Bailar, *Inorg. Chem.* **3**, 1085 (1964).

[4b] *Idem, Inorg. Chem.*, **3**, 1197 (1964).

cedures many other salts can be made by metathesis and, for ruthenium, the free acid, $H_4[Ru(CN)_6]$, has been isolated.

Both Ru^{II} and Os^{II} form complexes of the type $[M(diars)_2X_2]$, where X is a halide or SCN^-. These complexes are obtained by treating Ru^{III} halides or $[Os^{IV}X_6]^{2-}$ in alcohol with excess of the diarsine, which functions as a reducing agent. The complexes are yellow, orange, or brown and are nonelectrolytes. Nonelectrolyte monomeric triarsine complexes,[5] and a variety of mixed phosphine and arsine complexes exist (see below).

Ru^{II} has also been reported to form a series of complexes containing ammonia and one of the sulfur-containing ligands, SO_2, HSO_3^- or SO_3^{2-}, and perhaps also chloride ions. Typical ones are $[Ru(NH_3)_5SO_3]\cdot 2H_2O$, $[Ru(NH_3)_4SO_2Cl]Cl$ and $Na_4[Ru(NH_3)_2(SO_3)_2(SO_3H)_2]\cdot 6H_2O$. They are obtained by the action of sodium bisulfite on Ru^{III} ammine complexes. The complex $[Ru(NH_3)_4(SO_2)Cl]Cl$ has been studied by X-rays and the monodentate coordination of SO_2 through sulfur confirmed.[5a]

Nitric Oxide Complexes of Ruthenium and Osmium. Nitric oxide complexes of various types are known for Ru and Os, but the latter are not especially stable or important. However, for ruthenium, nitric oxide complexes are very numerous—more than for any other element—and are a most important feature of ruthenium chemistry. The ruthenium nitric oxide species contain the group RuNO, and this group can occur in both anionic and cationic octahedral complexes in which it is remarkably stable, being able to persist through a variety of substitution and oxidation–reduction reactions. Ruthenium solutions or compounds which have at any time been treated with nitric acid can be suspected of containing nitric oxide bound to the metal. Indeed, commercial Ru products may contain bound NO and should be tested before use in other preparations. The presence of NO is conveniently shown by the infrared spectrum since all RuNO complexes have a strong band in the region 1845–1930 cm^{-1}.

Almost all ligands can be associated with the RuNO group and some typical complexes are $K_2[RuNO(OH)(NO_2)_4]$, $K_2[RuNOCl_5]$, $K_2[RuNO(CN)_5]$, $[RuNO(NH_3)_4Cl]Cl_2$ and $RuNO[S_2CN(CH_3)_2]_2$. The complexes can be obtained in a variety of ways and the source of NO can be HNO_3, NO, NO_2 or NO_2^-. A few examples will illustrate the preparative methods. If RuO_4 in $\sim 8M$ HCl is evaporated with HNO_3, a purple solution is obtained from which the addition of ammonium chloride will precipitate the salt $(NH_4)_2[RuNOCl_5]$. If this salt is boiled with ammonia, it is converted to the golden-yellow salt $[RuNO(NH_3)_4Cl]Cl_2$. When commercial ruthenium "tetrachloride" in HCl solution is heated with NO and NO_2, a plum-colored solution is obtained from which brick-red $RuNOCl_3\cdot 5H_2O$

[5] J. G. Hartley and L. M. Venanzi, *J. Chem. Soc.*, **1962**, 182.

[5a] L. H. Vogt, Jr., J. L. Katz and S. E. Wiberley, *Inorg. Chem.*, **4**, 1157 (1965).

can be obtained.   The addition of base to the solution gives a dark brown gelatinous precipitate of $RuNO(OH)_3 \cdot H_2O$.   When this oxide is boiled with $8M$ HNO_3 and the solution evaporated, red solutions are obtained from which ion-exchange separation has allowed identification of species such as $[RuNO(NO_3)_4H_2O]^-$, $[RuNO(NO_3)_2(H_2O)_3]^+$, $[RuNO-(H_2O)_4]^{2+}$ and $[RuNO(H_2O)_5]^{3+}$; other complex anions are present as well as neutral species, of which the main one is $[RuNO(NO_3)_3((H_2O)_2]$ which can be extracted into tributylphosphate.[6]   The chloride system has also been studied by ion-exchange and species ranging from $[RuNOCl-(H_2O)_4]^{2+}$ to $[RuNOCl_5]^{2-}$ characterized; $[RuNOCl_4(H_2O)]^-$ and $[RuNOCl_3(H_2O)_2]$ are weak acids, dissociating to give hydroxo species.[7]

As noted above, the vast majority of RuNO complexes are of the general type $RuNOL_5$, in which the metal atom is *formally* in the divalent state, if we postulate electron transfer from NO to the metal as Ru^{III} followed by donation from NO^+.   For iron, very few such octahedral complexes are known except with cyanide as an associated ligand, and the different behavior of the two elements could be attributed in part to the relatively low stabilization energy of the $t_{2g}^3 e_g^2$ ion for ruthenium and the consequent readiness of Ru^{III} to accept an electron from NO giving Ru^{II} (t_{2g}^6); the larger size of Ru^{3+}, (~ 0.72) compared to Fe^{3+} (~ 0.64) would also favor better $d\pi$–$p\pi$ overlap for NO π bonding.   For osmium, nitric oxide complexes are rather scarce and they are less resistant than the ruthenium analogs, but here the difference may be due to the general low stability of divalent osmium complexes toward oxidation.   It is also, presumably, the ease of oxidation of the $+1$ states that does not allow two nitric oxide groups to be bound to any of these elements in octahedral complexes.

Some X-ray studies have indicated that the Ru—N—O bond is non-linear in some complexes, but in the only accurate one, that of $Na_2[Ru(NO_2)_4NO(OH)]$, the group is linear with a short Ru—N bond consistent with the configuration $R=N^+=\ddot{O}:$; the NO and OH groups are *trans* to each other.   The high *trans* position of NO has been shown by the ready replacement of ligands such as NH_3 or Cl^- *trans* to it.[9]

Carbonyl and Phosphine Complexes of Ruthenium(II) and Osmium(II).   In common with other platinum metals, Ru and Os readily form carbonyl species where the CO group is derived either from CO, from formic acid or from certain alcohols, especially in basic solutions; the latter reactions may

[6] R. M. Wallace, *J. Inorg. Nucl. Chem.*, **20**, 283 (1961); D. Scargill, *et al.*, *J. Inorg. Nucl. Chem.*, **27**, 161 (1965).

[7] E. E. Mercer, W. M. Campbell and R. M. Wallace, *Inorg. Chem.* **3**, 1018 (1964).

[8] S. H. Simonsen and M. H. Mueller, *J. Inorg. Nucl. Chem.*, **27**, 309 (1965).

[9] O. E. Zvjagintsev, N. M. Sinitsyn and V. N. Pitchkov, *Proc. I.C.C.*, 8, Springer-Verlag, Vienna, 1964, p. 142.

give hydrido species also. Most of the known derivatives are of Ru^{II} although there are some closely related compounds of Ru^{III}.

The action of CO on alcohol solutions of commercial $RuCl_3 \cdot 3H_2O$ can give a variety of species, examples of which are summarized in Figure 30-F-1, where the phosphine is usually PEt_2Ph, though other phosphines

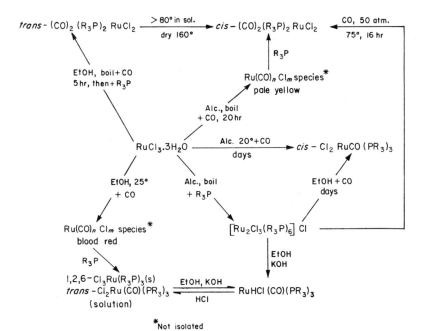

Fig. 30-F-1. Some carbonyl phosphine derivatives of ruthenium. EtOH = ethanol; Alc. = 2-methoxyethanol. Different phosphines sometimes give different reactions.

and arsines behave in similar, though not always identical ways.[10] The formation of the hydrido complex in the reaction with alkali in ethanol for complexes such as cis-$[PtCl_2(PEt_3)_2]$ or of hydridocarbonyl complexes as in the present case, is believed to occur through initial formation of an ethoxo complex, followed by transfer of H^- from the α-carbon atom:

$$CH_3{-}\underset{\underset{Cl}{|}}{\overset{\overset{H}{|}}{C}}{-}ORuL_4 \longrightarrow \left[CH_3{-}\underset{\underset{H}{|}}{C}{=}ORuL_4 \right] \xrightarrow{-CH_4} \left[C{\equiv}ORuL_4 \right] \longrightarrow O{\equiv}CRuHL_4$$

This particular reaction is not clean, and there are side reactions.

[10] (a) J. Chatt, B. L. Shaw and A. E. Field, *J. Chem. Soc.*, **1964,** 3466; (b) J. Chatt and J. M. Davidson, *J. Chem. Soc.*, **1965,** 843; (c) T. E. Stephenson and G. Wilkinson, *J. Inorg. Nucl. Chem.*, Vol. 28 (1966).

Some of the most interesting ruthenium compounds[10b] are those obtained by reducing the complex *trans*-$RuCl_2(Me_2PCH_2CH_2PMe_2)_2$ with sodium naphthalenide. They appear to be in tautomeric equilibria where a hydrogen atom bound to ruthenium can be transferred to the ligand, 30-F-I,

(30-F-I)   (30-F-II)

30-F-II. Such hydride transfers from a metal to a coordinated ligand, or vice versa, are doubtless involved in many of the reactions with alcohols referred to above and elsewhere and may well be involved in biological hydrogen transfer systems, but at present only this well-established example exists.

In the absence of π-bonding ligands, and using only catalytic amounts of ruthenium chloride, inter- and intramolecular hydrogen transfers can be effected using a variety of alcohols.[11]

Some similar types of complex are given by osmium and from $Os^{III}Cl_3(PEt_2Ph)_3$ the compound $Os^{II}HCl(CO)(PEt_2Ph)_3$ is obtained. Chelating diphosphine or diarsine halide complexes of Ru and Os can also be converted by action of LiR to alkyl derivatives[12] such as *cis*-$Ru^{II}(CH_3)Cl$ diars$_2$ or $Os^{II}(C_2H_5)Cl[Ph_2P(CH_2)_2PPh_2]_2$.

30-F-2. Complexes of Ruthenium(III) and Osmium(III), d^5

The somewhat greater stability of the trivalent state for ruthenium compared with osmium is apparent in their complexes. Ru^{III} complexes are considerably more numerous than those of Os^{III}.

The evaporation of solutions of RuO_4 in aqueous HCl in a stream of HCl affords the hydrate "$RuCl_3 \cdot 3H_2O$". Commercial hydrated "ruthenium trichloride" is a complex mixture of chloro or chlorohydroxo species, many of which are polymeric and contain mainly Ru^{IV}. The deep red

[11] J. K. Nicholson and B. L. Shaw, *Proc. Chem. Soc.*, **1963**, 282.
[12] J. Chatt and H. Hayter, *J. Chem. Soc.*, **1963**, 6017.

solutions of this material in water quickly darken due to hydrolysis.[13] In order to ensure the absence of Ru^{IV}, the commercial salt must be evaporated several times with concentrated HCl, when it is converted to chloro complex anions, mainly $[RuCl_5(H_2O)]^{2-}$.

Reduction of commercial "trichloride" in $0.3M$ HCl with mercury gives solutions containing Ru^{III} complexes, which are re-oxidized by air to Ru^{IV}. Ion exchange separation has allowed definite characterization of $[Ru(H_2O)_6]^{3+}$, $[RuCl(H_2O)_5]^{2+}$ and *cis*- and *trans*-$[RuCl_2(H_2O)_4]^+$ whose electronic spectra were recorded so that ready identification is possible.[14]

Aqueous or ethanolic solutions of osmium trichloride can be obtained but the precise nature of the species is uncertain; unlike the ruthenium solutions they are resistant to mild reducing agents or to boiling, but addition of alkalies to hot solutions gives a hydrous oxide.

Ammines. Ru^{III} ammines of several types are known. The colorless hexammine, $[Ru(NH_3)_6]Cl_3$, is best obtained by oxidation of $[Ru(NH_3)_6]^{2+}$ with $HgCl_2$. The standard potential of this Ru^{III}–Ru^{II} couple has been found to be 0.214 v.[15] The hexammine can be converted to the salt $[Ru(NH_3)_5Cl]Cl_2$ by boiling it with strong HCl. On treating the chloro pentammine with aqueous ammonia and then carefully acidifying, $[Ru(NH_3)_5(H_2O)]Cl_3$ can also be obtained. The base hydrolysis of $[Ru(NH_3)_5Cl]^{2+}$ is *ca* 10^6 times faster than acid hydrolysis,[16] thus resembling the corresponding Co^{III} complex, but differing from Cr^{III} and Rh^{III} analogs where base hydrolysis is slow. Tetraammines, $[Ru(NH_3)_4X_2]X$, are also known and two forms, considered to be *cis* and *trans* isomers, have been obtained for the chloro compound. Two unstable triammines, $[Ru(NH_3)_3X_3]$ (X = Cl, Br) are also known. Dipyridyl complexes like $[Rudipy_2Cl_2]Cl$ are best obtained from $Ru^{II}dipy_2ox$ as noted above.

Only a few osmium(III) ammine complexes have been described. There are the hexammines, $[Os(NH_3)_6]X_3$, obtained, among other products, by the action of liquid ammonia on hexabromoosmates(IV); there is a pentammine, $[Os(NH_3)_5Br]Br_2$, while dipyridyl and 1,10-phenathroline complexes[17] are known for both Os^{II} and Os^{III}.

Halogeno Complexes. No fluoro complexes of Os^{III} have yet been reported, but K_3RuF_6 can be prepared by treatment of $RuCl_3$ with molten KHF_2. It is a dark grey substance which is inert toward water but dissolves in dilute acids to give solutions in which the $[RuF_6]^{3-}$ ion

[13] F. Pantani, *J. Less Common Metals*, **4**, 116 (1962) and references therein.

[14] R. E. Connick and D. A. Fine, *J. Amer. Chem. Soc.*, **82**, 4187 (1960).

[15] J. F. Endicott and H. Taube, *Inorg. Chem.*, **4**, 437 (1965).

[16] J. A. Broomhead, F. Basolo and R. G. Pearson, *Inorg. Chem.*, **3**, 826 (1964).

[17] D. A. Buckingham, F. P. Dwyer, H. A. Goodwin and A. M. Sargeson. *Aust. J. Chem.*, **17**, 325 (1964).

apparently remains intact or is but little hydrolyzed. Ru^{III} occurs in quite a number of chloro complexes, some of which have less well-characterized bromo analogs, but no iodo complexes are known. The chloro complexes occur in the stoichiometric types $M^I RuCl_4 \cdot H_2O$, $M^I_2 RuCl_5$, $M^I_2 RuCl_5 \cdot H_2O$, $M^I_3 RuCl_6$ and $M^I_4 RuCl_7$. Although the hexachloro complexes (which incidentally have no bromo analogs) can probably be taken quite generally to contain the $[RuCl_6]^{3-}$ ion, the structures of the others have not been elucidated.

The only reported halo complexes of Os^{III} contain $[OsCl_6]^{3-}$ and $[OsBr_6]^{3-}$, though the latter is somewhat uncertain.

Other Species. Ru^{III} and Os^{III} form a few complexes in which the donor atoms are oxygen, such as the β-diketonates and oxalates,[18] $[Ruox_3]^{3-}$.

Both Ru and Os form rather stable complexes originally formulated $M^I_2[M^{III}(NO_2)_5]$, but these orange, water soluble salts have been shown by infrared studies to contain the ions $[M^{II}(NO_2)_4(OH)NO]^{2-}$ (see page 995).

The complex cations $[Ru(diars)_2 X_2]^+$ and $[Os(diars)_2 X_2]^+$ can be obtained on oxidation of the analogous Ru^{II} and Os^{II} complexes described earlier. Reaction of certain phosphines with Ru^{IV} and Os^{IV} hexahalo complexes yields complexes of the type $[MX_3(R_3P)_3]$.

All known complexes of Ru^{III} and Os^{III} are of the low-spin type, with one unpaired electron. In the approximation of exact octahedral symmetry of the ligand fields their electron configurations are $t_{2g}{}^5$. Study and interpretation of the spectra of these complexes has not been very conclusive. Transitions of the d–d type are rather difficult to observe because of strong charge-transfer bands appearing in the region where they would be expected. As noted in the introductory section of this chapter, the low-spin d^5 ions have normal magnetic behavior except when the quantity kT/λ becomes very small. Thus Ru^{III} complexes ($\lambda \approx 1.5 \times 10^3$ cm^{-1}) have magnetic moments in the range 1.8–2.1 BM at room temperature, and even for the Os^{III} complexes, where λ is quite large ($\sim 5 \times 10^3$ cm^{-1}), the moments are still almost "normal," i.e., in the range 1.6–1.95 BM.

30-F-3. Complexes of Ruthenium(IV) and Osmium(IV), d^4

Relatively few of these are known, and the most important ones are the *halogeno complexes*, particularly those of osmium.

Both Ru^{IV} and Os^{IV} can be obtained in hexafluoro complexes. The ruthenium complexes, K_2RuF_6 and Cs_2RuF_6, have been prepared by the

[18] R. W. Olliff and A. L. Odell. *J. Chem. Soc.*, **1964**, 2467.

action of water on the corresponding $M^I Ru^V F_6$ compounds, and a barium salt by direct fluorination of a mixture of $RuCl_3$ and $BaCl_2$. The barium compound is blue and the others yellow or pink, depending on the color of the corresponding Ru^V complex (see below). These compounds decompose slowly in moist air and cold aqueous solutions precipitate hydrous Ru^{IV} oxide on standing. Warm or alkaline solutions decompose rapidly. On treatment with hydrochloric or hydrobromic acid, they are converted to the $[RuCl_6]^{2-}$ or $[RuBr_6]^{2-}$ ions. The hexafluoroosmate(IV) ion is obtained by treating the $M^I OsF_6$ salts with aqueous alkali, and from such solutions the K, Cs, Na, NH_3 and Ba salts have been isolated. They are cream or white and stable toward water and dilute acids.

The $[RuCl_6]^{2-}$ and $[RuBr_6]^{2-}$ ions are known but are not particularly stable. On fusing ruthenium with potassium chlorate and adding excess potassium chloride to the dissolved product, or by passing chlorine through solutions of Ru^{III} containing excess chloride ion, the potassium salt may be obtained and others may be obtained from it by metathetical reactions. The larger the cation the less soluble these salts are, which is a useful rule in preparing others. The salts are dark brown or purple, and the presence of octahedral $[RuCl_6]^{2-}$ ion is demonstrated by their isomorphism with corresponding Os, Ir, Pd and Pt salts. In solution the $[RuCl_6]^{2-}$ ion is yellow, but the solutions fairly quickly decompose, turning black.

The corresponding black hexabromides are similar but even more easily hydrolyzed and hence of little importance.

Ru^{IV} chloride is known only in hydrated condition, $RuCl_4 \cdot 5H_2O$, and in the related hydroxochloride, $Ru(OH)Cl_3$. Both of these apparently occur as products of reduction or decomposition of RuO_4 in hydrochloric acid under various conditions. The hydrated chloride is obtained in the form of red, hygroscopic crystals, when a solution of the complex oxo-chloride, $(H_3O)_2RuO_2Cl_4$, in hydrochloric acid is heated with a stream of chlorine passing through it, and then evaporated over P_2O_5. It must be assumed that the water functions as the reducing agent in this curious reaction. The hydroxochloride can be isolated by evaporating a solution of RuO_4 in hydrochloric acid to dryness. It, too, is a dark red solid, extremely soluble in water. Their colors suggest that one or both of these substances may be similar in nature (though containing H_2O in place of NH_3) to the ruthenium reds (see page 1003) and hence much more complex than the simple formulas given would indicate.

The behavior of the Ru^{IV}–Cl system in aqueous solution of low chloride concentration is complicated—in regard to both kinetics and equilibrium—and not yet well understood. It appears less tractable than the Ru^{III} system. When chloride ions are added to a perchlorate solution containing Ru^{IV}, successive color changes take place, the sequence and persistence times being functions of the pH as well as of the Cl^- concentration. The sequence in solutions with $[Cl^-] > 0.1M$ and $[H^+] > 0.4M$ is

$$Ru^{IV}(reddish) \rightarrow yellow(I) \rightarrow violet \rightarrow yellow(II)$$

The yellow(I) state is thought to contain several fairly labile and probably polynuclear species. The main species in the violet stage is thought to be $[Ru(H_2O)_2(OH)_2Cl_2]$ which is transformed by additional chloride ion to yellow anionic complexes, $[Ru(H_2O)(OH)_2Cl_3]^-$ and $[Ru(OH)_2Cl_4]^{2-}$. These suggestions are rather speculative, however.

The salts of $[OsCl_6]^{2-}$ and $[OsBr_6]^{2-}$ are among the most important of osmium complexes, being quite commonly used as starting materials in the preparation of others. All of the salts are red to brown and give orange solutions; at low acidities they precipitate black $OsO_2 \cdot 2H_2O$ readily.[19] K_2OsCl_6 is prepared by heating osmium and potassium chloride in chlorine or by reducing OsO_4 with aqueous alcohol in presence of excess potassium chloride. Many other salts have been prepared from the potassium salt or from solutions which appear to contain the free acid. The latter are obtained on boiling solutions of $OsCl_4$ in hydrochloric acid until they turn brown and finally red. Clearly, $[OsCl_6]^{2-}$ is considerably more stable to aquation than $[RuCl_6]^{2-}$ or $[IrCl_6]^{2-}$.

Solutions of $H_2[OsBr_6]$ are obtained by boiling $OsCl_4$ in excess hydrobromic acid, and a variety of salts have been isolated. They are usually black and give dark purple solutions. Salts of the black and relatively unstable $[OsI_6]^{2-}$ are of little importance.

Hydroxohalo complexes, $M^I_2[RuCl_5(OH)]$, $M^I_2[OsCl_5(OH)]$ and $M^I_2[OsBr_5(OH)]$ have also been reported. The first of these has been shown, however, to be $M^I_4[RuCl_5ORuCl_5] \cdot H_2O$ and there is some evidence that the osmium complexes are similar.[19]

Ruthenium(IV) forms no authenticated cationic complexes and Os^{IV} forms only two types. Thus the Os^{III} diarsine complexes mentioned earlier resist oxidation by halogens, permanganate or ceric ion, but by using $15N$ nitric acid they can be converted to the $[Os(diars)_2X_2]^{2+}$ ions, which have been isolated as the perchlorates. There are also some Os^{IV} complexes which evidently contain ethylenediamine molecules which have lost a proton (en − H) from the nitrogen, namely, $[Os(en − H)_2(en)]^{2+}$ and $[Os(en − H)(en)_2X_3]$, but the structures are uncertain.

Of special interest is the compound $K_4[Ru_2Cl_{10}O] \cdot H_2O$, which was long formulated as $K_2[RuCl_5OH]$, on which basis its diamagnetism was difficult to explain. It is now known to contain a binuclear anion having the structure shown in Figure 30-F-2. Its diamagnetism can be understood using a simple molecular orbital treatment of the Ru—O—Ru group.

[19] R. R. Miano and C. S. Garner, *Inorg. Chem.*, **4**, 337 (1965).

Assuming these three atoms to lie along the z axis of a coordinate system, and assuming further that the ligand field around each Ru^{IV} ion is essentially octahedral, the ruthenium(IV) ions will then each have a $d_{xy}{}^2 d_{xz} d_{yz}$ configuration prior to interaction with the oxygen. By the interaction of the d_{xz} orbitals on each Ru^{IV} and the p_x orbital of oxygen, three three-center MO's, one bonding, one approximately nonbonding and one anti-bonding, will be formed. The four electrons (one from each Ru^{IV} and two

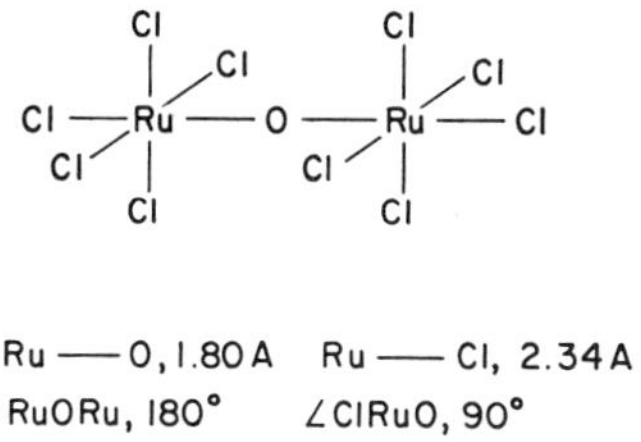

$$Ru \text{——} O, 1.80 A \quad Ru \text{——} Cl, 2.34 A$$
$$\angle RuORu, 180° \quad \angle ClRuO, 90°$$

Fig. 30-F-2. The structure of the $[Ru_2Cl_{10}O]^{4-}$ ion.

from oxygen) will occupy the lower two of these MO's. The same kind of interaction will occur in the Rud_{yz}—Op_y—Rud_{yz} set of orbitals, and thus all electron spins become paired.

Ruthenium Red. A characteristic of ruthenium complex ammine chemistry is the formation of highly colored red or brown species usually referred to as ruthenium reds. Thus, if commercial ruthenium "tetra-chloride," which consists largely of polynuclear Ru^{IV} complexes, is treated with ammonia in air for several days, a red solution is obtained. Alternatively, if the "tetrachloride" is reduced by refluxing with ethanol and the resulting trichloride in hydrochloric acid is treated with ammonia and exposed to air at 90° with addition of more ammonia at intervals, again a red solution is obtained. Crystallization of the solutions gives the diamagnetic ruthenium red. The structure of the species appears to be that of a trinuclear ion with oxygen bridges (presumably linear) between the metal atoms, $[(NH_3)_5Ru$—O—$Ru(NH_3)_4$—O—$Ru(NH_3)_5]^{6+}$; since the average oxidation state of Ru is $3\frac{1}{3}$, the metal atoms must be in different formal oxidation states. This ion can be oxidized in acid solution by air, Fe^{3+} or Ce^{4+} to a brown ion of the same constitution but with charge $+7$; the nitrate and the sulfate of the latter ion are paramagnetic with $\mu = 1.1$ BM. It is quite likely that there are corresponding trinuclear chloro complexes, such as $[Ru_3O_2Cl_6(H_2O)_6]$, in the violet aqueous solutions of $RuCl_3$, since ruthenium red is produced from these by action of ammonia.

Ru^{IV} and Os^{IV} complexes all have octahedral or distorted octahedral structures and should thus have $t_{2g}{}^4$ electron configurations. As discussed on pages 911–912, this configuration is especially subject to anomalous magnetic behavior when the spin-orbit coupling constant of the metal ion becomes high as it is in Os^{IV}. The chief effect in this case is that the effective magnetic moment is brought far below the spin-only value (2.84 BM), typical values for Os^{IV} complexes at room temperature being in the range 1.2–1.7 BM. As the temperature is lowered, μ_{eff} decreases as the square root of the absolute temperature. Ru^{IV} complexes have practically normal moments at room temperature (2.7–2.9 BM), but these also decrease with $T^{1/2}$ as the temperature is lowered.

Virtually nothing is known of the d–d transitions in Ru^{IV} and Os^{IV} complexes since the relevant absorption bands are severely masked by strong charge transfer bands.

30-F-4. Complexes of Ruthenium(V) and Osmium(V), d^3

This oxidation state is evidently an extremely unfavorable one for these elements, giving no simple compounds save the fluorides and a few complexes.

The hexafluoro complexes can be prepared by various nonaqueous reactions of which the following are representative:

$$RuCl_3 + M^ICl + F_2 \xrightarrow{\ 300°\ } M^I[RuF_6]$$
$$Ru + M^{II}Cl_2 + BrF_3 \longrightarrow M^{II}[RuF_6]_2$$
$$OsCl_4 + M^ICl + BrF_3 \longrightarrow M^I[OsF_6]$$

For several of them, X-ray studies have established that octahedral $[MF_6]^-$ ions are present. One curious feature of these compounds is that their colors vary with the method of preparation. For example, $KRuF_6$ samples prepared by high temperature fluorination are pale blue, whereas those from bromine trifluoride solution may be pale pink or cream. The colors are believed to be due to trace impurities.

The fluororuthenates(V) dissolve in water with evolution of oxygen undergoing reduction to $[RuF_6]^{2-}$ and also producing traces of RuO_4. The osmium salts dissolve in water without reaction, but when base is added oxygen is evolved and $[OsF_6]^{2-}$ is formed.

The $[MF_6]^-$ ions have t_{2g}^3 configurations with three unpaired electrons. Their magnetic moments are independent of temperature, averaging ~ 3.7 BM for the $[RuF_6]^-$ salts and ~ 3.2 BM for the $[OsF_6]^-$ salts. The differences from the spin-only moment (3.87 BM) may be due in part to certain second-order spin-orbit coupling effects but, since observed moments are perhaps lower than can be explained by this process alone, probably also to antiferromagnetic interactions.

A complex reported to have the formula $[Os(en - H)_3(en)I_2] \cdot 4H_2O$ is the only other Ru^V or Os^V complex for which there is any evidence. It has a magnetic moment of 1.78 BM and an apparent coordination number of 8. Such a singular compound should perhaps be more thoroughly investigated before complete reliance can be placed on the formula suggested.

30-F-5. Oxo Compounds of Ruthenium(VI), -(VII) and -(VIII) and of Osmium(VI) and -(VIII)

The highest oxidation states of ruthenium and osmium are best known in the tetroxides and oxo anions, and these species provide some of the more unusual as well as useful features of the chemistry. The main compounds or ions are shown in Table 30-F-2.

TABLE 30-F-2

Some Oxo Compounds and Ions of Ru and Os.

VIII	VII	VI
RuO_4	RuO_4^-	RuO_4^{2-}
		$RuO_2Cl_4^{2-}$
OsO_4		$[OsO_2(OH)_4]^{2-}$
OsO_3N^-		$[OsO_2X_4]^{2-}$ [a]
$OsO_4X_2^{2-}$ [a]	$OsOF_5$	$[OsO_2(OH)_2X_2]^{2-}$ [a]

[a] $X = Cl, CN, NO_2, 0.5ox$, etc.

The Tetroxides, RuO_4 and OsO_4. These volatile, crystalline solids (Table 30-E-2, page 984) are both very poisonous substances with characteristic, penetrating, ozone-like odors. OsO_4 is a particular hazard, especially to the eyes, on account of its facile reduction by organic matter to a black oxide, a fact utilized in its employment in dilute aqueous solution as a biological stain.

Ruthenium tetroxide is obtained when acid solutions containing ruthenium are heated with powerful oxidizing agents such as HIO_4, MnO_4^-, Ce^{4+}, BrO_3^- or Cl_2; the oxide can be distilled from the solutions or swept out by a gas stream. It may also be obtained by distillation from concentrated perchloric acid solutions or by acidification and oxidation of ruthenate(VI) solutions.

Osmium tetroxide can be obtained by burning osmium or by oxidation of osmium solutions with nitric acid (RuO_4 is *not* obtained by oxidation with nitric acid alone), peroxodisulfate in sulfuric acid or similar agents.

Both compounds have been shown to have a tetrahedral structure. They are extremely soluble in CCl_4 and can be extracted from aqueous solutions by it. RuO_4 is quite soluble, giving golden-yellow solutions, in dilute sulfuric acid; OsO_4 is sparingly soluble. The tetroxides are powerful oxidizing agents. Above $\sim 180°$, RuO_4 can explode, giving RuO_2 and O_2, and it is decomposed slowly by light; OsO_4 is more stable in both respects. OsO_4 finds limited use in organic chemistry since it can add to olefinic double bonds to give a *cis* ester which can be reduced to the *cis* dihydroxo compound by Na_2SO_3:

The oxide can be used catalytically for the same purpose in presence of H_2O_2 or ClO_3^-.

Both RuO_4 and OsO_4 are soluble in alkali hydroxide solutions, but the behavior is quite different. RuO_4 is reduced by hydroxide first to perruthenate(VII), which in turn is further reduced to ruthenate(VI).

$$4RuO_4 + 4OH^- = 4RuO_4^- + 2H_2O + O_2$$
$$4RuO_4^- + 4OH^- = 4RuO_4^{2-} + 2H_2O + O_2$$

On the other hand, OsO_4 gives the ion $[OsO_4(OH)_2]^{2-}$, discussed below. This difference between Ru and Os appears to be due to the ability of the $5d$ metal oxo anion to increase the coordination shell. Similar behavior occurs for ReO_4^-, which in concentrated alkali gives yellow *meso*-perrhenate

$$ReO_4^- + 2OH^- = ReO_4(OH)_2^{3-} = ReO_5^{3-} + H_2O$$

Ruthenates. There is a close similarity between Ru and Mn in the oxo anions, both MO_4^- and MO_4^{2-} being known.

The fusion of Ru or its compounds with alkali in presence of an oxidizing agent gives a green melt containing the *perruthenate* ion, RuO_4^-. Because of the high alkali concentration, on dissolution in water an orange solution of the stable RuO_4^{2-} is usually obtained. However, if RuO_4 is collected in ice-cold $1M$ KOH, black crystals of $KRuO_4$ can be obtained, which are quite stable when dry. Perruthenate solutions, which are a yellowish green, are reduced by hydroxyl ion, and kinetic studies suggest that unstable intermediates with coordinated OH^- are involved—this contrasts with the case of $3d$ metal oxo anions where there is no evidence for addition of OH^-. Since H_2O_2 is also formed in the reduction and RuO_4^- is incompletely reduced to RuO_4^{2-} by H_2O_2, a step such as

$$[RuO_4(OH)_2]^{2-} = RuO_4^{2-} + H_2O_2$$

is plausible.

The deep orange *ruthenate*(VI) ion, RuO_4^{2-}, is moderately stable in alkaline solution. It is paramagnetic with two unpaired electrons in contrast to osmate(VI) and has been shown to be tetrahedral. It may be noted that most ruthenium species in lower oxidation states are specifically oxidized to RuO_4^{2-} in alkaline solution by $KMnO_4$; hypochlorite gives a mixture of the RuO_4^- and RuO_4^{2-} ions while Br_2 gives RuO_4^-. The RuO_4^- ion can be conveniently reduced to RuO_4^{2-} by iodide ion, although further reduction can occur with excess I^-.

Osmates. OsO_4 is moderately soluble in water and its absorption spectrum in the solution is the same as in hexane, indicating that it is still tetrahedral. However, in strong alkaline solution coordination of OH^- ion occurs and a deep red solution is formed

$$OsO_4 + 2OH^- = [OsO_4(OH)_2]^{2-}$$

from which red salts such as $K_2[OsO_4(OH)_2]$ can be isolated. These "perosmates" or "osmenates" have *trans*-hydroxo groups according to infrared evidence.[20] The reduction of such perosmate solutions by alcohol or other agents gives the osmate(VI) ion, which is pink in aqueous solutions but blue in methanol. Its salts, which are also obtained in the alkaline oxidative fusion of the metal, are often formulated $K_2OsO_4 \cdot 2H_2O$, but the ion in solution and in salts has been shown to be the octahedral $[OsO_2(OH)_4]^{2-}$ ion. Unlike the corresponding RuO_4^{2-} ion, it is diamagnetic. The diamagnetism of the ion, its substituted derivatives such as $[OsO_2Cl_4]^{2-}$, and also of $[RuO_2Cl_4]^{2-}$ all of which have *trans* dioxo groups can be explained in terms of ligand field theory. If the z axis passes through the two oxide ligands and the x and y axes through OH, there will be a tetragonal splitting of the e_g level into two singlets, $d_{x^2-y^2}$ and d_{z^2}, whereas the t_{2g} level gives a singlet, d_{xy}, and a doublet, d_{xz}, d_{yz}. The oxide ligands will form Os=O bonds by π overlap mainly with d_{xz} and d_{yz} and will thus destabilize those orbitals, leaving a low-lying d_{xy} orbital which will be occupied by the two electrons leading to diamagnetism.

Other Oxo Anions. When RuO_4 is treated with gaseous HCl and Cl_2, hygroscopic crystals of $(H_3O)_2[RuO_2Cl_4]$ are produced, from which Rb and Cs salts can be obtained. The ion is instantly hydrolyzed by water

$$2Cs_2RuO_2Cl_4 + 2H_2O = RuO_4 + RuO_2 + 4CsCl + 4HCl$$

but there is evidence for other Ru^{VI} species in solution. If RuO_4 in dilute H_2SO_4 is reduced with $NaNO_2$, Na_2SO_3 or $FeSO_4$, green solutions are obtained. These contain Ru^{VI}; although the precise nature of the species is not known, it is probably $[RuO_2(SO_4)_2]^{2-}$. The green ion can be formed by mixing freshly prepared Ru^{IV} solutions, which are an intense brown, with RuO_4 in dilute H_2SO_4

$$Ru^{IV} + Ru^{VIII} = 2Ru^{VI}$$

[20] W. P. Griffith, *J. Chem. Soc.*, **1964**, 245.

The green solutions decompose within a few hours to Ru^{IV} and, like all ruthenium species in the VI, VII and VIII oxidation states, are reduced to Ru^{III} by excess iodide ion.

The osmate ion, $[OsO_2(OH)_4]^{2-}$, can undergo a variety of substitution reactions with various ions such as Cl^-, Br^-, CN^-, $C_2O_4{}^{2-}$, $NO_2{}^-$, etc., to give orange or red crystalline salts, sometimes referred to as osmyl derivatives. They can also be obtained directly from OsO_4 with which, for example, aqueous KCN gives the salt $K_2[OsO_2(CN)_4]$. This particular ion is unaffected by hydrochloric or sulfuric acids, but the other oxo anions are not very stable in aqueous solutions, although they are considerably more stable than the ruthenyl salts mentioned above.

There are also derivatives[21] of the type $[OsO_2(OH)_2X_2]^{2-}$, and the action of alkali fluorides on OsO_4 at low temperature gives red or brown salts of the ion $[OsO_4F_2]^{2-}$ which are soluble, but unstable, in water.

Nitrido Complexes of Osmium(VIII) and Osmium(VI).[22] The osmiamate ion, $[OsO_3N]^-$, was the first example to be prepared of complex ions in which nitrogen is bound to a transition metal by a multiple bond. Similar ions are now known, namely, $[MoO_3N]^{3-}$ and $[ReO_3N]^{2-}$.

When OsO_4 in KOH solution is treated with strong ammonia, the yellowish brown color of $[OsO_4(OH)_2]^{2-}$ changes to yellow and from the solution orange-yellow crystals of $K[OsO_3N]$ can be obtained. This ion has been shown to be distorted tetrahedral (C_{3v}). The infrared spectrum shows three main bands at 1023, 858 and 890 cm^{-1}, the first of which is displaced on isotopic substitution with ^{15}N, which confirms the assignment as the Os—N stretching frequency; the high value suggests considerable Os—N multiple bond character, and we can formally write this $Os\equiv N$.

Although the osmiamate ion is stable in alkaline solution, it is readily reduced by HCl or HBr, and from the resulting red solutions red crystals of salts such as $K_2[Os^{VI}NCl_5]$ can be obtained. This nitridochloro anion is diamagnetic and presumably has two electrons in a low-lying d level (cf. the osmyl derivatives above). On further reduction with acidified stannous chloride, salts of the ion $[Os^{III}NH_3Cl_5]^{2-}$ can be obtained.

The action of *tert*-butylamine on a petroleum solution of OsO_4 gives yellow crystals of $OsO_3NC(CH_3)_3$ which are soluble in organic solvents; this compound has an Os—N stretching frequency at 1184 cm^{-1}. Some other amines act similarly.

The action of liquid ammonia on OsO_4 gives volatile $OsO_4 \cdot NH_3$ and on dehydration, yellow anhydrous osmiamic acid and a trinuclear complex $Os_3N_7O_9H_{21}$ are obtained.[23]

[21] W. P. Griffith, *J. Chem. Soc.*, **1964**, 3249.

[22] For references see W. P. Griffith, *J. Chem. Soc.*, **1965**, 3694.

[23] G. W. Watt and W. C. McMordie, Jr., *J. Inorg. Nucl. Chem.*, **27**, 2013 (1965).

Addition Compounds of RuO$_4$ and OsO$_4$. The interaction of various donor ligands with both tetroxides has given black hygroscopic solids such as RuO_4PF_3, $(RuO_4)_2PF_3$ and $RuO_4(NO)_2$. The structures of these adducts are unknown.

Oxochlorides. The interaction of osmium with oxygen and chlorine at 400° gives brown needle crystals of what is believed to be $OsOCl_4$. If the solid is dissolved in concentrated hydrochloric acid and CsCl added to the deep green solution, a salt which may be of the ion $OsOCl_6^{2-}$ is obtained. Re-crystallization of the latter from $2N$ HCl, in which it gives an orange solution, provides $Cs_2OsO_2Cl_4$ as a buff solid.

The interaction of Os with Cl_2 and air at 650–700° gives a readily hydrolyzed compound, presumably $Cl_4OsOOsCl_4$.[24] Oxochlorides Ru_2OCl_4, Ru_2OCl_5 and Ru_2OCl_6 have been made by chlorination of dried commercial "$RuCl_3$ (aq)."[25]

30-G. RHODIUM AND IRIDIUM

Rhodium and iridium differ from the preceding elements in not forming oxo anions or high valent oxides. Their chemistry centers mainly around the valence states I and III for rhodium, and I, III and IV for iridium. Valence states higher than IV are limited to the hexafluorides and to salts of the IrF_6^- ion.

Rhodium and iridium have a much greater tendency to form cationic complexes than do the heavy elements of the preceding groups and rhodium-(III) resembles cobalt(III) in the existence of numerous amine complexes.

For both elements, the I state in square complexes is important, especially with CO, tertiary phosphines and olefins as ligands.

There is no evidence for any stable complexes in the divalent state comparable to the wellknown ones of cobalt(II), such as $[Co(NH_3)_6]^{2+}$ or $[CoX_4]^{2-}$ but Rh^{II} species may be intermediates in reduction reactions.

The oxidation states and stereochemistries are summarized in Table 30-G-1.

30-G-1. Rhodium(IV) and Iridium(IV), d^5, and -(V), d^4

The IV state is of little importance for Rh and only a few complexes are known though doubtless others can be made. The alkali salts $M^I_2[RhF_6]$ are obtained by the action of F_2 or BrF_3 on a stoichiometric mixture of

[24] R. L. Schaaf, *J. Inorg. Nucl. Chem.*, **25**, 903 (1963).
[25] J. M. Fletcher, *et al.*, *Nature*, **199**, 1089 (1963).

TABLE 30-G-1

Oxidation States and Stereochemistries of Rhodium and Iridium

Oxidation state	Coordination number	Geometry	Examples
Rh^{-I}, Ir^{-I}(?)	4	Tetrahedral(?)	$Rh(CO)_4{}^-$
	5?	?	$[Rh(NO)_2Cl]_4$(?)
Rh^0, Ir^0	?	?	$Rh_6(CO)_{16}$, $Ir(NH_3)_5$
Rh^I, Ir^I, d^8	4[a,b]	Planar	$[Rh(CO)_2Cl]_2$, $C_8H_{12}RhCl(AsPh_3)$, $IrClCO(PEt_3)_2$
	5	TBP	$HRh(diphos)_2$, $HIrCO(PPh_3)_3$, $(C_8H_{10})_2RhSnCl_3$
Rh^{II}, Ir^{II}, d^7	?	?	$[Rh_2I_2(CNPh)_8]^{2+}$
	4	Square	$[Rh\{S_2C_2(CN)_2\}_2]^{2-}$
	5	?	$[Rh(dipy)_2Cl]^+$
	5	Cu^{II} acetate struct.	$[Rh(OCOR)_2]_2$
	6	Cu^{II} acetate struct.	$[Ph_3PRh(OCOCH_3)_2]_2$
Rh^{III}, Ir^{III}, d^6	5	TBP	$IrH_3(PR_3)_2$
	6[a,b]	Octahedral	$[Rh(H_2O)_6]^{3+}$, $RhCl_6{}^{3-}$, $IrH_3(PPh_3)_3$, $RhCl_3(PEt_3)_3$, $IrCl_6{}^{3-}$, $[Rh(diars)_2Cl_2]^+$, RhF_3, IrF_3 (ReO_3 type)
Rh^{IV}, Ir^{IV}, d^5	6[b]	Octahedral	K_2RhF_6, $[Ir(C_2O_4)_3]^{2-}$, $IrCl_6{}^{2-}$ IrO_2 (rutile type)
Ir^V, d^4	6	Octahedral	$CsIrF_6$
Rh^{VI}, Ir^{VI}, d^3	6	Octahedral	RhF_6, IrF_6

[a] Most common states for Rh.
[b] Most common states for Ir.

$RhCl_3$ and, say, CsCl. The yellow solids are completely hydrolyzed by contact with water. The magnetic moments of ~ 1.8 BM are consistent with a $t_{2g}{}^5$ configuration.

Dark green Cs_2RhCl_6 is precipitated when Na_3RhCl_6 solutions are oxidized by Ce^{IV} in presence of CsCl; the salt is stable when dry.

Oxidation of Rh^{III} sulfate solutions with sodium bismuthate or O_3 produces red solutions of uncertain nature; higher oxidation states of V and VI have been postulated in reactions of Rh^{III} with hypobromite.[1]

The Ir^{IV} state is quite common, the most important complexes being $IrX_6{}^{2-}$, X = F, Cl, Br. A tris oxalato complex, $K_2[Irox_3] \cdot 4H_2O$, is also known and is shown to be kinetically inert by resolution into its optical isomers.

The $IrF_6{}^{2-}$ salts have been made only by indirect methods because F_2 or other strong fluorinating agents readily give Ir^V complexes. When $K[IrF_6]$ is treated with water, the $IrF_6{}^{2-}$ ion, which is apparently kinetically inert to water, acids and bases, is produced by reduction. The salts can also be made in dry ways.

[1] F. Pantani, *Talanta*, **9**, 15 (1962) and references therein.

Hexachloroiridates(IV) can be made by chlorination of a mixture of iridium powder and an alkali metal chloride, or, in solution, by adding the alkali metal chloride to a suspension of hydrous IrO_2 in aqueous HCl. The sodium salt Na_2IrCl_6 is the usual starting material for the preparation of other Ir complexes.

All of the salts of $[IrCl_6]^{2-}$ are dark red solids which form brownish red solutions fading to yellow on dilution. In general, solubility decreases with increasing cation size: thus $Na_2[IrCl_6]$ is extremely soluble in water, whereas the cesium salt and those of many large organic cations or complex cations (e.g., $[Co(NH_3)_6]^{3+}$) are only slightly soluble and easily isolated. The $[IrCl_6]^{2-}$ ion seems to be kinetically fairly inert; solutions are hydrolyzed only slowly, and in dilute hydrochloric acid the ion seems to be stable indefinitely.

The action of Cl_2 or aqua regia on $(NH_4)_2IrCl_6$ gives a hydrated form of $IrCl_4$, but this loses water and chlorine on heating and cannot be made pure. A cationic complex, $[Ir(H_2O)_3Cl_3]^+$, and also $[Ir(H_2O)_2Cl_4]$, has been identified.[2]

Hexabromoiridates(IV) are isolated from solutions of hydrous Ir^{IV} oxide in hydrobromic acid. The salts are deep blue-black crystals or dark blue powders, and the solutions are bright blue. Their solubilities as a function of cation size show the same trend as do the hexachloro analogs. The $[IrBr_6]^{2-}$ ion is also kinetically inert, but differs from its fluoro and chloro analogs in that its slow decomposition in solution involves not only hydrolysis but also evolution of free halogen. Solutions in dilute hydrobromic acid to which a small quantity of bromine has been added are evidently stable indefinitely.

Octahedrally coordinated Ir^{IV} has a t_{2g}^5 configuration with one unpaired electron. Magnetic susceptibility measurements on hexachloroiridates(IV) have revealed effective magnetic moments in pure compounds of 1.6–1.7 BM. Theory shows that the moment of the isolated $[IrCl_6]^{2-}$ ion should be 1.7–1.8 BM, and, in fact, studies of the variation of susceptibility of $[IrCl_6]^{2-}$ as a function of its concentration in isomorphous, diamagnetic $[PtCl_6]^{2-}$ salts, have shown quite clearly that antiferromagnetic interactions between $[IrCl_6]^{2-}$ ions, occurring by a superexchange mechanism across intervening chloride ions, cause the lowering from the theoretically expected value of the magnetic moment. The magnetic properties of Cs_2RhCl_6 are similar.[2a]

The spectra of the $[IrCl_6]^{2-}$ and $[IrBr_6]^{2-}$ ions have been studied. Their colors are due to the occurrence of moderately strong charge-transfer bands (molar absorbances of ~2500) in the visible region. Weak bands due to

[2] J. C. Chang and C. S. Garner, *Inorg. Chem.*, **4**, 209 (1965).
[2a] I. Feldman, R. S. Nyholm and E. Walton, *J. Chem. Soc.*, **1965**, 4724.

d–d transitions were not observed, and it may be that the orbital overlap in the complexes is sufficient to blur the distinction between these two types of band.

The only *rhodium-* and *iridium(V) complexes* known are the fluoro complexes of the types $M^I[MF_6]$ and $M^{II}[IrF_6]_2$. The Ir complexes are prepared by treating a stoichiometric mixture of $IrBr_3$ and M^ICl or $M^{II}Cl_2$ with bromine trifluoride. They are pink in color and paramagnetic, and they dissolve in water with evolution of oxygen and reduction of iridium, giving the $[IrF_6]^{2-}$ ion. They contain slightly distorted $[IrF_6]^-$ octahedra and would thus be expected to have t_{2g}^4 electron configurations. They have magnetic moments which are ~ 1.25 BM at room temperature and variable with temperature. Despite the presence of two unpaired electrons, an isolated $[IrF_6]^-$ ion would be expected to have a moment of only this magnitude at room temperature (and a marked temperature dependence) because of strong spin-orbit coupling (see page 911) and in addition there may be antiferromagnetic coupling between $[IrF_6]^-$ units in the lattice.

$CsRhF_6$ is obtained by interaction of CsF and RhF_5 in IF_5 solution; the red-brown salt is isomorphous with $CsPtF_6$.[3]

30-G-2. Rhodium(III) and Iridium(III), d^6

A large number of octahedral complexes, cationic, neutral and anionic, are known for both elements, but those of rhodium have been more extensively studied. In contrast to Co^{III} complexes, reduction of Rh^{III} or Ir^{III} does *not* give rise to divalent complexes (except in a few special cases). Thus, depending on the nature of the ligands and on the conditions, reduction may lead to the metal—usually with halogens, water or amine ligands present—or to hydridic species of M^{III} or to M^I when π-bonding ligands are involved.

While being similar to Co^{III} in giving complex anions with CN^- and NO_2^-, Rh and Ir differ in readily giving octahedral complexes with halides, e.g., $[RhCl_5H_2O]^{2-}$ and $[IrCl_6]^{3-}$, and with oxygen ligands such as oxalate, EDTA, etc.

The cationic and neutral complexes of all three elements are generally kinetically inert, but the anionic complexes of Rh^{III} are usually quite labile. By contrast, anionic Ir^{III} complexes are inert and the preparation of such complexes is significantly harder than for the corresponding Rh species.

In their magnetic and spectral properties the Rh^{III} complexes are fairly simple. All of the complexes, and indeed all compounds, of rhodium(III)

---

[3] J. H. Holloway, P. R. Rao and N. Bartlett, *Chem. Comm.*, **1965**, 306.

are diamagnetic. This includes even the $[RhF_6]^{3-}$ ion, of which the cobalt analog constitutes the only example of a high-spin Co^{III}, Rh^{III} or Ir^{III} ion in octahedral coordination. Thus the inherent tendency of the octahedral d^6 configuration to adopt the low-spin t_{2g}^6 arrangement (see page 670), together with the relatively high ligand field strengths prevailing in these complexes of tripositive higher transition series ions, as well as the fact that all $4d^n$ and $5d^n$ configurations are more prone to spin pairing than their $3d^n$ analogs, is a combination of factors which evidently leaves no possibility of there being any high-spin octahedral complexes of Rh^{III} or Ir^{III}.

The visible spectra of Rh^{III} complexes have the same explanation as do those of Co^{III} complexes. As illustrated in Figure 30-G-1 for the

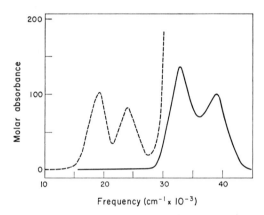

Fig. 30-G-1. The visible spectra of the $[RhCl_6]^{3-}$ (– – – – –) and $[Rh(NH_3)_6]^{3+}$ (———) ions.

$[Rh(NH_3)_6]^{3+}$ and $[RhCl_6]^{3-}$ ions, there are in general two bands toward the blue end of the visible, which, together with any additional absorption in the blue due to charge-transfer transitions (see page 713), are responsible for the characteristic orange, red, yellow or brown colors of rhodium(III) compounds.[4] These bands are assigned as transitions from the $^1A_{1g}$ ground state to the $^1T_{1g}$ and $^1T_{2g}$ upper states just as shown in the energy level diagram for Fe^{II} and Co^{III} (page 856). The spectra of Ir^{III} complexes have a similar interpretation.[4]

The Rhodium Aquo Ion. Unlike cobalt, rhodium gives a well-characterized yellow aquo ion, $[Rh(H_2O)_5]^{3+}$. It is obtained by dissolution of $Rh_2O_3(aq)$ in cold mineral acids, or, as the perchlorate, by repeated evaporation of

[4] H. H. Smidke, *Proc. I.C.C.* 8, Abstr. 7A3 (1964); *Z. Phys. Chem. (Frankfurt)*, **40**, 96 (1964), and references quoted.

$HClO_4$ solutions of $RhCl_3(aq)$. Exchange studies using $H_2{}^{18}O$ confirm the hydration number as 5.9 ± 0.4.[5] The ion is acidic, $pK_a \sim 3.3$, giving $[Rh(H_2O)_5OH]^{2+}$ in solutions less than about $0.1 M$ in acid. The crystalline deliquescent perchlorate is isomorphous with other salts containing octahedral cations, e.g., $[Co(NH_3)_6](ClO_4)_3$. The aquo ion also occurs in alums, $M^IRh(SO_4)_2 \cdot 12H_2O$, and in the yellow sulfate, $Rh_2(SO_4)_3 \cdot 14H_2O$, obtained by vacuum evaporation at $0°$ of solutions of $Rh_2O_3(aq)$ in H_2SO_4. A red sulfate, $Rh_2(SO_4)_3 \cdot 6H_2O$, obtained by evaporation of the yellow solutions at $100°$, gives no precipitate with Ba^{2+} ion and is presumably a sulfato complex.

An aquoiridium(III) ion does not appear to be established. A sulfite, $Ir_2(SO_3)_3 \cdot 6H_2O$, crystallizes from solutions of $Ir_2O_3(aq)$ in water saturated with SO_2 and a sulfate may be isolated from sulfuric acid solutions of the hydrous oxide with exclusion of air but the structures of these compounds are unknown.

The Rh^{III}–Cl System. The species formed when $[Rh(H_2O)_6]^{3+}$ is heated with dilute hydrochloric acid have been studied by ion-exchange and the yellow cations, $[RhCl(H_2O)_5]^{2+}$, and $[RhCl_2(H_2O)_4]^+$, and their formation constants and spectra characterized.[6] Additional acid gives *cis* and *trans* isomers of red $[RhCl_3(H_2O)_3]$, the red anions, $[RhCl_4(H_2O)_2]^-$ and $[RhCl_5(H_2O)]^{2-}$, and finally, the rose-pink $[RhCl_6]^{3-}$.

One of the most important of Rh^{III} compounds and the usual starting material for the preparation of rhodium complexes (see Figures 30-G-2 and 3) is the dark red, crystalline deliquescent trichloride, $RhCl_3 \cdot nH_2O$; n is usually 3 or 4. This is obtained by dissolving hydrous Rh_2O_3 in aqueous hydrochloric acid and evaporating the hot solutions. It is very soluble in water and alcohols giving red-brown solutions. The precise nature of the hydrate, or of its aqueous solutions, is uncertain. The fresh solutions do not give a precipitate with Ag^+ ion and presumably contain one or more neutral, probably polynuclear, chloro complexes. On boiling, the solution gives $[Rh(H_2O)_6]^{3+}$, and on heating with excess HCl, $[RhCl_6]^{3-}$. Hexachlororhodates are usually obtained by heating Rh metal and an alkali chloride (plus a little carbon) in chlorine, extracting the melt with water and crystallizing.

Rhodium trichloride has been used to catalyze a number of organic reactions, although the precise way in which it acts is uncertain. Thus in aqueous emulsions it induces the stereoregular polymerization of butadiene to all *trans*-polybutadiene.[7] It also catalyzes the isomerization of various

[5] W. Plumb and G. M. Harris, *Inorg. Chem.*, **3**, 542 (1964).

[6] W. C. Wolsey, C. A. Reynolds and J. Kleinberg, *Inorg. Chem.*, **2**, 463 (1963).

[7] P. Teyssié and R. Dauby, *J. Polymer Sci.*, Part B., *Polymer Letters*, **2**, 413 (1964) and quoted references.

olefins in ethanolic solutions (p. 792). Its reduction in presence of olefins and other π-bonding ligands is discussed later.

There are other poorly understood halogeno complexes, especially bromides, such as M^IRhX_4, $M^I_2RhX_5$, $M^I_4RhX_7$, $M^I_3Rh_2X_9$; these are doubtless polymeric with halogen bridges and possibly, metal–metal bonds. Salts of the RhF_6^{3-} ion have little resemblance to those of other halogeno ions and are hydrolyzed by water. They can be made by fusing $K_3[Rh(NO_2)_6]$ with KHF_2.

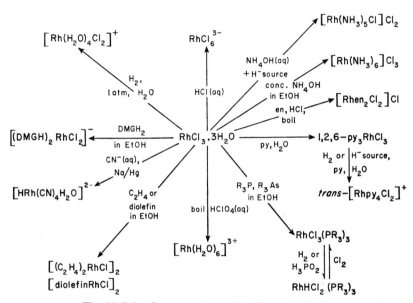

Fig. 30-G-2. Some reactions of rhodium trichloride.

Several dark green, hydrated Ir^{III} halides are obtained by dissolution of $Ir_2O_3(aq)$ in the appropriate acid. The nature of several species formed by aquation of $[IrCl_6]^{3-}$, e.g., $[Ir(H_2O)Cl_5]^{2-}$, $[Ir(H_2O)_2Cl_4]^-$, $[Ir(H_2O)_3Cl_3]$, have been studied in great detail.[2]

Cationic Complexes. Both Rh and Ir give cobalt-like ammines of the types $[ML_6]^{3+}$, $[ML_5X]^{2+}$, $[ML_4X_2]^+$, of which $[Rh(NH_3)_5Cl]Cl_2$ is a typical example. The salts are made in various ways, but usually by the interaction of aqueous solutions of $RhCl_3(aq)$ with the ligand.[8]

The formation of complex ions from $RhCl_3(aq)$, $[Rh(H_2O)Cl_5]^{2-}$ or $[RhCl_6]^{3-}$, is often catalyzed by the addition of reducing agents which can

[8] See e.g., (a) S. A. Johnson and F. Basolo, *Inorg. Chem.* **1**, 925 (1962); (b) R. D. Gillard and G. Wilkinson, *J. Chem. Soc.*, **1964**, 1224; (c) G. C. Kulasingam and W. R. McWhinnie, *J. Chem. Soc.*, **1965**, 7145.

furnish hydride ions; ligands such as ethylenediamine may also themselves act in this way. The effect of ethanol was discovered by Delépine long before the general nature of such catalysis was recognized.[9,10,11] It now appears that many rhodium complexes have been made only because ethanol was used as a solvent. One example of the catalysis is the interaction of pyridine, which with $RhCl_3(aq)$ gives mainly $Rhpy_3Cl_3$,[8b] or with aqueous $[Rh(H_2O)Cl_5]^{2-}$ gives $[Rhpy_2Cl_4]^-$.[9] On addition of alcohol, hydrazine, BH_4^- or other reducing substances—even molecular hydrogen at 25° and ≤ 1 atm[12]—conversion to $trans$-$[Rhpy_4Cl_2]^+$ rapidly occurs.

Similar catalysis of the formation of Ir^{III} complexes occurs, but the rates are still slow compared to rhodium systems. Thus to convert $Na_2Ir^{IV}Cl_6$ into $1,2,3$-py_3IrCl_3 and $trans$-$[Irpy_4Cl_2]Cl$ a bomb reaction is normally used. Quite rapid conversions are obtained[13] as follows:

$$Na_2IrCl_6 \xrightarrow[\text{boil 30 min.}]{NaH_2PO_2(aq)+py} 1,2,3\text{-}py_3IrCl_3 \xrightarrow{6\ hr} [Irpy_4Cl_2]Cl$$

$$H_2IrCl_6 \xrightarrow[\substack{2-\text{methoxyethanol,} \\ \text{boil 10 min.}}]{HCl\ in} IrCl_6^{3-} \xrightarrow[1\ hr]{+py.\ boil} 1,2,6\text{-}py_3IrCl_3$$

It is not fully established whether Rh^I species are intermediate in the catalyses[9] or whether hydrido species are involved.[10,11,12] The latter explanation is preferred since Rh—H bonds are known to be readily formed, and indeed $Rhpy_3Cl_3$ in solutions under hydrogen pressure gives an Rh—H bond detectable by nmr.[13]

Cationic hydrido species of Rh^{III} with amine ligands can indeed be isolated, and comparable, though less well characterized Ir^{III} complexes exist. Thus the action of aqueous BH_4^- as a source of nucleophilic hydride ion causes rapid displacements such as:

$$cis\text{- or } trans\text{-}[Rhen_2Cl_2]^+ \xrightarrow{H^-} [Rhen_2ClH]^+ \xrightarrow{H^-} [Rhen_2H_2]^+$$

which can be followed by electronic and nmr spectra.[14] The hydrido species are reasonably stable in alkaline solutions, but on acidification, or on heating, decompose giving some metal and Rh^{III} complexes.

Neutral Complexes. The interaction of acetylacetone with hydrous Rh_2O_3 gives the trisacetylacetonate, which has been resolved into d and l forms. It undergoes a variety of electrophilic substitution reactions of the

[9] J. V. Rund, F. Basolo and R. G. Pearson, *Inorg. Chem.*, **3,** 659 (1964).

[10] R. D. Gillard, J. A. Osborn and G. Wilkinson, *J. Chem. Soc.*, **1965,** 1951; 4107.

[11] B. N. Figgis, R. D. Gillard, R. S. Nyholm and G. Wilkinson, *J. Chem. Soc.*, **1964,** 5189.

[12] R. D. Gillard, J. A. Osborn, P. B. Stockwell and G. Wilkinson, *Proc. Chem. Soc.*, **1964,** 284.

[13] J. A. Osborn and G. Wilkinson, unpublished work.

[14] J. A. Osborn, R. D. Gillard and G. Wilkinson, *J. Chem. Soc.*, **1964,** 3168.

coordinated ligand, such as chlorination.[15] The stereochemistry and racemization of the *cis* and *trans* isomers of the unsymmetrical trifluoro-acetylacetonate have been studied by nmr; the compound is extremely stable to isomerization.[16]

Rhodium trichloride gives not only the neutral $Rhpy_3Cl_3$ noted above, but also, with various phosphines and arsines, complexes of the types $RhCl_3L_3$, $Rh_2Cl_2L_4$, $Rh_2Cl_6L_3$; the two last named appear to have two and three halogen bridges respectively.[17,18,19] Iridium gives similar complexes, e.g., $IrCl_3(OSMe_2)_3$, and with certain phosphine and arsine ligands, hydrido species of both metals, such as $MHCl_2L_3$, MH_2ClL_3 and MH_3L_3 can be obtained,[20] in some cases from the corresponding square M^I complex; the rhodium species are less stable and less well characterized than Ir species. Carbonyl complexes[17,20] of the type $IrX_3(CO)L_2$ can also be made, e.g., by action of CO on IrX_3L_3.

Octahedral Rh^{III} and Ir^{III} complexes with CO, PR_3, H, CH_3 and other ligands are also obtained by oxidation of the appropriate square M^I complex by the general reaction:

$$(30\text{-}G\text{-}1)$$

Some examples of these reactions are discussed later.

Finally we note that rhodium complexes $Rh(R_3P)_3Cl_3$ can act as catalysts for the homogeneous hydrogenation of olefins and acetylenes (see page 791), while $IrCl_3(OSMe_2)_3$ catalyzes hydrogen transfer from alcohols to ketones (cf. the Meerwein–Pondorff reduction).[21]

30-G-3. Rhodium(II) and Iridium(II), d^7

Only a few types of these compounds are known and some are certainly special cases. Early reports of rhodium(II) species with a variety of amine ligands have been shown to be incorrect, the products actually obtained

[15] J. P. Collman, R. P. Blair, R. L. Marshall and L. Slade, *Inorg. Chem.* **2**, 576 (1963).
[16] R. C. Fay and T. S. Piper, *Inorg. Chem.*, **3**, 348 (1964).
[17] J. Chatt, N. P. Johnson and B. L. Shaw, *J. Chem. Soc.*, **1964**, 1625, 2508.
[18] J. W. Collier and F. G. Mann, *J. Chem. Soc.*, **1964**, 1815.
[19] R. G. Hayter, *Inorg. Chem.*, **3**, 301 (1964).
[20] L. Malatesta, *et al.*, *J. Chem. Soc.*, **1964**, 961; **1965**, 6974; J. Chatt, R. S. Coffey and B. L. Shaw, *J. Chem. Soc.*, **1965**, 7390; R. C. Taylor, J. F. Young and G. Wilkinson, *Inorg. Chem.*, **5**, 26 (1965).
[21] Y. M. Y. Haddad, H. B. Henbest, Mrs. J. Husbands and T. R. B. Mitchell, *Proc. Chem. Soc.*, **1964**, 371.

being either hydrido species or, more commonly, Rh^{III} complexes made by reductive catalysis[10,11] (see page 1015-1016).

The interaction of $Rh_2O_3(aq)$ with acetic acid or other alkyl carboxylic acids leads to the formation of deep green compounds $[Rh(OCOR)_2]_2$ which have been shown by Russian workers to have the chromium(II) acetate structure (page 821). These compounds readily add water, alcohols or other donors at the end positions to give complexes such as $[Ph_3PRh(OCOR)_2]_2$. With π-bonding ligands the adducts are orange or red, but with oxygen donors, green or blue. Other carboxylates, e.g., the trifluoroacetate, can be made by exchange. All of the compounds[22] are diamagnetic so that here, as in other similar bridged carboxylates, there is a metal–metal interaction. Whether this is best regarded as an antiferromagnetic coupling of spins or a genuine metal–metal bond is uncertain.

The interaction of the acetate with sodium maleonitrile dithiolate and a quaternary ammonium hydroxide in methanol gives a red solution and a green salt containing the anion[23] 30-G-I.

(30-G-I)

This is the only square paramagnetic Rh^{II} species; because of the special nature of the ligand however (see page 756) the significance of the oxidation number of the metal is somewhat uncertain.

There are also some ill-characterized isonitrile derivatives which may contain Rh^{II}. Also, the reduction of dipyridyl and 1,10-phenanthroline complexes of Rh^{III} by BH_4^-, Na/Hg or Zn/Hg gives colored complexes which may contain Rh^{II} but perhaps more likely Rh^I; they are known not to be hydrides.

Finally, kinetic studies[24] of the reduction of $[(NH_3)_5RhX]^{2+}$ and its Ir^{III} analog by Cr^{2+} provide some evidence for the existence of a Rh^{II} ammine in solutions but the species was not conclusively identified.

Divalent iridium has been reported to occur in some complexes including ammines $[Ir(NH_3)_4]Cl_2$ and a sulfito complex, $Na_6[Ir(SO_3)_4] \cdot 10H_2O$, but none of these are unequivocally established.

[22] S. A. Johnson, H. R. Hunt and H. M. Neumann, *Inorg. Chem.*, **2**, 961 (1963); T. A. Stephenson, *et. al.*, *J. Chem. Soc.*, **1965**, 3632.

[23] E. Billig, *et. al.*, *J. Amer. Chem. Soc.*, **86**, 926 (1964); A. Davison, *et. al.*, *J. Amer. Chem. Soc.*, **86**, 4580 (1964).

[24] G. T. Takaki and R. T. M. Fraser, *Proc. Cnem. Soc.*, **1964**, 116.

30-G-4. Rhodium(I) and Iridium(I), d^8

There is an extensive chemistry for both elements in the I state but it is almost exclusively one involving π-bonding ligands (see also Chapters 27 and 28).

Planar Complexes. Rhodium(I) complexes are generally obtained when solutions of $RhCl_3$(aq) in ethanol or other alcoholic solutions are heated with π-acid ligands; the alcohol, or in some cases the ligand itself, acts as the reducing agent although more rapid reaction may occur when additional reducing agents are used. For example the halogen-bridged cycloocta-1,5-diene complex $[C_8H_{12}RhCl]_2$ can be made by direct interaction in ethanol over a period of hours, or at once by addition of stannous chloride. Some preparations and reactions of Rh^I complexes are shown in Figure 30-G-3.

One of the most important compounds and a convenient source material is the carbonyl chloride, $[Rh(CO)_2Cl]_2$. It is most easily obtained by passing CO over hydrated $RhCl_3$ at about $100°$, when it sublimes as red needles. It is diamagnetic and in solution it is dimeric with a dipole moment of 1.65 D. These data, together with certain characteristics of the infrared spectrum, led to the postulation of a chlorine-bridged structure with planar coordination about each Rh^I and a small dihedral angle along the Cl—Cl line. Such a structure has been proved by X-ray study to occur in the solid compound as shown in Figure 30-G-4. The cause of the dihedral angle is not known, but there may be some direct interaction between electrons in rhodium orbitals perpendicular to the planes of coordination. The carbonyl chloride and similar bridged complexes are cleaved[25] by donor ligands, or in some cases, also by Cl^- ion, e.g.,

$$[Rh(CO)_2Cl]_2 + 2Cl^- = 2[Rh(CO)_2Cl_2]^-$$
$$[C_8H_{12}RhCl]_2 + 2Ph_3P = 2C_8H_{12}RhClPPh_3$$

Rhodium trichloride hydrate may also be reduced in presence of tertiary phosphines by aldehydes, hot diethylene glycol or by CO in alcohols to give complexes of the type $Rh(R_3P)_2COCl$; Ir^{III} or Ir^{IV} halides or halide complexes behave similarly.[26] The carbon monoxide groups in $Rh(Ph_3P)COCl$ undergo rapid exchange despite the thermodynamic stability of the complex.[27] The complex is a very effective catalyst for the hydroformylation of olefins and acetylenes (page 790).

It is a general reaction of the neutral square complexes of Rh^I and Ir^I to add molecules such as HCl, CH_3I or H_2 to give octahedral complexes,[26]

[25] D. Lawson and G. Wilkinson, *J. Chem. Soc.*, **1965**, 1900; L. M. Vallarino, *Inorg. Chem.*, **4**, 161 (1965).

[26] See, e.g., R. F. Heck, *J. Amer. Chem. Soc.*, **86**, 2796 (1964); L. Vaska and J. W. DiLuzio, *J. Amer. Chem. Soc.*, **84**, 679 (1962).

[27] A. T. Brault, E. M. Thorsteinson and F. Basolo, *Inorg. Chem.*, **3**, 770 (1964).

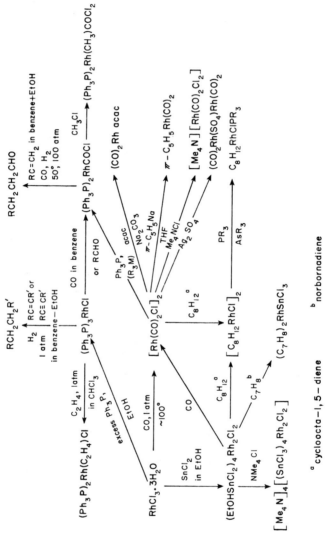

Fig. 30-G-3. Some preparations and reactions of rhodium(I) complexes.

^{a} cyclooocta-1, 5 - diene ^{b} norbornadiene

(eq. 30-G-1, page 1017). This addition fails in some cases, e.g., $RhCO(PPh_3)_2Cl$ does not add H_2 molecules, and the rhodium adducts are often unstable; the iridium(III) complexes so formed have been better characterized.

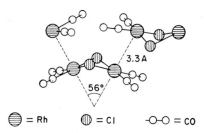

= Rh   = Cl   -O-O = CO

Fig. 30-G-4. The structure of crystalline $[Rh(CO)_2Cl]_2$.

Among the most interesting additions is the reversible uptake of molecular H_2, O_2 and SO_2 to give crystalline complexes,[28] e.g.,

$$IrClCO(PPh_3)_2 \underset{\text{vacuum}}{\overset{\text{O}_2 \text{ in benzene}}{\rightleftarrows}} O_2IrClCO(PPh_3)_2.$$

X-ray study[29] of the oxygen complex shows that the CO and Cl are randomly distributed, suggesting attack of O_2 from either side of the plane and that the two oxygen atoms occupy *cis* positions of the octahedron. The O—O distance is 1.30 A, i.e., it is characteristic of O_2^- (1.28 A) rather than O_2^{2-} (1.49 A) and the Ir—O distances are the same suggesting symmetrical bonding.

Another unusual case involves the formation of Ir—Hg bonds[30] by addition as in equation 30-G-2

(30-G-2)

The corresponding Rh^I complex is not oxidized by $HgCl_2$, but Rh—Hg bonds can be obtained by action of $HgCl_2$ on Rh—H bonds.[30]

[28] L. Vaska, *Science*, **140**, 800 (1963).
[29] S. J. LaPlaca and J. A. Ibers, *J. Amer. Chem. Soc.*, **87**, 258 (1965).
[30] R. S. Nyholm and K. Vrieze, *J. Chem. Soc.*, **1965**, 5331, 5337.

The interaction of Rh^{III} chloride solutions in water or ethanol with stannous chloride gives a deep red complex, which on addition of Me_4NCl, can be isolated as a crystalline salt. The salt has been shown to contain the ion 30-G-II, where $SnCl_3^-$ is acting as a donor ligand.[31] The ethanol

$$\left[\begin{array}{ccc} Cl_3Sn & \quad Cl & \quad SnCl_3 \\ & \diagdown\;\diagup\;\;\diagdown\;\diagup & \\ & Rh\qquad Rh & \\ & \diagup\;\diagdown\;\;\diagup\;\diagdown & \\ Cl_3Sn & \quad Cl & \quad SnCl_3 \end{array}\right]^{4-}$$

(30-G-II)

solutions are believed to contain a comparable complex with coordinated $SnCl_2(EtOH)$ groups. Addition of chelating diolefins to the solutions, or interaction with CO, provide useful routes to the complexes of these ligands.

The reduction of ethanolic solutions of $RhCl_3$ by excess triphenyl phosphine gives $(Ph_3P)_3RhCl$ as red crystals. This complex has been found to be an exceedingly effective catalyst for the homogeneous hydrogenation of olefins and acetylenes at 25° and 1 atm pressure (see page 792).

Five-coordinate Complexes. A number of these are known for both metals. Interaction of $Ph_2PCH_2CH_2PPh_2$ with $[Rh(CO)_2Cl]_2$ gives the yellow salt, $[Rh(diphos)_2]^+Cl^-$ which, with $LiAlH_4$ gives an air-sensitive orange hydride,[32] $HRh(diphos)_2$, whose dipole moment (4.35 D) suggests a distorted trigonal bipyramidal structure comparable to $HCo(CO)_4$. Other hydridic five-coordinate species of stoichiometry $HMCO(PPh_3)_3$ have been made by an unusual reaction[33]—the interaction of the square planar complex with hydrazine in ethanol—

$$2IrClCO(Ph_3P)_2(s) \xrightarrow{\text{N}_2\text{H}_4 \text{ in EtOH}} HIrCO(PPh_3)_3(s) + IrCO(PPh_3)(N_2H_4)(soln)$$
$$+ N_2H_5Cl + N_2$$

X-ray study of $HRhCO(PPh_3)_3$ shows that it has a distorted trigonal bipyramidal structure.[34a] $HRR(PF_3)_4$ and $HIr(PF_3)_4$ are presumably similar.[34b]

Non-hydridic complexes are known so far only where $SnCl_3$ is bound to Rh or Ir together with olefin or phosphine ligands as in $(C_8H_{12})_2IrSnCl_3$ or $(C_7H_8)_2RhSnCl_3$.[31] The former has been shown by X-rays to be five-coordinate.[35]

[31] J. F. Young, R. D. Gillard and G. Wilkinson, *J. Chem. Soc.*, **1964**, 5174.
[32] A. Sacco and R. Ugo, *J. Chem. Soc.*, **1964**, 3274.
[33] S. S. Bath and L. Vaska, *J. Amer. Chem. Soc.*, **85**, 3500 (1963).
[34a] S. J. LaPlaca and J. A. Ibers, *J. Amer. Chem. Soc.*, **85**, 3501 (1963).
[34b] Th. Kruck and W. Lang, *Angew. Chem. (Internat.)*, **4**, 870 (1965).
[35] H. M. Powell, *et. al.*, *Proc. I.C.C.C.* 8, Abs. 1133 (1964).

30-G-5. Iridium(0)

The zero valent state occurs in the carbonyls (page 727) and apparently also in a yellow and diamagnetic substance which approximates to the composition $Ir(NH_3)_5$. It is obtained by reducing a solution of $[(NH_3)_5IrBr]Br_2$ in liquid ammonia with potassium.

30-H. PALLADIUM AND PLATINUM

Palladium and platinum generally have similar chemistries in the II oxidation state. Some of the compounds are also similar to those of nickel(II), e.g., there are the isomorphous salts of the ions $[M(CN)_4]^{2-}$, (M = Ni, Pd, Pt).

Although some Ni^{III} complexes exist, there is no unequivocal evidence for Pd^{III} and Pt^{III} (see, however, page 756). A number of complexes which appear to contain M^{III} according to stoichiometry are now known to contain M^{II} and M^{IV}.

For both Pd and Pt the IV state is readily accessible and numerous compounds, some of great importance, are known.

Some further differences from nickel are: (a) the absence of binary carbonyls; (b) square complexes of Pd^{II} are moderately, and of Pt^{II} very inert, whereas those of Ni^{II} are kinetically labile; and (c) Pd^{II} and Pt^{II} are commonly square and are 5- or 6-coordinate only in special cases, while Ni^{II} is commonly 6-coordinate. The factors favoring square coordination for d^8 ions, especially the heavier ones, have been discussed earlier (page 712). However, there is evidence for axial interactions in a number of cases (see later).

Palladium and platinum have perhaps the greatest propensity among the transition metals for forming bonds to carbon; Pd^{II} readily gives allylic species while Pt^{II} commonly gives olefin complexes. Especially Pt^{IV}, also Pt^{II} and to a lesser extent Pd^{II} give stable σ bonds to carbon in complex compounds.

The oxidation states and stereochemistries are summarized in Table 30-H-1.

30-H-1. Complexes of Palladium(II) and Platinum(II), d^8

General Remarks. The characteristic shape of the predominant complexes of Pd^{II} and Pt^{II} is square. However, there are indications that additional, though weaker, bonds may be formed in the vacant octahedral sites. In solutions, such positions may be occupied by solvent molecules[1] and in catalytic reactions of these metal complexes or in ligand displacement reactions, initial attack presumably occurs in the axial positions.

[1] See S. E. Livingstone and B. Wheelahan, *Austral. J. Chem.*, **17**, 219 (1964).

TABLE 30-H-1

Oxidation States and Stereochemistry of Palladium and Platinum

Oxidation state	Coordination number	Geometry	Examples
Pd^0, Pt^0	?	?	$[Pd(NO)_2Cl_2]_n$, $Pt(NH_3)_5$, $Pten_2$, $Pd(Ph_3P)_3$
	4	Tetrahedral	$Pt(Ph_2PCH_2CH_2PPh_2)_2$, $Pd(PF_3)_4$
Pd^{II}, Pt^{II}, d^8	$4^{a,b}$	Planar	$[PdCl_2]_n$, $[Pd(NH_3)_4]Cl_2$, PdO, PtO, $PtCl_4^{2-}$, $HPtBr(PEt_3)_2$, $[Pd(CN)_4]^{2-}$, PtS, $[Pdpy_2Cl]_2$, PdS, $Pt(PEt_3)_2(C_6F_5)_2$
	5	TBP	$[Pd(diars)_2Cl]^+$, $[Pt(SnCl_3)_5]^{3-}$
	6	Octahedral	PdF_2(rutile type), $[PtNOCl_5]^{2-}$, $Pd(diars)_2I_2$, $Pd(DMGH)_2,^c$
Pd^{IV}, Pt^{IV}, d^6	6^b	Octahedral	$[Pt(en)_2Cl_2]^{2+}$, $PdCl_6^{2-}$, $[Pt(NH_3)_6]^{4+}$, $[Me_3PtCl]_4$.
Pt^V, d^5	?	?	PtF_5
	6	Octahedral	PtF_6^-
Pt^{VI}, d^4	?	?	$PtOF_4$, PtO_3
	6	Octahedral	PtF_6

[a] Most common states for Pd.

[b] Most common states for Pt.

[c] Has planar set of N atoms with weak Pd—Pd bonds completing a distorted octahedron.

There is evidence also of axial interactions in crystalline compounds between stacked square units, as in the dimethylglyoxime complex $Pd(DMGH)_2$. Like its Ni^{II} analog, this has chains of metal atoms, at a distance indicating some bonding, perpendicular to the planes. Unlike $Ni(DMGH)_2$ the palladium complex dissolves in bases,[2] again indicating additional coordination

$$Pd(DMGH)_2 + OH^- = [Pd(DMGH)_2OH]^-$$

The platinum complex, $Pt(DMGH)_2$, has a different structure where there is weak intermolecular interaction between each Pt atom and the oxygen atoms of adjacent $Pt(DMGH)_2$ units.

There also is increasing evidence that certain atoms of ligands bound to the metal can interact with axial positions. One example is the crystalline complex trans-$PdI_2(PMe_2Ph)_2$, (30-H-I), in which the α-hydrogen of the phenyl groups of the coordinated phosphines occupy axial positions, the trans axial position being occupied by an iodine of an adjacent molecule.[3] A distorted quasi 7-coordinate complex results.

Evidence of interaction of ligand atoms with nonbonding electron density comes from anomalous N—H stretching and deformation frequencies in complexes such as $[Pt(NH_3)_2Cl_2]$, where a type of hydrogen

[2] K. Burger and D. Dyrssen, Acta. Chem. Scand., **17**, 1489 (1963).

[3] N. A. Bailey, J. M. Jenkins, R. Mason and B. L. Shaw, Chem. Comm., **1965**, 296; cf. also the quasi-octahedral complex $RuCl_2(PPh_3)_3$ on page 993.

(30-H-I)

bonding interaction between H and filled d_{xy} or d_{xz} orbitals of the metal is postulated;[4a] palladium complexes do not show this effect, probably due to the relatively smaller spatial extension of the $4d$ orbitals. Similar types of interaction have been found in cyclopentadiene and cyclohexadienyl complexes of various transition metal complexes (see page 771).

We finally note another case where the groups on a ligand—the ethyl groups in the complex $[Pd(Et_4dien)Cl]^+$—block off the axial positions of the plane to give a quasi-octahedral complex. This is evidently the reason for the fact that with several reagents the ion reacts with half-lives of about 5 min at $25°$, where corresponding reactions with unsubstituted $[Pd(dien)Cl]^+$ are exceedingly rapid.[4b]

Normal octahedral complexes of Pd^{II} and Pt^{II} are quite rare and several cases which could have been examples have later been shown not to be so. Thus the complex obtained by ammonolysis of $Pt(MeCN)_2Cl_2$ and formulated $Pt(NH_3)_4(MeCN)_2Cl_2 \cdot H_2O$ actually contains the planar ion[5] *trans*-$[Pt(NH_3)_2\{HN{=}C(Me)NH_2\}_2]^{2+}$. In the acetylacetonates, $K[PtClacac_2]$ and $Na_2[PtCl_2acac_2] \cdot 5H_2O$, there is a unidentate acetylacetonate bound through the γ-carbon atom in the former, and two unidentate groups bound either through oxygen or carbon or a combination of both, in the latter. The coordination is again square.[6]

The possibility of 5-coordinate transition states of Pd^{II} and Pt^{II} has been discussed (page 174). A few crystalline compounds having 5-coordination are known (see later) and it is quite possible that more will be found.

As a general rule Pd^{II} complexes are somewhat less stable in both the

[4a] K. Nakamoto, *et al.*, *Inorg. Chem.*, **4**, 36 (1965) and references therein.
[4b] W. H. Baddley and F. Basolo, *J. Amer. Chem. Soc.*, **86**, 2075 (1964).
[5] N. C. Stephenson, *J. Inorg. Nucl. Chem.*, **24**, 801 (1962).
[6] R. A. D. Wentworth and C. H. Brubaker, Jr., *Inorg. Chem.*, **3**, 1472 (1964); J. Lewis, R. F. Long and C. Oldham, *J. Chem. Soc.*, **1965**, 6740.

33—A.I.C.

thermodynamic and kinetic sense than their Pt^{II} analogs, but otherwise the two series of complexes are usually similar. The kinetic inertness of the Pt^{II} (and also Pt^{IV}) complexes has allowed them to play a very important role in the development of coordination chemistry. Many studies of geometrical isomerism and reaction mechanisms have had a profound influence on our understanding of complex compounds. The inertness is shown, *inter alia*, by the fact that Pt^{II} complexes can be converted to Pt^{IV} complexes with retention of configuration, by oxidation with a variety of agents:

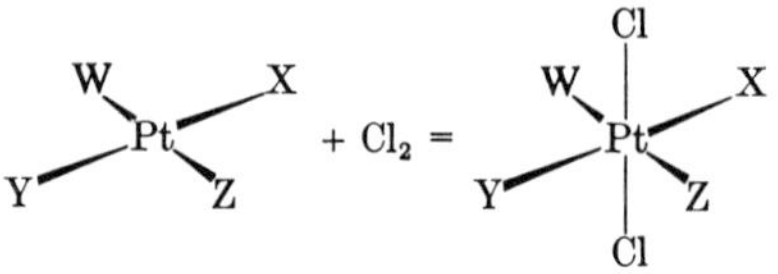

As with Rh^{I} and Ir^{I}, d^8, square complexes, molecules such as HCl or CH_3I can add across the plane (cf. page 1017).

All of the possible types of *mononuclear complexes*, namely, $[ML_4]^{2+}$, $[ML_3X]^+$, *cis-* and *trans-*$[ML_2X_2]$, $[MLX_3]^-$ and $[MX_4]^{2-}$, where M represents Pd^{II} or Pt^{II}, L represents a neutral ligand and X a uninegative acido group, are known as well as a number of internal salt type of bis-chelates with ligands such as β-diketones, dialkylglyoximes, salicylaldox-imines, etc. As a general rule, Pd^{II} and Pt^{II} show a great preference for nitrogen (in aliphatic amines and in NO_2), halogens, cyanide and heavy donor atoms, such as phosphorus, arsenic, sulfur and selenium, and relatively small affinity for oxygen and fluorine. The strong binding of the heavy atom donors is due in great measure to the formation of metal–ligand π bonds by overlap of filled $d\pi$ orbitals (d_{xz}, d_{xy} and d_{yz}) on the metal with empty $d\pi$ orbitals in the valence shells of the heavy atoms. This π bonding has already been discussed and illustrated in connection with theories of the *trans* effect on page 175. Cyanide ions, nitro groups and carbon monoxide are also bound in a manner involving π bonding which results in these cases from overlap of filled metal $d\pi$ orbitals with empty $p\pi$ antibonding molecular orbitals of these ligands.

The importance of π bonding in R_3P complexes of Pt is clearly shown by the Pt—P spin coupling constants determined from measurement[7] of ^{31}P and ^{195}Pt nuclear resonances (Fig. 30-H-1). For $Pt(R_3P)_2X_2$, the Pt—P $d\pi$–$d\pi$ bonding should be stronger in the *cis* isomer where the P atoms each have access to one out-of-plane $d\pi$ orbital (d_{xz}, d_{yz}) while sharing the in-plane $d\pi$ orbital (d_{xy}), whereas in the *trans* isomer, one of the out-of-plane orbitals is available to neither while they must share the other one.

[7] A. Pidcock, R. E. Richards and L. M. Venanzi, *Proc. Chem. Soc.*, **1962**, 184.

The value of J_{Pt-P} is seen to increase in just this way. Moreover, the cis–trans difference should be, and is, largest when the anion X^- has the lowest π-bonding capacity. Convincing evidence that the J_{Pt-P} values do measure π, rather than σ bonding comes from the comparison of cis-$[Pt\{(n\text{-}C_4H_9)_3P\}_2Cl_2]$ with cis-$[Pt\{(EtO)_3P\}_2Cl_2]$. The phosphite is a poorer σ donor than the phosphine, but a better π acceptor.

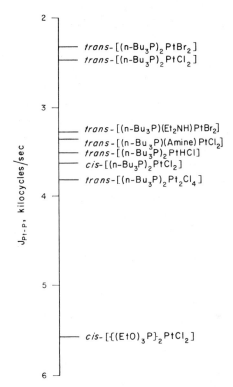

Fig. 30-H-1. ^{31}P—^{195}Pt nuclear spin coupling constants in some platinum phosphine complexes.

The evidence from coupling constants for these complexes is also in accord with chemical stabilities shown by the isomerization:

$$\text{trans-phosphite complex} \xrightarrow{\text{boil CHCl}_3} \text{cis-complex}$$

$$\text{trans-phosphine complex (95\%)} \underset{\text{benzene}}{\rightleftharpoons} \text{cis-complex (5\%)}$$

It is to be emphasized however that isomerization reactions alone are not conclusive because of the unknown magnitude of differences in solvation energies for any given pair of isomers. Relative stabilities are governed by solvation entropy effects: thus *trans* isomers which have negligible dipole moments are less polar and less solvated and hence less stable. Indeed the above comparison of reactions is actually a questionable one since the polar *cis* isomer may be favored more by the polar $CHCl_3$ than by the non-polar C_6H_6. In general therefore it is hazardous to draw any conclusions regarding π bonding from relative stabilities of *cis* and *trans* isomers. In addition to thermal isomerization, photo-isomerization can also occur, but here triplet states may be the intermediates rather than solvated or 5-coordinate intermediates.[8]

Other studies on *cis* and *trans* isomers of the type PtL_2X_2 involve measurement of stretching frequencies of the Pt—X bond in the far infrared as a function of the ligand, L. There is a rough inverse relationship between the *trans* directing influence of L and the stretching frequency. The cyclo-octa-1,5-diene (COD) complex, $CODPtX_2$, has a high Pt—X frequency despite the high *trans* effect of olefins. This agrees with other information that ligands exert their *trans* effects by both inductive and π-bonding mechanisms and that *trans* Pt—X bond weakening is associated mainly with the inductive one (cf. page 177).[9]

A recent elegant way of discriminating between these two electronic effects which contribute to the *trans* effect in nucleophilic substitutions (page 175) involves[10a,b] measurement of the ^{19}F nmr shielding parameters of *m* and *p*-fluorophenylplatinum complexes 30-H-II and -III.

(30-H-II)   (30-H-III)

The *meta* parameters vary with the σ-donor character of X; it is found that they parallel the basicity order $CH_3^- > C_6H_5^- > FC_6H_4^-$ and $CN^- > Cl^- > Br^- > I^-$. The *para* shifts vary with the π-acceptor nature of X since the metal $5d_{xy}$ orbital overlaps not only with the $p\pi$ orbital of the carbon bound to Pt but also with X. The results confirm other indications that CH_3 is a non-π-bonding ligand, that aryl ligands form substantial π bonds to Pt, and that halides may be weak π donors. Hence two types of ligand produce *trans* activation: (a) strong *donor* ligands such as Me or Ph which weaken the *trans* metal–ligand bond by polarization of the Pt atom. Presumably H^- is in this category. (b) Strong π-acceptor

[8] V. Balzani, *et. al.*, *Inorg. Chem.*, **4**, 1243 (1965).

[9] D. M. Adams, J. Chatt, J. Gerratt and A. D. Westland, *J. Chem. Soc.*, **1964**, 734.

[10a] G. W. Parshall, *J. Amer. Chem. Soc.*, **86**, 5367 (1964).

ligands, which can facilitate nucleophilic substitution in *trans* position by stabilizing the transition state during the substitution reaction. A combination of these effects accounts for the high *trans* position of ligands such as CN^- and R_3P which are both σ donors and π acceptors.

Finally, we note that there is a correlation between the *trans* effect of a ligand, the values of the Pt–H stretching frequencies and the position of the nmr line of the *trans* hydrogen bound to Pt in complexes of the type *trans*-$PtXH(PR_3)_2$ as shown in Table 30-H-2. It is of interest that for the

TABLE 30-H-2

Correlation of Spectroscopic Data with *trans* Effects in *trans*-$PtXH(PEt_3)_2$[a]

X	X in *trans*-$PtXH(PEt_3)_2$					
	Cl	Br	I	NCS	SnCl$_3$	CN
ν_{Pt-H} cm^{-1}	2183	2178	2156	2112	2105	2041
τ_H	26.8	25.6	22.7	23.0	19.2	17.8

[a] For references and other data, see J. Powell and B. L. Shaw, *J. Chem. Soc.*, **1965**, 3879.

unusual ligand $SnCl_3^-$, whose complexes are discussed later, the ^{19}F nmr method indicates[10b] that it is a weak σ donor and strong π acceptor, while these data confirm its high *trans* effect, comparable to CN^-.

The aquopalladium(II) ion; salts of oxo acids. The only aquo ion is $[Pd(H_2O)_4]^{2+}$, which is obtained when hydrous PdO dissolves in dilute nitric, perchloric or sulfuric acids. Brown deliquescent crystals of salts can be isolated. The dissolution of Pd metal in concentrated nitric acid occurs without gas evolution and nitrite or other complexes may be present in the solution.

When Pd is dissolved in glacial acetic acid containing HNO_3 and the solution boiled, brown crystals of a trimeric acetate $[Pd(OCOCH_3)_2]_3$ can be obtained.[11] The structure is not yet known. The acetate and other carboxylates are cleaved by amines and other ligands to give yellow *trans* complexes, $L_2Pd(OCOR)_2$. Platinous acetate, also a trimer, is not isomorphous with the Pd compound and is not cleaved by ligands.

A sublimable anhydrous nitrate, $[Pd(NO_3)_2]_n$ has been made by action of $N_2O_5(l)$ on the hydrated nitrate;[12] it appears to have both bridging and non-bridging groups.

Halogeno Anions. Among the most important compounds of Pd^{II}, and especially of Pt^{II}, are the red tetrachlorometallates. These are crystallized from solutions when various Pd^{II} and Pt^{II} compounds are dissolved in

[10b] R. V. Lindsay, Jr., G. W. Parshall and U. G. Stolberg, *J. Amer. Chem. Soc.*, **87**, 658 (1965).
[11] T. E. Stephenson, *et al.*, *J. Chem. Soc.*, **1965**, 3632.
[12] B. O. Field and C. J. Hardy, *J. Chem. Soc.*, **1965**, 4428.

hydrochloric acid and a univalent cation added. The chloroplatinates(II) can be also made by reduction of $PtCl_6{}^{2-}$ salts. Sodium or potassium chloroplatinate(II) are soluble in water and are common source materials for preparing platinum compounds.

Potassium tetrachlorometallates have planar anions stacked one above the other but at a distance too great to justify postulating true chemical bonding: the metal–metal distances are 4.10A in K_2PdCl_4 and 4.13 in K_2PtCl_4. However, there are some salts containing halogeno ions of the general type $[ML_4]^+[M'X_4]^-$ where M' is Pd or Pt, while M may be Pd, Pt or some other element such as Cu. L and X represent a neutral ligand and a halide or pseudohalide ion respectively.

One of the best known examples is Magnus' green salt, $[Pt(NH_3)_4][PtCl_4]$. Others include $[Pd(NH_3)_4][Pd(SCN)_4]$, $[Pt(CH_3NH_2)_4][PtBr_4]$ and $[Cu(NH_3)_4][PtCl_4]$. They generally have the same structure as Magnus' green salt in which anions and cations are stacked up with parallel planes creating chains of metal atoms. It appears that whenever *both* M and M' are Pt^{II} the substance shows a green color (although the constituent cations are colorless or pale yellow and the anions red). Marked dichroism with high absorption of light polarized in the direction of the metal chains has been observed. This has been interpreted in terms of Pt—Pt bonding.[13] If steric hindrance is too great, as in $[Pt(C_2H_5NH_2)_4][PtCl_4]$, a different structure is adopted and the compound has a pink color, which is merely the sum of the colors of its constituent ions.

It is convenient to note here a similar class of pleochroic compounds which have chain-like structures. Examples are $Pt(en)Br_3$ and $Pt(NH_3)_2Br_3$, each of which can be considered as build up of alternating square Pt^{II} complexes and octahedral Pt^{IV} complexes with *trans* Br^- ions from the Pt^{IV} complexes serving as bridges (Fig. 30-H-2). Other compounds which seem likely to be similarly constituted are known. These compounds generally have a quite different appearance than either of the Pt^{II} and Pt^{IV} complexes which may be considered as their constituents. Another complex, Wolfram's red salt, has octahedral $[Pt(EtNH_2)_4Cl_2]^+$ and planar $[Pt(EtNH_2)_4]^{2+}$ ions linked in chains through the chloride ion, together with four other chloride ions in the lattice.

Metal–metal interaction is evident also in various other complexes such as the salts of $[M(CN)_4]^{2-}$ (M = Ni, Pd, Pt) which have stacked anions and in "platinum blue,"[14] an acetamido complex of composition $Pt(MeCONH)_2$ obtained by hydrolysis of $(MeCN)_2PtCl_2$.

[13] J. R. Miller, *J. Chem. Soc.*, **1965**, 713 and references therein; see also G. Basu, G. M. Cook and R. L. Belford, *Inorg. Chem.*, **3**, 1361 (1964); D. S. Martin and C. A. Lenhart, *Inorg. Chem.*, **3**, 1368 (1964).

[14] R. D. Gillard and G. Wilkinson, *J. Chem. Soc.*, **1964**, 2835.

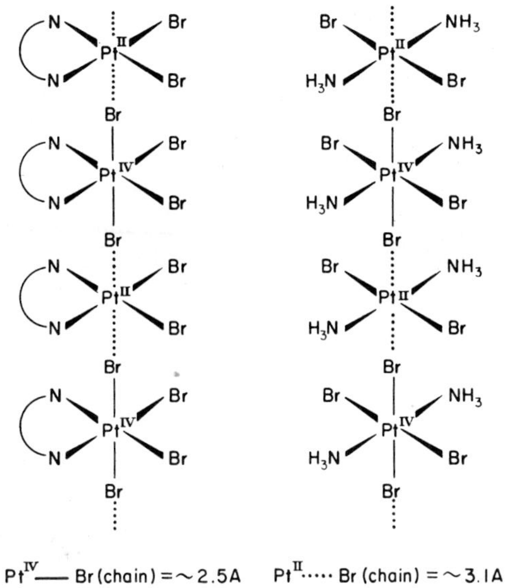

$$Pt^{IV}\text{——}Br\,(chain) = \sim 2.5A \quad Pt^{II}\cdots Br\,(chain) = \sim 3.1A$$

Fig. 30-H-2.   Diagram showing the chains of alternating Pt^{II} and Pt^{IV} atoms with bridging bromide ions in $PtenBr_3$ and $Pt(NH_3)_2Br_3$.

Bridged Binuclear Complexes.   Besides the mononuclear complexes there are a considerable number of the type 30-H-IV where the bridge

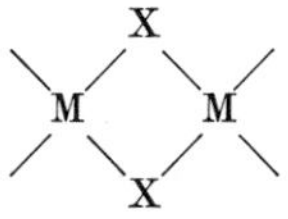

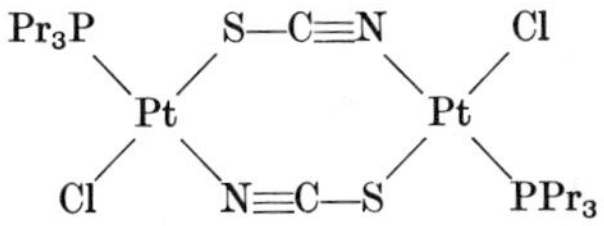

groups, X, are commonly halide ions, RS^- groups or thiocyanate ions. Bridging thiocyanate ions are coordinated by both sulfur and nitrogen as in 30-H-V.   Such bridged binuclear complexes quite generally are subject to attack by other ligands whereby the bridges are split and two mononuclear species are formed, for example,

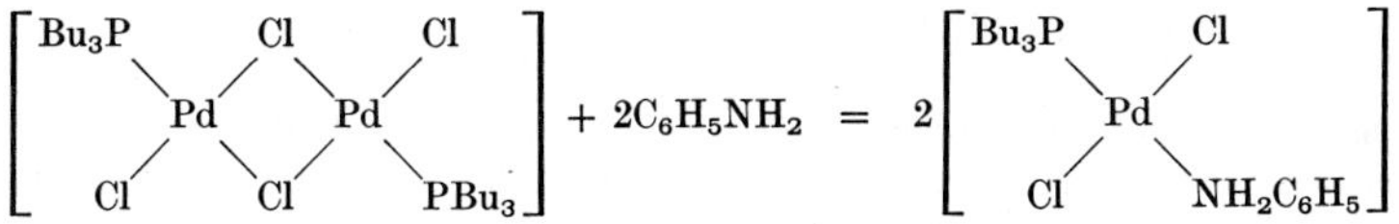

When Cl^- or Br^- are the bridges, the equilibria generally lie toward the mononuclear complexes.   It might be supposed that such bridge-splitting

reactions should give the *trans* mononuclear complexes, and indeed *trans* isomers are probably the initial product of cleavage reactions. However, since the relative stabilities of *cis* and *trans* isomers depend on the particular nature of the ligands involved and on the solvent (see earlier discussion page 1027) mixtures may result. In some cases, such as in the cleavage of phosphine complexes with CO or C_2H_4, *cis* products are obtained[15] presumably because they are thermodynamically more stable than the *trans* isomers due to the high *trans* effect of π-bonding ligands.

There are also complexes in which atoms or groups other than Cl^-, Br^- or CNS^- are bridging. Thus the action on NaOEt on dialkylphosphine or -arsine complexes leads to complexes with R_2P or R_2As bridges[16] (30-H-VI); these can also be made in other ways, as can species with SR bridges.

(30-H-VI)

The four-membered rings formed in such complexes may have some delocalized bonding due to overlap of filled metal d_{xz} and d_{yz} orbitals with similar empty orbitals on the bridge atom.

Hydride and Alkyl Complexes. As with other transition metals, the formation of stable bonds to hydrogen and also to alkyl groups (see also pages 203 and 786) is a feature of platinum(II) chemistry. The first platinum metal hydrides to be discovered were those of the type $Pt(R_3P)_2HX$.[17] The palladium complexes are less stable and have been less well studied, while the analogous Ni^{II} complexes as a class are very unstable and only a few have been characterized. So far no known platinum hydrido complexes have nitrogen ligands but a hydrido cyano complex exists.

[15] J. Chatt, N. P. Johnson and B. L. Shaw, *J. Chem. Soc.*, **1964**, 1662.

[16] R. G. Hayter and S. F. Humiec, *Inorg. Chem.*, **2**, 306 (1963); R. G. Hayter, *Inorg. Chem.*, **3**, 301 (1964); J. Chatt and J. M. Davidson, *J. Chem. Soc.*, **1964**, 2433, and references therein.

[17] J. Chatt and B. L. Shaw, *J. Chem. Soc.*, **1962**, 5075, and references therein; R. Eisenberg and J. A. Ibers, *Inorg. Chem.*, **4**, 773 (1965); see also ref. 28b.

The phosphine and arsine hydrides are obtained from the corresponding halides (the *cis* isomer is usually most reactive) by the action of a variety of hydrogen-transfer agents such as KOH in ethanol, H_2 at 50 atm/95°, $LiAlH_4$ in THF or, most conveniently, 90% aqueous hydrazine, e.g.,

$$cis\text{-}Pt(Et_3P)_2Br_2 \rightarrow trans\text{-}Pt(Et_3P)_2HBr$$

The KOH–alcohol reduction is a general one for the preparation of hydrido or hydridocarbonyl complexes, but detailed mechanistic studies are lacking (see page 998).

The hydrido compounds of Pt^{II} are usually air-stable, colorless, crystalline solids, soluble in organic solvents and sublimable. Their chemical reactions resemble those of other hydrido species. They will also add HCl or CH_3I to give octahedral Pt^{IV} complexes, but these usually readily lose the added molecules.

The *alkyls*, e.g., $Pt(R_3P)_2BrCH_3$, are generally made by standard methods using RMgBr or RLi.[18a] In certain cases the ethyls can be made from the hydride,

$$trans\text{-}Pt(Et_3P)_2ClH + C_2H_4 \underset{heat\ 180°}{\overset{\substack{40\ atm/95° \\ in\ cyclohexane}}{\rightleftharpoons}} Pt(Et_3P)_2ClEt$$

They also undergo carbonylation reactions to give acetyls, the palladium alkyls reacting at atmospheric pressure and temperature while platinum alkyls require 50–100 atm/90°,[18b]

$$Pt(R_3P)_2XR' \xrightarrow{CO} Pt(R_3P)_2X(COR')$$

Platinum complexes have also been made with bonds to germanium rather than to carbon, e.g.,

$$cis\text{- or } trans\text{-}(Et_3P)_2PtCl_2 + 2Ph_3GeLi \rightarrow (Et_3P)_2Pt(GePh_3)_2$$

These have the interesting property of cleaving with molecular hydrogen at room temperature and pressure:[19]

$$Pt(Et_3P)_2(GePh_3)_2 + H_2 = Pt(Et_3P)_2(H)GePh_3 + Ph_3GeH$$

Complexes of Pd^{II} and Pt^{II} with Coordination Numbers 5 and 6. In addition to the cases noted earlier where there are weak interactions above and below the plane in square complexes, authentic cases of higher coordination numbers exist.

For the complexes $[PtCl_5NO]^{2-}$ and $[Pt(NO_3)_3Cl_2NO]^{2-}$ the infrared spectra indicate that NO is formally NO^+ making these Pt^{II} complexes.[20]

[18a] See, e.g., D. T. Rosevear and F. G. A. Stone, *J. Chem. Soc.*, **1965**, 5275.
[18b] G. Booth and J. Chatt, *Proc. Chem. Soc.*, **1961**, 67.
[19] R. J. Cross and F. Glockling, *J. Chem. Soc.*, **1965**, 5422.
[20] R. Levitus and J. Raskovan, *J. Inorg. Nucl. Chem.*, **25**, 1534 (1963).

Complexes with a trigonal bipyramidal structure have been obtained[21] for Pd^{II} and Pt^{II} using tris(o-diphenylarsinophenyl)arsine (QAS) as salts of the type $[Pd(QAS)X]^+X$, which act as 1:1 electrolytes in solution. With bis(o-diphenylarsinophenyl)phenylarsine (TAS) a 5-coordinate complex $PdI_2(TAS)$ is obtained but this dissociates in nitrobenzene to give $[PdI(TAS)]^+$. Distorted square pyramidal Pd and Pt complexes can be made using a specific, rather complicated phosphine.[22] Although complexes of Pd or Pt with diphosphines, diarsines and Ph_3Sb generally appear to dissociate to 5-coordinate species in nonaqueous solvents,[23a] in the crystal the structure of the iodides $MdiarsI_2$ is certainly octahedral with *trans*-iodine atoms.[23b] The complexes $Pt(SbPh_3)_4(NO_3)_2$ show the highest dissociation, but it is not certain whether in $[Pt(SbPh_3)_4NO_3]^+$, the NO_3 is mono- or bidentate.

Although there is some evidence that the action of excess halide ion on chelates such as $[Pdphen_2]^{2+}$ and tetrahalogenopalladates(II) gives additional coordination,[24] the formation of higher coordination numbers by $PtCl_4^{2-}$ appears to be negligible under these conditions.

The only well-established cases of 5-coordinate species with a monodentate ligand are the ions $[Pt(SnCl_3)_5]^{3-}$, $[HPt(SnCl_3)_4]^{3-}$ and $[HPt-(SnCl_3)_2(PEt_3)_2]$.[25] The first of these is isolated as R_4N^+ or R_4P^+ salts from the red solutions obtained by adding excess $SnCl_3^-$ to $PtCl_4^{2-}$ in $3M$ HCl or $SnCl_2$ to ethanolic solutions of Na_2PtCl_4.[26,27] It is likely that the $[Pt(SnCl_3)_5]^{3-}$ ion exists only in the solid state. The nature of the $SnCl_3^--PtCl_4^{2-}$ solutions is exceedingly complex and depends on the concentrations, acidity, time and temperature. There are several displacement reactions involved, the first of which is

$$[PtCl_4]^{2-} + SnCl_3^- \rightleftharpoons [PtCl_3(SnCl_3)]^{2-} + Cl^-$$

The $SnCl_3^-$ ion has a strong *trans* effect (cf. page 1029) so that the *trans*-Cl^- would be expected to be labile, giving *trans*-$[PtCl_2(SnCl_3)_2]^{2-}$ readily. This appears to be so. Both the *trans* isomer and the more thermo-

[21] L. M. Venanzi, et al., J. Chem. Soc., **1965**, 2771, 5210, 5521; Angew. Chem. (Internat.), **3**, 453 (1964).

[22] J. W. Collier, F. G. Mann, D. G. Watson and H. R. Watson, J. Chem. Soc., **1964**, 1803.

[23a] A. D. Westland, J. Chem. Soc., **1965**, 3060.

[23b] N. C. Stephenson, J. Inorg. Nucl. Chem., **24**, 791, 797 (1962); N. C. Stephenson and G. A. Jeffrey, Proc. Chem. Soc., **1963**, 173.

[24] See, e.g., C. M. Harris, S. E. Livingstone and I. H. Rees, J. Chem. Soc., **1959**, 1505.

[25] R. D. Cramer, R. V. Lindsay, Jr., C. T. Prewitt and U. G. Stolberg, J. Amer. Chem. Soc., **87**, 658 (1965).

[26] J. F. Young, R. D. Gillard and G. Wilkinson, J. Chem. Soc., **1964**, 5176.

[27] R. D. Cramer, E. I. Jenner, R. V. Lindsay, Jr., and U. G. Stolberg, J. Amer. Chem. Soc., **85**, 1691 (1963).

dynamically stable yellow *cis* isomer can be present in solutions. At higher tin concentrations other species up to the maximum must exist; the equilibria appear also to be very labile. In acetone solution, there is obtained an anion $[Pt_3Sn_8Cl_{20}]^{4-}$, which is believed to have Pt_3Sn_2 clusters.[28a]

The Pt–Sn complexes catalyze the hydrogenation of ethylene and some other olefinic compounds;[27,28b] this action is doubtless connected with the ready dissociation of the complexes in solution, which leaves vacant sites for coordination of olefin and of hydrogen (cf. also page 791).

30-H-2. Complexes of Palladium(IV) and Platinum(IV)

Pd^{IV} is somewhat more stable in complexes than in simple compounds. Nevertheless, only a few complexes of Pd^{IV} are known, and they are not very common or important. Those known are of two types: $M^I_2[PdX_6]$ (X = F^-, Cl^- or Br^-) and diammines of the type $PdAm_2X_4$ (X = Cl^- or Br^-).

The hexahalo complexes are the more stable, those of chlorine and bromine being about equally easy to prepare and somewhat more stable than the fluoro one. X-ray study has shown that octahedral $[PdBr_6]^{2-}$ ions are present in $Rb_2[PdBr_6]$. The $[PdCl_6]^{2-}$ ion is formed when palladium is dissolved in aqua regia or on saturating a solution of Pd^{II} chloride with chlorine. It is stable to hydrolysis. The $[PdBr_6]^{2-}$ ion is formed when saturated solutions of $M^I_2PdBr_4$ salts are exposed to bromine vapor. Ammonium, K, Rb and Cs salts of both complex ions have been isolated. The $[PdCl_6]^{2-}$ salts are red, and the $[PdBr_6]^{2-}$ salts are black. They lose halogen on mild heating to leave the $M^I_2[PdX_4]$ salts. They react rapidly with concentrated aqueous ammonia evolving nitrogen, and they are decomposed by hot water to generate chlorine or bromine leaving the corresponding Pd^{II} complexes.

The three yellow $M^I_2[PdF_6]$ compounds, in which the alkali metal may be K, Rb or Cs, can be prepared by the action of bromine trifluoride on the $M^I_2[PdCl_4]$ or $M^I_2[PdCl_6]$ compounds or by the action of elemental fluorine on the $M^I_2[PdCl_4]$ compounds. X-ray studies have demonstrated the presence of octahedral $[PdF_6]^{2-}$ ions in the crystals. The $[PdF_6]^{2-}$ ion is immediately hydrolyzed by water with precipitation of hydrous palladium oxide.

The diammine complexes, such as $Pdpy_2Cl_4$, which is obtained as a deep orange crystalline powder when $Pdpy_2Cl_2$ suspended in chloroform is treated with chlorine, are of marginal stability. They lose chlorine or bromine rapidly on standing in moist air. However, complexes such as $Pd(NH_3)_2(NO_2)_2Cl_2$ are stable.

[28a] R. V. Lindsay, Jr., G. W. Parshall and U. G. Stolberg, *Inorg. Chem.*, **5**, 109 (1966).
[28b] J. C. Bailar and H. Itani, *Inorg. Chem.*, **4**, 1618 (1965).

In marked contrast to Pd^{IV}, platinum(IV) forms a vast number of very stable and kinetically inert complexes. As far as is known, Pt^{IV} complexes are invariably octahedral and, in fact, Pt^{IV} has such a pronounced tendency to be six coordinated that in some of its compounds quite unusual structures are adopted. An apparent exception to the rule is π-$C_5H_5Pt(CH_3)_3$ but, as with other π-C_5H_5 complexes, the ring can be considered as occupying three positions of an octahedron. Several interesting examples of this tendency of Pt^{IV} to be 6-coordinate exist where novel bonding is required for this to be achieved. The trimethylplatinum halides, as noted earlier (page 139) are tetrameric, $[Me_3PtX]_4$, with three-way halogen bridges. Tetramethylplatinum is now believed not to exist.[29a] The reported X-ray structure determination was evidently carried out on the trimethylplatinum hydroxide tetramer. In trimethylplatinum acetylacetonate, $[(CH_3)_3Pt(O_2C_5H_7)]_2$, long known to be a dimer in noncoordinating solvents, the structure is as shown in Figure 30-H-3. The acetylacetone functions as a tridentate ligand, the third donor atom, besides the two oxygen atoms which are normally the only donor atoms, being the middle carbon atom of the ring. The donor ability of this carbon atom can perhaps best be understood in terms of resonance structures of the chelate ring as shown in 30-H-VII. Ordinarily only 30-H-VIIa and 30-H-VIIb are considered, but 30-H-VIIc is also quite valid and must predominate in this platinum(IV) dimer. Other Me_3Pt derivatives also have octahedrally[29b] coordinated Pt.

In the monomeric compound, $(CH_3)_3Pt(dipy)(O_2C_5H_7)$, six rather than seven coordination is achieved by the formation of only one bond to the acetylacetonate ion (Fig. 30-H-4) as in the Pt^{II} complexes noted earlier.

(30-H-VIIa)　　　　(30-H-VIIb)　　　　(30-H-VIIc)

The great strength of the Pt—C bond is shown by the fact that in the preparation of this compound from $[(CH_3)_3Pt(O_2C_5H_7)]_2$ by the action of dipyridyl, it is the Pt—O bonds rather than Pt—C which are broken.

The most extensive and typical series of Pt^{IV} complexes are those which span the entire range from the hexammines, $[PtAm_6]X_4$, including all intermediates such as $[PtAm_4X_2]X_2$ and $M^I[PtAmX_5]$, to $M^I_2[PtX_6]$. Some of these have already been mentioned (page 126) as examples of the classical evidence which led Werner to assign the coordination number 6 to

[29a] Private communication from C. H. Brubaker.

[29b] For references see J. E. Lydon and M. R. Truter, J. Chem. Soc., 1965, 6899.

Pt^{IV}. The amines which occur in these complexes include ammonia, hydrazine, hydroxylamine and ethylenediamine, and the acido groups include the halogens, thiocyanate, hydroxide and the nitro group. Although not all of these groups are known to occur in all possible combinations in all types of compounds, it can be said that, with a few exceptions, they are generally interchangeable.

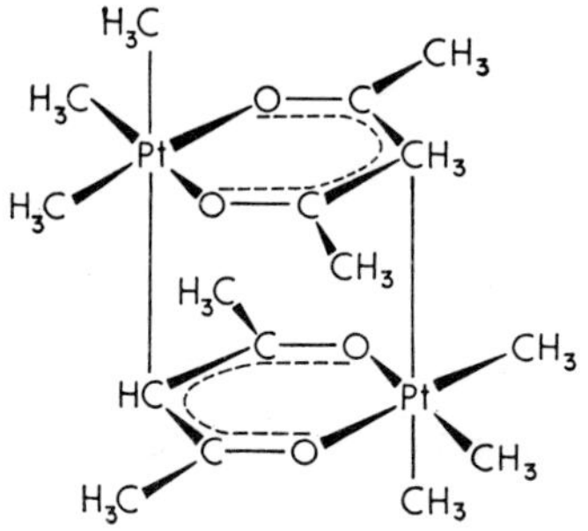

Fig. 30-H-3. The molecular structure of trimethylplatinum acetylacetonate dimer showing how the Pt^{IV} attains octahedral coordination.

One notable exception is the fluoride ion, which occurs only in the $[PtF_6]^{2-}$ ion. Alkali metal salts of this ion are made by the action of fluorine or bromine trifluoride on the corresponding $M^I_2[PtCl_6]$ compound

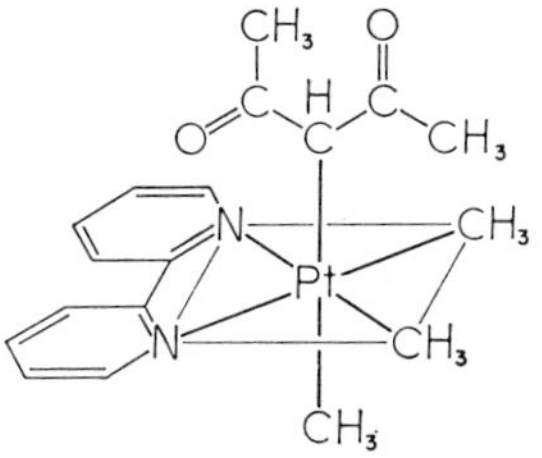

Fig. 30-H-4. Schematic representation of the molecular structure of the dipyridyl adduct of trimethylplatinum(IV) acetylacetonate.

and in other ways. In contrast to the behavior of $[PdF_6]^{2-}$, the $[PtF_6]^{2-}$ ion is only slowly hydrolyzed by water and the salts can be crystallized. It is known to be a regular octahedron.[30]

An unusual compound of stoichiometry $PtF_8(CO)_2$ may be $(FCO^+)_2[PtF_6^{2-}]$.

The *trans* effect, which plays such an important role in determining the

[30] N. Bartlett and D. H. Lohmann, *J. Chem. Soc.*, **1964**, 619.

stereochemical course of reaction in the planar complexes of Pd^{II} and Pt^{II}, operates also for substitutions in octahedral Pt^{IV} complexes, and considerable advantage may often be taken of it in designing stereospecific syntheses. As we have mentioned before, many Pt^{IV} complexes can be obtained stereospecifically from appropriate Pt^{II} complexes by oxidative addition of Cl_2, Br_2 or H_2O_2 (see page 1026).

30-H-3. Complexes of Platinum(V), d^5

The only examples are those derived from PtF_6 (see page 987); dioxygenylhexafluoroplatinate(V) may be treated with KI in IF_7 as solvent to give the potassium salt.[30]

30-H-4. Complexes of Palladium(0) and Platinum(0)

Although early reports of zerovalent compounds with phosphine ligands had to be reconsidered in view of the recognition that metal–hydrogen bonds are so readily formed, as we have seen, nevertheless there now appear to be several authentic zerovalent compounds.

The reduction by BH_4^- or sodium naphthalenide of chelating diarsine or diphosphine palladous salts of the type $[Pddiars_2]^{2+}$ gives colorless readily air-oxidized complexes, $[Pddiars_2]$. When a tridentate phosphine was used, two isomers, apparently differing in the number of points of attachment, were isolated. One isomer was postulated to be square planar and the other octahedral.[31]

Hydrazine reduction of $Pt[(C_6H_4F)_3P]_2Cl_2$ gives the yellow stable $Pt[(C_6H_4F)_3P]_3$, but whether this is truly 3-coordinate or not is uncertain[32] and the same doubt arises concerning the complexes[33] $Pt(Ph_3P)_2(olefin)$ (olefin = trans-stilbene, trans-4,4-dinitrostilbene and acenaphthylene). Triphenylphosphine complexes $Pt(Ph_3P)_4$ and $Pt(Ph_3P)_3$ also appear to be authentic.[34] It seems likely that these species may be in labile equilibria in solutions and may also acquire hydrogen atoms from solvents to give Pt—H bonds. It is also possible that in $Pt(Ph_3P)_3$, a coordination higher than 3 is present due to interaction of a ligand atom with the metal (cf. earlier discussion pages 771 and 1025) in crystals or with a solvent molecule in solutions.

[31] J. Chatt, F. A. Hart and H. R. Watson, *J. Chem. Soc.*, **1962**, 2537.

[32] A. D. Allen and C. D. Cook, *Proc. Chem. Soc.*, **1962**, 218.

[33] J. Chatt, B. L. Shaw and A. A. Williams, *J. Chem. Soc.*, **1962**, 3269.

[34] L. Malatesta and R. Ugo, *J. Chem. Soc.*, **1963**, 2080; cf. also, A. D. Allen and C. D. Cook, *Can. J. Chem.*, **42**, 1063 (1964).

Although carbonyls corresponding to $Ni(CO)_4$ do not exist, the analogs of $Ni(PF_3)_4$ have been obtained as volatile liquids which are thermally less stable than $Ni(PF_3)_4$. They can be obtained by the action of PF_3 at high pressure on $PdCl_2$ and $PtCl_2$ in presence of Cu at $100°$.[35a] There are also tertiary phosphine substituted carbonyls[35b] some of which, e.g., $Pt_3(CO)_4(PPh_3)_4$ are evidently cluster compounds.

30-I. SILVER AND GOLD

Like copper, these elements have a single s electron outside a completed d shell, but in spite of the similarity in electronic structures and ionization potentials there are few resemblances between Ag, Au and Cu, and there are no simple explanations for many of the differences.

Apart from obviously similar stoichiometries of compounds in the same oxidation state (which do not always have the same structure) there are some similarities within the group—or at least between two of the three elements:

1. The metals all crystallize with the same face-centered cubic (ccp) lattice.

2. Cu_2O and Ag_2O have the same body-centered cubic structure where the metal atom has two close oxygen neighbors and every oxygen is tetrahedrally surrounded by four metal atoms.

3. Although the stability constant sequence for halo complexes of many metals is $F > Cl > Br > I$, Cu^I and Ag^I belong to the group of ions of the more noble metals for which it is the reverse.

4. Cu^I and Ag^I (and to a lesser extent Au^I) form very much the same types of ions and compounds, such as $[M(CN)_2]^-$, $[Et_3AsMI]_4$ and K_2MCl_3.

5. Certain complexes of Cu^{II} and Ag^{II} are isomorphous, and Ag^{III}, Au^{III} and Cu^{III} also give similar complexes.

The only stable cationic species, apart from complex ions, is Ag^+. Gold(III) is invariably complexed in all solutions, usually as anionic species such as $[AuCl_3OH]^-$. The other oxidation states, Ag^{II}, Ag^{III} and Au^I, are either unstable to water or exist only in insoluble compounds or complexed species. Intercomparisons of the standard potentials are of limited utility, particularly since these strongly depend on the nature of the anion; some useful ones are, for silver:

$$Ag^{2+} \xrightarrow{\ 1.98\ } Ag^+ \xrightarrow{\ 0.799\ } Ag$$
$$Ag(CN)_2^- \xrightarrow{\ -0.31\ } Ag + 2CN^-$$

and for gold:

$$AuCl_4^- \xrightarrow{\ 1.00\ } Au + 4Cl^-$$
$$Au(CN)_2^- \xrightarrow{\ -0.6\ } Au + 2CN^-$$

[35a] G. F. Svatos and E. E. Flagg, *Inorg. Chem.*, **4**, 422 (1965); T. Kruck and K. Bauer, *Angew. Chem. (Internat.)*, **4**, 521 (1965).
[35b] G. Booth, J. Chatt and P. Chini, *Chem. Comm.*, **1965**, 639.

The oxidation states and stereochemistry are summarized in Table 30-I-1.

TABLE 30-I-1

Oxidation States and Stereochemistry of Silver and Gold

Oxidation state	Coordination number	Geometry	Examples
Ag^I, d^{10}	2a	Linear	$[Ag(CN)_2]^-$, $[Ag(NH_3)_2]^+$, AgSCN
	3	Trigonal(?)	$(Me_2NC_6H_4PEt_2)_2AgI$
	4a	Tetrahedral	$[Ag(SCN)_4]^{3-}$, $[AgIPR_3]_4$, $[AgSCNPPr_3]_n$, $[Ag(PPh_3)_4]^+ClO_4^-$
	6	Octahedral	AgF, AgCl, AgBr (NaCl structure)
Ag^{II}, d^9	4	Planar	$[Agpy_4]^{2+}$
Ag^{III}, d^8	4	Planar	AgF_4^-, $\frac{1}{2}$ of Ag atoms in AgO, $[Ag(ebg)_2]^{3+}$
	6	Octahedral(?)	$[Ag(IO_6)_2]^{7-}$
Au^I, d^{10}	2a	Linear	$[Au(CN)_2]^-$, $Et_3P \cdot AuC{\equiv}C \cdot C_6H_5$; $(AuI)_n$
	4	Tetrahedral	$[Au(diars)_2]^+I^-$
Au^{III}, d^8	4a	Planar	$AuBr_4^-$, Au_2Cl_6, $[(C_2H_5)_2AuBr]_2$, R_3PAuX_3
	5	Trigonal bipyramidal	$[Au(diars)_2I]^{2+}$
	6	Octahedral	$AuBr_6^{3-}$, $[Au(diars)_2I_2]^+$, $KAuF_4$ (distorted)

a Most common states.

There is no proof of the existence of divalent gold compounds (save possibly one, see page 1047). For silver(I) particularly, the stereochemistry is sensitive to the nature of the ligand, and, although the dominant coordination number is 2, there are some types of ligand which give four coordination.

30-I-1. The Elements

The elements are widely distributed in nature in the free state and in sulfides and arsenides; silver also occurs as the chloride, AgCl. Silver is often recovered from the work-up of copper and lead ores. The elements are usually extracted by treatment with cyanide solutions in presence of air and are recovered from them by addition of zinc. They are purified by electrodeposition.

Silver is a white, lustrous, soft, and malleable metal (m 961°) with the highest known electrical and thermal conductivity. It is chemically less reactive than copper, except toward sulfur and hydrogen sulfide, which rapidly blacken silver surfaces. The metal dissolves in oxidizing acids and in cyanide solutions in presence of oxygen or peroxide.

Gold is a soft, yellow metal (m 1063°) with the highest ductility and malleability of any element. It is chemically unreactive and is not attacked by oxygen or sulfur. Halogens react readily with gold as do solutions which generate them such as aqua regia. Gold dissolves in cyanide solutions in presence of air or peroxide, forming $[Au(CN)_2]^-$.

Since the chemistries of the compounds of these elements differ quite considerably, they will be treated separately.

30-I-2. Silver Compounds

Silver(I), d^{10}, Compounds. The argentous state is the normal and predominant oxidation state of silver. There is a well-defined, colorless argentous ion, Ag^+, in aqueous solution; the nature of the solvation shell is uncertain. Aquo ions do not seem to occur in argentous salts, practically all of which are normally anhydrous. There are several well-defined water-soluble salts, such as $AgNO_3$, $AgClO_3$ and $AgClO_4$, and a few rather sparingly soluble salts, such as Ag_2SO_4 and $AgOCOCH_3$. Such salts, as well as $AgNO_2$, appear to be primarily ionic on the basis of the Ag—O distances.[1] While AgCl and AgBr have the NaCl structure there appears to be appreciable covalent character in the $Ag \cdots X$ interactions, while in compounds such as AgCN and AgSCN, which have chain structures (30-I-I and 30-I-II), the bonds are considered to be predominantly covalent.

30-I-I   30-I-II

Ag^I and Au^I, along with Cu^I and Hg^{II}, show a pronounced tendency to exhibit linear, 2-fold coordination. It has been suggested[2] that this is due to a relatively small energy difference between the filled d orbitals and the unfilled s orbital ($4d$, $5s$ for Ag^I), which permits extensive hybridization of the d_{z^2} and s orbitals, as shown in Figure 30-I-1. The electron pair initially in the d_{z^2} orbital occupies ψ_1 giving a circular region of relatively high electron density from which ligands are somewhat repelled and regions above and below this ring in which the electron density is relatively low. Ligands are attracted to these regions. By further mixing of ψ_2 with the p_z orbital, two hybrid orbitals suitable for forming a pair of linear covalent bonds can be formed.

[1] R. E. Long and R. E. Marsh, *Acta Cryst.*, **15**, 448 (1962).
[2] L. E. Orgel, *J. Chem. Soc.*, **1958**, 4186.

Argentous Oxide. The addition of alkali hydroxide to Ag^+ solutions produces a dark brown precipitate which is difficult to free from alkali ions. It is strongly basic and its aqueous suspensions are alkaline

$$\tfrac{1}{2}Ag_2O(s) + \tfrac{1}{2}H_2O = Ag^+ + OH^- \qquad \log K = -7.42 \ (25°, 3M \ NaClO_4)$$
$$\tfrac{1}{2}Ag_2O(s) + \tfrac{1}{2}H_2O = AgOH \qquad \log K = -5.75$$

and absorb carbon dioxide from the air to give argentous carbonate. The oxide decomposes thermally above $\sim 160°$ and is readily reduced to the

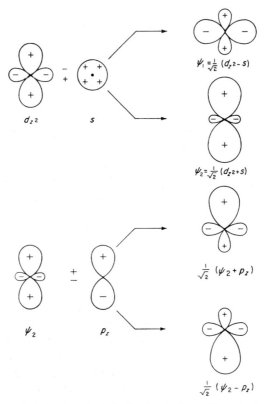

Fig. 30-I-1. Sketches showing the hybrid orbitals formed from a d_{z^2} and an s orbital, ψ_1 and ψ_2, and the hybrids which can be formed from ψ_2 and a p_z orbital. In each sketch the z axis is vertical and the actual orbital is the figure generated by rotating the sketch about the z axis.

metal by hydrogen. Silver oxide is more soluble in strong alkaline solution than in water, and it has been shown that $Ag(OH)_2^-$ species are formed. The treatment of water-soluble halides with a suspension of silver oxide is a useful way of preparing hydroxides, since the silver halides are insoluble.

Argentous Sulfide. The action of hydrogen sulfide on argentous solutions gives black Ag_2S, which is the least soluble in water of all silver compounds ($\log K_{SP} \approx -50$). The black coating often found on silver articles is the sulfide; the sulfide can be readily reduced by contact with aluminum in dilute sodium carbonate solution.

Argentous Halides. AgF is prepared by dissolving Ag_2O in aqueous hydrofluoric acid. Evaporation of the solution yields crystals of the very water-soluble hydrate $AgF \cdot 2H_2O$, which can be dehydrated above $40°$.

The water-insoluble compounds AgCl, AgBr and AgI are precipitated by the addition of the appropriate halide ion to an Ag^+ solution. The color and insolubility increase Cl < Br < I. Silver chloride is appreciably soluble in concentrated nitric acid and also in concentrated solutions of hydrochloric acid and alkali chlorides where chloro complexes are formed. The solubility of AgCl in concentrated $AgNO_3$ solutions gives evidence for species such as Ag_2Cl^+ and Ag_3Cl^{2+} and confirms the conclusion that AgCl is a weak electrolyte. It also readily dissolves in ammonia, cyanide and thiosulfate solutions to give complex ions. The bromide has similar solubility characteristics. The iodide is only sparingly soluble in ammonia, although it readily dissolves in cyanide and thiosulfate solutions since the formation constants are greater with these ligands than with NH_3.

Argentous Complexes. There are a great variety of silver complexes both in solution and in the solid state with π-bonding and non-π-bonding ligands. Oxygen is only feebly attached to silver, although the ion $[Ag(OH)_2]^-$ is known in strongly alkaline media. Since the most stable Ag^+ complexes have the linear structure, L—Ag—L, chelating ligands cannot form such simple ions and hence tend to give polynuclear complex ions. For monodentate ligands, the species AgL, AgL_2, AgL_3 and AgL_4 can exist, but the constants K_1 and K_2 are usually high whereas K_3 and K_4 are relatively small; hence the main species are usually of the linear AgL_2 type. The coordination number, however, is sensitive to the nature of the ligand and a variety of types can occur because of the possibilities of sp^2 and sp^3 bonding of Ag^+, in addition to the linear hybridization discussed earlier. For ligands with $d\pi$-bonding potential, especially S, Se, P and As ligands, the three- and four-coordinate species can predominate. Some formation constants are given in Figure 30-I-2 and in Table 30-I-2.

The ligands are of three main types: (1) ligands with little or no $d\pi$-bonding capacity, which show a marked inflection or a limiting value at $\bar{n} = 2$ in the complex constant curves (e.g., NH_3 gives only $[Ag(NH_3)_2]^+$ even in the highest concentrations of ammonia); (2) ligands having strong $d\pi$-bonding capacity which have a limit at $\bar{n} = 1$ or $\bar{n} = 3$ such as P, As, and I; and (3) ligands of intermediate $d\pi$-bonding capacity which show uniform formation up to $\bar{n} = 4$.

TABLE 30-I-2

Formation Constants of some Silver Complexes

Ligand	K_1, lmole^{-1}
Pyridine	110
Ethylamine	2340
Ammonia	1740
Chlorine	700
Bromine	1.4×10^4
Iodine	1.3×10^6
m-Ph$_2$PC$_6$H$_4$SO$_3^-$	1.4×10^8

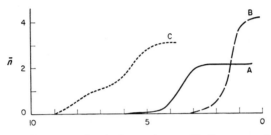

Fig. 30-I-2. Formation curves for Ag$^+$ complexes with three general classes of ligand L. A, Ligands with little or no π-bonding ability; B, ligands with intermediate π bonding ability; C, ligands with marked π-bonding ability.

Crystalline complexes of the type [AgL$_4$]ClO$_4$ can be obtained with phosphines[3] and with certain phosphites.[4]   A variety of other complexes of the types AgL$_2$X and AgL$_3$X are known.   The unusual tertiary phosphine 2-phenylphosphindoline (30-I-III) forms several types of Ag^I complex.[5]

(30-I-III)

Ethylenediamine also gives different types of complex depending on the conditions but 2-coordination of Ag^I appears to be preserved either by bridging as in ClAgNH$_2$CH$_2$CH$_2$NH$_2$AgCl or by polymerization.[6]

[3] F. A. Cotton and D. M. L. Goodgame, *J. Chem. Soc.*, **1960**, 5267.
[4] J. G. Verkade and T. S. Piper, *Inorg. Chem.*, **1**, 453 (1962).
[5] J. W. Colber, A. R. Fox, I. G. Minton and F. G. Mann, *J. Chem. Soc.*, **1964**, 1819.
[6] G. Newman and D. B. Powell, *J. Chem. Soc.*, **1962**, 3447.

Acetylene and Olefin Complexes. The action of acetylene on Ag^+ solutions gives an initial yellow precipitate which subsequently becomes white. This reaction is reversible

$$C_2H_2 + 2Ag^+ = AgC{\equiv}CAg + 2H^+$$

With strong solutions of $AgNO_3$, precipitates of $C_2Ag_3NO_3$ are obtained; it is possible that here there is π bonding similar to that discussed for the cuprous acetylene complexes. Substituted acetylenes in presence of phosphine ligands can give complexes such as $[(C_2H_5)_3PAgC{\equiv}C \cdot C_6H_5]_2$ which probably involve π bonding between the silver atom and the triple bond, as in Au^I acetylides (page 1048).

Virtually all olefins, and also many aromatic compounds, give complexes with silver ion (Chapter 28). Even where crystalline solids cannot be obtained, studies of the distribution of silver ion between aqueous and organic solvent phases allow equilibrium constants to be determined.

Silver(II), d^9, Compounds. Solutions of the argentic ion Ag^{2+} in perchloric and nitric acids may be prepared by oxidation of Ag^I with ozone. Kinetic evidence suggests that this oxidation occurs by a mechanism involving Ag^{III}:

$$Ag^+ + O_3 = AgO^+ + O_2$$
$$AgO^+ + Ag^+ + 2H^+ = 2Ag^{2+} + H_2O$$

The potentials for the Ag^{2+}/Ag^+ couple in $4M$ $HClO_4$, $+2.00$ v, and in $4M$ HNO_3, $+1.93$ v, show that Ag^{2+} is a powerful oxidizing agent. There is evidence for complexing by NO_3^-, SO_4^{2-} and ClO_4^- in solutions,[7] the electronic spectra in $HClO_4$ solutions being dependent on acid concentration, for example. The decomposition of Ag^{2+} in solutions appears to proceed[8]

$$2Ag^{2+} = Ag^+ + Ag^{3+} \quad \text{rapid}$$
$$Ag^{3+} + H_2O = AgO^+ + 2H^+ \quad \text{rapid}$$
$$AgO^+ = Ag^+ + \tfrac{1}{2}O_2 \quad \text{rate determining}$$

The concentration of Ag^{III} in solutions appears to be very small. The catalytic effect of Ag^+ ion in various oxidations by peroxodisulfate ion (page 549) is due to the formation of Ag^{2+} and/or Ag^{III} intermediates. In one case studied in detail,[8b] the Ag^+ catalyzed reduction of Co^{III} in $HClO_4$ is due to rapid oxidation

$$Co^{III} + Ag^I = Ag^{II} + Co^{II}$$

followed by decomposition of Ag^{II} as above.

Only two well-defined binary compounds are known, namely, the oxide, AgO, and the fluoride, AgF_2. Argentic oxide is best prepared by peroxodisulfate oxidation of Ag_2O in basic medium at $\sim 90°$. It can also be obtained

[7] G. A. Rechnitz and S. B. Zamochnick, *Talanta*, **11**, 1645 (1964).

[8] J. B. Kirvin, F. D. Peat, P. J. Proll and L. H. Sutcliffe, (a) *J. Phys. Chem.*, **67**, 1617 (1963); (b) **67**, 2288 (1963).

by peroxodisulfate oxidation in neutral or HNO_3 media, whereby substances of compositions $Ag_{14}O_{16}SO_4$ or $Ag_7O_8NO_3$ are produced as black precipitates yielding AgO on boiling 2–3 hours in water. Black AgO is a semiconductor, stable to $\sim 100°$, and it dissolves in acids evolving oxygen but giving some Ag^{2+} in solution. It is a powerful oxidizing agent. Since AgO is diamagnetic, it cannot in fact be Ag^{II} oxide and chemical evidence rules out the possibility of its being a peroxide. Neutron diffraction has shown that it is $Ag^I Ag^{III} O_2$ since there are two types of silver atoms in the lattice, one with linear coordination to two oxygen atoms (Ag^I) and the other square planar with respect to oxygen (Ag^{III}). When AgO is dissolved in acid Ag^{II} is formed, probably according to the equation

$$AgO^+ + Ag^+ + 2H^+ = 2Ag^{2+} + H_2O$$

but in presence of complexing agents in alkaline solution, Ag^{III} complexes are obtained[9] (see below). If AgF is heated with F_2 or other fluorinating agents, AgF_2, a dark brown crystalline solid, is obtained. This appears to be an authentic Ag^{II} compound. It is antiferromagnetic, having an effective moment at room temperature well below the spin-only value for one unpaired electron. It is both a strong oxidizing agent and a strong fluorinating agent.

Quite a number of Ag^{II} complexes are known. The cationic yellow to red complexes $[Agpy_4]^{2+}$, $[Ag(dipy)_2]^{2+}$ and $[Ag(phen)_2]^{2+}$ are obtained as crystalline peroxodisulfates when Ag^+ is oxidized by peroxodisulfate in presence of the appropriate ligand. Other salts of nonreducing anions, for example, NO_3^-, ClO_3^-, ClO_4^- and HSO_4^-, can be obtained metathetically. The salt $[Agpy_4]S_2O_8$ is isomorphous with its copper(II) analog, and so the $[Agpy_4]^{2+}$ ion is probably square. Similarly the bis-picolinate complex (30-I-IV) is isomorphous with its Cu^{II} analog which has been

(30-I-IV)

shown to have a *trans*-planar structure. In all cases studied, Ag^{II} complexes have magnetic moments of 1.75–2.2 BM in accord with expectation for the d^9 configuration; spectra are consistent with a planar structure.[10a]

[9] G. L. Cohen and G. Atkinson, *Inorg. Chem.*, **3**, 1741 (1964).
[10a] R. S. Banerjee and S. Basu, *J. Inorg. Nucl. Chem.*, **26**, 821 (1964).

Silver(III), d^8, Compounds. Anodic oxidation of Ag^I in alkaline solutions gives a black oxide claimed to be impure Ag_2O_3. It is not readily purified, and its formulation as Ag_2O_3 is not conclusive, though supported by the most recent work.

When 1:1 mixtures of potassium or cesium halides with silver halides are heated in a stream of fluorine, yellow $KAgF_4$ and $CsAgF_4$ are obtained. They are diamagnetic and extremely sensitive to moisture. Periodato and tellurato salts, diamagnetic and yellow in color, are obtained by peroxodisulfate oxidation of Ag^+ in strongly basic solutions containing periodate or tellurate ions. Representative compounds are: $K_6H[Ag(IO_6)_2]\cdot10H_2O$, and $Na_6H_3[Ag(TeO_6)_2]\cdot18H_2O$. These species are analogous to those of Cu^{III} and, by analogy, the structure of the periodate anion[9] is probably of the type 30-I-V, where one or more of the oxygen atoms bound to iodine can be protonated and such OH groups H-bonded to water. An Ag^{III} complex of remarkable stability is the one with ethylenedibiguanide (30-I-VI),

(30-I-V)   (30-I-VI)

which is obtained as the red sulfate when Ag_2SO_4 is treated with aqueous potassium peroxodisulfate in the presence of ethylenedibiguanidinium sulfate. The hydroxide, nitrate and perchlorate have been prepared metathetically. These salts are diamagnetic and oxidize two equivalents of iodide ion per gram-atom of silver.

30-I-3. Gold Compounds

Gold(I), d^{10}, Compounds. The chemistry of Au^I is essentially a chemistry of complex compounds, and in this respect it resembles Pt^{II}. No simple cations exist in aqueous solution. The aurous ion, Au^+, like the cuprous ion, cannot exist except in vanishingly small concentrations, and even $AuCl$ is decomposed by water to give gold and hydrolyzed gold(III) species. The aqueous chemistry of Au^I is thus mainly of complex *anions* such as $AuCl_2^-$ or $Au(CN)_2^-$. There is no evidence of any stable bivalent gold compounds at the present time, other than the dithiomaleonitrile complexes,[10b] $[Au(MNT)_2]^{2-}$ (see page 756).

[10b] J. H. Waters and H. B. Gray, *J. Amer. Chem. Soc.*, **87**, 3534 (1965).

Aurous oxide has not been well characterized.

Thermal decomposition of auric chloride, Au_2Cl_6, at about 185°, gives *aurous chloride* as a pale yellow powder. This compound is thermally unstable and is also decomposed by water, although it can be converted by alkali chlorides to the chloroaurates(I). The action of iodide ion on $Au^{III}Cl_4^-$ solutions precipitates *aurous iodide*, AuI, which is insoluble in water. Similarly the addition of cyanide ion precipitates AuCN, which, like the iodide, has continuous zigzag chains through the crystal lattice.

There are several aurous complexes stable in aqueous solution, the most important ones being $Au(CN)_2^-$, $AuCl_2^-$ and the thiosulfate species. The cyanide complex is very stable ($K = 4 \times 10^{28}$) and is formed when AuCN is treated with excess cyanide or, more usually, when gold is treated with alkali cyanides in presence of air or hydrogen peroxide. Crystalline compounds such as $K[Au(CN)_2]$ can be obtained, and the free acid, $HAu(CN)_2$, is isolable by evaporation of its solutions. Numerous complexes of Au^I with substituted phosphine, arsine and sulfide ligands as well as carbon monoxide can be obtained. Unlike the copper(I) and silver(I) complexes, which are polymeric with four-coordinated metal atoms, the gold(I) complexes are usually, though not invariably, monomeric. Thus the action of phosphorus trichloride or trialkyl phosphines on auric chloride in ether reduces the Au^{III} to give crystals of R_3PAuCl. Halides of this type can be reacted in the standard way with sodium salts, and compounds with metal–metal bonds such as $Ph_3PAuCo(CO)_4$ can be made.[11] Alkyls of the type R_3PAuR' have long been known and are quite stable.

The interaction of phenylacetylene or $t\text{-}C_4H_9C{\equiv}CH$ with reduced $HAuCl_4$ solutions gives polymeric yellow materials. The butyl complex is tetrameric and may have the structure 30-I-VII. Treatment of such complexes with tertiary phosphines or other ligands gives monomeric acetylides such as $Et_3PAu{-}C{\equiv}CPh$.[12]

Gold alkyl mercaptides and gold compounds derived from sulfurized veins are used for gold plating since they are highly soluble in organic solvents ("liquid gold") and decompose at fairly low temperatures.

(30-I-VII)

[11] A. S. Kasenally, *et al.*, *J. Chem. Soc.*, **1965**, 3407.
[12] G. E. Coates and C. Parkin, *J. Chem. Soc.*, **1962**, 3220.

Gold(III), d^8, Compounds. Auric compounds are mostly complexes and are powerful oxidizing agents.

The addition of alkali hydroxide to $AuCl_4^-$ solutions gives a yellow-brown precipitate, $Au(OH)_3$, which can be dehydrated to brown Au_2O_3. The latter is unstable above $\sim 150°$, decomposing to give what is presumed to be a mixture of gold and aurous oxide. The hydroxide is weakly acidic and is soluble in alkalies to give anionic species of the type $[Au(OH)_4]^-$ or $[AuO_2]^-$(aq).

Gold is soluble in bromine trifluoride, and a crystalline salt, $AuBrF_6$, (presumably $BrF_2^+AuF_4^-$) can be obtained. The latter is decomposed at $300°$ to crystalline AuF_3, which is stable to $\sim 500°$, but decomposed at once by water. AuF_3 is not isomorphous with any known trifluoride and possibly has planar AuF_4 units linked into spiral chains.[13a] Fluoroaurates such as $KAuF_4$, in which Au appears to have distorted octahedral coordination, can also be made.

Auric chloride and *auric bromide* are obtained by direct interaction of the elements at about $200°$. They are both dimeric in the red crystals and in the vapor. The halides are soluble in water, in which they are partially hydrolyzed to species such as $[AuCl_3OH]^-$; on addition of excess halogen acid, the ions $AuCl_4^-$ and $AuBr_4^-$ are formed. Chloroauric acid is the product obtained by dissolution of gold in aqua regia, and it can be obtained as yellow crystals, $H_3O^+AuCl_4^- \cdot 3H_2O$. Well-defined salts such as $KAuCl_4$ are formed. The anhydrous halides, as well as the acids, are soluble in organic donor solvents. Gold(III) in dilute aqueous acid solutions can be extracted with a high partition coefficient into ethyl acetate or diethyl ether as $[AuCl_3OH]^-$, which is presumably associated in an ion pair with an oxonium ion.

Although coordination numbers higher than 4 for gold(III) are rare, the tetrabromoaurate(III) ion reacts with bromide ion in nitrobenzene solution or in nitromethane, and some evidence for the ions $AuBr_6^{3-}$, $AuBr_5^{2-}$ and $Au_2Br_{10}^{4-}$ has been obtained. Salts of the $[Au(CN)_4]^-$ ion as well as substituted ions such as $[Au(CN)_2Cl_2]^-$ are known; unlike the $[Ni(CN)_4]^{2-}$ ion, but like the Pd and Pt species, no additional CN^- ion can be taken up.[13b]

Gold(III) salts of oxo anions are not very stable or important, but complex auric sulfates and nitrates, for example, $[Au(NO_3)_4]^-$, can be prepared. There are numerous four-coordinate complexes such as $[AuCl_2py_2]Cl$, $[AuphenCl_2]Cl$, etc. Chloroauric acid reacts with diethylenetriamine to give the ammonium tetrachloroaurate, $[AudienCl]Cl_2$ or $[Au(dien-H)Cl]Cl$,

[13a] L. B. Asprey, F. H. Kruse, K. H. Jack and R. Maitland, *Inorg. Chem.*, **3**, 602 (1964).
[13b] J. M. Smith, L. H. Jones, I. K. Kressin and R. A. Penneman, *Inorg. Chem.*, **4**, 369 (1965).

depending on the concentration and pH.[14] The kinetics of substitution of various anions in $[AudienCl]^{2+}$ have been compared with those for planar Pt^{II}; there is evidence that axial interactions occur here also in solution, e.g.,

Electronic spectra have been interpreted on an MO basis.

Important gold(III) complexes have been obtained using a chelating diarsine ligand from the interaction of sodium tetrachloroaurate(III) in presence of sodium iodide. The iodide $[Au(diars)_2I_2]I$ and other cations $[Au(diars)_2I]^{2+}$ and $[Au(diars)_2]^{3+}$ can be obtained. It is held that these are species with six, five and four coordination for Au^{III} with octahedral, trigonal bipyramidal and planar structures, respectively. The planar one is presumably dsp^2, whereas in the five-coordinate ion the $6p$ orbital, and in the six-coordinate ion the $6p6d$ hybrid orbitals, are being used for additional bonding. Chelating phosphine complexes also exist.[15]

Gold alkyls were among the first organometallic compounds of transition metals to be obtained. There are several types, but the dialkyls, R_2AuX $(X = Cl^-, Br^-, CN^-, SO_4^{2-}, etc.)$, are stable and the most important. Of these the halides are dimeric in solution with halogen bridges, whereas the cyanides are tetrameric, presumably owing to the impossibility of forming cyanide bridges of the type given by bridging carbon monoxide groups. The cyanides are square planar with $Au{\leftarrow}N{\equiv}C{-}Au$ bridges. Trialkyls such as $(Me_3Au)_2en$ can be cleaved by tertiary phosphines to give complexes such as Me_3PAuMe_3.[16]

[14] W. H. Baddley, F. Basolo, C. Nölting and A. J. Poë, *Inorg. Chem.*, **2**, 921 (1963); W. H. Baddley and F. Basolo, *Inorg. Chem.*, **3**, 1087 (1964).
[15] M. Davis and F. G. Mann, *J. Chem. Soc.*, **1964**, 3791.
[16] G. E. Coates and C. Parkin, *J. Chem. Soc.*, **1963**, 421.

References

Avtokratova, T. D., *Analytical Chemistry of Ruthenium*, Israel Program for Scientific Translations, Jerusalem, 1963. (Oldbourne Press, London.) This Russian work contains a vast amount of ruthenium chemistry, including preparative details, in addition to analytical matters.

Chaston, J. C., *Platinum Metals Review*, **8**, 50 (1964) ; **9**, 51 (1965). Reactions of O_2 and Pt metals at high temperatures.

Colton, R., *The Chemistry of Rhenium and Technetium*, Interscience—Wiley, London, 1965.

Colton, R., and R. D. Peacock, *Quart. Rev.*, **16**, 299 (1962). Review on technetium chemistry.

Engelhard Industries Technical Bulletin. Reviews, abstracts, uses and patents in platinum metal chemistry.

Griffith, W. P. G., *Quart. Rev.*, **19**, 254 (1965). Review on osmium compounds.

Haraldsen, H., *Angew. Chem. (Internat.)*, **5**, 58 (1966). Chalconides of 2nd and 3rd series elements.

Harris, C. M., and S. E. Livingstone, *Rev. Pure Appl. Chem.*, **12**, 16 (1962). Short review on d^8(Ni^{II}, Pd^{II}, Pt^{II}, Au^{III}) chemistry.

Jamrack, W. D., *Rare Metal Extraction*, Pergamon Press, London, 1963. Chemical engineering techniques for obtaining metal from ores for Ti, Zr, Hf, V, Nb, Ta, U and Th.

McMillan, J. A., *Chem. Rev.*, **62**, 65 (1962). An extensive review on higher oxidation states of silver.

Miller, J. R., *Adv. Inorg. Chem. Radiochem.*, **4**, 133 (1962). An extensive comparison of the chemistries of Ni, Pd and Pt with numerous references.

Pascal's Nouveau Traité de Chimie Minérale, Masson, Paris. This series contains recent volumes on 2nd and 3rd series elements which are more up-to-date than *Gmelin's Handbuch*, but are rather less comprehensive.

Peacock, R. D., *The Chemistry of Technetium and Rhenium*, Elsevier, London, 1965.

Platinum Metals Review, Johnson Matthey Ltd., London. This quarterly contains reviews on chemistry, uses, history, etc., of platinum metals as well as abstracts and patents.

Powell, A. R., in *Comprehensive Analytical Chemistry*, C. L. Wilson and D. W. Wilson, eds., Elsevier, Vol. I, Part C, 1962. An extensive treatment of analytical chemistry of platinum metals but one containing much useful chemistry.

———, in *Thorpe's Dictionary of Applied Chemistry*, 4th ed., Longmans, London. General accounts of platinum metals including refining methods.

Ramette, R., *J. Chem. Educ.*, **37**, 348 (1960). Solubility and equilibria of silver chloride.

Ronser, B. W., ed., *Rhenium*, Elsevier, New York, 1962. Monographs on the metal, its extraction, uses and analysis.

Shukla, S. K., *Ann. de Chim.*, **13**, 1383 (1961). Contains many references to rhodium complexes in aqueous solution.

Solovkin, A. S., and S. V. Tsvetkova, *Russ. Chem. Rev.*, **1962**, 655. The existence of "zirconyl" ion.

Tribalat, S., Mme, *Rhenium et Technétium*, Gauthier Villars, Paris, 1957.

Walsh, T. J., and E. A. Hausman, in *Treatise on Analytical Chemistry*. Interscience-Wiley, Part II, Vol. 8, 1963. Occurrence, separations and analysis of platinum metals; includes detailed physical properties of the metals and other useful information.

Wise, E. M., ed., *Gold: Recovery, Properties and Applications*, Van Nostrand, New York, 1964. Sources, extraction and metallurgy.

31

The Lanthanides; Scandium and Yttrium

31-1. Introduction

The lanthanides—or lanthanons, as they are sometimes called—are strictly the fourteen elements following lanthanum in which the fourteen $4f$ electrons are being successively added to the lanthanum configuration. Since the term lanthanide is used to indicate that these elements form a closely allied group, for the chemistry of which lanthanum is the prototype,

TABLE 31-1

Outer Electronic Configurations of Lanthanide Atoms and Ions[a,b] and Radii of M^{3+}[c,d]

Atomic number	Name	Symbol	Atom	M^{2+}	M^{3+}	M^{4+}	Radii M^{3+}
57	Lanthanum	La	$5d6s^2$	—	[Xe]	—	1.061
58	Cerium	Ce	$4f^26s^2$	—	$4f$	[Xe]	1.034
59	Praseodymium	Pr	$4f^36s^2$	—	$4f^2$	$4f$	1.013
60	Neodymium	Nd	$4f^46s^2$	$4f^4$	$4f^3$	$4f^2$	0.995
61	Promethium	Pm	$4f^56s^2$	—	$4f^4$	—	0.979
62	Samarium	Sm	$4f^66s^2$	$4f^6$	$4f^5$	—	0.964
63	Europium	Eu	$4f^76s^2$	$4f^7$	$4f^6$	—	0.950
64	Gadolinium	Gd	$4f^75d6s^2$	—	$4f^7$	—	0.938
65	Terbium	Tb	$4f^96s^2$	—	$4f^8$	$4f^7$	0.923
66	Dysprosium	Dy	$4f^{10}6s^2$	—	$4f^9$	$4f^8$	0.908
67	Holmium	Ho	$4f^{11}6s^2$	—	$4f^{10}$	—	0.894
68	Erbium	Er	$4f^{12}6s^2$	—	$4f^{11}$	—	0.881
69	Thulium	Tm	$4f^{13}6s^2$	$4f^{13}$	$4f^{12}$	—	0.869
70	Ytterbium	Yb	$4f^{14}6s^2$	$4f^{14}$	$4f^{13}$	—	0.858
71	Lutetium	Lu	$4f^{14}5d6s^2$	—	$4f^{14}$	—	0.848

[a] Only the valence shell electrons, that is, those outside of the [Xe] shell, are given.

[b] A dash indicates that this oxidation state is not known in any isolable compound. Properties of M^{2+} ions stabilized by substitution for Ca^{2+} in a CaF_2 lattice have been studied. See D. S. McClure and Z. Kiss, *J. Chem. Phys.*, **39**, 3251 (1963), and page 1070.

[c] D. H. Templeton and C. H. Dauben, *J. Amer. Chem. Soc.*, **76**, 5237 (1954).

[d] Radius of $Y^{3+} = 0.88$ A, and of $Sc^{3+} = 0.68$ A; W. H. Zachariasen in G. T. Seaborg and J. J. Katz, *The Actinide Elements*, McGraw-Hill, New York (1954).

the term is often taken as including lanthanum itself. Table 31-1 gives some principal characteristics of the lanthanide atoms and ions.

The chemistry of these highly electropositive elements is largely ionic and is determined by the size of the M^{3+} ion. Since yttrium, which lies above lanthanum in transition group III and has a similar $+3$ ion with a noble-gas core, has both atomic and ionic radii lying close to the corresponding values for terbium and dysprosium (a fact resulting from the lanthanide "contraction" to be discussed subsequently), this element is also considered here. It is generally found in nature along with the lanthanides and resembles terbium(III) and dysprosium(III) in its compounds.

The lighter element in group III, scandium, also has only the single oxidation state Sc^{III}; the scandium ion has a smaller radius, which does not fall within the range of the lanthanide ion radii, so that although scandium does show some similarities to the other elements discussed here, it is sufficiently different in many details to warrant separate treatment.

31-2. Occurrence

The lanthanide elements were originally known as the Rare Earth elements from their occurrence in oxide (or in old usage, earth) mixtures. They are not, however, particularly rare elements. Substantial deposits are located in Scandinavia, India, the Soviet Union and the United States, with a wide occurrence in smaller deposits in many other places. Many minerals make up these deposits, one of the most important being *monazite*, which usually occurs as a heavy dark sand of variable composition. Monazite is essentially a lanthanide orthophosphate, but significant amounts of thorium (up to 30%) occur in most monazite sands. The distribution of the individual lanthanides in minerals is usually such that La, Ce, Pr and Nd make up about 90%, with yttrium and the heavier elements together constituting the remainder. Monazite and other minerals carrying lanthanides in the $+3$ oxidation state are usually poor in europium which, because of its relatively strong tendency to give the $+2$ state, is often more concentrated in the calcium group minerals. The absolute abundances of the lanthanides in the lithosphere are relatively high. Thus even the least abundant, thulium, is as common as bismuth ($\sim 2 \times 10^{-5}$ wt. %) and more common than As, Cd, Hg or Se, elements not usually considered rare.

31-3. Promethium

Promethium, $_{61}Pm$, does not occur in nature except in vanishingly small traces as a spontaneous fission fragment of uranium in uranium ores. As early as 1926, several groups of workers reported optical and X-ray evidence for the existence of element 61 in various lanthanide concentrates, and the names Illinium, Il, and Florentium, Fl, were proposed by workers at the Universities of Illinois and Florence.

From considerations of nuclear stability systematics it is now believed that all isotopes of element 61 must be unstable with respect to β^-, β^+ or electron capture decay and have quite short half-lives. Although tracer amounts had probably been made in cyclotron bombardments previously, it was only during World War II that Coryell and co-workers at Oak Ridge were able to isolate from fission products sufficient amounts of the isotope of mass 147 to allow conclusive identification. The element was given the name Promethium. Eleven isotopes, ^{141}Pm to ^{151}Pm, have now been identified. ^{147}Pm is the longest-lived (2.64 years), and milligram quantities of the pink ^{147}Pm^{3+} salts have been isolated.

Other lanthanide elements contain several naturally occurring radio-isotopes, viz., ^{176}Lu (β^-, γ, 4.6×10^{10} years), ^{138}La (K, β^-, $\sim 2 \times 10^{11}$ years), ^{144}Nd (α, $\sim 5 \times 10^{15}$ years) and ^{147}Sm (α, 1.14×10^{11} years).

31-4. Electronic Structures; Oxidation States

The position of the lanthanides in the periodic table has been discussed earlier (page 627). The electronic structures are shown in Table 31-1, along with the electronic configurations of the various known lanthanide ions. Not all of these electronic configurations are known with complete certainty owing to the great complexity of the electronic spectra of the atoms and ions and the attendant difficulty of analysis.

All of the lanthanides form M^{3+} ions and so do Sc and Y, which have the atomic structures $[Ar]3d4s^2$ and $[Kr]4d5s^2$, respectively. For several of the lanthanides other oxidation states occur although these are always less stable than the characteristic group valency. To a certain extent, the occurrence of the oxidation states $+2$ and $+4$ can be correlated with the electronic structures if we assume that there is a special stability associated with an empty, half-filled or filled f shell just as, to a lesser degree, the same phenomenon is seen in the regular transition series (notably, Mn^{2+}) and in the ionization potentials of the first short period (cf. Fig. 7-1). Thus Sc, Y and La form only the M^{3+} ions since removal of three electrons leaves the noble-gas configuration. Lutetium and Gd form only the tripositive ions since the latter then have the stable $4f^{14}$ and $4f^7$ configurations, respectively. In all of these five cases, removal of *less* than three electrons under chemical conditions does not occur because the M^{2+} or M^+ ions would be much larger than the M^{3+} ions. Thus the energy saved in the ionization step would be less than the additional lattice or hydration energies of the salts of the small M^{3+} ions as compared with the lattice or hydration energies of the M^{2+} or M^+ ions.

The most stable di- and tetrapositive ions are formed by elements which can attain the f^0, f^7 and f^{14} configurations by so doing. Thus cerium and terbium attain the f^0 and f^7 configurations, respectively, by going to the IV oxidation state, whereas europium and ytterbium have the f^7 and f^{14} configurations, respectively, in the II oxidation state. These facts seem to support the view that "special stability" of the f^0, f^7 and f^{14} configurations is important in determining the existence of oxidation states other than III for the lanthanides. This argument becomes less convincing however when we note that samarium and thulium give M^{2+} species having f^6 and f^{13} configurations but no M^+ ions, whereas praseodymium and neodymium give M^{4+} ions with configurations f^1 and f^2 but no penta- or hexavalent species. Admittedly, the Sm^{II} and especially Tm^{II}, Pr^{IV} and Nd^{IV} states are very unstable indeed, but the idea that stability is favored even by the mere *approach* to an f^0, f^7 or f^{14} configuration, even though such a configuration is not actually attained, is of dubious validity. The existence of Nd^{2+}, f^4, and evidence even for Pr^{2+} and Ce^{2+} in lattices, provides particularly cogent evidence for believing that although the special stability of f^0, f^7, f^{14} may be one factor, there are other thermodynamic and kinetic factors which are of equal or greater importance in determining the stability of oxidation states.

31-5. The Lanthanide Contraction

The lanthanide contraction has been alluded to previously in discussing the elements of the third transition series, since it has certain important effects on their properties. It consists of a significant and steady decrease in the size of the atoms and ions with increasing atomic number; that is, lanthanum has the greatest, and lutetium the smallest, radius (see Table 31-1). Note that the radius of La^{3+} is about 0.18 A larger than that of Y^{3+}, so that if the fourteen lanthanide elements did not intervene we might have expected Hf^{4+} to have a radius ~ 0.2 A greater than that of Zr^{4+}. Instead, the lanthanide contraction, amounting to 0.21 A, almost exactly wipes out this expected increase and results in almost identical radii for Hf^{4+} and Zr^{4+}, as noted previously.

The cause of the lanthanide contraction is the same as the cause of the less spectacular contractions which occur in the d-block transition series, namely, the imperfect shielding of one electron by another in the same subshell. As we proceed through the lanthanide series, the nuclear charge and the number of $4f$ electrons increases by one at each step. The shielding of one $4f$ electron by another is quite imperfect (much more so than with d

electrons) owing to the shapes of the orbitals, so that at each increase the effective nuclear charge experienced by each $4f$ electron increases, thus causing a reduction in size of the entire $4f^n$ shell. The accumulation of these successive contractions is the total lanthanide contraction.

It should be noted also that the decrease, though steady, is not quite regular, the biggest decreases occurring with the first f electrons added; there also appears to be a larger decrease after f^7, that is, between Tb and Gd. Certain chemical properties of lanthanide compounds show corresponding divergences from regularity as a consequence of the ionic size; thus for ion exchange elution there is a break in the regularity in the separations between Gd and Tb, and, in the extraction of lanthanides from strong nitric acid solutions by tributyl phosphate in carbon tetrachloride, there are changes in the distribution constants at Gd. A half-filled shell effect has also been noted from stabilities of lanthanide complexes of ethylenediaminetetraacetic acid.

31-6. Magnetic and Spectral Properties

In several aspects, the magnetic and spectral behavior of the lanthanides is fundamentally different from that of the d-block transition elements. The basic reason for the differences lies in the fact that the electrons responsible for the magnetic spectral properties of lanthanide ions are $4f$ electrons, and the $4f$ orbitals are very effectively shielded from interaction with external forces by the overlying $5s^2$ and $5p^6$ shells. Hence the states arising from the various $4f^n$ configurations are only slightly affected by the surroundings of the ions and remain practically invariant for a given ion in all of its compounds.

The states of the $4f^n$ configurations are all given, to a useful approximation, by the Russell–Saunders coupling scheme. In addition, the spin-orbit coupling constants are quite large (order of 1000 cm^{-1}). The result of all this is that, with only a few exceptions, the lanthanide ions have ground states with a single well-defined value of the total angular momentum, J, with the next lowest J state at energies many times kT (at ordinary temperatures equal to ~ 200 cm^{-1}) above and hence virtually unpopulated (Fig. 31-1a). Thus the susceptibilities and magnetic moments should be given straightforwardly by formulas considering only this one well-defined J state, and indeed such calculations give results which are, with only two exceptions, in excellent agreement with experimental values (Fig. 31-2). For Sm^{3+} and Eu^{3+}, it turns out that the first excited J state is sufficiently close to the ground state (Fig. 31-1b) that this state (and in the case of Eu^{3+} even the second and third excited states) is appreciably populated at ordinary temperatures. Since these excited states have higher J values than the ground state, the actual magnetic moments are higher than those calculated considering the ground states only. Calculations taking into account the population of excited states afford results in excellent agreement with experiment (Fig. 31-2).

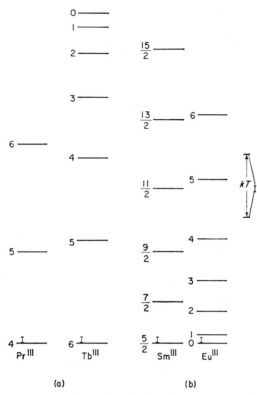

Fig. 31-1. J states for several trivalent lanthanides: (a) two of the several cases where the J states are widely separated compared to kT and (b) the two cases where the separations are of the same order as or less than kT.

It should be emphasized that magnetic behavior depending on J values is qualitatively different from that depending on S values—that is the "spin-only" behavior—which gives a fair approximation for many of the regular transition elements. Only for the f^0, f^7 and f^{14} cases, where there is no orbital angular momentum ($J = S$), do the two treatments give the same answer. For the lanthanides the external fields do not either appreciably split the free ion terms or quench the orbital angular momentum.

Because the f orbitals are so well shielded from the surroundings of the ions, the various states arising from the f^n configurations are split by

34+A.I.C.

external fields only to the extent of ~ 100 cm^{-1}. Thus when electronic transitions, called f–f transitions, occur from one J state of an f^n configuration to another J state of this configuration, the absorption bands are extremely sharp. They are similar to those for free atoms and are

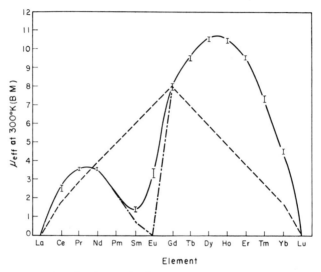

Fig. 31-2. Measured and calculated effective magnetic moments (BM) of lanthanide M^{3+} ions at 300° K. I's are ranges of experimental values; —————gives values calculated for appropriate J ground states and allowing for the Sm and Eu anomalies; —·—·— gives values calculated without allowing for the Sm and Eu anomalies; –––– gives calculated spin-only values.

quite unlike those for the d–d transitions. Virtually all of the absorption bands found in the visible and near-ultraviolet spectra of the lanthanide ions have this line-like character. There are, however, bands found in some cases which are quite broad; these may be assigned to transitions in which an f electron is excited to an outer d, s or p orbital. Since these outer levels *are* very much broadened by external fields, the breadth of the absorption bands due to such transitions is attributable to the breadth of these upper states. There are also some broad bands,[1] due to ligand to metal charge transfer with reducing ligands.

The colors and electronic ground states of the tripositive ions are given in Table 31-2. Note the novel arrangement, which emphasizes that the color sequence in the La–Gd series is accidentally repeated in the series Lu–Gd. As implied by the earlier discussion, insofar as the colors are due

[1] J. C. Barns, *J. Chem. Soc.*, **1964**, 3880.

to f–f transitions they are virtually independent of the environment of the ions.

TABLE 31-2

Colors and Electronic Ground States of the M^{3+} Ions

Ion	Ground state	Color	Ion	Ground state
La	$^1S_0$	Colorless	Lu	$^1S_0$
Ce	$^2F_{5/2}$	Colorless	Yb	$^2F_{7/2}$
Pr	$^3H_4$	Green	Tm	$^3H_6$
Nd	$^4I_{9/2}$	Reddish	Er	$^4I_{15/2}$
Pm	$^5I_4$	Pink; yellow	Ho	$^5I_8$
Sm	$^6H_{5/2}$	Yellow	Dy	$^6H_{15/2}$
Eu	$^7F_0$	Pale pink	Tb	$^7F_6$
Gd	$^8S_{7/2}$	Colorless	Gd	$^8S_{7/2}$

31-7. The Metals

The lighter metals (La, Ce, Pr, Nd, Gd) are obtained by reduction of the trichlorides with calcium, at 1000° or more, whereas for the others (Tb, Dy, Ho, Er, Tm and also Y) the trifluorides are used because the chlorides are too volatile. Pm is made by reduction of PmF_3 with lithium. Eu, Sm and Yb trichlorides are reduced only to the dihalides by calcium, but the metals can be prepared by reduction of the sesquioxides, M_2O_3, with lanthanum at high temperatures.

The metals are silvery white and very reactive. They tarnish readily in air and all burn easily to give the sesquioxides except cerium, which gives CeO_2. Yttrium is remarkably resistant to air even up to 1000° due to the formation of a protective oxide coating.[2] The metals react exothermically with hydrogen, though heating to 300–400° is often required to initiate the reaction. The resulting MH_2 and MH_3 phases, which are usually in a defect state, are remarkably thermally stable, in some cases up to 900°. The MH_2 phases have a fluorite structure and are of salt-like character, being ionic type rather than interstitial type hydrides; they react readily with oxygen, water and with NH_3 at about 800° to give nitrides.[3] The metals also react readily with carbon, nitrogen, silicon, phosphorus, sulfur, halogens and other nonmetals at elevated temperatures. They all react directly with water, slowly in the cold, rapidly on heating, to liberate hydrogen. Their high potentials (Table 31-3) are in accord with their electropositive character.

The atomic volumes, densities and some other properties of the metals change smoothly except for Eu and Yb, and occasionally Sm and Tm.

---

[2] H. J. Borchardt, *J. Inorg. Nucl. Chem.*, **26**, 711 (1964).

[3] D. E. LaValle, *J. Inorg. Nucl. Chem.*, **24**, 930 (1962).

TABLE 31-3

Standard Potentials of the Lanthanides

Element	E^0, v	Element	E^0, v
La	−2.52	Tb	−2.39
Ce	−2.48	(Y	−2.37)
Pr	−2.47	Dy	−2.35
Nd	−2.44	Ho	−2.32
Pm	−2.42	Er	−2.30
Sm	−2.41	Tm	−2.28
Eu	−2.41	Yb	−2.27
Gd	−2.40	Lu	−2.25
		(Sc	−1.88)

For example, Figure 31-3 shows a plot of atomic volumes and heats of vaporization. It is obvious that the deviations occur with just those lanthanides which have the greatest tendency to exist in the divalent state. Presumably these elements tend to donate only two electrons to the conduction bands of the metal, thus leaving larger cores and affording lower binding forces.

Europium and ytterbium metals dissolve in liquid ammonia at −78° to give characteristic blue solutions (cf. the alkalies and alkaline earths), but samarium is insoluble.[3a]

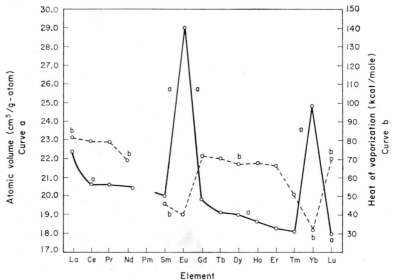

Fig. 31-3. The atomic volumes (curve a) and heats of vaporization (curve b) of the lanthanide metals.

[3a] R. Catherall and M. C. R. Symons, *J. Chem. Soc.*, **1965**, 3763.

CHEMISTRY OF THE TRIVALENT
LANTHANIDES AND YTTRIUM

31-8. General Chemistry

The trivalent state is the characteristic one for all of the lanthanides. They form *oxides*, M_2O_3, which resemble the Ca, Sr, Ba group oxides and absorb carbon dioxide and water from the air to form carbonates and hydroxides, respectively. The *hydroxides*, $M(OH)_3$, are definite compounds, having hexagonal structures, and not merely hydrous oxides. The basicity of the hydroxides decreases with increasing atomic number as would be expected because of the decrease in ionic radius. The hydroxides are precipitated from aqueous solutions by ammonia or dilute alkalies as gelatinous precipitates. They are not amphoteric.

Among the *halides*, the fluorides are of particular importance because of their insolubility. Addition of hydrofluoric acid or fluoride ions precipitates the fluorides from lanthanide ion solutions even $3M$ in nitric acid and is a characteristic test for lanthanide ions. The fluorides, particularly of the heavier lanthanides, are slightly soluble in excess HF owing to complex formation. They may be redissolved in $3N$ nitric acid saturated with boric acid which removes F^- as BF_4^-. The chlorides are soluble in water, from which they crystallize as hydrates. The anhydrous chlorides cannot easily be obtained from the hydrates because these lose hydrochloric acid on heating—to give the oxochlorides, MOCl—more readily than they lose water. (Scandium and cerium give Sc_2O_3 and CeO_2, respectively, however.) The anhydrous chlorides are best made by heating oxides (or oxalates, etc.) with ammonium chloride at about 300°.

$$M_2O_3 + 6NH_4Cl = 2MCl_3 + 3H_2O + 6NH_3$$

The bromides and iodides are rather similar to the chlorides.

Lanthanide *salts of most oxo acids*—sulfates, nitrates, perchlorates, bromates, etc.—are known. They are generally soluble and crystallize as hydrates. The carbonates, phosphates and oxalates are insoluble, and precipitation of the oxalates from dilute nitric acid solution is a quantitative and fairly specific separation procedure for the lanthanides; lanthanides can be determined gravimetrically in this way, after ignition to the oxides. The actual nature of the oxalate precipitate depends on conditions.[4] In nitric acid solutions, where the main ion is Hox^-, ammonium ion gives double salts $NH_4Mox_2 \cdot yH_2O$ ($y = 1$ or 3). In neutral solution, ammonium oxalate gives the normal oxalate with lighter, but mixtures with heavier

[4] M. F. Barrett, T. R. R. McDonald and N. E. Topp, *J. Inorg. Nucl. Chem.*, **26**, 931 (1964).

lanthanides. Washing the double salts with $0.1N$ HNO_3 gives, with some ions, normal oxalates.

Double salts are very common, the most important ones being the double nitrates and double sulfates, such as $2M(NO_3)_3 \cdot 3Mg(NO_3)_2 \cdot 24H_2O$, $M(NO_3)_3 \cdot 2NH_4NO_3 \cdot 4H_2O$ and $M_2(SO_4)_3 \cdot 3Na_2SO_4 \cdot 12H_2O$. The solubilities of double sulfates of the latter type fall into two rough classes: the cerium group, La–Eu, and the yttrium group, Gd–Lu and Y. Those of the cerium group are only sparingly soluble in sodium sulfate, whereas those of the yttrium group are appreciably soluble. Thus a fairly rapid separation of the entire group of lanthanides into two main groups is possible. Various of the double nitrates were used in the past for further separations by fractional crystallization procedures.

The lanthanides form many well-defined compounds with nonmetals and metalloids other than oxygen and halogens. The general preparation of all of these compounds is by direct combination of the elements at elevated temperatures. Among these are sulfides, M_2S_3 (not of europium, however), selenides, M_2Se_3, and oxosulfides, M_2O_2S. Nitrides, phosphides, arsenides, antimonides and bismuthides, MN, MP, MAs, MSb and MBi, crystallize in the NaCl structure. Borides of the types MB_6 and MB_4 are well characterized as are various carbides, and previously mentioned hydride phases MH_2 and MH_3. There are certain differences occasionally through the lanthanides; thus the carbide, M_3C, which has a *ccp* type lattice except that it is deficient in carbon is found for the elements Sm–Lu, inclusive, but not for La, Ce, Pr or Nd. A similar structural change in the middle of the series occurs for halides. Thus the iodides are orthorhombic at the start and hexagonal at the end of the series. A similar change occurs for actinide tribromides and $NpBr_3$ is actually dimorphic.[5]

The M^{3+} aquo ions are slightly hydrolyzed according to

$$[M(H_2O)_n]^{3+} + H_2O = [M(H_2O)_{n-1}(OH)]^{2+} + H_3O^+$$

and the tendency to hydrolysis increases with increasing atomic number as would be expected from the contraction in radii. Scandium and yttrium similarly[6] give predominantly MOH^{2+} and also $M_2(OH)_2^{4+}$ ions; however, for Ce^{3+} only 1% of the metal ion is hydrolyzed[7] without giving a precipitate, and here the main equilibrium appears to be

$$3Ce^{3+} + 5H_2O \rightleftharpoons Ce_3(OH)_5^{4+} + 5H^+$$

Compared to the *d*-block transition elements, the lanthanides form few

[5] L. B. Asprey, T. K. Keenan and F. M. Kruse, *Inorg. Chem.*, **3**, 1137 (1964).
[6] G. Biedermann and L. Ciavatta, *Arkiv Kemi*, **22**, 233 (1964).
[7] G. Biedermann and L. Newman, *Arkiv Kemi*, **22**, 303 (1964).

complexes, and these are mostly with oxygen compounds. This is due in part to the unavailability of the f orbitals to form hybrid orbitals which might lead to covalent bond strength, and also to the fact that the lanthanide ions are rather large (radii 0.85–1.06) compared with those of the transition elements (e.g., Cr^{3+} and Fe^{3+} with radii of 0.60–0.65 A), which lowers electrostatic forces of attraction. The only stable complexes which are at all common or important are those with chelate ligands. β-Diketones such as acetylacetone, dibenzoylmethane and thenoyltrifluoroacetone, form complexes of stoichiometry $M(\beta\text{-diketonate})_3$, which generally crystallize with solvent, perhaps indicating coordination numbers above 6. The lanthanides can also be extracted from aqueous solutions into organic solvents using certain complexing agents, such as tributyl phosphate in the presence of concentrated hydrochloric acid. Chelate ligands giving water-soluble complexes are hydroxo acids such as tartaric or citric, and various amino acids of the types $RN(CH_2COOH)_2$, $N(CH_2COOH)_3$ and $EDTAH_4$. Although some complexes appear to be octahedral, higher coordination numbers, as in $[Nd(H_2O)_9](BrO_3)_3$, and some 8-, 9- and 10-coordinate species have been characterized.[8] Examples[9] are anions such as $[Euacac_4]^-$ and $[La(OH_2)_4EDTAH]\cdot 3H_2O$; the insolubility of some lanthanide tropolonates also suggests cross-linkages leading to coordination numbers exceeding 6, and even scandium forms an 8-coordinate tropolonate ion, ScT_4^-.[9c]

Since the lanthanides are so highly electropositive, they have little or no tendency to form complexes with π-bonding ligands. However, 1, 10-phenanthrolene gives complexes, $[phen_2MCl(H_2O)]Cl_2$ and $[phen_3M](SCN)_3$, which are insoluble in organic solvents and decomposed by water;[10] also, dipyridyl complexes $[dipy_2M(H_2O)_n]$ are obtained from ethanol solutions of the chlorides and nitrates. Some of these chelates are fluorescent,[9b] particularly those containing tetra(β-ketoenolate) anions like $[Eu(PhCOCHCOPh)_4]^-$, or luminescent, and may have properties suitable for laser operation. A europium activated yttrium vanadate is used as a red phosphor in color television tubes.

Studies on chelates such as 2-picolyliminoacetic acid suggest[11] that the affinity of such N-donors is approximately comparable to OH^-.

The only complexes of sulfur ligands are the readily hydrolyzed tris-dithiocarbamates.

[8] M. D. Lind, B. Lee and J. L. Hoard, J. Amer. Chem. Soc., **87**, 1611, 1612 (1965).

[9] L. R. Melby, N. J. Rose, E. Abramson and J. C. Cairns, J. Amer. Chem. Soc., **86**, 5117 (1964); (b) H. Bauer, J. Blanc and D. L. Ross, J. Amer. Chem. Soc., **86**, 5125 (1964); (c) E. L. Muetterties and C. M. Wright, J. Amer. Chem. Soc., **87**, 4706 (1965).

[10] F. A. Hart and F. P. Lanning, J. Inorg. Nucl. Chem., **26**, 579 (1964).

[11] L. C. Thompson, Inorg. Chem., **3**, 1015 (1964).

The only example of *zero valent compounds* are the tris-dipyridyls of Sc and Y which are obtained by reduction of the corresponding chlorides with Li in THF.[12]

Organo compounds similarly are not known with the exception of the thermally very stable but air-sensitive cyclopentadienides, $(C_5H_5)_3M$, $C_5H_5MCl_2 \cdot 3THF$ and $(C_5H_5)_3MCNC_6H_{11}$.[13] These are ionic and have magnetic moments similar to the M^{3+} ions themselves; although they sublime in vacuum at $\sim 200°$, presumably as molecules, their structures are not known. The divalent species are known for Eu and Yb.

31-9. Separation of the Lanthanides

Prior to the advent of ion exchange techniques, separation of the rare earths was an extraordinarily laborious task even on a small scale. For many years the only techniques used were fractional crystallization, most commonly of double sulfates, fractional precipitation or fractional decomposition, but these were later supplemented by procedures involving the removal of cerium as Ce^{IV} and europium, samarium and ytterbium in their divalent states. All such procedures, except in special cases (notably the removal of europium) have been rendered obsolete by ion exchange resin separations. Although the chemistries of all the lanthanides in the III oxidation state are almost identical, there are slight quantitative differences which vary systematically from La through Lu (Y being placed approximately between Dy and Ho). The ion exchange separation is based upon the fact that the steady decrease in size and consequent decrease in basicity means that there is a steady increase with increasing atomic number in the binding of ligands. The first consequence of this is that the *hydrated* radii of the lanthanide(III) ions increase with increasing atomic number; since the binding of cations to the anionic sites of the exchange resin seems to involve electrostatic attraction of the hydrated cation by the negative site, it is found that the larger the hydrated radius of the ion, the less strongly it is bound. Thus this effect alone tends to give a separation of the lanthanide(III) ions when a solution containing several of them passes slowly through a column of a cation exchange resin, with the heavier members coming through first. This situation may be expressed using equilibria of the type

$$3H^+_R + M^{3+}(aq) = M^{3+}_R + 3H^+(aq) \qquad K = \frac{[H^+(aq)]^3}{[H^+_R]^3} \cdot \frac{[M^{3+}_R]}{[M^{3+}(aq)]}$$

[12] S. Hertzog and K. Gustav, *Z. Naturforsch.*, **176**, 62 (1962).
[13] E. O. Fischer and H. Fischer, *J. Organomet. Chem.*, **3**, 181 (1965); *Angew Chem. (Internat.)*, **4**, 246 (1965).

where H^+_R and M^{3+}_R represent hydrogen ions and lanthanide ions bound to the resin, and the constants decrease with increasing atomic number of the lanthanide because $[M^{3+}_R]/[M^{3+}(aq)]$ decreases.

The separation obtainable because of differing preferences of the hydrated cations for the exchange resin can be significantly enhanced by the use of complexing agents at appropriate pH. EDTAH$_4$ and a variety of other hydroxo or amino carboxylic acids may be used, but for laboratory separations citrate at pH 2.8–3.4 is a convenient eluant. The lanthanide ions are introduced at the top of columns from chloride solution. Just as the smaller radius of the heavier of two lanthanide ions will cause it to have the larger hydrated radius and hence the smaller tendency to be held by the resin, its smaller radius will cause it to form stronger complexes thus positively enhancing its preference for the aqueous phase. Figure 31-4

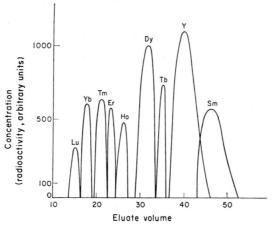

Fig. 31-4. A typical elution curve of lanthanide ions on a Dowex-50 column using buffered ammonium citrate solution as eluate. The eluate volume is given by number of sample tube from a rotary sample collector; the concentrations were measured by radioactive counting of tracers.

illustrates a typical elution profile on a cation exchange resin. Further discussion of ion exchange procedures for both lanthanide and actinide elements appears on page 1111. Large-scale column techniques allow the separation in a very pure state of kilogram quantities of the lanthanides.

Although cerium(IV) nitrate (and other +4 nitrates such as those of Zr, Th and Pu) is readily extracted from nitric acid solutions by tributyl phosphate dissolved in kerosene or other inert solvent and can thus be readily separated from the +3 lanthanide ions, the trivalent lanthanide nitrates can also be extracted under suitable conditions with various phosphate esters or acids. Extractability under given conditions increases

34*

with increasing atomic number; it is higher in strong acid or high nitrate concentrations.

THE CHEMISTRY OF SCANDIUM

Scandium, with an electron configuration $[Ar]3d4s^2$, is a congener of aluminum, but is decidedly more basic in its properties; it is in many respects quite similar to yttrium and the lanthanides, although the distinctly smaller radius of the scandium(III) ion (~ 0.7 A, compared to a range of 0.85–1.06 for yttrium and the lanthanides) makes for some differences in chemistry. It is not a rare element, being as common as arsenic and twice as abundant as boron, but its chemistry is not on the whole well known. This is due partly to the absence of rich sources of the element and also to the difficulty (until recently) of obtaining it in a pure state. Scandium has only the III oxidation state in which it gives the oxide, Sc_2O_3, halides, ScX_3 and oxohalides, $ScOX$, as well as numerous salts of oxo acids. The possibility of there being a dipositive oxidation state has been rather carefully examined and there is no evidence for its existence.

The scandium ion, being smaller, has a much greater tendency to hydrolysis than the lanthanide ions, and polymeric species of the type 31-I

$$\left[Sc\left(\begin{smallmatrix} OH \\ OH \end{smallmatrix}\right)Sc\right)_n\right]^{(n+3)+}$$

(31-I)

have been shown to arise with chain length increasing as pH increases. It is perhaps to be expected that, since it is closely related to both aluminum and the elements of the first transition series, scandium ion forms complexes far more readily than do the lanthanides. Thus, in perchloric acid solutions, complexes such as $ScCl_2^+$ and $ScCl^{2+}$ are formed on adding Cl^- ions.[14]

Some significant differences between the chemistries of scandium and the trivalent lanthanides are the following:

1. Scandium forms a double sulfate $K_2SO_4 \cdot Sc_2(SO_4)_3 \cdot nH_2O$ which is very insoluble in K_2SO_4 solution. It can also be precipitated as potassium double fluoride, as ammonium double tartrate or by disodium hydrogen phosphate.

2. In presence of thiocyanate ion, it gives a yellow thiocyanate, $Sc(NCS)_3$, which can be extracted into ether.

3. The thenoyltrifluoroacetone complex of scandium may be extracted from aqueous solutions into excess TTA in a solvent such as benzene at

[14] G. L. Reed, K. J. Sutton and D. F. C. Morris, *J. Inorg. Nucl. Chem.*, **26**, 1227 (1964).

pH's of 1.5–2.0, unlike the corresponding lanthanide complexes. Solvent extraction of the scandium oxine chelate by chloroform can also be made quantitative in one operation. Scandium acetylacetonate may be sublimed ($\sim 200°$), whereas acetylacetonates of the lanthanides are pyrolyzed.

4. Scandium does not appear to form a definite hydroxide, but only a hydrous oxide, $Sc_2O_3 \cdot nH_2O$, although a definite hydrated oxide containing OH is known, namely ScO(OH), which is similar in structure to AlO(OH). The "hydroxide" readily dissolves in concentrated NaOH and $Na_3[Sc(OH)_6] \cdot 2H_2O$ can be crystallized; this complex hydrolyzes at NaOH concentrations less than $8M$. Scandium oxide is more basic than aluminum oxide but less so than those of the lanthanides. If the oxide is heated with Li_2O or Na_2O, the readily hydrolyzed compounds $Li(Na)ScO_2$ are formed.

Scandium resembles the lanthanides in many ways, of course, having, for instance, an insoluble oxalate, phosphate, carbonate and fluoride. The fluoride, however, is readily soluble in excess HF or NH_4F and definite fluoro complexes, e.g., ScF_6^{3-}, exist. The chloride, $ScCl_3$, sublimes at a much lower temperature than the lanthanide chlorides, but is monomeric in the vapor and has no activity as a Friedel–Crafts catalyst (unlike volatile $AlCl_3$).

THE IV OXIDATION STATE

31-10. Cerium(IV)

This is the only tetrapositive lanthanide species sufficiently stable to exist in aqueous solution as well as in solid compounds. The terms ceric and cerous are commonly used to designate the IV and III valence states of cerium. The only known binary, solid compounds of Ce^{IV} are the oxide, CeO_2, the hydrous oxide, $CeO_2 \cdot nH_2O$, and the fluoride, CeF_4. CeO_2, white when pure, is obtained by heating cerium metal, $Ce(OH)_3$, or any of several Ce^{III} salts of oxo acids such as the oxalate, carbonate or nitrate in air or oxygen. It is a rather inert substance, not attacked by either strong acids or alkalies. It can, however, be dissolved by acids in the presence of reducing agents (H_2O_2, Sn^{2+}, etc.) giving then Ce^{III} solutions. Hydrous ceric oxide, $CeO_2 \cdot nH_2O$, is a yellow, gelatinous precipitate obtained on treating Ce^{IV} solutions with bases. It redissolves fairly easily in acids. CeF_4 is prepared by treating anhydrous $CeCl_3$ or CeF_3 with fluorine at room temperature; it is relatively inert to cold water and is reduced to CeF_3 by hydrogen at 200–300°.

Ce^{IV} in solution is obtained by treatment of Ce^{III} solutions with very powerful oxidizing agents, for example, peroxodisulfate or bismuthate in nitric acid. The aqueous chemistry of Ce^{IV} is similar to that of Zr, Hf and, particularly, tetravalent actinides. Thus Ce^{IV} gives phosphates insoluble in $4N$ HNO_3 and iodates insoluble in $6N$ HNO_3, as well as an insoluble oxalate. The phosphate and iodate precipitations can be used to separate Ce^{IV} from the trivalent lanthanides. Ce^{IV} is also much more readily extracted into organic solvents by tributyl phosphate and similar extractants than are the M^{III} lanthanide ions.

The very highly charged Ce^{4+} ion has a pronounced tendency to hydrate, and the hydrated ion, $[Ce(H_2O)_n]^{4+}$, is a fairly strong acid. Thus, except at very low pH, hydrolysis and polymerization of ceric ion are considerable. It is probable that the $[Ce(H_2O)_n]^{4+}$ ion exists only in concentrated perchloric acid solution. In other acid media coordination of anions doubtless occurs. This affords an explanation of the dependence of the potential of the Ce^{IV}/Ce^{III} couple on the nature of the acid medium, as shown by the following figures:

$$Ce^{IV} + e = Ce^{III} \qquad E^0 = +1.28 \ (2M \ HCl), \ +1.44 \ (1M \ H_2SO_4),$$
$$+1.61 \ (1M \ HNO_3), \ +1.70 \ (1M \ HClO_4)$$

Comparison of the potential in sulphuric acid with that for the oxidation of water

$$O_2 + 4H^+ + 4e = 2H_2O \qquad E^0 = +1.229$$

indicates that the acid Ce^{IV} solutions commonly used in analysis are metastable. The oxidation of water is kinetically controlled but can be temporarily catalyzed by fresh glass surfaces.[15]

Cerium(IV) forms double salts readily, the best-known one being ceric ammonium nitrate, $Ce(NO_3)_4 \cdot 2NH_4NO_3$, which can be crystallized from nitric acid solutions. Although many complex cationic and anionic Ce^{IV} species are doubtless present in solution, few have been isolated. Whether complex anions are present in many double salts, for example, $Ce(NO_3)_6^{2-}$ in the one mentioned above, is uncertain. Although concentrated aqueous HCl is oxidized to Cl_2 by Ce^{IV}, the reaction of CeO_2 with HCl in dioxane gives orange needles of the dioxanate of hexachloroceric acid, $H_2CeCl_6 \cdot 4C_4H_8O_2$. The pyridinium salt is stable enough to be dried in vacuum at $120°$.

This pyridinium salt is used to prepare ceric alkoxides,

$$(C_5H_5NH)_2CeCl_6 + 4ROH + 6NH_3 = Ce(OR)_4 + 2C_5H_5N + 6NH_4Cl$$

The isopropoxide is a crystalline solid, subliming in vacuum at $170°$, but other alkoxides, prepared from the isopropyl compound by alcohol exchange, are nonvolatile and presumably polymerized by Ce—O(R)—Ce bridges. Fluoro complexes such as Na_2CeF_6 and Cs_3CeF_7 can be made by fluorination of $M^ICl + CeO_2$.

[15] D. Grant, *J. Inorg. Nucl. Chem.*, **26**, 335 (1964).

31-11. Praseodymium(IV)

Praseodymium(IV) is known only in a few solid compounds. The Pr—O system has a very complex phase diagram. On heating praseodymium salts in air a black material having the approximate composition Pr_6O_{11} is obtained; this is believed to be $Pr_{32}O_{58}$ or $Pr_{32}O_{59}$ with some vacant oxygen sites like the intermediate oxides of Tb (Section 31-12) and derived from the ideal $M_{32}O_{64}$ phase. PrO_2 can be obtained by heating finely divided $PrO_n (n < 2)$ with oxygen at 100 atm at 500° for 8–12 hours. This oxide has a fluorite structure. Even using ozone, no Pr—O compound containing Pr beyond the IV state has been obtained. PrF_4 is not obtained by fluorination of PrF_3, but in mixed systems Pr^{IV} can be obtained by fluorination. For example, the compounds $NaPrF_5$, Na_2PrF_6, K_2PrF_6, Rb_2PrF_6 and Cs_2PrF_6 are obtained when alkali fluorides, mixed in correct stoichiometric ratio with praseodymium salts, are treated with fluorine gas at 300–500°. The tetravalence of Pr in these compounds has been firmly established by magnetic, spectral and X-ray data.

Pr^{IV} is a very powerful oxidizing agent, the Pr^{IV}/Pr^{III} couple being estimated as $+2.9$ v. This potential is such that Pr^{IV} would oxidize water itself so that its nonexistence in solution is not surprising. Pr_6O_{11} dissolves in acids to give aqueous Pr^{III} and to liberate oxygen, chlorine, etc., depending on the acid used.

There is some evidence that $Pr(NO_3)_4$ is partially formed by action of N_2O_5 and O_3 on PrO_2.[16]

31-12. Terbium(IV)

The chemistry of terbium(IV) appears to resemble that of Pr^{IV}, although it is rather less known. The Tb–O system is complex. When terbium or its common oxo acid salts are ignited under ordinary conditions, an oxide of approximately the composition Tb_4O_7 is obtained. Actually, this formula ($TbO_{1.75}$) is not the correct formula for the stable phase obtained, but is the nearest approach, using small whole numbers, to the true formula, which may be anywhere from $TbO_{1.71}$ to $TbO_{1.81}$ depending on details of ignition temperature, oxygen pressure and rate of cooling. Thus nonstoichiometry is characteristic of this system. For the average formula Tb_4O_7, Tb^{III} and Tb^{IV} are present in equal amounts. TbO_2, with a fluorite structure, can be obtained by oxidation of Tb_2O_3 with atomic oxygen at 450°. Colorless TbF_4, isostructural with CeF_4 and ThF_4, is obtained by reacting gaseous fluorine with TbF_3 at 300–400°. Also, compounds of the

[16] J. Soriano and Y. Marcus, *Inorg. Chem.*, **3**, 901 (1964).

type $M_nTbF_{n+4}(M = K, Rb$ or $Cs; n \geqslant 2)$ have been reported, but not yet fully described. No numerical estimate has been given for the Tb^{IV}/Tb^{III} potential, but it must certainly be more positive than $+1.23$ v since dissolution of any oxide containing Tb^{IV} gives only Tb^{III} in solution and oxygen is evolved. TbF_4 is even less reactive than CeF_4 and does not react rapidly even with hot water.

31-13. Neodymium(IV) and Dysprosium(IV)

Although there are many reports of the preparation of higher oxides of these elements, supposedly containing Nd^{IV} and Dy^{IV}, recent studies leave little doubt that these claims are erroneous. Even treatment of Nd_2O_3 with atomic oxygen gave no Nd^{IV}-containing product. Only in the products of fluorination of mixtures of RbCl and CsCl with $NdCl_3$ and $DyCl_3$ is there fair evidence for the existence of Nd^{IV} and Dy^{IV}. Apparently such compounds as Cs_3NdF_7 and Cs_3DyF_7 can be formed, at least partially, in this way.

THE II OXIDATION STATE

31-14. Europium(II)

Of the five divalent species given by the lanthanides, Eu^{II} is by far the most stable. This is reflected, for example, in the potential of the Eu^{III}/Eu^{II} couple, -0.43 v. Aqueous solutions of Eu^{II}, which are colorless, are obtained by treating Eu^{III} solutions with various reducing agents such as magnesium, aluminum, iron or zinc, and the reduction may also be carried out electrolytically at a mercury cathode. The solid halides are usually made by reducing the solid trihalides with hydrogen or ammonia or by thermal decomposition,

$$EuI_3 \rightarrow EuI_2 + \tfrac{1}{2}I_2(g)$$

Other salts can be made by metathetical reactions with the halides.

A large number of compounds containing Eu^{II} are known, including the halides, the sulfate, phosphate, perchlorate, hydroxide, carbonate, oxide, sulfide, selenide and telluride. The structures of many of these have been studied, and in most cases isomorphism with other M^{II} salts, especially Ba and Sr salts, is found. Eu^{II} ion has a crystallographic radius of about 1.10 A (cf. Eu^{III} with $r = 0.95$ A). The oxide, sulfide, selenide and telluride have the rock salt structure as do many $M^{II}O$ compounds. $EuSO_4$ is isostructural with $BaSO_4$. $EuCl_2$ is isostructural with $PbCl_2$, as is $NdCl_2$

(see below); $EuBr_2$ is isostructural with $SrBr_2$, but EuI_2 is not isostructural with SrI_2 and its structure is not known in detail.

Eu^{II} in solution is a mild reducing agent, but otherwise similar in its chemistry to barium. The hydroxide is soluble in water, and the other lanthanides can be separated from Eu^{II} by precipitation of their hydroxides with carbonate-free ammonia; alternatively, europous sulfate can be precipitated and removed.

31-15. Samarium(II)

Sm^{II} is much less stable than Eu^{II} and less stable even than Yb^{II}. The most recent estimates of its standard potential give a value of about -1.55 v, which accords with its behavior as a very powerful reducing agent; indeed, aqueous solutions are not stable because water is reduced by Sm^{II}. Aqueous solutions containing blood-red Sm^{II} are prepared by treating aqueous Sm^{III} with alkali metal amalgams or electrolytically. The divalent halides are obtained by reduction of anhydrous Sm^{III} halides with hydrogen or ammonia at high temperatures. SmI_2 but not the other dihalides can be obtained by thermal decomposition of the Sm^{III} compound. Other compounds may be obtained by metathetical reactions of aqueous solutions of the halides. All compounds of Sm^{II} are thermodynamically unstable with respect to oxidation by water or oxygen but are stable indefinitely in an inert atmosphere.

A number of compounds of Sm^{II} are known including the halides, sulfate, chromate, phosphate, hydroxide, carbonate and oxide, and the structures of some of these are known. The ionic radius of Sm^{II} is about 1.11 A. SmO has the rock salt structure. SmF_2 has the fluorite structure but readily dissolves SmF_3 and is thus difficult to obtain pure. $SmCl_2$ and $SmBr_2$ are isostructural with $SrCl_2$ and $SrBr_2$, while SmI_2 is isostructural with EuI_2 but not with SrI_2. $SmSO_4$ and $SmCO_3$ are isostructural with the corresponding barium compounds.

In their chemical as well as structural properties, Sm^{II} compounds resemble those of barium insofar as the strongly reducing character of Sm^{II} permits comparisons.

31-16. Ytterbium(II)

The green Yb^{II} ion is a powerful reducing agent and is rapidly oxidized by water in aqueous solution. Its standard potential appears to be about -1.15 v according to the most recent estimates.

Yb^{II} is in general more stable than Sm^{II}, but distinctly less so than Eu^{II}. It has been prepared in aqueous solution mainly by electrolytic reduction of Yb^{III} at mercury or amalgamated lead cathodes or by electrolysis with a lithium amalgam.

Among the solid compounds known are the halides, sulfate, carbonate, oxide, sulfide, selenide and telluride. Methods of preparation are analogous to those described above for corresponding Eu^{II} and Sm^{II} compounds. Solid Yb^{II} salts are stable in the absence of air and water. The oxide, selenide and telluride have the NaCl structure and the carbonate is iso-structural with $BaCO_3$. The sulfate has a structure like $CePO_4$. The fluoride has a fluorite structure, but, like EuF_2 and SmF_2, it dissolves the trifluoride extensively and pure YbF_2 has probably never been obtained. The structures of $YbCl_2$ and $YbBr_2$ are not known in detail; YbI_2 is isostructural with CdI_2. The ionic radius of Yb^{II} is about 0.93 A.

31-17. Thulium(II) and Neodymium(II)

These species are very unstable and of very rare occurrence. Definite evidence for their existence has been obtained only recently. Although there had been some inconclusive evidence for Tm^{II}, the preparation of the iodide, in 1959, by reduction of TmI_3 with Tm at 500–600° represents the only unequivocal evidence for the occurrence of Tm^{II}. The iodide has, like YbI_2, the CdI_2 structure. Tm^{II} is a very powerful reducing agent, reacting violently with water, and its standard potential is believed to be more negative than -1.5 v.

Study of the NdX_3–Nd systems shows that in addition to the stoichio-metric compound $NdCl_2$, the intermediate phases $NdCl_{2.3_7}$, and $NdCl_{2.2_7}$, and $NdI_{1.95}$ exist.[17] The black chlorides and red-violet iodide are air-sensitive and react with water. Magnetic measurements show that the Nd^{2+} ion $(4f^2)$ is present. $NdCl_2$, like $SmCl_2$ and $EuCl_2$, has the $PbCl_2$ structure.

31-18. Other Dihalides

From melts of La, Ce, Pr and Gd iodides containing the respective metal, solids of stoichiometry MI_2 can be obtained.[18] However, these do *not* contain M^{2+} ions but are metallic in nature. For LaI_2 it has been shown that the substance must be regarded as $La^{3+}(I^-)_2 \, e$ with the odd valence electron located in a metallic conduction band, formed presumably by overlap of metal orbitals via the iodide ions. The substances thus resemble the monosulfides (e.g., golden yellow LaS) and acetylides which can

[17] R. A., Sallach and J. D. Corbett, *Inorg. Chem.*, **3**, 993 (1964) and references therein.
[18] J. E. Mee and J. D. Corbett, *Inorg. Chem.*, **4**, 88 (1965).

similarly be formulated $M^{3+}(S^{2-})\ e$, and $M^{3+}(C_2^{2-})\ e$, since they show metal-like conductivity. However, Gd appears to give a chloride, $GdCl_{1.6}$, which appears to contain some reduced Gd species and there is evidence that Ce^{2+} and Pr^{2+} can exist in host lattices. There is no evidence for lower states in Sc–$ScCl_3$ melts.[19]

[19] J. D. Corbett and B. N. Ramsey, *Inorg. Chem.*, **4**, 261 (1965).

References

Asprey, L. B., and B. B. Cunningham, *Prog. Inorg. Chem.*, **2**, 267 (1960). Unusual oxidation states of some actinide and lanthanide elements.

Boyd, G. E., *J. Chem. Educ.*, **36**, 3 (1959). Promethium.

Cunningham, B. B., *Rare Earth Research*, E. V. Kleber, Ed., Macmillan, New York, 1961, pp. 127–134. Comparison of lanthanide and actinide chemistry.

Eyring, Le Roy, ed., *Progress in the Science and Technology of the Rare Earths*, Pergamon Press, London, 1964. Reviews on extraction, solution chemistry, magnetic properties, analysis, etc.

Moeller, T., *The Chemistry of the Lanthanides*, Reinhold, New York, 1963. An introductory treatment, but authoritative and thorough at its level.

Nachod, J. F., and C. E. Lundin, *Rare Earth Research*, Gordon and Beach, New York, 1962. Conference proceedings.

Prog. Sci. Tech. Rare Earths, Vol. 1, McMillan, New York, 1964. Various articles on alloys, separations, etc.

Rare Earths. Special report, *Chem. and Eng. News*, 1965, May 10th, page 78. General survey of mining economics and uses.

Spedding, F. H., and A. M. Daane, Eds., *The Rare Earths*, Wiley, New York, 1961. Contains detailed discussions of occurrence, extraction procedures, preparation, and properties of metals and alloys; also describes applications.

Taylor, M. D., *Chem. Rev*, **62**, 503 (1962). Preparation of anhydrous lanthanide halides.

Topp, N. E., *J. Less Common Metals*, **7**, 411 (1964). Review on lanthanide separations.

———, *The Chemistry of the Rare Earth Elements*, Elsevier, New York, 1965.

Trifonov, D. N., *The Rare Earth Elements*, Macmillan, New York, 1964. A cursory general treatment, emphasizing historical development.

Vickery, R. C., *Analytical Chemistry of the Rare Earths*, Pergamon Press, London, 1961.

———, *Chemistry of the Lanthanons*, Academic Press, New York, 1953. A general account of the elements.

———, *Chemistry of Yttrium and Scandium*, Pergamon Press, London, 1960.

Wybourne, B. G., *Spectroscopic Properties of Rare Earths*, Wiley, New York, 1965. Comprehensive discussion of atomic spectra and especially of spectra of salts.

Yost, D. M., H. Russell and C. S. Garner, *The Rare Earth Elements and Their Compounds*, Wiley, New York, 1947. A classical book containing early references; still of value.

32

The Actinide Elements

32-1. Occurrence

The actinide elements, all of whose isotopes are radioactive, are listed in Table 32-1.

TABLE 32-1

The Actinide Elements: Electronic Structures and Ionic Radii[a]

Z	Symbol	Name	Electronic structure of valence shells	Radius M^{3+}, A	Radius M^{4+}, A
89	Ac	Actinium	$6d7s^2$	1.11	
90	Th	Thorium	$6d^27s^2$		0.99
91	Pa	Protactinium	$5f^26d7s^2$ or $5f^16d^27s^2$		0.96
92	U	Uranium	$5f^36d7s^2$	1.03	0.93
93	Np	Neptunium	$5f^57s^2$	1.01	0.92
94	Pu	Plutonium	$5f^67s^2$	1.00	0.90
95	Am	Americium	$5f^77s^2$	0.99	0.89
96	Cm	Curium	$5f^76d7s^2$	0.98	0.88
97	Bk	Berkelium	$5f^86d7s^2$ or $5f^97s^2$		
98	Cf	Californium	$5f^{10}7s^2$		
99	Es	Einsteinium	$5f^{11}7s^2$		
100	Fm	Fermium	$5f^{12}7s^2$		
101	Md	Mendelevium	$5f^{13}7s^2$		
102[b]			$5f^{14}7s^2$		
103	Lw	Lawrencium	$5f^{14}6d7s^2$		

[a] In the octahedral fluorides, MF_6, the M—F bond distance also decreases with increasing Z, namely, U—F, 1.994 A; Np—F, 1.981 A; Pu—F, 1.969 A.

[b] The name "nobelium" was given to an unconfirmed isotope; established isotopes of element 102 are now known but no name has yet been assigned.

TABLE 32-2

Principal Actinide Isotopes Available in Macroscopic Amounts[a]

Isotope	Half-life	Source
^{227}Ac	21.7 yr.	Natural; ^{226}Ra$(n\gamma)^{227}$Ra $\xrightarrow[41.2 \text{ min.}]{\beta^-}$ ^{227}Ac
^{232}Th	1.39×10^{10} yr.	Natural; 100% abundance.
^{231}Pa	3.28×10^5 yr.	Natural; 0.34 p.p.m. of U in uranium ores
^{235}U	7.13×10^8 yr.	Natural; 0.72% abundance
^{238}U	4.50×10^9 yr.	Natural; 99.274% abundance
^{237}Np	2.20×10^6 yr.	^{235}U$(n\gamma)^{236}$U$(n\gamma)^{237}$U $\xrightarrow[6.75 \text{ d.}]{\beta^-}$ ^{237}Np
^{238}Pu	86.4 yr.	^{237}Np$(n\gamma)^{238}$Np $\xrightarrow[2.1 \text{ d.}]{\beta^-}$ ^{238}Pu
^{239}Pu	24,360 yr.	^{238}U$(n\gamma)^{239}$U $\xrightarrow[23.5 \text{ min.}]{\beta^-}$ ^{239}Np $\xrightarrow[2.35 \text{ d.}]{\beta^-}$ ^{239}Pu
^{242}Pu	3.79×10^5 yr.	Successive $n\gamma$ in ^{239}Pu
^{241}Am	458 yr.	^{239}Pu$(n\gamma)^{240}$Pu$(n\gamma)^{241}$Pu $\xrightarrow[13.2 \text{ yr.}]{\beta^-}$ ^{241}Am
^{243}Am	7951 yr.	Successive $n\gamma$ on ^{239}Pu
^{242}Cm	162.5 d.	^{241}Am$(n\gamma)^{242m}$Am $\xrightarrow[160. \text{ hr.}]{\beta^-}$ ^{242}Cm
^{244}Cm	17.6 yr.	^{239}Pu$(4n\gamma)^{243}$Pu $\xrightarrow[5.0 \text{ hr.}]{\beta^-}$ ^{243}Am$(n\gamma)^{244}$Am $\xrightarrow[26 \text{ min.}]{\beta^-}$ ^{244}Cm
^{252}Cf	2.2 yr.	Successive $n\gamma$ on ^{242}Pu

[a] Other long-lived isotopes are known but several, such as ^{248}Cm, ^{254}Es and ^{255}Fm, can probably not be obtained in macroscopic amounts. ^{237}Np and ^{239}Pu are available in multi-kilogram quantities, ^{241}Am, ^{242}Pu and ^{244}Cm in amounts of 100 g or above, ^{249}Bk, $^{249-252}$Cf in quantities approaching milligrams, and $^{253-4}$Es in μg.

The terrestrial occurrence of actinium, protactinium, uranium and thorium is due to the half-lives of the isotopes ^{235}U, ^{238}U and ^{232}Th which are sufficiently long to have enabled the species to persist since genesis. They are the prime sources of actinium and protactinium (and also the other radioactive isotopes formed in the decay series), which are found in uranium and thorium ores. The half-lives of the most stable isotopes of the trans-uranium elements are such that any primordial amounts of these elements would have disappeared long ago. However, neptunium and plutonium have been isolated in trace quantities from uranium minerals in which they are formed continuously by neutron reactions such as

$$^{238}\text{U} \xrightarrow{n\gamma} {}^{239}\text{U} \xrightarrow{\beta^-} {}^{239}\text{Np} \xrightarrow{\beta^-} {}^{239}\text{Pu}$$

The neutrons arise from spontaneous fission of ^{235}U or from α,n reactions of light elements present in uranium minerals. In Congo uranium ore, the mass ratio $^{237}\text{Np}/^{238}\text{U}$ does not exceed 1.8×10^{-12}, whereas in Canada pitchblende the ratio $^{238}\text{Pu}/^{238}\text{U}$ is 7.1×10^{-12}.

Neptunium and plutonium were obtained in tracer amounts from bombardments of uranium by McMillan and Abelson and by Seaborg, McMillan, Kennedy and Wahl, respectively, in 1940. Both elements are obtained in substantial quantities from the uranium fuel elements of nuclear reactors. Only plutonium is normally recovered and is used as a nuclear fuel since, like ^{235}U, it undergoes fission; its nuclear properties apparently preclude its use in hydrogen bombs. The heavier elements are obtained by successive neutron capture in ^{239}Pu in reactors giving high neutron fluxes ($> 10^{14}$ neutrons/cm^2/sec); they can be obtained in tracer quantities by appropriate nuclear reactions of Pu, Am or Cm isotopes with accelerated heavy ions of B, C, N, O or Ne. The present detailed knowledge of the actinide elements as a whole—and indeed of many other elements such as those encountered as fission products or those used in nuclear technology—is primarily a result of the development of nuclear energy. The impact of these developments has also led further to revolutionary advances and progress in methods and techniques. Thus procedures such as ion exchange separations, solvent extraction and handling of microgram quantities of material or of reactive or intensely radioactive substances, have been perfected in the nuclear energy programs.

32-2. Electronic Structures—Comparison with Lanthanides

The electronic structures of the neutral gaseous atoms are given in Table 32-1 from which it will be seen that there is still uncertainty in allocation in a few cases. In the actinide elements, the fourteen $5f$ electrons are added formally, though not necessarily actually, from thorium, $Z = 90$, onward, and the $5f$ shell is complete at element 103; element 104 should be hafnium-like in its properties.

Since f shells are being filled, the actinides have a close and instructive relation with the lanthanides. Thus actinium and lanthanum occupy corresponding positions as prototypes for the two series of elements. Although important similarities do exist between the actinides and lanthanides, very important differences also occur. The differences arise mainly from the relatively lower binding energies and less effective shielding by the outer electrons of the $5f$ as compared to the $4f$ electrons. In the elements preceding the lanthanides the $4f$ orbitals have relatively high energy and extend spatially outside the $5s$ and $5p$ shells, but over a small range of atomic numbers, at and after cerium, they become lower energy inner orbitals. As inner orbitals they are not accessible for bonding purposes, and the lanthanide elements have virtually no complexes or covalent compounds in which 4f orbitals are used.

For the 5f orbitals the change from outer to inner orbitals is similar to the 4f case. There is reason to believe that 5f electrons are not present in thorium or probably in protactinium, but for uranium and succeeding elements 5f electrons are present. A rough qualitative picture for the binding energies of the weakest bound 5f and 6d electrons is shown in Figure 32-1; it appears from spectroscopic, chemical and other data that

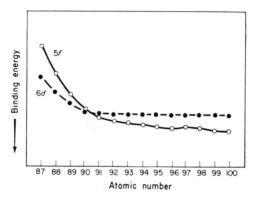

Fig. 32-1. Qualitative representation of electronic binding energies in the heaviest elements (J. J. Katz and G. T. Seaborg, *The Chemistry of the Actinide Elements*, Methuen, London, 1957, p. 465).

the 5f level becomes progressively lower in energy compared to the 6d with increasing atomic number. The relative point of change is thus different in the two series and also the fall in energy and shrinkage in size are not so precipitous for the 5f orbitals compared to the 4f orbitals. The 5f orbitals thus have a greater spatial extension relative to the 6s and 6p orbitals than the 4f orbitals have relative to the 5s and 5p orbitals. The greater spacial extension of the 5f orbitals has been shown experimentally; the electron spin resonance spectrum of UF_3 in a CaF_2 lattice shows structure attributable to the interaction of fluorine nuclei with the electron spin of the U^{3+} ion. This implies a small overlap of 5f orbitals with fluorine and constitutes an f covalent contribution to the ionic bonding. With the neodymium ion a similar effect is *not* observed.

In the actinide series, therefore, we have a situation in which the energies of the 5f, 6d, 7s and 7p orbitals are about comparable over a range of atomic numbers (especially U–Am), and, since the orbitals also overlap spacially, bonding can involve any or all of them. In the chemistries, this situation is indicated by the fact that the actinides are much more prone to complex formation than are the lanthanides where the bonding is almost exclusively ionic. Indeed the actinides can even form complexes with π-bonding ligands such as alkylphosphines, thioethers and π-cyclopentadienyl as well as forming complexes with halide, sulfate and other ions. The difference from lanthanide chemistry is usually attributed to the contribution of covalent-hybrid bonding involving $5f$ electrons.

A further point is that since the energies of the $5f$, $6d$, $7s$ and $7p$ levels are comparable, the energies involved in an electron shifting from one to another, say $5f$ to $6d$, may lie *within* the range of chemical binding energies. Thus the electronic structure of the element in a given oxidation state may vary between compounds and in solution be dependent on the nature of the ligands. It is accordingly also often impossible to say *which* orbitals are being utilized in bonding or to decide meaningfully whether the bonding is covalent or ionic.

32-3. Oxidation States of the Actinide Elements

The known oxidation states are given in Table 32-3. The common and dominant oxidation state, as in the lanthanides, is $+3$, and the behavior of actinides and lanthanides in this state is very similar. For thorium and protactinium, the $+3$ state is unimportant, and for these elements the $+4$ and $+5$ oxidation states, respectively, predominate; accordingly thorium to some extent resembles hafnium and protactinium resembles tantalum, and there has been some rather pedantic argument as to whether or not they should be placed in groups IV and V.

From uranium onward there is a very closely related group, U, Np, Pu and Am, in which the stability of the higher oxidation states falls. This fall is shown by the reduction potentials of the ions in solution and in simple compounds such as the halides, where the higher halides either do not exist, for example, $PuCl_5$, or require more vigorous conditions to prepare, for example, AmF_6.

All of the actinide elements form cationic species, the principal ions being M^{3+}, M^{4+}, MO_2^+ and MO_2^{2+} for the oxidation states $+3$ to $+6$, respectively. The general behavior of compounds or ions of different elements in the same oxidation state is the same, excepting differences in ease of oxidation or reduction. Most compounds of the same type are isomorphous. The oxo ions, MO_2^+ and MO_2^{2+}, are remarkably stable with respect to the strength of the M—O bond (see below). Unlike some other oxo ions they can persist through a variety of chemical changes, and they behave like cations whose properties are intermediate between those of M^+ or M^{2+} ions and those of ions of similar size but greater charge. The MO_2 group even appears more or less as an "yl" group in certain oxide and oxo ion structures, as noted later. Further, whereas MoO_2F_2 or WO_2F_2 are molecular halides, in UO_2F_2 there is a linear O—U—O group with F-bridges. The stability of UO_2^{2+} and PuO_2^{2+} ions in aqueous solution is shown by the very long half-life for exchange with $H_2^{18}O$ of $>10^4$ hours; the exchange can be catalyzed by the presence of reduced states or, for PuO_2^{2+}, by self-reduction due to radiation effects.[1]

TABLE 32-3

Oxidation States of the Actinide Elements

Ac	Th	Pa	U	Np	Pu	Am	Cm	Bk	Cf	Es	Fm	Md
_3_[a]	_3_[b]	3	3	3	3	_3_	_3_	_3_	3	3	3	3
	_4_	4	4	_4_	4	4	4	4				
		5	5	5	5	5						
			6	6	6	6						

[a] Italic number signifies most stable state.
[b] Solid state only.

The possibility of several cationic species introduces complexity into the aqueous chemistries, particularly of U, Np, Pu and Am. Thus for Pu, all four oxidation states can coexist in appreciable concentrations in a solution. The solution chemistries and the oxidation–reduction potentials are further complicated by the existence of *complex species* with ions other than perchlorate—cationic, neutral and anionic species being known—by *hydrolysis*, even in solutions of low pH to give polymeric ions, and finally by *disproportionation* reactions which can occur in some cases and are particularly pH dependent.

Since extrapolation to infinite dilution is not possible for most of the actinide ions, owing to hydrolysis—for example, Pu^{4+} cannot exist in solution below $0.05M$ in acid—only approximate oxidation potentials can sometimes be given. The potentials are sensitive to the anions and other conditions. In Table 32-4 are given the potentials for $1M$ perchloric acid solutions, from which it can clearly be seen that the electropositive character of the metals increases with atomic number and the stability of the higher oxidation states falls off.

A comparison of the various actinide ions is given in Table 32-5.

In addition to the above complications it must also be borne in mind that for comparatively short-lived isotopes decaying by α-emission or spontaneous fission, heating and chemical effects due to the high level of radioactivity occur in both solids and aqueous solutions, e.g., for ^{238}Pu,

[1] B. J. Masters and S. W. Rabideau, *Inorg. Chem.*, **2**, 1 (1963).

TABLE 32-4

Formal Reduction Potentials of the Actinides for $1M$ Perchloric Acid Solutions at 25°.

(In volts; brackets [ ] indicate estimate)

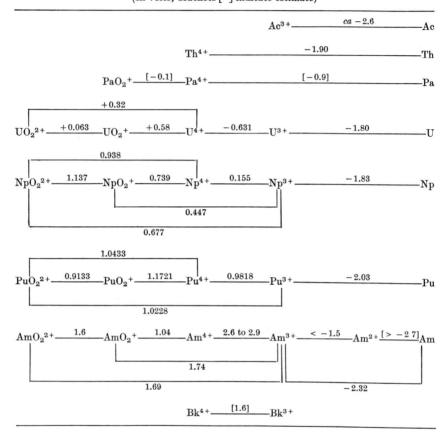

Notes:

1. $PaO_2^+ + 4H^+ = Pa + 2H_2O$, $E = [-1.0]$.

2. Couples involving oxygen transfer, for example, $UO_2^{2+} + 4H^+ + 2e = U^{4+} + 2H_2O$ are *irreversible* and are of course hydrogen ion dependent. Couples such as PuO_2^{2+}/PuO_2^+ *are* reversible.

[241]Am and [242]Cm the heat output is calculated as 0.5, 0.1 and 122 watts/g, respectively. Radiation-induced decomposition of water leads to H and OH radicals, H_2O_2 production, etc., and in solution higher oxidation states such as Pu^V, Pu^{VI}, Am^{IV-VI} are reduced. Chemical reactions observable with a short-lived isotope, e.g., [242]Cm (163 days) may differ when a longer-lived isotope is used; thus Cm^{IV} can be observed only when [244]Cm (17.6 years) is employed.

TABLE 32-5

The Principal Actinide Ions[a] in Aqueous Solution

Ion	Color[b]	Preparation	Stability
U^{3+}	Red-brown	Na or Zn/Hg on UO_2^{2+}	Slowly oxidized by H_2O, rapidly by air to U^{4+}
Np^{3+}	Purplish	$H_2(Pt)$ or electrolytic	Stable in water; oxidized by air to Np^{4+}
Pu^{3+}	Blue-violet	SO_2, NH_2OH on higher states	Stable to water and air; easily oxidized to Pu^{4+}
Am^{3+}	Pink	I^-, SO_2, etc., on higher states	Stable; difficult to oxidize
Cm^{3+}	Pale yellow		Stable; not oxidized chemically
U^{4+}	Green	Air or O_2 on U^{3+}	Stable; slowly oxidized by air to UO_2^{2+}
Np^{4+}	Yellow-green	SO_2 on NpO_2^+ in H_2SO_4	Stable; slowly oxidized by air to NpO_2^+
Pu^{4+}	Tan	SO_2 or NO_2^- on PuO_2^{2+}	Stable in $6M$ acid; disproportionates in low acid $\rightarrow Pu^3 + PuO_2^{2+}$
Am^{4+c}	Pink-red	$Am(OH)_4$ in $15M$ NH_4F	Stable in $15M$ NH_4F; reduced by I^-
Cm^{4+c}	Pale yellow	Cm_4F in $15M$ CsF	Stable only 1 hour at $25°$.
UO_2^+	?	Transient species	Stability greatest pH 2–4; disproportionates to U^{4+} and UO_2^{2+}
NpO_2^+	Green	Np^{4+} and hot HNO_3	Stable; disproportionates only in strong acid
PuO_2^+	?	Hydroxylamine on PuO_2^{2+}	Always disproportionates; most stable at low acidity
AmO_2^+	Pale yellow	Am^{3+} with OCl^-, cold $S_2O_8^{2-}$	Disproportionates in strong acid; reduced (2% per hour) by products of own α-radiation
UO_2^{2+}	Yellow	Oxidize U^{4+} with HNO_3, etc.	Very stable; difficult to reduce
NpO_2^{2+}	Pink		Stable; easily reduced
PuO_2^{2+}	Yellow-pink	Oxidize lower states with Ce^{4+}, MnO_4^-, O_3, BrO_3^-, etc.	Stable; fairly easy to reduce
AmO_2^{2+}	Rum		Reduced (4% per hour) by products from own α-radiation

[a] Ac^{3+}, Th^{4+}, Cm^{3+} and ions of Pa are colorless.
[b] Depends on concentration and nature of ions.
[c] As fluoro complex, MF_6^{2-}.

32-4. Ionic Radii

The ionic radii are listed in Table 32-1 and are also shown together with the lanthanide radii in Figure 32-2. There is clearly an "actinide con-

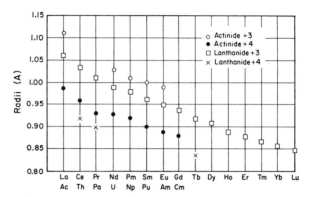

Fig. 32-2. Radii of actinide and lanthanide ions.

traction" similar to that for the lanthanide ions and the trends are very similar indeed. As would be expected, the chemistries of lanthanides and actinides in the M^{3+} and M^{4+} states are quite similar, and, if we compare an actinide and a lanthanide with the same radius for, say, M^{3+}, physical properties, such as thermochemical data for hydrolysis reactions, which depend closely on the ionic radius, are very similar. Actinide compounds in the same oxidation state have the same crystal structures differing only in the parameters. Despite the ease of oxidation of Pa^{4+} and the non-existence of Am^{4+} and Cm^{4+} in solution except as fluoro anions, the dioxides MO_2 are stable owing to the high lattice energy of their fluorite lattice.

Although the lanthanide metals with the exception of Eu and Yb have also a steady decrease in the atomic volumes and metal radii, Pa, U, Np and Pu metals have complicated structures which have no counterpart among the metals of the lanthanides. Americium is the first metal to show a similarity to the crystal structures of the lanthanide metals.

32-5. Absorption Spectra and Magnetic Properties

The absorption spectra of the actinide ions, like those of the lanthanide ions, consist of narrow bands in the visible, near-ultraviolet and near-infrared regions which are less influenced by ligand fields than are the spectral bands of d transition metal ions. The bands, which are due to electronic transition within the $5f^n$ levels, are generally about ten times as intense as the lanthanide bands. Spectra involving only one f electron are simple, consisting of only a single transition $^2F_{5/2}$–$^2F_{7/2}$. For the f^7 configuration (Cm^{3+}; cf. Gd^{3+}) the lowest excited state lies about 4 ev above the ground level so that these ions show only charge-transfer absorption in the ultra-violet.

The magnetic properties of the actinide ions are considerably more difficult to interpret than those of the lanthanide ions, and the situation is not yet fully understood. The experimental magnetic moments are usually lower than the values calculated using Russell–Saunders coupling, and this appears to be due both to ligand field effects similar to those operating in the d transition series and to inadequacy of this coupling scheme. It is now quite certain that $5f$ orbitals can participate to some extent in covalent bonding so that ligand effects are to be expected.

For the ions Pu^{3+} and Am^{3+}, the same phenomenon noted for Sm^{3+} and Eu^{3+} is found; since the multiplet levels are comparable to kT, anomalous temperature dependence of the susceptibilities is found.

32-6. Stereochemistry

Although there is certainly some doubt concerning the extent of covalent bonding in actinide compounds, the angular distributions and relative strengths of various orbital combinations using f orbitals have been worked out theoretically in a manner similar to that for the familiar schemes in light elements. Examples are: sf, linear; sf^3, tetrahedral; sf^2d, square; and d^2sf^3, octahedral. These hybridizations *could* be considered to hold in PuO_2^{2+}, $NpCl_4$ and UCl_6, for example. However, in view of the close-ness in the energy levels of electrons in the valence shells, and the mutual overlap of orbitals of comparable size in these heavy atoms, several equally valid descriptions can be chosen in a particular case. In such circum-stances, the orbitals actually used must be some mixture of all the possible limiting sets and it is not justified to treat the bonding in terms of any single set, except as a convenient first approximation.

The actinides have a far greater tendency to complex formation than the lanthanides. Thus there are extensive series of halogeno complexes and complex ions are given with most oxo anions such as NO_3^-, SO_4^{2-}, ox^{2-}, CO_3^{2-}, phosphate, etc. A vast amount of data exists on complex ion formation in solution since this has been of primary importance in con-nection with solvent extraction, ion-exchange behavior and precipitation reactions involved in the technology of actinide elements. The general tendency to complex ion formation decreases in the direction controlled by factors such as ionic size and charge, so that the order is generally M^{4+} >

$MO_2^{2+} > M^{3+} > MO_2^+$. For anions, the order of complexing ability is generally: uninegative ions, $F^- > NO_3^- > Cl^- > ClO_4^-$; binegative ions, $CO_3^{2-} > ox^{2-} > SO_4^{2-}$. Complexes are also formed between halides and neutral ligands but very few complexes indeed are formed by π-bonding ligands (other than oxygen), providing a notable contrast to the d-block transition elements. Thus there is no evidence for bonding of CO, NO or olefins to actinide ions; no compounds are known in which the formal oxidation states are lower than +3. The only organo compounds are the π-cyclopentadienyls, e.g., $(\pi\text{-}C_5H_5)_3Am$[1a] and $(\pi\text{-}C_5H_5)_3UCl$, for which "sandwich type" bonding can be explained by appropriate hybridization schemes involving f orbitals.

Examples of the stereochemistry of actinide compounds and complexes are given in Table 32-6. For the +3 oxidation state, where the resemblance

TABLE 32-6

Stereochemistry of Actinides

Oxidation state	Coordination number	Geometry[a]	Examples
+3	5	TBP	AcF_3, $BaUF_6$ (LaF$_3$-type)
	6	Octahedral	Macac$_3$, $[M(H_2O)_6]^{3+}$
	8		UI_3
	9		UCl_3, $AmCl_3$ (also La–GdCl$_3$)
+4	6	Octahedral	UCl_6^-, UCl_6^{2-}, $UCl_4(PEt_3)_2$
	8	Dodecahedral?	$K_4[U(NCS)_8]$, AmF_8^{4-}
		Dodecahedral	[Th ox$_4$]$^{4-}$
		Fluorite str.	ThO_2, UO_2
		Square antiprism	$ThI_4(s)$, $Uacac_4$
	9	?	Th nitriloacetate complex
	12	Irreg. icosahedral	$[Th(NO_3)_6]^{2-}$
+5	6	Octahedral	UF_6^-, α–UF$_5$ (infinite chain)
	7		β–UF$_5$
	9	Complex	PaF_7^{2-} in K_2PaF_7
+6	6	Octahedral	UF_6, Li_4UO_5 (distorted), UCl_6
	6–8	See text	MO_2^+ and MO_2^{2+} complexes
	8	?	$M_2^1UF_8$
	10	?	$[M(tropolonate)_5]^-$, $M = Th, U$

[a] For detailed discussion of crystal structures, many of which are most complicated, see A. F. Wells, *Structural Inorganic Chemistry*, 3rd ed., Oxford University Press, 1962, p. 959.

to the lanthanides is distinct, octahedral coordination is often found, but higher coordination numbers (e.g., 9 in UCl_3) are also common. Eight coordination is especially a characteristic of the +4 oxidation state. An example here is Thacac$_4$, which is isomorphous with the uranium analog

[1a] F. Baumgartner, *et al.*, *Angew. Chem.* (*Internat.*), **5**, 134 (1966).

and has a structure based on a slightly distorted square antiprism. This structure is the one predicted on purely electrostatic grounds, and the volatility of the compound is no criterion of covalent bonding but is only a reflection of the almost spherical nature of the molecules and valence saturation of the outer atoms. Well-defined 10-coordinate anions, [M(tropolonate)$_5$]$^-$, have been prepared for Th^{IV} and U^{IV}.[2a]

The Oxo Ions MO$_2^+$ and MO$_2^{2+}$. Although some structural evidence in the past suggested non-linearity of the O—M—O groups, it is now generally agreed that in both crystalline compounds and in solutions the oxo ions are *linear*. The oxo ions form a great variety of complexes with negative ions and neutral molecules. Crystallographic data show that four, five or six ligand atoms can lie in the equatorial plane of the O—M—O group; the ligand atoms may or may not be entirely coplanar depending on the circumstances. Planar 5- and 6-coordination in the equatorial plane is commonest and appears to be the more stable geometry compared to puckered hexagonal configurations. Planar 5-coordination best allows the rationalization of a number of hydroxide and other structures, as well as the behavior of polynuclear uranyl ions in hydrolyzed solutions.[2b] An example is the structure of the anion in the complex salt sodium uranyl acetate shown in Figure 32-3; the carboxyl groups are bidentate and

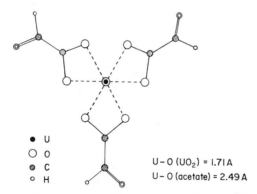

●	U
○	O
◉	C
○	H

U – O (UO$_2$) = 1.71 A
U – O (acetate) = 2.49 A

Fig. 32-3. Structure of anion in Na[UO$_2$(OCOCH$_3$)$_3$].

equivalent. Similar structures have been found in other species such as UO$_2$(NO$_3$)$_2$[OP(OEt$_3$)]$_2$ and Rb[UO$_2$(NO$_3$)$_3$].

For such heavy atoms there are difficulties in accurately locating oxygen atoms and assessing M—O distances but it is certain that the M—O distances are *not constant*. Thus for UO$_2^{2+}$ the range appears to be from

[2a] E. L. Muetterties, *J. Amer. Chem. Soc.*, **88**, 305 (1966).
[2b] H. T. Evans, Jr., *Science*, **141**, 154 (1963).

ca 1.6 to *ca* 2.0 A. Accordingly there has been extensive use of infrared data[3] for correlating bond lengths and force constants using Badger's rule:

$$R = \beta F^{-1/3} + d$$

where R = bond length in A, F = force constant in millidynes/A, β = an empirical constant, 1.08, d = a constant estimated from crystallographic data to be 1.17. Where intercomparison is possible, the rule generally agrees with X-ray data.

For MO_2^{2+} the bond strengths evidently decrease in the order U > Np > Pu > Am. It also appears that the force constants for U—O bonds are high, indicating a multiplicity greater than two. The suggestion that the U—O bond can be regarded as having a formal order of three $\ddot{O}{=}U{=}\ddot{O}$ was first made by Dyatkina.[4] Appropriate combinations of d and f orbitals can be combined into molecular orbitals to give one σ- plus two π-bonds. The treatment allows detailed interpretation of spectroscopic and magnetic data for the oxo ions. It also provides an explanation of the U–Am stability sequence and for the non-existence of PaO_2^{2+}. The latter is connected with the fact that for Pa, the $6d$ level is higher than the $5f$, whereas for $U(5f^3 6d^1 7s^2)$ it is the reverse, so that for Pa, the $5f\sigma{-}2p\sigma$ metal–oxygen overlap is poor. The instability of UO_2^+ (see later) is probably also connected with the sensitivity of the energy of the $5f$ electrons to total charge thus critically affecting the U—O overlap.

ACTINIUM

32-7. The Element and its Compounds

Actinium was originally isolated from uranium minerals in which it occurs in trace amounts, but it is now made on a milligram scale by neutron capture in radium and β decay of ^{227}Ra (Table 32-3). The actinium +3 ion is separated from excess radium and isotopes of Th, Po, Bi and Pb, also formed by decay or in the bombardment, by ion exchange elution or by solvent extraction with thenoyltrifluoroacetone. Precipitation of AcF_3 from solutions and reduction of the dry fluoride with lithium vapor at 1100–1275° or $AcCl_3$ with potassium vapor at 350° gives the silvery white metal (m 1050°). The metal glows in the dark owing to its radioactivity. Like lanthanum, it is a very reactive metal and oxidizes in moist air; the intense radioactivity contributes to its reactivity.

The general chemistry of the Ac^{3+} ion in both solid compounds and in

---

[3] For examples, discussion and references see H. R. Hoekstra, *Inorg. Chem.*, **2**, 492 (1963).
[4] M. E. Dyatkina, V. P. Markov, I. V. Tsapkina and Y. N. Mikhailov, *Russ. J. Inorg. Chem.*, **6**, 293 [575] (1961); for more detailed discussion and MO treatment see S. P. McGlynn and J. K. Smith, *J. Mol. Spect.*, **6**, 164, 188 (1961).

solution, where known, is very similar to that of lanthanum as would be expected from the similarity in position in the periodic table and in radii (Ac^{3+}, 1.10; La^{3+}, 1.06 A) together with the noble-gas structure of the ion. Thus actinium is a true member of group III, the only difference from lanthanum being in the expected increased basicity. The increased basic character is shown by the stronger absorption of the hydrated ion on cation exchange resins, the poorer extraction of the ion from strong nitric acid solutions by tributyl phosphate, and by the hydrolysis of the tri-halides with water vapor at $\sim 1000°$ to the oxohalides AcOX; the lanthanum halides are hydrolyzed to oxide by water vapor at 1000°.

The crystal structures of actinium compounds where they have been studied, for example, in AcH_3, AcF_3, Ac_2S_3 and AcOCl, are the same as those of the analogous lanthanum compounds.

The study of even milligram amounts of actinium is rather difficult owing to the intense γ radiation of its decay products which rapidly build up in the initially pure material.

THORIUM

32-8. The Element

Thorium is widely distributed in nature and there are large deposits of the principal mineral, *monazite*, a complex phosphate containing uranium, cerium and other lanthanides. The extraction of thorium from monazite is complicated, the main problem being the destruction of the resistant sand and the separation of thorium from cerium and phosphate. One method involves a digestion with sodium hydroxide; the insoluble hydroxides are removed and dissolved in hydrochloric acid. On adjusting the pH of the solution to 5.8, all of the thorium and uranium, together with about 3% of the lanthanides, are precipitated as hydroxides. The thorium is recovered by tributyl phosphate extraction from $> 6M$ hydrochloric acid solution or by extraction with methylisobutyl or other ketone from nitric acid solutions in presence of excess of a salt such as aluminum nitrate as a "salting-out" agent.

The metal is made by calcium reduction of the tetrafluoride in presence of zinc chloride as a flux, by reduction of the oxide or tetrachloride by calcium, magnesium or sodium, or by electrolysis of a fused mixture of ThF_4, KCN and NaCl. Very pure metal can be made by the thermal decomposition of the vapor of ThI_4 on an incandescent filament. The metal has a high melting point, 1750°, and is quite electropositive in behavior, being comparable to the lanthanide metals in its chemical reactivity. Thus it tarnishes in air and is pyrophoric when finely divided; it is attacked by boiling water, by oxygen at 250° and by nitrogen at 800°. Dilute hydrofluoric, nitric and sulfuric acids and concentrated phosphoric and hydrochloric acids attack thorium only slowly, whereas strong nitric acid makes it passive. The attack of hot $12N$ hydrochloric acid on thorium gives a black residue which appears to be a complex hydride approximating to $ThO_{1.3}Cl_{0.7}H_{1.3}$.[5]

32-9. Binary Compounds of Thorium

Some typical thorium compounds are listed in Table 32-7.

TABLE 32-7

Some Thorium Compounds

Compound	Form	Melting point, °C	Properties
ThO_2	White, crystalline; fluorite structure	3220	Stable, refractory; soluble in HF + HNO_3
ThN	Refractory solid	2500	Slowly hydrolyzed by water
ThS_2	Purple solid	1905	Metal-like; soluble in acids
$ThCl_4$	Tetragonal white crystals	770	Soluble in and hydrolyzed by H_2O; Lewis acid
$Th(NO_3)_4 \cdot 5H_2O$	White crystals, orthorhombic		Very soluble in H_2O, alcohols, ketones, ethers
$Th(IO_3)_4$	White crystalline solid		Precipitated from 50% HNO_3; very insoluble
$Th(C_5H_7O_2)_4$	White crystals	171	Sublimes in vacuum 160°
$Th(BH_4)_4$	White crystals	204	Sublimes in vacuum about 40°
$Th(C_2O_4)_2 \cdot 6H_2O$	White crystals		Precipitated from up to $2M$ HNO_3 solution

Oxide and Hydroxide. The only oxide, ThO_2, is obtained by ignition of oxo acid salts or of the hydroxide. The latter is insoluble in excess alkali hydroxides, although it is readily peptized by heating with Th^{4+} or Fe^{3+} ions or dilute acids; the colloid exists as fibers which are coiled into spheres in concentrated sols but which uncoil on dilution. The addition of hydrogen peroxide to Th^{4+} salts gives a highly insoluble white precipitate of variable composition which contains excess anions in addition to peroxide; the composition is approximately $Th(O_2)_{3.2}X_{0.5}{}^-O_{0.15}{}^{2-}$ but it is usually referred to as thorium peroxide.

Halides. The anhydrous halides may be prepared by dry reactions such as:

$$ThO_2 + 4HF(g) \overset{600°}{=} ThF_4 + 2H_2O$$

$$ThO_2 + CCl_4 \overset{600°}{=} ThCl_4 + CO_2$$

They are all white crystalline solids which, with the exception of ThF_4,

[5] R. S. Newbury and A. W. Searcy, *Inorg. Chem.*, **1**, 794 (1962); L. I. Katzin, L. Kaplan and T. Steitz, *Inorg. Chem.*, **1**, 963 (1962).

can be sublimed in vacuum at 500–600°. The hydrated tetrafluoride is precipitated by aqueous hydrofluoric acid from Th^{4+} solutions; it can be dehydrated by heating in an atmosphere of hydrogen fluoride. The other halides are soluble in acid and are partially hydrolyzed by water. They behave as Lewis acids and form complexes with ammonia, amines, ketones, alcohols and donor molecules generally.

The *oxohalides*, $ThOX_2$, can be obtained by interactions of ThO_2 and ThX_4 at 600°; they appear to have —Th—O—Th—O chains.[6]

Other Binary Compounds. Various borides, sulfides, carbides, nitrides, etc., have been obtained by direct interaction of the elements at elevated temperatures. Like other actinide and lanthanide metals, thorium also reacts at elevated temperatures with hydrogen. Products with a range of compositions can be obtained, but two definite phases, ThH_2 and Th_4H_{15}, have been characterized.

32-10. Oxo Salts, Aqueous Solutions and Complexes of Thorium

Thorium salts of strong mineral acids usually have varying amounts of water of crystallization. The most common salt and the usual starting material for preparation of other thorium compounds is the nitrate, $Th(NO_3)_4 \cdot 5H_2O$. This salt is very soluble in water as well as in alcohols, ketones, ethers and esters. Various reagents give insoluble precipitates with thorium solutions, the most important being hydroxide, peroxide, fluoride, iodate, oxalate and phosphate; the last four give precipitates even from strongly acid ($6M$) solutions and provide useful separations of thorium from elements other than those having $+3$ or $+4$ cations with similar properties.

The thorium ion, Th^{4+}, is more resistant to hydrolysis than other $4+$ ions but undergoes extensive hydrolysis in aqueous solution at pH higher than ~ 3; the species formed are complex and dependent on the conditions of pH, nature of anions, concentration, etc.[7] In perchlorate solutions the main ions appear to be $Th(OH)^{3+}$, $Th(OH)_2^{2+}$, $Th_2(OH)_2^{2+}$, $Th_4(OH)_8^{8+}$, while the final product is the hexamer $Th_6(OH)_{15}^{9+}$; all of these species carry additional water of course. Hexameric ions exist also for Nb^V and for Ce^{VI} and U^{IV}; $[M_6O_4(OH)_4]^{12+}$ ions are found in crystals of the sulfates.[8] The metal atoms are linked by hydroxo or oxo bridges. In crystals of the hydroxide, $Th(OH)_4$, or the compound $Th(OH)_2CrO_4 \cdot H_2O$, chain-like structures have been identified, the repeating unit being $Th(OH)_2^{2+}$; in

[6] D. E. Scaife, A. G. Turnbull and A. W. Wylie, *J. Chem. Soc.*, **1965**, 1432.

[7] C. F. Baes, Jr., N. J. Meyer and C. E. Roberts, *Inorg. Chem.*, **4**, 518 (1965); F. C. Hentz, Jr., and S. Y. Tyree, *Inorg. Chem.*, **4**, 873 (1965).

[8] S. Hietanen and L. G. Sillén, *Acta Chem. Scand.*, **18**, 1018 (1964).

solution, the polymers may have similar form (32-I) or may additionally be crosslinked.

(32-Ia)   (32-Ib)

The high charge on Th^{4+} makes it susceptible to complex formation, and in solutions with anions other than perchlorate, complexed species, which may additionally be partially hydrolyzed and polymeric, are formed. Equilibrium constants for reactions such as the following have been measured:

$$Th^{4+} + nCl^- = ThCl_n^{4-n}$$
$$Th^{4+} + NO_3^- = Th(NO_3)^{3+}$$
$$Th^{4+} + 2HSO_4^- = Th(HSO_4, SO_4)^+ + H^+$$

$EDTAH_4$ and similar complexing agents give complex anions,[9] one, with diethylenetriaminepentaacetic acid (H_5L) being 8-coordinate $H[ThL]^- \cdot H_2O$, while in a mixed chelate of nitriloacetate and N,2-hydroxy-ethyl-N',N'-ethylenediaminetriacetate there is some evidence for 9-coordination.[10]

Like Zr, Hf and U, Th also gives salts such as $K_4[Thox_4] \cdot nH_2O$, but these hydrolyze extensively in water. Taking the simple view of d^4sp^3 hybridization, a vacant d orbital is then available for additional coordination and subsequent hydrolysis. Any possibility of resolution of optical isomers, which theoretically can exist for both dodecahedral and square antiprism structures, is thus precluded.[11]

A series of nitrato complexes, $M^{II}[Th(NO_3)_6] \cdot 8H_2O$, can be made and the Mg salt has been shown to contain the 12-coordinate anion[12] with chelated NO_3 groups.

32-11. Lower Oxidation States of Thorium

There is no evidence for any reduction of Th^{IV} in solutions.

In the solid state, the only evidence for lower states is the existence of a black triiodide and of two forms of a golden diiodide.[13] The precise nature of these materials, which are air-sensitive and vigorously attacked by water, is not fully established. The triiodide is believed to contain Th^{3+}

[9] R. E. Sievers and J. C. Bailar, *Inorg. Chem.*, **1**, 175 (1962).
[10] G. H. Carey, R. F. Bogucki and A. E. Martell, *Inorg. Chem.*, **3**, 1288 (1964).
[11] F. A. Johnson and E. M. Larson, *Inorg. Chem.*, **1**, 159 (1962).
[12] S. Ščavničar and B. Prodič, *Acta Cryst.*, **18**, 698 (1965).
[13] D. E. Scaife and A. W. Wylie, *J. Chem. Soc.*, **1964**, 5450.

ions, but the diiodides may well have the structure $Th^{4+}(I^-)_2(e)_2$ similar to the diiodides of certain lanthanides (page 1072).

Sulfides such as ThS and Th_2S_3 appear to have Th^{4+} and S^{2-} ions with electrons in conduction bands.

PROTACTINIUM

32-12. The Element

Protactinium as ^{231}Pa occurs in pitchblende, but even the richest ores contain only about 1 part Pa in 10^7. The isolation of protactinium from residues in the extraction of uranium from its minerals is difficult, as indeed is the study of protactinium chemistry generally, owing to the extreme tendency of the compounds to hydrolyze. In aqueous solution, polymeric ionic species and colloidal particles are formed, and these are carried on precipitates and adsorbed on vessels; in solutions other than those containing appreciable amounts of mineral acids or complexing agents or ions such as F^-, the difficulties are almost insuperable.

Protactinium can be recovered from solutions $2-8M$ in nitric or hydrochloric acids by extraction with tributyl phosphate, methyl isobutyl ketone, or other organic solvents. The protactinium can be stripped from the solvent by aqueous acid fluoride solutions; the addition to these solutions of Al^{3+} ion or boric acid, which form stronger complexes with fluoride ion than protactinium, then allows re-extraction and further purification of protactinium. Anion exchange procedures using mixtures of hydrofluoric and hydrochloric acids as eluants can also be used, since in these solutions anionic protactinium fluoro or chloro anions are formed. About 125 g of protactinium was isolated in a twelve-stage process from 60 tons of accumulated sludges of uranium extraction from Belgian Congo ore by the United Kingdom Atomic Energy Authority; previously only about 1 g had ever been isolated. The method involved leaching of Pa from the residues with $4M$ $HNO_3-0.5M$ HF, followed by extraction of Pa^V from these solutions by 20% tributylphosphate in kerosene. After collection of the Pa on a hydrous alumina precipitate it was purified further by extraction from HCl–HF solution with dibutyl ketone, anion-exchange separation from HCl solution and finally precipitation from dilute H_2SO_4 by H_2O_2.

The metal, which is obtained by barium reduction of the tetrafluoride at 1400°, is shiny and malleable, but tarnishes in air. The series of metal radii Th, Pa and U, 1.80, 1.63 and 1.54 A, respectively, are similar to the Zr, Nb, Mo series rather than to those of $4f$ metals and this suggests the absence of $5f$ electrons in Pa metal.

32-13. Protactinium(V) Compounds

Comparatively few compounds have been characterized and some of these and their preparations are given in Figure 32-4.

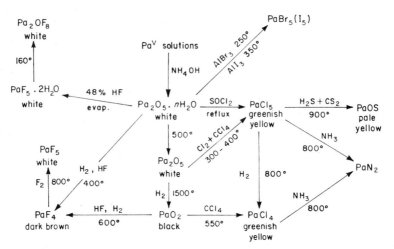

Fig. 32-4.   Some preparations of protactinium compounds.

The *pentoxide*, Pa_2O_5, obtained by ignition of other compounds in air has a cubic lattice; on heating *in vacuo*, a black sub-oxide phase $PaO_{2.3}$ and finally PaO_2 are obtained, but the situation is more complex than this brief summary implies.

The *pentafluoride* is obtained as a white hygroscopic solid by fluorination of PaF_4;[14] it is less volatile than the pentafluorides of V, Nb or Ta but does sublime *in vacuo* above 500°. It is very soluble in $1M$ or stronger HF; from solutions of Pa_2O_5 in 48% HF, evaporation at 110° gives white needles of the hydrate $PaF_5 \cdot 2H_2O$; on heating this gives Pa_2OF_8 which is isomorphous with U_2F_9 and hence probably has the structure $F_4PaOPaF_4$.[14]

The other halides are known; $PaCl_5$, which sublimes at 160° *in vacuo*, is monoclinic and is not isomorphous with $TaCl_5$. It is readily hydrolyzed in air and is soluble in THF.

Sulfato and selenato complexes, e.g., $H_3PaO(SO_4)_3$, have been obtained but the structures are uncertain.[15]

Aqueous Chemistry.   The chemistry of Pa^V in solution is somewhat like that of Nb and Ta, but Pa is even less tractable because of hydrolysis. Cationic species of sorts appear to exist in 1–3M mineral acids but it is

[14] L. Stein, *Inorg. Chem.*, **3**, 995 (1964).
[15] K. W. Bagnall, D. Brown and P. J. Jones, *J. Chem. Soc.*, **1965**, 176.

unlikely that the ion is PaO_2^+; the species are probably of the type $Pa(OH)_nX_m^{5-n-m}(H_2O)_l$; hydrolysis to insoluble products readily occurs.

Anionic complexes are well established. The fluoro, oxalato and sulfato complexes resist hydrolysis and the very stable citrate and tartrate complexes are unaffected by acids or ammonia. The precise nature of complex anions is not well known. Alkali metal salts of the ions PaF_6^{2-}, PaF_7^{2-} and PaF_8^{3-} are known. The nature of the species in solution may, of course, be different depending on the conditions. In K_2PaF_7 the metal atom is 9-coordinate with PaF_9 groups linked by double fluorine bridges into infinite chains.[16a] Yellow hexa- and octachloroprotactinates(V), e.g., $CsPaCl_6$ and $(Me_4N)_3PaCl_8$, have been made by interaction of MCl with $PaCl_5$ in $SOCl_2$ solution.[16b] Solutions with SCN^-, NO_3^-, Cl^-, etc., also contain complex anions. Neutral complexes with β-diketones, especially TTA, cupferron and alkylphosphate esters, can be extracted into benzene or CCl_4 from aqueous solutions.

32-14. Protactinium(IV) Compounds

The fluoride, chloride and oxide are well established. PaF_4 is high melting and is insoluble in HNO_3–HF solution and this and $PaCl_4$ are isomorphous with corresponding Th and U halides. PaO_2 is isomorphous with the dioxides of Th–Am inclusive. The lower oxidation state can also be obtained in solution by reduction of Pa^V solutions with Cr^{2+} or Zn amalgam, but the solutions are rapidly oxidized by air. The solutions of $PaCl_4$ in HCl, H_2SO_4 and $HClO_4$ have very similar absorption spectra being similar to $Ce^{III}(4f^1)$. Further, the absorption and esr spectra of Pa^{IV} incorporated in Cs_2ZrCl_6 are more compatible with a $5f^1$ configuration for Pa^{IV} than with a $6d^1$ configuration, and similar studies where U^{IV} is incorporated again indicate $5f^2$ configuration for the ion.

URANIUM

32-15. The Element

Uranium was discovered by Klaproth in 1789. Until the discovery of uranium fission by Hahn and Strassman in 1939, uranium had little commercial importance; its ores were sources of radium and small quantities were used for coloring glass and ceramics, but the bulk of the uranium was discarded. Uranium is now important as a nuclear fuel; its chemical importance lies in its being the prototype for the succeeding three elements.

[16a] D. Brown and A. J. Smith, *Chem. Comm.*, **1965**, 554.
[16b] K. W. Bagnall and D. Brown, *J. Chem. Soc.*, **1964**, 3021.

Uranium has three isotopes: ^{238}U (99.2739 ± 0.0007%), ^{235}U (0.7204 ± 0.0007%), and ^{234}U (0.0057 ± 0.007%); ^{238}U is the parent of the $(4n + 2)$ radioactive decay series and ^{235}U the parent of the $(4n + 3)$ series, whereas ^{234}U is formed in the ^{238}U decay sequence. Uranium-235 is of great significance since it undergoes nuclear fission with neutrons, for example

$$^{235}_{92}U + n = {}^{140}_{56}Ba + {}^{96}_{36}Kr + 3n + \sim 200 \text{ mev}$$

In this process two main groups of fission products are obtained with the release of about 200 mev per fission (1 mev = 10^6 ev; 1 ev per atom = 23.06 kcal/mole) owing to the total mass difference between the fission product isotopes and ^{235}U + n. In addition, since the process gives a distribution of fission fragments, about 2.5 neutrons per fission are liberated; these neutrons are very energetic and in pure ^{235}U can sustain a chain reaction leading to a nuclear explosion provided the mass of ^{235}U exceeds a certain critical value (a few kilograms). The fission neutrons can be slowed down or moderated by collisions with hydrogen, deuterium or carbon atoms, and under these conditions a self-sustaining but controlled chain reaction can be set up using natural uranium in an appropriate reactor. In nuclear reactors where ^{235}U is consumed as fuel, the ^{238}U of natural uranium undergoes neutron capture reactions in the high neutron fluxes and plutonium, ^{239}Pu, is built up (Table 32-2).

The most important of the widely distributed sources of uranium is *pitchblende*, an oxide of variable composition approximating to UO_2. The methods of extraction of uranium are numerous and complex. The final stages of purification usually employ solvent extraction of uranyl nitrate from aqueous solutions. The metal, which must be extraordinarily pure for use in nuclear reactions and free from elements with high neutron-absorbing properties, for example, B or Cd, is obtained by reduction of the tetrafluoride with magnesium or calcium:

$$UF_4 + 2Mg = U + 2MgF_2$$

Other methods involve reduction of oxides or halides with electropositive metals or electrolysis of fused fluoride mixtures.

Uranium is one of the densest of metals (19.04 g/cm^3 at 25°) and has three crystalline modifications below its melting point of 1132°. It forms a wide range of intermetallic compounds—U_6Mn, U_6Ni, USn_3, etc.—but, owing to the unique nature of its crystal structures, cannot form extensive ranges of solid solutions. Uranium is chemically reactive and combines directly with most elements in the periodic table. In air, the surface is rapidly converted to a yellow and subsequently a black nonprotective film. Powdered uranium is frequently pyrophoric. The reaction with water is complex; boiling water forms UO_2 and hydrogen, the latter reacting with the metal to form hydride, which causes disintegration. Uranium dissolves rapidly in hydrochloric acid (a black residue often remains, cf. Th) and nitric acid, but slowly in sulfuric, phosphoric or hydrofluoric acid. It is unaffected by alkalies.

32-16. Uranium Compounds

The chemistry of uranium is varied and complex and has been intensively studied—indeed the chemistry is one of the best known of all metal chemistries. Accordingly we can discuss only some of the more important aspects; some representative compounds are given in Table 32-8.

TABLE 32-8

Some Representative Compounds of Uranium[a] (see also Table 32-9)

Compound	Form	Melting point, °C	Properties
UO_2	Brown-black face-centered cubic crystals	2800	Soluble in nitric acid, chemically inert
UC	Black	2500	NaCl structure; hydrolyzed by acids
U_3Si_2	Tetragonal crystals	1665	Chemically inert, metallic
$U(C_5H_7O_2)_4$	Green	175	Soluble in organic solvents, sublimes in vacuum
$U(OC_2H_5)_5$	Dark brown		Distillable liquid; readily hydrolyzed by H_2O
$(\pi\text{-}C_5H_5)_3UCl$	Red crystals	260	Air-sensitive; soluble in H_2O giving cation
$UO_2(NO_3)_2 6H_2O$	Yellow crystals		Soluble in water, ethers, alcohols, esters, etc.
UO_2Cl_2	Yellow solid	578	Soluble in water; forms hydrates
$NaUO_2(C_2H_3O_2)_3$	Pale yellow crystalline solid		Insoluble in sodium acetate

[a] The stoichiometries structures, and properties of Np, Pu, and Am compounds, where they have been studied, are usually closely similar to those of the uranium analogs; the +3 and +4 compounds are also often similar to lanthanide compounds.

Uranium Hydride. Uranium metal reacts rapidly with hydrogen at 250–300° to give a black powder. The reaction is reversible,

$$U + \tfrac{3}{2}H_2 = UH_3$$

the hydride decomposing at somewhat higher temperatures to give extremely reactive, finely divided metal. A study of the isostructural deuteride by X-ray and neutron diffraction shows that the deuterium atoms lie in a distorted tetrahedron equidistant from four uranium atoms; no U—U bonds appear to be present and the U—D distance is 2.32 A. The stoichiometric hydride, UH_3, can be obtained, but the stability of the product with a slight deficiency of hydrogen is greater.

The hydride is chemically very reactive and can inflame in air; it is often more suitable for the preparation of uranium compounds than is the massive metal (Fig. 32-5).

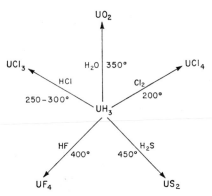

Fig. 32-5.   Some reactions of UH_3

Uranium Oxides.   The U—O system is one of the most complex oxide systems known, owing in part to the multiplicity of oxidation states of comparable stability; deviations from stoichiometry are the rule rather than the exception, and stoichiometric formulas must be considered as ideal compositions.[17]   In the dioxide, UO_2, for example, about 10% excess oxygen atoms can be added before any notable structural changes are observable, and the UO_2 phase extends from UO_2 to $\sim UO_{2.25}$.   The main oxides are UO_2, brown-black; U_3O_8, greenish black; and UO_3, orange-yellow.   Each of these oxides has several crystalline modifications of different thermal and thermodynamic stabilities and colors.   The trioxide, UO_3,[18] is obtained by decomposition at 350° of uranyl nitrate, or better, of ammonium diuranate

$$(NH_4)_2U_2O_7 = 2UO_3 + H_2O + 2NH_3$$

One polymorph has a structure which can be considered as uranyl ion linked by U—O—U bonds through the equatorial oxygens to give layers. The same type of structure occurs also in UO_2F_2 (F-bridges) and certain uranates.   The other oxides can be obtained by the reactions:

$$3UO_3 \overset{700°}{=} U_3O_8 + \tfrac{1}{2}O_2$$

$$UO_3 + CO \overset{350°}{=} UO_2 + CO_2$$

---

[17] M. J. M. Leask, L. E. J. Roberts, A. J. Walter and W. P. Wolf, *J. Chem. Soc.*, **1963**, 4788; magnetic properties and references.
[18] V. J. Wheeler, R. M. Dell and E. Wait, *J. Inorg. Nucl. Chem.*, **26**, 1829 (1964); detailed discussion of UO_3 polymorphs and hydrates.

All the oxides readily dissolve in nitric acid to give UO_2^{2+} salts. The addition of hydrogen peroxide to uranyl solution at pH 2.5–3.5 gives a pale yellow precipitate, of formula approximately $UO_4 \cdot 2H_2O$. Broad-line nmr studies coupled with peroxide analyses show this to be a uranyl peroxide, $UO_2^{2+}(O_2^{2-}) \cdot 2H_2O$, which contains ca 15% of $UO(OH)_3(OOH)$ or $UO(OH)_2(O_2)H_2O$.

Uranates. The fusion of uranium oxides with alkali or alkaline earth carbonates, or thermal decomposition of salts of the uranyl acetate anion, gives orange or yellow materials generally referred to as uranates,[19] e.g.,

$$2UO_3 + Li_2CO_3 = Li_2U_2O_7 + CO_2$$
$$Li_2U_2O_7 + Li_2CO_3 = 2Li_2UO_4 + CO_2$$
$$Li_2UO_4 + Li_2CO_3 = Li_4UO_5 + CO_2$$

Other metal oxides can be incorporated in addition and such ternary substances are best regarded as mixed oxides.[20] The uranates are generally of stoichiometry $M^I_2U_xO_{3x+1}$ but $M^I_4UO_5$, $M^{II}_3UO_6$, etc., are known. A common useful compound, ammonium diuranate referred to above, is obtained by addition of aqueous ammonia to uranyl nitrate solutions. Unlike Mo or W there do not seem to be iso- or heteropolyuranium ions in solutions.

Alkaline-earth uranates do not contain discrete ions such as UO_4^{2-} but have unsymmetrical oxygen coordination such that two U—O bonds are short, ca 1.92 A, constituting a sort of uranyl group, with other longer U—O bonds in the plane normal to this UO_2 axis linked into chain or layer lattices. However, Na_4UO_5 and M_3UO_6 do not have such uranyl groups and the former has strings of UO_6 octahedra sharing opposite corners so as to give infinite —U—O—U—O— chains with a planar UO_4 group normal to the chain; the U—O bonds in the chain are longer than those in the UO_4 group.

Uranium Halides. The principal halides are given in Table 32-9; they

TABLE 32-9

Uranium Halides

+3	+4		+5	+6
UF_3 green	UF_4 green	U_2F_9 black	UF_5 white-blue	UF_6 white
UCl_3 red	UCl_4 green	U_4F_{14} black	UCl_5 red-brown	UCl_6 black
UBr_3 red	UBr_4 brown		—	—
UI_3 black	UI_4 black		—	—

[19] H. Hoekstra and S. Siegel, *J. Inorg. Nucl. Chem.*, **26**, 693 (1964); J. C. Allpress, *J. Inorg. Nucl. Chem.*, **26**, 1874 (1964); H. Hoekstra, *J. Inorg. Nucl. Chem.*, **27**, 801 (1965); C. Kellar, *et al.*, *J. Inorg. Nucl. Chem.*, **27**, 1205, 1225 (1965).

[20] See, e.g., A. W. Sleight and R. Ward, *Inorg. Chem.*, **1**, 790 (1962).

have been studied in great detail and their chemical, structural and thermodynamic properties are well established. Uranium trifluoride is a high melting, nonvolatile, crystalline solid resembling the lanthanum fluorides, and it is insoluble in water or dilute acids; the preparation is by the aluminum reduction of UF_4:

$$UF_4 + Al \overset{900°}{=} UF_3 + AlF$$

The hydrated tetrafluoride can be obtained by precipitation from U^{4+} solution, the anhydrous fluoride by reactions such as

$$UO_2 \xrightarrow[500-600°]{C_2Cl_4F_2} UF_4$$

The nonvolatile solid is insoluble in water but is readily soluble in solutions of oxidizing agents. The hexafluoride, UF_6, is obtained by the action of fluorine on the lower fluorides; it forms colorless crystals, m 64.1° with a vapor pressure at 25° of 115 mm. It is the only readily accessible volatile uranium compound, and its physical properties have been intensively studied, primarily because it is used in the separation of uranium isotopes by gaseous diffusion in order to produce pure ^{235}U nuclear fuel. The structure has been shown to be octahedral in the gas and with a small tetragonal distortion in the molecular crystals. UF_6 is a powerful fluorinating agent, converting many substances to fluoro compounds, e.g., CS_2 to SF_4, $(CF_3)_2S_3$, etc.,[21] and it is also hydrolyzed rapidly by water. The intermediate fluorides, UF_5, U_2F_9 and U_4F_{14}, are made by interaction of UF_6 and UF_4; they disproportionate quite readily, e.g.,

$$3UF_5 \rightleftarrows U_2F_9(s) + UF_6(g)$$

UF_5 is made by treating UF_4 with fluorine at 240° or UF_6 with HBr at 65°;[22] it has a polymeric chain structure. U_2F_9 has crystallographically identical U atoms, each 9-coordinate; the black color evidently results from charge transfer transitions giving formally $+4$ and $+5$ atoms in the excited state.

Uranium trichloride can be made only in anhydrous conditions, for example, by the action of hydrogen chloride on UH_3; the aqueous solutions obtained by reduction of acid solutions of UO_2^{2+} by zinc amalgam are readily reoxidized to U^{4+} by air. The most important chloride is UCl_4, which is best made by liquid phase chlorination of UO_3 by refluxing with hexachloropropene. The primary product is believed to be UCl_6 which thermally decomposes. UCl_4 is soluble in polar organic solvents and in water. The penta- and hexachlorides are both soluble in carbon tetrachloride; they are violently hydrolyzed by water. UCl_5 disproportionates

[21] L. E. Trevorrow, J. Fischer and W. H. Gunter, *Inorg. Chem.*, **2**, 1281 (1963).
[22] A. S. Wolf, W. E. Hobbs and K. E. Rapp, *Inorg. Chem.*, **4**, 755 (1965).

on heating but can be isolated by chilling the gaseous products in the reaction scheme:

$$UCl_4 + \tfrac{1}{2}Cl_2 \xrightarrow{500°} UCl_5 \xrightarrow{120°} UCl_4 + UCl_6$$

The bromides and iodides are made by direct interaction; the tetraiodide is unstable.

Halogeno Complexes. All of the halides can form halogeno complexes, those with F^- and Cl^- being the best known. They can be obtained by interaction of the halide with alkali halides in melts or in solvents such as $SOCl_2$, or in the case of fluorides sometimes in aqueous solution.

Thus for U^{IV} and U^V yellow salts such as K_2UCl_6, $(Me_4N)UCl_6$ and $(Me_4N)_3UCl_8$ are known;[23] UCl_5 also reacts with PCl_5 to give $[PCl_4]^+[UCl_6]^-$.

Fluoride complexes such as green UF_5^-, $UF_6{}^{2-}$, $UF_7{}^{3-}$ and $UF_8{}^{4-}$ can be made by sealed-tube reactions,[24a,b] or by dissolution of UF_4 in RbF, but perhaps the most interesting is the stabilization of U^V in aqueous solutions (see below) as a fluoro complex ion.[25a] Thus the deep blue solutions of UF_5 in 48% HF are only slowly oxidized by air and on cooling give large blue crystals of $HUF_6 \cdot 2.5H_2O$. On dilution with water, hydrolysis to $UO_2{}^{2+}$ and insoluble UF_4 occurs, but addition of Rb or Cs fluorides gives stable blue salts which are isostructural with $CsNb(Ta)F_6$. These salts are best made[25b] by interaction of ClF_5 and MF in liquid HF as solvent. Absorption spectra indicate nearly octahedral symmetry.[26a]

For U^{VI} the ions UF_7^- and $UF_8{}^{2-}$ are established in sodium and potassium salts.[26b]

Oxohalides. The stable uranyl compounds, UO_2X_2, are soluble in water. They are made by reactions such as

$$UCl_4 + O_2 \overset{350°}{=} UO_2Cl_2 + Cl_2$$

$$UO_3 + 2HF \overset{400°}{=} UO_2F_2 + H_2O$$

Other Binary Compounds. Direct interaction of uranium with B, C, Si, N, P, As, Sb, Se, S, Te, etc., leads to semimetallic compounds which are often nonstoichiometric, resembling the oxides. Some of them, for example, the silicides, are chemically inert, and the sulfides, notably US, can be used as refractories.

[23] J. Morrey, *Inorg. Chem.*, **2**, 163 (1963); K. W. Bagnall, D. Brown and J. G. H. du Preez, *J. Chem. Soc.*, **1964**, 2603; **1965**, 5217; P. Gans and B. C. Smith, *J. Chem. Soc.*, **1964**, 4177.

[24a] R. Benz, R. M. Douglas, F. H. Kruse and R. A. Penneman, *Inorg. Chem.*, **2**, 799 (1963).

[24b] F. H. Kruse and L. B. Asprey, *Inorg. Chem.*, **1**, 137 (1962).

[25a] L. B. Asprey and R. A. Penneman, *Inorg. Chem.*, **3**, 727 (1964).

[25b] G. D. Sturgeon, R. A. Penneman, F. H. Kruse and L. B. Asprey, *Inorg. Chem.*, **4**, 748 (1965).

[26a] M. J. Reisfeld and G. A. Crosby, *Inorg. Chem.*, **4**, 65 (1965).

[26b] J. G. Malm, H. Selig and S. Siegel, *Inorg. Chem.*, **5**, 130 (1966).

32-17. Aqueous Chemistry of Uranium

Uranium ions in aqueous solution can give very complex species because, in addition to the four oxidation states, complexing reactions with all ions other than ClO_4^- as well as hydrolytic reactions leading to polymeric ions occur under appropriate conditions. The formal potentials for $1M$ $HClO_4$ have been given in Table 32-4; in presence of other anions the values differ, thus the U^{4+}/U^{3+} couple in $1M$ $HClO_4$ is -0.631 v, but in $1M$ HCl it is -0.640 v. The simple ions and their properties are also listed in Table 32-5. Aqueous solutions of uranium salts have an acid reaction due to hydrolysis which increases in the order $U^{3+} < UO_2^{2+} < U^{4+}$. The uranyl and U^{4+} solutions have been particularly well studied. The main hydrolyzed species of UO_2^{2+} at $25°$ are UO_2OH^+, $(UO_2)_2(OH)_2^{2+}$ and $(UO_2)_3(OH)_5^+$ but the system is a complex one and the species present depend on the medium; at higher temperatures the monomer is most stable but the rate of hydrolysis to UO_3 of course increases.[27] The solubility of large amounts of UO_3 in UO_2^{2+} solutions is also attributable to formation of UO_2OH^+ and polymerized hydroxo bridged species.[28]

The U^{4+} ion is only slightly hydrolyzed in molar acid solutions:

$$U^{4+} + H_2O = U(OH)^{3+} + H^+ \qquad K_{25°} = 0.027 \ (1M \ HClO_4, NaClO_4)$$

but can also give polynuclear species in less acid solutions.

The U^{4+} ion gives insoluble precipitates with F^-, PO_4^{3-} and IO_3^- from acid solutions (cf. Th^{4+}).

The uranium(V) ion, UO_2^+, is extraordinarily unstable towards disproportionation and has a transistory existence under most conditions, although evidence for its occurrence can be obtained polarographically. It is also an intermediate in photochemical reduction reactions of uranyl ions in presence of sucrose and similar substances. The ion is most stable in the pH range 2.0–4.0 where the disproportionation reaction to give U^{4+} and UO_2^{2+} is negligibly slow, and millimolar solutions can be obtained by electrolytic reduction of UO_2^{2+} or by dissolving UCl_5. As noted above it can be stabilized in HF solutions as UF_6^-.

Spectroscopic and other studies have shown that in aqueous solutions of UO_2^{2+} and U^{4+}, complex ions are often readily formed, for example,

$$
\begin{aligned}
U^{4+} + Cl^- &= UCl^{3+} & K &= 1.21 \ (\mu = 2.0; 25°) \\
U^{4+} + 2HSO_4^- &= U(SO_4)_2 + 2H^+ & K &= 7.4 \times 10^3 \ (\mu = 2.0; 25°) \\
UO_2^{2+} + Cl^- &= UO_2Cl^+ & K &= 0.88 \ (\mu = 2.0; 25°) \\
UO_2^{2+} + 2SO_4^{2-} &= UO_2(SO_4)_2^{2-} & K &= 7.1 \times 10^2 \ (\mu = 2.0; 25°)
\end{aligned}
$$

Nitrate complexes also exist, and nitrate solutions of U^{IV} contain

---

[27] C. F. Baes, Jr., and N. J. Meyer, *Inorg. Chem.*, **1**, 780 (1962).
[28] Cf. J. R. Lacher, K. Ensley and J. D. Park, *Inorg. Chem.*, **1**, 944 (1962).

$[UNO_3(H_2O)_4]^{3+}$ and similar species; in concentrated nitric acid it appears that $[U(NO_3)_6]^{2-}$ can be formed and the cesium salt can be precipitated.[29]

The nature of the reduction of UO_2^{2+} especially by Cr^{2+} has been studied and it appears that there is a bright green intermediate complex ion,[30] probably $[(H_2O)_5Cr^{III}—O—UO(H_2O)_n]^{4+}$, which reacts further to give Cr^{III} and U^{IV}. A similar intermediate occurs in the reduction of PuO_2^{2+}, and for Np an intermediate has been separated by ion-exchange.[31] It is pertinent to note here that the reverse process, oxidation of U^{4+} by various agents, has been studied in detail;[32] this is possible only because of the slow exchange of UO_2^{2+} with water. Using ^{18}O tracer it was found that PbO_2, H_2O_2 or MnO_2 gave UO_2^{2+} where virtually all the O came from the solid oxidant whereas for O_2 and O_3 only one oxygen is transferred from the oxidant to U^{IV}.

Complex ions are also formed with citrate and anions of other organic acids, thiocyanate, dialkyl dithiocarbamates and phosphates. The latter are important in view of the occurrence of uranium in phosphate minerals, and species such as $UO_2H_2PO_4^+$, $UO_2H_3PO_3^{2+}$, and at high concentrations anionic complexes are known.

32-18. Uranyl Salts

These are the only common uranium salts and the most important one is the nitrate which crystallizes with six, three or two molecules of water, depending on whether it is obtained from dilute, strong or fuming nitric acid. The most unusual and significant property of the nitrate is its solubility in numerous ethers, alcohols, ketones and esters, when it distributes itself between the organic and an aqueous phase. The nitrate is also readily extracted from aqueous solutions, and this operation has become classical for the separation and purification of uranium since, with the exception of the other actinide MO_2^{2+} ions, few other metal nitrates have any extractability. A great deal of information is available, and phase diagrams for the $UO_2(NO_3)_2$–H_2O–solvent systems have been determined. The effect of added salts, for example, $Ca(NO_3)_2$ or NH_4NO_3, as "salting-out" agents is to increase substantially the extraction ratio to technically usable values. Studies of the organic phase have shown that $UO_2(NO_3)_2$ is accompanied into the solvents by $4H_2O$ molecules, but there is little or no ionization and the nitrate is undoubtedly coordinated in the

[29] H. A. C. McKay and J. L. Woodward, *J. Chem. Soc.*, **1964**, 717

[30] T. W. Newton and F. B. Baker, *Inorg. Chem.*, **1**, 369 (1962); G. Gordon, *Inorg. Chem.*, **2**, 1277 (1963).

[31] J. C. Sullivan, *J. Amer. Chem. Soc.*, **84**, 4256 (1962).

[32] G. Gordon and H. Taube, *Inorg. Chem.*, **1**, 69 (1962).

equatorial plane of the UO_2 system.   An important extractant for uranyl nitrate which does not require a salting-out agent for useful ratios is tributyl phosphate.   Anhydrous uranyl nitrate[33] is obtained by the reactions:

$$U + N_2O_4(l) \xrightarrow{\text{MeCN}} UO_2(NO_3)_2 \cdot N_2O_4 \cdot 2MeCN \xrightarrow{163°} UO_2(NO_3)_2$$

Other uranyl salts are given by organic acids, sulfate, halides, etc.; the water-soluble acetate in presence of excess sodium acetate in dilute acetic acid gives a crystalline precipitate of $NaUO_2(OCOCH_3)_3$.

NEPTUNIUM, PLUTONIUM AND AMERICIUM

32-19. Isolation of the Elements

Although several isotopes of these elements are known, the most important long-lived ones that can be obtained in macroscopic amounts are given in Table 32-2.   Both ^{237}Np and ^{239}Pu are found in the uranium fuel elements of nuclear reactors, from which plutonium is isolated on a kilogram scale. ^{237}Np occurs in small amounts and is recovered primarily for conversion to ^{238}Pu, by neutron irradiation of NpO_2, which is used as a power source for satellites.[34]   Americium is produced from intense neutron irradiations of pure plutonium.   The problems involved in the extraction of these elements involve the recovery of the expensive starting material and the removal of hazardous fission products which are formed simultaneously in amounts comparable to the amounts of the synthetic elements themselves.   Not only are the chemical problems themselves quite formidable, but the handling of highly radioactive solutions or solids (in the case of plutonium the exceedingly high toxicity is an additional hazard since even a μg is potentially a lethal dose) has necessitated the development of remote control operations.   For the large-scale extractions from fuel elements, detailed studies of the effects of radiation on structural and process materials have also been required.   There are numerous procedures for the separation of Np, Pu and Am, variously involving precipitation, solvent extraction, differential volatility of compounds and so on, and we can give only the briefest outline.   The most important separation methods are based on the following chemistry.

1. *Stabilities of oxidation states.*   The stabilities of the major ions involved are: UO_2^{2+}, $NpO_2^{2+} > PuO_2^{2+} > AmO_2^{2+}$; $Am^{3+} > Pu^{3+} \gg Np^{3+}$, U^{4+}.   It is thus possible (see also Table 32-5) by choice of suitable oxidizing or reducing agents to obtain a solution containing the elements in different

[33] C. C. Addison, *et al.*, *J. Chem. Soc.*, **1964**, 2354.
[34] *Chem. and Eng. News*, Aug. 5 (1963), p. 47.

oxidation states; they can then be separated by precipitation or solvent extraction. For example, Pu can be oxidized to PuO_2^{2+} while Am remains as Am^{3+}—the former could be removed by solvent extraction or the latter by precipitation of AmF_3.

2. *Extractability into organic solvents.* As noted previously, the MO_2^{2+} ions can be extracted from nitrate solutions into organic solvents. The M^{4+} ions can be extracted into tributyl phosphate in kerosene from $6M$ nitric acid solutions; the M^{3+} ions can be similarly extracted from 10–$16M$ nitric acid; and neighboring actinides can be separated by a choice of conditions.

3. *Precipitation reactions.* Only M^{3+} and M^{4+} give insoluble fluorides or phosphates from acid solutions; the higher oxidation states give either no precipitate or precipitation can be prevented by complex formation with sulfate or other ions.

4. *Ion exchange procedures.* Although ion exchange procedures, both cationic and anionic, can be used to separate the actinide ions, they are best suited for small amounts of material. Since they have found most use in the separation of the trans-americium elements, these procedures are discussed later.

The following examples are for the separation of plutonium from uranium; similar procedures using the same basic principles have been devised to separate Np and Am. The initial starting material in plutonium extraction is a solution of the uranium fuel element (plus its aluminum or other protective jacket) in nitric acid. The combination of oxidation–reduction cycles coupled with solvent extraction and/or precipitation methods remove the bulk of fission products (FP's); however, certain elements—notably ruthenium, which forms cationic, neutral and anionic nitrosyl complexes—may require special elimination steps. The initial uranyl nitrate solution contains Pu^{4+} since nitric acid cannot oxidize this to Pu^V or Pu^{VI}.

1. *Methyl isobutyl ketone (hexone) method.* This is shown in Scheme 32-1.

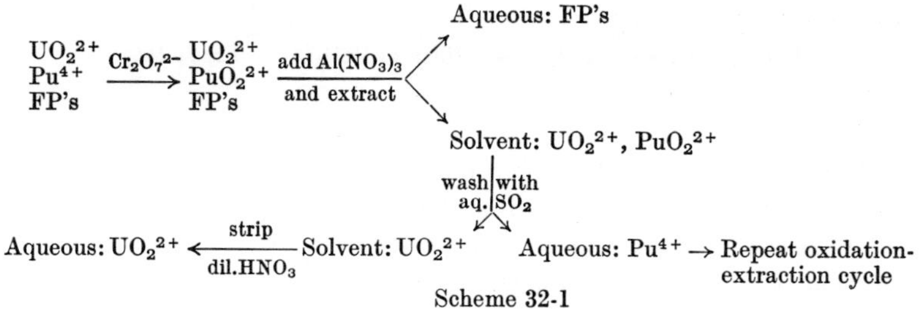

Aqueous: FP's

$$\begin{matrix} UO_2^{2+} \\ Pu^{4+} \\ FP's \end{matrix} \xrightarrow{Cr_2O_7^{2-}} \begin{matrix} UO_2^{2+} \\ PuO_2^{2+} \\ FP's \end{matrix} \xrightarrow[\text{and extract}]{\text{add } Al(NO_3)_3}$$

Solvent: UO_2^{2+}, PuO_2^{2+}

wash with aq. SO_2

Aqueous: UO_2^{2+} $\xleftarrow[\text{dil.HNO}_3]{\text{strip}}$ Solvent: UO_2^{2+} Aqueous: Pu^{4+} → Repeat oxidation-extraction cycle

Scheme 32-1

2. *Tributyl phosphate method.* The extraction coefficients from $6N$ nitric acid solutions are $Pu^{4+} > PuO_2^{2+}$; $Np^{4+} \sim NpO_2^+ \gg Pu^{3+}$; $UO_2^{2+} >$

$NpO_2^+ > PuO_2^{2+}$; the M^{3+} have very low extraction coefficients in $6M$ acid, but from $12M$ hydrochloric acid or $16M$ nitric acid the extraction increases and the order is Np < Pu < Am < Cm < Bk.

Thus in the U–Pu separation, after addition of NO_2^- to adjust all of the plutonium to Pu^{4+}, we have Scheme 32-2.

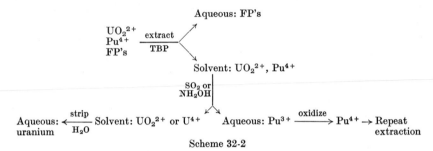

Scheme 32-2

The extraction of ^{237}Np involves similar principles of adjustment of oxidation state and solvent extraction;[35] Pu is reduced by ferrous sulfamate plus hydrazine to unextractable Pu^{III} while Np^{IV} remains in the solvent from which it is differentially stripped by water to separate it from U.

3. *Lanthanum fluoride cycle.* This classical procedure was first developed by McMillan and Abelson for the isolation of neptunium, but it is applicable elsewhere and is of great utility. For the U–Pu separation again, we have

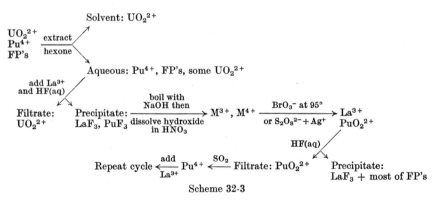

Scheme 32-3

Scheme 32-3. The cycle shown is repeated with progressively smaller amounts of lanthanum carrier and smaller volumes of solution until plutonium becomes the bulk phase. This fluoride cycle has also been used in combination with an initial precipitation step for Pu^{4+} using bismuth phosphate as a carrier.

[35] *Chem. and Eng. News.*, Feb. 3 (1964), p. 50.

32-20. The Elements and Binary Compounds

The metals of Np, Pu and Am[36] are prepared in the same way as uranium—by Li or Ba reduction of the fluorides at $\sim 1200°$; they are silvery metals and chemically very reactive. Plutonium metal has some unique properties; it has at least six allotropic forms below its melting point, each with different densities, coefficients of expansion and resistivities and, most curiously, if the phase expands on heating the resistance decreases. In its physical properties, americium metal resembles the lanthanide metals much more than U, Np or Pu.

Oxides. All three oxide systems have various solid solutions and other nonstoichiometric complications. The monoxides are interstitial compounds. The important oxides of Np, Pu and Am are the *dioxides*, which are obtained on heating the nitrates or hydroxides of any oxidation state in air; they are isostructural with UO_2. Ordinarily, PuO_2 is nonstoichiometric and may have different colors, but ignition at $1200°$ gives the stoichiometric oxide.[37] The oxide Np_3O_8, isomorphous with U_3O_8, can be obtained under specific conditions. The action of ozone on suspensions of the M^{IV} hydroxides gives rise to the hydrated *trioxides*,[38] brown $NpO_3 \cdot 2H_2O$ and $NpO_3 \cdot H_2O$, and red-gold $PuO_3 \cdot 0.8H_2O$, but unlike U, which also gives $UO_3 \cdot 0.8H_2O$, no anhydrous trioxides are known. Above $300°$ black Np_2O_5 is obtained. $NpO_3 \cdot 2H_2O$ and Np_2O_5 can also be made by oxidation in $LiClO_4$ melts.[39] Reduction of AmO_2 with hydrogen at $600°$ gives the reddish brown dimorphic Am_2O_3, which is the first lanthanide-like sesquioxide in the actinide series.

Halides. The halides are listed in Table 32-10.

The Np, Pu and Am halides, which are isostructural with and chemically similar to those of uranium, clearly show the decrease in stability of compounds in the higher oxidation states, and this trend continues in the succeeding elements. The preparative methods used are also similar to those for uranium, for example,

$$NpO_2 + \tfrac{1}{2}H_2 + 3HF(g) \xrightarrow{500°} NpF_3 + 2H_2O$$

$$PuF_4 + F_2 \xrightarrow{500°} PuF_6$$

$$AmO_2 + 2CCl_4 \xrightarrow{800°} AmCl_3 + 2COCl_2 + \tfrac{1}{2}Cl_2$$

The fluorides, MF_3 and MF_4, can be precipitated from aqueous solutions

[36] D. B. McWhan, B. B. Cunningham and J. C. Wallman, *J. Inorg. Nucl. Chem.*, **24**, 1025 (1962). A detailed and instructive account of preparation of milligram quantities.

[37] E. R. Gardner, T. L. Markin and R. S. Street, *J. Inorg. Nucl. Chem.*, **27**, 541 (1965).

[38] K. W. Bagnall and J. B. Laidler, *J. Chem. Soc.*, **1964**, 2693.

[39] D. Cohen, *Inorg. Chem.*, **2**, 867 (1963); D. Cohen and A. D. Walter, *J. Chem. Soc.*, **1964**, 2696.

TABLE 32-10

Halides of Np, Pu and Am[a]

+3	+4	+6
NpF_3, purple-black	NpF_4, green	NpF_6, orange, m $55.1°$
PuF_3, purple	PuF_4, brown	PuF_6, red-brown m $51.6°$
AmF_3, pink	AmF_4, tan	—
$NpCl_3$, white	$NpCl_4$, red-brown	
$PuCl_3$, emerald	—	
$AmCl_3$, pink	—	
$NpBr_3$, green	$NpBr_4$, red-brown	
$PuBr_3$, green	—	
$AmBr_3$, white	—	
NpI_3, brown	—	
PuI_3, green	—	
AmI_3, yellow		

[a] Oxohalides PuOX and AmOCl also exist.

in hydrated form. The hexafluorides have been much studied since they are volatile; the melting points and stabilities decrease U > Np > Pu. PuF_6 is so very much less stable than UF_6, that at equilibrium, the partial pressure of PuF_6 is only 0.004% of the fluorine pressure. Hence PuF_6 formed by fluorination of PuF_4 at $750°$ must be quenched immediately by a liquid nitrogen probe. The compound also undergoes self destruction by α-radiation damage especially in the solid; it must also be handled with extreme care due to the toxicity of Pu. PuF_6 contains two nonbonding $5f$ electrons and should be paramagnetic; however, like UF_6, where all the valence electrons are involved in bonding, it shows only a small temperature-independent paramagnetism. This observation has been explained by ligand field splitting of the f levels to give a lower-lying orbital which is doubly occupied.

NpF_6 has a $5f^1$ configuration according to esr and absorption spectra, the octahedral field splitting the seven-fold orbital degeneracy of the $5f$ electron leaving a ground state that has only spin degeneracy. This quenching of the orbital angular momentum is similar to that in the first-row d-transition group. It provides further evidence for the closeness of the energy levels of the $5f$ and valence electrons in actinides as contrasted with the much lower energies of the $4f$ electrons in lanthanides. NpF_6 is slightly distorted in the solid and its magnetic behavior depends on its environment when diluted with UF_6.

Other Compounds. A substantial number of compounds, particularly of plutonium, are known, and most of them closely resemble their uranium analogs. The hydride systems of Np, Pu and Am are more like that of thorium than that of uranium and are complex. Thus nonstoichiometry up to $MH_{2.7}$ is found in addition to stoichiometric hydrides such as PuH_2 and AmH_2.

As with uranium, many complex salts are known, e.g., Cs_2PuCl_6, $NaPuF_5$, $KPuO_2F_3$, $NaPu(SO_4)_2 \cdot 7H_2O$, $CsNp(NO_3)_6$. A simple solid hydrated nitrate, $Pu(NO_3)_4$, is obtained by evaporation of Pu^{IV} nitrate solution; at 150–180° in air this gives $PuO_2(NO_3)_2$. Pu^V also occurs in salts of the $PuF_7{}^{2-}$ and $PuF_6{}^{-}$ ions.[40]

32-21. Aqueous Chemistry of Neptunium, Plutonium and Americium

The formal reduction potentials have been given in Table 32-4 and the general stabilities of the ions in Table 32-5.

Aqueous solutions of Pu and Am V and VI and especially Am^{IV} undergo rapid self-reduction due to their α-radiation.

For Np, the potentials of the four oxidation states are separated, like those of uranium, but in this case the $NpO_2{}^+$ state is comparatively stable. Earlier evidence that $NpO_2{}^{2+}$ was reduced by Cl^- has been shown to be due to catalysis by platinum and the rate is very slow.[41a] With Pu, however, the potentials are not well separated and in $1M$ $HClO_4$ all four species can coexist in appreciable concentrations; $PuO_2{}^+$ becomes increasingly stable with decreasing acidity since the couples are strongly hydrogen ion dependent. The Am ions stable enough to exist in finite concentrations are Am^{3+}, $AmO_2{}^+$ and $AmO_2{}^{2+}$ and the Am^{3+} ion is the usual state since powerful oxidation is required to achieve the higher oxidation states. Alkaline solutions are more favorable for the stabilization of Am^{IV}, and for $1M$ basic solution the $Am(OH)_4$–$Am(OH)_3$ couple has a value of $+0.5$ v, nearly 2 v less than the Am^{4+}/Am^{3+} couple in acid solution. Thus pink $Am(OH)_3$ can be readily converted to black $Am(OH)_4$ (or $AmO_2(aq)$) by the action of hypochlorite. This black hydroxide is also soluble in $13M$ ammonium fluoride solutions to give stable solutions from which $(NH_4)_4AmF_8$ can be precipitated; the anion in this salt probably has the square antiprism structure as does AmF_4.[41b]

As with uranium, the solution chemistry is complicated owing to hydrolysis and polynuclear ion formation, complex formation with anions other than perchlorate, and disproportionation reactions of some oxidation states. The tendency of ions to displace a proton from water increases with increasing charge and decreasing ion radius, so that the tendency to hydrolysis increases in the same order for each oxidation state, that is,

[40] R. H. Penneman, et al., J. Amer. Chem. Soc., **87**, 5803 (1965).
[41a] D. Cohen and B. Taylor, J. Inorg. Nucl. Chem., **22**, 151 (1961).
[41b] L. B. Asprey and R. A. Penneman, Inorg. Chem., **1**, 134 (1962).

Am > Pu > Np > U and M^{4+} > MO_2^{2+} > M^{3+} > MO_2^+; simple ions such as NpO_2OH or $PuOH^{3+}$ are known in addition to polymeric species, which in the case of plutonium can have molecular weights up to 10^{10}.

The complexing tendencies decrease in the same orders as the hydrolytic tendencies on the whole. The formation of complexes shifts the oxidation

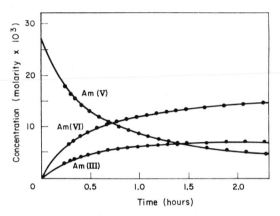

Fig. 32-6. Disproportionation of AmO_2^+ in $6M$ perchloric acid at $25°$. Net reaction: $3AmO_2^+ + 4H^+ = 2AmO_2^{2+} + Am^{3+} + H_2O$. (Reprinted with permission from J. S. Coleman, *Inorg. Chem.*, **2**, 53 (1963).)

potentials, sometimes influencing the relative stabilities of oxidation states; thus the formation of sulfate complexes of Np^{4+} and NpO_2^{2+} is strong enough to cause disproportionation of NpO_2^+. The disproportionation reactions have been studied in some detail; Figures 32-6 and 32-7 illustrate some of the complexities involved.

Typical of these disproportionations are the following at low acidity

$$3Pu^{4+} + 2H_2O = PuO_2^{2+} + 2Pu^{3+} + 4H^+$$
$$2Pu^{4+} + 2H_2O = PuO_2^+ + Pu^{3+} + 4H^+$$
$$PuO_2^+ + Pu^{4+} = PuO_2^{2+} + Pu^{3+}$$

At $25°$ and $1M$ $HClO_4$,

$$K = \frac{[Pu^{VI}][Pu^{III}]}{[Pu^V][Pu^{IV}]} = 10.7$$

which indicates that measurable amounts of all four states can be present.

An example of complex formation is provided by carbonate; for Am this provides a useful separation from Cm since $Cm(OH)_3$ is insoluble in $NaHCO_3$ and cannot be oxidized to soluble complexes. However, treatment of Am^{3+} in $2M$ Na_2CO_3 with O_3 at $25°$ gives a red-brown Am^{VI}

carbonato complex anion of uncertain composition; however, at 90°, reduction to the ion $[Am^{V}O_2CO_3]^-$ occurs unless $S_2O_8^{2-}$ is present.[42] The Am^{VI}/Am^V couple in $0.1M$ $NaHCO_3$ is estimated to be *ca* 1 volt. Np^V, Pu^V and Am^V carbonate complexes can also be obtained by oxidation of dilute HNO_3 solutions with O_3, reduction of MO_2^{2+} with KI, and addition of $KHCO_3$. The $KM^VO_2CO_3$ salts are isostructural with layers held together by K^+ ions;[43] uranium gives complexes $UO_2(CO_3)_2^{2-}$ and $UO_2(CO_3)_3^{4-}$, but no U^V complexes are known.

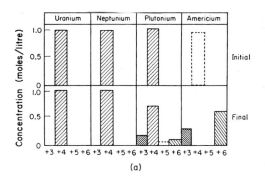

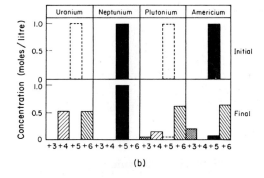

Fig. 32-7.   Disproportionation reactions of (a) tetra- and (b) pentapositive ions in $1M$ acid at 5°. (Reprinted with permission from J. J. Katz and G. T. Seaborg, *The Chemistry of the Actinide Elements*, Methuen, London, 1957, p. 420.)

Hexacoordinate AmF_6^{2-} salts also exist.[24b] The precipitation reactions of Np, Pu, and Am are generally similar to those of uranium in the corresponding oxidation states, for example, of $NaM^{VI}O_2(OCOCH_3)_3$ or MF_3.

[42] J. S. Coleman, T. K. Keenan, L. H. Jones, W. T. Carnall and R. A. Penneman, *Inorg. Chem.*, **2**, 58 (1963).
[43] T. K. Keenan and F. H. Kruse, *Inorg. Chem.*, **3**, 1231 (1964).

THE TRANS-AMERICIUM ELEMENTS

32-22. General Remarks

The isotope ^{242}Cm was first isolated among the products of α-bombardment of ^{239}Pu, and its discovery actually preceded that of americium. Isotopes of the other elements were first identified in products from the first hydrogen bomb explosion or in cyclotron bombardments. Although Cm, Bk and Cf have been obtained in macro amounts (Table 32-2) much of the chemical information has been obtained on the tracer scale. The remaining elements have been characterized only by their chemical behavior on the tracer scale in conjunction with their specific nuclear decay characteristics.

For these elements, the correspondence of the actinide and lanthanide series becomes most clearly revealed. The position of curium corresponds to that of gadolinium where the f shell is half-filled. For curium, the $+3$ oxidation state is the normal state in solution, although, unlike gadolinium, a solid tetrafluoride, CmF_4, has been obtained. Berkelium has $+3$ and $+4$ oxidation states, as would be expected from its position relative to terbium, but the $+4$ state of terbium does not exist in solution whereas for Bk it does.

The remaining elements, from Cf onward, have only the $+3$ state. The great similarity between the $+3$ ions of Am and the trans-americium elements has meant that the more conventional chemical operations successful for the separation of the previous actinide elements are inadequate, and most of the separations require the highly selective procedures of ion exchange discussed below; solvent extraction of the M^{3+} ions from 10–$16M$ nitric acid by tributyl phosphate also gives reasonable separations.

32-23. Curium, Berkelium and Californium

Curium is isolated as macro amounts and the metal has been prepared on a microgram scale by reduction of CmF_3 with barium at $1275°$. The metal is similar to the other actinides, but corrodes more rapidly, partially because of self-heating by radioactive decay.

A few solid curium compounds are known, for example, CmF_3, CmF_4, $CmCl_3$, $CmBr_3$, white Cm_2O_3 and black CmO_2. Where X-ray structural studies have been made—and these are difficult since amounts of the order of 0.5×10^{-6} g must be used in order to avoid fogging of the film by radioactivity and because of destruction of the lattice by emitted particles—the compounds are isomorphous with other actinide compounds.

In view of the position of Cm in the actinide series, numerous experiments have been made to ascertain if Cm has only the $+3$ state in solution; no evidence for a lower state has been found. Concerning the $+4$ state, the potential of the Cm^{4+}/Cm^{3+} couple must be greater than that of Am^{4+}/Am^{3+}, which is 2.6 to 2.9 v, so that solutions of Cm^{4+} must be unstable. It has been found that if CmF_4, prepared by dry fluorination of CmF_3, is treated with $15M$ CsF at $0°$, a pale yellow solution is obtained which appears to contain Cm^{4+} as a fluoro complex. This solution exists for only an hour or so at $10°$; its spectrum resembles that of the isoelectronic Am^{3+} ion.

The solution reactions of Cm^{3+} closely resemble the lanthanide and actinide $+3$ ions, and the fluoride, oxalate, phosphate, iodate and hydroxide are insoluble. There is some evidence for complexing in solution, although the complexes appear to be weaker than those of preceding elements.

Magnetic measurements on CmF_3 diluted in LaF_3 and also the close resemblance of the absorption spectra of CmF_3 and GdF_3 supported the hypothesis that the ion has the $5f^7$ configuration.

Berkelium. Only a few solid compounds have been made, notably the yellow oxide BkO_2 which has the fluorite structure.

Californium. The oxide, Cf_2O_3, and halides, $CfCl_3$ and $CfOCl$, have been made.

32-24. Ion Exchange Separations

Ion exchange has been indispensable in the characterization of the transamericium elements and is also important for some of the preceding elements as well, particularly for tracer quantities of material. We have seen in the case of the lanthanides (Chapter 31) that the $+3$ ions can be eluted from a cation exchange column by various complexing agents, such as buffered citrate, lactate or α-hydroxybutyrate solutions, and that the elution order follows the order of the hydrated ionic radii so that the lutetium is eluted first and lanthanum last. Using the actinide hypothesis and extrapolating from data obtained with the lighter actinides such as U^{3+}, Np^{3+} and Pu^{3+}, it has been possible to predict quite precisely, *even to the exact drop*, where the heavier actinide ions should be eluted under prescribed conditions. Consummate use of these principles has allowed Seaborg and his collaborators to isolate and characterize the heavier actinides even when only a few *atoms* of the element have been present in the solution.

The main problems in this work have been twofold: (*a*) the separation of the actinides as a group from the lanthanide ions (which are formed as fission fragments in the bombardments which produce the actinides) and (*b*) the separation of the actinide elements from one another.

The first problem can be solved by the use of strong hydrochloric acid as an eluting agent; since the actinide ions form chloride complexes more easily, they are desorbed first from a cation exchange resin, thus effecting a *group* separation; conversely, the actinides are more strongly adsorbed on anion exchange resins. Although some of the actinide ions are themselves separated in the strong hydrochloric acid elutions on cationic columns, the resolution is not too satisfactory, particularly for Cf and Es. A more effective group separation employs $10M$ LiCl as eluant for a moderately cross-linked, strongly basic anion exchange column operating at elevated temperatures up to $\sim 90°$. In addition to affording a lanthanide–actinide separation, fractionation of the actinide elements into groups Pu, Am–Cm, Bk and Cf–Es can be obtained. Except for unexplained reversals observed in the elution order of Gd, Ho and of Cm and Es, the elution sequences proceed in the order of increasing Z, with La being the least strongly absorbed.

The actinide ions are effectively separated from each other by elution with citrate or similar eluants; some typical elution curves in which the relative positions of the corresponding lanthanides are also given are displayed in Figure 32-8. It will be noted that a very striking similarity

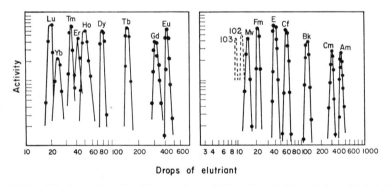

Fig. 32-8. Elution of lanthanide $+3$ ions (left) and actinide $+3$ ions (right) from Dowex 50 cation exchange resin. Buffered ammonium α-hydroxybutyrate was the eluant. The predicted positions of elements 102 and 103 (unobserved here) are shown by broken lines. (Reprinted with permission from J. J. Katz and G. T. Seaborg, *The Chemistry of the Actinide Elements*, Methuen, London, 1957, p. 435.)

occurs in the spacings of corresponding elements in the two series. There is a distinct break between Gd and Tb and between Cm and Bk, which can be attributed to the small change in ionic radius occasioned by the half-filling of the 4f and 5f shells, respectively. The elution order is not always as regular as that in Figure 32-8. With some complexing agents, for example, thiocyanate, complicated elution orders are found for the actinides. After the separation on ion exchange columns, the actinide ions are usually collected on an insoluble fluoride precipitate.

32-25. Chemical Properties of the Trans-americium Elements

The chemical properties have been deduced from ion exchange behavior and from experiments with tracer quantities of material using other non-radioactive $+3$ ions as carriers.

Berkelium is the analog of Tb, and in addition to the $+3$ state could be expected to give a $+4$ ion. If Bk^{3+} solutions in nitric acid are oxidized with bromate or other powerful oxidant, the berkelium can be precipitated by phosphate, iodate or phenylarsenate using Ce^{4+} or Zr^{4+} as carrier substance. By comparing the amounts of radioactive Ce^{4+} and Bk^{4+} carried by zirconium precipitates, it was concluded that the Bk^{4+}/Bk^{3+} couple lies within about 60 mv of the Ce^{4+}/Ce^{3+} couple, so that the formal potential can be estimated to be about $+1.62$ v. In the $+4$ state, berkelium can be readily solvent extracted (cf. Ce^{4+}) by hexane solutions of bis(2-ethylhexyl) hydrogen phosphate or similar complexing agents.

There is no evidence that Cf exists in the $+4$ state in aqueous solution, but it behaves as a typical $+3$ ion, being coprecipitated with the fluoride, oxalate or hydroxide of lanthanum; the ions of Es, Fm and Md, insofar as they have been studied, also have only the $+3$ oxidation state.

We may finally note the origin of the names of the new synthetic elements. Neptunium and plutonium follow uranium in being named after the planets; americium was named in honor of the Americas and corresponds to europium in the lanthanides; curium was named after the Curies since the corresponding lanthanide was named after the lanthanide pioneer Gadolin; berkelium, from Berkeley, is the homolog of terbium, which was named after Ytterby in Sweden where lanthanide ores were found; californium was named in honor of the university and state where the element was discovered; einsteinium and fermium were named after the great physicists Einstein and Fermi, lawrencium after Lawrence, originator of the cyclotron, and mendelevium in honor of the great Russian originator of the periodic table.

References

Asprey, L. B., and B. B. Cunningham, *Prog. Inorg. Chem.*, **2**, 267 (1960). Unusual oxidation states of some actinide and lanthanide elements.

Bagnall, K. W., *Science Progress*, **52**, 66 (1964). Short review on trans-uranium elements; contains crystallographic and other data on halides, oxides, etc.

Brown, D., and A. G. Maddock, *Quart. Rev.*, **17**, 289 (1963). Comprehensive review on protactinium.

Comyns, A. E., *Chem. Rev.*, **60**, 115 (1960). A comprehensive review of the coordination chemistry of the actinides.

Friedlander, G., J. W. Kennedy and J. M. Miller, *Nuclear and Radiochemistry*, 2nd ed., Wiley, New York, 1964. Discussion of radioactivity and nuclear stability.

Gittus, J. H., *Uranium*, Butterworths, London, 1963. Ores, production, properties and applications of the metal.

Hindman, J. C., T. K. Keenan, B. B. Cunningham and G. T. Seaborg, *J. Chem. Educ.*, **36**, 15 (1959). Articles on trans-uranium elements.

Hodge, N., *Adv. Fluorine Chem.*, **2**, 138 (1961). Fluorides of the actinide elements.

Hyde, E. K., I. Perlman and G. T. Seaborg, *The Nuclear Properties of the Heavy Elements*, Vols. I–III, Prentice-Hall, New Jersey, 1964. Comprehensive reference treatise on nuclear structure, radioactive properties and fission.

Katz, J. J., and G. T. Seaborg, *The Chemistry of the Actinide Elements*, Methuen, London, 1957. A lucidly written reference text containing most of the information on these elements.

Katz, J. J., and I. Sheft, *Adv. Inorg. Chem. Radiochem.*, **2**, 195 (1960). Detailed account of the halides of the actinides with a collection of physical data.

Keller, C., *Angew. Chem. (Internat.)*, **4**, 903 (1965). Synthesis of trans-curium elements by heavy ion bombardments.

———, *Angew. Chem. (Internat.)*, **5**, 23 (1966). Extensive review of the chemistry of protactinium.

Makarov, E. S., *Crystal Chemistry of Simple Compounds of U, Th, Pu and Np* (trans.), Consultants Bureau, New York, 1959.

Martin, F. S., and G. L. Miles, *Chemical Processing of Nuclear Fuels*, Butterworths, London, 1958. Procedures for isolating actinides from reactor fuels.

Rabinowitch, E., and R. Linn Belford, *Spectroscopy and Photochemistry of Uranyl Compounds*, Macmillan, New York, 1964. Extensive review.

Rand, M. H., and O. Kubaschewski, *The Thermodynamic Properties of Uranium Compounds*, Wiley, New York, 1963.

Roberts, L. E. J., *Quart. Rev.*, **15**, 442 (1961). The actinide oxides.

Seaborg, G. T., *Man-Made Transuranium Elements*, Prentice-Hall, 1963. Lucid and well illustrated introduction enriched with historical development.

Weinstock, B., *Record of Chem. Progress*, **23**, 23 (1962). Comprehensive reviews of hexafluorides including actinides, especially thermodynamic and spectroscopic properties.

Appendix

A. ENERGY UNITS

In discussions of the energy changes which occur in physical and chemical processes, several energy units and conventions are commonly used and occur throughout this book. The *calorie*, or "small" calorie, is approximately the amount of heat required to raise the temperature of 1 gram of water 1°, but its exact definition is in terms of electrical units. Chemical energies of a relatively weak nature are frequently expressed in units of calories per mole (cal/mole). Normal chemical bonds and differences in energies of the principal levels of atoms and molecules, however, are usually of the order of thousands of calories per mole. These are usually expressed in terms of the *kilocalorie*, which is, by definition, 1000 calories. For example, the energies required to separate the molecules O_2, I_2 and H_2 into atoms are 118, 36 and 103 kcal/mole, respectively.

A larger unit is the *electron volt* (ev), which is the kinetic energy acquired by an electron when it passes through a potential difference of 1 volt. One electron volt is equal to 23.063 kcal/mole.

One of the main sources of information about the energy levels in atoms and molecules is their spectra. Usually the wavelengths of spectral lines are measured directly. The most common units for their expression are

$$Angstrom \ (A): 1 \ A = 10^{-8} \ cm$$
$$Micron \ (\mu): 1 \ \mu = 10^{-4} \ cm = 10^{-3} \ mm$$
$$Millimicron \ (m\mu): 1 \ m\mu = 10^{-3} \ \mu$$

Energy cannot conveniently be measured in any wavelength units, but, because of the relation

$$E = h\nu$$

can be expressed in frequency units. In the above equation Planck's constant is in its usual units of erg-second, and the frequency is in cycles per second. For various reasons, cycles per second is not a convenient frequency unit, and the one most commonly used is the *reciprocal centimeter* (cm^{-1}), also called a *wave number* (no abbreviation) or a *Kayser* (K). Since the frequency, f, in cycles per second is related to the wavelength, λ, in centimeters by the relation $f = c/\lambda$, where c is the velocity of light, energy in ergs is given by E (ergs) $= hc \times$ frequency (in cm^{-1}). Applying suitable conversion factors, the wave number, as a unit of energy, is related to other energy units as follows:

$$1 \text{ kcal/mole} = 349.75 \text{ cm}^{-1}$$
$$1 \text{ ev} = 8066.0 \text{ cm}^{-1}$$

In any description of a change in energy, it is necessary to have a convention regarding the algebraic sign to be given to the energy released or absorbed. We use the convention which states that the energy of any exothermic process is negative (energy released or lost by the system) and the energy of any endothermic process is positive (energy gained by the system).

B. ENERGY LEVEL DIAGRAMS

On the following two pages are a complete set of semiquantitative energy level diagrams for the d^2–d^8 configurations in octahedral symmetry. (After Tanabe and Sugano, *J. Phys. Soc. Japan*, **9**, 753 (1954).)

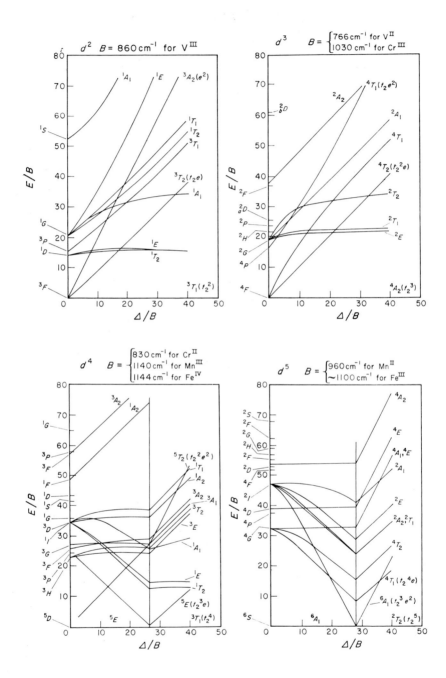

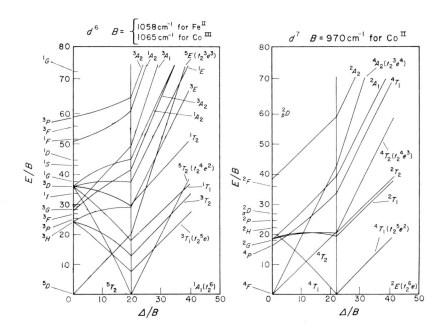

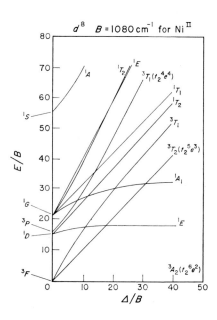

General References

More specialized references to aspects of the chemistries of the elements have been listed at the end of each chapter. Here are given some useful general sources of information in inorganic chemistry.

Reference Texts

There are several works in English which contain more detailed accounts of the chemistry of the elements than appear in this book, and they provide a useful first stage in the search for additional information.

Remy, H., *Treatise on Inorganic Chemistry* (translated by J. S. Anderson), Vols. I, II, Elsevier, New York, 1956. This book contains much detailed information on the elements and their compounds.

Sidgwick, N. V., *The Chemical Elements and Their Compounds*, Vols. I, II, Oxford University Press, 1950. This unique and personal book contains much useful and curious information and should be carefully read by all serious students.

Sneed, M. C., J. L. Maynard and R. C. Brasted (with other contributors), *Comprehensive Inorganic Chemistry*, Van Nostrand, New York. A series of volumes on the elements, their compounds and some other selected topics which are useful sources of information but less exhaustive than those listed below.

Wells, A. F., *Structural Inorganic Chemistry*, 3rd ed., Clarendon Press, Oxford, 1962. The third edition of this well-known book is an exceedingly comprehensive source book for experimental methods of structural chemistry and detailed solid-state structures of oxides, sulfides, silicates, metals and alloys, etc., as well as of compounds of a number of the elements. It can be strongly recommended as general reading for the student.

Comprehensive Treatises

Gmelin's Handbuch der anorganischen Chemie, Verlag Chemie, Weinheim. This series contains exhaustive treatments of all phases of inorganic and some physical chemistry. Some volumes are old, but supplementary volumes (which are still about ten years behind in literature coverage) are being issued regularly. The new volumes have subheadings in English.

Mellor's Comprehensive Treatise on Inorganic and Theoretical Chemistry, Longmans, Green, London, and Wiley, New York. Similar to Gmelin but less comprehensive. There are recent supplements.

Pascal's Nouveau traité de chimie minérale, Masson, Paris. Similar to Gmelin, though less comprehensive, but recent volumes are more up to date and critical.

Annual Reviews of Current Work

The *Annual Reports on the Progress of Chemistry* of the Chemical Society, London, provide a review with many references of approximately the latest year's work; the coverage is by no means exhaustive however.

There are several series of annual reviews specifically on inorganic chemistry or closely allied fields, such as organometallic chemistry, of which the following may be mentioned:

Carlin, R. L., ed., *Progress in Transition Metal Chemistry*, Dekker, New York, Vol. 1, 1965.

Cotton, F. A., ed., *Progress in Inorganic Chemistry*, Interscience–Wiley, New York, Vol. 1, 1959.

Eméleus, H. J., and A. G. Sharpe, eds., *Advances in Inorganic Chemistry and Radiochemistry*, Academic Press, New York, Vol. 1, 1959.

Seyferth, D., and R. B. King, *Annual Survey of Organometallic Chemistry*, Elsevier, New York, Vol. 1 (covering 1964), 1965.

Stone, F. G. A., and R. West, eds., *Advances in Organometallic Chemistry*, Academic Press, New York, Vol. 1, 1964.

More Specialized Text and Reference Books

Bailar, J. C., ed., *The Chemistry of Coordination Compounds* (American Chemical Society Monograph, No. 131), Reinhold, New York, 1956.

Basolo, F., and R. G. Pearson, *Mechanism of Inorganic Reactions*, Wiley, New York, 1958. An excellent account and reference source for transition metal complex reactions.

Brauer, G., ed., *Handbook of Preparative Inorganic Chemistry*, 2nd ed., Vols. I and II, Academic Press, New York, 1963. Contains descriptions of techniques and tested methods of preparation for many compounds.

Coates, G. E., *Organometallic Compounds*, 2nd ed., Methuen, London, 1960. Discusses the organo derivatives of the more metallic elements in a lucid and authoritative way.

Fluck, E., *Die kernmagnetische Resonanz und ihre Anwendung in der anorganischen Chemie*, Springer-Verlag, Berlin, 1963. Good review on nuclear magnetic resonance studies on inorganic compounds; see also article by E. L. Muetterties and W. D. Phillips in *Adv. Inorg. Chem. Radiochem.*, **4**, 231 (1962).

Inorganic Syntheses, McGraw-Hill, New York. This series gives tested, detailed synthetic procedures for several hundred important inorganic compounds and also brief descriptions of their properties.

Jolly, W. L., ed., *Preparative Inorganic Reactions*, Interscience–Wiley, New York. A continuing series of volumes describing and illustrating preparative methods for classes of compounds.

Jonassen, H. B., and A. Weissberger, eds., *Technique of Inorganic Chemistry*, Interscience–Wiley, New York. A series of volumes containing articles on particular experimental methods.

Latimer, W. M., *The Oxidation States of the Elements and Their Potentials in Aqueous Solution*, 2nd ed., Prentice-Hall, New York, 1952. Provides a detailed account of aqueous chemistry with particular reference to potentials, free energy changes, and entropies. The latter data are best obtained from the circulars of the National Bureau of Standards, Washington, D.C.

Lewis, J., and R. G. Wilkins, eds., *Modern Coordination Chemistry*, Interscience, New York–London, 1959. Contains authoritative reviews on several aspects of coordination chemistry.

Nakamoto, K., *Infrared Spectra of Inorganic and Coordination Compounds*, Wiley, New York, 1963. A useful but far from complete collection of data.

Wyckoff, R. W. G., *Crystal Structures*, Interscience, New York. An exhaustive compilation of crystal and molecular structures periodically supplemented to bring it up to date. Fully referenced.

Index

A